Prealgebra & Introductory Algebra

Julie Miller
Daytona State College

Molly O'Neill
Daytona State College

Nancy Hyde
Professor Emeritus
Broward College

Special Edition

Mc Graw Hill Education

1 2 3 4 5 6 7 8 9 0 SCI SCI 15 14 13

ISBN-13: 978-1-259-12709-0
ISBN-10: 1-259-12709-5

Learning Solutions Consultant: Kimberly Wollschlager
Associate Project Manager: Carman Bakey

Letter from the Authors

Dear Colleagues,

We originally embarked on this textbook project because we were seeing a lack of student success in our developmental math sequence. In short, we were not getting the results we wanted from our students with the materials and textbooks that we were using at the time. The primary goal of our project was to create teaching and learning materials that would get better results.

Now, as course needs continue to change, we are continuously working to adapt our series to meet the needs of instructors and students. We now have the opportunity to introduce the newest text in our series, *Prealgebra and Introductory Algebra,* combined. Recently, we have become more conscious of the need to create a text that combines these 2 course areas to help accommodate schools that are

- focused on acceleration and persistence through these developmental math courses
- sensitive to textbook prices, and
- Implementing curriculum and course redesigns where these disciplines are sequenced as one course.

As we have seen movement towards the Beginning and Intermediate Algebra combined courses, we knew that we must also create this combined option. We have worked to design a table of contents by involving instructors that teach these courses or are looking to redesign their courses with this format.

Our textbook series has been a true collaboration with our Board of Advisors and colleagues in developmental mathematics around the country. We are sincerely humbled by those of you who have adopted our series and the over 400 colleagues around the country who partnered with us providing valuable feedback and suggestions through reviews, symposia, focus groups, and being on our Board of Advisors. You partnered with us to create materials that will help students get better results. For that we are immeasurably grateful.

As an author team, we have an ongoing commitment to provide the best possible text materials for instructors and students. With your continued help and suggestions we will continue the quest to help all of our students get better results.

Sincerely,

Julie Miller
julie.miller.math@gmail.com

Molly O'Neill
molly.s.oneill@gmail.com

Nancy Hyde
nhyde@montanasky.com

Contents

Chapter 7 Measurement and Geometry   453

Chapter 8 Introduction to Statistics   547

Chapter 9 Linear Equations and Inequalities   593

Chapter 13 Factoring Polynomials 877

Chapter 14 Rational Expressions 939

Connect Math Hosted by ALEKS Corporation is an exciting, new ehomework platform combining the strengths of McGraw-Hill Higher Education and ALEKS Corporation. Connect Math Hosted by ALEKS Corporation is the first platform on the market to combine an artificially-intelligent, diagnostic assessment with an intuitive ehomework platform designed to meet your needs.

Connect Math Hosted by ALEKS Corporation is the culmination of a one-of-a-kind market development process involving full-time and adjunct Math faculty at every step of the process. This process enables us to provide you with a solution that best meets your needs.

Connect Math Hosted by ALEKS Corporation is built by Math educators for Math educators!

1 ***Your students want a well-organized homepage where key information is easily viewable.***

Modern Student Homepage

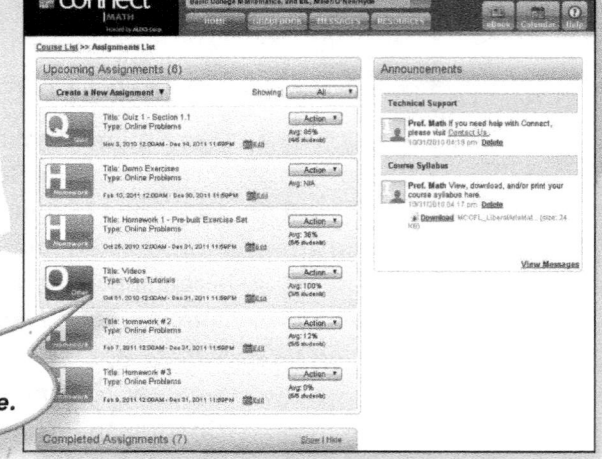

▶ This homepage provides a dashboard for students to immediately view their assignments, grades, and announcements for their course. (Assignments include HW, quizzes, and tests.)

▶ Students can access their assignments through the course Calendar to stay up-to-date and organized for their class.

Modern, intuitive, and simple interface.

2 ***You want a way to identify the strengths and weaknesses of your class at the beginning of the term rather than after the first exam.***

Integrated ALEKS® Assessment

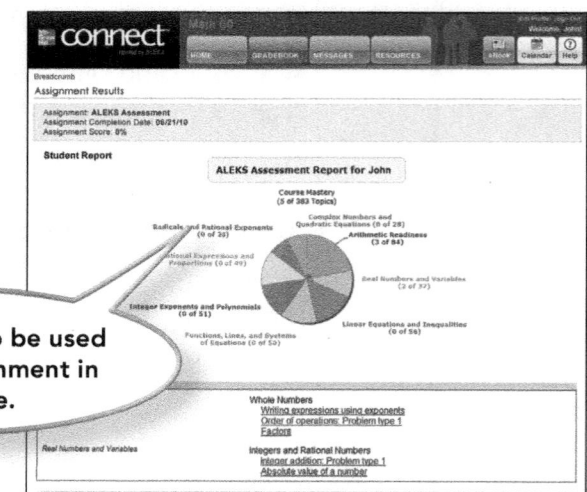

▶ This artificially-intelligent (AI), diagnostic assessment identifies precisely what a student knows and is ready to learn next.

▶ Detailed assessment reports provide instructors with specific information about where students are struggling most.

▶ This AI-driven assessment is the only one of its kind in an online homework platform.

Recommended to be used as the first assignment in any course.

ALEKS is a registered trademark of ALEKS Corporation.

Resources for Online Homework

3 *Your students want an assignment page that is easy to use and includes lots of extra help resources.*

Efficient Assignment Navigation

▶ Students have access to immediate feedback and help while working through assignments.

▶ Students have direct access to a media-rich eBook for easy referencing.

▶ Students can view detailed, step-by-step solutions written by instructors who teach the course, providing a unique solution to each and every exercise.

Students can easily monitor and track their progress on a given assignment.

4 *You want a more intuitive and efficient assignment creation process because of your busy schedule.*

Assignment Creation Process

▶ Instructors can select textbook-specific questions organized by chapter, section, and objective.

▶ Drag-and-drop functionality makes creating an assignment quick and easy.

▶ Instructors can preview their assignments for efficient editing.

Connect
Learn
Succeed™

Mc Graw Hill CONNECT |MATH
Hosted by ALEKS Corp.

5   *Your students want an interactive eBook with rich functionality integrated into the product.*

Integrated Media-Rich eBook

▶ A Web-optimized eBook is seamlessly integrated within ConnectPlus Math Hosted by ALEKS Corp. for ease of use.

▶ Students can access videos, images, and other media in context within each chapter or subject area to enhance their learning experience.

▶ Students can highlight, take notes, or even access shared instructor highlights/notes to learn the course material.

▶ The integrated eBook provides students with a cost-saving alternative to traditional textbooks.

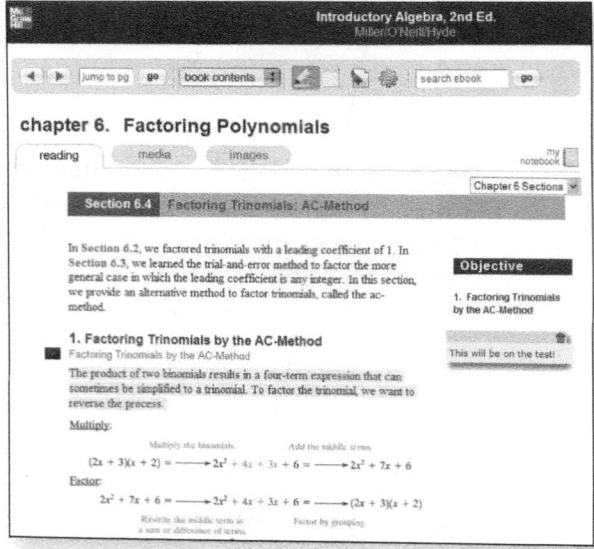

6   *You want a flexible gradebook that is easy to use.*

Flexible Instructor Gradebook

▶ Based on instructor feedback, Connect Math Hosted by ALEKS Corp.'s straightforward design creates an intuitive, visually pleasing grade management environment.

▶ Assignment types are color-coded for easy viewing.

▶ The gradebook allows instructors the flexibility to import and export additional grades.

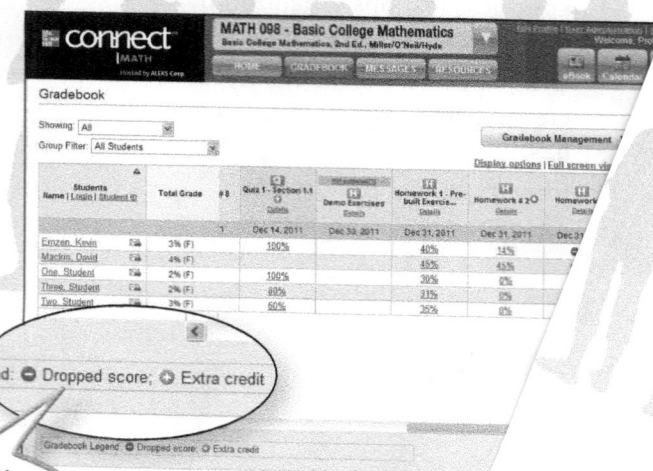

Instructors have the ability to drop grades as well as assign extra credit.

Built by Math Educators for Math Educators

 7 **You want algorithmic content that was developed by math faculty to ensure the content is pedagogically sound and accurate.**

Digital Content Development Story

As the usage of online homework progresses and evolves, McGraw-Hill understands the need to involve instructors while developing the digital content to ensure that what students see in the online homework system is consistent with what they see in their textbooks. For the Miller, O'Neill, and Hyde developmental math series, we partnered with instructors that have taught from the series to help ensure a seamless transition from print to digital offerings.

The development of McGraw-Hill's Connect Math Hosted by ALEKS Corporation content involved collaboration between McGraw-Hill, our authors, experienced instructors, and ALEKS Corporation, a company known for its high-quality digital content. The result of this process, outlined below, is accurate content created with your students in mind. It is available in a simple-to-use interface with all the functionality tools needed to manage your course.

1. McGraw-Hill selected experienced instructors to work as Digital Contributors.

2. The Digital Contributors selected the textbook exercises to be included in the algorithmic content to ensure appropriate coverage of the textbook content.

3. The Digital Contributors created detailed, stepped-out solutions for use in the Guided Solution and Solve It features, matching the voice of the authors.

4. The Digital Contributors provided detailed instructions for authoring the algorithm specific to each exercise to maintain the original intent and integrity of each unique exercise.

5. Each algorithm was reviewed by the Contributor, went through a detailed quality control process by ALEKS Corporation, and was copyedited prior to being posted live.

> Solutions in Connect Math Hosted by ALEKS match the procedure and language of the text.

| Previous | 1 | 2 | 3 | 4 | 5 |

Question 6 of 7 (1 point)

Factor completely.

$$100u^2 - 80u + 16$$

Step 1:
Factor out the GCF of 4.

Step 2:
$$100u^2 - 80u + 16 = 4(25u^2 - 20u + 4)$$

Step 3:
Can we factor again? Yes.

Step 4:
Notice that the first and last terms in the trinomial are perfect squares.
$$25u^2 - 20u + 4 = (5u)^2 - 20u + (-2)^2$$

The middle term is $2 \cdot 5u \cdot (-2) = -20u$.

Try Another · *Solve It* · *Guided Solution* · *Show Example* · *Ask My Instructor* · *Link to Textbook*

Result = Truly Vetted, Consistent Digital Content That Is Built By Math Educators And Supported By ALEKS Corporation.

Lead Digital Contributors

[D]onna Gerken, *Miami Dade College*
[Ni]cole Lloyd, *Lansing Community College*
[Ste]phen Toner, *Victor Valley College*

Digital Contributors

Jody Harris, *Broward College*
Lizette Hernandez Foley, *Broward College*
Linda Schott, *Ozarks Technical Community College*
Michael Larkin, *Pacific University*
Alina Coronel, *Miami Dade College*

Connect Learn Succeed™

ALEKS 360: A Total Course Solution

With **eBook** Integration

Connect
Learn
Succeed™

A cost-effective total course solution: fully integrated, interactive eBook combined with ALEKS individualized assessment and learning.

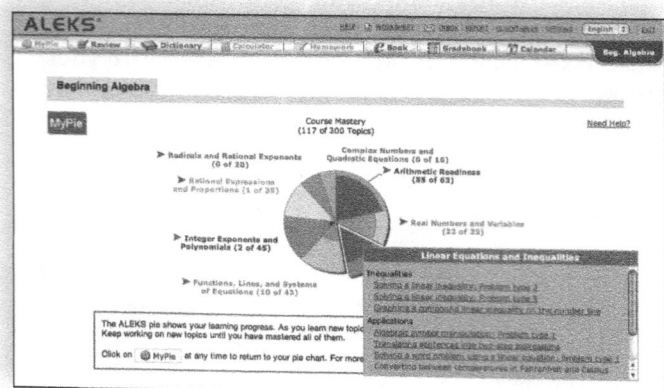

Individualized Learning

- The ALEKS Pie summarizes a student's current knowledge and provides individualized learning on the exact topics the student is **ready to learn**

- Artificial intelligence successfully targets gaps by assessing precisely a student's knowledge and periodically reassessing for long-term retention

- Adaptive, open-response environment avoids multiple-choice and includes problems, explanations, and realistic answer input tools

Interactive eBook

- eBook access provides worked examples, videos, and additional support

- Robust virtual features include highlighting, bookmarking, and note-taking capabilities

- Students can easily access the eBook, multimedia resources, and their notes from within their ALEKS Student Accounts

Learn More: www.aleks.com/highered/math

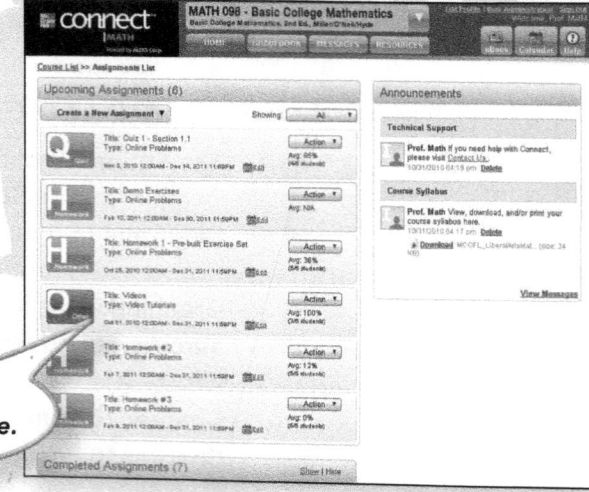

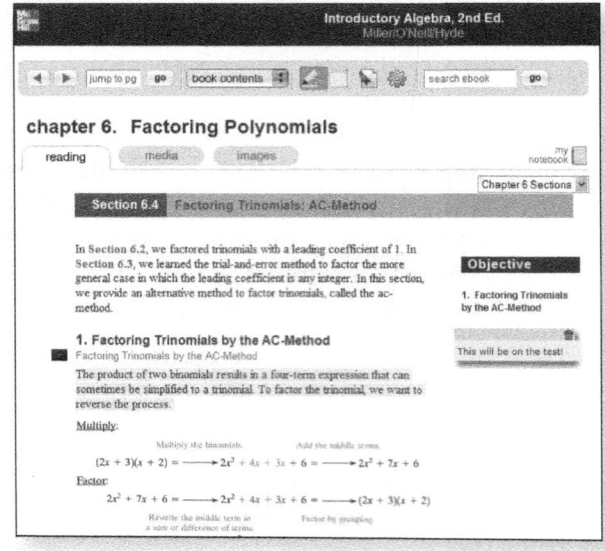

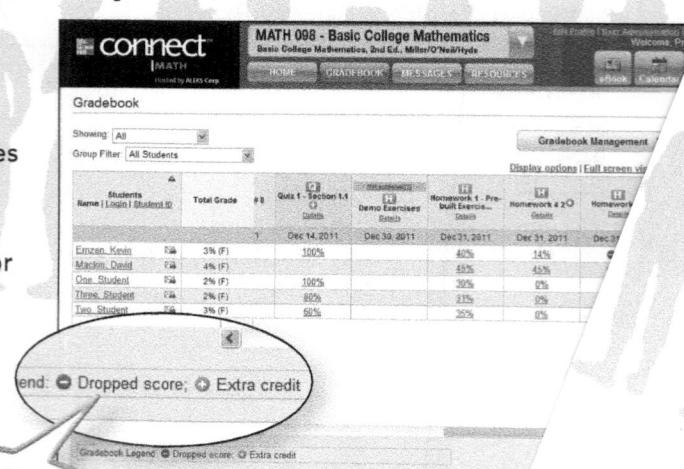

ALEKS 360: A Total Course Solution

A cost-effective total course solution: fully integrated, interactive eBook combined with ALEKS individualized assessment and learning.

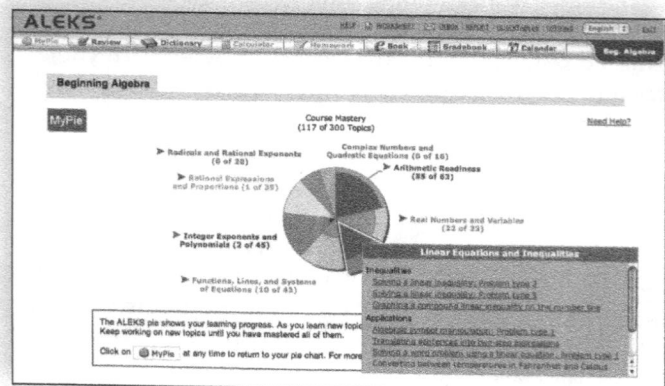

Individualized Learning

- The ALEKS Pie summarizes a student's current knowledge and provides individualized learning on the exact topics the student is **ready to learn**

- Artificial intelligence successfully targets gaps by assessing precisely a student's knowledge and periodically reassessing for long-term retention

- Adaptive, open-response environment avoids multiple-choice and includes problems, explanations, and realistic answer input tools

Interactive eBook

- eBook access provides worked examples, videos, and additional support

- Robust virtual features include highlighting, bookmarking, and note-taking capabilities

- Students can easily access the eBook, multimedia resources, and their notes from within their ALEKS Student Accounts

Learn More: www.aleks.com/highered/math/aleks360

ALEKS Course Management Tools

Dynamic, Automated Reporting

- Automated reports dynamically track student and class learning progress so instructors can effectively direct classroom instruction

- Detailed reports identify precisely what each student knows, and more importantly, what each student is ready to learn next

  - Time and Topic Report offers up-to-the-minute daily progress, including time logged, topics attempted, and topics mastered

Course Control and Customization

- Align ALEKS topics with a textbook or course syllabus
- Create and customize course objectives and modules
- Set due dates for course objectives to pace student progress
- Assign automatically-graded homework, quizzes, and tests
- Seamlessly track and adjust student scores with the customizable gradebook

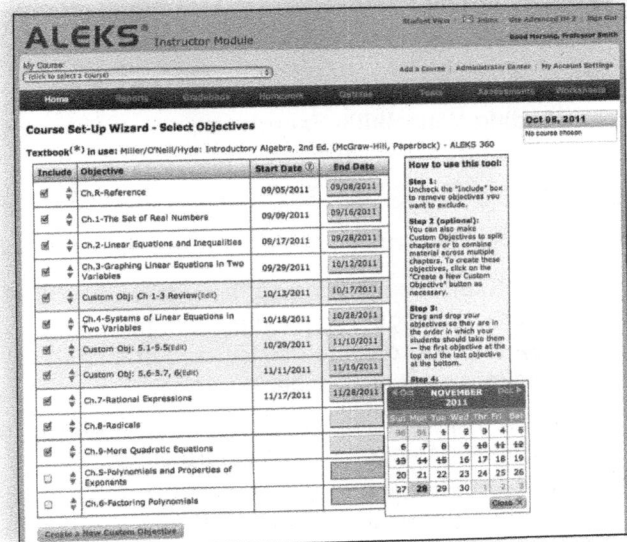

How Will Miller/O'Neill/Hyde Help Your Students *Get Better Results?*

Better Clarity, Quality, and Accuracy

Julie Miller, Molly O'Neill, and Nancy Hyde know what students need to be successful in mathematics. Better results come from clarity in their exposition, quality of step-by-step worked examples, and accuracy of their exercises sets; but it takes more than just great authors to build a textbook series to help students achieve success in mathematics. Our authors worked with a strong mathematical team of instructors from around the country to ensure that the clarity, quality, and accuracy you expect from the Miller/O'Neill/Hyde series was included in this edition.

> "I would describe it as an excellent text written by teachers! It has easy to understand explanations for students. The examples are good and the mathematics is solid. The students should find it "easy to read."
>
> —Teresa Hasenauer, *Indian River State College*

Better Exercise Sets!

Comprehensive sets of exercises are available for every student level. Julie Miller, Molly O'Neill, and Nancy Hyde worked with a national board of advisors from across the country to offer the appropriate depth and breadth of exercises for your students. **Problem Recognition Exercises** were created to improve student performance while testing.

Our practice exercise sets help students progress from skill development to conceptual understanding. Student tested and instructor approved, the Miller/O'Neill/Hyde exercise sets will help your student *get better results*.

- ▶ **Problem Recognition Exercises**
- ▶ **Skill Practice Exercises**
- ▶ **Study Skills Exercises**
- ▶ **Mixed Exercises**
- ▶ **Expanding Your Skills Exercises**

> "Extremely interesting and effective practice exercises. I love the study skills component that reminds students of essential habits that will help students achieve success. Review is a great reinforcement technique for recently mastered skills. The exercise are innovative and there are plenty of relevant applications from several fields and disciplines."
>
> —Corinna Goehring, *Jackson State Community C*

Better Step-By-Step Pedagogy!

Prealgebra provides enhanced step-by-step learning tools to help students *get better results*.

- ▶ **Worked Examples** provide an "easy-to-understand" approach, clearly guiding each student through a step-by-step approach to master each practice exercise for better comprehension.
- ▶ **TIPs** offer students extra cautious direction to help improve understanding through hints and further insight.
- ▶ **Avoiding Mistakes** boxes alert students to common errors and provide practical ways to avoid them. Both of these learning aids will help students get better results by showing how to work through a problem us defined step-by-step methodology that has been class tested and student approved.

> "MOH seems to look into the heads o and see what mistakes they make a help the students to avoid them—r the Avoiding Mistakes help with th TIPs along the way also help."
>
> —Linda Schott, *Ozark Technical C*

Better Learning Tools

Chapter Openers

Tired of students not being prepared? The Miller/O'Neill/Hyde *Chapter Openers* help students get better results through engaging *Puzzles and Games* that introduce the chapter concepts and ask "Are You Prepared?"

> "I really like the puzzle idea! I like for the chapter opener to be an activity instead of just reading. That way, students don't even realize they are preparing themselves for the concepts ahead and it is not nearly as boring."
>
> —Jacqui Fields, *Wake Technical Community College*

Chapter 7

In this chapter, we present the concept of percent. Percents are used to measure the number of parts per hundred of some whole amount. As a consumer, it is important to have a working knowledge of percents.

Are You Prepared?

To prepare for your work with percents, take a minute to review multiplying and dividing by a power of 10. Also practice solving equations and proportions. Work the problems on the left. Record the answers in the spaces on the right, according to the number of digits to the left and right of the decimal point. Then write the letter of each choice to complete the sentence below. If you need help, review Sections 5.3, 5.4, and 3.4.

1. 0.582×100 **2.** 0.002×100

4. 318×0.01

6. Solve. $\dfrac{34}{160} = \dfrac{x}{100}$

$= \dfrac{36}{100}$ **8.** Solve. $0.3x = 16.2$

S.	__ • __ __ __
F.	__ __ • __ __
P.	__ __ __ __ •
O.	• __
I.	__ __ •
E.	• __ __ __
H.	__ __ • __
U.	• __ __

...cian's bakery was called   __ __ __ __ __   __ __   __ __ .
                              1 2 3 4 5   2 6   7 8

TIP and Avoiding Mistakes Boxes

TIP and Avoiding Mistakes boxes have been created based on the authors' classroom experiences—they have also been integrated into the **Worked Examples**. These pedagogical tools will help students get better results by learning how to work through a problem using a clearly defined step-by-step methodology.

Example 1   Adding and Subtracting Like Fractions

Add. Write the answer as a fraction or whole number.

a. $\dfrac{1}{4} + \dfrac{5}{4}$ **b.** $\dfrac{2}{15} + \dfrac{1}{15} - \dfrac{13}{15}$

Avoiding Mistakes

Notice that when adding fractions, we do not add the denominators. We add *only* the numerators.

Solution:

a. $\dfrac{1}{4} + \dfrac{5}{4} = \dfrac{1+5}{4}$ Add the numerators.

$= \dfrac{6}{4}$ Write the sum over the common denominator.

$= \dfrac{\overset{3}{\cancel{6}}}{\underset{2}{\cancel{4}}}$ Simplify to lowest terms.

Avoiding Mistakes Boxes:

Avoiding Mistakes boxes are integrated throughout the textbook to alert students to common errors and how to avoid them.

> "The MOH text does a better job of pointing out the common mistakes students make."
>
> —Kaye Black, *Bluegrass Community & Technical College*

TIP Boxes

Teaching tips are usually revealed only in the classroom. Not anymore! TIP boxes offer students helpful hints and extra direction to help improve understanding and further insight.

> "I think that one of the best features of this chapter (and probably will continue throughout the text) is the TIP section."
>
> —Ena Salter, *Manatee Community College*

TIP: Example 1(a) can also be solved by using a percent proportion.

$\dfrac{5.5}{100} = \dfrac{x}{20{,}000}$ What is 5.5% of 20,000?

$(5.5)(20{,}000) = 100x$

$110{,}000 = 100x$

$\dfrac{110{,}000}{100} = \dfrac{100x}{100}$ Divide both sides by 100.

$1100 = x$ The sales tax is $1100.

Better Exercise Sets

Better Exercise Sets! Better Practice! Better Results!

▶ Do your students have trouble with problem solving?

▶ Do you want to help students overcome math anxiety?

▶ Do you want to help your students improve performance on math assessments?

Problem Recognition Exercises

Problem Recognition Exercises present a collection of problems that look similar to a student upon first glance, but are actually quite different in the manner of their individual solutions. Students sharpen critical thinking skills and better develop their "solution recall" to help them distinguish the method needed to solve an exercise—an essential skill in developmental mathematics.

Problem Recognition Exercises, tested in a developmental mathematics classroom, were created to improve student performance while testing.

"I like how this author doesn't title all the sections within this PRE. I believe that would be important during testing-anxiety situations. How many times do our students say they did not know what to do and (are) not sure what they were being asked?"

—Christine Baade, *San Juan College*

Problem Recognition Exercises

Operations on Fractions versus Solving Proportions

For Exercises 1–6, identify the problem as a proportion or as a product of fractions. Then solve the proportion or multiply the fractions.

1. a. $\dfrac{x}{4} = \dfrac{15}{8}$ b. $\dfrac{1}{4} \cdot \dfrac{15}{8}$ 2. a. $\dfrac{2}{5} \cdot \dfrac{3}{10}$ b. $\dfrac{2}{5} = \dfrac{y}{10}$

3. a. $\dfrac{2}{7} \times \dfrac{3}{14}$ b. $\dfrac{2}{7} = \dfrac{n}{14}$ 4. a. $\dfrac{m}{5} = \dfrac{6}{15}$ b. $\dfrac{3}{5} \times \dfrac{6}{15}$

5. a. $\dfrac{48}{p} = \dfrac{16}{3}$ b. $\dfrac{48}{8} \cdot \dfrac{16}{3}$ 6. a. $\dfrac{10}{7} \cdot \dfrac{28}{5}$ b. $\dfrac{10}{7} = \dfrac{28}{t}$

For Exercises 7–10, solve the proportion or perform the indicated operation on fractions.

7. a. $\dfrac{3}{7} = \dfrac{6}{z}$ b. $\dfrac{3}{7} \div \dfrac{6}{35}$ c. $\dfrac{3}{7} + \dfrac{6}{35}$ d. $\dfrac{3}{7} \cdot \dfrac{6}{35}$

8. a. $\dfrac{4}{5} \div \dfrac{20}{3}$ b. $\dfrac{4}{v} = \dfrac{20}{3}$ c. $\dfrac{4}{5} \times \dfrac{20}{3}$ d. $\dfrac{4}{5} - \dfrac{20}{3}$

9. a. $\dfrac{14}{5} \cdot \dfrac{10}{7}$ b. $\dfrac{14}{5} = \dfrac{x}{7}$ c. $\dfrac{14}{5} - \dfrac{10}{7}$ d. $\dfrac{14}{-} \div$

10. a. $\dfrac{11}{-} = \dfrac{66}{y}$ b. $\dfrac{11}{3} + \dfrac{66}{11}$ c. $\dfrac{11}{3} \div \dfrac{66}{11}$

"These are brilliant! [...] such things in clas[...] across a point, an[...] seen them in a te[...]"

—Russell Penner, [...] Cor[...]

"This book does a much better job of pairing similar problems for students to be able to practice recognizing different exercises— and as an instructor, I can use these exercises as part of a review and lecture about the need to understand a problem versus just memorizing a process."

—Vicki Lucido, *St. Louis Community College–Florissant Valley*

Dynamic Math Animations

The Miller/O'Neill/Hyde author team has developed a series of Flash animations to illustrate difficult concepts where static images and text fall short. The animations leverage the use of on-screen movement and morphing shapes to enhance conceptual learning.

Modeling Using a Linear Equation in Two Variables

x Time (hr)	y Height (in.)
1	7.5
1.4	10.5
1.8	13.5
2.7	20.25
3.6	27
4.4	33
5.3	39.75
6.1	45.75

Water Level vs. Time

Click on the "*Get data point*" button several times.

Copyright © 2008 Julie Miller

2. Graphing Linear Equations i

In the introduction to this section, we found
$x + y = 4$. If we graph these solutions, notice
Figure 9-9.)

Equation: $x + y = 4$

Several solutions: $(2, 2)$

$(1, 3)$

$(4, 0)$

$(-1, 5)$

The equation actually has infinitely many soluti
This is because there are infinitely many comb
tions of x and y whose sum is 4. The graph o
solutions to this equation makes up the line sh
each end indicate that the line extends infinitely. This is called the *graph of the equation.*

The graph of a linear equation is a line. Therefore, we need to plot at least two points and then draw the line between them. This is demonstrated in Example 4.

Skill Practice

Graph the equation.
7. $-x + y = 4$

Example 4 **Graphing a Linear Equation**

Graph the equation. $-x + y = 2$

Solution:

We will find three ordered pairs that are solutions to $-x + y = 2$. To find the ordered pairs, choose arbitrary values for x or y, such as those shown in the table. Then complete the table.

x	y
3	
	-2
-1	

$(3, \ )$
$(\ , -2)$
$(-1, \ )$

Complete: $(3, \ )$

$-x + y = 2$
$-(3) + y = 2$
$-3 + 3 + y = 2 + 3$
$y = 5$

Complete: $(\ , -2)$

$-x + y = 2$
$-x + (-2) = 2$
$-x - 2 + 2 = 2 + 2$
$-x = 4$
$x = -4$

Complete: $(-1, \ )$

$-x + y = 2$
$-(-1) + y = 2$
$1 + y = 2$
$1 - 1 + y = 2 - 1$
$y = 1$

Answer
7.
$-x + y = 4$

Through their classroom experience, the authors recognize that such media assets are great teaching tools for the classroom and excellent for online learning. The Miller/O'Neill/Hyde animations are interactive and quite diverse in their use. Some provide a virtual laboratory for which an application is simulated and where students can collect data points for analysis and modeling. Others provide interactive question-and-answer sessions to test conceptual learning. For word problem applications, the animations ask students to estimate answers and practice "number sense."

Julie Miller has been on the faculty in the School of Mathematics at Daytona State College for 20 years, where she has taught developmental and upper-level courses. Prior to her work at DSC, she worked as a software engineer for General Electric in the area of flight and radar simulation. Julie earned a bachelor of science in applied mathematics from Union College in Schenectady, New York, and a master of science in mathematics from the University of Florida. In addition to this textbook, she has authored several course supplements for college algebra, trigonometry, and precalculus, as well as several short works of fiction and nonfiction for young readers.

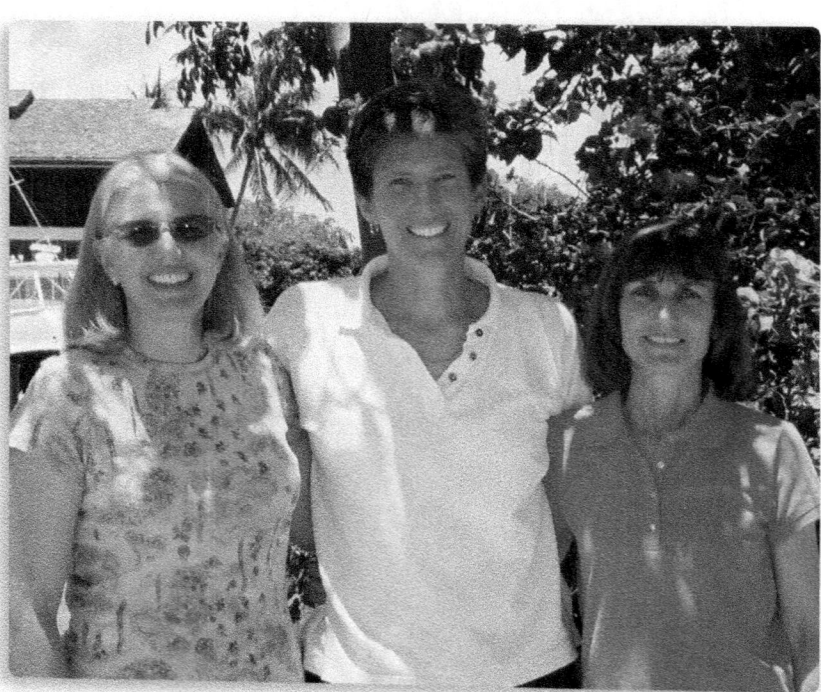

"My father is a medical researcher, and I got hooked on math and science when I was young and would visit his laboratory. I can remember using graph paper to plot data points for his experiments and doing simple calculations. He would then tell me what the peaks and features in the graph meant in the context of his experiment. I think that applications and hands-on experience made math come alive for me and I'd like to see math come alive for my students."

—Julie Miller

Molly O'Neill is also from Daytona State College, where she has taught for 22 years in the School of Mathematics. She has taught a variety of courses from developmental mathematics to calculus. Before she came to Florida, Molly taught as an adjunct instructor at the University of Michigan–Dearborn, Eastern Michigan University, Wayne State University, and Oakland Community College. Molly earned a bachelor of science in mathematics and a master of arts and teaching from Western Michigan University in Kalamazoo, Michigan. Besides this textbook, she has authored several course supplements for college algebra, trigonometry, and precalculus and has reviewed texts for developmental mathematics.

"I differ from many of my colleagues in that math was not always easy for me. But in seventh grade I had a teacher who taught me that if I follow the rules of mathematics, even I could solve math problems. Once I understood this, I enjoyed math to the point of choosing it for my career. I now have the greatest job because I get to do math every day and I have the opportunity to influence my students just as I was influenced. Authoring the text has given me another avenue to reach even more students."

—Molly O'Neill

Nancy Hyde served as a full-time faculty member of the Mathematics Department at Broward College for 24 years. During this time she taught the full spectrum of courses from developmental math through differential equations. She received a bachelor of science degree in math education from Florida State University and a master's degree in math education from Florida Atlantic University. She has conducted workshops for both students and teachers on the use of technology in the classroom. In addition to this text she has authored a graphing calculator supplement for *College Algebra*.

"I grew up in Brevard County, Florida, with my father working at Cape Canaveral. I was always interested in mathematics and physics in relation to the space program. As I studied higher levels of mathematics I became more intrigued by its abstract nature and infinite possibilities. It is enjoyable and rewarding to bring this perspective to students while helping them to understand mathematics."

—Nancy Hyde

360° Development Process

McGraw-Hill's 360° Development Process is an ongoing, never-ending, market-oriented approach to building accurate and innovative print and digital products. It is dedicated to continual large-scale and incremental improvement that is driven by multiple customer-feedback loops and checkpoints. This is initiated during the early planning stages of our new products, and intensifies during the development and production stages—then begins again upon publication, in anticipation of the next edition.

A key principle in the development of any mathematics text is its ability to adapt to teaching specifications in a universal way. The only way to do so is by contacting those universal voices—and learning from their suggestions. We are confident that our book has the most current content the industry has to offer, thus pushing our desire for accuracy to the highest standard possible. In order to accomplish this, we have moved through an arduous road to production. Extensive and open-minded advice is critical in the production of a superior text.

Here is a brief overview of the initiatives included in the 360° Development Process:

Board of Advisors

A hand-picked group of trusted teachers' active in developmental math courses course served as chief advisors and consultants to the author and editorial team with regards to manuscript development. The Board of Advisors reviewed parts of the manuscript; served as a sounding board for pedagogical, media, and design concerns; consulted on organizational changes; and attended a focus group to confirm the manuscript's readiness for publication.

Prealgebra
Vanetta Grier-Felix, *Seminole State College of Florida*
Teresa Hasenauer, *Indian River State College*
Shelbra Jones, *Wake Technical Community College*
Nicole Lloyd, *Lansing Community College*
Kausha Miller, *Bluegrass Community and Technical College*
Linda Schott, *Ozarks Technical Community College*
Renee Sundrud, *Harrisburg Area Community College*

Basic College Mathematics
Vernon Bridges, *Durham Technical Community College*
Lynette King, *Gadsden State Community College*
Sharon Morrison, *St. Petersburg College*
Deanna Murphy, *Lane County Community College*
Rod Oberdick, *Delaware Technical and Community College*
Matthew Robinson, *Tallahassee Community College*
Pat Rome, *Delgado Community College-City Park*

Introductory Algebra
Mark Billiris, *St. Petersburg Community College*
Pauline Chow, *Harrisburg Community College*
John Close, *Salt Lake Community College*
Barbara Elzy, *Bluegrass Community College*
Lori Grady, *University of Wisconsin-Whitewater*
Mike Kirby, *Tidewater Community College*
Patricia Roux, *Delgado Community College*

Intermediate Algebra
Susan Dimick, *Spokane Community College*
Sue Duff, *Guilford Technical Community College*
Alicia Giovinazzo, *Miami Dade College*
Charlotte Newsome, *Tidewater Community College*
Ena Salter, *Manatee Community College*

Acknowledgments and Reviewers

The development of this textbook series would never have been possible without the creative ideas and feedback offered by many reviewers. We are especially thankful to the following instructors for their careful review of the manuscript.

Reviewers of the Miller/O'Neill/Hyde Developmental Mathematics Series

Ken Aeschliman, *Oakland Community College*
Darla Aguilar, *Pima Community College–Desert Vista*
Joyce Ahlgren, *California State University–San Bernardino*
Ebrahim Ahmadizadeh, *Northampton Community College*
Khadija Ahmed, *Monroe County Community College*
Sara Alford, *North Central Texas College*
Theresa Allen, *University of Idaho*
Sheila Anderson, *Housatonic Community College*
Lane Andrew, *Arapahoe Community College*
Victoria Anemelu, *San Bernardino Valley College*
Jan Archibald, *Ventura College*
Carla Arriola, *Broward College–North*
Yvonne Aucoin, *Tidewater Community College–Norfolk*
Eric Aurand, *Mohave Community College*
Christine Baade, *San Juan College*
Sohrab Bakhtyari, *St. Petersburg College*
Anna Bakman, *Los Angeles Trade Technical*
Andrew Ball, *Durham Technical Community College*
Russell Banks, *Guilford Technical Community College*
Carlos Barron, *Mountain View College*
Suzanne Battista, *St. Petersburg College*
Kevin Baughn, *Kirtland Community College*
Sarah Baxter, *Gloucester County College*
Lynn Beckett-Lemus, *El Camino College*
Edward Behder, *Century College*
Monika Bender, *Central Texas College*
Emilie Berglund, *Utah Valley State College*
Rebecca Berthiaume, *Edison College–Fort Myers*
John Beyers, *Miami Dade College–Hialeah*
Laila Bicksler, *Delgado Community College–City Park*
Norma Bisulca, *University of Maine–Augusta*
Kaye Black, *Bluegrass Community and Technical College*
Deronn Bowen, *Broward College–Central*
Timmy Bremer, *Broome Community College*
Donald Bridgewater, *Broward College*
Peggy Brock, *TVI Community College*
Kelly Brooks, *Pierce College*
Susan D. Caire, *Delgado Community College–West Bank*
Susan Caldiero, *Cosumnes River College*
Peter Carlson, *Delta College*
Judy Carter, *North Shore Community College*
Veena Chadha, *University of Wisconsin–Eau Claire*
Zhixiong Chen, *New Jersey City University*
Julie Chung, *American River College*
Tyrone Clinton, *Saint Petersburg College–Gibbs*
John Close, *Salt Lake Community College*

William Coe, *Montgomery College*
Lois Colpo, *Harrisburg Area Community College*
Eugenia Cox, *Palm Beach State College*
Julane Crabtree, *Johnson Community College*
Mark Crawford, *Waubonsee Community College*
Natalie Creed, *Gaston College*
Greg Cripe, *Spokane Falls Community College*
Anabel Darini, *Suffolk County Community College–Brentwood*
Antonio David, *Del Mar College*
Ann Davis, *Pasadena Area Community College*
Ron Davis, *Kennedy-King College–Chicago*
Laurie Delitsky, *Nassau Community College*
Patti D'Emidio, *Montclair State University*
Bob Denton, *Orange Coast College*
Robert Diaz, *Fullerton College*
Robert Doran, *Palm Beach State College*
Deborah Doucette, *Erie Community College–North Campus—Williamsville*
Thomas Drucker, *University of Wisconsin–Whitewater*
Michael Dubrowsky, *Wayne Community College*
Barbara Duncan, *Hillsborough Community College–Dale Mabry*
Jeffrey Dyess, *Bishop State Community College*
Elizabeth Eagle, *University of North Carolina–Charlotte*
Marcial Echenique, *Broward College–North*
Sabine Eggleston, *Edison College–Fort Myers*
Lynn Eisenberg, *Rowan-Cabarrus Community College*
Monette Elizalde, *Palo Alto College*
Barb Elzey, *Bluegrass Community and Technical College*
Nerissa Felder, *Polk State College*
Mark Ferguson, *Chemeketa Community College*
Jacqui Fields, *Wake Technical Community College*
Diane Fisher, *Louisiana State University–Eunice*
Rhoderick Fleming, *Wake Technical Community College*
David French, *Tidewater Community College–Chesapeake*
Dot French, *Community College of Philadelphia*
Deborah Fries, *Wor-Wic Community College*
Robert Frye, *Polk State College*
Lori Fuller, *Tunxis Community College*
Jesse M. Fuson, *Mountain State University*
Patricia Gary, *North Virginia Community College–Manassas*
Calvin Gatson, *Alabama State University*
Donna Gerken, *Miami Dade College–Kendall*
Mehrnaz Ghaffarian, *Tarrant County College South*
Mark Glucksman, *El Camino College*
Judy Godwin, *Collin County Community College*
Corinna Goehring, *Jackson State Community College*

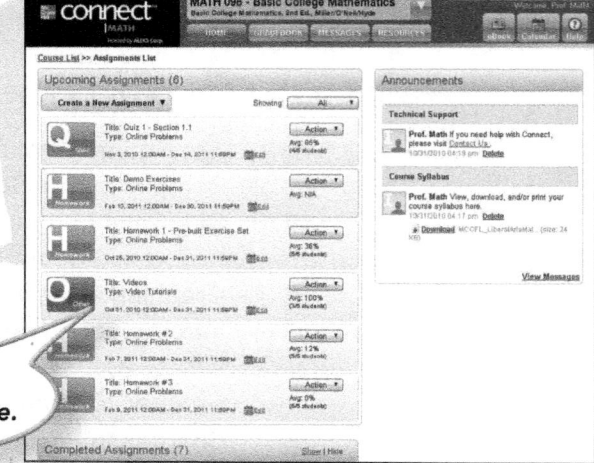

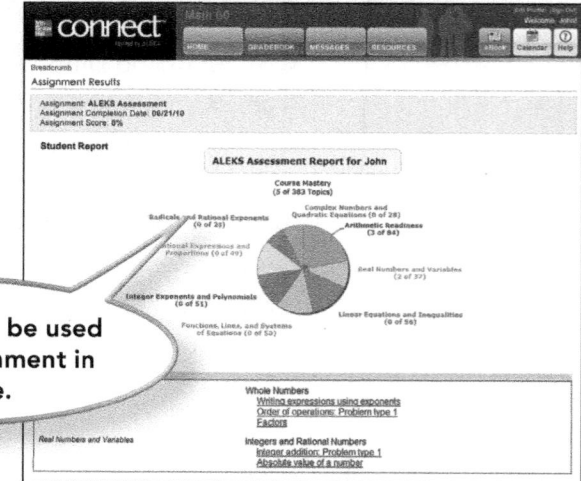

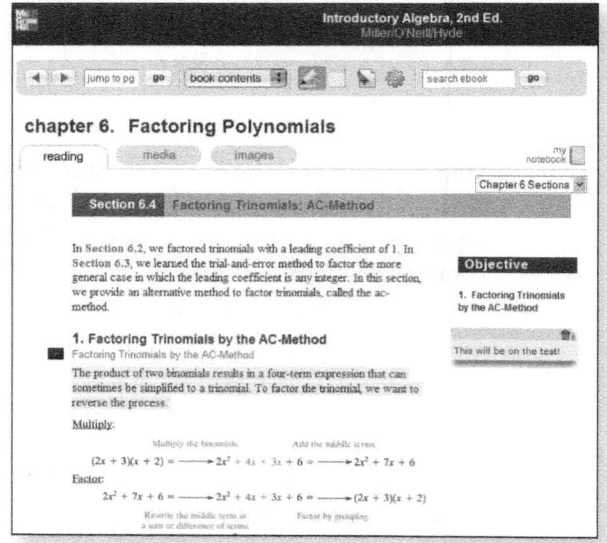

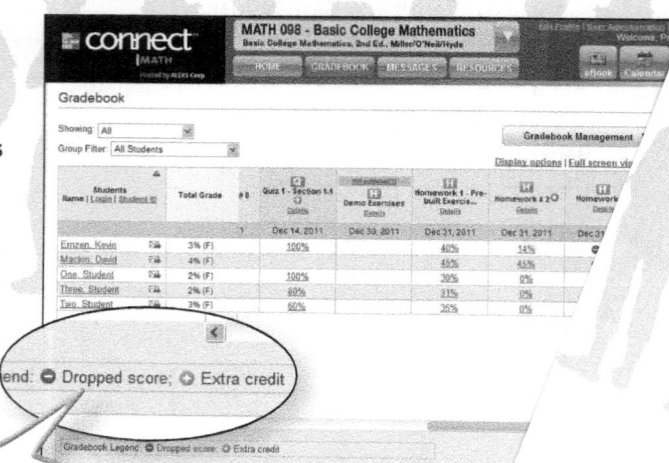

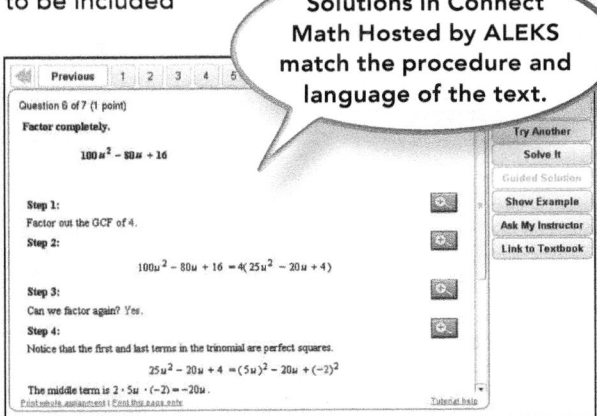

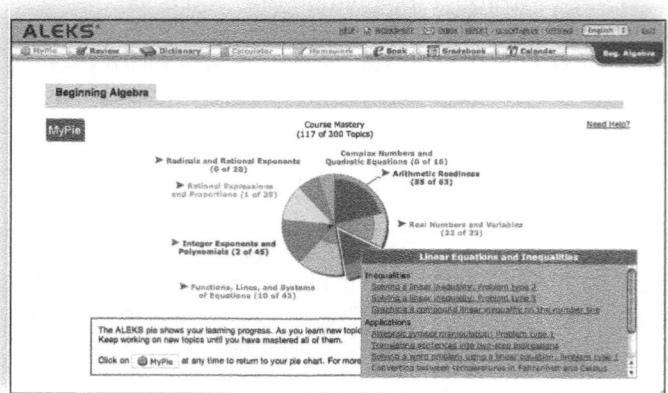

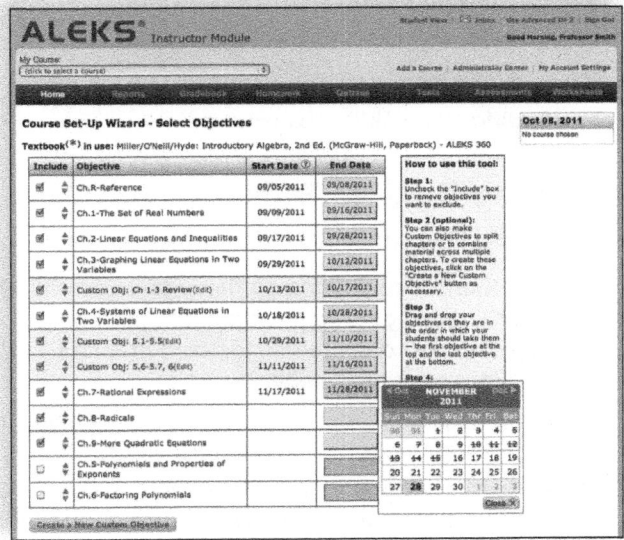

How Will Miller/O'Neill/Hyde Help Your Students *Get Better Results?*

Better Clarity, Quality, and Accuracy

Julie Miller, Molly O'Neill, and Nancy Hyde know what students need to be successful in mathematics. Better results come from clarity in their exposition, quality of step-by-step worked examples, and accuracy of their exercises sets; but it takes more than just great authors to build a textbook series to help students achieve success in mathematics. Our authors worked with a strong mathematical team of instructors from around the country to ensure that the clarity, quality, and accuracy you expect from the Miller/O'Neill/Hyde series was included in this edition.

> "I would describe it as an excellent text written by teachers! It has easy to understand explanations for students. The examples are good and the mathematics is solid. The students should find it "easy to read."
>
> —Teresa Hasenauer, *Indian River State College*

Better Exercise Sets!

Comprehensive sets of exercises are available for every student level. Julie Miller, Molly O'Neill, and Nancy Hyde worked with a national board of advisors from across the country to offer the appropriate depth and breadth of exercises for your students. **Problem Recognition Exercises** were created to improve student performance while testing.

Our practice exercise sets help students progress from skill development to conceptual understanding. Student tested and instructor approved, the Miller/O'Neill/Hyde exercise sets will help your student *get better results*.

- ► **Problem Recognition Exercises**
- ► **Skill Practice Exercises**
- ► **Study Skills Exercises**
- ► **Mixed Exercises**
- ► **Expanding Your Skills Exercises**

> "Extremely interesting and effective practice exercises. I love the study skills component that reminds students of essential habits that will help students achieve success. Review is a great reinforcement technique for recently mastered skills. The exercises are innovative and there are plenty of relevant applications from several fields and disciplines."
>
> —Corinna Goehring, *Jackson State Community College*

Better Step-By-Step Pedagogy!

Prealgebra provides enhanced step-by-step learning tools to help students *get better results*.

- ► **Worked Examples** provide an "easy-to-understand" approach, clearly guiding each student through a step-by-step approach to master each practice exercise for better comprehension.
- ► **TIPs** offer students extra cautious direction to help improve understanding through hints and further insight.
- ► **Avoiding Mistakes** boxes alert students to common errors and provide practical ways to avoid them. Both of these learning aids will help students get better results by showing how to work through a problem using a clearly defined step-by-step methodology that has been class tested and student approved.

> "MOH seems to look into the heads of students and see what mistakes they make and then help the students to avoid them—not only do the Avoiding Mistakes help with this, but the TIPs along the way also help."
>
> —Linda Schott, *Ozark Technical Community College*

Get Better Results

Better Exercise Sets

Better Exercise Sets! Better Practice! Better Results!

▶ Do your students have trouble with problem solving?

▶ Do you want to help students overcome math anxiety?

▶ Do you want to help your students improve performance on math assessments?

Problem Recognition Exercises

Problem Recognition Exercises present a collection of problems that look similar to a student upon first glance, but are actually quite different in the manner of their individual solutions. Students sharpen critical thinking skills and better develop their "solution recall" to help them distinguish the method needed to solve an exercise—an essential skill in developmental mathematics.

Problem Recognition Exercises, tested in a developmental mathematics classroom, were created to improve student performance while testing.

"I like how this author doesn't title all the sections within this PRE. I believe that would be important during testing-anxiety situations. How many times do our students say they did not know what to do and (are) not sure what they were being asked?"

—Christine Baade, *San Juan College*

Problem Recognition Exercises

Operations on Fractions versus Solving Proportions

For Exercises 1–6, identify the problem as a proportion or as a product of fractions. Then solve the proportion or multiply the fractions.

1. **a.** $\dfrac{x}{4} = \dfrac{15}{8}$ **b.** $\dfrac{1}{4} \cdot \dfrac{15}{8}$ 2. **a.** $\dfrac{2}{5} \cdot \dfrac{3}{10}$ **b.** $\dfrac{2}{5} = \dfrac{y}{10}$

3. **a.** $\dfrac{2}{7} \times \dfrac{3}{14}$ **b.** $\dfrac{2}{7} = \dfrac{n}{14}$ 4. **a.** $\dfrac{m}{5} = \dfrac{6}{15}$ **b.** $\dfrac{3}{5} \times \dfrac{6}{15}$

5. **a.** $\dfrac{48}{p} = \dfrac{16}{3}$ **b.** $\dfrac{48}{8} \cdot \dfrac{16}{3}$ 6. **a.** $\dfrac{10}{7} \cdot \dfrac{28}{5}$ **b.** $\dfrac{10}{7} = \dfrac{28}{t}$

For Exercises 7–10, solve the proportion or perform the indicated operation on fractions.

7. **a.** $\dfrac{3}{7} = \dfrac{6}{z}$ **b.** $\dfrac{3}{7} \div \dfrac{6}{35}$ **c.** $\dfrac{3}{7} + \dfrac{6}{35}$ **d.** $\dfrac{3}{7} \cdot \dfrac{6}{35}$

8. **a.** $\dfrac{4}{5} \div \dfrac{20}{3}$ **b.** $\dfrac{4}{v} = \dfrac{20}{3}$ **c.** $\dfrac{4}{5} \times \dfrac{20}{3}$ **d.** $\dfrac{4}{5} - \dfrac{20}{3}$

9. **a.** $\dfrac{14}{5} \cdot \dfrac{10}{7}$ **b.** $\dfrac{14}{5} = \dfrac{x}{7}$ **c.** $\dfrac{14}{5} - \dfrac{10}{7}$ **d.** $\dfrac{14}{5} \div \cdots$

10. **a.** $\dfrac{11}{\,} \cdot \dfrac{66}{y}$ **b.** $\dfrac{11}{3} + \dfrac{66}{11}$ **c.** $\dfrac{11}{3} \div \dfrac{66}{11}$

"These are brilliant! I often do such things in class to get across a point, and I haven't seen them in a text before."

—Russell Penner, *Mohawk Valley Community College*

"This book does a much better job of pairing similar problems for students to be able to practice recognizing different exercises— and as an instructor, I can use these exercises as part of a review and lecture about the need to understand a problem versus just memorizing a process."

—Vicki Lucido, *St. Louis Community College–Florissant Valley*

Julie Miller has been on the faculty in the School of Mathematics at Daytona State College for 20 years, where she has taught developmental and upper-level courses. Prior to her work at DSC, she worked as a software engineer for General Electric in the area of flight and radar simulation. Julie earned a bachelor of science in applied mathematics from Union College in Schenectady, New York, and a master of science in mathematics from the University of Florida. In addition to this textbook, she has authored several course supplements for college algebra, trigonometry, and precalculus, as well as several short works of fiction and nonfiction for young readers.

"My father is a medical researcher, and I got hooked on math and science when I was young and would visit his laboratory. I can remember using graph paper to plot data points for his experiments and doing simple calculations. He would then tell me what the peaks and features in the graph meant in the context of his experiment. I think that applications and hands-on experience made math come alive for me and I'd like to see math come alive for my students."

—Julie Miller

Molly O'Neill is also from Daytona State College, where she has taught for 22 years in the School of Mathematics. She has taught a variety of courses from developmental mathematics to calculus. Before she came to Florida, Molly taught as an adjunct instructor at the University of Michigan–Dearborn, Eastern Michigan University, Wayne State University, and Oakland Community College. Molly earned a bachelor of science in mathematics and a master of arts and teaching from Western Michigan University in Kalamazoo, Michigan. Besides this textbook, she has authored several course supplements for college algebra, trigonometry, and precalculus and has reviewed texts for developmental mathematics.

"I differ from many of my colleagues in that math was not always easy for me. But in seventh grade I had a teacher who taught me that if I follow the rules of mathematics, even I could solve math problems. Once I understood this, I enjoyed math to the point of choosing it for my career. I now have the greatest job because I get to do math every day and I have the opportunity to influence my students just as I was influenced. Authoring these texts has given me another avenue to reach even more students."

—Molly O'Neill

Nancy Hyde served as a full-time faculty member of the Mathematics Department at Broward College for 24 years. During this time she taught the full spectrum of courses from developmental math through differential equations. She received a bachelor of science degree in math education from Florida State University and a master's degree in math education from Florida Atlantic University. She has conducted workshops and seminars for both students and teachers on the use of technology in the classroom. In addition to this textbook, she has authored a graphing calculator supplement for *College Algebra*.

"I grew up in Brevard County, Florida, with my father working at Cape Canaveral. I was always excited by mathematics and physics in relation to the space program. As I studied higher levels of mathematics I became more intrigued by its abstract nature and infinite possibilities. It is enjoyable and rewarding to convey this perspective to students while helping them to understand mathematics."

—Nancy Hyde

William Graesser, *Ivy Tech Community College*

Victoria Gray, *Scott Community College*

Edna Greenwood, *Tarrant County College–Northwest*

Kimberly Gregor, *Delaware Technical Community College–Wilmington*

Vanetta Grier-Felix, *Seminole State College of Florida*

Kathy Grigsby, *Moraine Valley Community College*

Susan Grody, *Broward College–North*

Joseph Guiciardi, *Community College of Allegheny County–Monroeville*

Kathryn Gundersen, *Three Rivers Community College*

Susan Haley, *Florence-Darlington Technical College*

Safa Hamed, *Oakton Community College*

Kelli Hammer, *Broward College–South*

Mary Lou Hammond, *Spokane Community College*

Joseph Harris, *Gulf Coast Community College*

Lloyd Harris, *Gulf Coast Community College*

Mary Harris, *Harrisburg Area Community College–Lancaster*

Susan Harrison, *University of Wisconsin–Eau Claire*

Teresa Hasenauer, *Indian River State College*

Kristen Hathcock, *Barton County Community College*

Mary Beth Headlee, *Manatee Community College*

Rebecca Heiskell, *Mountain View College*

Paul Hernandez, *Palo Alto College*

Marie Hoover, *University of Toledo*

Linda Hoppe, *Jefferson College*

Joe Howe, *St. Charles County Community College*

Glenn Jablonski, *Triton College*

Erin Jacob, *Corning Community College*

Ted Jenkins, *Chaffey College*

Juan Jimenez, *Springfield Technical Community College*

Jennifer Johnson, *Delgado Community College*

Yolanda Johnson, *Tarrant County College South*

Shelbra Jones, *Wake Technical Community College*

Joe Jordan, *John Tyler Community College*

Cheryl Kane, *University of Nebraska–Lincoln*

Ryan Kasha, *Valencia College–West*

Ismail Karahouni, *Lamar University*

Mike Karahouni, *Lamar University–Beaumont*

Susan Kautz, *Cy Fair College*

Joanne Kawczenski, *Luzerne County Community College*

Elaine Keane, *Miami Dade College–North*

Miriam Keesey, *San Diego State University*

Joe Kemble, *Lamar University–Beaumont*

Joanne Kendall, *Cy Fair College*

Patrick Kimani, *Morrisville State College*

Sonny Kirby, *Gadsden State Community College*

Terry Kidd, *Salt Lake Community College*

Vicky Kirkpatrick, *Lane Community College*

Barbara Kistler, *Lehigh Carbon Community College*

Marcia Kleinz, *Atlantic Cape Community College*

Bernadette Kocyba, *J. Sargent Reynolds Community College*

Ron Koehn, *Southwestern Oklahoma State University*

Jeff Koleno, *Lorain County Community College*

Rosa Kontos, *Bergen Community College*

Kathy Kopelousos, *Lewis and Clark Community College*

Randa Kress, *Idaho State University*

Gayle Krzemie, *Pikes Peak Community College*

Gayle Kulinsky, Carla, *Salt Lake Community College*

Linda Kuroski, *Erie Community College*

Gayle Krzemien, *Pikes Peak Community College*

Carla Kulinsky, *Salt Lake Community College*

Catherine Laberta, *Erie Community College–North Campus—Williamsville*

Myrna La Rosa, *Triton College*

Kristi Laird, *Jackson State Community College*

Lider Lamar, *Seminole State College–Lake Mary*

Joyce Langguth, *University of Missouri–St. Louis*

Betty Larson, *South Dakota State University*

Katie Lathan, *Tri-County Technical College*

Kathryn Lavelle, *Westchester Community College*

Alice Lawson-Johnson, *Palo Alto College*

Patricia Lazzarino, *North Virginia Community College–Manassas*

Julie Letellier, *University of Wisconsin–Whitewater*

Mickey Levendusky, *Pima Community College*

Jeanine Lewis, *Aims Community College–Main*

Lisa Lindloff, *McLennan Community College*

Barbara Little, *Central Texas College*

David Liu, *Central Oregon Community College*

Nicole Lloyd, *Lansing Community College*

Maureen Loiacano, *Montgomery College*

Wanda Long, *St. Charles County Community College*

Kerri Lookabill, *Mountain State University*

Barbara Lott, *Seminole State College–Lake Mary*

Ann Loving, *J. Sargeant Reynolds Community College*

Jessica Lowenfield, *Nassau Community College*

Vicki Lucido, *St. Louis Community College–Florissant Valley*

Diane Lussier, *Pima Community College*

Judy Maclaren, *Trinidad State Junior College*

J Robert Malena, *Community College of Allegheny County-South*

Barbara Manley, *Jackson State Community College*

Linda Marable, *Nashville State Technical Community College*

Mark Marino, *Erie Community College–North Campus—Williamsville*

Diane Martling, *William Rainey Harper College*

Dorothy Marshall, *Edison College–Fort Myers*

Diane Masarik, *University of Wisconsin–Whitewater*

Louise Mataox, *Miami Dade College*

Cindy McCallum, *Tarrant County College South*

Joyce McCleod, *Florida Community College–South Campus*

Victoria Mcclendon, *Northwest Arkansas Community College*

Roger McCoach, *County College of Morris*

Stephen F. McCune, *Austin State University*

Ruth McGowan, *St. Louis Community College–Florissant Valley*

Hazel Ennis McKenna, *Utah Valley State College*

Harry McLaughlin, *Montclair State University*

Valerie Melvin, *Cape Fear Community College*

Trudy Meyer, *El Camino College*

Kausha Miller, *Bluegrass Community and Technical College*

Angel Miranda, *Valencia College–Osceola*

Danielle Morgan, *San Jacinto College–South*

Richard Moore, *St. Petersburg College–Seminole*

Reviewers of the Miller/O'Neill/Hyde Developmental Mathematics Series *(continued)*

Elizabeth Morrison, *Valencia College*
Sharon Morrison, *St. Petersburg College*
Shauna Mullins, *Murray State University*
Linda Murphy, *Northern Essex Community College*
Michael Murphy, *Guilford Technical Community College*
Kathy Nabours, *Riverside Community College*
Roya Namavar, *Rogers State University*
Tony Nelson, *Tulsa Community College*
Melinda Nevels, *Utah Valley State College*
Charlotte Newsom, *Tidewater Community College–Virginia Beach*
Brenda Norman, *Tidewater Community College*
David Norwood, *Alabama State University*
Rhoda Oden, *Gadsden State Community College*
Kathleen Offenholley, *Brookdale Community College*
Maria Parker, *Oxnard College*
Tammy Payton, *North Idaho College*
Melissa Pedone, *Valencia College–Osceola*
Russell Penner, *Mohawk Valley Community College*
Shirley Pereira, *Grossmont College*
Pete Peterson, *John Tyler Community College*
Suzie Pickle, *St. Petersburg College*
Sheila Pisa, *Riverside Community College–Moreno Valley*
Marilyn Platt, *Gaston College*
Richard Ponticelli, *North Shore Community College*
Tammy Potter, *Gadsden State Community College*
Sara Pries, *Sierra College*
Joel Rappaport, *Florida Community College*
Kumars Ranjbaran, *Mountain View College*
Ali Ravandi, *College of the Mainland*
Sherry Ray, *Oklahoma City Community College*
Linda Reist, *Macomb Community College*
Nancy Ressler, *Oakton Community College*
Natalie Rivera, *Estrella Mountain Community College*
Angelia Reynolds, *Gulf Coast Community College*
Suellen Robinson, *North Shore Community College*
Jeri Rogers, *Seminole State College–Oviedo*
Trisha Roth, *Gloucester County College*
Pat Rowe, *Columbus State Community College*
Richard Rupp, *Del Mar College*
Dave Ruszkiewicz, *Milwaukee Area Technical College*
Kristina Sampson, *Cy Fair College*
Nancy Sattler, *Terra Community College*
Vicki Schell, *Pensacola Junior College*
Rainer Schochat, *Triton College*
Linda Schott, *Ozarks Technical Community College*
Nyeita Schult, *St. Petersburg College*
Sally Sestini, *Cerritos College*
Wendiann Sethi, *Seton Hall University*
Dustin Sharp, *Pittsburg Community College*
Kathleen Shepherd, *Monroe County Community College*
Rose Shirey, *College of the Mainland*
Marvin Shubert, *Hagerstown Community College*
Plamen Simeonov, *University of Houston–Downtown*

Carolyn Smith, *Armstrong Atlantic State University*
Melanie Smith, *Bishop State Community College*
Domingo Soria-Martin, *Solano Community College*
Joel Spring, *Broward College–South*
Melissa Spurlock, *Anne Arundel Community College*
John Squires, *Cleveland State Community College*
Sharon Staver, Judith, *Florida Community College–South Campus*
Shirley Stewart, *Pikes Peak Community College*
Sharon Steuer, *Nassau Community College*
Trudy Streilein, *North Virginia Community College–Annandale*
Barbara Strauch, *Devry University–Tinley Park*
Jennifer Strehler, *Oakton Community College*
Renee Sundrud, *Harrisburg Area Community College*
Gretchen Syhre, *Hawkeye Community College*
Katalin Szucs, *Pittsburg Community College*
Shae Thompson, *Montana State University–Bozeman*
John Thoo, *Yuba College*
Mike Tiano, *Suffolk County Community College*
Joseph Tripp, *Ferris State University*
Stephen Toner, *Victor Valley College*
Mary Lou Townsend, *Wor-Wic Community College*
Susan Twigg, *Wor-Wic Community College*
Matthew Utz, *University of Arkansas–Fort Smith*
Joan Van Glabek, *Edison College–Fort Myers*
Laura Van Husen, *Midland College*
John Van Kleef, *Guilford Technical Community College*
Diane Veneziale, *Burlington County College–Pemberton*
Andrea Vorwark, *Metropolitan Community College–Maple Woods*
Edward Wagner, *Central Texas College*
David Wainaina, *Coastal Carolina Community College*
Karen Walsh, *Broward College–North*
James Wang, *University of Alabama*
Richard Watkins, *Tidewater Community College–Virginia Beach*
Sharon Wayne, *Patrick Henry Community College*
Leben Wee, *Montgomery College*
Jennifer Wilson, *Tyler Junior College*
Betty Vix Weinberger, *Delgado Community College–City Park*
Christine Wetzel-Ulrich, *Northampton Community College*
Jackie Wing, *Angelina College*
Michelle Wolcott, *Pierce College*
Deborah Wolfson, *Suffolk County Community College–Brentwood*
Mary Wolyniak, *Broome Community College*
Rick Woodmansee, *Sacramento City College*
Susan Working, *Grossmont College*
Karen Wyrick, *Cleveland State Community College*
Alan Yang, *Columbus State Community College*
Michael Yarbrough, *Cosumnes River College*
Kevin Yokoyama, *College of the Redwoods*
William Young, Jr, *Century College*
Vasilis Zafiris, *University of Houston*
Vivian Zimmerman, *Prairie State College*

Supplements

For the Instructor

Instructor's Resource Manual

The *Instructor's Resource Manual (IRM)*, written by the authors, is a printable electronic supplement available through Connect Math Hosted by ALEKS Corp. The *IRM* includes discovery-based classroom activities, worksheets for drill and practice, materials for a student portfolio, and tips for implementing successful cooperative learning. Numerous classroom activities are available for each section of text and can be used as a complement to the lectures or can be assigned for work outside of class. The activities are designed for group or individual work and take about 5–10 minutes each. With increasing demands on faculty schedules, these ready-made lessons offer a convenient means for both full-time and adjunct faculty to promote active learning in the classroom. This supplement is also available as a Student Resource Manual. Students can follow along with their instructor or use the manual individually as needed.

Instructor's Test Bank

Among the supplements is a **computerized test bank** utilizing Brownstone Diploma® algorithm-based testing software to create customized exams quickly. This user-friendly program enables instructors to search for questions by topic, format, or difficulty level; to edit existing questions or to add new ones; and to scramble questions and answer keys for multiple versions of a single test. Hundreds of text-specific, open-ended, and multiple-choice questions are included in the question bank. Sample chapter tests are also provided.

Annotated Instructor's Edition

In the *Annotated Instructor's Edition (AIE)*, **answers to all exercises and tests appear adjacent to each exercise,** in a color used *only* for annotations. The *AIE* also contains **Instructor Notes** that appear in the margin. The notes may assist with lecture preparation. Also found in the *AIE* are icons within the Practice Exercises that serve to guide instructors in their preparation of homework assignments and lessons.

Another significant feature new to this edition is the inclusion of ***Classroom Examples*** for the instructor. In the Annotated Instructor's Edition of the text, we include references to even-numbered exercises at the end of the section for instructors to use as *Classroom Examples*. These exercises mirror the examples in the text. Therefore, if an instructor covers these exercises as classroom examples, then all the major objectives in that section will have been covered. This feature was added because we recognize the growing demands on faculty time, and to assist new faculty, adjunct faculty, and graduate assistants. Furthermore, because these exercises appear in the student edition of the text, students will not waste valuable class time copying down complicated examples from the board.

Instructor's Solutions Manual

The *Instructor's Solutions Manual* provides comprehensive, worked-out solutions to all exercises in the Chapter Openers; the Practice Exercises; the Problem Recognition Exercises; the end-of-chapter Review Exercises; the Chapter Tests; and the Cumulative Review Exercises.

For the Student

ALEKS Prep for Developmental Mathematics

ALEKS Prep for Beginning Algebra and Prep for Intermediate Algebra focus on prerequisite and introductory material for Beginning Algebra and Intermediate Algebra. These prep products can be used during the first 3 weeks of a course to prepare students for future success in the course and to increase retention and pass rates. Backed by two decades of National Science Foundation funded research, ALEKS interacts with students much like a human tutor, with the ability to precisely asses a student's preparedness and provide instruction on the topics the student is most likely to learn.

ALEKS Prep Course Products Feature:

- Artificial Intelligence Targets Gaps in Individual Students Knowledge
- Assessment and Learning Directed Toward Individual Students Needs
- Open Response Environment with Realistic Input Tools
- Unlimited Online Access-PC & Mac Compatible

Free trial at www.aleks.com/free_trial/instructor

Student's Solutions Manual

The *Student's Solutions Manual* provides comprehensive, worked-out solutions to the odd-numbered exercises in the Practice Exercise sets; the Problem Recognition Exercises, the end-of-chapter Review Exercises, the Chapter Tests, and the Cumulative Review Exercises. Answers to the odd- and even-numbered entries to the Chapter Opener Puzzles are also provided.

NEW Lecture Videos created by Julie Miller

Julie Miller began creating these lecture videos for her own students to use when they were absent and unable to attend one of her lectures. She found them to be so helpful, that she decided to create the lecture videos for her entire developmental math book series. In these new videos, Julie walks students through the learning objectives using the same language and procedures outlined in the book. Students are able to learn and review right alongside the author! Students can also access the note files that accompany the videos so that they can take their notes while following the video just like a classroom lecture. These videos as well as the exercise videos are available online through Connect Math Hosted by ALEKS Corp.

The videos are closed-captioned for the hearing-impaired, and meet the Americans with Disabilities Act Standards for Accessible Design. Instructors may use them as resources in a learning center, for online courses, and to provide additional help for students who require extra practice.

Exercise Video Series

The video series is based on examples and exercises from the textbook. Each presenter works through selected problems or examples, following the solution methodology employed in the text. The video series is available online as part of Connect Hosted by ALEKS Corp. The videos are closed-captioned for the hearing impaired, and meet the Americans with Disabilities Act Standards for Accessible Design.

Whole Numbers

1

Chapter 1

Chapter 1 begins with adding, subtracting, multiplying, and dividing whole numbers. We also include rounding, estimating, and applying the order of operations.

Are You Prepared?

Before you begin this chapter, check your skill level by trying the exercises in the puzzle. If you have trouble with any of these problems, come back to the puzzle as you work through the chapter and fill in the answers that gave you trouble.

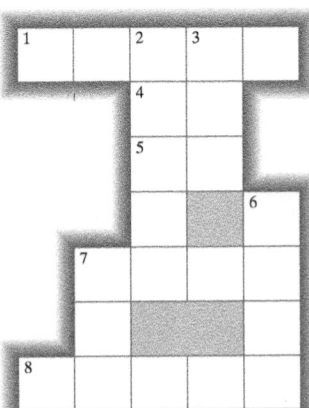

Across

1. $24{,}159 - 3168$
4. 8^2
5. 2^5
7. $1600 \div 4 \times 8$
8. $3^3 \cdot 1000$

Down

2. $39{,}504 + 56{,}798$
3. $11{,}304 \div 12$
6. $(13 - \sqrt{9})^3$
7. $100 - 5 \cdot 4 + 277$

Section 1.1   Study Tips

Objectives

1. Before the Course
2. During the Course
3. Preparation for Exams
4. Where to Go for Help

In taking a course in algebra, you are making a commitment to yourself, your instructor, and your classmates. Following some or all of the study tips below can help you be successful in this endeavor. The features of this text that will assist you are printed in blue.

1. Before the Course

- Purchase the necessary materials for the course before the course begins or on the first day.
- Obtain a three-ring binder to keep and organize your notes, homework, tests, and any other materials acquired in the class. We call this type of notebook a *portfolio*.
- Arrange your schedule so that you have enough time to attend class and to do homework. A common rule is to set aside at least 2 hours for homework for every hour spent in class. That is, if you are taking a 4-credit-hour course, plan on at least 8 hours a week for homework. If you experience difficulty in mathematics, plan for more time. A 4-credit-hour course will then take *at least* 12 hours each week—about the same as a part-time job.
- Communicate with your employer and family members the importance of your success in this course so that they can support you.
- Be sure to find out the type of calculator (if any) that your instructor requires.

2. During the Course

- Read the section in the text *before* the lecture to familiarize yourself with the material and terminology.
- Attend every class and be on time.
- Take notes in class. Write down all of the examples that the instructor presents. Read the notes after class and add any comments to make your notes clearer to you. Use a tape recorder to record the lecture if the instructor permits the recording of lectures.
- Ask questions in class.
- Read the section in the text *after* the lecture and pay special attention to the Tip boxes and Avoiding Mistakes boxes.
- After you read an example, try the accompanying Skill Practice problem in the margin. The skill practice problem mirrors the example and tests your understanding of what you have read.
- Do homework every night. Even if your class does not meet every day, you should still do some work every night to keep the material fresh in your mind.
- Check your homework with the answers that are supplied in the back of this text. Correct the exercises that do not match and circle or star those that you cannot correct yourself. This way you can easily find them and ask your instructor the next day.
- Write the definition and give an example of each Key Term found at the beginning of the Practice Exercises.
- The Problem Recognition Exercises are located in most chapters. These provide additional practice distinguishing among a variety of problem types. Sometimes the most difficult part of learning mathematics is retaining all that you learn. These exercises are excellent tools for retention of material.

- Form a study group with fellow students in your class and exchange phone numbers. You will be surprised by how much you can learn by talking about mathematics with other students.
- If you use a calculator in your class, read the Calculator Connections boxes to learn how and when to use your calculator.
- Ask your instructor where you might obtain extra help if necessary.

3. Preparation for Exams

- Look over your homework. Pay special attention to the exercises you have circled or starred to be sure that you have learned that concept.
- Read through the Summary at the end of the chapter. Be sure that you understand each concept and example. If not, go to the section in the text and reread that section.
- Give yourself enough time to take the Chapter Test uninterrupted. Then check the answers. For each problem you answered incorrectly, go to the Review Exercises and do all of the problems that are similar.
- To prepare for the final exam, complete the Cumulative Review Exercises at the end of each chapter, starting with Chapter 2. If you complete the cumulative reviews after finishing each chapter, then you will be preparing for the final exam throughout the course. The Cumulative Review Exercises are another excellent tool for helping you retain material.

4. Where to Go for Help

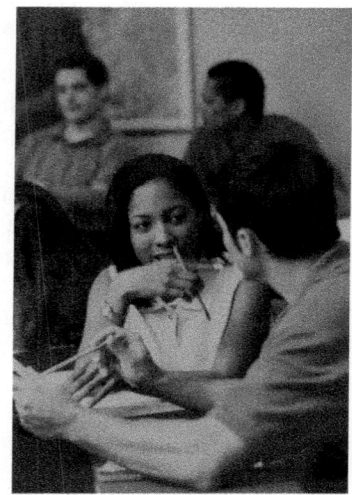

- At the first sign of trouble, see your instructor. Most instructors have specific office hours set aside to help students. Don't wait until after you have failed an exam to seek assistance.
- Get a tutor. Most colleges and universities have free tutoring available.
- When your instructor and tutor are unavailable, use the Student Solutions Manual for step-by-step solutions to the odd-numbered problems in the exercise sets.
- Work with another student from your class.
- Work on the computer. Many mathematics tutorial programs and websites are available on the Internet, including the website that accompanies this text: www.mhhe.com/moh

Group Activity

Becoming a Successful Student

Materials: Computer with Internet access and textbook

Estimated time: 15 minutes

Group Size: 4

Good time management, good study skills, and good organization will help you be successful in this course. Answer the following questions and compare your answers with your group members.

1. To motivate yourself to complete a course, it is helpful to have clear reasons for taking the course. List your goals for taking this course and discuss them with your group.

2. For the following week, write down the times each day that you plan to study math.

Monday	Tuesday	Wednesday	Thursday	Friday	Saturday	Sunday

3. Write down the date of your next math test. _____

4. Taking 12 credit-hours is the equivalent of a full-time job. Often students try to work too many hours while taking classes at school.

a. Write down the number of hours you work per week and the number of credit hours you are taking this term.

number of hours worked per week _____

number of credit-hours this term _____

b. The table gives a recommended limit to the number of hours you should work for the number of credit hours you are taking at school. (Keep in mind that other responsibilities in your life such as your family might also make it necessary to limit your hours at work even more.) How do your numbers from part (a) compare to those in the table? Are you working too many hours?

Number of Credit-Hours	Maximum Number of Hours of Work per Week
3	40
6	30
9	20
12	10
15	0

5. Look through the book in Chapter 2 and find the page number corresponding to each feature in the book. Discuss with your group members how you might use each feature.

Problem Recognition Exercises: page _____

Chapter Summary: page _____

Chapter Review Exercises: page _____

Chapter Test: page _____

Cumulative Review Exercises: page _____

6. Look at the Skill Practice exercises in the margin (for example, find Skill Practice exercises 2–4 in Section 1.2). Where are the answers to these exercises located? Discuss with your group members how you might use the Skill Practice exercises.

7. Discuss with your group members places where you can go for extra help in math. Then write down three of the suggestions.

_____

_____

_____

8. Do you keep an organized notebook for this class? Can you think of any suggestions that you can share with your group members to help them keep their materials organized?

9. Do you think that you have math anxiety? Read the following list for some possible solutions. Check the activities that you can realistically try to help you overcome this problem.

_____ Read a book on math anxiety.

_____ Search the Web for helpful tips on handling math anxiety.

_____ See a counselor to discuss your anxiety.

_____ See your instructor to inform him or her about your situation.

_____ Evaluate your time management to see if you are trying to do too much. Then adjust your schedule accordingly.

10. Some students favor different methods of learning over others. For example, you might prefer:

• Learning through listening and hearing.

• Learning through seeing images, watching demonstrations, and visualizing diagrams and charts.

• Learning by experience through a hands-on approach by doing things.

• Learning through reading and writing.

Most experts believe that the most effective learning comes when a student engages in *all* of these activities. However, each individual is different and may benefit from one activity more than another. You can visit a number of different websites to determine your "learning style." Try doing a search on the Internet with the key words *"learning styles assessment."* Once you have found a suitable website, answer the questionnaire, and the site will give you feedback on what method of learning works best for you.

Introduction to Whole Numbers

Section 1.2

1. Place Value

Objectives

Numbers provide the foundation that is used in mathematics. We begin this chapter by discussing how numbers are represented and named. All numbers in our numbering system are composed from the **digits** 0, 1, 2, 3, 4, 5, 6, 7, 8, and 9. In mathematics, the numbers 0, 1, 2, 3, 4, 5, 6, 7, 8, 9, 10, 11, 12, . . . are called the *whole numbers.* (The three dots are called *ellipses* and indicate that the list goes on indefinitely.)

1. Place Value
2. Standard Notation and Expanded Notation
3. Writing Numbers in Words
4. The Number Line and Order

For large numbers, commas are used to separate digits into groups of three called **periods**. For example, the number of live births in the United States in a recent year was 4,058,614 (*Source: The World Almanac*). Numbers written in this way are said to be in **standard form**. The position of each digit within a number determines the place value of the digit. To interpret the number of births in the United States, refer to the place value chart (Figure 1-1).

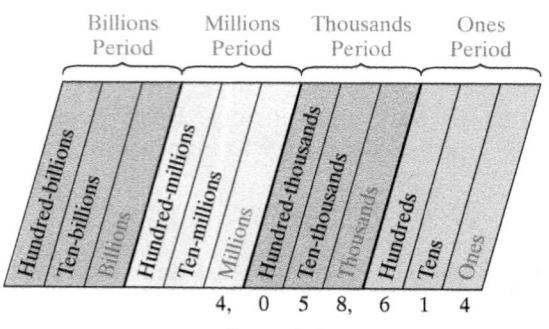

Billions Period   Millions Period   Thousands Period   Ones Period

4, 0 5 8, 6 1 4

Figure 1-1

The digit 5 in the number 4,058,614 represents 5 ten-thousands because it is in the ten-thousands place. The digit 4 on the left represents 4 millions, whereas the digit 4 on the right represents 4 ones.

Skill Practice

Determine the place value of the digit 4 in each number.

2. 547,098,632
3. 1,659,984,036
4. 6420

Example 1   **Determining Place Value**

Determine the place value of the digit 2 in each number.

a. 417,216,900   b. 724   c. 502,000,700

Solution:

a. 417,216,900   hundred-thousands

b. 724   tens

c. 502,000,700   millions

Skill Practice

5. Alaska is the largest state geographically. Its land area is 571,962 square miles (mi²). Give the place value for each digit.

Example 2   **Determining Place Value**

The altitude of Mount Everest, the highest mountain on earth, is 29,035 feet (ft). Give the place value for each digit in this number.

Solution:

29,035

— ones
— tens
— hundreds
— thousands
— ten-thousands

Answers

1. First 3 (on the left) represents 3 hundreds, while the second 3 (on the right) represents 3 ones.
2. Ten-millions
3. Thousands
4. Hundreds
5. 5: hundred-thousands
   7: ten-thousands
   1: thousands   9: hundreds
   6: tens   2: ones

2. Standard Notation and Expanded Notation

A number can also be written in an expanded form by writing each digit with its place value unit. For example, the number 287 can be written as

$$287 = 2 \text{ hundreds} + 8 \text{ tens} + 7 \text{ ones}$$

This is called **expanded form**.

Example 3 Converting Standard Form to Expanded Form

Convert to expanded form.

a. 4672   **b.** 257,016

Solution:

a. 4672   4 thousands + 6 hundreds + 7 tens + 2 ones

b. 257,016   2 hundred-thousands + 5 ten-thousands +
                    7 thousands + 1 ten + 6 ones

┌─ **Skill Practice** ─────┐
Convert to expanded form.
  6. 837
  7. 4,093,062
└──────────────────────────┘

Example 4 Converting Expanded Form to Standard Form

Convert to standard form.

a. 2 hundreds + 5 tens + 9 ones

b. 1 thousand + 2 tens + 5 ones

Solution:

a. 2 hundreds + 5 tens + 9 ones = 259

b. Each place position from the thousands place to the ones place must contain a digit. In this problem, there is no reference to the hundreds place digit. Therefore, we assume 0 hundreds. Thus,

1 thousand + 0 hundreds + 2 tens + 5 ones = 1025

┌─ **Skill Practice** ─────┐
Convert to standard form.
  8. 8 thousands + 5 hundreds +
      5 tens + 1 one
  9. 5 hundred-thousands +
      4 thousands + 8 tens +
      3 ones
└──────────────────────────┘

3. Writing Numbers in Words

The word names of some two-digit numbers appear with a hyphen, while others do not. For example:

Number	Number Name
12	twelve
68	sixty-eight
40	forty
42	forty-two

To write a three-digit or larger number, begin at the leftmost group of digits. The number named in that group is followed by the period name, followed by a comma. Then the next period is named, and so on.

Answers
6. 8 hundreds + 3 tens + 7 ones
7. 4 millions + 9 ten-thousands +
    3 thousands + 6 tens + 2 ones
8. 8551   **9.** 504,083

Example 5   **Writing a Number in Words**

Write the number 621,417,325 in words.

Solution:

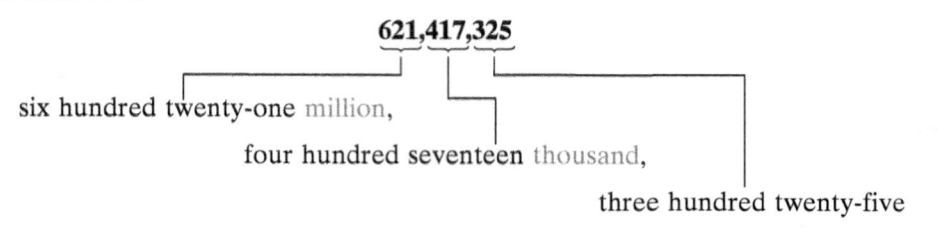

Notice from Example 5 that when naming numbers, the name of the ones period is not attached to the last group of digits. Also note that for whole numbers, the word *and* should not appear in word names. For example, the number 405 should be written as four hundred five.

Example 6   **Writing a Number in Standard Form**

Write the number in standard form.

Six million, forty-six thousand, nine hundred three

Solution:

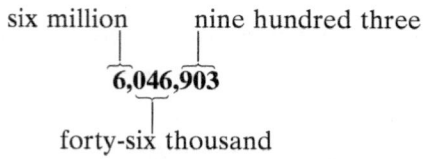

We have seen several examples of writing a number in standard form, in expanded form, and in words. Standard form is the most concise representation. Also note that when we write a four-digit number in standard form, the comma is often omitted. For example, the number 4,389 is often written as 4389.

4. The Number Line and Order

Whole numbers can be visualized as equally spaced points on a line called a *number line* (Figure 1-2).

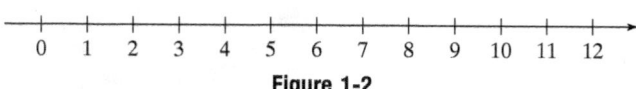

Figure 1-2

The whole numbers begin at 0 and are ordered from left to right by increasing value.

A number is graphed on a number line by placing a dot at the corresponding point. For any two numbers graphed on a number line, the number to the left is less than the number to the right. Similarly, a number to the right is greater than the number to the left. In mathematics, the symbol $<$ is used to denote "is less than," and the symbol $>$ means "is greater than." Therefore,

$3 < 5$ means   3 is less than 5
$5 > 3$ means   5 is greater than 3

Example 7   **Determining Order of Two Numbers**

Fill in the blank with the symbol $<$ or $>$.

a. 7 ☐ 0   **b.** 30 ☐ 82

Solution:

a. 7 $\boxed{>}$ 0

b. 30 $\boxed{<}$ 82

To visualize the numbers 82 and 30 on the number line, it may be necessary to use a different scale. Rather than setting equally spaced marks in units of 1, we can use units of 10. The number 82 must be somewhere between 80 and 90 on the number line.

Skill Practice

Fill in the blank with the symbol $<$ or $>$.
12. 9 ☐ 5
13. 8 ☐ 18

Answers
12. $>$ **13.** $<$

Section 1.2   Practice Exercises

Study Skills Exercises

In this text, we provide skills for you to enhance your learning experience. Many of the practice exercises begin with an activity that focuses on one of seven areas: learning about your course, using your text, taking notes, doing homework, taking an exam (test and math anxiety), managing your time, and studying for the final exam.

Each activity requires only a few minutes and will help you pass this class and become a better math student. Many of these skills can be carried over to other disciplines and help you become a model college student.

1. To begin, write down the following information.

   a. Instructor's name

   b. Instructor's office number

   c. Instructor's telephone number

   d. Instructor's email address

   e. Instructor's office hours

   f. Days of the week that the class meets

   g. The room number in which the class meets

   h. Is there a lab requirement for this course? If so, where is the lab located and how often must you go?

2. Define the key terms.

   a. Digit   **b. Standard form**   **c. Periods**   **d. Expanded form**

Objective 1: Place Value

3. Name the place value for each digit in the number 8,213,457.

4. Name the place value for each digit in the number 103,596.

For Exercises 5–24, determine the place value for each underlined digit. **(See Example 1.)**

5. 3<u>2</u>1	**6.** 6<u>8</u>9	**7.** 21<u>4</u>	**8.** 73<u>8</u>
9. 8<u>7</u>10	**10.** 2<u>2</u>93	**11.** <u>1</u>430	**12.** <u>3</u>101
13. <u>4</u>52,723	**14.** 6<u>5</u>5,878	**15.** 1,023,676,207	**16.** <u>3</u>,111,901,211
17. <u>2</u>2,422	**18.** <u>5</u>8,106	**19.** 51,<u>0</u>33,201	**20.** 93,<u>9</u>71,224

21. The number of U.S. travelers abroad in a recent year was <u>1</u>0,677,881. **(See Example 2.)**

22. The area of Lake Superior is 31,820 square miles (mi²).

23. For a recent year, the total number of U.S. $1 bills in circulation was <u>7</u>,653,468,440.

24. For a certain flight, the cruising altitude of a commercial jet is 3<u>1</u>,000 ft.

Objective 2: Standard Notation and Expanded Notation

For Exercises 25–32, convert the numbers to expanded form. **(See Example 3.)**

25. 58	**26.** 71	**27.** 539	**28.** 382
29. 5203	**30.** 7089	**31.** 10,241	**32.** 20,873

For Exercises 33–40, convert the numbers to standard form. **(See Example 4.)**

33. 5 hundreds + 2 tens + 4 ones

34. 3 hundreds + 1 ten + 8 ones

35. 1 hundred + 5 tens

36. 6 hundreds + 2 tens

37. 1 thousand + 9 hundreds + 6 ones

38. 4 thousands + 2 hundreds + 1 one

39. 8 ten-thousands + 5 thousands + 7 ones

40. 2 ten-thousands + 6 thousands + 2 ones

41. Name the first four periods of a number (from right to left).

42. Name the first four place values of a number (from right to left).

Objective 3: Writing Numbers in Words

For Exercises 43–50, write the number in words. **(See Example 5.)**

43. 241   **44.** 327   **45.** 603   **46.** 108

47. 31,530   **48.** 52,160   **49.** 100,234   **50.** 400,199

51. The Shuowen jiezi dictionary, an ancient Chinese dictionary that dates back to the year 100, contained 9535 characters. Write the number 9535 in words.

52. Interstate I-75 is 1377 miles (mi) long. Write the number 1377 in words.

53. The altitude of Mt. McKinley in Alaska is 20,320 ft. Write the number 20,320 in words.

54. There are 1800 seats in the Regal Champlain Theater in Plattsburgh, New York. Write the number 1800 in words.

55. Researchers calculate that about 590,712 stone blocks were used to construct the Great Pyramid. Write the number 590,712 in words.

56. In the United States, there are approximately 60,000,000 cats living in households. Write the number 60,000,000 in words.

For Exercises 57–62, convert the number to standard form. **(See Example 6.)**

57. Six thousand, five

58. Four thousand, four

59. Six hundred seventy-two thousand

60. Two hundred forty-eight thousand

61. One million, four hundred eighty-four thousand, two hundred fifty

62. Two million, six hundred forty-seven thousand, five hundred twenty

Objective 4: The Number Line and Order

For Exercises 63–64, graph the numbers on the number line.

63. a. 6   **b.** 13   **c.** 8   **d.** 1

64. a. 5   **b.** 3   **c.** 11   **d.** 9

65. On a number line, what number is 4 units to the right of 6?

66. On a number line, what number is 8 units to the left of 11?

67. On a number line, what number is 3 units to the left of 7?

68. On a number line, what number is 5 units to the right of 0?

For Exercises 69–72, translate the inequality to words.

69. $8 > 2$ **70.** $6 < 11$ **71.** $3 < 7$ **72.** $14 > 12$

For Exercises 73–84, fill in the blank with the inequality symbol $<$ or $>$. **(See Example 7.)**

73. 6 ☐ 11   **74.** 14 ☐ 13   **75.** 21 ☐ 18   **76.** 5 ☐ 7

77. 3 ☐ 7   **78.** 14 ☐ 24   **79.** 95 ☐ 89   **80.** 28 ☐ 30

81. 0 ☐ 3   **82.** 8 ☐ 0   **83.** 90 ☐ 91   **84.** 48 ☐ 47

Expanding Your Skills

85. Answer true or false. The number 12 is a digit.

86. Answer true or false. The number 26 is a digit.

87. What is the greatest two-digit number?

88. What is the greatest three-digit number?

89. What is the greatest whole number?

90. What is the least whole number?

91. How many zeros are there in the number ten million?

92. How many zeros are there in the number one hundred billion?

93. What is the greatest three-digit number that can be formed from the digits 6, 9, and 4? Use each digit only once.

94. What is the greatest three-digit number that can be formed from the digits 0, 4, and 8? Use each digit only once.

Section 1.3   **Addition and Subtraction of Whole Numbers and Perimeter**

Objectives

1. Addition of Whole Numbers
2. Properties of Addition
3. Subtraction of Whole Numbers
4. Translations and Applications Involving Addition and Subtraction
5. Perimeter

1. Addition of Whole Numbers

We use addition of whole numbers to represent an increase in quantity. For example, suppose Jonas typed 5 pages of a report before lunch. Later in the afternoon he typed 3 more pages. The total number of pages that he typed is found by adding 5 and 3.

$$5 \text{ pages} + 3 \text{ pages} = 8 \text{ pages}$$

The result of an addition problem is called the **sum**, and the numbers being added are called **addends**. Thus,

$$5 + 3 = 8$$

addends   sum

--- Concept Connections ---

1. Identify the addends and the sum.
$$3 + 7 + 12 = 22$$

Answer

1. Addends: 3, 7, and 12; sum: 22

The number line is a useful tool to visualize the operation of addition. To add 5 and 3 on a number line, begin at 5 and move 3 units to the right. The final location indicates the sum.

0   1   2   3   4   5   6   7   8   9   10

The sum
is 8.

You can use a number line to find the sum of any pair of digits. The sums for all possible pairs of one-digit numbers should be memorized (see Exercise 7). Memorizing these basic addition facts will make it easier for you to add larger numbers.

To add whole numbers with several digits, line up the numbers vertically by place value. Then add the digits in the corresponding place positions.

Example 1 **Adding Whole Numbers**

Add. $261 + 28$

Solution:

```
    261  ┌─ Add digits in
  +  28  │   ones column.
  ─────  ├─ Add digits in
    289 ─┘   tens column.
         └─ Add digits in
             hundreds column.
```

┌─ **Skill Practice** ─┐
2. Add.
    $4135 + 210$

Sometimes when adding numbers, the sum of the digits in a given place position is greater than 9. If this occurs, we must do what is called *carrying* or *regrouping*. Example 2 illustrates this process.

Example 2 **Adding Whole Numbers with Carrying**

Add. $35 + 48$

Solution:

$$35 = 3 \text{ tens} + 5 \text{ ones}$$
$$+ 48 = 4 \text{ tens} + 8 \text{ ones}$$
$$\overline{7 \text{ tens} + 13 \text{ ones}}$$

The sum of the digits in the ones place exceeds 9. But 13 ones is the same as 1 ten and 3 ones. We can *carry* 1 ten to the tens column while leaving the 3 ones in the ones column. Notice that we placed the carried digit above the tens column.

$$\overset{1\overset{1 \text{ ten}}{}}{35} = 3 \text{ tens} + 5 \text{ ones}$$
$$+ 48 = 4 \text{ tens} + 8 \text{ ones}$$
$$\overline{83 = 8 \text{ tens} + 3 \text{ ones}}$$

The sum is 83.

┌─ **Skill Practice** ─┐
3. Add.
    $43 + 29$

Answers
2. 4345   **3.** 72

Addition of numbers may include more than two addends.

Example 3 **Adding Whole Numbers**

Add. $21{,}076 + 84{,}158 + 2419$

Solution:

$$
\begin{array}{r}
\overset{\scriptstyle 1\,2}{21{,}076} \\
84{,}158 \\
+\ \ \ 2{,}419 \\
\hline
107{,}653
\end{array}
$$

In this example, the sum of the digits in the ones column is 23. Therefore, we write the 3 and carry the 2.

In the tens column, the sum is 15. Write the 5 in the tens place and carry the 1.

2. Properties of Addition

A **variable** is a letter or symbol that represents a number. The following are examples of variables: a, b, and c. We will use variables to present three important properties of addition.

   Most likely you have noticed that 0 added to any number is that number. For example:

$$6 + 0 = 6 \qquad 527 + 0 = 527 \qquad 0 + 88 = 88 \qquad 0 + 15 = 15$$

In each example, the number in red can be replaced with any number that we choose, and the statement would still be true. This fact is stated as the addition property of 0.

> **PROPERTY** **Addition Property of 0**
> For any number a,
> $$a + 0 = a \quad \text{and} \quad 0 + a = a$$
> The sum of any number and 0 is that number.

The order in which we add two numbers does not affect the result. For example: $11 + 20 = 20 + 11$. This is true for any two numbers and is stated in the next property.

> **PROPERTY** **Commutative Property of Addition**
> For any numbers a and b,
> $$a + b = b + a$$
> Changing the order of two addends does not affect the sum.

In mathematics we use parentheses ( ) as grouping symbols. To add more than two numbers, we can group them and then add. For example:

$(2 + 3) + 8$ Parentheses indicate that $2 + 3$ is added first. Then 8 is added to the result.

$= 5 + 8$

$= 13$

2 + (3 + 8)   Parentheses indicate that 3 + 8 is added first. Then the
= 2 + 11   result is added to 2.
= 13

PROPERTY **Associative Property of Addition**

For any numbers $a, b,$ and $c,$

$$(a + b) + c = a + (b + c)$$

The manner in which addends are grouped does not affect the sum.

Example 4 **Applying the Properties of Addition**

a. Rewrite 9 + 6, using the commutative property of addition.

b. Rewrite (15 + 9) + 5, using the associative property of addition.

Solution:

a. 9 + 6 = 6 + 9   Change the order of the addends.

b. (15 + 9) + 5 = 15 + (9 + 5)   Change the grouping of the addends.

Skill Practice

5. Rewrite 3 + 5, using the commutative property of addition.
6. Rewrite (1 + 7) + 12, using the associative property of addition.

3. Subtraction of Whole Numbers

Jeremy bought a case of 12 sodas, and on a hot afternoon he drank 3 of the sodas. We can use the operation of subtraction to find the number of sodas remaining.

12 sodas − 3 sodas   =   9 sodas

The symbol "−" between two numbers is a subtraction sign, and the result of a subtraction is called the **difference**. The number being subtracted (in this case, 3) is called the **subtrahend**. The number 12 from which 3 is subtracted is called the **minuend**.

12 − 3 = 9   is read as   "12 minus 3 is equal to 9"

minuend subtrahend difference

Subtraction is the reverse operation of addition. To find the number of sodas that remain after Jeremy takes 3 sodas away from 12 sodas, we ask the following question:

"3 added to what number equals 12?"

That is,

12 − 3 = ?   is equivalent to   ? + 3 = 12

Answers
5. 3 + 5 = 5 + 3
6. (1 + 7) + 12 = 1 + (7 + 12)

Subtraction can also be visualized on the number line. To evaluate $7 - 4$, start from the point on the number line corresponding to the minuend (7 in this case). Then move to the *left* 4 units. The resulting position on the number line is the difference.

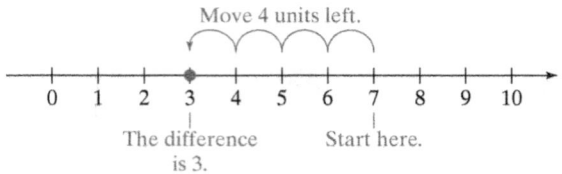

Move 4 units left.

0 1 2 3 4 5 6 7 8 9 10

The difference is 3.   Start here.

To check the result, we can use addition.

$$7 - 4 = 3 \qquad \text{because} \qquad 3 + 4 = 7$$

Skill Practice

Subtract. Check by using addition.

7. $11 - 5$ **8.** $8 - 0$
9. $7 - 2$ **10.** $5 - 5$

Example 5   **Subtracting Whole Numbers**

Subtract and check the answer by using addition.

a. $8 - 2$ **b.** $10 - 6$ **c.** $5 - 0$ **d.** $3 - 3$

Solution:

a. $8 - 2 = 6$ because $6 + 2 = 8$

b. $10 - 6 = 4$ because $4 + 6 = 10$

c. $5 - 0 = 5$ because $5 + 0 = 5$

d. $3 - 3 = 0$ because $0 + 3 = 3$

When subtracting large numbers, it is usually more convenient to write the numbers vertically. We write the minuend on top and the subtrahend below it. Starting from the ones column, we subtract digits having corresponding place values.

Skill Practice

Subtract. Check by using addition.

11. 472   **12.** 3947
      $-\ 261$ $-\ 137$

Example 6   **Subtracting Whole Numbers**

Subtract and check the answer by using addition.

a.   976   **b.** 2498
      $-\ 124$ $-\ 197$

Solution:

a.   976   Check: 852
      $-\ 124$ $+\ 124$
       852   976 ✓

Subtract the ones column digits.
Subtract the tens column digits.
Subtract the hundreds column digits.

b. 2498   Check: 2301
      $-\ 197$ $+\ 197$
       2301   2498 ✓

When a digit in the subtrahend (bottom number) is larger than the corresponding digit in the minuend (top number), we must "regroup" or borrow a value from the column to the left.

$$92 = 9 \text{ tens} + 2 \text{ ones}$$
$$- 74 = 7 \text{ tens} + 4 \text{ ones}$$

In the ones column, we cannot take 4 away from 2. We will regroup by borrowing 1 ten from the minuend. Furthermore, 1 ten = 10 ones.

$$\overset{8\ +10}{9\ 2} = \overset{8}{9} \text{ tens} + \overset{+10\text{ ones}}{2} \text{ ones} \Big\}$$
$$- 7\ 4 = 7 \text{ tens} + 4 \text{ ones}$$

We now have 12 ones in the minuend.

$$\overset{8\ \ 12}{9\ 2} = \overset{8}{9} \text{ tens} + 12 \text{ ones}$$
$$- 7\ 4 = 7 \text{ tens} + \ \ 4 \text{ ones}$$
$$\overline{1\ 8 = 1 \text{ ten} + \ \ 8 \text{ ones}}$$

TIP: The process of *borrowing* in subtraction is the reverse operation of *carrying* in addition.

Example 7   **Subtracting Whole Numbers with Borrowing**

Subtract and check the result with addition.

$$134{,}616$$
$$- \ 53{,}438$$

Solution:

$$\begin{array}{r} \overset{0\ 16}{1\ 3\ 4{,}6\cancel{1}\cancel{6}} \\ - \ \ 5\ 3{,}4\ 3\ 8 \\ \hline 8 \end{array}$$

In the ones place, 8 is greater than 6. We borrow 1 ten from the tens place.

$$\begin{array}{r} \overset{\ \ \ \ \ \overset{10}{\cancel{0}}\ 16}{\overset{5}{1\ 3\ 4{,}\cancel{6}\cancel{1}\cancel{6}}} \\ - \ \ 5\ 3{,}4\ 3\ 8 \\ \hline 7\ 8 \end{array}$$

In the tens place, 3 is greater than 0. We borrow 1 hundred from the hundreds place.

$$\begin{array}{r} \overset{0\ 13\ \ \ \ \ \overset{10}{\cancel{0}}\ 16}{\overset{5}{\cancel{1}\cancel{3}\ 4{,}\cancel{6}\cancel{1}\cancel{6}}} \\ - \ \ 5\ 3{,}4\ 3\ 8 \\ \hline 8\ 1{,}1\ 7\ 8 \end{array}$$

In the ten-thousands place, 5 is greater than 3. We borrow 1 hundred-thousand from the hundred-thousands place.

Check:
$$\overset{1\ 1}{81{,}178}$$
$$+ \ 53{,}438$$
$$\overline{134{,}616} \ \checkmark$$

Skill Practice

Subtract. Check by addition.
13.   23,126
      −   6,048

Answer
13. 17,078

Example 8 **Subtracting Whole Numbers with Borrowing**

Subtract and check the result with addition.   500 − 247

Solution:

$$\begin{array}{r} 500 \\ -\,247 \\ \hline \end{array}$$
  In the ones place, 7 is greater than 0. We try to borrow 1 ten from the tens place. However, the tens place digit is 0. Therefore we must first borrow from the hundreds place.

$$\begin{array}{r} {}^{4\ 10}\!\!\!\not5\not0\ 0 \\ -\,2\ 4\ 7 \\ \hline \end{array}$$
  ←—1 hundred = 10 tens

$$\begin{array}{r} {}^{9}\!\!\!{}^{4\ \not{10}\ 10}\!\!\!\not5\not0\not0 \\ -\,2\ 4\ 7 \\ \hline 2\ 5\ 3 \end{array}$$
  ←—Now we can borrow 1 ten to add to the ones place.

Subtract.

Check: $\begin{array}{r} {}^{1\ 1} \\ 253 \\ +\,247 \\ \hline 500\ \checkmark \end{array}$

4. Translations and Applications Involving Addition and Subtraction

In the English language, there are many different words and phrases that imply addition. A partial list is given in Table 1-1.

Table 1-1

Word/Phrase	Example	In Symbols
Sum	The sum of 6 and x	$6 + x$
Added to	3 added to 8	$8 + 3$
Increased by	y increased by 2	$y + 2$
More than	10 more than 6	$6 + 10$
Plus	8 plus 3	$8 + 3$
Total of	The total of a and b	$a + b$

Example 9 **Translating an English Phrase to a Mathematical Statement**

Translate each phrase to an equivalent mathematical statement and simplify.

a. 12 added to 109

b. The sum of 1386 and 376

Solution:

a. $109 + 12$

$$\overset{1}{109}$$
$$+\ \ 12$$
$$\overline{121}$$

b. $1386 + 376$

$$\overset{1\ 1}{1386}$$
$$+\ \ 376$$
$$\overline{1762}$$

Table 1-2 gives several key phrases that imply subtraction.

Table 1-2

Word/Phrase	Example	In Symbols
Minus	15 minus x	$15 - x$
Difference	The difference of 10 and 2	$10 - 2$
Decreased by	a decreased by 1	$a - 1$
Less than	5 less than 12	$12 - 5$
Subtract . . . from	Subtract 3 from 8	$8 - 3$
Subtracted from	6 subtracted from 10	$10 - 6$

In Table 1-2, make a note of the last three entries. The phrases *less than, subtract . . . from* and *subtracted from* imply a specific order in which the subtraction is performed. In all three cases, begin with the second number listed and subtract the first number listed.

Example 10 **Translating an English Phrase to a Mathematical Statement**

Translate the English phrase to a mathematical statement and simplify.

a. The difference of 150 and 38   **b.** 30 subtracted from 82

Solution:

a. From Table 1-2, the *difference* of 150 and 38 implies $150 - 38$.

$$\overset{4\ 10}{1\cancel{5}0}$$
$$-\ \ \ 38$$
$$\overline{112}$$

b. The phrase "30 subtracted from 82" implies that 30 is taken away from 82. We have $82 - 30$.

$$82$$
$$-30$$
$$\overline{52}$$

We noted earlier that addition is commutative. That is, the order in which two numbers are added does not affect the sum. This is *not* true for subtraction. For example, $82 - 30$ is not equal to $30 - 82$. The symbol $\neq$ means "is not equal to." Thus, $82 - 30 \neq 30 - 82$.

In Examples 11 and 12, we use addition and subtraction of whole numbers to solve application problems.

Example 11 **Solving an Application Problem Involving a Table**

The table gives the number of gold, silver, and bronze medals won in the 2006 Winter Olympics for selected countries.

a. Find the total number of medals won by Canada.

b. Determine the total number of silver medals won by these three countries.

	Gold	Silver	Bronze
Germany	11	12	6
United States	9	9	7
Canada	7	10	7

Solution:

a. The number of medals won by Canada appears in the last row of the table. The word "total" implies addition.

$7 + 10 + 7 = 24$ Canada won 24 medals.

b. The number of silver medals is given in the middle column. The total is

$12 + 9 + 10 = 31$ There were 31 silver medals won by these countries.

Example 12 **Solving an Application Problem**

The number of reported robberies in the United States has fluctuated for selected years, as shown in the graph.

a. Find the increase in the number of robberies from the year 2000 to 2005.

b. Find the decrease in the number of robberies from the year 1995 to 2000.

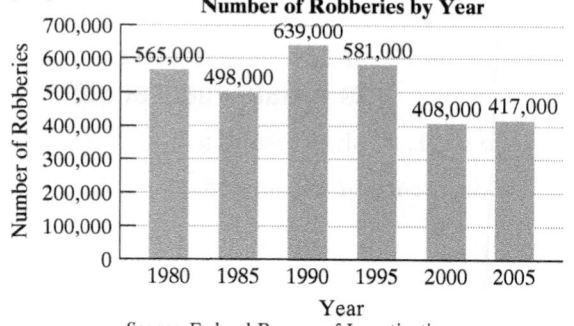

Solution:

For the purpose of finding an amount of increase or decrease, we will subtract the smaller number from the larger number.

a. Because the number of robberies went *up* from 2000 to 2005, there was an *increase*. To find the amount of increase, subtract the smaller number from the larger number.

$$
\begin{array}{r}
{\scriptstyle 0\ 17}\\
4\,\cancel{1}\,\cancel{7},000\\
-\ 4\,0\,8,000\\
\hline
9,000
\end{array}
$$

From 2000 to 2005, there was an increase of 9000 robberies in the United States.

Answers
19. a. 20 **b.** 25
20. a. decreased **b.** 164,000 robberies

b. Because the number of robberies went *down* from 1995 to 2000, there was a *decrease*. To find the amount of decrease, subtract the smaller number from the larger number.

$$\begin{array}{r} \overset{7\ \ 11}{5\,8\,1,0\,0\,0} \\ -\ 4\,0\,8,0\,0\,0 \\ \hline 1\,7\,3,0\,0\,0 \end{array}$$

From 1995 to 2000 there was a decrease of 173,000 robberies in the United States.

5. Perimeter

One special application of addition is to find the perimeter of a polygon. A **polygon** is a flat closed figure formed by line segments connected at their ends. Familiar figures such as triangles, rectangles, and squares are examples of polygons. See Figure 1-3.

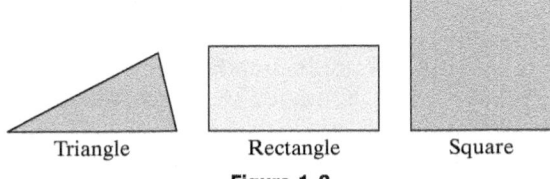

Triangle   Rectangle   Square
Figure 1-3

The **perimeter** of any polygon is the distance around the outside of the figure. To find the perimeter, add the lengths of the sides.

Example 13 **Finding Perimeter**

A paving company wants to edge the perimeter of a parking lot with concrete curbing. Find the perimeter of the parking lot.

Solution:

The perimeter is the sum of the lengths of the sides.

$$\begin{array}{r} \overset{3}{190}\ \text{ft} \\ 50\ \text{ft} \\ 60\ \text{ft} \\ 50\ \text{ft} \\ 250\ \text{ft} \\ +\ 100\ \text{ft} \\ \hline 700\ \text{ft} \end{array}$$

The distance around the parking lot (the perimeter) is 700 ft.

Skill Practice

21. Find the perimeter of the garden.

Answer
21. 240 yd

Section 1.3 Practice Exercises

Boost your GRADE at ALEKS.com!

ALEKS version 3.0

- Practice Problems
- Self-Tests
- NetTutor
- e-Professors
- Videos

Study Skills Exercises

1. It is very important to attend class every day. Math is cumulative in nature, and you must master the material learned in the previous class to understand the lesson for the next day. Because this is so important, many instructors tie attendance to the final grade. Write down the attendance policy for your class.

2. Define the key terms.

   a. **Sum**   b. **Addends**   c. **Polygon**   d. **Perimeter**

   e. **Difference**   f. **Subtrahend**   g. **Minuend**   h. **Variable**

Review Exercises

For Exercises 3–6, write the number in the form indicated.

3. Write 351 in expanded form.

4. Write in standard form: two thousand, four

5. Write in standard form: four thousand, twelve

6. Write in standard form: 6 thousands + 2 hundreds + 6 ones

Objective 1: Addition of Whole Numbers

7. Fill in the table.

+	0	1	2	3	4	5	6	7	8	9
0										
1										
2										
3										
4										
5										
6										
7										
8										
9										

For Exercises 8–10, identify the addends and the sum.

8. $11 + 10 = 21$ 9. $1 + 13 + 4 = 18$ 10. $5 + 8 + 2 = 15$

For Exercises 11–18, add. **(See Example 1.)**

11. $\begin{array}{r} 42 \\ + 33 \\ \hline \end{array}$

12. $\begin{array}{r} 21 \\ + 53 \\ \hline \end{array}$

13. $\begin{array}{r} 12 \\ 15 \\ + 32 \\ \hline \end{array}$

14. $\begin{array}{r} 10 \\ 8 \\ + 30 \\ \hline \end{array}$

15. $890 + 107$

16. $444 + 354$

17. $4 + 13 + 102$

18. $11 + 221 + 5$

For Exercises 19–32, add the whole numbers with carrying. **(See Examples 2–3.)**

19.   76
　　+ 45

20.   25
　　+ 59

21.   87
　　+ 24

22.   38
　　+ 77

23.   658
　　+ 231

24.   642
　　+ 295

25.   152
　　+ 549

26.   462
　　+ 388

27. $79 + 112 + 12$ ● **28.** $62 + 907 + 34$ **29.** $4980 + 10,223$ **30.** $23,112 + 892$

31. $10,223 + 25,782 + 4980$ **32.** $92,377 + 5622 + 34,659$

Objective 2: Properties of Addition

For Exercises 33–36, rewrite the addition problem, using the commutative property of addition. **(See Example 4.)**

33. $101 + 44 = \square + \square$ **34.** $8 + 13 = \square + \square$ **35.** $x + y = \square + \square$ **36.** $t + q = \square + \square$

●

For Exercises 37–40, rewrite the addition problem using the associative property of addition, by inserting a pair of parentheses. **(See Example 4.)**

● **37.** $(23 + 9) + 10 = 23 + 9 + 10$ **38.** $7 + (12 + 8) = 7 + 12 + 8$

39. $r + (s + t) = r + s + t$ **40.** $(c + d) + e = c + d + e$

41. Explain the difference between the commutative and associative properties of addition.

42. Explain the addition property of 0. Then simplify the expressions.

　　a. $423 + 0$ **b.** $0 + 25$ **c.**   67
　　　　　　　　　　　　　　　　　　　　+ 0   **d.** $0 + x$

Objective 3: Subtraction of Whole Numbers

For Exercises 43–44, identify the minuend, subtrahend, and the difference.

43. $12 - 8 = 4$ **44.**   9
　　　　　　　　　　　　　　− 6
　　　　　　　　　　　　　　―――
　　　　　　　　　　　　　　　3

For Exercises 45–48, write the subtraction problem as a related addition problem. For example, $19 - 6 = 13$ can be written as $13 + 6 = 19$.

45. $27 - 9 = 18$ **46.** $20 - 8 = 12$ **47.** $102 - 75 = 27$ **48.** $211 - 45 = 166$

For Exercises 49–52, subtract, then check the answer by using addition. **(See Example 5.)**

49. $8 - 3$ Check: $\square + 3 = 8$ **50.** $7 - 2$ Check: $\square + 2 = 7$

51. $4 - 1$ Check: $\square + 1 = 4$ **52.** $9 - 1$ Check: $\square + 1 = 9$

For Exercises 53–56, subtract and check the answer by using addition. **(See Example 6.)**

● **53.**   1347
　　− 221

54.   4865
　　− 713

55. $14,356 - 13,253$ **56.** $34,550 - 31,450$

For Exercises 57–72, subtract the whole numbers involving borrowing. **(See Examples 7–8.)**

57.   76
         − 59

58.   64
         − 48

59.   710
         − 189

60.   850
         − 303

61.   6002
         − 1238

62.   3000
         − 2356

63.   10,425
         − 9,022

64.   23,901
         − 8,064

65.   62,088
         − 59,871

66.   32,112
         − 28,334

67. 3700 − 2987

68. 8000 − 3788

69. 32,439 − 1498

70. 21,335 − 4123

71. 8,007,234 − 2,345,115

72. 3,045,567 − 1,871,495

73. Use the expression $7 - 4$ to explain why subtraction is not commutative.

74. Is subtraction associative? Use the numbers 10, 6, 2 to explain.

Objective 4: Translations and Applications Involving Addition and Subtraction

For Exercises 75–92, translate the English phrase to a mathematical statement and simplify. **(See Examples 9–10.)**

75. The sum of 13 and 7

76. The sum of 100 and 42

77. 45 added to 7

78. 81 added to 23

79. 5 more than 18

80. 2 more than 76

81. 1523 increased by 90

82. 1320 increased by 448

83. The total of 5, 39, and 81

84. 78 decreased by 6

85. Subtract 100 from 422.

86. Subtract 42 from 89.

87. 72 less than 1090

88. 60 less than 3111

89. The difference of 50 and 13

90. The difference of 405 and 103

91. Subtract 35 from 103.

92. Subtract 14 from 91.

93. Three top television shows entertained the following number of viewers in one week: 26,548,000 for *American Idol,* 26,930,000 for *Grey's Anatomy,* and 20,805,000 for *House.* Find the sum of the viewers for these shows.

94. To schedule enough drivers for an upcoming week, a local pizza shop manager recorded the number of deliveries each day from the previous week: 38, 54, 44, 61, 97, 103, 124. What was the total number of deliveries for the week?

95. The table gives the number of desks and chairs delivered each quarter to an office supply store. Find the total number of desks delivered for the year. **(See Example 11.)**

	Chairs	Desks
1st Quarter	220	115
2nd Quarter	185	104
3rd Quarter	201	93
4th Quarter	198	111

96. A portion of Jonathan's checking account register is shown. What is the total amount of the three checks written?

Check No.	Description	Debit	Credit	Balance
1871	Electric	$60		$180
1872	Groceries	82		98
	Payroll		$1256	1354
1874	Restaurant	58		1296
	Deposit		150	1446

97. The altitude of White Mountain Peak in California is 14,246 ft. Denali in Alaska is 20,320 ft. How much higher is Denali than White Mountain Peak?

98. There are 55 DVDs to shelve one evening at a video rental store. If Jason puts away 39 before leaving for the day, how many are left for Patty to put away?

For Exercises 99–102, use the information from the graph. **(See Example 12.)**

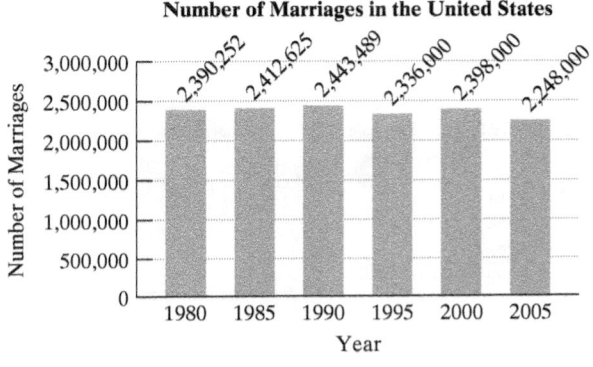

Source: National Center for Health Statistics

Figure for Exercises 99–102

99. What is the difference in the number of marriages between 1980 and 2000?

100. Find the decrease in the number of marriages in the United States between the years 2000 and 2005.

101. What is the difference in the number of marriages between the year having the greatest and the year having the least?

102. Between which two 5-year periods did the greatest increase in the number of marriages occur? What is the increase?

103. The staff for U.S. public schools is categorized in the graph. Determine the number of staff other than teachers.

104. The pie graph shows the costs incurred in managing Sub-World sandwich shop for one month. From this information, determine the total cost for one month.

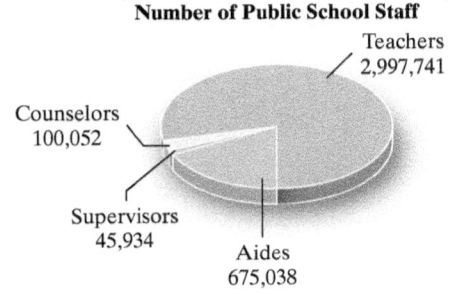

Number of Public School Staff

Teachers 2,997,741
Counselors 100,052
Supervisors 45,934
Aides 675,038

Source: National Center for Education Statistics

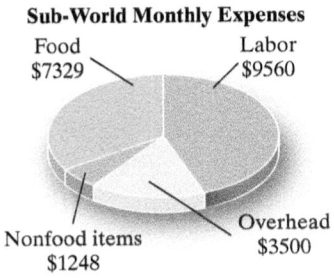

Sub-World Monthly Expenses

Food $7329
Labor $9560
Nonfood items $1248
Overhead $3500

105. Pinkham Notch Visitor Center in the White Mountains of New Hampshire has an elevation of 2032 ft. The summit of nearby Mt. Washington has an elevation of 6288 ft. What is the difference in elevation?

106. A recent report in *USA Today* indicated that the play *The Lion King* had been performed 4043 times on Broadway. At that time, the play *Hairspray* had been performed 2064 times on Broadway. How many more times had *The Lion King* been performed than *Hairspray*?

107. Jeannette has two children who each attended college in Boston. Her son Ricardo attended Bunker Hill Community College where the yearly tuition and fees came to $2600. Her daughter Ricki attended M.I.T. where the yearly tuition and fees totaled $26,960. If Jeannette paid the full amount for both children to go to school, what was her total expense for tuition and fees for 1 year?

108. Clyde and Mason each leave a rest area on the Florida Turnpike. Clyde travels north and Mason travels south. After 2 hr, Clyde has gone 138 mi and Mason, who ran into heavy traffic, traveled only 96 mi. How far apart are they?

Objective 5: Perimeter

For Exercises 109–112, find the perimeter. **(See Example 13.)**

109.

110.

111.

112.
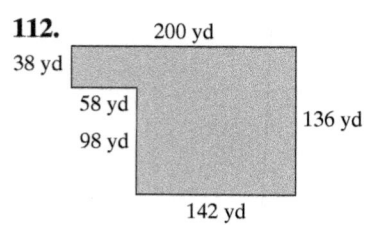

113. Find the perimeter of an NBA basketball court.

114. A major league baseball diamond is in the shape of a square. Find the distance a batter must run if he hits a home run.

For Exercises 115–116, find the missing length.

115. The perimeter of the triangle is 39 m.

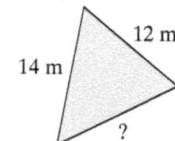

116. The perimeter of the figure is 547 cm.

Calculator Connections

Topic: Adding and Subtracting Whole Numbers

The following keystrokes demonstrate the procedure to add numbers on a calculator. The **ENTER** key (or on some calculators, the ⎸ **=** ⎸key or **EXE** key) tells the calculator to complete the calculation. Notice that commas used in large numbers are not entered into the calculator.

Expression	Keystrokes	Result
92,406 + 83,168	92406 ⎸ **+** ⎸ 83168 **ENTER**	175574

Your calculator may use the
⎸ **=** ⎸key or **EXE** key.

To subtract numbers on a calculator, use the subtraction key, ⎸ **−** ⎸. Do not confuse the subtraction key with the ⎸ **(−)** ⎸key. The ⎸ **(−)** ⎸will be presented later to enter negative numbers.

Expression	Keystrokes	Result
345,899 − 43,018	345899 ⎸ **−** ⎸ 43018 **ENTER**	302881

Calculator Exercises

For Exercises 117–122, perform the indicated operation by using a calculator.

117. 45,418
         81,990
          9,063
     + 56,309

118. 9,300,050
         7,803,513
         3,480,009
     +   907,822

119. 3,421,019
           822,761
         1,003,721
     +   9,678

120. 4,905,620
     −   458,318

121. 953,400,415
     −   56,341,902

122. 82,025,160
     − 79,118,705

For Exercises 123–126, refer to the table showing the land area for five states.

State	Land Area (mi^2)
Rhode Island	1045
Tennessee	41,217
West Virginia	24,078
Wisconsin	54,310
Colorado	103,718

123. Find the difference in the land area between Colorado and Wisconsin.

124. Find the difference in the land area between Tennessee and West Virginia.

125. What is the combined land area for Rhode Island, Tennessee, and Wisconsin?

126. What is the combined land area for all five states?

Section 1.4 Rounding and Estimating

1. Rounding

Rounding a whole number is a common practice when we do not require an exact value. For example, Madagascar lost 3956 mi² of rainforest between 1990 and 2008. We might round this number to the nearest thousand and say that approximately 4000 mi² was lost. In mathematics, we use the symbol ≈ to read "is approximately equal to." Therefore, 3956 mi² ≈ 4000 mi².

A number line is a helpful tool to understand rounding. For example, the number 48 is closer to 50 than it is to 40. Therefore, 48 rounded to the nearest ten is 50.

Round up to 50.

Concept Connections

1. Is the number 82 closer to 80 or to 90? Round 82 to the nearest ten.
2. Is the number 65 closer to 60 or to 70? Round the number to the nearest ten.

The number 43, on the other hand, is closer to 40 than to 50. Therefore, 43 rounded to the nearest ten is 40.

Round down to 40.

The number 45 is halfway between 40 and 50. In such a case, our convention will be to round *up* to the next-larger ten.

Round up to 50.

The decision to round up or down to a given place value is determined by the digit to the *right* of the given place value. The following steps outline the procedure.

PROCEDURE Rounding Whole Numbers

Step 1 Identify the digit one position to the right of the given place value.

Step 2 If the digit in Step 1 is a 5 or greater, then add 1 to the digit in the given place value. If the digit in Step 1 is less than 5, leave the given place value unchanged.

Step 3 Replace each digit to the right of the given place value by 0.

Answers

1. Closer to 80; 80
2. The number 65 is the same distance from 60 and 70; round up to 70.

Example 1 **Rounding a Whole Number**

Round 3741 to the nearest hundred.

Solution:

3 7 ④ 1 ≈ 3700

hundreds
place

This is the digit to the right of the hundreds place. Because 4 is less than 5, leave the hundreds digit unchanged. Replace the digits to its right by zeros.

Skill Practice

3. Round 12,461 to the nearest thousand.

Example 1 could also have been solved by drawing a number line. Use the part of a number line between 3700 and 3800 because 3741 lies between these numbers.

Round down to 3700.

Example 2 **Rounding a Whole Number**

Round 1,790,641 to the nearest hundred-thousand.

Solution:

1,7 ⑨ 0,6 4 1 ≈ 1,800,000

hundred-
thousands
place

This is the digit to the right of the given place value. Because 9 is greater than 5, add 1 to the hundred-thousands place, add: 7 + 1 = 8. Replace the digits to the right of the hundred-thousands place by zeros.

Skill Practice

4. Round 147,316 to the nearest ten-thousand.

Example 3 **Rounding a Whole Number**

Round 1503 to the nearest thousand.

Solution:

1 ⑤ 0 3 ≈ 2000

thousands
place

This is the digit to the right of the thousands place. Because this digit is 5, we round up. We increase the thousands place digit by 1. That is, 1 + 1 = 2. Replace the digits to its right by zeros.

Skill Practice

5. Round 7,521,460 to the nearest million.

Answers
3. 12,000   4. 150,000
5. 8,000,000

Skill Practice

6. Round 39,823 to the nearest thousand.

Example 4 **Rounding a Whole Number**

Round the number 24,961 to the hundreds place.

Solution:

$$24,9\overset{+1}{\boxed{6}}1 \approx 25,000$$

This is the digit to the right of the hundreds place. Because 6 is greater than 5, add 1 to the hundreds place digit. Replace the digits to the right of the hundreds place with 0.

2. Estimation

We use the process of rounding to estimate the result of numerical calculations. For example, to estimate the following sum, we can round each addend to the nearest ten.

31	rounds to	$\longrightarrow$	30
12	rounds to	$\longrightarrow$	10
+ 49	rounds to	$\longrightarrow$	+ 50
			90

The estimated sum is 90 (the actual sum is 92).

Skill Practice

7. Estimate the sum by rounding each number to the nearest hundred.

$3162 + 4931 + 2206$

Example 5 **Estimating a Sum**

Estimate the sum by rounding to the nearest thousand.

$$6109 + 976 + 4842 + 11,619$$

Solution:

6,109	rounds to	$\longrightarrow$	$\overset{1}{}6,000$
976	rounds to	$\longrightarrow$	1,000
4,842	rounds to	$\longrightarrow$	5,000
+ 11,619	rounds to	$\longrightarrow$	+ 12,000
			24,000

The estimated sum is 24,000 (the actual sum is 23,546).

Skill Practice

8. Estimate the difference by rounding each number to the nearest million.

$35,264,000 - 21,906,210$

Example 6 **Estimating a Difference**

Estimate the difference $4817 - 2106$ by rounding each number to the nearest hundred.

Solution:

4817	rounds to	$\longrightarrow$	4800
− 2106	rounds to	$\longrightarrow$	− 2100
			2700

The estimated difference is 2700 (the actual difference is 2711).

Answers

6. 40,000   **7.** 10,300
8. 13,000,000

3. Using Estimation in Applications

Example 7 Estimating a Sum in an Application

A driver for a delivery service must drive from Chicago, Illinois, to Dallas, Texas, and make several stops on the way. The driver follows the route given on the map. Estimate the total mileage by rounding each distance to the nearest hundred miles.

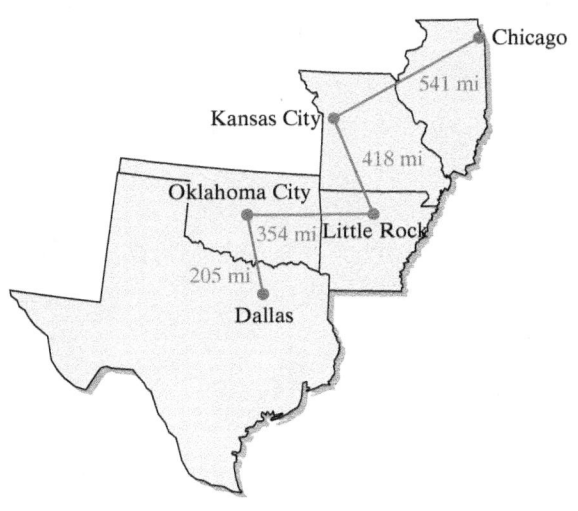

Solution:

541	rounds to ⟶	500
418	rounds to ⟶	400
354	rounds to ⟶	400
+ 205	rounds to ⟶	+ 200
		1500

The driver traveled approximately 1500 mi.

Example 8 Estimating a Difference in an Application

In a recent year, the U.S. Census Bureau reported that the number of males over the age of 18 was 100,994,367. The same year, the number of females over 18 was 108,133,727. Round each value to the nearest million. Estimate how many more females over 18 there were than males over 18.

Solution:

The number of males was approximately 101,000,000. The number of females was approximately 108,000,000.

$$\begin{array}{r} 108,000,000 \\ -\ 101,000,000 \\ \hline 7,000,000 \end{array}$$

There were approximately 7 million more women over age 18 in the United States than men.

Skill Practice

9. The two countries with the largest areas of rainforest are Brazil and the Democratic Republic of Congo. The rainforest areas are 4,776,980 square kilometers (km^2) and 1,336,100 km^2, respectively. Round the values to the nearest hundred-thousand. Estimate the total area of rainforest for these two countries.

Skill Practice

10. In a recent year, there were 135,073,000 persons over the age of 16 employed in the United States. During the same year, there were 6,742,000 persons over the age of 16 who were unemployed. Approximate each value to the nearest million. Use these values to approximate how many more people were employed than unemployed.

Answers

9. 6,100,000 km^2
10. 128,000,000

Section 1.4   Practice Exercises

Study Skills Exercises

1. After doing a section of homework, check the odd-numbered answers in the back of the text. Choose a method to identify the exercises that gave you trouble (i.e., circle the number or put a star by the number). List some reasons why it is important to label these problems.

2. Define the key term **rounding**.

Review Exercises

For Exercises 3–6, add or subtract as indicated.

3.   59   4.   130   5.   4009   6.   12,033
   − 33   − 98   + 998   + 23,441

7. Determine the place value of the digit 6 in the number 1,860,432.

8. Determine the place value of the digit 4 in the number 1,860,432.

Objective 1: Rounding

9. Explain how to round a whole number to the hundreds place.

10. Explain how to round a whole number to the tens place.

For Exercises 11–28, round each number to the given place value. **(See Examples 1–4.)**

11. 342; tens   12. 834; tens   13. 725; tens

14. 445; tens   15. 9384; hundreds   16. 8363; hundreds

17. 8539; hundreds   18. 9817; hundreds   19. 34,992; thousands

20. 76,831; thousands   21. 2578; thousands   22. 3511; thousands

23. 9982; hundreds   24. 7974; hundreds   25. 109,337; thousands

26. 437,208; thousands   27. 489,090; ten-thousands   28. 388,725; ten-thousands

29. In the first weekend of its release, the movie *Spider-Man 3* grossed $148,431,020. Round this number to the millions place.

30. The average per capita personal income in the United States in a recent year was $33,050. Round this number to the nearest thousand.

31. The average center-to-center distance from the Earth to the Moon is 238,863 mi. Round this to the thousands place.

32. A shopping center in Edmonton, Alberta, Canada, covers an area of 492,000 square meters (m^2). Round this number to the hundred-thousands place.

Objective 2: Estimation

For Exercises 33–36, estimate the sum or difference by first rounding each number to the nearest ten. **(See Examples 5–6.)**

33. 57
        82
      + 21

34. 33
        78
      + 41

35. 639
      − 422

36. 851
      − 399

For Exercises 37–40, estimate the sum or difference by first rounding each number to the nearest hundred. **(See Examples 5–6.)**

37. 892
      + 129

38. 347
      + 563

39. 3412
      − 1252

40. 9771
      − 4544

Objective 3: Using Estimation in Applications

For Exercises 41–42, refer to the table.

Brand	Manufacturer	Sales ($)
M&Ms	Mars	97,404,576
Hershey's Milk Chocolate	Hershey Chocolate	81,296,784
Reese's Peanut Butter Cups	Hershey Chocolate	54,391,268
Snickers	Mars	53,695,428
KitKat	Hershey Chocolate	38,168,580

41. Round the individual sales to the nearest million to estimate the total sales brought in by the Mars company. **(See Example 7.)**

42. Round the sales to the nearest million to estimate the total sales brought in by the Hershey Chocolate Company.

43. Neil Diamond earned $71,339,710 in U.S. tours in one year while Paul McCartney earned $59,684,076. Round each value to the nearest million dollars to estimate how much more Neil Diamond earned. **(See Example 8.)**

44. The number of women in the 45–49 age group who gave birth in 1981 is 1190. By 2001 this number increased to 4844. Round each value to the nearest thousand to estimate how many more women in the 45–49 age group gave birth in 2001.

For Exercises 45–48, use the given table.

45. Round each revenue to the nearest hundred-thousand to estimate the total revenue for the years 2000 through 2002.

46. Round the revenue to the nearest hundred-thousand to estimate the total revenue for the years 2003 through 2005.

47. a. Determine the year with the greatest revenue. Round this revenue to the nearest hundred-thousand.

Beach Parking Revenue for Daytona Beach, Florida	
Year	Revenue
2000	$3,316,897
2001	3,272,028
2002	3,360,289
2003	3,470,295
2004	3,173,050
2005	1,970,380

Source: Daytona Beach News Journal

Table for Exercises 45–48

   b. Determine the year with the least revenue. Round this revenue to the nearest hundred-thousand.

48. Estimate the difference between the year with the greatest revenue and the year with the least revenue.

For Exercises 49–52, use the graph provided.

49. Determine the state with the greatest number of students enrolled in grades 6–12. Round this number to the nearest thousand.

50. Determine the state with the least number of students enrolled in grades 6–12. Round this number to the nearest thousand.

51. Use the information in Exercises 49 and 50 to estimate the difference between the number of students in the state with the greatest enrollment and that of the least enrollment.

52. Estimate the total number of students enrolled in grades 6–12 in the selected states by first rounding the number of students to the thousands place.

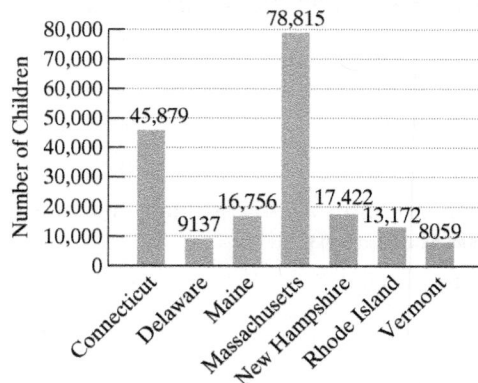

Number of Students Enrolled in Grades 6–12 for Selected States

Source: National Center for Education Statistics
Figure for Exercises 49–52

Expanding Your Skills

For Exercises 53–56, round the numbers to estimate the perimeter of each figure. (Answers may vary.)

53.

3045 mm
1892 mm   1892 mm
3045 mm

54.

1851 cm
1782 cm   1782 cm
1851 cm

55.

105 in.
57 in.   57 in.
57 in.   57 in.
105 in.

56.

182 ft
169 ft
121 ft
169 ft
182 ft

Section 1.5   Multiplication of Whole Numbers and Area

Objectives

1. **Introduction to Multiplication**
2. **Properties of Multiplication**
3. **Multiplying Many-Digit Whole Numbers**
4. **Estimating Products by Rounding**
5. **Applications Involving Multiplication**
6. **Area of a Rectangle**

1. Introduction to Multiplication

Suppose that Carmen buys three cartons of eggs to prepare a large family brunch. If there are 12 eggs per carton, then the total number of eggs can be found by adding three 12s.

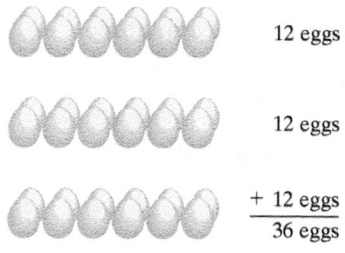

12 eggs

12 eggs

+ 12 eggs
36 eggs

When each addend in a sum is the same, we have what is called *repeated* addition. Repeated addition is also called **multiplication**. We use the multiplication sign × to express repeated addition more concisely.

$$12 + 12 + 12 \quad \text{is equal to} \quad 3 \times 12$$

The expression 3×12 is read "3 times 12" to signify that the number 12 is added 3 times. The numbers 3 and 12 are called **factors**, and the result, 36, is called the **product**.

The symbol · may also be used to denote multiplication such as in the expression $3 \cdot 12 = 36$. Two factors written adjacent to each other with no other operator between them also implies multiplication. The quantity $2y$, for example, is understood to be 2 times y. If we use this notation to multiply two numbers, parentheses are used to group one or both factors. For example:

$$3(12) = 36 \quad (3)12 = 36 \quad \text{and} \quad (3)(12) = 36$$

all represent the product of 3 and 12.

TIP: In the expression 3(12), the parentheses are necessary because two adjacent factors written together with no grouping symbol would look like the number 312.

The products of one-digit numbers such as $4 \times 5 = 20$ and $2 \times 7 = 14$ are basic facts. All products of one-digit numbers should be memorized (see Exercise 6).

Example 1 **Identifying Factors and Products**

Identify the factors and the product.

a. $6 \times 3 = 18$ **b.** $5 \cdot 2 \cdot 7 = 70$

Solution:

a. Factors: 6, 3; product: 18 **b.** Factors: 5, 2, 7; product: 70

2. Properties of Multiplication

Recall from Section 1.3 that the order in which two numbers are added does not affect the sum. The same is true for multiplication. This is stated formally as the *commutative property of multiplication*.

PROPERTY **Commutative Property of Multiplication**

For any numbers, a and b,

$$a \cdot b = b \cdot a$$

Changing the order of two factors does not affect the product.

The following rectangular arrays help us visualize the commutative property of multiplication. For example $2 \cdot 5 = 5 \cdot 2$.

$2 \cdot 5 = 10$ 2 rows of 5

$5 \cdot 2 = 10$ 5 rows of 2

Multiplication is also an associative operation. For example,

$$(3 \cdot 5) \cdot 2 = 3 \cdot (5 \cdot 2).$$

PROPERTY **Associative Property of Multiplication**

For any numbers, a, b, and c,

$$(a \cdot b) \cdot c = a \cdot (b \cdot c)$$

The manner in which factors are grouped under multiplication does not affect the product.

TIP: The variable "x" is commonly used in algebra and can be confused with the multiplication symbol "$\times$." For this reason it is customary to limit the use of "$\times$" for multiplication.

Example 2 **Applying Properties of Multiplication**

a. Rewrite the expression $3 \cdot 9$, using the commutative property of multiplication. Then find the product.

b. Rewrite the expression $(4 \cdot 2) \cdot 3$, using the associative property of multiplication. Then find the product.

Solution:

a. $3 \cdot 9 = 9 \cdot 3$. The product is 27.

b. $(4 \cdot 2) \cdot 3 = 4 \cdot (2 \cdot 3)$.

To find the product, we have

$$4 \cdot (2 \cdot 3)$$
$$= 4 \cdot (6)$$
$$= 24$$

The product is 24.

Two other important properties of multiplication involve factors of 0 and 1.

> **PROPERTY** Multiplication Property of 0
>
> For any number a,
>
> $$a \cdot 0 = 0 \quad \text{and} \quad 0 \cdot a = 0$$
>
> The product of any number and 0 is 0.

The product $5 \cdot 0 = 0$ can easily be understood by writing the product as repeated addition.

$$\underbrace{0 + 0 + 0 + 0 + 0}_{\text{Add 0 five times.}} = 0$$

> **PROPERTY** Multiplication Property of 1
>
> For any number a,
>
> $$a \cdot 1 = a \quad \text{and} \quad 1 \cdot a = a$$
>
> The product of any number and 1 is that number.

The next property of multiplication involves both addition and multiplication. First consider the expression $2(4 + 3)$. By performing the operation within parentheses first, we have

$$2(4 + 3) = 2(7) = 14$$

We get the same result by multiplying 2 times each addend within the parentheses:

$$2(4 + 3) = (2 \cdot 4) + (2 \cdot 3) = 8 + 6 = 14$$

This result illustrates the distributive property of multiplication over addition (sometimes we simply say *distributive property* for short).

> **PROPERTY** Distributive Property of Multiplication over Addition
>
> For any numbers a, b, and c,
>
> $$a(b + c) = a \cdot b + a \cdot c$$
>
> The product of a number and a sum can be found by multiplying the number by each addend.

Example 3 Applying the Distributive Property of Multiplication Over Addition

Apply the distributive property and simplify.

a. $3(4 + 8)$ **b.** $7(3 + 0)$

Solution:

a. $3(4 + 8) = (3 \cdot 4) + (3 \cdot 8) = 12 + 24 = 36$

b. $7(3 + 0) = (7 \cdot 3) + (7 \cdot 0) = 21 + 0 = 21$

Skill Practice

Apply the distributive property and simplify.

6. $2(6 + 4)$

7. $5(0 + 8)$

Answers

6. $(2 \cdot 6) + (2 \cdot 4)$; 20
7. $(5 \cdot 0) + (5 \cdot 8)$; 40

3. Multiplying Many-Digit Whole Numbers

When multiplying numbers with several digits, it is sometimes necessary to carry. To see why, consider the product 3 · 29. By writing the factors in expanded form, we can apply the distributive property. In this way, we see that 3 is multiplied by both 20 and 9.

$$3 \cdot 29 = 3(20 + 9) = (3 \cdot 20) + (3 \cdot 9)$$
$$= 60 + 27$$
$$= 6 \text{ tens} + 2 \text{ tens} + 7 \text{ ones}$$
$$= 8 \text{ tens} + 7 \text{ ones}$$
$$= 87$$

Now we will multiply 29 · 3 in vertical form.

$$\begin{array}{r} \overset{2}{2}9 \\ \times \quad 3 \\ \hline 7 \end{array}$$

Multiply 3 · 9 = 27. Write the 7 in the ones column and carry the 2.

$$\begin{array}{r} \overset{2}{2}9 \\ \times \quad 3 \\ \hline 8\,7 \end{array}$$

Multiply 3 · 2 tens = 6 tens. Add the carry: 6 tens + 2 tens = 8 tens. Write the 8 in the tens place.

Example 4   **Multiplying a Many-Digit Number by a One-Digit Number**

Multiply.

$$\begin{array}{r} 368 \\ \times \quad 5 \\ \hline \end{array}$$

Solution:

Using the distributive property, we have

$$5(300 + 60 + 8) = 1500 + 300 + 40 = 1840$$

This can be written vertically as:

$$\begin{array}{r} 368 \\ \times \quad 5 \\ \hline 40 \\ 300 \\ + \ 1500 \\ \hline 1840 \end{array}$$

Multiply 5 · 8.
Multiply 5 · 60.
Multiply 5 · 300.
Add.

The numbers 40, 300, and 1500 are called *partial sums*. The product of 386 and 5 is found by adding the partial sums. The product is 1840.

The solution to Example 4 can also be found by using a shorter form of multiplication. We outline the procedure:

$$\begin{array}{r} \overset{4}{3}68 \\ \times \quad 5 \\ \hline 0 \end{array}$$

Multiply 5 · 8 = 40. Write the 0 in the ones place and carry the 4.

$$\begin{array}{r} \overset{3\,4}{368} \\ \times \quad 5 \\ \hline 40 \end{array}$$

Multiply $5 \cdot 6$ tens = 300. Add the carry. $300 + 4$ tens = 340.
Write the 4 in the tens place and carry the 3.

$$\begin{array}{r} \overset{3\,4}{368} \\ \times \quad 5 \\ \hline 1840 \end{array}$$

Multiply $5 \cdot 3$ hundreds = 1500. Add the carry.
$1500 + 3$ hundreds = 1800. Write the 8 in the hundreds
place and the 1 in the thousands place.

Example 5 demonstrates the process to multiply two factors with many digits.

Example 5 **Multiplying a Two-Digit Number by a Two-Digit Number**

Multiply.

$$\begin{array}{r} 72 \\ \times\ 83 \end{array}$$

Solution:

Writing the problem vertically and computing the partial sums, we have

$$\begin{array}{r} \overset{1}{72} \\ \times\ 83 \\ \hline 216 \\ +\ 5760 \\ \hline 5976 \end{array}$$

Multiply $3 \cdot 72$.
Multiply $80 \cdot 72$.
Add.

The product is 5976.

Skill Practice

9. Multiply.
$$\begin{array}{r} 59 \\ \times\ 26 \end{array}$$

Example 6 **Multiplying Two Multidigit Whole Numbers**

Multiply.   368(497)

Solution:

$$\begin{array}{r} \overset{2\,3}{} \\ \overset{6\,7}{} \\ \overset{4\,5}{368} \\ \times\ 497 \\ \hline 2576 \\ 33120 \\ +\ 147200 \\ \hline 182{,}896 \end{array}$$

Multiply $7 \cdot 368$.
Multiply $90 \cdot 368$.
Multiply $400 \cdot 368$.

Skill Practice

10. Multiply.
$$\begin{array}{r} 274 \\ \times\ 586 \end{array}$$

4. Estimating Products by Rounding

A special pattern occurs when one or more factors in a product ends in zero.
Consider the following products:

$12 \cdot 20 = 240$	$120 \cdot 20 = 2400$
$12 \cdot 200 = 2400$	$1200 \cdot 20 = 24{,}000$
$12 \cdot 2000 = 24{,}000$	$12{,}000 \cdot 20 = 240{,}000$

Answers
9. 1534   10. 160,564

Notice in each case the product is $12 \cdot 2 = 24$ followed by the total number of zeros from each factor. Consider the product $1200 \cdot 20$.

$$\begin{array}{r|l} 12 & 00 \\ \times \ \ 2 & 0 \\ \hline 24 & 000 \end{array}$$

Shift the numbers 1200 and 20 so that the zeros appear to the right of the multiplication process. Multiply $12 \cdot 2 = 24$.
Write the product 24 followed by the total number of zeros from each factor.

Skill Practice

11. Estimate the product 421(869) by rounding each factor to the nearest hundred.

Example 7 Estimating a Product

Estimate the product 795(4060) by rounding 795 to the nearest hundred and 4060 to the nearest thousand.

Solution:

$$\begin{array}{llll} 795 & \text{rounds to} \longrightarrow & 800 & \ \ 8\,|\,00 \\ 4060 & \text{rounds to} \longrightarrow & 4000 & \underline{\times\ \ 4\,|\,000} \\ & & & 32\,|\,00000 \end{array}$$

The product is approximately 3,200,000.

Skill Practice

12. A small newspaper has 16,850 subscribers. Each subscription costs $149 per year. Estimate the revenue for the year by rounding the number of subscriptions to the nearest thousand and the cost to the nearest ten.

Example 8 Estimating a Product in an Application

For a trip from Atlanta to Los Angeles, the average cost of a plane ticket was $495. If the plane carried 218 passengers, estimate the total revenue for the airline. (*Hint*: Round each number to the hundreds place and find the product.)

Solution:

$$\begin{array}{llll} \$495 & \text{rounds to} \longrightarrow & \$\ 5\,|\,00 \\ 218 & \text{rounds to} \longrightarrow & \underline{\times 2\,|\,00} \\ & & \$10\,|\,0000 \end{array}$$

The airline received approximately $100,000 in revenue.

5. Applications Involving Multiplication

In English there are many different words that imply multiplication. A partial list is given in Table 1-3.

Table 1-3

Word/Phrase	Example	In Symbols
Product	The product of 4 and 7	$4 \cdot 7$
Times	8 times 4	$8 \cdot 4$
Multiply ... by ...	Multiply 6 by 3	$6 \cdot 3$

Multiplication may also be warranted in applications involving unit rates. In Example 8, we multiplied the cost per customer ($495) by the number of customers (218). The value $495 is a unit rate because it gives the cost per one customer (per one unit).

Answers

11. 360,000   **12.** $2,550,000

Example 9	Solving an Application Involving Multiplication

The average weekly income for production workers is $489. How much does a production worker make in 1 year. (Assume there are 52 weeks in 1 year.)

Solution:

The value $489 per week is a unit rate. The total earnings for 1 year is given by $489 · 52.

$$
\begin{array}{r}
{\scriptstyle 4\,4} \\
{\scriptstyle 1\,1} \\
489 \\
\times\ 52 \\
\hline
978 \\
+\ 24450 \\
\hline
25{,}428
\end{array}
$$
The yearly earnings total $25,428.

> **TIP:** This product can be estimated quickly by rounding the factors.
>
> | 489 | rounds to → | 5|00 |
> |---|---|---|
> | 52 | rounds to → | × 5|0 |
> | | | 25|000 |
>
> The total yearly income is approximately $25,000. Estimating gives a quick approximation of a product. Furthermore, it also checks for the reasonableness of our exact product. In this case $25,000 is close to our exact value of $25,428.

6. Area of a Rectangle

Another application of multiplication of whole numbers lies in finding the area of a region. **Area** measures the amount of surface contained within the region. For example, a square that is 1 in. by 1 in. occupies an area of 1 square inch, denoted as $1\ \text{in.}^2$. Similarly, a square that is 1 centimeter (cm) by 1 cm occupies an area of 1 square centimeter. This is denoted by $1\ \text{cm}^2$.

1 square inch = 1 in.^{2}

1 in.

1 in.

1 square centimeter = 1 cm^2

1 cm

1 cm

The units of square inches and square centimeters (in.^{2} and cm^2) are called *square units*. To find the area of a region, measure the number of square units occupied in that region. For example, the region in Figure 1-4 occupies 6 cm^2.

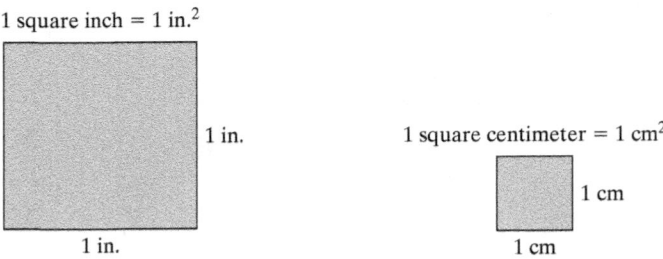

Area = 6 cm^2

2 cm

3 cm

Figure 1-4

Answer
13. 2925 words

The 3-cm by 2-cm region in Figure 1-4 suggests that to find the **area of a rectangle**, multiply the length by the width. If the area is represented by A, the length is represented by l, and the width is represented by w, then we have

$$\textbf{Area of rectangle} = (\text{length}) \cdot (\text{width})$$

$$A = l \cdot w$$

The letters A, l, and w are variables because their values *vary* as they are replaced by different numbers.

Example 10 **Finding the Area of a Rectangle**

Find the area and perimeter of the rectangle.

4 yd

7 yd

Solution:

Area:

$$A = l \cdot w$$

$$A = (7 \text{ yd}) \cdot (4 \text{ yd})$$

$$= 28 \text{ yd}^2$$

Avoiding Mistakes

Notice that area is measured in square units (such as yd^2) and perimeter is measured in units of length (such as yd). It is important to apply the correct units of measurement.

Recall from Section 1.3 that the perimeter of a polygon is the sum of the lengths of the sides. In a rectangle the opposite sides are equal in length.

Perimeter:

$$P = 7 \text{ yd} + 4 \text{ yd} + 7 \text{ yd} + 4 \text{ yd}$$

$$= 22 \text{ yd}$$

The area is 28 yd^2 and the perimeter is 22 yd.

7 yd

4 yd   4 yd

7 yd

Skill Practice

15. A house sits on a rectangular lot that is 192 ft by 96 ft. Approximate the area of the lot by rounding the length and width to the nearest hundred.

Example 11 **Finding Area in an Application**

The state of Wyoming is approximately the shape of a rectangle (Figure 1-5). Its length is 355 mi and its width is 276 mi. Approximate the total area of Wyoming by rounding the length and width to the nearest ten.

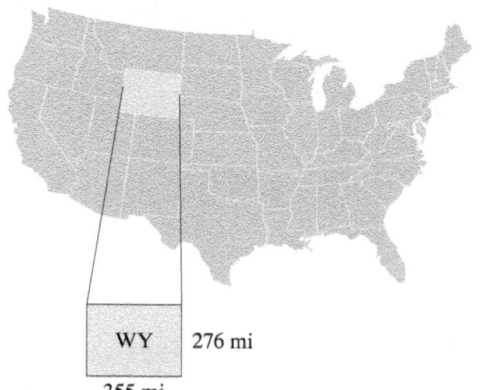

WY   276 mi

355 mi

Figure 1-5

Solution:

$$
\begin{array}{rcl}
355 & \text{rounds to} \longrightarrow & \overset{\overset{1}{4}}{3}6\,|\,0 \\
276 & \text{rounds to} \longrightarrow & \times\ 28\,|\,0 \\
\hline
& & 288 \\
& & 720 \\
\hline
& & 1008\,|\,00
\end{array}
$$

The area of Wyoming is approximately 100,800 mi^2.

Section 1.5   Practice Exercises

Study Skills Exercises

1. Sometimes you may run into a problem with homework, or you may find that you are having trouble keeping up with the pace of the class. A tutor can be a good resource. Answer the following questions.

   a. Does your college offer tutoring?   b. Is it free?

   c. Where would you go to sign up for a tutor?

2. Define the key terms.

   a. **Multiplication**   b. **Factor**   c. **Product**

   d. **Area**   e. **Area of a rectangle**

Review Exercises

For Exercises 3–5, estimate the answer by rounding to the indicated place value.

3. $869,240 + 34,921 + 108,332$; ten-thousands   4. $907,801 - 413,560$; hundred-thousands

5. $8821 - 3401$; hundreds

Objective 1: Introduction to Multiplication

6. Fill in the table of multiplication facts.

×	0	1	2	3	4	5	6	7	8	9
0										
1										
2										
3										
4										
5										
6										
7										
8										
9										

For Exercises 7–10, write the repeated addition as multiplication and simplify.

7. $5 + 5 + 5 + 5 + 5 + 5$ 8. $2 + 2 + 2 + 2 + 2 + 2 + 2 + 2 + 2$

9. $9 + 9 + 9$ 10. $7 + 7 + 7 + 7$

For Exercises 11–14, identify the factors and the product. (See Example 1.)

11. $13 \times 42 = 546$ 12. $26 \times 9 = 234$

13. $3 \cdot 5 \cdot 2 = 30$ 14. $4 \cdot 3 \cdot 8 = 96$

15. Write the product of 5 and 12, using three different notations. (Answers may vary.)

16. Write the product of 23 and 14, using three different notations. (Answers may vary.)

Objective 2: Properties of Multiplication

For Exercises 17–22, match the property with the statement.

17. $8 \cdot 1 = 8$

a. Commutative property of multiplication

18. $6 \cdot 13 = 13 \cdot 6$

b. Associative property of multiplication

19. $2(6 + 12) = 2 \cdot 6 + 2 \cdot 12$

c. Multiplication property of 0

20. $5 \cdot (3 \cdot 2) = (5 \cdot 3) \cdot 2$

d. Multiplication property of 1

21. $0 \cdot 4 = 0$

e. Distributive property of multiplication over addition

22. $7(14) = 14(7)$

For Exercises 23–28, rewrite the expression, using the indicated property. **(See Examples 2–3.)**

23. $14 \cdot 8$; commutative property of multiplication

24. $3 \cdot 9$; commutative property of multiplication

25. $6 \cdot (2 \cdot 10)$; associative property of multiplication

26. $(4 \cdot 15) \cdot 5$; associative property of multiplication

27. $5(7 + 4)$; distributive property of multiplication over addition

28. $3(2 + 6)$; distributive property of multiplication over addition

Objective 3: Multiplying Many-Digit Whole Numbers

For Exercises 29–60, multiply. **(See Examples 4–6.)**

29. $\begin{array}{r} 24 \\ \times\ 6 \\ \hline \end{array}$	**30.** $\begin{array}{r} 18 \\ \times\ 5 \\ \hline \end{array}$	**31.** $\begin{array}{r} 26 \\ \times\ 2 \\ \hline \end{array}$	**32.** $\begin{array}{r} 71 \\ \times\ 3 \\ \hline \end{array}$
33. $\begin{array}{r} 131 \\ \times\ 5 \\ \hline \end{array}$	**34.** $\begin{array}{r} 725 \\ \times\ 3 \\ \hline \end{array}$	**35.** $\begin{array}{r} 344 \\ \times\ 4 \\ \hline \end{array}$	**36.** $\begin{array}{r} 105 \\ \times\ 9 \\ \hline \end{array}$
37. $\begin{array}{r} 1410 \\ \times\ 8 \\ \hline \end{array}$	**38.** $\begin{array}{r} 2016 \\ \times\ 6 \\ \hline \end{array}$	**39.** $\begin{array}{r} 3312 \\ \times\ 7 \\ \hline \end{array}$	**40.** $\begin{array}{r} 4801 \\ \times\ 5 \\ \hline \end{array}$
41. $\begin{array}{r} 42,014 \\ \times\ 9 \\ \hline \end{array}$	**42.** $\begin{array}{r} 51,006 \\ \times\ 8 \\ \hline \end{array}$	**43.** $\begin{array}{r} 32 \\ \times\ 14 \\ \hline \end{array}$	**44.** $\begin{array}{r} 41 \\ \times\ 21 \\ \hline \end{array}$
45. $68 \cdot 24$	**46.** $55 \cdot 41$	**47.** $72 \cdot 12$	**48.** $13 \cdot 46$
49. $(143)(17)$	**50.** $(722)(28)$	**51.** $(349)(19)$	**52.** $(512)(31)$

53.   151
        × 127

54.   703
        × 146

55.   222
        × 841

56.   387
        × 506

57.   3532
        × 6014

58.   2810
        × 1039

● **59.**   4122
        × 982

60.   7026
        × 528

Objective 4: Estimating Products by Rounding

For Exercises 61–68, multiply the numbers, using the method found on page 40. **(See Example 7.)**

61.   600
        × 40

62.   900
        × 50

63.   3000
        × 700

64.   4000
        × 400

65.   8000
        × 9000

66.   1000
        × 2000

● **67.**   90,000
        × 400

68.   50,000
        × 6000

For Exercises 69–72, estimate the product by first rounding the number to the indicated place value.

69. 11,784 · 5201; thousands place

70. 45,046 · 7812; thousands place

71. 82,941 · 29,740; ten-thousands place

72. 630,229 · 71,907; ten-thousands place

73. Suppose a hotel room costs $189 per night. Round this number to the nearest hundred to estimate the cost for a five-night stay. **(See Example 8.)**

74. The science department of Comstock High School must purchase a set of calculators for a class. If the cost of one calculator is $129, estimate the cost of 28 calculators by rounding the numbers to the tens place.

75. The average price for a ticket to see Kenny Chesney is $137. If a concert stadium seats 10,256 fans, estimate the amount of money received during that performance by rounding the number of seats to the nearest ten-thousand.

76. A breakfast buffet at a local restaurant serves 48 people. Estimate the maximum revenue for one week (7 days) if the price of a breakfast is $12.

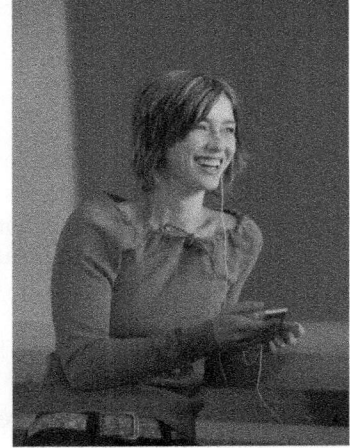

Objective 5: Applications Involving Multiplication

77. The 4-gigabyte (4-GB) iPod nano is advertised to store approximately 1000 songs. Assuming the average length of a song is 4 minutes (min), how many minutes of music can be stored on the iPod nano? **(See Example 9.)**

78. One CD can hold 700 megabytes (MB) of data. How many megabytes can 15 CDs hold?

79. It costs about $45 for a cat to have a medical exam. If a humane society has 37 cats, find the cost of medical exams for its cats.

80. The Toyota Prius gets 55 miles per gal (mpg) on the highway. How many miles can it go on 20 gal of gas?

81. A can of Coke contains 12 fluid ounces (fl oz). Find the number of ounces in a case of Coke containing 12 cans.

82. A 3 credit-hour class at a college meets 3 hours (hr) per week. If a semester is 16 weeks long, for how many hours will the class meet during the semester?

83. PaperWorld shipped 115 cases of copy paper to a business. There are 5 reams of paper in each case and 500 sheets of paper in each ream. Find the number of sheets of paper delivered to the business.

84. A dietary supplement bar has 14 grams (g) of protein. If Kathleen eats 2 bars a day for 6 days, how many grams of protein will she get from this supplement?

85. Tylee's car gets 31 miles per gallon (mpg) on the highway. How many miles can he travel if he has a full tank of gas (12 gal)?

86. Sherica manages a small business called Pizza Express. She has 23 employees who work an average of 32 hr per week. How many hours of work does Sherica have to schedule each week?

Objective 6: Area of a Rectangle

For Exercises 87–90, find the area. **(See Example 10.)**

87.

88.

89.

90.

91. The state of Colorado is approximately the shape of a rectangle. Its length is 388 mi and its width is 269 mi. Approximate the total area of Colorado by rounding the length and width to the nearest ten. **(See Example 11.)**

92. A parcel of land has a width of 132 yd and a length of 149 yd. Approximate the total area by rounding each dimension to the nearest ten.

93. The front of a building has windows that are 44 in. by 58 in.

    a. Approximate the area of one window.

    b. If the building has three floors and each floor has 14 windows, how many windows are there?

    c. What is the approximate total area of all of the windows?

94. The length of a carport is 51 ft and its width is 29 ft. Approximate the area of the carport.

95. Mr. Slackman wants to paint his garage door that is 8 ft by 16 ft. To decide how much paint to buy, he must find the area of the door. What is the area of the door?

96. To carpet a rectangular room, Erika must find the area of the floor. If the dimensions of the room are 10 yd by 15 yd, how much carpeting does she need?

Division of Whole Numbers

1. Introduction to Division

Suppose 12 pieces of pizza are to be divided evenly among 4 children (Figure 1-6). The number of pieces that each child would receive is given by $12 \div 4$, read "12 divided by 4."

Objectives

1. **Introduction to Division**
2. **Properties of Division**
3. **Long Division**
4. **Dividing by a Many-Digit Divisor**
5. **Translations and Applications Involving Division**

Figure 1-6

The process of separating 12 pieces of pizza evenly among 4 children is called **division**. The statement $12 \div 4 = 3$ indicates that each child receives 3 pieces of pizza. The number 12 is called the **dividend**. It represents the number to be divided. The number 4 is called the **divisor**, and it represents the number of groups. The result of the division (in this case 3) is called the **quotient**. It represents the number of items in each group.

Division can be represented in several ways. For example, the following are all equivalent statements.

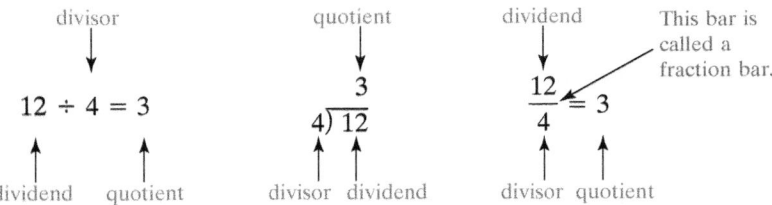

Recall that subtraction is the reverse operation of addition. In the same way, division is the reverse operation of multiplication. For example, we say $12 \div 4 = 3$ because $3 \cdot 4 = 12$.

Example 1 Identifying the Dividend, Divisor, and Quotient

Simplify each expression. Then identify the dividend, divisor, and quotient.

a. $48 \div 6$ **b.** $9\overline{)36}$ **c.** $\dfrac{63}{7}$

Solution:

a. $48 \div 6 = 8$ because $8 \cdot 6 = 48$

The dividend is 48, the divisor is 6, and the quotient is 8.

b. $9\overset{4}{\overline{)36}}$ because $4 \cdot 9 = 36$

The dividend is 36, the divisor is 9, and the quotient is 4.

c. $\dfrac{63}{7} = 9$ because $9 \cdot 7 = 63$

The dividend is 63, the divisor is 7, and the quotient is 9.

Skill Practice

Identify the dividend, divisor, and quotient.

1. $56 \div 7$
2. $4\overline{)20}$
3. $\dfrac{18}{2}$

Answers

1. Dividend: 56; divisor: 7; quotient: 8
2. Dividend: 20; divisor: 4; quotient: 5
3. Dividend: 18; divisor: 2; quotient: 9

2. Properties of Division

> **PROPERTY Properties of Division**
>
> **1.** $a \div a = 1$ for any number a, where $a \neq 0$.
> Any nonzero number divided by itself is 1.   Example: $9 \div 9 = 1$
> **2.** $a \div 1 = a$ for any number a.
> Any number divided by 1 is the number itself.   Example: $3 \div 1 = 3$
> **3.** $0 \div a = 0$ for any number a, where $a \neq 0$.
> Zero divided by any nonzero number is zero.   Example: $0 \div 5 = 0$
> **4.** $a \div 0$ is undefined for any number a.
> Any number divided by zero is undefined.   Example: $9 \div 0$ is undefined.

Example 2 illustrates the important properties of division.

Skill Practice

Divide.

4. $3\overline{)3}$ **5.** $5 \div 5$

6. $\dfrac{4}{1}$ **7.** $8 \div 0$

8. $\dfrac{0}{7}$ **9.** $3\overline{)0}$

Example 2   **Dividing Whole Numbers**

Divide.

a. $8 \div 8$ **b.** $\dfrac{6}{6}$ **c.** $5 \div 1$ **d.** $1\overline{)7}$

e. $0 \div 6$ **f.** $\dfrac{0}{4}$ **g.** $6 \div 0$ **h.** $\dfrac{10}{0}$

Solution:

a. $8 \div 8 = 1$ because $1 \cdot 8 = 8$

b. $\dfrac{6}{6} = 1$ because $1 \cdot 6 = 6$

c. $5 \div 1 = 5$ because $5 \cdot 1 = 5$

d. $\begin{array}{r} 7 \\ 1\overline{)7} \end{array}$ because $7 \cdot 1 = 7$

e. $0 \div 6 = 0$ because $0 \cdot 6 = 0$

f. $\dfrac{0}{4} = 0$ because $0 \cdot 4 = 0$

> **Avoiding Mistakes**
>
> There is no mathematical symbol to describe the result when dividing by 0. We must write out the word *undefined* to denote that we cannot divide by 0.

g. $6 \div 0$ is *undefined* because there is no number that when multiplied by 0 will produce a product of 6.

h. $\dfrac{10}{0}$ is *undefined* because there is no number that when multiplied by 0 will produce a product of 10.

Concept Connections

10. Which expression is undefined?

$\dfrac{5}{0}$ or $\dfrac{0}{5}$

11. Which expression is equal to zero?

$0\overline{)4}$ or $4\overline{)0}$

You should also note that unlike addition and multiplication, division is neither commutative nor associative. In other words, reversing the order of the dividend and divisor may produce a different quotient. Similarly, changing the manner in which numbers are grouped with division may affect the outcome. See Exercises 31 and 32.

Answers

4. 1   **5.** 1   **6.** 4   **7.** Undefined

8. 0   **9.** 0   **10.** $\dfrac{5}{0}$ **11.** $4\overline{)0}$

3. Long Division

To divide larger numbers we use a process called **long division**. This process uses a series of estimates to find the quotient. We illustrate long division in Example 3.

Example 3 **Using Long Division**

Divide. $7\overline{)161}$

Solution:

Estimate $7\overline{)161}$ by first estimating $7\overline{)16}$ and writing the result above the tens place of the dividend. Since $7 \cdot 2 = 14$, there are at least 2 sevens in 16.

$$
\begin{array}{r}
2 \\
7\overline{)161} \\
-140 \\
\hline
21
\end{array}
$$

The 2 in the tens place represents 20 in the quotient.
←—Multiply $7 \cdot 20$ and write the result under the dividend.
Subtract 140. We see that our estimate leaves 21.

Repeat the process. Now divide $7\overline{)21}$ and write the result in the ones place of the quotient.

$$
\begin{array}{r}
23 \\
7\overline{)161} \\
-140 \\
\hline
21 \\
-21 \\
\hline
0
\end{array}
$$

←— Multiply $7 \cdot 3$.
Subtract.

The quotient is 23.

Check: $\begin{array}{r} 23 \\ \times\, 7 \\ \hline 161 \end{array}$ ✔

Skill Practice

12. Divide.
   $8\overline{)136}$

We can streamline the process of long division by "bringing down" digits of the dividend one at a time.

Example 4 **Using Long Division**

Divide. $6138 \div 9$

Solution:

$$
\begin{array}{r}
682 \\
9\overline{)6138} \\
-54 \\
\hline
73 \\
-72 \\
\hline
18 \\
-18 \\
\hline
0
\end{array}
$$

$61 \div 9$ is estimated at 6. Multiply $9 \cdot 6 = 54$ and subtract.

$73 \div 9$ is estimated at 8. Multiply $9 \cdot 8 = 72$ and subtract.

$18 \div 9 = 2$. Multiply $9 \cdot 2 = 18$ and subtract.

The quotient is 682.

Check: $\begin{array}{r} {}^{7\,1} \\ 682 \\ \times\ \ 9 \\ \hline 6138 \end{array}$ ✔

Skill Practice

13. Divide.
   $2891 \div 7$

Answers

12. 17 **13.** 413

In many instances, quotients do not come out evenly. For example, suppose we had 13 pieces of pizza to distribute among 4 children (Figure 1-7).

Figure 1-7

The mathematical term given to the "leftover" piece is called the **remainder**. The division process may be written as

$$
\begin{array}{r}
3 \text{ R}1 \\
4\overline{)13} \\
-12 \\
\hline
1
\end{array}
$$

The remainder is written next to the 3.

The **whole part of the quotient** is 3, and the remainder is 1. Notice that the remainder is written next to the whole part of the quotient.

We can check a division problem that has a remainder. To do so, multiply the divisor by the whole part of the quotient and then add the remainder. The result must equal the dividend. That is,

$$(\text{Divisor})(\text{whole part of quotient}) + \text{remainder} = \text{dividend}$$

Thus,

$$(4)(3) + 1 \stackrel{?}{=} 13$$
$$12 + 1 \stackrel{?}{=} 13$$
$$13 = 13 \ \checkmark$$

Skill Practice

14. Divide.

$5107 \div 5$

Example 5   **Using Long Division**

Divide. $1253 \div 6$

Solution:

$$
\begin{array}{r}
208 \text{ R}5 \\
6\overline{)1253} \\
-12 \\
\hline
05 \\
-00 \\
\hline
53 \\
-48 \\
\hline
5
\end{array}
$$

$6 \cdot 2 = 12$ and subtract.

Bring down the 5.

Note that 6 does not divide into 5, so we put a 0 in the quotient.

Bring down the 3.

$6 \cdot 8 = 48$ and subtract.

The remainder is 5.

To check, verify that $(6)(208) + 5 = 1253$. ✔

Answer

14. 1021 R2

4. Dividing by a Many-Digit Divisor

When the divisor has more than one digit, we still use a series of estimations to find the quotient.

Example 6   **Dividing by a Two-Digit Number**

Divide. $32\overline{)1259}$

Solution:

To estimate the leading digit of the quotient, estimate the number of times 30 will go into 125. Since $30 \cdot 4 = 120$, our estimate is 4.

$$\begin{array}{r} 4 \\ 32\overline{)1259} \\ -128 \end{array}$$

$32 \cdot 4 = 128$ is too big. We cannot subtract 128 from 125. Revise the estimate in the quotient to 3.

$$\begin{array}{r} 3 \\ 32\overline{)1259} \\ -96\downarrow \\ \hline 299 \end{array}$$

$32 \cdot 3 = 96$ and subtract.
Bring down the 9.

Now estimate the number of times 30 will go into 299. Because $30 \cdot 9 = 270$, our estimate is 9.

$$\begin{array}{r} 39 \ \text{R}11 \\ 32\overline{)1259} \\ -96\downarrow \\ \hline 299 \\ -288 \\ \hline 11 \end{array}$$

$32 \cdot 9 = 288$ and subtract.
The remainder is 11.

To check, verify that $(32)(39) + 11 = 1259$. ✔

Skill Practice

15. Divide.
$63\overline{)4516}$

Example 7   **Dividing by a Many-Digit Number**

Divide. $\dfrac{82{,}705}{602}$

Solution:

$$\begin{array}{r} 137 \ \text{R}231 \\ 602\overline{)82{,}705} \\ -602\downarrow \\ \hline 2250 \\ -1806\downarrow \\ \hline 4445 \\ -4214 \\ \hline 231 \end{array}$$

$602 \cdot 1 = 602$ and subtract.
Bring down the 0.
$602 \cdot 3 = 1806$ and subtract.
Bring down the 5.
$602 \cdot 7 = 4214$ and subtract.
The remainder is 231.

To check, verify that $(602)(137) + 231 = 82{,}705$. ✔

Skill Practice

16. Divide.
$304\overline{)62{,}405}$

Answers
15. 71 R43   **16.** 205 R85

5. Translations and Applications Involving Division

Several words and phrases imply division. A partial list is given in Table 1-4.

Table 1-4

Word/Phrase	Example	In Symbols		
Divide	Divide 12 by 3	$12 \div 3$ or	$\dfrac{12}{3}$ or	$3\overline{)12}$
Quotient	The quotient of 20 and 2	$20 \div 2$ or	$\dfrac{20}{2}$ or	$2\overline{)20}$
Per	110 mi per 2 hr	$110 \div 2$ or	$\dfrac{110}{2}$ or	$2\overline{)110}$
Divides into	4 divides into 28	$28 \div 4$ or	$\dfrac{28}{4}$ or	$4\overline{)28}$
Divided, or shared equally among	64 shared equally among 4	$64 \div 4$ or	$\dfrac{64}{4}$ or	$4\overline{)64}$

── Skill Practice ──

17. Four people play Hearts with a standard 52-card deck of cards. If the cards are equally distributed, how many cards does each player get?

Example 8   **Solving an Application Involving Division**

A painting business employs 3 painters. The business collects $1950 for painting a house. If all painters are paid equally, how much does each person make?

Solution:

This is an example where $1950 is shared equally among 3 people. Therefore, we divide.

$$
\begin{array}{r}
650 \\
3\overline{)1950} \\
\end{array}
$$

$$
\begin{array}{rl}
650 & \\
3\overline{)1950} & \\
-18\downarrow & \quad 3 \cdot 6 = 18 \text{ and subtract.} \\
\hline
15 & \quad \text{Bring down the 5.} \\
-15\downarrow & \quad 3 \cdot 5 = 15 \text{ and subtract.} \\
\hline
00 & \quad \text{Bring down the 0.} \\
-0 & \quad 3 \cdot 0 = 0 \text{ and subtract.} \\
\hline
0 & \quad \text{The remainder is 0.}
\end{array}
$$

Each painter makes $650.

Answer

17. 13 cards

Example 9   Solving an Application Involving Division

The graph in Figure 1-8 depicts the number of calories burned per hour for selected activities.

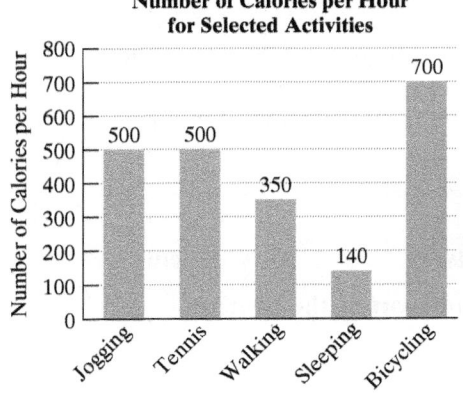

Number of Calories per Hour for Selected Activities

Figure 1-8

a. Janie wants to burn 3500 calories per week exercising. For how many hours must she jog?

b. For how many hours must Janie bicycle to burn 3500 calories?

Solution:

a. The total number of calories must be divided into 500-calorie increments. Thus, the number of hours required is given by 3500 ÷ 500.

$$\begin{array}{r} 7 \\ 500\overline{)3500} \\ -3500 \\ \hline 0 \end{array}$$

Janie requires 7 hr of jogging to burn 3500 calories.

b. 3500 calories must be divided into 700-calorie increments. The number of hours required is given by 3500 ÷ 700.

$$\begin{array}{r} 5 \\ 700\overline{)3500} \\ -3500 \\ \hline 0 \end{array}$$

Janie requires 5 hr of bicycling to burn 3500 calories.

Skill Practice

18. The cost for four different types of pastry at a French bakery is shown in the graph.

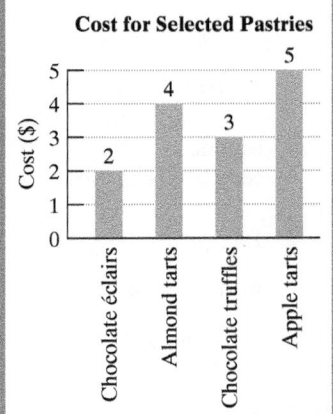

Cost for Selected Pastries

Melissa has $360 to spend on desserts.
a. If she spends all the money on chocolate éclairs, how many can she buy?
b. If she spends all the money on apple tarts, how many can she buy?

Answer
19. a. 180 chocolate éclairs
    b. 72 apple tarts

Section 1.6 Practice Exercises

Study Skills Exercises

1. In your next math class, take notes by drawing a vertical line about three-fourths of the way across the paper, as shown. On the left side, write down what your instructor puts on the board or overhead. On the right side, make your own comments about important words, procedures, or questions that you have.

2. Define the key terms.

   a. Division   b. Dividend   c. Divisor   d. Quotient

   e. Long division   f. Remainder   g. Whole part of the quotient

Review Exercises

For Exercises 3–10, add, subtract, or multiply as indicated.

3. $48 \cdot 103$ 4. $678 - 83$ 5. $1008 + 245$ 6. $14(220)$

7. $5230 \cdot 127$ 8. $789(25)$ 9. $4890 - 3988$ 10. $38{,}002 + 3902$

Objective 1: Introduction to Division

For Exercises 11–16, simplify each expression. Then identify the dividend, divisor, and quotient. **(See Example 1.)**

11. $72 \div 8$ 12. $32 \div 4$ ⊙ 13. $8\overline{)64}$

14. $5\overline{)35}$ 15. $\dfrac{45}{9}$ 16. $\dfrac{20}{5}$

Objective 2: Properties of Division

⊙ 17. In your own words, explain the difference between dividing a number by zero and dividing zero by a number.

18. Explain what happens when a number is either divided or multiplied by 1.

For Exercises 19–30, use the properties of division to simplify the expression, if possible. **(See Example 2.)**

19. $15 \div 1$ 20. $21\overline{)21}$ 21. $0 \div 10$ 22. $\dfrac{0}{3}$

23. $0\overline{)9}$ 24. $4 \div 0$ 25. $\dfrac{20}{20}$ 26. $1\overline{)9}$

27. $\dfrac{16}{0}$ 28. $\dfrac{5}{1}$ 29. $8\overline{)0}$ 30. $13 \div 13$

31. Show that $6 \div 3 = 2$ but $3 \div 6 \neq 2$ by using multiplication to check.

32. Show that division is not associative, using the numbers 36, 12, and 3.

Objective 3: Long Division

33. Explain the process for checking a division problem when there is no remainder.

34. Show how checking by multiplication can help us remember that $0 \div 5 = 0$ and that $5 \div 0$ is undefined.

For Exercises 35–46, divide and check by multiplying. **(See Examples 3 and 4.)**

35. $78 \div 6$
Check: $6 \cdot \square = 78$

36. $364 \div 7$
Check: $7 \cdot \square = 364$

37. $5\overline{)205}$
Check: $5 \cdot \square = 205$

38. $8\overline{)152}$
Check: $8 \cdot \square = 152$

39. $\dfrac{972}{2}$

40. $\dfrac{582}{6}$

41. $1227 \div 3$

42. $236 \div 4$

43. $5\overline{)1015}$

44. $5\overline{)2035}$

45. $\dfrac{4932}{6}$

46. $\dfrac{3619}{7}$

For Exercises 47–54, check the following division problems. If it does not check, find the correct answer.

47. $4\overline{)224}^{\,56}$

48. $7\overline{)574}^{\,82}$

49. $761 \div 3 = 253$

50. $604 \div 5 = 120$

51. $\dfrac{1021}{9} = 113\ R4$

52. $\dfrac{1311}{6} = 218\ R3$

53. $8\overline{)203}^{\,25\ R6}$

54. $7\overline{)821}^{\,117\ R5}$

For Exercises 55–70, divide and check the answer. **(See Example 5.)**

55. $61 \div 8$

56. $89 \div 3$

57. $9\overline{)92}$

58. $5\overline{)74}$

59. $\dfrac{55}{2}$

60. $\dfrac{49}{3}$

61. $593 \div 3$

62. $801 \div 4$

63. $\dfrac{382}{9}$

64. $\dfrac{428}{8}$

65. $3115 \div 2$

66. $4715 \div 6$

67. $6014 \div 8$

68. $9013 \div 7$

69. $6\overline{)5012}$

70. $2\overline{)1101}$

Objective 4: Dividing by a Many-Digit Divisor

For Exercises 71–86, divide. **(See Examples 6 and 7.)**

71. $9110 \div 19$

72. $3505 \div 13$

73. $24\overline{)1051}$

74. $41\overline{)8104}$

75. $\dfrac{8008}{26}$

76. $\dfrac{9180}{15}$

77. $68{,}012 \div 54$

78. $92{,}013 \div 35$

79. $\dfrac{1650}{75}$

80. $\dfrac{3649}{89}$

81. $520\overline{)18{,}201}$

82. $298\overline{)6278}$

83. $69{,}712 \div 304$

84. $51{,}107 \div 221$

85. $114\overline{)34{,}428}$

86. $421\overline{)87{,}989}$

Objective 5: Translations and Applications Involving Division

For Exercises 87–92, for each English sentence, write a mathematical expression and simplify.

87. Find the quotient of 497 and 71.

88. Find the quotient of 1890 and 45.

89. Divide 877 by 14.

90. Divide 722 by 53.

91. Divide 6 into 42.

92. Divide 9 into 108.

93. There are 392 students signed up for Anatomy 101. If each classroom can hold 28 students, find the number of classrooms needed.   **(See Example 8.)**

94. A wedding reception is planned to take place in the fellowship hall of a church. The bride anticipates 120 guests, and each table will seat 8 people. How many tables should be set up for the reception to accommodate all the guests?

95. A case of tomato sauce contains 32 cans. If a grocer has 168 cans, how many cases can he fill completely? How many cans will be left over?

96. Austin has $425 to spend on dining room chairs. If each chair costs $52, does he have enough to purchase 8 chairs? If so, will he have any money left over?

97. At one time, Seminole Community College had 3000 students who registered for Beginning Algebra. If the average class size is 25 students, how many Beginning Algebra classes will the college have to offer?

98. Eight people are to share equally in an inheritance of $84,480. How much money will each person receive?

99. The Honda Hybrid gets 45 mpg in stop-and-go traffic. How many gallons will it use in 405 mi of stop-and-go driving?

100. A couple traveled at an average speed of 52 mph for a cross-country trip. If the couple drove 1352 mi, how many hours was the trip?

101. Suppose Genny can type 1234 words in 22 min. Round each number to estimate her rate in words per minute.

102. On a trip to California from Illinois, Lavu drove 2780 mi. The gas tank in his car allows him to travel 405 mi. Round each number to the hundreds place to estimate the number of tanks of gas needed for the trip.

103. A group of 18 people goes to a concert. Ticket prices are given in the graph. If the group has $450, can they all attend the concert? If so, which type of seats can they buy?   **(See Example 9.)**

104. The graph gives the average annual income for four professions: teacher, professor, CEO, and programmer. Find the monthly income for each of the four professions.

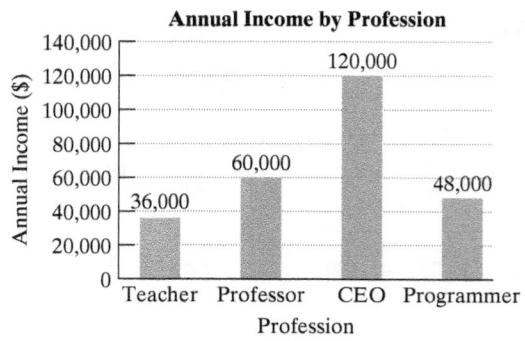

Calculator Connections

Topic: Multiplying and Dividing Whole Numbers

To multiply and divide numbers on a calculator, use the $\times$ and $\div$ keys, respectively.

Expression	Keystrokes	Result
38,319 × 1561	38319 × 1561 ENTER	59815959
2,449,216 ÷ 6248	2449216 ÷ 6248 ENTER	392

Calculator Exercises

For Exercises 105–108, solve the problem. Use a calculator to perform the calculations.

105. The United States consumes approximately 21,000,000 barrels (bbl) of oil per day. (*Source:* U.S. Energy Information Administration) How much does it consume in 1 year?

106. The average time to commute to work for people living in Washington state is 26 min (round trip 52 min). (*Source:* U.S. Census Bureau) How much time does a person spend commuting to and from work in 1 year if the person works 5 days a week for 50 weeks per year?

107. The budget for the U.S. federal government for 2008 was approximately $2532 billion dollars. (*Source:* U.S. Department of the Treasury) How much could the government spend each month and still stay within its budget?

108. At a weigh station, a truck carrying 96 crates weighs in at 34,080 lb. If the truck weighs 9600 lb when empty, how much does each crate weigh?

Problem Recognition Exercises

Operations on Whole Numbers

For Exercises 1–14, perform the indicated operations.

1. a. 96 + 24   **b.** 96 − 24   **c.** 96 × 24   **d.** 24)96

2. a. 550 + 25   **b.** 550 − 25   **c.** 550 × 25   **d.** 25)550

3. a. 612 + 334   **b.** 946 − 334   **4. a.** 612 − 334   **b.** 278 + 334

5. a. 5500 − 4299   **b.** 1201 + 4299   **6. a.** 22,718 + 12,137   **b.** 34,855 − 12,137

7. a. 50 · 400   **b.** 20,000 ÷ 50   **8. a.** 548 · 63   **b.** 34,524 ÷ 63

9. a. 5060 ÷ 22   **b.** 230 · 22   **10. a.** 1875 ÷ 125   **b.** 125 · 15

11. a. 4)1312   **b.** 328)1312   **12. a.** 547)4376   **b.** 8)4376

13. a. 418 · 10   **b.** 418 · 100   **c.** 418 · 1000   **d.** 418 · 10,000

14. a. 350,000 ÷ 10   **b.** 350,000 ÷ 100   **c.** 350,000 ÷ 1000   **d.** 350,000 ÷ 10,000

Section 1.7 Exponents, Algebraic Expressions, and the Order of Operations

Objectives

1. Exponents
2. Square Roots
3. Order of Operations
4. Algebraic Expressions

1. Exponents

Thus far in the text we have learned to add, subtract, multiply, and divide whole numbers. We now present the concept of an **exponent** to represent repeated multiplication. For example, the product

$$3 \cdot 3 \cdot 3 \cdot 3 \cdot 3 \quad \text{can be written as} \quad 3^5$$

(exponent — 5; base — 3)

The expression 3^5 is written in exponential form. The exponent, or **power**, is 5 and represents the number of times the **base**, 3, is used as a factor. The expression 3^5 is read as "three to the fifth power." Other expressions in exponential form are shown next.

5^2 is read as "five squared" or "five to the second power"

5^3 is read as "five cubed" or "five to the third power"

5^4 is read as "five to the fourth power"

5^5 is read as "five to the fifth power"

TIP: The expression $5^1 = 5$. Any number without an exponent explicitly written has a power of 1.

Exponential form is a shortcut notation for repeated multiplication. However, to simplify an expression in exponential form, we often write out the individual factors.

Skill Practice

Evaluate.
1. 8^2 2. 4^3 3. 2^5

Example 1   Evaluating Exponential Expressions

Evaluate.

a. 6^2 **b.** 5^3 **c.** 2^4

Solution:

a. $6^2 = 6 \cdot 6$ — The exponent, 2, indicates the number of times the base, 6, is used as a factor.

$= 36$

b. $5^3 = 5 \cdot 5 \cdot 5$ — When three factors are multiplied, we can group the first two factors and perform the multiplication.

$= (5 \cdot 5) \cdot 5$

$= (25) \cdot 5$ — Then multiply the product of the first two factors by the last factor.

$= 125$

c. $2^4 = 2 \cdot 2 \cdot 2 \cdot 2$

$= (2 \cdot 2) \cdot 2 \cdot 2$ — Group the first two factors.

$= 4 \cdot 2 \cdot 2$ — Multiply the first two factors.

$= (4 \cdot 2) \cdot 2$ — Multiply the product by the next factor to the right.

$= 8 \cdot 2$

$= 16$

Answers

1. 64   **2.** 64   **3.** 32

One important application of exponents lies in recognizing **powers of 10**, that is, 10 raised to a whole-number power. For example, consider the following expressions.

$$10^1 = 10$$
$$10^2 = 10 \cdot 10 = 100$$
$$10^3 = 10 \cdot 10 \cdot 10 = 1000$$
$$10^4 = 10 \cdot 10 \cdot 10 \cdot 10 = 10{,}000$$
$$10^5 = 10 \cdot 10 \cdot 10 \cdot 10 \cdot 10 = 100{,}000$$
$$10^6 = 10 \cdot 10 \cdot 10 \cdot 10 \cdot 10 \cdot 10 = 1{,}000{,}000$$

From these examples, we see that a power of 10 results in a 1 followed by several zeros. The number of zeros is the same as the exponent on the base of 10.

2. Square Roots

To square a number means that we multiply the base times itself. For example, $5^2 = 5 \cdot 5 = 25$.

To find a positive **square root** of a number means that we reverse the process of squaring. For example, finding the square root of 25 is equivalent to asking, "What positive number, when squared, equals 25?" The symbol $\sqrt{\ }$, (called a *radical sign*) is used to denote the positive square root of a number. Therefore, $\sqrt{25}$ is the positive number, that when squared, equals 25. Thus, $\sqrt{25} = 5$ because $(5)^2 = 25$.

Example 2   Evaluating Square Roots

Find the square roots.

a. $\sqrt{9}$ **b.** $\sqrt{64}$ **c.** $\sqrt{1}$ **d.** $\sqrt{0}$

Solution:

a. $\sqrt{9} = 3$ because $(3)^2 = 3 \cdot 3 = 9$
b. $\sqrt{64} = 8$ because $(8)^2 = 8 \cdot 8 = 64$
c. $\sqrt{1} = 1$ because $(1)^2 = 1 \cdot 1 = 1$
d. $\sqrt{0} = 0$ because $(0)^2 = 0 \cdot 0 = 0$

Skill Practice
Find the square roots.
4. $\sqrt{4}$
5. $\sqrt{100}$
6. $\sqrt{400}$
7. $\sqrt{121}$

TIP: To simplify square roots, it is advisable to become familiar with the following squares and square roots.

$$0^2 = 0 \rightarrow \sqrt{0} = 0 \qquad 7^2 = 49 \rightarrow \sqrt{49} = 7$$
$$1^2 = 1 \rightarrow \sqrt{1} = 1 \qquad 8^2 = 64 \rightarrow \sqrt{64} = 8$$
$$2^2 = 4 \rightarrow \sqrt{4} = 2 \qquad 9^2 = 81 \rightarrow \sqrt{81} = 9$$
$$3^2 = 9 \rightarrow \sqrt{9} = 3 \qquad 10^2 = 100 \rightarrow \sqrt{100} = 10$$
$$4^2 = 16 \rightarrow \sqrt{16} = 4 \qquad 11^2 = 121 \rightarrow \sqrt{121} = 11$$
$$5^2 = 25 \rightarrow \sqrt{25} = 5 \qquad 12^2 = 144 \rightarrow \sqrt{144} = 12$$
$$6^2 = 36 \rightarrow \sqrt{36} = 6 \qquad 13^2 = 169 \rightarrow \sqrt{169} = 13$$

Answers
4. 2   **5.** 10   **6.** 20   **7.** 11

3. Order of Operations

A numerical expression may contain more than one operation. For example, the following expression contains both multiplication and subtraction.

$$18 - 5(2)$$

The order in which the multiplication and subtraction are performed will affect the overall outcome.

Multiplying first yields	**Subtracting first yields**
$18 - 5(2) = 18 - 10$	$18 - 5(2) = 13(2)$
$= 8$ (correct)	$= 26$ (incorrect)

To avoid confusion, mathematicians have outlined the proper order of operations. In particular, multiplication is performed before addition or subtraction. The guidelines for the order of operations are given next. These rules must be followed in all cases.

Animation

PROCEDURE   Order of Operations

Step 1 First perform all operations inside parentheses or other grouping symbols.

Step 2 Simplify any expressions containing exponents or square roots.

Step 3 Perform multiplication or division in the order that they appear from left to right.

Step 4 Perform addition or subtraction in the order that they appear from left to right.

Skill Practice

Simplify.

8. $18 + 6 \div 2 - 4$

9. $(20 - 4) \div 2 + 1$

10. $2^3 - \sqrt{16 + 9}$

Example 3   Using the Order of Operations

Simplify.

a. $15 - 10 \div 2 + 3$ **b.** $(5 - 2) \cdot 7 - 1$ **c.** $\sqrt{64 + 36} - 2^3$

Solution:

a. $15 - \underbrace{10 \div 2} + 3$

$= 15 - \underbrace{5 + 3}$ Perform the division $10 \div 2$ first.

$=\quad 10 + 3$ Perform addition and subtraction from left to right.

$=\quad 13$ Add.

b. $\underbrace{(5 - 2)} \cdot 7 - 1$

$= \underbrace{(3) \cdot 7} - 1$ Perform the operation inside parentheses first.

$=\quad 21 - 1$ Perform multiplication before subtraction.

$=\quad 20$ Subtract.

Answers

8. 17   **9.** 9   **10.** 3

c. $\sqrt{64 + 36} - 2^3$

$= \sqrt{100} - 2^3$　　　The radical sign is a grouping symbol. Perform the operation within the radical first.

$= 10 - 8$　　　Simplify any expressions with exponents or square roots. Note that $\sqrt{100} = 10$, and $2^3 = 2 \cdot 2 \cdot 2 = 8$.

$= 2$　　　Subtract.

Example 4　**Using the Order of Operations**

Simplify.

a. $300 \div (7 - 2)^2 \cdot 2^2$　　　**b.** $36 + (7^2 - 3)$　　　**c.** $\dfrac{3^2 + 6 \cdot 1}{10 - 7}$

Solution:

a. $300 \div \underbrace{(7 - 2)}^2 \cdot 2^2$　　Perform the operation within parentheses first.

$= 300 \div \underbrace{(5)^2 \cdot 2^2}$　　Simplify exponents: $5^2 = 5 \cdot 5 = 25$ and $2^2 = 2 \cdot 2 = 4$.

$= \underbrace{300 \div 25} \cdot 4$　　From left to right, division appears before multiplication.

$= \quad 12 \cdot 4$　　Multiply.

$= \quad\quad 48$

b. $\quad 36 + \underbrace{(7^2 - 3)}$

$= 36 + \underbrace{(49 - 3)}$　　Perform the operations within parentheses first. The guidelines indicate that we simplify the expression with the exponent before we subtract: $7^2 = 49$.

$= 36 + \quad 46$　　Add.

$= 82$

c. $\dfrac{3^2 + 6 \cdot 1}{10 - 7}$

$= \dfrac{9 + 6}{3}$　　Simplify the expressions above and below the fraction bar by using the order of operations.

$= \dfrac{15}{3}$　　Simplify.

$= 5$　　Divide.

Skill Practice

Simplify.

11. $40 \div (3 - 1)^2 \cdot 5^2$

12. $42 - (50 - 6^2)$

13. $\dfrac{6^2 - 3 \cdot 4}{8 \cdot 3}$

TIP: A division bar within an expression acts as a grouping symbol. In Example 4(c), we must simplify the expressions above and below the division bar first before dividing.

Sometimes an expression will have parentheses within parentheses. These are called *nested parentheses*. The grouping symbols ( ), [ ], or { } are all used as parentheses. The different shapes make it easier to match up the pairs of parentheses. For example,

$$\{300 - 4[4 + (5 + 2)^2] + 8\} - 31$$

When nested parentheses are present, simplify the innermost set first. Then work your way out.

Answers

11. 250　**12.** 28　**13.** 1

Skill Practice

14. Simplify.

$4^2 - 2[12 - (3 + 6)]$

Example 5 **Using the Order of Operations**

Simplify. $\{300 - 4[4 + (5 + 2)^2] + 8\} - 31$

Solution:

$\{300 - 4[4 + (5 + 2)^2] + 8\} - 31$ Simplify within the innermost parentheses first ( ).

$= \{300 - 4[4 + (7)^2] + 8\} - 31$ Simplify the exponent.

$= \{300 - 4[4 + 49] + 8\} - 31$ Simplify within the next innermost parentheses [ ].

$= \{300 - 4[53] + 8\} - 31$ Multiply before adding.

$= \{300 - 212 + 8\} - 31$ Subtract and add in order from left to right within the parentheses { }.

$= \{88 + 8\} - 31$ Simplify within the parentheses { }.

$= 96 - 31$ Simplify.

$= 65$

4. Algebraic Expressions

In Section 1.5, we introduced the formula $A = l \cdot w$. This represents the area of a rectangle in terms of its length and width. The letters A, l, and w are called variables. **Variables** are used to represent quantities that are subject to change. Quantities that do not change are called **constants**. Variables and constants are used to build algebraic expressions. The following are all examples of algebraic expressions.

$$n + 30, \qquad x - y, \qquad 3w, \qquad \frac{a}{4}$$

The value of an algebraic expression depends on the values of the variables within the expression. In Examples 6 and 7, we practice evaluating expressions for given values of the variables.

Skill Practice

15. Evaluate $x + 7y$ for $x = 8$ and $y = 4$.

Example 6 **Evaluating an Algebraic Expression**

Evaluate the expression for the given values of the variables.

$$5a + b \quad \text{for } a = 6 \text{ and } b = 10$$

Solution:

$5a + b$

$= 5(\;) + (\;)$ When we substitute a number for a variable, use parentheses in place of the variable.

$= 5(6) + (10)$ Substitute 6 for a and 10 for b, by placing the values within the parentheses.

$= 30 + 10$ Apply the order of operations. Multiplication is performed before addition.

$= 40$

Answers

14. 10   **15.** 36

Example 7 **Evaluating an Algebraic Expression**

Evaluate the expression for the given values of the variables.

$$(x - y + z)^2 \quad \text{for } x = 12, y = 9, \text{ and } z = 4$$

Solution:

$(x - y + z)^2$

$= [( ) - ( ) + ( )]^2$ Use parentheses in place of the variables.

$= [(12) - (9) + (4)]^2$ Substitute 12 for x, 9 for y, and 4 for z.

$= [3 + 4]^2$ Subtract and add within the grouping symbols from left to right.

$= (7)^2$

$= 49$ The value $7^2 = 7 \cdot 7 = 49$.

Skill Practice

16. Evaluate $(m - n)^2 + p$ for $m = 11$, $n = 5$, and $p = 2$.

Answer

16. 38

Section 1.7 Practice Exercises

Boost *your* **GRADE at ALEKS.com!**

ALEKS version 3.0

- Practice Problems
- Self-Tests
- NetTutor
- e-Professors
- Videos

Study Skills Exercises

1. Look over the notes that you took today. Do you understand what you wrote? If there were any rules, definitions, or formulas, highlight them so that they can be easily found when studying for the test. You may want to begin by highlighting the order of operations.

2. Define the key terms.

    a. Exponent   **b. Power**   **c. Base**   **d. Power of 10**

    e. Square root   **f. Variable**   **g. Constant**

Review Exercises

For Exercises 3–8, write true or false for each statement.

3. Addition is commutative; for example, $5 + 3 = 3 + 5$.

4. Subtraction is commutative; for example, $5 - 3 = 3 - 5$.

5. $6 \cdot 0 = 6$ **6.** $0 \div 8 = 0$ **7.** $0 \cdot 8 = 0$ **8.** $5 \div 0$ is undefined

Objective 1: Exponents

9. Write an exponential expression with 9 as the base and 4 as the exponent.

10. Write an exponential expression with 3 as the base and 8 as the exponent.

For Exercises 11–14, write the repeated multiplication in exponential form. Do not simplify.

 11. $3 \cdot 3 \cdot 3 \cdot 3 \cdot 3 \cdot 3$ **12.** $7 \cdot 7 \cdot 7 \cdot 7$ **13.** $4 \cdot 4 \cdot 4 \cdot 4 \cdot 2 \cdot 2 \cdot 2$ **14.** $5 \cdot 5 \cdot 5 \cdot 10 \cdot 10 \cdot 10$

For Exercises 15–18, expand the exponential expression as a repeated multiplication. Do not simplify.

15. 8^4 **16.** 2^6 **17.** 4^8 **18.** 6^2

For Exercises 19–30, evaluate the exponential expressions. **(See Example 1.)**

19. 2^3 **20.** 4^2 **21.** 3^2 **22.** 5^2

23. 3^3 **24.** 11^2 **25.** 5^3 **26.** 10^3

27. 2^5 **28.** 6^3 **29.** 3^4 **30.** 5^4

31. Evaluate 1^2, 1^3, 1^4, and 1^5. Explain what happens when 1 is raised to any power.

For Exercises 32–35, evaluate the powers of 10.

32. 10^2 **33.** 10^3 **34.** 10^4 **35.** 10^5

36. Explain how to get 10^9 *without* performing the repeated multiplication. **(See Exercises 32–35.)**

Objective 2: Square Roots

For Exercises 37–44, evaluate the square roots. **(See Example 2.)**

37. $\sqrt{4}$ **38.** $\sqrt{9}$ **39.** $\sqrt{36}$ **40.** $\sqrt{81}$

41. $\sqrt{100}$ **42.** $\sqrt{49}$ **43.** $\sqrt{0}$ **44.** $\sqrt{16}$

Objective 3: Order of Operations

45. Does the order of operations indicate that addition is always performed before subtraction? Explain.

46. Does the order of operations indicate that multiplication is always performed before division? Explain.

For Exercises 47–87, simplify using the order of operations. **(See Examples 3–4.)**

47. $6 + 10 \cdot 2$ **48.** $4 + 3 \cdot 7$ **49.** $10 - 3^2$ **50.** $11 - 2^2$

51. $(10 - 3)^2$ **52.** $(11 - 2)^2$ **53.** $36 \div 2 \div 6$ **54.** $48 \div 4 \div 2$

55. $15 - (5 + 8)$ **56.** $41 - (13 + 8)$ **57.** $(13 - 2) \cdot 5 - 2$ **58.** $(8 + 4) \cdot 6 + 8$

59. $4 + 12 \div 3$ **60.** $9 + 15 \div \sqrt{25}$ **61.** $30 \div 2 \cdot \sqrt{9}$ **62.** $55 \div 11 \cdot 5$

63. $7^2 - 5^2$ **64.** $3^3 - 2^3$ **65.** $(7 - 5)^2$ **66.** $(3 - 2)^3$

67. $100 \div 5 \cdot 2$ **68.** $60 \div 3 \cdot 2$ **69.** $20 - 5(11 - 8)$ **70.** $38 - 6(10 - 5)$

71. $\sqrt{36 + 64} + 2(9 - 1)$ **72.** $\sqrt{16 + 9} + 3(8 - 3)$ **73.** $\dfrac{36}{2^2 + 5}$ **74.** $\dfrac{42}{3^2 - 2}$

75. $80 - 20 \div 4 \cdot 6$ **76.** $300 - 48 \div 8 \cdot 40$ **77.** $\dfrac{42 - 26}{4^2 - 8}$ **78.** $\dfrac{22 + 14}{2^2 \cdot 3}$

79. $(18 - 5) - (23 - \sqrt{100})$ **80.** $(\sqrt{36} + 11) - (31 - 16)$ **81.** $80 \div (9^2 - 7 \cdot 11)^2$

82. $108 \div (3^3 - 6 \cdot 4)^2$ **83.** $22 - 4(\sqrt{25} - 3)^2$ **84.** $17 + 3(7 - \sqrt{9})^2$

85. $96 - 3(42 \div 7 \cdot 6 - 5)$ **86.** $50 - 2(36 \div 12 \cdot 2 - 4)$ **87.** $16 + 5(20 \div 4 \cdot 8 - 3)$

For Exercises 88–93, simplify the expressions with nested parentheses. **(See Example 5.)**

88. $3[4 + (6 - 3)^2] - 15$

89. $2[5(4 - 1) + 3] \div 6$

90. $8^2 - 5[12 - (8 - 6)]$

91. $3^3 - 2[15 - (2 + 1)^2]$

92. $5\{21 - [3^2 - (4 - 2)]\}$

93. $4\{18 - [(10 - 8) + 2^3]\}$

Objective 4: Algebraic Expressions

For Exercises 94–101, evaluate the expressions for the given values of the variables. $x = 12, y = 4, z = 25,$ and $w = 9.$ **(See Examples 6 – 7.)**

94. $10y - z$

95. $8w - 4x$

96. $3x + 6y + 9w$

97. $9y - 4w + 3z$

98. $(z - x - y)^2$

99. $(y + z - w)^2$

100. $\sqrt{z}$

101. $\sqrt{w}$

Calculator Connections

Topic: Evaluating Expressions with Exponents

Many calculators use the $\boxed{x^2}$ key to square a number. To raise a number to a higher power, use the $\boxed{\wedge}$ key (or on some calculators, the $\boxed{x^y}$ key or $\boxed{y^x}$ key).

Expression	Keystrokes	Result
26^2	26 $\boxed{x^2}$ $\boxed{\text{ENTER}}$	676
	↑ On some calculators, you do not need to press $\boxed{\text{ENTER}}$.	
3^4	3 $\boxed{\wedge}$ 4 $\boxed{\text{ENTER}}$	81
or	3 $\boxed{y^x}$ 4 $\boxed{=}$	81

Calculator Exercises

For Exercises 102–107, use a calculator to perform the indicated operations.

102. 156^2 **103.** 418^2 **104.** 12^5 **105.** 35^4 **106.** 43^3 **107.** 71^3

For Exercises 108–113, simplify the expressions by using the order of operations. For each step use the calculator to simplify the given operation.

108. $8126 - 54{,}978 \div 561$

109. $92{,}168 + 6954 \times 29$

110. $(3548 - 3291)^2$

111. $(7500 \div 625)^3$

112. $\dfrac{89{,}880}{384 + 2184}$ *Hint:* This expression has implied grouping symbols. $\dfrac{89{,}880}{(384 + 2184)}$

113. $\dfrac{54{,}137}{3393 - 2134}$ *Hint:* This expression has implied grouping symbols. $\dfrac{54{,}137}{(3393 - 2134)}$

Section 1.8   Mixed Applications and Computing Mean

Objectives

1. Applications Involving Multiple Operations
2. Computing a Mean (Average)

1. Applications Involving Multiple Operations

Sometimes more than one operation is needed to solve an application problem.

Example 1   Solving a Consumer Application

Jorge bought a car for $18,340. He paid $2500 down and then paid the rest in equal monthly payments over a 4-year period. Find the amount of Jorge's monthly payment (not including interest).

Solution:

Familiarize and draw a picture.

Given: total price: $18,340
down payment: $2500

payment plan: 4 years
(48 months)

Find: monthly payment

$18,340   Original cost of car

−2,500   Minus down payment

$15,840   Amount to be paid off

Divide payments over 4 years (48 months)

Operations:

1. The amount of the loan to be paid off is equal to the original cost of the car minus the down payment. We use subtraction:

$$\begin{array}{r} \$18{,}340 \\ -\ 2{,}500 \\ \hline \$15{,}840 \end{array}$$

2. This money is distributed in equal payments over a 4-year period. Because there are 12 months in 1 year, there are $4 \cdot 12 = 48$ months in a 4-year period. To distribute $15,840 among 48 equal payments, we divide.

$$\begin{array}{r} 330 \\ 48)\overline{15{,}840} \\ \underline{-144} \\ 144 \\ \underline{-144} \\ 00 \end{array}$$

Jorge's monthly payments will be $330.

TIP: The solution to Example 1 can be checked by multiplication. Forty-eight payments of $330 each amount to 48($330) = $15,840. This added to the down payment totals $18,340 as desired.

Answer

1. $135 per month

Example 2 | **Solving a Travel Application**

Linda must drive from Clayton to Oakley. She can travel directly from Clayton to Oakley on a mountain road, but will only average 40 mph. On the route through Pearson, she travels on highways and can average 60 mph. Which route will take less time?

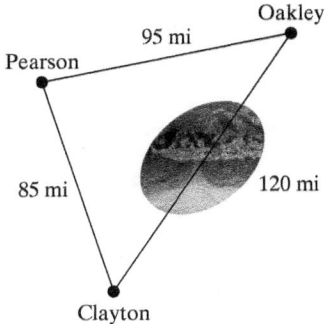

Skill Practice

2. Taylor makes $18 per hour for the first 40 hr worked each week. His overtime rate is $27 per hour for hours exceeding the normal 40-hr workweek. If his total salary for one week is $963, determine the number of hours of overtime worked.

Solution:

Read and familiarize: A map is presented in the problem.

Given: The distance for each route and the speed traveled along each route

Find: Find the time required for each route. Then compare the times to determine which will take less time.

Operations:

1. First note that the total distance of the route through Pearson is found by using addition.

$$85 \text{ mi} + 95 \text{ mi} = 180 \text{ mi}$$

2. The speed of the vehicle gives us the distance traveled per hour. Therefore, the time of travel equals the total distance divided by the speed.

From Clayton to Oakley through the mountains, we divide 120 mi by 40-mph increments to determine the number of hours.

$$\text{Time} = \frac{120 \text{ mi}}{40 \text{ mph}} = 3 \text{ hr}$$

From Clayton to Oakley through Pearson, we divide 180 mi by 60-mph increments to determine the number of hours.

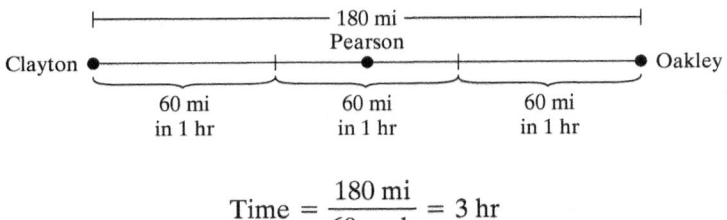

$$\text{Time} = \frac{180 \text{ mi}}{60 \text{ mph}} = 3 \text{ hr}$$

Therefore, each route takes the same amount of time, 3 hr.

Answer

2. 9 hr overtime

— **Skill Practice** —

3. Alain wants to put molding around the base of the room shown in the figure. No molding is needed where the door, closet, and bathroom are located. Find the total cost if molding is $2 per foot.

Example 3 **Solving a Construction Application**

A rancher must fence the corral shown in Figure 1-9. However, no fencing is required on the side adjacent to the barn. If fencing costs $4 per foot, what is the total cost?

Figure 1-9

Solution:

Read and familiarize: A figure is provided.

Strategy

With some application problems, it helps to work backward from your final goal. In this case, our final goal is to find the total cost. However, to find the total cost, we must first find the total distance to be fenced. To find the total distance, we add the lengths of the sides that are being fenced.

$$
\begin{array}{r}
275 \text{ ft} \\
200 \text{ ft} \\
200 \text{ ft} \\
475 \text{ ft} \\
+\ 300 \text{ ft} \\
\hline
1450 \text{ ft}
\end{array}
$$

Therefore,

$$
\left(\begin{array}{c}\text{Total cost}\\\text{of fencing}\end{array}\right) = \left(\begin{array}{c}\text{total}\\\text{distance}\\\text{in feet}\end{array}\right)\left(\begin{array}{c}\text{cost}\\\text{per foot}\end{array}\right)
$$

$$
= (1450 \text{ ft})(\$4 \text{ per ft})
$$

$$
= \$5800
$$

The total cost of fencing is $5800.

2. Computing a Mean (Average)

The order of operations must be used when we compute an average. The technical term for the average of a list of numbers is the **mean** of the numbers. To find the mean of a set of numbers, first compute the sum of the values. Then divide the sum by the number of values. This is represented by the formula

$$
\text{Mean} = \frac{\text{sum of the values}}{\text{number of values}}
$$

Answer

3. $124

Example 4 **Computing a Mean (Average)**

Ashley took 6 tests in Chemistry. Find her mean (average) score.

$$89, 91, 72, 86, 94, 96$$

Solution:

$$\text{Average score} = \frac{89 + 91 + 72 + 86 + 94 + 96}{6}$$

$$= \frac{528}{6} \qquad \text{Add the values in the list first.}$$

$$= 88 \qquad \text{Divide.} \qquad \begin{array}{r} 88 \\ 6\overline{)528} \\ -48 \\ \hline 48 \\ -48 \\ \hline 0 \end{array}$$

Ashley's mean (average) score is 88.

TIP: The division bar in $\dfrac{89 + 91 + 72 + 86 + 94 + 96}{6}$ is also a grouping symbol and implies parentheses:

$$\frac{(89 + 91 + 72 + 86 + 94 + 96)}{6}$$

Skill Practice

4. The ages (in years) of 5 students in an algebra class are given here. Find the mean age.

   22, 18, 22, 32, 46

Answer

4. 28 years

Section 1.8 Practice Exercises

Boost *your* GRADE at ALEKS.com!

ALEKS version 3.0

- Practice Problems
- Self-Tests
- NetTutor
- e-Professors
- Videos

Study Skills Exercises

1. Check yourself.

Yes _____ No _____ Did you have sufficient time to study for the test on this chapter? If not, what could you have done to create more time for studying?

Yes _____ No _____ Did you work all the assigned homework problems in this chapter?

Yes _____ No _____ If you encountered difficulty in this chapter, did you see your instructor or tutor for help?

Yes _____ No _____ Have you taken advantage of the textbook supplements such as the *Student Solution Manual*?

2. Define the key term, **mean**.

Review Exercises

For Exercises 3–13, translate the English phrase into a mathematical statement and simplify.

3. 71 increased by 14

4. 16 more than 42

5. Twice 14

6. The difference of 93 and 79

7. Subtract 32 from 102

8. Divide 12 into 60

9. The product of 10 and 13

10. The total of 12, 14, and 15

11. The quotient of 24 and 6

12. 41 less than 78

13. The sum of 5, 13, and 25

Objective 1: Applications Involving Multiple Operations

14. Jackson purchased a car for $16,540. He paid $2500 down and paid the rest in equal monthly payments over a 36-month period. How much were his monthly payments?

15. Lucio purchased a refrigerator for $1170. He paid $150 at the time of purchase and then paid off the rest in equal monthly payments over 1 year. How much was his monthly payment? **(See Example 1.)**

16. Monika must drive from Watertown to Utica. She can travel directly from Watertown to Utica on a small county road, but will only average 40 mph. On the route through Syracuse, she travels on highways and can average 60 mph. Which route will take less time?

17. Rex has a choice of two routes to drive from Oklahoma City to Fort Smith. On the interstate, the distance is 220 mi and he can drive 55 mph. If he takes the back roads, he can only travel 40 mph, but the distance is 200 mi. Which route will take less time? **(See Example 2.)**

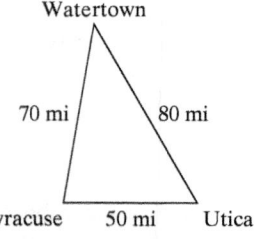

Figure for Exercise 16

18. If you wanted to line the outside of a garden with a decorative border, would you need to know the area of the garden or the perimeter of the garden?

19. If you wanted to know how much sod to lay down within a rectangular backyard, would you need to know the area of the yard or the perimeter of the yard?

20. Alexis wants to buy molding for a room that is 12 ft by 11 ft. No molding is needed for the doorway, which measures 3 ft. See the figure. If molding costs $2 per foot, how much money will it cost?

21. A homeowner wants to fence her rectangular backyard. The yard is 75 ft by 90 ft. If fencing costs $5 per foot, how much will it cost to fence the yard? **(See Example 3.)**

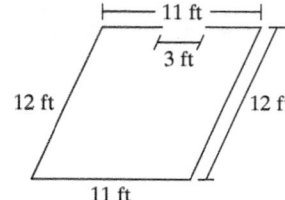

22. What is the cost to carpet the room whose dimensions are shown in the figure? Assume that carpeting costs $34 per square yard and that there is no waste.

23. What is the cost to tile the room whose dimensions are shown in the figure? Assume that tile costs $3 per square foot.

24. The balance in Gina's checking account is $278. If she writes checks for $82, $59, and $101, how much will be left over?

25. The balance in Jose's checking account is $3455. If he write checks for $587, $36, and $156, how much will be left over?

26. A community college bought 72 new computers and 6 new printers for a computer lab. If computers were purchased for $2118 each and the printers for $256 each, what was the total bill (not including tax)?

27. Tickets to the San Diego Zoo in California cost $22 for children aged 3–11 and $33 for adults. How much money is required to buy tickets for a class of 33 children and 6 adult chaperones?

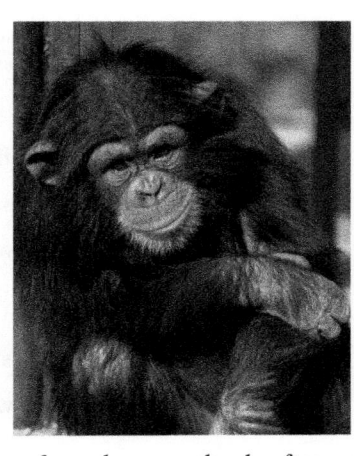

28. A discount music store buys used CDs from its customers for $3. Furthermore, a customer can buy any used CD in the store for $8. Latayne sells 16 CDs.

   a. How much money does she receive by selling the 16 CDs?

   b. How many CDs can she then purchase with the money?

29. Shevona earns $8 per hour and works a 40-hr workweek. At the end of the week, she cashes her paycheck and then buys two tickets to a Beyoncé concert.

   a. How much is her paycheck?

   b. If the concert tickets cost $64 each, how much money does she have left over from her paycheck after buying the tickets?

30. During his 13-year career with the Chicago Bulls, Michael Jordan scored 12,192 field goals (worth 2 points each). He scored 581 three-point shots and 7327 free-throws (worth 1 point each). How many total points did he score during his career with the Bulls?

31. A matte is to be cut and placed over five small square pictures before framing. Each picture is 5 in. wide, and the matte frame is 37 in. wide, as shown in the figure. If the pictures are to be equally spaced (including the space on the left and right edges), how wide is the matte between them?

32. Mortimer the cat was prescribed a suspension of methimazole for hyperthyroidism. This suspension comes in a 60 milliliter bottle with instructions to give 1 milliliter twice a day. The label also shows there is one refill, but it must be called in 2 days ahead. Mortimer had his first two doses on September 1.

   a. For how many days will one bottle last?

   b. On what day, at the latest, should his owner order a refill to avoid running out of medicine?

33. Recently, the American Medical Association reported that there were 630,300 male doctors and 205,900 female doctors in the United States.

   a. What is the difference between the number of male doctors and the number of female doctors?

   b. What is the total number of doctors?

34. On a map, 1 in. represents 60 mi.

   a. If Las Vegas and Salt Lake City are approximately 6 in. apart on the map, what is the actual distance between the cities?

   b. If Madison, Wisconsin, and Dallas, Texas, are approximately 840 mi apart, how many inches would this represent on the map?

35. On a map, each inch represents 40 mi.

   a. If Wichita, Kansas, and Des Moines, Iowa, are approximately 8 in. apart on the map, what is the actual distance between the cities?

   b. If Seattle, Washington, and Sacramento, California, are approximately 600 mi apart, how many inches would this represent on the map?

36. A textbook company ships books in boxes containing a maximum of 12 books. If a bookstore orders 1250 books, how many boxes can be filled completely? How many books will be left over?

37. A farmer sells eggs in containers holding a dozen eggs. If he has 4257 eggs, how many containers will be filled completely? How many eggs will be left over?

38. Marc pays for an $84 dinner with $20 bills.

  a. How many bills must he use?

  b. How much change will he receive?

39. Byron buys three CDs for a total of $54 and pays with $10 bills.

  a. How many bills must he use?

  b. How much change will he receive?

40. Ling has three jobs. He works for a lawn maintenance service 4 days a week. He also tutors math and works as a waiter on weekends. His hourly wage and the number of hours for each job are given for a 1-week period. How much money did Ling earn for the week?

	Hourly Wage	Number of Hours
Tutor	$30/hr	4
Waiter	10/hr	16
Lawn maintenance	8/hr	30

41. An electrician, a plumber, a mason, and a carpenter work at a construction site. The hourly wage and the number of hours each person worked are summarized in the table. What was the total amount paid for all four workers?

	Hourly Wage	Number of Hours
Electrician	$36/hr	18
Plumber	28/hr	15
Mason	26/hr	24
Carpenter	22/hr	48

Objective 2: Computing a Mean (Average)

For Exercises 42–44, find the mean (average) of each set of numbers. (See Example 4.)

42. 19, 21, 18, 21, 16

43. 105, 114, 123, 101, 100, 111

44. 1480, 1102, 1032, 1002

45. Neelah took six quizzes and received the following scores: 19, 20, 18, 19, 18, 14. Find her quiz average.

46. Shawn's scores on his last four tests were 83, 95, 87, and 91. What is his average for these tests?

47. At a certain grocery store, Jessie notices that the price of bananas varies from week to week. During a 3-week period she buys bananas for 89¢ per pound, 79¢ per pound, and 66¢ per pound. What does Jessie pay on average per pound?

48. On a trip, Stephen had his car washed four times and paid $7, $10, $8, and $7. What was the average amount spent per wash?

49. The monthly rainfall for Seattle, Washington, is given in the table. All values are in millimeters (mm).

	Jan.	Feb.	Mar.	Apr.	May	Jun.	Jul.	Aug.	Sep.	Oct.	Nov.	Dec.
Rainfall	122	94	80	52	47	40	15	21	44	90	118	123

Find the average monthly rainfall for the months of November, December, and January.

50. The monthly snowfall for Alpena, Michigan, is given in the table. All values are in inches.

	Jan.	Feb.	Mar.	Apr.	May	Jun.	Jul.	Aug.	Sep.	Oct.	Nov.	Dec.
Snowfall	22	16	13	5	1	0	0	0	0	1	9	20

Find the average monthly snowfall for the months of November, December, January, February, and March.

Chapter 1   Summary

Section 1.2   Introduction to Whole Numbers

Key Concepts

The place value for each **digit** of a number is shown in the chart.

	Billions Period			Millions Period			Thousands Period			Ones Period		
	Hundred-billions	Ten-billions	Billions	Hundred-millions	Ten-millions	Millions	Hundred-thousands	Ten-thousands	Thousands	Hundreds	Tens	Ones
			3,	4	0	9,	1	1	2			

Numbers can be written in different forms, for example:

Standard Form: 3,409,112

Expanded Form: 3 millions + 4 hundred-thousands + 9 thousands + 1 hundred + 1 ten + 2 ones

Words: three million, four hundred nine thousand, one hundred twelve

The order of whole numbers can be visualized by placement on a number line.

Examples

Example 1

The digit 9 in the number 24,891,321 is in the ten-thousands place.

Example 2

The standard form of the number forty-one million, three thousand, fifty-six is 41,003,056.

Example 3

The expanded form of the number 76,903 is 7 ten-thousands + 6 thousands + 9 hundreds + 3 ones.

Example 4

In words the number 2504 is two thousand, five hundred four.

Example 5

To show that $8 > 4$, note the placement on the number line: 8 is to the right of 4.

| Section 1.3 | Addition and Subtraction of Whole Numbers and Perimeter |

Key Concepts

The **sum** is the result of adding numbers called **addends**.

Addition is performed with and without carrying (or regrouping).

Addition Property of Zero:

The sum of any number and zero is that number.

Commutative Property of Addition:

Changing the order of the addends does not affect the sum.

Associative Property of Addition:

The manner in which the addends are grouped does not affect the sum.

There are several words and phrases that indicate addition, such as *sum, added to, increased by, more than, plus,* and *total of.*

The **perimeter** of a **polygon** is the distance around the outside of the figure. To find perimeter, take the sum of the lengths of all sides of the figure.

The **difference** is the result of subtracting the **subtrahend** from the **minuend**.

Subtract numbers with and without borrowing.

There are several words and phrases that indicate subtraction, such as *minus, difference, decreased by, less than,* and *subtract from.*

Examples

Example 1

For $2 + 7 = 9$, the addends are 2 and 7, and the sum is 9.

Example 2

$$\begin{array}{r} 23 \\ +\ 41 \\ \hline 64 \end{array} \qquad \begin{array}{r} {}^{1\ 1} \\ 189 \\ +\ 76 \\ \hline 265 \end{array}$$

Example 3

$16 + 0 = 16$ Addition property of zero

$3 + 12 = 12 + 3$ Commutative property of addition

$2 + (9 + 3) = (2 + 9) + 3$ Associative property of addition

Example 4

18 added to 4 translates to $4 + 18$.

Example 5

The perimeter is found by adding the lengths of all sides.

Perimeter $= 42$ in. $+ 38$ in. $+ 31$ in.

        $= 111$ in.

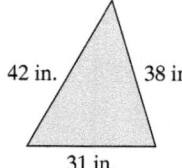

42 in.   38 in.

31 in.

Example 6

For $19 - 13 = 6$, the minuend is 19, the subtrahend is 13, and the difference is 6.

Example 7

$$\begin{array}{r} 398 \\ -\ 227 \\ \hline 171 \end{array} \qquad \begin{array}{r} {}^{\quad 9} \\ {}^{1\ \cancel{10}\ 14} \\ 2\ \cancel{0}\ 4 \\ -\ 88 \\ \hline 116 \end{array}$$

Example 8

The difference of 15 and 7 translates to $15 - 7$.

Section 1.4 Rounding and Estimating

Key Concepts

To **round a number**, follow these steps.

Step 1 Identify the digit one position to the right of the given place value.

Step 2 If the digit in step 1 is a 5 or greater, then add 1 to the digit in the given place value. If the digit in step 1 is less than 5, leave the given place value unchanged.

Step 3 Replace each digit to the right of the given place value by 0.

Use rounding to estimate sums and differences.

Examples

Example 1

Round each number to the indicated place.

a. 4942; hundreds place $\longrightarrow$ 4900
b. 3712; thousands place $\longrightarrow$ 4000
c. 135; tens place $\longrightarrow$ 140
d. 199; tens place $\longrightarrow$ 200

Example 2

Round to the thousands place to estimate the sum: $3929 + 2528 + 5452$.

$4000 + 3000 + 5000 = 12,000$

The sum is approximately 12,000.

Section 1.5 Multiplication of Whole Numbers and Area

Key Concepts

Multiplication is repeated addition.

The **product** is the result of multiplying **factors**.

Properties of Multiplication

1. Commutative Property of Multiplication: Changing the order of the factors does not affect the product.
2. Associative Property of Multiplication: The manner in which the factors are grouped does not affect the product.
3. Multipliction Property of 0: The product of any number and 0 is 0.
4. Multiplication Property of 1: The product of any number and 1 is that number.
5. Distributive Property of Multiplication over Addition

Examples

Example 1

$16 + 16 + 16 + 16 = 4 \cdot 16 = 64$

Example 2

For $3 \cdot 13 \cdot 2 = 78$ the factors are 3, 13, and 2, and the product is 78.

Example 3

1. $4 \cdot 7 = 7 \cdot 4$

2. $6 \cdot (5 \cdot 7) = (6 \cdot 5) \cdot 7$

3. $43 \cdot 0 = 0$

4. $290 \cdot 1 = 290$

5. $5 \cdot (4 + 8) = (5 \cdot 4) + (5 \cdot 8)$

Multiply whole numbers.	**Example 4** $3 \cdot 14 = 42$ $7(4) = 28$ $\begin{array}{r} 312 \\ \times\ 23 \\ \hline 936 \\ 6240 \\ \hline 7176 \end{array}$
The **area of a rectangle** with length l and width w is given by $A = l \cdot w$.	**Example 5** Find the area of the rectangle. 23 cm 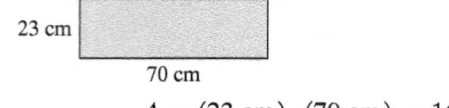 70 cm $A = (23\text{ cm}) \cdot (70\text{ cm}) = 1610\text{ cm}^2$

Section 1.6   Division of Whole Numbers

Key Concepts

A **quotient** is the result of dividing the **dividend** by the **divisor**.

Examples

Example 1

For $36 \div 4 = 9$, the dividend is 36, the divisor is 4, and the quotient is 9.

Properties of Division:

1. Any nonzero number divided by itself is 1.
2. Any number divided by 1 is the number itself.
3. Zero divided by any nonzero number is zero.
4. A number divided by zero is undefined.

Example 2

1. $13 \div 13 = 1$

2. $\begin{array}{r} 37 \\ 1\overline{)37} \end{array}$

3. $\dfrac{0}{2} = 0$

Example 3

$\dfrac{2}{0}$ is undefined.

Long division, with and without a **remainder**

Example 4

$$
\begin{array}{r}
263 \\
3\overline{)789} \\
-6 \\
\hline
18 \\
-18 \\
\hline
09 \\
-9 \\
\hline
0
\end{array}
\qquad
\begin{array}{r}
41\ \text{R}\ 12 \\
21\overline{)873} \\
-84 \\
\hline
33 \\
-21 \\
\hline
12
\end{array}
$$

Section 1.7 Exponents, Algebraic Expressions, and the Order of Operations

Key Concepts

A number raised to an **exponent** represents repeated multiplication.

For 6^3, 6 is the **base** and 3 is the exponent or **power**.

The **square root** of 16 is 4 because $4^2 = 16$. That is, $\sqrt{16} = 4$.

Order of Operations

1. First perform all operations inside parentheses or other grouping symbols.
2. Simplify any expressions containing exponents or square roots.
3. Perform multiplication or division in the order that they appear from left to right.
4. Perform addition or subtraction in the order that they appear from left to right.

Powers of 10

$10^1 = 10$

$10^2 = 100$

$10^3 = 1000$ and so on.

Variables are used to represent quantities that are subject to change. Quantities that do not change are called **constants**. Variables and constants are used to build **algebraic expressions**.

Examples

Example 1

$$9^4 = 9 \cdot 9 \cdot 9 \cdot 9 = 6561$$

Example 2

$$\sqrt{49} = 7$$

Example 3

$$32 \div \sqrt{16} + (9 - 6)^2$$
$$= 32 \div \sqrt{16} + (3)^2$$
$$= 32 \div 4 + 9$$
$$= 8 + 9$$
$$= 17$$

Example 4

$10^5 = 100{,}000$ 1 followed by 5 zeros

Example 5

Evaluate the expression $3x + y^2$ for $x = 10$ and $y = 5$.

$$3x + y^2 = 3(\quad) + (\quad)^2$$
$$= 3(10) + (5)^2$$
$$= 3(10) + 25$$
$$= 30 + 25$$
$$= 55$$

Section 1.8   Mixed Applications and Computing Mean

Key Concepts

Many applications require several steps and several mathematical operations.

The **mean** is the average of a set of numbers. To find the mean, add all the values and divide by the number of values.

Examples

Example 1

Nolan received a doctor's bill for $984. His insurance will pay $200, and the balance can be paid in 4 equal monthly payments. How much will each payment be?

Solution:

To find the amount not paid by insurance, subtract $200 from the total bill.

$$984 - 200 = 784$$

To find Nolan's 4 equal payments, divide the amount not covered by insurance by 4.

$$784 \div 4 = 196$$

Nolan must make 4 payments of $196 each.

Example 2

Find the mean (average) of Michael's scores from his homework assignments.

40, 41, 48, 38, 42, 43

Solution:

$$\frac{40 + 41 + 48 + 38 + 42 + 43}{6} = \frac{252}{6} = 42$$

The average is 42.

Chapter 1   Review Exercises

Section 1.2

For Exercises 1–2, determine the place value for each underlined digit.

1. 1̲0,024

2. 8̲21,811

For Exercises 3–4, convert the numbers to standard form.

3. 9 ten-thousands + 2 thousands + 4 tens + 6 ones

4. 5 hundred-thousands + 3 thousands + 1 hundred + 6 tens

For Exercises 5–6, convert the numbers to expanded form.

5. 3,400,820

6. 30,554

For Exercises 7–8, write the numbers in words.

7. 245

8. 30,861

For Exercises 9–10, write the numbers in standard form.

9. Three thousand, six-hundred two

10. Eight hundred thousand, thirty-nine

For Exercises 11–12, place the numbers on the number line.

11. 2

12. 7

For Exercises 13–14, determine if the inequality is true or false.

13. $3 < 10$

14. $10 > 12$

Section 1.3

For Exercises 15–16, identify the addends and the sum.

15. $105 + 119 = 224$

16.
$$\begin{array}{r} 53 \\ + 21 \\ \hline 74 \end{array}$$

For Exercises 17–20, add.

17. $18 + 24 + 29$

18. $27 + 9 + 18$

19.
$$\begin{array}{r} 8403 \\ + 9007 \end{array}$$

20.
$$\begin{array}{r} 68,421 \\ + 2,221 \end{array}$$

21. For each of the mathematical statements, identify the property used. Choose from the commutative property or the associative property.

    a. $6 + (8 + 2) = (8 + 2) + 6$

    b. $6 + (8 + 2) = (6 + 8) + 2$

    c. $6 + (8 + 2) = 6 + (2 + 8)$

For Exercises 22–23, identify the minuend, subtrahend, and difference.

22. $14 - 8 = 6$

23.
$$\begin{array}{r} 102 \\ - 78 \\ \hline 24 \end{array}$$

For Exercises 24–25, subtract and check your answer by addition.

24.
$$\begin{array}{r} 37 \\ - 11 \end{array}$$
Check: ☐ $+ 11 = 37$

25.
$$\begin{array}{r} 61 \\ - 41 \end{array}$$
Check: ☐ $+ 41 = 61$

For Exercises 26–29, subtract.

26.
$$\begin{array}{r} 2005 \\ - 1884 \end{array}$$

27. $1389 - 299$

28. $86,000 - 54,981$

29. $67,000 - 32,812$

For Exercises 30–37, translate the English phrase to a mathematical statement and simplify.

30. The sum of 403 and 79

31. 92 added to 44

32. 38 minus 31

33. 111 decreased by 15

34. 7 more than 36

35. 23 increased by 6

36. Subtract 42 from 251.

37. The difference of 90 and 52

38. The table gives the number of cars sold by three dealerships during one week.

	Honda	Ford	Toyota
Bob's Discount Auto	23	21	34
AA Auto	31	25	40
Car World	33	20	22

    a. What is the total number of cars sold by AA Auto?

    b. What is the total number of Fords sold by these three dealerships?

Use the bar graph to answer exercises 39–41. The graph represents the distribution of the U.S. population by age group for a recent year.

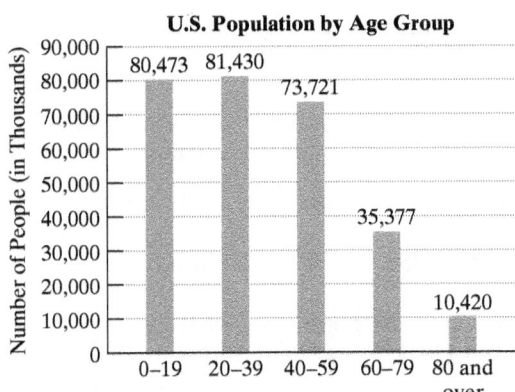

Source: U.S. Census Bureau

39. Determine the number of seniors (aged 60 and over).

40. Compute the difference in the number of people in the 20–39 age group and the number in the 40–59 age group.

41. How many more people are in the 0–19 age group than in the 60–79 age group?

42. For a recent year, 95,192,000 tons of watermelon and 23,299,000 tons of cantaloupe were grown. Determine the difference between the amount of watermelon grown and the amount of cantaloupe grown.

43. Tiger Woods earned $57,940,144 from the PGA tour as of 2006. If Phil Mickelson earned $36,167,360, find the difference in their winnings.

44. Find the perimeter of the figure.

30 m 44 m
25 m   25 m
53 m

Section 1.4

For Exercises 45–46, round each number to the given place value.

45. 5,234,446; millions

46. 9,332,945; ten-thousands

For Exercises 47–48, estimate the sum or difference by rounding to the indicated place value.

47. 894,004 − 123,883; hundred-thousands

48. 330 + 489 + 123 + 571; hundreds

49. In 2004, the population of Russia was 144,112,353, and the population of Japan was 127,295,333. Estimate the difference in their populations by rounding to the nearest million.

50. The state of Missouri has two dams: Fort Peck with a volume of 96,050 cubic meters (m^3) and Oahe with a volume of 66,517 m^3. Round the numbers to the nearest thousand to estimate the total volume of these two dams.

Section 1.5

51. Identify the factors and the product. $33 \cdot 40 = 1320$

52. Indicate whether the statement is equal to the product of 8 and 13.

   a. 8(13)   **b.** (8) · 13   **c.** (8) + (13)

For Exercises 53–57, for each property listed, choose an expression from the right column that demonstrates the property.

53. Associative property of multiplication   **a.** 3(4) = 4(3)

54. Distributive property of multiplication over addition   **b.** $19 \cdot 1 = 19$

55. Multiplication property of 0   **c.** $(1 \cdot 8) \cdot 3 = 1 \cdot (8 \cdot 3)$

56. Commutative property of multiplication   **d.** $0 \cdot 29 = 0$

57. Multiplication property of 1   **e.** $4(3 + 1) = 4 \cdot 3 + 4 \cdot 1$

For Exercises 58–60, multiply.

58. 142
  × 43

59. (1024)(51)

60. 6000
  × 500

61. A discussion group needs to purchase books that are accompanied by a workbook. The price of the book is $26, and the workbook costs an additional $13. If there are 11 members in the group, how much will it cost the group to purchase both the text and workbook for each student?

62. Orcas, or killer whales, eat 551 pounds (lb) of food a day. If Sea World has two adult killer whales, how much food will they eat in 1 week?

Section 1.6

For Exercises 63–64, perform the division. Then identify the divisor, dividend, and quotient.

63. $42 \div 6$ **64.** $4\overline{)52}$

For Exercises 65–68, use the properties of division to simplify the expression, if possible.

65. $3 \div 1$ **66.** $3 \div 3$

67. $3 \div 0$ **68.** $0 \div 3$

69. Explain how you check a division problem if there is no remainder.

70. Explain how you check a division problem if there is a remainder.

For Exercises 71–73, divide and check the answer.

71. $348 \div 6$ **72.** $11\overline{)458}$ **73.** $\dfrac{1043}{20}$

For Exercises 74–75, write the English phrase as a mathematical expression and simplify.

74. The quotient of 72 and 4

75. 108 divided by 9

76. Quinita has 105 photographs that she wants to divide equally among herself and three siblings. How many photos will each person receive? How many photos will be left over?

77. Ashley has $60 to spend on souvenirs at a surf shop. The prices of several souvenirs are given in the graph.

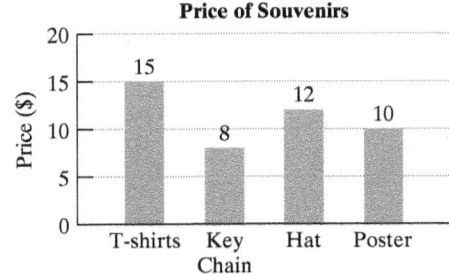

Price of Souvenirs

a. How many souvenirs can Ashley buy if she chooses all T-shirts?

b. How many souvenirs can Ashley buy if she chooses all hats?

Section 1.7

For Exercises 78–79, write the repeated multiplication in exponential form. Do not simplify.

78. $8 \cdot 8 \cdot 8 \cdot 8 \cdot 8$

79. $2 \cdot 2 \cdot 2 \cdot 2 \cdot 5 \cdot 5 \cdot 5$

For Exercises 80–83, evaluate the exponential expressions.

80. 5^3 **81.** 4^4 **82.** 1^7 **83.** 10^6

For Exercises 84–85, evaluate the square roots.

84. $\sqrt{64}$ **85.** $\sqrt{144}$

For Exercises 86–92, evaluate the expression using the order of operations.

86. $14 \div 7 \cdot 4 - 1$ **87.** $10^2 - 5^2$

88. $90 - 4 + 6 \div 3 \cdot 2$

89. $2 + 3 \cdot 12 \div 2 - \sqrt{25}$

90. $6^2 - [4^2 + (9 - 7)^3]$

91. $26 - 2(10 - 1) + (3 + 4 \cdot 11)$

92. $\dfrac{5 \cdot 3^2}{7 + 8}$

For Exercises 93–96, evaluate the expressions for $a = 20$, $b = 10$, and $c = 6$.

93. $a + b + 2c$ **94.** $5a - b^2$

95. $\sqrt{b + c}$ **96.** $(a - b)^2$

Section 1.8

97. Doris drives her son to extracurricular activities each week. She drives 5 mi round-trip to baseball practice 3 times a week and 6 mi round-trip to piano lessons once a week.

a. How many miles does she drive in 1 week to get her child to his activities?

b. Approximately how many miles does she travel during a school year consisting of 10 months (there are approximately 4 weeks per month)?

98. At one point in his baseball career, Alex Rodriquez signed a contract for $252,000,000 for a 9-year period. Suppose federal taxes amount to $75,600,000 for the contract. After taxes, how much did Alex receive per year?

99. Aletha wants to buy plants for a rectangular garden in her backyard that measures 12 ft by 8 ft. She wants to divide the garden into 2-square-foot (2 ft²) areas, one for each plant.

a. How many plants should Aletha buy?

b. If the plants cost $3 each, how much will it cost Aletha for the plants?

c. If she puts a fence around the perimeter of the garden that costs $2 per foot, how much will it cost for the fence?

d. What will be Aletha's total cost for this garden?

100. Find the mean (average) for the set of numbers 7, 6, 12, 5, 7, 6, 13.

101. Carolyn's electric bills for the past 5 months have been $80, $78, $101, $92, and $94. Find her average monthly charge.

102. The table shows the number of homes sold by a realty company in the last 6 months. Determine the average number of houses sold per month for these 6 months.

Month	Number of Houses
May	6
June	9
July	11
August	13
September	5
October	4

Chapter 1   Test

1. Determine the place value for the underlined digit.

    a. 4<u>9</u>2   **b.** 2<u>3</u>,441   **c.** <u>2</u>,340,711   **d.** 3<u>4</u>0,592

2. Fill in the table with either the word name for the number or the number in standard form.

	Population	
State / Province	**Standard Form**	**Word Name**
a. Kentucky		Four million, sixty-five thousand
b. Texas	21,325,000	
c. Pennsylvania	12,287,000	
d. New Brunswick, Canada		Seven hundred twenty-nine thousand
e. Ontario, Canada	11,410,000	

3. Translate the phrase by writing the numbers in standard form and inserting the appropriate inequality. Choose from < or >.

    a. Fourteen is greater than six.

    b. Seventy-two is less than eighty-one.

For Exercises 4–17, perform the indicated operation.

4.   51
    + 78

5.   82
    × 4

6.   154
    − 41

7. 4)908

8. 58 · 49

9. 149 + 298

10. 324 ÷ 15

11. 3002 − 2456

12. 10,984 − 2881

13. $\dfrac{840}{42}$

14. (500,000)(3000) **15.** 34 + 89 + 191 + 22

16. 403(0) **17.** $0\overline{)16}$

18. For each of the mathematical statements, identify the property used. Choose from the commutative property of multiplication and the associative property of multiplication. Explain your answer.

   a. $(11 \cdot 6) \cdot 3 = 11 \cdot (6 \cdot 3)$

   b. $(11 \cdot 6) \cdot 3 = 3 \cdot (11 \cdot 6)$

19. Round each number to the indicated place value.

   a. 4850; hundreds **b.** 12,493; thousands

   c. 7,963,126; hundred-thousands

20. The attendance to the Van Gogh and Gauguin exhibit in Chicago was 690,951. The exhibit moved to Amsterdam, and the attendance was 739,117. Round the numbers to the ten-thousands place to estimate the total attendance for this exhibit.

For Exercises 21–24, simplify, using the order of operations.

   21. $8^2 \div 2^4$ **22.** $26 \cdot \sqrt{4} - 4(8 - 1)$

   23. $36 \div 3(14 - 10)$ **24.** $65 - 2(5 \cdot 3 - 11)^2$

For Exercises 25–26, evaluate the expressions for $x = 5$ and $y = 16$.

   25. $x^2 + 2y$ **26.** $x + \sqrt{y}$

27. Brittany and Jennifer are taking an online course in business management. Brittany has taken 6 quizzes worth 30 points each and received the following scores: 29, 28, 24, 27, 30, and 30. Jennifer has only taken 5 quizzes so far, and her scores are 30, 30, 29, 28, and 28. At this point in the course, which student has a higher average?

28. The use of the cell phone has grown every year for the past 13 years. See the graph.

   a. Find the change in the number of phones used from 2003 to 2004.

b. Of the years presented in the graph, between which two years was the increase the greatest?

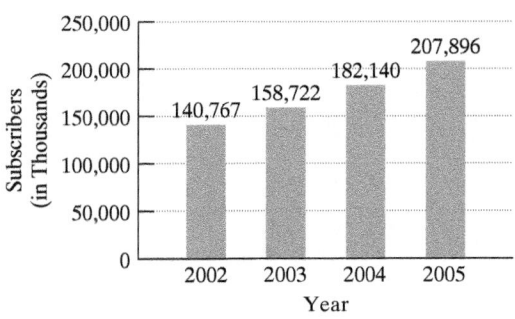

Cell Phone Use in the United States

(Bar graph — Subscribers (in Thousands) vs. Year)
2002: 140,767
2003: 158,722
2004: 182,140
2005: 207,896

29. The table gives the number of calls to three fire departments during a selected number of weeks. Find the number of calls per week for each department to determine which department is the busiest.

	Number of Calls	Time Period (Number of Weeks)
North Side Fire Department	80	16
South Side Fire Department	72	18
East Side Fire Department	84	28

30. Find the perimeter of the figure.

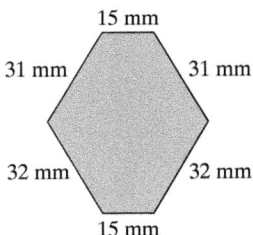

15 mm
31 mm 31 mm
32 mm 32 mm
15 mm

31. Find the perimeter and the area of the rectangle.

47 ft
128 ft

32. Round to the nearest hundred to estimate the area of the rectangle.

2379 m
1872 m

Integers and Algebraic Expressions

2

Chapter 2

In this chapter, we begin our study of algebra by learning how to add, subtract, multiply, and divide positive and negative numbers. These are necessary skills to continue in algebra.

Are You Prepared?

To help you prepare for this chapter, try the following problems to review the order of operations. As you simplify the expressions, fill out the boxes labeled A through M. Then fill in the remaining part of the grid so that every row, every column, and every 2 × 3 box contains the digits 1 through 6.

A. $12 - 10 - 1 + 4$

B. $22 - 3 \cdot 6 - 1$

C. $24 \div 8 \cdot 2$

D. 2^2

E. $32 \div 4 \div 2$

F. $9^2 - 4(30 - 2 \cdot 5)$

G. $13 - 8 \div 2 \cdot 3$

H. $\sqrt{16 - 3 \cdot 4}$

I. $\sqrt{10^2 - 8^2}$

J. $50 \div 2 \div 5$

K. $18 \div 9 \cdot 3$

L. $\dfrac{50 - 40}{5 - 3}$

M. $\sqrt{5^2 - 3^2}$

	A	2	B		6
C		D			1
E				F	6
5	G				H
3			I		J
	K	L	1	M	

Section 2.1 Integers, Absolute Value, and Opposite

Objectives

1. Integers
2. Absolute Value
3. Opposite

1. Integers

The numbers $1, 2, 3, \ldots$ are **positive numbers** because they lie to the right of zero on the number line (Figure 2-1).

Figure 2-1

In some applications of mathematics we need to use *negative* numbers. For example:

• On a winter day in Buffalo, the low temperature was 3 degrees below zero: $-3°$
• Tiger Woods' golf score in the U.S. Open was 7 below par: -7
• Carmen is \$128 overdrawn on her checking account. Her balance is: $-\$128$

The values $-3°$, -7, and $-\$128$ are negative numbers. **Negative numbers** lie to the *left* of zero on a number line (Figure 2-2). The number 0 is neither negative nor positive.

Figure 2-2

The numbers $\ldots -3, -2, -1, 0, 1, 2, 3, \ldots$ and so on are called **integers**.

Skill Practice

Write an integer that denotes each number.

1. The average temperature at the South Pole in July is 65°C below zero.
2. Sylvia's checking account is overdrawn by \$156.
3. The price of a new car is \$2000 more than it was one year ago.

Example 1 Writing Integers

Write an integer that denotes each number.

a. Liquid nitrogen freezes at 346°F below zero.

b. The shoreline of the Dead Sea on the border of Israel and Jordan is the lowest land area on Earth. It is 1300 ft below sea level.

c. Jenna's 10-year-old daughter weighs 14 lb more than the average child her age.

Solution:

a. $-346°F$

b. -1300 ft

c. 14 lb

Answers
1. $-65°C$ 2. $-\$156$
3. \$2000

Example 2 Locating Integers on the Number Line

Locate each number on the number line.

a. −4 **b.** −7 **c.** 0 **d.** 2

Solution:

On the number line, negative numbers lie to the left of 0, and positive numbers lie to the right of 0.

Locate each number on the number line.

4. −5 **5.** −1 **6.** 4

As with whole numbers, the order between two integers can be determined using the number line.

- A number a is less than b (denoted $a < b$) if a lies to the left of b on the number line (Figure 2-3).
- A number a is greater than b (denoted $a > b$) if a lies to the right of b on the number line (Figure 2-4).

a is less than b.
$a < b$

Figure 2-3

a is greater than b.
$a > b$

Figure 2-4

Example 3 Determining Order Between Two Integers

Skill Practice

Use the number line from Example 2 to fill in the blank with $<$ or $>$ to make a true statement.

a. −7 ☐ −4 **b.** 0 ☐ −4 **c.** 2 ☐ −7

Fill in the blank with $<$ or $>$.
7. −3 ☐ −8
8. −3 ☐ 8
9. 0 ☐ −11

Solution:

a. −7 $\boxed{<}$ −4   −7 lies to the *left* of −4 on the number line. Therefore, −7 < −4.

b. 0 $\boxed{>}$ −4   0 lies to the *right* of −4 on the number line. Therefore, 0 > −4.

c. 2 $\boxed{>}$ −7   2 lies to the *right* of −7 on the number line. Therefore, 2 > −7.

2. Absolute Value

On the number line, pairs of numbers like 4 and −4 are the same distance from zero (Figure 2-5). The distance between a number and zero on the number line is called its **absolute value**.

Figure 2-5

Answers
4–6

7. > **8.** < **9.** >

> **DEFINITION Absolute Value**
>
> The absolute value of a number a is denoted $|a|$. The value of $|a|$ is the distance between a and 0 on the number line.

From the number line, we see that $|-4| = 4$ and $|4| = 4$.

Example 4 **Finding Absolute Value**

Determine the absolute value.

   a. $|-5|$ **b.** $|3|$ **c.** $|0|$

Solution:

   a. $|-5| = 5$ The number -5 is 5 units from 0 on the number line.

$$|-5| = 5$$

-5 -4 -3 -2 -1 0 1 2 3 4 5

   b. $|3| = 3$ The number 3 is 3 units from 0 on the number line.

$$|3| = 3$$

-5 -4 -3 -2 -1 0 1 2 3 4 5

   c. $|0| = 0$ The number 0 is 0 units from 0 on the number line.

$$|0| = 0$$

-5 -4 -3 -2 -1 0 1 2 3 4 5

TIP: The absolute value of a nonzero number is always positive. The absolute value of zero is 0.

3. Opposite

Two numbers that are the same distance from zero on the number line, but on opposite sides of zero, are called **opposites**. For example, the numbers -2 and 2 are opposites (see Figure 2-6).

Same distance

-4 -3 -2 -1 0 1 2 3 4

Figure 2-6

The opposite of a number, a, is denoted $-(a)$.

Original number a	Opposite $-(a)$	Simplified Form	
5	$-(5)$	-5	} The opposite of a positive number is a negative number.
-7	$-(-7)$	7	} The opposite of a negative number is a positive number.

The opposite of a negative number is a positive number. Thus, for a positive value, a ($a > 0$), we have

$$-(-a) = a$$ This is sometimes called the *double negative property*.

Example 5   Finding the Opposite of an Integer

Find the opposite.

a. 4   b. −99

Solution:

a. If a number is positive, its opposite is negative. The opposite of 4 is −4.

b. If a number is negative, its opposite is positive. The opposite of −99 is 99.

> **TIP:** To find the opposite of a number, change the sign.

Example 6   Simplifying Expressions

Simplify.

a. −(−9)   b. −|−12| c. −|7|

Solution:

a. −(−9) = 9   This represents the opposite of −9, which is 9.

b. −|−12| = −12   This represents the opposite of |−12|. Since |−12| is equal to 12, the opposite is −12.

c. −|7| = −7   This represents the opposite of |7|. Since |7| is equal to 7, the opposite is −7.

Avoiding Mistakes

In Example 6(b) two operations are performed. First take the absolute value of −12. Then determine the opposite of the result.

Section 2.1   Practice Exercises

Study Skills Exercises

1. When working with signed numbers, keep a simple example in your mind, such as temperature. We understand that 10 degrees below zero is colder than 2 degrees below zero, so the inequality −10 < −2 makes sense. Write down another example involving signed numbers that you can easily remember.

2. Define the key terms.

   a. **Absolute value**   b. **Integers**   c. **Negative numbers**

   d. **Opposite**   e. **Positive numbers**

Objective 1: Integers

For Exercises 3–12, write an integer that represents each numerical value. **(See Example 1.)**

3. Death Valley, California, is 86 m below sea level.

4. In a card game, Jack lost $45.

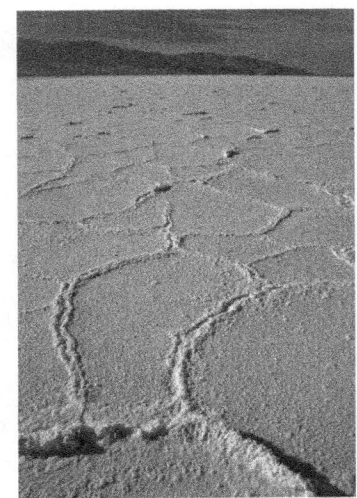

Figure for Exercise 3

5. Playing *Wheel of Fortune*, Sally won $3800.

6. Jim's golf score is 5 over par.

7. Rena lost $500 in the stock market in 1 month.

8. LaTonya earned $23 in interest on her saving account.

9. Patrick lost 14 lb on a diet.

10. A plane descended 2000 ft.

11. The number of Internet users rose by about 1,400,000.

12. A small business experienced a loss of $20,000 last year.

Figure for Exercise 6

Figure for Exercise 11

For Exercises 13–14, graph the numbers on the number line. **(See Example 2.)**

13. $-6, 0, -1, 2$

14. $-2, 4, -5, 1$

15. Which number is closer to -4 on the number line? -2 or -7

16. Which number is closer to 2 on the number line? -5 or 8

For Exercises 17–24, fill in the blank with $<$ or $>$ to make a true statement. **(See Example 3.)**

17. $0 \;\square\; -3$ **18.** $-1 \;\square\; 0$ **19.** $-8 \;\square\; -9$ **20.** $-5 \;\square\; -2$

21. $8 \;\square\; 9$ **22.** $5 \;\square\; 2$ **23.** $-226 \;\square\; 198$ **24.** $408 \;\square\; -416$

Objective 2: Absolute Value

For Exercises 25–32, determine the absolute value. **(See Example 4.)**

25. $|-2|$ **26.** $|-9|$ **27.** $|2|$ **28.** $|9|$

29. $|-427|$ **30.** $|-615|$ **31.** $|100,000|$ **32.** $|64,000|$

33. a. Which is greater, -12 or -8?
  b. Which is greater, $|-12|$ or $|-8|$?

34. a. Which is greater, -14 or -20?
  b. Which is greater, $|-14|$ or $|-20|$?

35. a. Which is greater, 5 or 7?
  b. Which is greater, $|5|$ or $|7|$?

36. a. Which is greater, 3 or 4?
  b. Which is greater, $|3|$ or $|4|$?

37. Which is greater, -5 or $|-5|$?

38. Which is greater -9 or $|-9|$?

39. Which is greater 10 or $|10|$?

40. Which is greater 256 or $|256|$?

Objective 3: Opposite

For Exercises 41–48 find the opposite. **(See Example 5.)**

41. 5   **42.** 31   **43.** -12 **44.** -25

45. 0   **46.** 1   **47.** -1 **48.** -612

For Exercises 49–60, simplify the expression. **(See Example 6.)**

49. $-(-15)$ **50.** $-(-4)$ **51.** $-|-15|$ **52.** $-|-4|$

53. $-|15|$ **54.** $-|4|$ **55.** $|-15|$ **56.** $|-4|$

57. $-(-36)$ **58.** $-(-19)$ **59.** $-|-107|$ **60.** $-|-26|$

Mixed Exercises

For Exercises 61–64, simplify the expression.

61. a. $|-6|$ **b.** $-(-6)$ **c.** $-|6|$ **d.** $|6|$ **e.** $-|-6|$

62. a. $-(-12)$ **b.** $|12|$ **c.** $|-12|$ **d.** $-|-12|$ **e.** $-|12|$

63. a. $-|8|$ **b.** $|8|$ **c.** $-|-8|$ **d.** $-(-8)$ **e.** $|-8|$

64. a. $-|-1|$ **b.** $-(-1)$ **c.** $|1|$ **d.** $|-1|$ **e.** $-|1|$

For Exercises 65–74, write in symbols, do not simplify.

65. The opposite of 6

66. The opposite of 23

67. The opposite of negative 2

68. The opposite of negative 9

69. The absolute value of 7

70. The absolute value of 11

71. The absolute value of negative 3

72. The absolute value of negative 10

73. The opposite of the absolute value of 14

74. The opposite of the absolute value of 42

For Exercises 75–84, fill in the blank with $<$, $>$, or $=$.

75. $|-12|\ \square\ |12|$ **76.** $-(-4)\ \square\ -|-4|$ **77.** $|-22|\ \square\ -(22)$ **78.** $-8\ \square\ -10$

79. $-44\ \square\ -54$ **80.** $-|0|\ \square\ -|1|$ **81.** $|-55|\ \square\ -(-65)$ **82.** $-(82)\ \square\ |46|$

83. $-|32|\ \square\ |0|$ **84.** $-|22|\ \square\ 0$

For Exercises 85–91, refer to the contour map for wind chill temperatures for a day in January. Give an *estimate* of the wind chill for the given city. For example, the wind chill in Phoenix is between 30°F and 40°F, but closer to 30°F. We might estimate the wind chill in Phoenix to be 33°F.

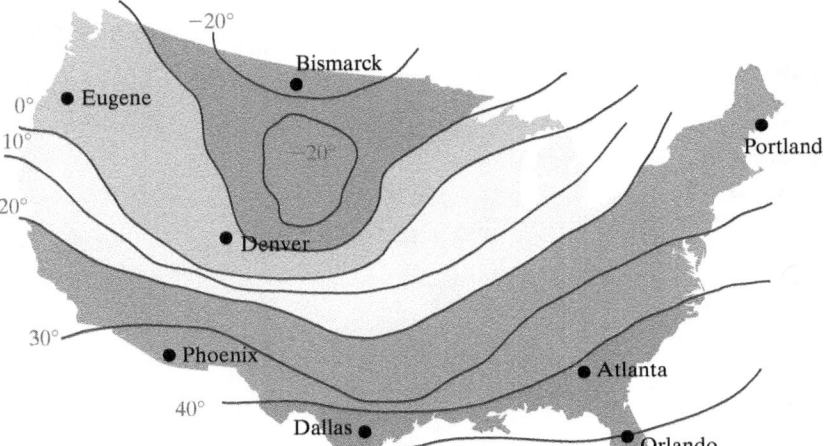
Wind Chill Temperatures, °F

85. Portland   **86.** Atlanta

87. Bismarck   **88.** Denver

89. Eugene   **90.** Orlando

91. Dallas

Late spring and summer rainfall in the Lake Okeechobee region in Florida is important to replenish the water supply for large areas of south Florida. Each bar in the graph indicates the number of inches of rainfall above or below average for the given month. Use the graph for Exercises 92–94.

92. Which month had the greatest amount of rainfall *below* average? What was the departure from average?

93. Which month had the greatest amount of rainfall *above* average?

94. Which month had the average amount of rainfall?

Rainfall Amounts Above or Below Average

Expanding Your Skills

For Exercises 95–96, rank the numbers from least to greatest.

95. $-|-46|, -(-24), -60, 5^2, |-12|$

96. $-15, -(-18), -|20|, 4^2, |-3|^2$

97. If a represents a negative number, then what is the sign of $-a$?

98. If b represents a negative number, then what is the sign of $|b|$?

99. If c represents a negative number, then what is the sign of $-|c|$?

100. If d represents a negative number, then what is the sign of $-(-d)$?

Section 2.2	Addition of Integers

Objectives

1. Addition of Integers by Using a Number Line
2. Addition of Integers
3. Translations and Applications of Addition

Skill Practice

Use a number line to add.

1. $3 + 2$

2. $-3 + 2$

1. Addition of Integers by Using a Number Line

Addition of integers can be visualized on a number line. To do so, we locate the first addend on the number line. Then to add a positive number, we move to the right on the number line. To add a negative number, we move to the left on the number line. This is demonstrated in Example 1.

Example 1	Using a Number Line to Add Integers

Use a number line to add.

a. $5 + 3$ **b.** $-5 + 3$

Solution:

a. $5 + 3 = 8$

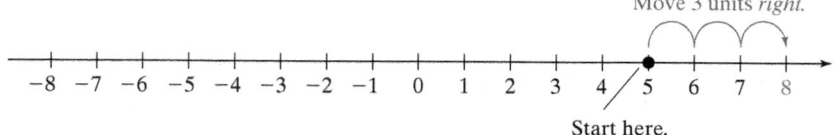

Move 3 units *right.*

Start here.

Begin at 5. Then, because we are adding *positive* 3, move to the *right* 3 units. The sum is 8.

Answers

1. 5   **2.** −1

b. $-5 + 3 = -2$

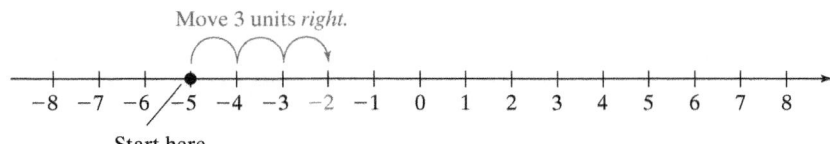

Move 3 units *right*.

Start here.

Begin at -5. Then, because we are adding *positive* 3, move to the *right* 3 units. The sum is -2.

Example 2   **Using a Number Line to Add Integers**

Use a number line to add.

a. $5 + (-3)$ **b.** $-5 + (-3)$

Solution:

a. $5 + (-3) = 2$

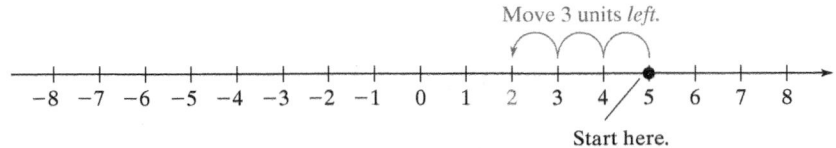

Move 3 units *left*.

Start here.

Begin at 5. Then, because we are adding *negative* 3, move to the *left* 3 units. The sum is 2.

b. $-5 + (-3) = -8$

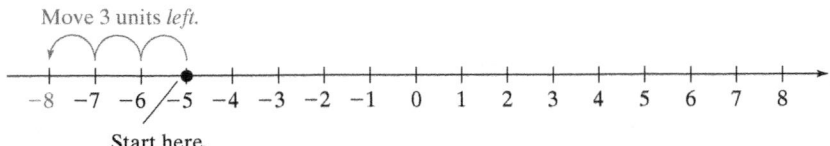

Move 3 units *left*.

Start here.

Begin at -5. Then, because we are adding *negative* 3, move to the *left* 3 units. The sum is -8.

Skill Practice

Use a number line to add.

3. $3 + (-2)$

4. $-3 + (-2)$

TIP: In Example 2, parentheses are inserted for clarity. The parentheses separate the number -3 from the symbol for addition, $+$.

$5 + (-3)$ and $-5 + (-3)$

---

2. Addition of Integers

It is inconvenient to draw a number line each time we want to add signed numbers. Therefore, we offer two rules for adding integers. The first rule is used when the addends have the *same* sign (that is, if the numbers are both positive or both negative).

PROCEDURE   Adding Numbers with the Same Sign

To add two numbers with the same sign, add their absolute values and apply the common sign.

Answers

3. 1   **4.** -5

Example 3 **Adding Integers with the Same Sign**

Add.

a. $-2 + (-4)$ **b.** $-12 + (-37)$ **c.** $10 + 66$

Solution:

a. $-2 + (-4)$ First find the absolute value of each addend.
                     $|-2| = 2$ and $|-4| = 4$.

   $= -(2 + 4)$ Add their absolute values and apply the common sign
                       (in this case, the common sign is negative).
Common sign is negative.

   $= -6$ The sum is -6.

b. $-12 + (-37)$ First find the absolute value of each addend.
                       $|-12| = 12$ and $|-37| = 37$.

   $= -(12 + 37)$ Add their absolute values and apply the common sign
                       (in this case, the common sign is negative).
Common sign is negative.

   $= -49$ The sum is -49.

c. $10 + 66$ First find the absolute value of each addend.
                       $|10| = 10$ and $|66| = 66$.

   $= +(10 + 66)$ Add their absolute values and apply the common sign
                       (in this case, the common sign is positive).
Common sign is positive.

   $= 76$ The sum is 76.

The next rule helps us add two numbers with different signs.

PROCEDURE **Adding Numbers with Different Signs**

To add two numbers with different signs, subtract the smaller absolute value from the larger absolute value. Then apply the sign of the number having the larger absolute value.

Example 4 **Adding Integers with Different Signs**

Add.

a. $2 + (-7)$ **b.** $-6 + 24$ **c.** $-8 + 8$

Solution:

a. $2 + (-7)$ First find the absolute value of each addend.
             $|2| = 2$ and $|-7| = 7$

             Note: The absolute value of -7 is greater than the absolute value of 2. Therefore, the sum is negative.

   $= -(7 - 2)$ Next, subtract the smaller absolute value from the larger
                    absolute value.
Apply the sign of the number with the larger absolute value.

   $= -5$

b. $-6 + 24$ First find the absolute value of each addend.

$|-6| = 6$ and $|24| = 24$

Note: The absolute value of 24 is greater than the absolute value of -6. Therefore, the sum is positive.

$= +(24 - 6)$ Next, subtract the smaller absolute value from the larger absolute value.

└─ Apply the sign of the number with the larger absolute value.

$= 18$

c. $-8 + 8$ First find the absolute value of each addend.

$|-8| = 8$ and $|8| = 8$

$= (8 - 8)$ The absolute values are equal. Therefore, their difference is 0. The number zero is neither positive nor negative.

$= 0$

> **TIP:** Parentheses are used to show that the absolute values are subtracted *before* applying the appropriate sign.

Example 4(c) illustrates that the sum of a number and its opposite is zero. For example:

$$-8 + 8 = 0 \qquad -12 + 12 = 0 \qquad 6 + (-6) = 0$$

PROPERTY Adding Opposites

For any number a,

$$a + (-a) = 0 \quad \text{and} \quad -a + a = 0$$

That is, the sum of any number and its opposite is zero. (This is also called the *additive inverse property*.)

Example 5   **Adding Several Integers**

Simplify. $-30 + (-12) + 4 + (-10) + 6$

Solution:

$-30 + (-12) + 4 + (-10) + 6$ Apply the order of operations by adding from left to right.

$= -42 + 4 + (-10) + 6$

$= -38 + (-10) + 6$

$= -48 + 6$

$= -42$

> **Skill Practice**
>
> **13.** Simplify.
> $-24 + (-16) + 8 + 2 + (-20)$

TIP: When several numbers are added, we can reorder and regroup the addends using the commutative property and associative property of addition. In particular, we can group all the positive addends together, and we can group all the negative addends together. This makes the arithmetic easier. For example,

positive addends   negative addends

$-30 + (-12) + 4 + (-10) + 6 = 4 + 6 + (-30) + (-12) + (-10)$

$= 10 + (-52)$

$= -42$

Answer

13. -50

3. Translations and Applications of Addition

Example 6 **Translating an English Phrase to a Mathematical Expression**

Translate to a mathematical expression and simplify.

$$-6 \text{ added to the sum of 2 and } -11$$

Solution:

$[2 + (-11)] + (-6)$ Translate: −6 added to the sum of 2 and −11

Notice that the sum of 2 and −11 is written first, and then −6 is added to that value.

$= -9 + (-6)$ Find the sum of 2 and −11 first. $2 + (-11) = -9$.

$= -15$

Example 7 **Applying Addition of Integers to Determine Rainfall Amount**

Late spring and summer rainfall in the Lake Okeechobee region in Florida is important to replenish the water supply for large areas of south Florida. The graph indicates the number of inches of rainfall above or below average for given months.

   Find the total departure from average rainfall for these months. Do the results show that the region received above average rainfall for the summer or below average?

Solution:

From the graph, we have the following departures from the average rainfall.

Month	Amount (in.)
May	2
June	−6
July	−4
Aug.	0
Sept.	4

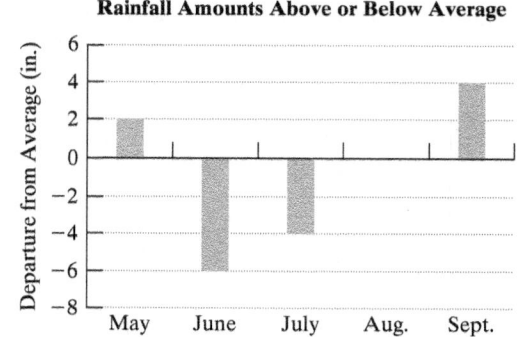

Rainfall Amounts Above or Below Average

To find the total, we can group the addends conveniently.

Total: $\underbrace{(-6) + (-4)}_{= -10} + \underbrace{2 + 0 + 4}_{6}$

$= -10 \quad + \quad 6$

$= -4$ The total departure from average is −4 in. The region received below average rainfall.

Answers

14. $[-8 + (-10) + 5] + (-2); -15$

15. The total score is 7. Jonas' score is above par.

Section 2.2 Practice Exercises

Study Skill Exercise

1. Instructors vary in what they emphasize on tests. For example, test material may come from the textbook, notes, handouts, homework, etc. What does your instructor emphasize?

Review Exercises

For Exercises 2–8, place the correct symbol ($>$, $<$, or $=$) between the two numbers.

2. $-6 \,\square\, -5$ **3.** $-33 \,\square\, -44$ **4.** $|-4| \,\square\, -|4|$ **5.** $|6| \,\square\, |-6|$

6. $0 \,\square\, -6$ **7.** $-|-10| \,\square\, 10$ **8.** $-(-2) \,\square\, 2$

Objective 1: Addition of Integers by Using a Number Line

For Exercises 9–20, refer to the number line to add the integers. **(See Examples 1–2.)**

$$\begin{array}{c} \xleftarrow{\hspace{0.5em}}\!\!-8\ -7\ -6\ -5\ -4\ -3\ -2\ -1\ \ 0\ \ 1\ \ 2\ \ 3\ \ 4\ \ 5\ \ 6\ \ 7\ \ 8\xrightarrow{\hspace{0.5em}} \end{array}$$

9. $-3 + 5$ **10.** $-6 + 3$ **11.** $2 + (-4)$ **12.** $5 + (-1)$

13. $-4 + (-4)$ **14.** $-2 + (-5)$ **15.** $-3 + 9$ **16.** $-1 + 5$

17. $0 + (-7)$ **18.** $(-5) + 0$ **19.** $-1 + (-3)$ **20.** $-4 + (-3)$

Objective 2: Addition of Integers

21. Explain the process to add two numbers with the same sign.

For Exercises 22–29, add the numbers with the same sign. **(See Example 3.)**

22. $23 + 12$ **23.** $12 + 3$ **24.** $-8 + (-3)$ **25.** $-10 + (-6)$

26. $-7 + (-9)$ **27.** $-100 + (-24)$ **28.** $23 + 50$ **29.** $44 + 45$

30. Explain the process to add two numbers with different signs.

For Exercises 31–42, add the numbers with different signs. **(See Example 4.)**

31. $7 + (-10)$ **32.** $-8 + 2$ **33.** $12 + (-7)$ **34.** $-3 + 9$

35. $-90 + 66$ **36.** $-23 + 49$ **37.** $78 + (-33)$ **38.** $10 + (-23)$

39. $2 + (-2)$ **40.** $-6 + 6$ **41.** $-13 + 13$ **42.** $45 + (-45)$

Mixed Exercises

For Exercises 43–66, simplify. **(See Example 5.)**

43. $12 + (-3)$ **44.** $-33 + (-1)$ **45.** $-23 + (-3)$

46. $-5 + 15$ **47.** $4 + (-45)$ **48.** $-13 + (-12)$

49. $(-103) + (-47)$

50. $119 + (-59)$

51. $0 + (-17)$

52. $-29 + 0$

53. $-19 + (-22)$

54. $-300 + (-24)$

55. $6 + (-12) + 8$

56. $20 + (-12) + (-5)$

 57. $-33 + (-15) + 18$

58. $3 + 5 + (-1)$

59. $7 + (-3) + 6$

60. $12 + (-6) + (-9)$

61. $-10 + (-3) + 5$

62. $-23 + (-4) + (-12) + (-5)$

63. $-18 + (-5) + 23$

64. $14 + (-15) + 20 + (-42)$

65. $4 + (-12) + (-30) + 16 + 10$

66. $24 + (-5) + (-19)$

Objective 3: Translations and Applications of Addition

For Exercises 67–72, translate to a mathematical expression. Then simplify the expression. **(See Example 6.)**

67. The sum of -23 and 49

68. The sum of 89 and -11

69. The total of $3, -10,$ and 5

70. The total of $-2, -4, 14,$ and 20

71. -5 added to the sum of -8 and 6

72. -15 added to the sum of -25 and 7

73. The graph gives the number of inches below or above the average snowfall for the given months for Marquette, Michigan. Find the total departure from average. Is the snowfall for Marquette above or below average? **(See Example 7.)**

74. The graph gives the number of inches below or above the average rainfall for the given months for Hilo, Hawaii. Find the total departure from average. Is the total rainfall for these months above or below average?

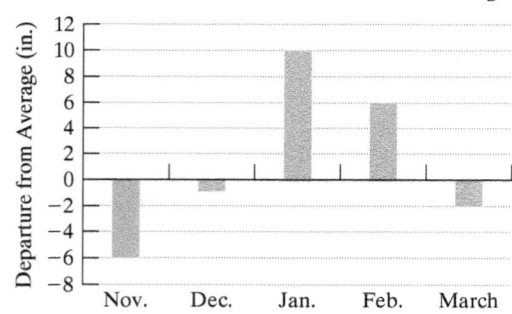

Snowfall Amounts Above or Below Average

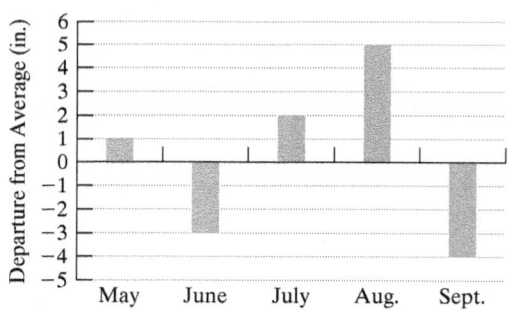

Amount of Rainfall Above or Below Average

For Exercises 75–76, refer to the table. The table gives the scores for the top two finishers at a recent PGA Open golf tournament.

75. Compute Tiger Woods' total score.

76. Compute Woody Austin's total score.

	Round 1	Round 2	Round 3	Round 4
Tiger Woods	1	−7	−1	−1
Woody Austin	−2	0	−1	−3

 77. At 6:00 A.M. the temperature was $-4°$F. By noon, the temperature had risen by $12°$F. What was the temperature at noon?

78. At midnight the temperature was $-14°$F. By noon, the temperature had risen $10°$F. What was the temperature at noon?

79. Jorge's checking account is overdrawn. His beginning balance was −$56. If he deposits his paycheck for $389, what is his new balance?

80. Ellen's checking account balance is $23. If she writes a check for $40, what is her new balance?

81. A contestant on *Jeopardy* scored the following amounts for several questions he answered. Determine his total score.

    −$200, −$400, $1000, −$400, $600

82. The number of yards gained or lost by a running back in a football game are given. Find the total number of yards.

    3, 2, −8, 5, −2, 4, 21

83. Christie Kerr won the U.S. Open Women's Golf Championship for a recent year. The table gives her scores for the first 9 holes in the first round. Find the sum of the scores.

Hole	1	2	3	4	5	6	7	8	9
Score	0	2	−1	−1	0	−1	1	0	0

84. Se Ri Pak tied for fourth place in the U.S. Open Women's Golf Championship for a recent year. The table gives her scores for the first 9 holes in the first round. Find the sum of the scores.

Hole	1	2	3	4	5	6	7	8	9
Score	1	1	0	0	−1	−1	0	0	2

Expanding Your Skills

85. Find two integers whose sum is −10. Answers may vary.

86. Find two integers whose sum is −14. Answers may vary.

87. Find two integers whose sum is −2. Answers may vary.

88. Find two integers whose sum is 0. Answers may vary.

Calculator Connections

Topic: Adding Integers on a Calculator

To enter negative numbers on a calculator, use the ⌊(−)⌋ key or the ⌊+○−⌋ key. To use the ⌊(−)⌋ key, enter the number the same way that it is written. That is, enter the negative sign first and then the number, such as: ⌊(−)⌋ 5. If your calculator has the ⌊+○−⌋ key, type the number first, followed by the ⌊+○−⌋ key. Thus, −5 is entered as: 5 ⌊+○−⌋. Try entering the expressions below to determine which method your calculator uses.

Expression	Keystrokes		Result
−10 + (−3)	⌊(−)⌋ 10 ⌊+⌋ ⌊(−)⌋ 3 **ENTER**	or 10 ⌊+○−⌋ ⌊+⌋ 3 ⌊+○−⌋ ⌊=⌋	−13
−4 + 6	⌊(−)⌋ 4 ⌊+⌋ 6 **ENTER**	or 4 ⌊+○−⌋ ⌊+⌋ 6 ⌊=⌋	2

Calculator Exercises

For Exercises 89–94, add using a calculator.

89. 302 + (−422)

90. −900 + 334

91. −23,991 + (−4423)

92. −1034 + (−23,291)

93. 23 + (−125) + 912 + (−99)

94. 891 + 12 + (−223) + (−341)

Section 2.3   Subtraction of Integers

Objectives

1. **Subtraction of Integers**
2. **Translations and Applications of Subtraction**

1. Subtraction of Integers

In Section 2.2, we learned the rules for adding integers. Subtraction of integers is defined in terms of the addition process. For example, consider the following subtraction problem. The corresponding addition problem produces the same result.

$$6 - 4 = 2 \quad \Leftrightarrow \quad 6 + (-4) = 2$$

In each case, we start at 6 on the number line and move to the *left* 4 units. Adding the *opposite* of 4 produces the same result as subtracting 4. This is true in general. To subtract two integers, add the opposite of the second number to the first number.

> **PROCEDURE Subtracting Signed Numbers**
>
> For two numbers a and b, $a - b = a + (-b)$.
>
> Therefore, to perform subtraction, follow these steps:
>
> **Step 1** Leave the first number (the minuend) unchanged.
> **Step 2** Change the subtraction sign to an addition sign.
> **Step 3** Add the opposite of the second number (the subtrahend).

Concept Connections

Fill in the blank to change subtraction to addition of the opposite.

1. $9 - 3 = 9 + \square$
2. $-9 - 3 = -9 + \square$
3. $9 - (-3) = 9 + \square$
4. $-9 - (-3) = -9 + \square$

For example:

$$\left.\begin{array}{l} 10 - 4 = 10 + (-4) = 6 \\ -10 - 4 = -10 + (-4) = -14 \end{array}\right\} \text{ Subtracting 4 is the same as adding } -4.$$

$$\left.\begin{array}{l} 10 - (-4) = 10 + (4) = 14 \\ -10 - (-4) = -10 + (4) = -6 \end{array}\right\} \text{ Subtracting } -4 \text{ is the same as adding 4.}$$

Skill Practice

Subtract.

5. $12 - 19$
6. $-8 - 14$
7. $30 - (-3)$

Example 1   Subtracting Integers

Subtract.   **a.** $15 - 20$ **b.** $-7 - 12$ **c.** $40 - (-8)$

Solution:

Add the opposite of 20.

a. $15 - \boxed{20} = 15 + (-20) = -5$ Rewrite the subtraction in terms of addition. Subtracting 20 is the same as adding -20.

Change subtraction to addition.

b. $-7 - 12 = -7 + (-12)$ Rewrite the subtraction in terms of addition. Subtracting 12 is the same as adding -12.

$ = -19$

c. $40 - (-8) = 40 + (8)$ Rewrite the subtraction in terms of addition. Subtracting -8 is the same as adding 8.

$ = 48$

Answers

1. -3 2. -3 3. 3   4. 3
5. -7 6. -22 7. 33

> **TIP:** After subtraction is written in terms of addition, the rules of addition are applied.

Example 2   **Adding and Subtracting Several Integers**

Simplify. $-4 - 6 + (-3) - 5 + 8$

Solution:

$-4 - 6 + (-3) - 5 + 8$

$= -4 + (-6) + (-3) + (-5) + 8$ Rewrite all subtractions in terms of addition.

$= \quad -10 + (-3) + (-5) + 8$ Add from left to right.

$= \quad\quad -13 + (-5) + 8$

$= \quad\quad\quad -18 + 8$

$= \quad\quad\quad\quad -10$

Skill Practice

8. Simplify.
$-8 - 10 + (-6) - (-1) + 4$

2. Translations and Applications of Subtraction

Recall from Section 1.3 that several key words imply subtraction.

Word/Phrase	Example	In Symbols
a minus b	-15 minus 10	$-15 - 10$
The difference of a and b	The difference of 10 and -2	$10 - (-2)$
a decreased by b	9 decreased by 1	$9 - 1$
a less than b	-12 less than 5	$5 - (-12)$
Subtract a from b	Subtract -3 from 8	$8 - (-3)$
b subtracted from a	-2 subtracted from -10	$-10 - (-2)$

Example 3   **Translating to a Mathematical Expression**

Translate to a mathematical expression. Then simplify.

a. The difference of -52 and 10.

b. -35 decreased by -6.

Solution:

a.   the difference of

$\quad -52 \;-\; 10$ Translate: The difference of -52 and 10.

$= -52 + (-10)$ Rewrite subtraction in terms of addition.

$= -62$ Add.

b.   decreased by

$\quad -35 \;-\; (-6)$ Translate: -35 decreased by -6.

$= -35 + (6)$ Rewrite subtraction in terms of addition.

$= -29$ Add.

Skill Practice

Translate to a mathematical expression. Then simplify.
9. The difference of -16 and 4
10. -8 decreased by -9

Avoiding Mistakes

Subtraction is not commutative. The order of the numbers being subtracted is important.

Answers
   8. -19 **9.** $-16 - 4; -20$
   10. $-8 - (-9); 1$

Example 4 **Translating to a Mathematical Expression**

Translate each English phrase to a mathematical expression. Then simplify.

a. 12 less than −8   **b.** Subtract 27 from 5.

Solution:

a. To translate "12 less than −8," we must *start* with −8 and subtract 12.

$$-8 - 12 \qquad \text{Translate: 12 less than } -8.$$
$$= -8 + (-12) \qquad \text{Rewrite subtraction in terms of addition.}$$
$$= -20 \qquad \text{Add.}$$

b. To translate "subtract 27 from 5," we must *start* with 5 and subtract 27.

$$5 - 27 \qquad \text{Translate: Subtract 27 from 5.}$$
$$= 5 + (-27) \qquad \text{Rewrite subtraction in terms of addition.}$$
$$= -22 \qquad \text{Add.}$$

Example 5 **Applying Subtraction of Integers**

A helicopter is hovering at a height of 200 ft above the ocean. A submarine is directly below the helicopter 125 ft below sea level. Find the difference in elevation between the helicopter and the submarine.

Solution:

$$\begin{pmatrix} \text{Difference between} \\ \text{elevation of helicopter} \\ \text{and submarine} \end{pmatrix} = \begin{pmatrix} \text{Elevation of} \\ \text{helicopter} \end{pmatrix} - \begin{pmatrix} \text{"Elevation" of} \\ \text{submarine} \end{pmatrix}$$

$$= 200 \text{ ft} - (-125 \text{ ft})$$
$$= 200 \text{ ft} + (125 \text{ ft}) \qquad \text{Rewrite as addition.}$$
$$= 325 \text{ ft}$$

The helicopter and submarine are 325 ft apart.

Section 2.3 Practice Exercises

Boost *your* GRADE at ALEKS.com!

- Practice Problems
- Self-Tests
- NetTutor
- e-Professors
- Videos

Study Skills Exercise

1. Which activities might you try when working in a study group to help you learn and understand the material?

☐ Quiz one another by asking one another questions.

☐ Practice teaching one another.

☐ Share and compare class notes.

☐ Support and encourage one another.

☐ Work together on exercises and sample problems.

Review Exercises

For Exercises 2–7, simplify.

2. $34 + (-13)$

3. $-34 + (-13)$

4. $-34 + 13$

5. $-|-26|$

6. $-(-32)$

7. $-9 + (-8) + 5 + (-3) + 7$

Objective 1: Subtraction of Integers

8. Explain the process to subtract integers.

For Exercises 9–16, rewrite the subtraction problem as an equivalent addition problem. Then simplify. **(See Example 1.)**

9. $2 - 9 = $ ___ $+$ ___ $=$ ___

10. $5 - 11 = $ ___ $+$ ___ $=$ ___

11. $4 - (-3) = $ ___ $+$ ___ $=$ ___

12. $12 - (-8) = $ ___ $+$ ___ $=$ ___

13. $-3 - 15 = $ ___ $+$ ___ $=$ ___

14. $-7 - 21 = $ ___ $+$ ___ $=$ ___

15. $-11 - (-13) = $ ___ $+$ ___ $=$ ___

16. $-23 - (-9) = $ ___ $+$ ___ $=$ ___

For Exercises 17–46, simplify. **(See Examples 1–2.)**

17. $35 - (-17)$

18. $23 - (-12)$

19. $-24 - 9$

20. $-5 - 15$

21. $50 - 62$

22. $38 - 46$

23. $-17 - (-25)$

24. $-2 - (-66)$

25. $-8 - (-8)$

26. $-14 - (-14)$

27. $120 - (-41)$

28. $91 - (-62)$

29. $-15 - 19$

30. $-82 - 44$

31. $3 - 25$

32. $6 - 33$

33. $-13 - 13$

34. $-43 - 43$

35. $24 - 25$

36. $43 - 98$

37. $-6 - (-38)$

38. $-75 - (-21)$

39. $-48 - (-33)$

40. $-29 - (-32)$

41. $2 + 5 - (-3) - 10$

42. $4 - 8 + 12 - (-1)$

43. $-5 + 6 + (-7) - 4 - (-9)$

44. $-2 - 1 + (-11) + 6 - (-8)$

45. $25 - 13 - (-40)$

46. $-35 + 15 - (-28)$

Objective 2: Translations and Applications of Subtraction

47. State at least two words or phrases that would indicate subtraction.

48. Is subtraction commutative. For Example, does $3 - 7 = 7 - 3$?

For Exercises 49–60, translate each English phrase to a mathematical expression. Then simplify. **(See Examples 3–4.)**

49. 14 minus 23

50. 27 minus 40

51. The difference of 105 and 110

52. The difference of 70 and 98

53. 320 decreased by -20

54. 150 decreased by 75

55. Subtract 12 from 5.

56. Subtract 10 from 16.

57. 21 less than -34

58. 22 less than -90

59. Subtract 24 from -35

60. Subtract 189 from 175

61. The liquid hydrogen in the space shuttle's main engine is $-423°F$. The temperature in the engine's combustion chamber reaches $6000°F$. Find the difference between the temperature in the combustion chamber and the temperature of the liquid hydrogen. **(See Example 5.)**

62. Temperatures on the moon range from $-184°C$ during its night to $214°C$ during its day. Find the difference between the highest temperature on the moon and the lowest temperature.

63. Ivan owes $320 on his credit card; that is, his balance is $-\$320$. If he charges $55 for a night out, what is his new balance?

64. If Justin's balance on his credit card was $-\$210$ and he made the minimum payment of $25, what is his new balance?

65. The Campus Food Court reports its total profit or loss each day. During a 1-week period, the following profits or losses were reported. If the Campus Food Court's balance was $17,476 at the beginning of the week, what is the balance at the end of the reported week?

Monday	$1786
Tuesday	$-\$2342$
Wednesday	$-\$754$
Thursday	$321
Friday	$1597

66. Jeff's balance in his checking account was $2036 at the beginning of the week. During the week, he wrote two checks, made two deposits, and made one ATM withdrawal. What is his ending balance?

Check	$-\$150$
Check	$-\$25$
Paycheck (deposit)	$480
ATM	$-\$200$
Cash (deposit)	$80

For Exercises 67–70, refer to the graph indicating the change in value of the Dow Jones Industrial Average for a given week.

67. What is the difference in the change in value between Tuesday and Wednesday?

68. What is the difference in the change in value between Thursday and Friday?

69. What is the total change for the week?

70. Based on the values in the graph, did the Dow gain or lose points for the given week?

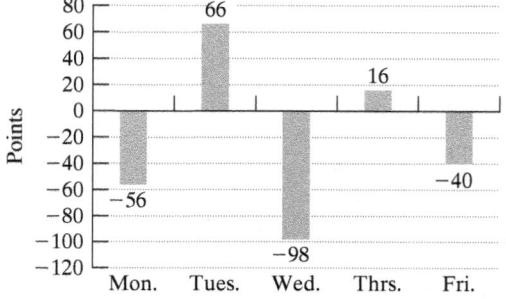

For Exercises 71–72, find the range. The *range* of a set of numbers is the difference between the highest value and the lowest value. That is, range = highest − lowest.

71. Low temperatures for 1 week in Anchorage (°C): −4°, −8°, 0°, 3°, −8°, −1°, 2°

72. Low temperatures for 1 week in Fargo (°C): −6°, −2°, −10°, −4°, −12°, −1°, −3°

73. Find two integers whose difference is −6. Answers may vary.

74. Find two integers whose difference is −20. Answers may vary.

For Exercises 75–76, write the next three numbers in the sequence.

75. 5, 1, −3, −7, ____, ____, ____

76. −13, −18, −23, −28, ____, ____, ____

Expanding Your Skills

For Exercises 77–84, assume $a > 0$ (this means that a is positive) and $b < 0$ (this means that b is negative). Find the sign of each expression.

77. $a - b$

78. $b - a$

79. $|a| + |b|$

80. $|a + b|$

81. $-|a|$

82. $-|b|$

83. $-(a)$

84. $-(b)$

Calculator Connections

Topic: Subtracting Integers on a Calculator

The [−] key is used for subtraction. This should not be confused with the [(−)] key or [+◦−] key, which is used to enter a negative number.

Expression	Keystrokes	Result
−7 − 4	[(−)] 7 [−] 4 [ENTER] or 7 [+◦−] [−] 4 [=]	−11

Calculator Exercises

For Exercises 85–90, subtract the integers using a calculator.

85. −190 − 223

86. −288 − 145

87. −23,624 − (−9001)

88. −14,593 − (−34,499)

89. 892,904 − (−23,546)

90. 104,839 − (−24,938)

91. The height of Mount Everest is 29,029 ft. The lowest point on the surface of the Earth is −35,798 ft (that is, 35,798 ft below sea level) occurring at the Mariana Trench on the Pacific Ocean floor. What is the difference in altitude between the height of Mt. Everest and the Mariana Trench?

92. Mt. Rainier is 4392 m at its highest point. Death Valley, California, is 86 m below sea level (−86 m) at the basin, Badwater. What is the difference between the altitude of Mt. Rainier and the altitude at Badwater?

Section 2.4 Multiplication and Division of Integers

Concept Connections

1. Write $4(-5)$ as repeated addition.

1. Multiplication of Integers

We know from our knowledge of arithmetic that the product of two positive numbers is a positive number. This can be shown by using repeated addition.

For example: $3(4) = 4 + 4 + 4 = 12$

Now consider a product of numbers with different signs.

For example: $3(-4) = -4 + (-4) + (-4) = -12$ (3 times -4)

This example suggests that the product of a positive number and a negative number is *negative*.

Now what if we have a product of two negative numbers? To determine the sign, consider the following pattern of products.

$$3 \cdot -4 = -12$$
$$2 \cdot -4 = -8$$
$$1 \cdot -4 = -4$$
$$0 \cdot -4 = 0$$
$$-1 \cdot -4 = 4$$
$$-2 \cdot -4 = 8$$
$$-3 \cdot -4 = 12$$

The pattern increases by 4 with each row.

The product of two negative numbers is *positive*.

From the first four rows, we see that the product increases by 4 for each row. For the pattern to continue, it follows that the product of two negative numbers must be *positive*.

Avoiding Mistakes

Try not to confuse the rule for multiplying two negative numbers with the rule for adding two negative numbers.

- The product of two negative numbers is positive.
- The sum of two negative numbers is negative.

PROCEDURE   Multipliying Signed Numbers

1. The product of two numbers with the *same* sign is positive.

   Examples: $(5)(6) = 30$
   $(-5)(-6) = 30$

2. The product of two numbers with *different* signs is negative.

   Examples: $4(-10) = -40$
   $-4(10) = -40$

3. The product of any number and zero is zero.

   Examples: $3(0) = 0$
   $0(-6) = 0$

Answer

1. $-5 + (-5) + (-5) + (-5)$

Example 1 **Multiplying Integers**

Multiply.

a. $-8(-7)$ **b.** $-5 \cdot 10$ **c.** $(18)(-2)$ **d.** $16 \cdot 2$ **e.** $-3 \cdot 0$

Solution:

a. $-8(-7) = 56$ Same signs. Product is positive.

b. $-5 \cdot 10 = -50$ Different signs. Product is negative.

c. $(18)(-2) = -36$ Different signs. Product is negative.

d. $16 \cdot 2 = 32$ Same signs. Product is positive.

e. $-3 \cdot 0 = 0$ The product of any number and zero is zero.

── **Skill Practice** ──

Multiply.
 2. $-2(-6)$
 3. $3 \cdot (-10)$
 4. $-14(3)$
 5. $8 \cdot 4$
 6. $-5 \cdot 0$

Recall that the terms *product*, *multiply*, and *times* imply multiplication.

Example 2 **Translating to a Mathematical Expression**

Translate each phrase to a mathematical expression. Then simplify.

a. The product of 7 and -8 **b.** -3 times -11

Solution:

a. $7(-8)$ Translate: The product of 7 and -8.

   $= -56$ Different signs. Product is negative.

b. $(-3)(-11)$ Translate: -3 times -11.

   $= 33$ Same signs. Product is positive.

── **Skill Practice** ──

Translate each phrase to a
mathematical expression. Then
simplify.
 7. The product of -4
  and -12.
 8. Eight times -5.

2. Multiplying Many Factors

In each of the following products, we can apply the order of operations and multiply from left to right.

two negative factors	three negative factors	four negative factors	five negative factors
$(-2)(-2)$	$(-2)(-2)(-2)$	$(-2)(-2)(-2)(-2)$	$(-2)(-2)(-2)(-2)(-2)$
$= 4$	$= 4(-2)$	$= 4(-2)(-2)$	$= 4(-2)(-2)(-2)$
Product is positive.	$= -8$	$= (-8)(-2)$	$= (-8)(-2)(-2)$
	Product is negative.	$= 16$	$= 16(-2)$
		Product is positive.	$= -32$
			Product is negative.

── **Concept Connections** ──

Multiply.
 9. $(-1)(-1)$
 10. $(-1)(-1)(-1)$
 11. $(-1)(-1)(-1)(-1)$
 12. $(-1)(-1)(-1)(-1)(-1)$

These products indicate the following rules.

• The product of an *even* number of negative factors is *positive*.
• The product of an *odd* number of negative factors is *negative*.

Answers

2. 12   **3.** -30 **4.** -42
5. 32   **6.** 0   **7.** $(-4)(-12)$; 48
8. $8(-5)$; -40 **9.** 1
10. -1 **11.** 1 **12.** -1

Skill Practice

Multiply.
13. $(-3)(-4)(-8)(-1)$
14. $(-1)(-4)(-6)(5)$

Example 3 **Multiplying Several Factors**

Multiply.

a. $(-2)(-5)(-7)$ **b.** $(-4)(2)(-1)(5)$

Solution:

a. $(-2)(-5)(-7)$ This product has an odd number of negative factors.

  $= -70$ The product is negative.

b. $(-4)(2)(-1)(5)$ This product has an even number of negative factors.

  $= 40$ The product is positive.

3. Exponential Expressions

Be particularly careful when evaluating exponential expressions involving negative numbers. An exponential expression with a negative base is written with parentheses around the base, such as $(-3)^4$.

To evaluate $(-3)^4$, the base -3 is multiplied 4 times:

$$(-3)^4 = (-3)(-3)(-3)(-3) = 81$$

If parentheses are *not* used, the expression -3^4 has a different meaning:

- The expression -3^4 has a base of 3 (not -3) and can be interpreted as $-1 \cdot 3^4$. Hence,

$$-3^4 = -1 \cdot (3)(3)(3)(3) = -81$$

- The expression -3^4 can also be interpreted as "the opposite of 3^4." Hence,

$$-3^4 = -(3 \cdot 3 \cdot 3 \cdot 3) = -81$$

Skill Practice

Simplify.
15. $(-5)^2$ **16.** -5^2
17. $(-2)^3$ **18.** -2^3

Example 4 **Simplifying Exponential Expressions**

Simplify.

a. $(-4)^2$ **b.** -4^2 **c.** $(-5)^3$ **d.** -5^3

Solution:

a. $(-4)^2 = (-4)(-4)$ The base is -4.

  $= 16$ Multiply.

b. $-4^2 = -(4)(4)$ The base is 4. This is equal to $-1 \cdot 4^2 = -1 \cdot (4)(4)$.

  $= -16$ Multiply.

c. $(-5)^3 = (-5)(-5)(-5)$ The base is -5.

  $= -125$ Multiply.

d. $-5^3 = -(5)(5)(5)$ The base is 5. This is equal to $-1 \cdot 5^3 = -1 \cdot (5)(5)(5)$.

  $= -125$ Multiply.

Avoiding Mistakes

In Example 4(b) the base is positive because the negative sign is not enclosed in parentheses with the base.

Answers

13. 96   **14.** -120
15. 25   **16.** -25
17. -8 **18.** -8

4. Division of Integers

From Section 1.6, we learned that when we divide two numbers, we can check our result by using multiplication. Because multiplication and division are related in this way, it seems reasonable that the same sign rules that apply to multiplication also apply to division. For example:

$24 \div 6 = 4$	Check:	$6 \cdot 4 = 24 ✓$
$-24 \div 6 = -4$	Check:	$6 \cdot (-4) = -24 ✓$
$24 \div (-6) = -4$	Check:	$-6 \cdot (-4) = 24 ✓$
$-24 \div (-6) = 4$	Check:	$-6 \cdot 4 = -24 ✓$

We summarize the rules for dividing signed numbers along with the properties of division learned in Section 1.6.

> **PROCEDURE Dividing Signed Numbers**
>
> **1.** The quotient of two numbers with the *same* sign is positive.
>
> Examples: $20 \div 5 = 4$ and $-20 \div (-5) = 4$
>
> **2.** The quotient of two numbers with different signs is negative.
>
> Examples: $16 \div (-8) = -2$ and $-16 \div 8 = -2$
>
> **3.** Zero divided by any nonzero number is zero.
>
> Examples: $0 \div 12 = 0$ and $0 \div (-3) = 0$
>
> **4.** Any nonzero number divided by zero is undefined.
>
> Examples: $-5 \div 0$ is undefined

Example 5 Dividing Integers

Divide.

a. $50 \div (-5)$ **b.** $\dfrac{-42}{-7}$ **c.** $\dfrac{-39}{3}$ **d.** $0 \div (-7)$ **e.** $\dfrac{-8}{0}$

Solution:

a. $50 \div (-5) = -10$ Different signs. The quotient is negative.

b. $\dfrac{-42}{-7} = 6$ Same signs. The quotient is positive.

c. $\dfrac{-39}{3} = -13$ Different signs. The quotient is negative.

d. $0 \div (-7) = 0$ Zero divided by any nonzero number is 0.

e. $\dfrac{-8}{0}$ is undefined.   Any nonzero number divided by 0 is undefined.

Skill Practice

Divide.
19. $-40 \div 10$
20. $\dfrac{-36}{-12}$
21. $\dfrac{18}{-2}$
22. $0 \div (-12)$
23. $\dfrac{-2}{0}$

TIP: In Example 5(e), $\frac{-8}{0}$ is undefined because there is no number that when multiplied by 0 will equal -8.

Answers
19. -4 **20.** 3
21. -9 **22.** 0
23. Undefined

Skill Practice

Translate the phrase into a mathematical expression. Then simplify.

24. The quotient of -40 and -4
25. 60 divided by -3
26. -8 divided into -24

Example 6 **Translating to a Mathematical Expression**

Translate the phrase into a mathematical expression. Then simplify.

a. The quotient of 26 and -13 **b.** -45 divided by 5

c. -4 divided into -24

Solution:

a. The word quotient implies division. The quotient of 26 and -13 translates to $26 \div (-13)$.

$$26 \div (-13) = -2 \qquad \text{Simplify.}$$

b. -45 divided by 5 translates to $-45 \div 5$.

$$-45 \div 5 = -9 \qquad \text{Simplify.}$$

c. -4 divided into -24 translates to $-24 \div (-4)$.

$$-24 \div (-4) = 6 \qquad \text{Simplify.}$$

Skill Practice

27. A severe cold front blew through Atlanta and the temperature change over a 6-hr period was $-24°$F. Find the average hourly change in temperature.

Example 7 **Applying Division of Integers**

Between midnight and 6:00 A.M., the change in temperature was $-18°$F. Find the average hourly change in temperature.

Solution:

In this example, we have a change of $-18°$F in temperature to distribute evenly over a 6-hr period (from midnight to 6:00 A.M. is 6 hr). This implies division.

$$-18 \div 6 = -3 \qquad \text{Divide } -18°\text{F by 6 hr.}$$

The temperature changed by $-3°$F per hour.

Answers

24. $-50 \div (-5)$; 10
25. $60 \div (-3)$; -20
26. $-24 \div (-8)$; 3   **27.** $-4°$F

Section 2.4 Practice Exercises

Study Skills Exercise

1. Students often learn a rule about signs that states "two negatives make a positive." This rule is incomplete and therefore not always true. Note the following combinations of two negatives:

$-2 + (-4)$	the sum of two negatives
$-(-5)$	the opposite of a negative
$-\lvert -10 \rvert$	the opposite of an absolute value
$(-3)(-6)$	the product of two negatives

Simplify the expressions to determine which are negative and which are positive. Then write the rule for multiplying two numbers with the same sign.

$$-2 + (-4) \underline{\hspace{3cm}}$$

$$-(-5) \underline{\hspace{3cm}}$$

$$-|-10| \underline{\hspace{3cm}}$$

$$(-3)(-6) \underline{\hspace{3cm}}$$

When multiplying two numbers with the same sign, the product is $\underline{\hspace{3cm}}$.

Review Exercises

2. Simplify.

   a. $|-5|$ **b.** $|5|$ **c.** $-|5|$ **d.** $-|-5|$ **e.** $-(-5)$

For Exercises 3–8, add or subtract as indicated.

3. $14 - (-5)$ **4.** $-24 - 50$ **5.** $-33 + (-11)$

6. $-7 - (-23)$ **7.** $23 - 12 + (-4) - (-10)$ **8.** $9 + (-12) - 17 - 4 - (-15)$

Objective 1: Multiplication of Integers

For Exercises 9–24, multiply the integers. **(See Example 1.)**

9. $-3(5)$ **10.** $-2(13)$ **11.** $(-5)(-8)$ **12.** $(-12)(-2)$

13. $7(-3)$ **14.** $5(-12)$ **15.** $-12(-4)$ **16.** $-6(-11)$

17. $-15(3)$ **18.** $-3(25)$ **19.** $9(-8)$ **20.** $8(-3)$

21. $-14 \cdot 0$ **22.** $-8 \cdot 0$ **23.** $-95(-1)$ **24.** $-144(-1)$

For Exercises 25–30, translate to a mathematical expression. Then simplify. **(See Example 2.)**

25. Multiply -3 and -1 **26.** Multiply -12 and -4 **27.** The product of -5 and 3

28. The product of 9 and -2 **29.** 3 times -5 **30.** -3 times 6

Objective 2: Multiplying Many Factors

For Exercises 31–40, multiply. **(See Example 3.)**

31. $(-5)(-2)(-4)(-10)$ **32.** $(-3)(-5)(-2)(-4)$ **33.** $(-11)(-4)(-2)$

34. $(-20)(-3)(-1)$ **35.** $(24)(-2)(0)(-3)$ **36.** $(3)(0)(-13)(22)$

37. $(-1)(-1)(-1)(-1)(-1)(-1)$ **38.** $(-1)(-1)(-1)(-1)(-1)(-1)(-1)$

39. $(-2)(2)(2)(-2)(2)$ **40.** $(2)(-2)(2)(2)$

Objective 3: Exponential Expressions

For Exercises 41–56, simplify. **(See Example 4.)**

41. -10^2 **42.** -8^2 **43.** $(-10)^2$ **44.** $(-8)^2$

45. -10^3 **46.** -8^3 **47.** $(-10)^3$ **48.** $(-8)^3$

49. -5^4 **50.** -4^4 **51.** $(-5)^4$ **52.** $(-4)^4$

53. $(-1)^2$ **54.** $(-1)^3$ **55.** -1^4 **56.** -1^5

Objective 4: Division of Integers

For Exercises 57–72, divide the real numbers, if possible. **(See Example 5.)**

57. $60 \div (-3)$ **58.** $46 \div (-2)$ **59.** $\dfrac{-56}{-8}$ **60.** $\dfrac{-48}{-3}$

61. $\dfrac{-15}{5}$ **62.** $\dfrac{30}{-6}$ **63.** $-84 \div (-4)$ **64.** $-48 \div (-6)$

65. $\dfrac{-13}{0}$ **66.** $\dfrac{-41}{0}$ **67.** $\dfrac{0}{-18}$ **68.** $\dfrac{0}{-6}$

69. $(-20) \div (-5)$ **70.** $(-10) \div (-2)$ **71.** $\dfrac{204}{-6}$ **72.** $\dfrac{300}{-2}$

For Exercises 73–78, translate the English phrase to a mathematical expression. Then simplify. **(See Example 6.)**

73. The quotient of -100 and 20 **74.** The quotient of 46 and -23 **75.** -64 divided by -32

76. -108 divided by -4 **77.** 13 divided into -52 **78.** -15 divided into -45

79. During a 10-min period, a SCUBA diver's depth changed by -60 ft. Find the average change in depth per minute. **(See Example 7.)**

80. When a severe winter storm moved through Albany, New York, the change in temperature between 4:00 P.M. and 7:00 P.M. was $-27°F$. What was the average hourly change in temperature?

81. One of the most famous blizzards in the United States was the blizzard of 1888. In one part of Nebraska, the temperature plunged from $40°F$ to $-25°F$ in 5 hr. What was the average change in temperature during this time?

82. A submarine descended from a depth of -528 m to -1804 m in a 2-hr period. What was the average change in depth per hour during this time?

83. Travis wrote five checks to the employees of his business, each for $225. If the original balance in his checking account was $890, what is his new balance?

84. Jennifer's checking account had $320 when she wrote two checks for $150, and one check for $82. What is her new balance?

85. During a severe drought in Georgia, the water level in Lake Lanier dropped. During a 1-month period from June to July, the lake's water level changed by -3 ft. If this continued for 6 months, by how much did the water level change?

86. During a drought, the change in elevation for a retention pond was -9 in. over a 1-month period. At this rate, what will the change in elevation be after 5 months?

Mixed Exercises

For Exercises 87–102, perform the indicated operation.

87. $18(-6)$ **88.** $24(-2)$ **89.** $18 \div (-6)$ **90.** $24 \div (-2)$

91. $(-9)(-12)$ **92.** $-36 \div (-12)$ **93.** $-90 \div (-6)$ **94.** $(-5)(-4)$

95. $\dfrac{0}{-2}$ **96.** $-24 \div 0$ **97.** $-90 \div 0$ **98.** $\dfrac{0}{-5}$

99. $(-2)(-5)(4)$ **100.** $(10)(-2)(-3)(-5)$ **101.** $(-7)^2$ **102.** -7^2

103. a. What number must be multiplied by -5 to obtain -35?

   b. What number must be multiplied by -5 to obtain 35?

104. a. What number must be multiplied by -4 to obtain -36?

   b. What number must be multiplied by -4 to obtain 36?

Expanding Your Skills

The electrical charge of an atom is determined by the number of protons and number of electrons an atom has. Each proton gives a positive charge ($+1$) and each electron gives a negative charge (-1). An atom that has a total charge of 0 is said to be electrically neutral. An atom that is not electrically neutral is called an ion. For Exercises 105–108, determine the total charge for an atom with the given number of protons and electrons.

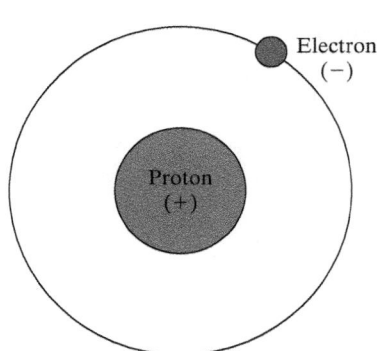

The Hydrogen Atom

105. 1 proton, 0 electrons   **106.** 17 protons, 18 electrons

107. 8 protons, 10 electrons   **108.** 20 protons, 18 electrons

For Exercises 109–114, assume $a > 0$ (this means that a is positive) and $b < 0$ (this means that b is negative). Find the sign of each expression.

109. $a \cdot b$ **110.** $b \div a$ **111.** $|a| \div b$

112. $a \cdot |b|$ **113.** $-a \div b$ **114.** $a(-b)$

Calculator Connections

Topic: Multiplying and Dividing Integers on a Calculator

Knowing the sign of the product or quotient can make using the calculator easier. For example, look at $\frac{-78}{-26}$. Note the keystrokes if we enter this into the calculator as written:

Expression	Keystrokes	Result
$\dfrac{-78}{-26}$	78 +⊙- ÷ 26 +⊙- =	3
	or (−) 78 ÷ (−) 26 =	3

But since we know that the quotient of two negative numbers is positive, we can simply enter:

78 ÷ 26 =   3

Calculator Exercises

For Exercises 115–118, use a calculator to perform the indicated operations.

115. $(-413)(871)$ **116.** $-6125 \cdot (-97)$

117. $\dfrac{-576,828}{-10,682}$ **118.** $5,945,308 \div (-9452)$

Problem Recognition Exercises

Operations on Integers

1. Perform the indicated operations

    a. $(-24)(-2)$

    b. $(-24) - (-2)$

    c. $(-24) + (-2)$

    d. $(-24) \div (-2)$

2. Perform the indicated operations.

    a. $12(-3)$

    b. $12 - (-3)$

    c. $12 + (-3)$

    d. $12 \div (-3)$

For Exercises 3–14, translate each phrase to a mathematical expression. Then simplify.

3. The sum of -5 and -3

4. The product of 9 and -5

5. The difference of -3 and -7

6. The quotient of 28 and -4

7. -23 times -2

8. 18 subtracted from -4

9. 42 divided by -2

10. -13 added to -18

11. -12 subtracted from 10

12. -7 divided into -21

13. The product of -6 and -9

14. The total of $-7, 4, 8, -16,$ and -5

For Exercises 15–37, perform the indicated operations.

15. a. $15 - (-5)$ **b.** $15(-5)$ **c.** $15 + (-5)$ **d.** $15 \div (-5)$

16. a. $-36(-2)$ **b.** $-36 - (-2)$ **c.** $\dfrac{-36}{-2}$ **d.** $-36 + (-2)$

17. a. $20(-4)$ **b.** $-20(-4)$ **c.** $-20(4)$ **d.** $20(4)$

18. a. $-5 - 9 - 2$ **b.** $-5(-9)(-2)$ **19. a.** $10 + (-3) + (-12)$ **b.** $10 - (-3) - (-12)$

20. a. $(-1)(-2)(-3)(-4)$ **b.** $(-1)(-2)(3)(4)$ **c.** $(-1)(-2)(-3)(4)$ **d.** $(-1)(2)(3)(4)$

21. a. $|-50|$ **b.** $-(-50)$ **c.** $|50|$ **d.** $-|-50|$

22. $\dfrac{0}{-8}$ **23.** $-55 \div 0$ **24.** $-615 - (-705)$ **25.** $-184 - 409$

26. $420 \div (-14)$ **27.** $-3600 \div (-90)$ **28.** $-44 - (-44)$ **29.** $-37 - (-37)$

30. $(-9)^2$ **31.** $(-2)^5$ **32.** -9^2 **33.** -2^5

34. $\dfrac{-46}{0}$ **35.** $0 \div (-16)$ **36.** $-15,042 + 4893$ **37.** $-84,506 + (-542)$

Order of Operations and Algebraic Expressions | Section 2.5

1. Order of Operations

The order of operations was first introduced in Section 1.7. The order of operations also applies when simplifying expressions with integers.

Objectives

1. Order of Operations
2. Translations Involving Variables
3. Evaluating Algebraic Expressions

> **PROCEDURE** Applying the Order of Operations
>
> 1. First perform all operations inside parentheses and other grouping symbols.
> 2. Simplify expressions containing exponents, square roots, or absolute values.
> 3. Perform multiplication or division in the order that they appear from left to right.
> 4. Perform addition or subtraction in the order that they appear from left to right.

Example 1   Applying the Order of Operations

Simplify. $-12 - 6(7 - 5)$

Solution:

$$-12 - 6(7 - 5)$$
$$= -12 - 6(2) \qquad \text{Simplify within parentheses first.}$$
$$= -12 - 12 \qquad \text{Multiply before subtracting.}$$
$$= -24 \qquad \text{Subtract. } \textit{Note: } -12 - 12 = -12 + (-12) = -24.$$

— Skill Practice —

Simplify.
1. $8 - 2(3 - 10)$

Example 2   Applying the Order of Operations

Simplify. $6 + 48 \div 4 \cdot (-2)$

Solution:

$$6 + \underbrace{48 \div 4} \cdot (-2) \qquad \text{Perform division and multiplication from left to right before addition.}$$
$$= 6 + \underbrace{12 \cdot (-2)} \qquad \text{Perform multiplication before addition.}$$
$$= 6 + (-24) \qquad \text{Add.}$$
$$= -18$$

— Skill Practice —

Simplify.
2. $-10 + 24 \div 2 \cdot (-3)$

Answers
1. 22   **2.** -46

Skill Practice

Simplify.

3. $8^2 - 2^3 \div (-7 + 5)$

Example 3 **Applying the Order of Operations**

Simplify. $\quad 3^2 - 10^2 \div (-1 - 4)$

Solution:

$3^2 - 10^2 \div (-1 - 4)$

$= 3^2 - 10^2 \div (-5)$ Simplify within parentheses.
                              Note: $-1 - 4 = -1 + (-4) = -5$.

$= 9 - 100 \div (-5)$ Simplify exponents.
                              Note: $3^2 = 3 \cdot 3 = 9$ and $10^2 = 10 \cdot 10 = 100$.

$= 9 - (-20)$ Perform division before subtraction.
                              Note: $100 \div (-5) = -20$.

$= 29$ Subtract. *Note:* $9 - (-20) = 9 + (20) = 29$.

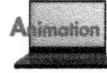

Skill Practice

Simplify.

4. $\dfrac{|50 + (-10)|}{-2^2}$

5. $1 - 3[5 - (8 - 1)]$

Example 4 **Applying the Order of Operations**

Simplify.

a. $\dfrac{|-8 + 24|}{5 - 3^2}$ **b.** $5 - 2[8 + (-7 - 5)]$

Solution:

a. $\dfrac{|-8 + 24|}{5 - 3^2}$ Simplify the expressions above and below the division bar by first adding within the absolute value and simplifying exponents.

$= \dfrac{|16|}{5 - 9}$

$= \dfrac{16}{-4}$ Simplify the absolute value and subtract $5 - 9$.

$= -4$ Divide.

b. $5 - 2[8 + (-7 - 5)]$

$= 5 - 2[8 + (-12)]$ First simplify the expression within the innermost parentheses.

$= 5 - 2[-4]$ Continue simplifying within parentheses.

$= 5 - (-8)$ Perform multiplication before subtraction.

$= 13$ Subtract. *Note:* $5 - (-8) = 5 + 8 = 13$

2. Translations Involving Variables

Recall that **variables** are used to represent quantities that are subject to change. For this reason, we can use variables and algebraic expressions to represent one or more unknowns in a word problem.

Answers

3. 68   **4.** −10   **5.** 7

Example 5 **Using Algebraic Expressions in Applications**

a. At a discount CD store, each CD costs $8. Suppose *n* is the number of CDs that a customer buys. Write an expression that represents the cost for *n* CDs.

b. The length of a rectangle is 5 in. longer than the width *w*. Write an expression that represents the length of the rectangle.

Solution:

a. The cost of 1 CD is 8(1) dollars.
The cost of 2 CDs is 8(2) dollars.
The cost of 3 CDs is 8(3) dollars.
The cost of *n* CDs is 8(*n*) dollars or simply 8*n* dollars.

From this pattern, we see that the total cost is the cost per CD times the number of CDs.

b. The length of a rectangle is 5 in. more than the width. The phrase "more than" implies addition. Thus, the length (in inches) is represented by

$$\text{length} = w + 5$$

w

w + 5

Example 6 **Translating to an Algebraic Expression**

Write each phrase as an algebraic expression.

a. The product of −6 and *x*

b. *p* subtracted from 7

c. The quotient of *c* and *d*

d. Twice the sum of *y* and 4

Solution:

a. The product of −6 and *x*: −6*x*   "Product" implies multiplication.

b. *p* subtracted from 7: 7 − *p*   To subtract *p* from 7, we must "start" with 7 and then perform the subtraction.

c. The quotient of *c* and *d*: $\dfrac{c}{d}$ "Quotient" implies division.

d. Twice the sum of *y* and 4: 2(*y* + 4)   The word "twice the sum" implies that we multiply the *sum* by 2. The sum must be enclosed in parentheses so that the entire quantity is doubled.

---

3. Evaluating Algebraic Expressions

The value of an algebraic expression depends on the values of the variables within the expression.

Answers

6. 7*p*   7. *L* − 44   8. $\dfrac{w}{-4}$
9. *x* − 11   10. −9*p*   11. 4(*m* + *n*)

Example 7 Evaluating an Algebraic Expression

Evaluate the expression for the given values of the variables.

$$3x - y \quad \text{for } x = 7 \text{ and } y = -3$$

Solution:

$3x - y$

$= 3(\ \ ) - (\ \ )$ When substituting a number for a variable, use parentheses in place of the variable.

$= 3(7) - (-3)$ Substitute 7 for x and -3 for y.

$= 21 + 3$ Apply the order of operations. Multiplication is performed before subtraction.

$= 24$

Example 8 Evaluating an Algebraic Expression

Evaluate the expressions for the given values of the variables.

a. $-|-z|$ for $z = -6$ **b.** x^2 for $x = -4$ **c.** $-y^2$ for $y = -6$

Solution:

a. $-|-z|$

$= -|-(\ \ )|$ Replace the variable with empty parentheses.

$= -|\underbrace{-(-6)}|$ Substitute the value -6 for z. Apply the order of operations. Inside the absolute value bars, we take the opposite of -6, which is 6.

$= \quad -|6|$

$= -6$ The opposite of $|6|$ is -6.

b. x^2

$= (\ \ )^2$ Replace the variable with empty parentheses.

$= (-4)^2$ Substitute -4 for x.

$= (-4)(-4)$ The expression $(-4)^2$ has a base of -4. Therefore,

$= 16$ $(-4)^2 = (-4)(-4) = 16$.

c. $-y^2$

$= -(\ \ )^2$ Replace the variable with empty parentheses.

$= -(-6)^2$ Substitute -6 for y.

$= -(36)$ Simplify the expression with exponents first. The expression $(-6)^2 = (-6)(-6) = 36$.

$= -36$

Example 9	**Evaluating an Algebraic Expression**

Evaluate the expression for the given values of the variables.

$$-5|x - y + z|, \quad \text{for } x = -9, y = -4, \text{ and } z = 2$$

Solution:

$-5|x - y + z|$

$= -5|(\ \ ) - (\ \ ) + (\ \ )|$	Replace the variables with empty parentheses.
$= -5|(-9) - (-4) + (2)|$	Substitute -9 for x, -4 for y, and 2 for z.
$= -5|-9 + 4 + 2|$	Simplify inside absolute value bars first. Rewrite subtraction in terms of addition.
$= -5|-3|$	Add within the absolute value bars.
$= -5 \cdot 3$	Evaluate the absolute value before multiplying.
$= -15$	

TIP: Absolute value bars act as grouping symbols. Therefore, you must perform the operations within the absolute value first.

Skill Practice

16. Evaluate the expression for the given value of the variable.
$$3 - |a + b + 4| \quad \text{for}$$
$$a = -5 \text{ and } b = -12$$

Answer

16. -10

Section 2.5 Practice Exercises

Boost your GRADE at ALEKS.com!

 ALEKS version 3.0

- Practice Problems
- Self-Tests
- NetTutor
- e-Professors
- Videos

Study Skills Exercises

1. When you take a test, go through the test and do all the problems that you know first. Then go back and work on the problems that were more difficult. Give yourself a time limit for how much time you spend on each problem (maybe 3 to 5 minutes the first time through). Circle the importance of each statement.

	Not important	Somewhat important	Very important
a. Read through the entire test first.	1	2	3
b. If time allows, go back and check each problem.	1	2	3
c. Write out all steps instead of doing the work in your head.	1	2	3

2. Define the key term **variable**.

Review Exercises

For Exercises 3–8, perform the indicated operation.

3. $-100 \div (-4)$ **4.** $-100 - (-4)$ **5.** $-100(-4)$

6. $-100 + (-4)$ **7.** $(-12)^2$ **8.** -12^2

Objective 1: Order of Operations

For Exercises 9–54, simplify using the order of operations. **(See Examples 1–4.)**

9. $-1 - 5 - 8 - 3$

10. $-2 - 6 - 3 - 10$

11. $(-1)(-5)(-8)(-3)$

12. $(-2)(-6)(-3)(-10)$

13. $5 + 2(3 - 5)$

14. $6 - 4(8 - 10)$

15. $-2(3 - 6) + 10$

16. $-4(1 - 3) - 8$

17. $-8 - 6^2$

18. $-10 - 5^2$

19. $120 \div (-4)(5)$

20. $36 \div (-2)(3)$

21. $40 - 32 \div (-4)(2)$

22. $48 - 36 \div (6)(-2)$

23. $100 - 2(3 - 8)$

24. $55 - 3(2 - 6)$

25. $|-10 + 13| - |-6|$

26. $|4 - 9| - |-10|$

27. $\sqrt{100 - 36} - 3\sqrt{16}$

28. $\sqrt{36 - 11} + 2\sqrt{9}$

29. $5^2 - (-3)^2$

30. $6^2 - (-4)^2$

31. $-3 + (5 - 9)^2$

32. $-5 + (3 - 10)^2$

33. $12 + (14 - 16)^2 \div (-4)$

34. $-7 + (1 - 5)^2 \div 4$

35. $-48 \div 12 \div (-2)$

36. $-100 \div (-5) \div (-5)$

37. $90 \div (-3) \cdot (-1) \div (-6)$

38. $64 \div (-4) \cdot 2 \div (-16)$

39. $[7^2 - 9^2] \div (-5 + 1)$

40. $[(-8)^2 - 5^2] \div (-4 + 1)$

41. $2 + 2^2 - 10 - 12$

42. $14 - 4^2 + 2 - 10$

43. $\dfrac{3^2 - 27}{-9 + 6}$

44. $\dfrac{8 + (-2)^2}{-5 + (-1)}$

45. $\dfrac{13 - (2)(4)}{-1 - 2^2}$

46. $\dfrac{10 - (-3)(5)}{-9 - 4^2}$

47. $\dfrac{|-23 + 7|}{5^2 - (-3)^2}$

48. $\dfrac{|10 - 50|}{6^2 - (-4)^2}$

49. $21 - [4 - (5 - 8)]$

50. $15 - [10 - (20 - 25)]$

51. $-17 - 2[18 \div (-3)]$

52. $-8 - 5(-45 \div 15)$

53. $4 + 2[9 + (-4 + 12)]$

54. $-13 + 3[11 + (-15 + 10)]$

Objective 2: Translations Involving Variables

55. Carolyn sells homemade candles. Write an expression for her total revenue if she sells x candles for \$15 each. **(See Example 5.)**

56. Maria needs to buy 12 wine glasses. Write an expression of the cost of 12 glasses at p dollars each.

57. Jonathan is 4 in. taller than his brother. Write an expression for Jonathan's height if his brother is t inches tall. **(See Example 5.)**

58. It takes Perry 1 hr longer than David to mow the lawn. If it takes David h hours to mow the lawn, write an expression for the amount of time it takes Perry to mow the lawn.

59. A sedan travels 6 mph slower than a sports car. Write an expression for the speed of the sedan if the sports car travels v mph.

60. Bill's daughter is 30 years younger than he is. Write an expression for his daughter's age if Bill is A years old.

61. The price of gas has doubled over the last 3 years. If gas cost g dollars per gallon 3 years ago, write an expression of the current price per gallon.

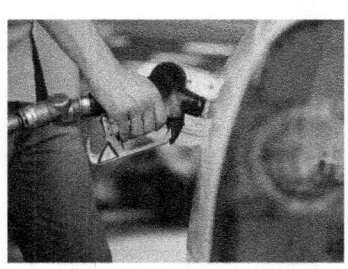

62. Suppose that the amount of rain that fell on Monday was twice the amount that fell on Sunday. Write an expression for the amount of rain on Monday, if Sunday's amount was t inches.

For Exercises 63–74, write each phrase as an algebraic expression. **(See Example 6.)**

63. The product of -12 and n

64. The product of -3 and z

65. x subtracted from -9

66. p subtracted from -18

67. The quotient of t and -2

68. The quotient of -10 and w

69. -14 added to y

70. -150 added to c

71. Twice the sum of c and d

72. Twice the sum of a and b

73. The difference of x and -8

74. The difference of m and -5

Objective 3: Evaluating Algebraic Expressions

For Exercises 75–94, evaluate the expressions for the given values of the variables. **(See Examples 7–9.)**

75. $x + 9z$ for $x = -10$ and $z = -3$

76. $a + 7b$ for $a = -3$ and $b = -6$

77. $x + 5y + z$ for $x = -10, y = 5,$ and $z = 2$

78. $9p + 4t + w$ for $p = 2, t = 6,$ and $w = -50$

79. $a - b + 3c$ for $a = -7, b = -2,$ and $c = 4$

80. $w + 2y - z$ for $w = -9, y = 10,$ and $z = -3$

81. $-3mn$ for $m = -8$ and $n = -2$

82. $-5pq$ for $p = -4$ and $q = -2$

83. $|-y|$ for $y = -9$

84. $|-z|$ for $z = -18$

85. $-|-w|$ for $w = -4$

86. $-|-m|$ for $m = -15$

87. x^2 for $x = -3$

88. n^2 for $n = -9$

89. $-x^2$ for $x = -3$

90. $-n^2$ for $n = -9$

91. $-4|x + 3y|$ for $x = 5$ and $y = -6$

92. $-2|4a - b|$ for $a = -8$ and $b = -2$

93. $6 - |m - n^2|$ for $m = -2$ and $n = 3$

94. $4 - |c^2 - d^2|$ for $c = 3$ and $d = -5$

Expanding Your Skills

95. Find the average temperature: $-8°, -11°, -4°, 1°, 9°, 4°, -5°$

96. Find the average temperature: $15°, 12°, 10°, 3°, 0°, -2°, -3°$

97. Find the average score: $-8, -8, -6, -5, -2, -3, 3, 3, 0, -4$

98. Find the average score: $-6, -2, 5, 1, 0, -3, 4, 2, -7, -4$

Group Activity

Checking Weather Predictions

Materials: A computer with online access

Estimated time: 2–3 minutes each day for 10 days

Group Size: 3

1. Go to a website such as http://www.weather.com/ to find the predicted high and low temperatures for a 10-day period for a city of your choice.

2. Record the predicted high and low temperatures for each of the 10 days. Record these values in the second column of each table.

Day	Predicted High	Actual High	Difference (error)
1			
2			
3			
4			
5			
6			
7			
8			
9			
10			

Day	Predicted Low	Actual Low	Difference (error)
1			
2			
3			
4			
5			
6			
7			
8			
9			
10			

3. For the next 10 days, record the actual high and low temperatures for your chosen city for that day. Record these values in the third column of each table.

4. For each day, compute the difference between the predicted and actual temperature and record the results in the fourth column of each table. We will call this difference the *error*.

$$\text{error} = (\text{predicted temperature}) - (\text{actual temperature})$$

5. If the error is *negative*, does this mean that the weather service overestimated or underestimated the temperature?

6. If the error is *positive*, does this mean that the weather service overestimated or underestimated the temperature?

Chapter 2 Summary

Section 2.1 Integers, Absolute Value, and Opposite

Key Concepts

The numbers ... $-3, -2, -1, 0, 1, 2, 3, \ldots$ and so on are called **integers**. The negative integers lie to the left of zero on the number line.

Negative numbers   Zero   Positive numbers

The **absolute value** of a number a is denoted $|a|$. The value of $|a|$ is the distance between a and 0 on the number line.

Two numbers that are the same distance from zero on the number line, but on opposite sides of zero are called **opposites**.

The double negative property states that the opposite of a negative number is a positive number. That is, $-(-a) = a$, for $a > 0$.

Examples

Example 1

The temperature 5° below zero can be represented by a negative number: $-5°$.

Example 2

a. $|5| = 5$ b. $|-13| = 13$ c. $|0| = 0$

Example 3

The opposite of 12 is $-(12) = -12$.

Example 4

The opposite of -23 is $-(-23) = 23$.

Section 2.2 Addition of Integers

Key Concepts

To add integers using a number line, locate the first number on the number line. Then to add a positive number, move to the right on the number line. To add a negative number, move to the left on the number line.

Integers can be added using the following rules:

Adding Numbers with the Same Sign

To add two numbers with the same sign, add their absolute values and apply the common sign.

Adding Numbers with Different Signs

To add two numbers with different signs, subtract the smaller absolute value from the larger absolute value. Then apply the sign of the number having the larger absolute value.

An English phrase can be translated to a mathematical expression involving addition of integers.

Examples

Example 1

Add $-2 + (-4)$ using the number line.

Move 4 units to the *left*.

Start here.

$-2 + (-4) = -6$

Example 2

a. $5 + 2 = 7$
b. $-5 + (-2) = -7$

Example 3

a. $6 + (-5) = 1$
b. $(-6) + 5 = -1$

Example 4

-3 added to the sum of -8 and 6 translates to $(-8 + 6) + (-3)$.

Section 2.3   Subtraction of Integers

Key Concepts

Subtraction of Signed Numbers

For two numbers a and b,

$$a - b = a + (-b)$$

To perform subtraction, follow these steps:

1. Leave the first number (the minuend) unchanged.
2. Change the subtraction sign to an addition sign.
3. Add the opposite of the second number (the subtrahend).

An English phrase can be translated to a mathematical expression involving subtraction of integers.

Examples

Example 1

a. $3 - 9 = 3 + (-9) = -6$

b. $-3 - 9 = -3 + (-9) = -12$

c. $3 - (-9) = 3 + (9) = 12$

d. $-3 - (-9) = -3 + (9) = 6$

Example 2

2 decreased by -10 translates to $2 - (-10)$.

Section 2.4   Multiplication and Division of Integers

Key Concepts

Multiplication of Signed Numbers

1. The product of two numbers with the same sign is positive.
2. The product of two numbers with different signs is negative.
3. The product of any number and zero is zero.

The product of an *even* number of negative factors is *positive*.
The product of an *odd* number of negative factors is *negative*.

When evaluating an exponential expression, attention must be given when parentheses are used.
That is, $(-2)^4 = (-2)(-2)(-2)(-2) = 16$,
while $-2^4 = -1 \cdot (2)(2)(2)(2) = -16$.

Division of Signed Numbers

1. The quotient of two numbers with the same sign is positive.
2. The quotient of two numbers with different signs is negative.
3. Division by zero is undefined.
4. Zero divided by a nonzero number is 0.

Examples

Example 1

a. $-8(-3) = 24$

b. $8(-3) = -24$

c. $-8(0) = 0$

Example 2

a. $(-5)(-4)(-1)(-3) = 60$

b. $(-2)(-1)(-6)(-3)(-2) = -72$

Example 3

a. $(-3)^2 = (-3)(-3) = 9$

b. $-3^2 = -(3)(3) = -9$

Example 4

a. $-36 \div (-9) = 4$ b. $\dfrac{42}{-6} = -7$

Example 5

a. $-15 \div 0$ is undefined.   b. $0 \div (-3) = 0$

Section 2.5   Order of Operations and Algebraic Expressions

Key Concepts

Order of Operations

1. First perform all operations inside parentheses and other grouping symbols.
2. Simplify expressions containing exponents, square roots, or absolute values.
3. Perform multiplication or division in the order that they appear from left to right.
4. Perform addition or subtraction in the order that they appear from left to right.

Evaluating an Algebraic Expression

To evaluate an expression, first replace the variable with parentheses. Then insert the values and simplify using the order of operations.

Examples

Example 1

$$-15 - 2(8 - 11)^2 = -15 - 2(-3)^2$$
$$= -15 - 2 \cdot 9$$
$$= -15 - 18$$
$$= -33$$

Example 2

Evaluate $4x - 5y$ for $x = -2$ and $y = 3$.
$$4x - 5y = 4(\ \ ) - 5(\ \ )$$
$$= 4(-2) - 5(3)$$
$$= -8 - 15$$
$$= -23$$

Chapter 2   Review Exercises

Section 2.1

For Exercises 1–2, write an integer that represents each numerical value.

1. The plane descended 4250 ft.

2. The company's profit fell by $3,000,000.

For Exercises 3–6, graph the numbers on the number line.

3. -2 4. -5 5. 0 6. 3

For Exercises 7–8, determine the opposite and the absolute value for each number.

7. -4 8. 6

For Exercises 9–16, simplify.

9. $|-3|$ 10. $|-1000|$ 11. $|74|$

12. $|0|$ 13. $-(-9)$ 14. $-(-28)$

15. $-|-20|$ 16. $-|-45|$

For Exercises 17–20, fill in the blank with $<$, $>$, or $=$, to make a true statement.

17. $-7\ \square\ |-7|$ 18. $-12\ \square\ -5$

19. $-(-4)\ \square\ -|-4|$ 20. $-20\ \square\ -|-20|$

Section 2.2

For Exercises 21–24, add the integers using the number line.

21. $6 + (-2)$ 22. $-3 + 6$

23. $-3 + (-2)$ 24. $-3 + 0$

25. State the rule for adding two numbers with the same sign.

26. State the rule for adding two numbers with different signs.

For Exercises 27–32, add the integers.

27. $35 + (-22)$ 28. $-105 + 90$

29. $-29 + (-41)$ **30.** $-98 + (-42)$

31. $-3 + (-10) + 12 + 14 + (-10)$

32. $9 + (-15) + 2 + (-7) + (-4)$

For Exercises 33–38, translate each phrase to a mathematical expression. Then simplify the expression.

33. The sum of 23 and -35 **34.** 57 plus -10

35. The total of $-5, -13,$ and 20

36. -42 increased by 12 **37.** 3 more than -12

38. -89 plus -22

39. The graph gives the number of inches below or above the average snowfall for the given months for Caribou, Maine. Find the total departure from average. Is the snowfall for Caribou above or below average?

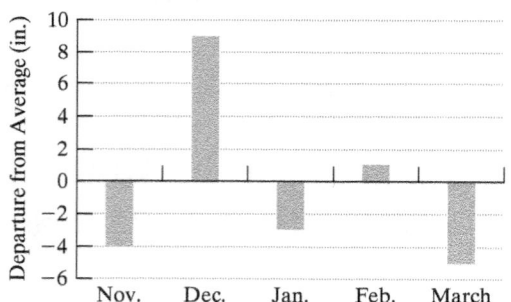

40. The table gives the scores for golfer Ernie Els at a recent PGA Open golf tournament. Find Ernie's total score after all four rounds.

	Round 1	Round 2	Round 3	Round 4
Ernie Els	2	-2	-1	-4

Section 2.3

41. State the steps for subtracting two numbers.

For Exercises 42–49, simplify.

42. $4 - (-23)$ **43.** $19 - 44$

44. $-2 - (-24)$ **45.** $-289 - 130$

46. $2 - 7 - 3$ **47.** $-45 - (-77) + 8$

48. $-16 - 4 - (-3)$ **49.** $99 - (-7) - 6$

50. Translate the phrase to a mathematical expression. Then simplify.

    a. The difference of 8 and 10

    b. 8 subtracted from 10

For Exercises 51–52, translate the mathematical statement to an English phrase. Answers will vary.

51. $-2 - 14$

52. $-25 - (-7)$

53. The temperature in Fargo, North Dakota, rose from $-6°F$ to $-1°F$. By how many degrees did the temperature rise?

54. Sam's balance in his checking account was $-\$40$, so he deposited $132. What is his new balance?

55. Find the average of the golf scores: $-3, 4, 0, 9, -2, -1, 0, 5, -3$ (These scores are the number of holes above or below par.)

56. A missile was launched from a submarine from a depth of -1050 ft below sea level. If the maximum height of the missile is 2400 ft, find the vertical distance between its greatest height and its depth at launch.

Section 2.4

For Exercises 57–72, simplify.

57. $6(-3)$ **58.** $\dfrac{-12}{4}$

59. $\dfrac{-900}{-60}$ **60.** $(-7)(-8)$

61. $-36 \div 9$ **62.** $60 \div (-5)$

63. $(-12)(-4)(-1)(-2)$

64. $(-1)(-8)(2)(1)(-2)$

65. $-15 \div 0$ **66.** $\dfrac{0}{-5}$

67. -5^3 **68.** $(-5)^3$

69. $(-6)^2$ **70.** -6^2

71. $(-1)^{10}$ **72.** $(-1)^{21}$

73. What is the sign of the product of three negative factors?

74. What is the sign of the product of four negative factors?

For Exercises 75–76, translate the English phrase to a mathematical expression. Then simplify.

75. The quotient of -45 and -15

76. The product of -4 and 19

77. Between 8:00 P.M. and midnight, the change in temperature was $-12°$F. Find the average hourly change in temperature.

78. Suzie wrote four checks to a vendor, each for $160. If the original balance in her checking account was $550, what is her new balance?

Section 2.5

For Exercises 79–88, simplify using the order of operations.

79. $50 - 3(6 - 2)$

80. $48 - 8 \div (-2) + 5$

81. $28 \div (-7) \cdot 3 - (-1)$

82. $(-4)^2 \div 8 - (-6)$

83. $[10 - (-3)^2] \cdot (-11) + 4$

84. $[-9 - (-7)]^2 \cdot 3 \div (-6)$

85. $\dfrac{100 - 4^2}{(-7)(6)}$ **86.** $\dfrac{18 - 3(-2)}{4^2 - 8}$

87. $5 - 2[-3 + (2 - 5)]$

88. $-10 + 3[4 - (-2 + 7)]$

89. Michael is 8 years older than his sister. Write an expression for Michael's age if his sister is a years old.

90. At a movie theater, drinks are $3 each. Write an expression for the cost of n drinks.

For Exercises 91–96, write each phrase as an algebraic expression.

91. The product of -5 and x

92. The difference of p and 12

93. Two more than the sum of a and b

94. The quotient of w and 4

95. -8 subtracted from y

96. Twice the sum of 5 and z

For Exercises 97–104, evaluate the expression for the given values of the variable.

97. $3x - 2y$ for $x = -5$ and $y = 4$

98. $5(a - 4b)$ for $a = -3$ and $b = 2$

99. $-2(x + y)^2$ for $x = 6$ and $y = -9$

100. $-3w^2 - 2z$ for $w = -4$ and $z = -9$

101. $-|x|$ for $x = -2$

102. $-|-x|$ for $x = -5$

103. $-(-x)$ for $x = -10$

104. $-(-x)$ for $x = 5$

Chapter 2   Test

For Exercises 1–2, write an integer that represents the numerical value.

1. Dwayne lost $220 during in his last trip to Las Vegas.

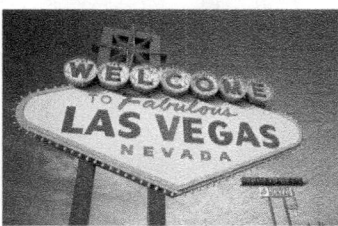

2. Garth Brooks has 26 more platinum albums than Elvis Presley.

For Exercises 3–8, fill in the blank with $>$, $<$, or $=$ to make the statement true.

3. $-5 \,\square\, -2$

4. $|-5| \,\square\, |-2|$

5. $0 \,\square\, -(-2)$

6. $-|-12| \,\square\, -12$

7. $-|-9| \,\square\, 9$

8. $-5^2 \,\square\, (-5)^2$

9. Determine the absolute value of -10.

10. Determine the opposite of -10.

For Exercises 11–22, perform the indicated operations.

11. $9 + (-14)$

12. $-23 + (-5)$

13. $-4 - (-13)$

14. $-30 - 11$

15. $-15 + 21$

16. $5 - 28$

17. $6(-12)$

18. $(-11)(-8)$

19. $\dfrac{-24}{-12}$

20. $\dfrac{54}{-3}$

21. $\dfrac{-44}{0}$

22. $(-91)(0)$

For Exercises 23–28, translate to a mathematical expression. Then simplify the expression.

23. The product of -3 and -7

24. 8 more than -13

25. Subtract -4 from 18.

26. The quotient of 6 and -2

27. -8 increased by 5

28. The total of $-3, 15, -6,$ and -1

29. The graph gives the number of inches below or above the average rainfall for the given months for Atlanta, Georgia. Find the total departure from average. Is the total rainfall for these months above or below average?

Amount of Rainfall Above or Below Average

30. The "Great White Hurricane" was a severe winter blizzard that dumped 50 in. of snow in Connecticut and Massachusetts. In one part of Connecticut, between 3:00 P.M. and 8:00 P.M., the change in temperature was $-35°F$. Find the average hourly change in temperature.

31. Simplify the expressions.
   a. $(-8)^2$ **b.** -8^2
   c. $(-4)^3$ **d.** -4^3

For Exercises 32–37, simplify the expressions.

32. $-14 + 22 - (-5) + (-10)$

33. $(-3)(-1)(-4)(-1)(-5)$

34. $16 - 2[5 - (1 - 4)]$

35. $-20 \div (-2)^2 + (-14)$

36. $12 \cdot (-6) + [20 - (-12)] - 15$

37. $\dfrac{24 - 2|3 - 9|}{8 - 2^2}$

38. A high school student sells magazine subscriptions at $18 each. Write an expression that represents the total value sold for m magazines.

For Exercises 39–40, evaluate the expressions for the given values of the variables.

39. $-x^2 + y^2$ for $x = 4$ and $y = -1$

40. $-4m - 3n$ for $m = -6$ and $n = 4$

Chapters 1–2   Cumulative Review Exercises

1. For the number 6,8<u>7</u>3,129 identify the place value of the underlined digit.

2. Write the following inequality in words: $130 < 244$

3. Approximate the perimeter of the triangle by first rounding the numbers to the hundreds place.

589 ft
132 ft
490 ft

For Exercises 4–7, add or subtract as indicated.

4. $73 + 41$

5. $71 + (-4) + 81 + (-106)$

6. $284 - 171 - (-84) - 393$

7. $\begin{array}{r} 1001 \\ -235 \\ \hline \end{array}$

For Exercises 8–13, multiply or divide as indicated.

8. $31 \cdot (-8)$

9. $-386 \div (-2)$

10. $737 \div 7$

11. $\begin{array}{r} 409 \\ \times\ 228 \\ \hline \end{array}$

12. $\dfrac{0}{-61}$

13. $0\overline{)341}$

14. Find the area of the rectangle.

28 m
5 m

15. Simplify the expressions.

  a. $-|-4|$ **b.** $-(-4)$

  c. -4^2 **d.** $(-4)^2$

16. Simplify the expression using the order of operations: $-14 - 2(9 - 5^2)$

For Exercises 17–18, evaluate the expressions for $x = -4$ and $y = 1$.

17. $x^2 - x + y$ **18.** $|x - y|$

19. Torie is taking a natural herb in capsule form. She purchased four bottles containing 30 capsules each. The directions state that she can take either 2 or 3 capsules a day.

  a. How many days will the capsules last if Torie takes 3 a day?

  b. How many days will the capsules last if she takes only 2 a day?

20. The low temperatures for Fairbanks, Alaska, are given for a 1-week period. Find the average low temperature.

  $-8°F, \quad -11°F, \quad 3°F, \quad 6°F, \quad 0°F, \quad -8°F, \quad -10°F$

Solving Equations

3

Chapter 3

In this chapter, we continue our study of algebra by learning how to solve linear equations. An *equation* is a statement indicating that two expressions are equal. A *solution* to an equation is a value of the variable that makes the right-hand side of an equation equal to the left-hand side of the equation.

Are You Prepared?

To help you prepare for this chapter, try the following exercises. Substitute the given value into the equation in place of the variable. Then determine if this value is a solution to the equation. That is, determine if the right-hand side equals the left-hand side.

1. $x + 12 = 16$ Is 4 a solution to this equation?   yes or no

2. $y - 7 = 18$ Is 11 a solution to this equation?   yes or no

3. $\dfrac{w}{-3} = 8$ Is -24 a solution to this equation?   yes or no

4. $18 = -3 + z$ Is 15 a solution to this equation?   yes or no

5. $120 = -5p$ Is -24 a solution to this equation?   yes or no

6. $3x - 7 = 29$ Is 12 a solution to this equation?   yes or no

7. $44 = 4 - 5x$ Is 8 a solution to this equation?   yes or no

8. $11x - 6 = 12x + 2$ Is -8 a solution to this equation?   yes or no

Section 3.1   Simplifying Expressions and Combining *Like* Terms

Objectives

1. Identifying *Like* Terms
2. Commutative, Associative, and Distributive Properties
3. Combining *Like* Terms
4. Simplifying Expressions

1. Identifying *Like* Terms

A **term** is a number or the product or quotient of numbers and variables. An algebraic expression is the sum of one or more terms. For example, the expression

$$-8x^3 + xy - 40 \quad \text{can be written as} \quad -8x^3 + xy + (-40)$$

This expression consists of the terms $-8x^3$, xy, and -40. The terms $-8x^3$ and xy are called **variable terms** because the value of the term will change when different numbers are substituted for the variables. The term -40 is called a **constant term** because its value will never change.

It is important to distinguish between a term and the factors within a term. For example, the quantity xy is one term, and the values x and y are factors within the term. The **coefficient** of the term is the numerical factor of the term.

> **TIP:** Variables without a coefficient explicitly written have a coefficient of 1. Thus, the term xy is equal to $1xy$. The 1 is understood.

Term	Coefficient of the Term
$-8x^3$	-8
xy or $1xy$	1
-40	-40

Terms are said to be *like* **terms** if they each have the same variables, and the corresponding variables are raised to the same powers. For example:

Like Terms	Unlike Terms	
$-4x$ and $6x$	$-4x$ and $6y$	(different variables)
$18ab$ and $4ba$	$18ab$ and $4a$	(different variables)
$7m^2n^5$ and $3m^2n^5$	$7m^2n^5$ and $3mn^5$	(different powers of m)
$5p$ and $-3p$	$5p$ and 3	(different variables)
8 and 10	8 and $10x$	(different variables)

Skill Practice

For Exercises 1–2, use the expression:

$$-48y^5 + 8y^2 - y - 8$$

1. List the terms of the expression.
2. List the coefficient of each term.
3. Are the terms $5x$ and x like terms?
4. Are the terms $-6a^3b^2$ and a^3b^2 like terms?

Example 1   Identifying Terms, Coefficients, and *Like* Terms

a. List the terms of the expression: $14x^3 - 6x^2 + 3x + 5$

b. Identify the coefficient of each term: $14x^3 - 6x^2 + 3x + 5$

c. Which two terms are *like* terms? $-6x, 5, -3y,$ and $4x$

d. Are the terms $3x^2y$ and $5xy^2$ *like* terms?

Solution:

a. The expression $14x^3 - 6x^2 + 3x + 5$ can be written as $14x^3 + (-6x^2) + 3x + 5$

Therefore, the terms are $14x^3, -6x^2, 3x,$ and 5.

b. The coefficients are $14, -6, 3,$ and 5.

c. The terms $-6x$ and $4x$ are *like* terms.

d. $3x^2y$ and $5xy^2$ are not *like* terms because the exponents on the x variables are different, and the exponents on the y variables are different.

Answers

1. $-48y^5, 8y^2, -y, -8$
2. $-48, 8, -1, -8$
3. Yes   4. Yes

2. Commutative, Associative, and Distributive Properties

Several important properties of whole numbers were introduced in Sections 1.3 and 1.5 involving addition and multiplication of whole numbers. These properties also hold for integers and algebraic expressions and will be used to simplify expressions (Tables 3-1 through 3-3).

Table 3-1   Commutative Properties

Property	In Symbols/Examples	Comments/Notes
Commutative property of addition	$a + b = b + a$ ex: $-4 + 7 = 7 + (-4)$ $x + 3 = 3 + x$	The order in which two numbers are added does not affect the sum.
Commutative property of multiplication	$a \cdot b = b \cdot a$ ex: $-5 \cdot 9 = 9 \cdot (-5)$ $8y = y \cdot 8$	The order in which two numbers are multiplied does not affect the product.

> **Avoiding Mistakes**
>
> In an expression such as $x + 3$, the two terms x and 3 cannot be combined into one term because they are not *like* terms. Addition of *like* terms will be discussed in Examples 6 and 7.

Table 3-2   Associative Properties

Property	In Symbols/Examples	Comments/Notes
Associative property of addition	$(a + b) + c = a + (b + c)$ ex: $(5 + 8) + 1 = 5 + (8 + 1)$ $(t + n) + 3 = t + (n + 3)$	The manner in which three numbers are grouped under addition does not affect the sum.
Associative property of multiplication	$(a \cdot b) \cdot c = a \cdot (b \cdot c)$ ex: $(-2 \cdot 3) \cdot 6 = -2 \cdot (3 \cdot 6)$ $3 \cdot (m \cdot n) = (3 \cdot m) \cdot n$	The manner in which three numbers are grouped under multiplication does not affect the product.

Table 3-3   Distributive Property of Multiplication over Addition

Property	In Symbols/Examples	Comments/Notes
Distributive property of multiplication over addition*	$a \cdot (b + c) = a \cdot b + a \cdot c$ ex: $-3(2 + x) = -3(2) + (-3)(x)$ $= -6 + (-3)x$ $= -6 - 3x$	The factor outside the parentheses is multiplied by each term in the sum.

*Note that the distributive property of multiplication over addition is sometimes referred to as the *distributive property*.

Example 2 demonstrates the use of the commutative properties.

Skill Practice

Apply the commutative property of addition or multiplication to rewrite the expression.
5. $x + 3$ **6.** $z(2)$
7. $-12 + p$ **8.** ab

Example 2 **Applying the Commutative Properties**

Apply the commutative property of addition or multiplication to rewrite the expression.

a. $6 + p$ **b.** $-5 + n$ **c.** $y(7)$ **d.** xy

Solution:

a. $6 + p = p + 6$ Commutative property of addition

b. $-5 + n = n + (-5)$ or $n - 5$ Commutative property of addition

c. $y(7) = 7y$ Commutative property of multiplication

d. $xy = yx$ Commutative property of multiplication

Recall from Section 1.3 that subtraction is not a commutative operation. However, if we rewrite the difference of two numbers $a - b$ as $a + (-b)$, then we can apply the commutative property of addition. For example:

$$x - 9 = x + (-9) \qquad \text{Rewrite as addition of the opposite.}$$
$$= -9 + x \qquad \text{Apply the commutative property of addition.}$$

Example 3 demonstrates the associative properties of addition and multiplication.

Skill Practice

Use the associative property of addition or multiplication to rewrite the expression. Then simplify the expression.
9. $6 + (14 + x)$
10. $2(8w)$

Example 3 **Applying the Associative Properties**

Use the associative property of addition or multiplication to rewrite each expression. Then simplify the expression.

a. $12 + (45 + y)$ **b.** $5(7w)$

Solution:

a. $12 + (45 + y) = (12 + 45) + y$ Apply the associative property of addition.
$$= 57 + y \qquad \text{Simplify.}$$

b. $5(7w) = (5 \cdot 7)w$ Apply the associative property of multiplication.

$$= 35w \qquad \text{Simplify.}$$

Note that in most cases, a detailed application of the associative properties will not be given. Instead the process will be written in one step, such as:

$$12 + (45 + y) = 57 + y, \qquad 5(7w) = 35w$$

Example 4 demonstrates the use of the distributive property.

Answers
5. $3 + x$ **6.** $2z$
7. $p + (-12)$ or $p - 12$ **8.** ba
9. $(6 + 14) + x$; $20 + x$
10. $(2 \cdot 8)w$; $16w$

Example 4 **Applying the Distributive Property**

Apply the distributive property.

a. $3(x + 4)$ **b.** $2(3y - 5z + 1)$

Solution:

a. $3(x + 4) = 3(x) + 3(4)$ Apply the distributive property.

$\qquad\quad = 3x + 12$ Simplify.

b. $2(3y - 5z + 1) = 2[3y + (-5z) + 1]$ First write the subtraction as addition of the opposite.

$\qquad\quad = 2[3y + (-5z) + 1]$ Apply the distributive property.

$\qquad\quad = 2(3y) + 2(-5z) + 2(1)$

$\qquad\quad = 6y + (-10z) + 2$ Simplify.

$\qquad\quad = 6y - 10z + 2$

TIP: In Example 4(b), we rewrote the expression by writing the subtraction as addition of the opposite. Often this step is not shown and fewer steps are shown overall. For example:

$$2(3y - 5z + 1) = 2(3y) + 2(-5z) + 2(1)$$
$$= 6y - 10z + 2$$

Skill Practice
Apply the distributive property.
11. $4(2 + m)$
12. $6(5p - 3q + 1)$

Avoiding Mistakes
Note that $6y - 10z + 2$ cannot be simplified further because $6y$, $-10z$, and 2 are not *like* terms.

Example 5 **Applying the Distributive Property**

Apply the distributive property.

a. $-8(2 - 5y)$ **b.** $-(-4a + b + 3c)$

Solution:

a. $-8(2 - 5y)$

$\quad = -8[2 + (-5y)]$ Write the subtraction as addition of the opposite.

$\quad = -8[2 + (-5y)]$ Apply the distributive property.

$\quad = -8(2) + (-8)(-5y)$

$\quad = -16 + 40y$ Simplify.

b. $-(-4a + b + 3c)$ The negative sign preceding the parentheses indicates that we take the opposite of the expression within parentheses. This is equivalent to multiplying the expression within parentheses by -1.

$\quad = -1 \cdot (-4a + b + 3c)$

$\quad = -1(-4a) + (-1)(b) + (-1)(3c)$ Apply the distributive property.

$\quad = 4a - b - 3c$ Simplify.

Skill Practice
Apply the distributive property.
13. $-4(6 - 10x)$
14. $-(2x - 3y + 4z)$

TIP: Notice that a negative factor outside the parentheses changes the signs of all terms to which it is multiplied.

$$-1 \cdot (-4a + b + 3c)$$
$$= +4a - b - 3c$$

Answers
11. $8 + 4m$ **12.** $30p - 18q + 6$
13. $-24 + 40x$ **14.** $-2x + 3y - 4z$

3. Combining *Like* Terms

Two terms may be combined if they are *like* terms. To add or subtract *like* terms, we use the distributive property as shown in Example 6.

— **Skill Practice** —

Add or subtract as indicated.
15. $-4w + 11w$
16. $6a^3b^2 - 11a^3b^2$
17. $z - 4z + 22z$

Example 6 **Using the Distributive Property to Add and Subtract *Like* Terms**

Add or subtract as indicated.

a. $8y + 6y$ **b.** $7x^2y - 10x^2y$ **c.** $-15w + 4w - w$

Solution:

a. $8y + 6y = (8 + 6)y$ Apply the distributive property.

$\qquad = 14y$ Simplify.

b. $7x^2y - 10x^2y = (7 - 10)x^2y$ Apply the distributive property.

$\qquad = -3x^2y$ Simplify.

c. $-15w + 4w - w = -15w + 4w - 1w$ First note that $w = 1w$.

$\qquad = (-15 + 4 - 1)w$ Apply the distributive property.

$\qquad = (-12)w$ Simplify within parentheses.

$\qquad = -12w$

Although the distributive property is used to add and subtract *like* terms, it is tedious to write each step. Observe that adding or subtracting *like* terms is a matter of adding or subtracting the coefficients and leaving the variable factors unchanged. This can be shown in one step.

$$8y + 6y = 14y \qquad \text{and} \qquad -15w + 4w - 1w = -12w$$

This shortcut will be used throughout the text.

— **Skill Practice** —

Simplify.
18. $4a - 10b - a + 16b + 9$

Example 7 **Adding and Subtracting *Like* Terms**

Simplify by combining *like* terms. $-3x + 8y + 4x - 19 - 10y$

Solution:

$-3x + 8y + 4x - 19 - 10y$

$= -3x + 4x + 8y - 10y - 19$ Arrange *like* terms together.

$= 1x - 2y - 19$ Combine *like* terms.

$= x - 2y - 19$ Note that $1x = x$. Also note that the remaining terms cannot be combined further because they are not *like*. The variable factors are different.

TIP: The commutative and associative properties enable us to arrange *like* terms together.

Answers

15. $7w$ **16.** $-5a^3b^2$
17. $19z$ **18.** $3a + 6b + 9$

4. Simplifying Expressions

For expressions containing parentheses, it is necessary to apply the distributive property before combining *like* terms. This is demonstrated in Examples 8 and 9. Notice that when we apply the distributive property, the parentheses are dropped. This is often called *clearing parentheses*.

Example 8 **Clearing Parentheses and Combining *Like* Terms**

Simplify by clearing parentheses and combining *like* terms. $6 - 3(2y + 9)$

Solution:

$6 - 3(2y + 9)$ The order of operations indicates that we must perform multiplication before subtraction.

It is also important to understand that a factor of -3 (not 3) will be multiplied to all terms within the parentheses. To see why, we can rewrite the subtraction in terms of addition of the opposite.

$6 - 3(2y + 9) = 6 + (-3)(2y + 9)$ Rewrite subtraction as addition of the opposite.

$\quad\quad\quad = 6 + (-3)(2y) + (-3)(9)$ Apply the distributive property.

$\quad\quad\quad = 6 + (-6y) + (-27)$ Simplify.

$\quad\quad\quad = -6y + 6 + (-27)$ Arrange *like* terms together.

$\quad\quad\quad = -6y + (-21)$ or $-6y - 21$ Combine *like* terms.

Skill Practice

Simplify.
19. $8 - 6(w + 4)$

Avoiding Mistakes

Multiplication is performed before subtraction. It is incorrect to subtract $6 - 3$ first.

Example 9 **Clearing Parentheses and Combining *Like* Terms**

Simplify by clearing parentheses and combining *like* terms.

$$-8(x - 4) - 5(x + 7)$$

Solution:

$-8(x - 4) - 5(x + 7)$

$= -8[x + (-4)] + (-5)(x + 7)$ Rewrite subtraction as addition of the opposite.

$= -8[x + (-4)] + (-5)(x + 7)$ Apply the distributive property.

$= -8(x) + (-8)(-4) + (-5)(x) + (-5)(7)$

$= -8x + 32 - 5x - 35$ Simplify.

$= -8x - 5x + 32 - 35$ Arrange *like* terms together.

$= -13x - 3$ Combine *like* terms.

Skill Practice

Simplify.
20. $-5(10 - m) - 2(m + 1)$

Answers
19. $-6w - 16$ **20.** $3m - 52$

Section 3.1   Practice Exercises

Boost your GRADE at ALEKS.com!

ALEKS
version 3.0

- Practice Problems
- Self-Tests
- NetTutor
- e-Professors
- Videos

Study Skills Exercises

1. After you get a test back, it is a good idea to correct the test so that you do not make the same errors again. One recommended approach is to use a clean sheet of paper and divide the paper down the middle vertically, as shown. For each problem that you missed on the test, rework the problem correctly on the left-hand side of the paper. Then write a written explanation on the right-hand side of the paper. Take the time this week to make corrections from your last test.

Perform the correct math here.	Explain the process here.
↓	↓
$2 + 4(5)$ $= 2 + 20$ $= 22$	Do multiplication before addition.

2. Define the key terms.

   a. **Coefficient**   b. **Constant term**   c. *Like* **terms**

   d. **Term**   e. **Variable term**

Review Exercises

For Exercises 3–8, simplify.

3. $-4 - 2(9 - 3)$

4. $6 - 4^2 \div (-2)$

5. $|-9 + 3|$

6. $|-9| + |3|$

7. -12^2

8. $(-12)^2$

Objective 1: Identifying *Like* Terms

For Exercises 9–12, for each expression, list the terms and identify each term as a variable term or a constant term. **(See Example 1.)**

9. $2a + 5b^2 + 6$

10. $-5x - 4 + 7y$

11. $8 + 9a$

12. $12 - 8k$

For Exercises 13–16, identify the coefficients for each term. **(See Example 1.)**

13. $6p - 4q$

14. $-5a^3 - 2a$

15. $-h - 12$

16. $8x - 9$

For Exercises 17–24, determine if the two terms are *like* terms or unlike terms. If they are unlike terms, explain why. **(See Example 1.)**

17. $3a, -2a$

18. $8b, 12b$

19. $4xy, 4y$

20. $-9hk, -9h$

21. $14y^2, 14y$

22. $25x, 25x^2$

23. $17, 17y$

24. $-22t, -22$

Objective 2: Commutative, Associative, and Distributive Properties

For Exercises 25–32, apply the commutative property of addition or multiplication to rewrite each expression. **(See Example 2.)**

25. $5 + w$

26. $t + 2$

27. $r(2)$

28. $a(-4)$

29. $t(-s)$

30. $d(-c)$

31. $-p + 7$

32. $-q + 8$

For Exercises 33–40, apply the associative property of addition or multiplication to rewrite each expression. Then simplify the expression. **(See Example 3.)**

33. $3 + (8 + t)$

34. $7 + (5 + p)$

35. $-2(6b)$

36. $-3(2c)$

37. $3(6x)$

38. $9(5k)$

39. $-9 + (-12 + h)$

40. $-11 + (-4 + s)$

For Exercises 41–52, apply the distributive property. **(See Examples 4–5.)**

41. $4(x + 8)$

42. $5(3 + w)$

43. $4(a + 4b - c)$

44. $2(3q - r + s)$

45. $-2(p + 4)$

46. $-6(k + 2)$

47. $-(3x + 9 - 5y)$

48. $-(a - 8b + 4c)$

49. $-4(3 - n^2)$

50. $-2(13 - t^2)$

51. $-3(-5q - 2s - 3t)$

52. $-2(-10p - 12q + 3)$

For Exercises 53–60, apply the appropriate property to simplify the expression.

53. $6(2x)$

54. $-3(12k)$

55. $6(2 + x)$

56. $-3(12 + k)$

57. $-8 + (4 - p)$

58. $3 + (25 - m)$

59. $-8(4 - p)$

60. $-3(25 - m)$

Objective 3: Combining *Like* Terms

For Exercises 61–72, combine the *like* terms. **(See Examples 6–7.)**

61. $6r + 8r$

62. $4x + 21x$

63. $-4h + 12h - h$

64. $9p - 13p + p$

65. $4a^2b - 6a^2b$

66. $13xy^2 + 8xy^2$

67. $10x - 12y - 4x - 3y + 9$

68. $14a - 5b + 3a - b - 3$

69. $-8 - 6k - 9k + 12k + 4$

70. $-5 - 11p + 23p - p + 4$

71. $-8uv + 6u + 12uv$

72. $9pq - 9p + 13pq$

Objective 4: Simplifying Expressions

For Exercises 73–94, clear parentheses and combine *like* terms. **(See Examples 8–9.)**

73. $5(t - 6) + 2$

74. $7(a - 4) + 8$

75. $-3(2x + 1) - 13$

76. $-2(4b + 3) - 10$

77. $4 + 6(y - 3)$

78. $11 + 2(p - 8)$

79. $21 - 7(3 - q)$

80. $10 - 5(2 - 5m)$

81. $-3 - (2n + 1)$

82. $-13 - (6s + 5)$

83. $10(x + 5) - 3(2x + 9)$

84. $6(y - 9) - 5(2y - 5)$

85. $-(12z + 1) + 2(7z - 5)$

86. $-(8w + 5) + 3(w - 15)$

87. $3(w + 3) - (4w + y) - 3y$

88. $2(s + 6) - (8s - t) + 6t$

89. $20a - 4(b + 3a) - 5b$

90. $16p - 3(2p - q) + 7q$

91. $6 - (3m - n) - 2(m + 8) + 5n$

92. $12 - (5u + v) - 4(u - 6) + 2v$

93. $15 + 2(w - 4) - (2w - 5z^2) + 7z^2$

94. $7 + 3(2a - 5) - (6a - 8b^2) - 2b^2$

Mixed Exercises

95. Demonstrate the commutative property of addition by evaluating the expressions for $x = -3$ and $y = 9$.

    a. $x + y$　　　　　**b.** $y + x$

96. Demonstrate the commutative property of addition by evaluating the expressions for $m = -12$ and $n = -5$.

    a. $m + n$　　　　　**b.** $n + m$

97. Demonstrate the associative property of addition by evaluating the expressions for $x = -7$, $y = 2$, and $z = 10$.

    a. $(x + y) + z$　　　　**b.** $x + (y + z)$

98. Demonstrate the associative property of addition by evaluating the expressions for $a = -4$, $b = -6$, and $c = 18$.

    a. $(a + b) + c$　　　　**b.** $a + (b + c)$

99. Demonstrate the commutative property of multiplication by evaluating the expressions for $x = -9$ and $y = 5$.

    a. $x \cdot y$　　　　　**b.** $y \cdot x$

100. Demonstrate the commutative property of multiplication by evaluating the expressions for $c = 12$ and $d = -4$.

    a. $c \cdot d$　　　　　**b.** $d \cdot c$

101. Demonstrate the associative property of multiplication by evaluating the expressions for $x = -2$, $y = 6$, and $z = -3$.

    a. $(x \cdot y) \cdot z$　　　　**b.** $x \cdot (y \cdot z)$

102. Demonstrate the associative property of multiplication by evaluating the expressions for $b = -4$, $c = 2$, and $d = -5$.

    a. $(b \cdot c) \cdot d$　　　　**b.** $b \cdot (c \cdot d)$

Section 3.2　Addition and Subtraction Properties of Equality

Objectives

1. Definition of a Linear Equation in One Variable
2. Addition and Subtraction Properties of Equality

1. Definition of a Linear Equation in One Variable

An **equation** is a statement that indicates that two quantities are equal. The following are equations.

$$x = 7 \qquad z + 3 = 8 \qquad -6p = 18$$

All equations have an equal sign. Furthermore, notice that the equal sign separates the equation into two parts, the left-hand side and the right-hand side. A **solution to an equation** is a value of the variable that makes the equation a true statement. Substituting a solution to an equation for the variable makes the right-hand side equal to the left-hand side.

Equation	**Solution**	**Check**	
$x = 7$	7	$x = 7$ $\downarrow$ $7 \stackrel{?}{=} 7 \checkmark$	Substitute 7 for x. The right-hand side equals the left-hand side.
$z + 3 = 8$	5	$z + 3 = 8$ $\downarrow$ $5 + 3 \stackrel{?}{=} 8$ $8 \stackrel{?}{=} 8 \checkmark$	Substitute 5 for z. The right-hand side equals the left-hand side.
$-6p = 18$	-3	$-6p = 18$ $\downarrow$ $-6(-3) \stackrel{?}{=} 18$ $18 \stackrel{?}{=} 18 \checkmark$	Substitute -3 for p. The right-hand side equals the left-hand side.

Avoiding Mistakes

It is important to distinguish between an equation and an expression. An equation has an equal sign, whereas an expression does not. For example:

$$2x + 4 = 16 \qquad \text{equation}$$
$$7x - 9 \qquad \text{expression}$$

Example 1 **Determining Whether a Number Is a Solution to an Equation**

Determine whether the given number is a solution to the equation.

a. $2x - 9 = 3; \quad 6$ **b.** $20 = 8p - 4; \quad -2$

Solution:

a. $2x - 9 = 3$

$2(6) - 9 \overset{?}{=} 3$ Substitute 6 for x.

$12 - 9 \overset{?}{=} 3$ Simplify.

$3 \overset{?}{=} 3$ ✓   The right-hand side equals the left-hand side. Thus, 6 is a solution to the equation $2x - 9 = 3$.

b. $20 = 8p - 4$

$20 \overset{?}{=} 8(-2) - 4$ Substitute -2 for p.

$20 \overset{?}{=} -16 - 4$ Simplify.

$20 \neq -20$ The right-hand side does not equal the left-hand side. Thus, -2 is *not* a solution to the equation $20 = 8p - 4$.

In the study of algebra, you will encounter a variety of equations. In this chapter, we will focus on a specific type of equation called a linear equation in one variable.

DEFINITION **Linear Equation in One Variable**

Let a, b, and c be numbers such that $a \neq 0$. A **linear equation in one variable** is an equation that can be written in the form

$$ax + b = c$$

Note: A linear equation in one variable contains only one variable and the exponent on the variable is 1.

2. Addition and Subtraction Properties of Equality

Given the equation $x = 3$, we can easily determine that the solution is 3. The solution to the equation $2x + 14 = 20$ is also 3. These two equations are called **equivalent equations** because they have the same solution. However, while the solution to $x = 3$ is obvious, the solution to $2x + 14 = 20$ is not obvious. Our goal in this chapter is to learn how to *solve* equations.

To solve an equation we use algebraic principles to write an equation like $2x + 14 = 20$ in an equivalent but simpler form, such as $x = 3$. The addition and subtraction properties of equality are the first tools we will use to solve an equation.

> **PROPERTY** **Addition and Subtraction Properties of Equality**
> Let $a, b,$ and c represent algebraic expressions.
> 1. The **addition property of equality:**   If $a = b,$
>   then, $a + c = b + c$
> 2. The **subtraction property of equality:**   If $a = b,$
>   then, $a - c = b - c$

The addition and subtraction properties of equality indicate that adding or subtracting the same quantity to each side of an equation results in an equivalent equation. This is true because if two equal quantities are increased (or decreased) by the same amount, then the resulting quantities will also be equal (Figure 3-1).

Figure 3-1

Skill Practice

Solve the equation and check the solution.

5. $y - 4 = 12$
6. $-18 = w + 5$
7. $-9 + z = 2$

| **Example 2** | **Applying the Addition Property of Equality** |

Solve the equations and check the solutions.

a. $x - 6 = 18$ **b.** $-12 = x - 7$ **c.** $-4 + y = 5$

Solution:

To solve an equation, the goal is to isolate the variable on one side of the equation. That is, we want to create an equivalent equation of the form $x = number$. To accomplish this, we can use the fact that the sum of a number and its opposite is zero.

a. $x - 6 = 18$

$x - 6 + 6 = 18 + 6$ To isolate x, add 6 to both sides, because $-6 + 6 = 0$.

$x + 0 = 24$ Simplify.

$x = 24$ The variable is isolated (by itself) on the left-hand side of the equation. The solution is 24.

Check: $x - 6 = 18$ Original equation

$(24) - 6 \overset{?}{=} 18$ Substitute 24 for x.

$18 \overset{?}{=} 18$ ✓   True

b. $-12 = x - 7$

$-12 + 7 = x - 7 + 7$ To isolate x, add 7 to both sides, because $-7 + 7 = 0$.

$-5 = x + 0$ Simplify.

$-5 = x$ The variable is isolated on the right-hand side of the equation. The solution is -5.

The equation $-5 = x$ is equivalent to $x = -5$.

TIP: Notice that the variable may be isolated on *either* side of the equal sign. In Example 2(a), the variable appears on the left. In Example 2(b), the variable appears on the right.

Answers

5. 16   **6.** -23 **7.** 11

Check: $-12 = x - 7$ — Original equation

$-12 \overset{?}{=} (-5) - 7$ — Substitute -5 for x.

$-12 \overset{?}{=} -12$ ✓ — True

c. $-4 + y = 5$

$-4 + 4 + y = 5 + 4$ — To isolate y, add 4 to both sides, because $-4 + 4 = 0$.

$0 + y = 9$ — Simplify.

$y = 9$ — The solution is 9.

Check: $-4 + y = 5$ — Original equation

$-4 + (9) \overset{?}{=} 5$ — Substitute 9 for y.

$5 \overset{?}{=} 5$ ✓ — True

In Example 3, we apply the subtraction property of equality. This indicates that we can subtract the same quantity from both sides of the equation to obtain an equivalent equation.

Example 3 **Applying the Subtraction Property of Equality**

Solve the equations and check.

a. $z + 11 = 14$ **b.** $-8 = 2 + q$

Skill Practice

Solve the equation and check the solution.
8. $m + 8 = 21$
9. $-16 = 1 + z$

Solution:

a. $z + 11 = 14$

$z + 11 - 11 = 14 - 11$ — To isolate z, subtract 11 from both sides, because $11 - 11 = 0$.

$z + 0 = 3$ — Simplify.

$z = 3$ — The solution is 3.

Check: $z + 11 = 14$ — Original equation

$(3) + 11 \overset{?}{=} 14$ — Substitute 3 for z.

$14 \overset{?}{=} 14$ ✓ — True

b. $-8 = 2 + q$

$-8 - 2 = 2 - 2 + q$ — To isolate q, subtract 2 from both sides, because $2 - 2 = 0$.

$-10 = 0 + q$ — Simplify.

$-10 = q$ — The solution is -10.

Check: $-8 = 2 + q$ — Original equation

$-8 \overset{?}{=} 2 + (-10)$ — Substitute -10 for q.

$-8 \overset{?}{=} -8$ ✓ — True

Answers
8. 13 **9.** -17

The equations in Example 4 require that we simplify the expressions on both sides of the equation, then apply the addition or subtraction property as needed. As you read through each example, remember that you want to isolate the variable.

Skill Practice

Solve the equations.

10. $15 + 6y - 5y = 4 - 9$

11. $-1 = 3(x + 4) - 2x$

Example 4 **Applying the Addition and Subtraction Properties of Equality**

Solve the equations.

a. $-8 + 3x - 2x = 12 - 9$ **b.** $-5 = 2(y + 1) - y$

Solution:

a. $-8 + 3x - 2x = 12 - 9$

$$-8 + x = 3 \qquad \text{Combine like terms.}$$

$$-8 + 8 + x = 3 + 8 \qquad \text{To isolate } x, \text{ add 8 to both sides, because } -8 + 8 = 0.$$

$$x = 11 \qquad \text{The solution is 11.}$$

$$\underline{\text{Check:}} \qquad -8 + 3x - 2x = 12 - 9$$

$$-8 + 3(11) - 2(11) \stackrel{?}{=} 12 - 9$$

$$-8 + 33 - 22 \stackrel{?}{=} 3$$

$$25 - 22 \stackrel{?}{=} 3$$

$$3 \stackrel{?}{=} 3 \checkmark \quad \text{True}$$

b. $-5 = 2(y + 1) - y$

$$-5 = 2y + 2 - y \qquad \text{Apply the distributive property to clear parentheses.}$$

$$-5 = y + 2 \qquad \text{Combine like terms.}$$

$$-5 - 2 = y + 2 - 2 \qquad \text{To isolate } y, \text{ subtract 2 from both sides, because } 2 - 2 = 0.$$

$$-7 = y \qquad \text{The solution is } -7.$$

$$\underline{\text{Check:}} \quad -5 = 2(y + 1) - y$$

$$-5 \stackrel{?}{=} 2(-7 + 1) - (-7)$$

$$-5 \stackrel{?}{=} 2(-6) + 7$$

$$-5 \stackrel{?}{=} -12 + 7$$

$$-5 \stackrel{?}{=} -5 \checkmark \quad \text{True}$$

Answers

10. -20 **11.** -13

Section 3.2   Practice Exercises

Study Skills Exercises

1. Does your school have a learning resource center or a tutoring center? If so, do you remember the location and hours of operation? Write them here.

Location of learning resource center or tutoring center: _____

Hours of operation: _____

2. Define the key terms.

    a. Addition property of equality   **b. Equation**

    c. Equivalent equations   **d. Linear equation in one variable**

    e. Solution to an equation   **f. Subtraction property of equality**

Review Exercises

For Exercises 3–8, simplify the expression.

    3. $-10a + 3b - 3a + 13b$ **4.** $4 - 23y^2 + 11 - 16y^2$ **5.** $-(-8h + 2k - 13)$

    6. $3(-4m + 3) - 12$ **7.** $5z - 8(z - 3) - 20$ **8.** $-(7p - 12) - 10(1 - p) + 6$

Objective 1: Definition of a Linear Equation in One Variable

For Exercises 9–16, determine whether the given number is a solution to the equation. **(See Example 1.)**

    9. $5x + 3 = -2$; -1 **10.** $3y - 2 = 4$; 2 **11.** $-z + 8 = 20$; 12

    12. $-7 - w = -10$; -3 **13.** $13 = 13 + 6t$; 0 **14.** $25 = 25 - 2x$; 0

    15. $15 = -2q + 9$; 3 **16.** $39 = -7p + 4$; 5

For Exercises 17–22, identify as an expression or an equation.

    17. $8x - 9 = 7$ **18.** $24 - 5x = 12 + x$ **19.** $8x - 9 - 7$

    20. $24 - 5x + 12 + x$ **21.** $2(x - 4) - x = 1$ **22.** $2(x - 4) - x + 1$

Objective 2: Addition and Subtraction Properties of Equality

For Exercises 23–28, fill in the blank with the appropriate number.

    23. $13 + (-13) = $ _____   **24.** $6 + $ _____ $= 0$ **25.** _____ $+ (-7) = 0$

    26. $1 + (-1) = $ _____   **27.** $0 = -3 + $ _____   **28.** $0 = 9 + $ _____

For Exercises 29–40, solve the equation using the addition property of equality. **(See Example 2.)**

29. $x - 23 = 14$ **30.** $y - 12 = 30$ **31.** $-4 + k = 12$

32. $-16 + m = 4$ **33.** $-18 = n - 3$ **34.** $-9 = t - 6$

35. $9 = -7 + t$ **36.** $-6 = -10 + z$ **37.** $k - 44 = -122$

38. $a - 465 = -206$ **39.** $13 = -21 + w$ **40.** $2 = -17 + p$

For Exercises 41–46, fill in the blank with the appropriate number.

41. $52 - \underline{\hspace{1cm}} = 0$ **42.** $2 - 2 = \underline{\hspace{1cm}}$ **43.** $18 - 18 = \underline{\hspace{1cm}}$

44. $\underline{\hspace{1cm}} - 15 = 0$ **45.** $\underline{\hspace{1cm}} - 100 = 0$ **46.** $21 - \underline{\hspace{1cm}} = 0$

For Exercises 47–58, solve the equation using the subtraction property of equality. **(See Example 3.)**

47. $x + 34 = 6$ **48.** $y + 12 = 4$ **49.** $17 + b = 20$

50. $5 + c = 14$ **51.** $-32 = t + 14$ **52.** $-23 = k + 11$

53. $82 = 21 + m$ **54.** $16 = 88 + n$ **55.** $z + 145 = 90$

56. $c + 80 = -15$ **57.** $52 = 10 + k$ **58.** $43 = 12 + p$

Mixed Exercises

For Exercises 59–78, solve the equation using the appropriate property. **(See Example 4.)**

59. $1 + p = 0$ **60.** $r - 12 = 13$ **61.** $-34 + t = -40$

62. $7 + q = 4$ **63.** $-11 = w - 23$ **64.** $-9 = p - 10$

65. $16 = x + 21$ **66.** $-4 = y + 18$ **67.** $5h - 4h + 4 = 3$

68. $10x - 9x - 11 = 15$ **69.** $-9 - 4x + 5x = 3 - 1$ **70.** $11 - 7x + 8x = -4 - 2$

71. $3(x + 2) - 2x = 5$ **72.** $4(x - 1) - 3x = 2$ **73.** $3(r - 2) - 2r = -2 + 6$

74. $4(k + 2) - 3k = -6 + 9$ **75.** $9 + (-2) = 4 + t$ **76.** $-13 + 15 = p + 5$

77. $-2 = 2(a - 15) - a$ **78.** $-1 = 6(t - 4) - 5t$

Multiplication and Division Properties of Equality

1. Multiplication and Division Properties of Equality

Adding or subtracting the same quantity on both sides of an equation results in an equivalent equation. The same is true when we multiply or divide both sides of an equation by the same nonzero quantity.

> **PROPERTY   Multiplication and Division Properties of Equality**
>
> Let a, b, and c represent algebraic expressions, $c \neq 0$.
>
> **1.** The **multiplication property of equality:**   If $a = b$,
> then, $a \cdot c = b \cdot c$
>
> **2.** The **division property of equality:**   If $a = b$
> then, $\dfrac{a}{c} = \dfrac{b}{c}$

Objectives

1. Multiplication and Division Properties of Equality
2. Comparing the Properties of Equality

To understand the multiplication property of equality, suppose we start with a true equation such as $10 = 10$. If both sides of the equation are multiplied by a constant such as 3, the result is also a true statement (Figure 3-2).

$$10 = 10$$
$$3 \cdot 10 = 3 \cdot 10$$
$$30 = 30$$

Figure 3-2

To solve an equation in the variable x, the goal is to write the equation in the form $x =$ number. In particular, notice that we want the coefficient of x to be 1. That is, we want to write the equation as $1 \cdot x =$ number. Therefore, to solve an equation such as $3x = 12$, we can *divide* both sides of the equation by the 3. We do this because $\frac{3}{3} = 1$, and that leaves $1x$ on the left-hand side of the equation.

$$3x = 12$$

$$\frac{3x}{3} = \frac{12}{3} \qquad \text{Divide both sides by 3.}$$

$$1 \cdot x = 4 \qquad \text{The coefficient of the } x \text{ term is now 1.}$$

$$x = 4 \qquad \text{Simplify.}$$

> **TIP:** Recall that the quotient of a nonzero real number and itself is 1. For example:
>
> $$\frac{3}{3} = 1 \quad \text{and} \quad \frac{-5}{-5} = 1$$

Example 1 **Applying the Division Property of Equality**

Solve the equations.

a. $10x = 50$ **b.** $28 = -4p$ **c.** $-y = 34$

Solution:

a. $10x = 50$

$\dfrac{10x}{10} = \dfrac{50}{10}$ To obtain a coefficient of 1 for the x term, divide both sides by 10, because $\frac{10}{10} = 1$.

$1x = 5$ Simplify.

$x = 5$ The solution is 5.

Check: $10x = 50$ Original equation

$10(5) \stackrel{?}{=} 50$ Substitute 5 for x.

$50 \stackrel{?}{=} 50$ ✓ True

b. $28 = -4p$

$\dfrac{28}{-4} = \dfrac{-4p}{-4}$ To obtain a coefficient of 1 for the p term, divide both sides by -4, because $\frac{-4}{-4} = 1$.

$-7 = 1p$ Simplify.

$-7 = p$ The solution is -7 and checks in the original equation.

c. $-y = 34$

$-1y = 34$ Note that $-y$ is the same as $-1 \cdot y$. To isolate y, we need a coefficient of *positive* 1.

$\dfrac{-1y}{-1} = \dfrac{34}{-1}$ To obtain a coefficient of 1 for the y term, divide both sides by -1.

$1y = -34$ Simplify.

$y = -34$ The solution is -34 and checks in the original equation.

The multiplication property of equality indicates that multiplying both sides of an equation by the same nonzero quantity results in an equivalent equation. For example, consider the equation $\frac{x}{2} = 6$. The variable x is being divided by 2. To solve for x, we need to reverse this process. Therefore, we will *multiply* by 2.

$\dfrac{x}{2} = 6$

$2 \cdot \dfrac{x}{2} = 2 \cdot 6$ Multiply both sides by 2.

$\dfrac{2}{2} \cdot x = 12$ The expression $2 \cdot \frac{x}{2}$ can be written as $\frac{2}{2} \cdot x$. This process is called *regrouping factors*.

$1 \cdot x = 12$ The x coefficient is 1, because $\frac{2}{2}$ equals 1.

$x = 12$ The solution is 12.

| Example 2 | **Applying the Multiplication Property of Equality** |

Solve the equations.

a. $\dfrac{x}{4} = -5$ **b.** $2 = \dfrac{t}{-8}$

Solution:

a. $\dfrac{x}{4} = -5$

$4 \cdot \dfrac{x}{4} = 4 \cdot (-5)$ To isolate x, multiply both sides by 4.

$\dfrac{4}{4} \cdot x = -20$ Regroup factors.

$1x = -20$ The x coefficient is now 1, because $\frac{4}{4}$ equals 1.

$x = -20$ The solution is -20.   Check: $\dfrac{x}{4} = -5$

$\dfrac{(-20)}{4} \stackrel{?}{=} -5$

$-5 \stackrel{?}{=} -5$ ✓ True

b. $2 = \dfrac{t}{-8}$

$-8 \cdot (2) = -8 \cdot \dfrac{t}{-8}$ To isolate t, multiply both sides by -8.

$-16 = \dfrac{-8}{-8} \cdot t$ Regroup factors.

$-16 = 1 \cdot t$ The coefficient on t is now 1.

$-16 = t$ The solution is -16 and checks in the original equation.

2. Comparing the Properties of Equality

It is important to determine which property of equality should be used to solve an equation. For example, compare equations:

$$4 + x = 12 \quad \text{and} \quad 4x = 12$$

In the first equation, the operation between 4 and x is addition. Therefore, we want to reverse the process by *subtracting* 4 from both sides. In the second equation, the operation between 4 and x is multiplication. To isolate x, we reverse the process by *dividing* by 4.

$$4 + x = 12 \qquad\qquad 4x = 12$$
$$4 - 4 + x = 12 - 4 \qquad \dfrac{4x}{4} = \dfrac{12}{4}$$
$$x = 8 \qquad\qquad x = 3$$

In Example 3, we practice distinguishing which property of equality to use.

Answers
4. -18 **5.** -50

Skill Practice

Solve the equations.

6. $\dfrac{t}{5} = -8$

7. $x + 46 = 12$

8. $10 = 5p - 7p$

9. $-5 + 20 =$
$\qquad -3 + 6w - 5(w + 1)$

Example 3 **Solving Linear Equations**

Solve the equations.

a. $\dfrac{m}{12} = -3$ **b.** $x + 18 = 2$

c. $20 + 8 = -10t + 3t$ **d.** $-4 + 10 = 4t - 3(t + 2) - 1$

Solution:

a. $\dfrac{m}{12} = -3$ — The operation between m and 12 is division. To obtain a coefficient of 1 for the m term, *multiply* both sides by 12.

$12 \cdot \dfrac{m}{12} = 12(-3)$ — Multiply both sides by 12.

$\dfrac{12}{12} \cdot m = 12(-3)$ — Regroup.

$m = -36$ — Simplify both sides. The solution -36 checks in the original equation.

b. $x + 18 = 2$ — The operation between x and 18 is addition. To isolate x, *subtract* 18 from both sides.

$x + 18 - 18 = 2 - 18$ — Subtract 18 on both sides.

$x = -16$ — Simplify. The solution is -16 and checks in the original equation.

c. $20 + 8 = -10t + 3t$ — Begin by simplifying both sides of the equation.

$28 = -7t$ — The relationship between t and -7 is multiplication. To obtain a coefficient of 1 on the t-term, we *divide* both sides by -7.

$\dfrac{28}{-7} = \dfrac{-7t}{-7}$ — Divide both sides by -7.

$-4 = t$ — Simplify. The solution is -4 and checks in the original equation.

d. $-4 + 10 = 4t - 3(t + 2) - 1$ — Begin by simplifying both sides of the equation.

$6 = 4t - 3t - 6 - 1$ — Apply the distributive property on the right-hand side.

$6 = t - 7$ — Combine *like* terms on the right-hand side.

$6 + 7 = -7 + 7 + t$ — To isolate the t term, *add* 7 to both sides. This is because $-7 + 7 = 0$.

$13 = t$ — The solution is 13 and checks in the original equation.

Answers

6. -40 **7.** -34

8. -5 **9.** 23

Section 3.3   Practice Exercises

Study Skills Exercises

1. One way to know that you really understand a concept is to explain it to someone else. In your own words, explain the circumstances in which you would apply the multiplication property of equality or the division property of equality.

2. Define the key terms.   **a. Division property of equality**   **b. Multiplication property of equality**

Review Exercises

For Exercises 3–6, simplify the expression.

3. $-3x + 5y + 9x - y$ **4.** $-4ab - 2b - 3ab + b$ **5.** $3(m - 2n) - (m + 4n)$ **6.** $2(5w - z) - (3w + 4z)$

For Exercises 7–10, solve the equation.

7. $p - 12 = 33$ **8.** $-8 = 10 + k$ **9.** $24 + z = -12$ **10.** $-4 + w = 22$

Objective 1: Multiplication and Division Properties of Equality

For Exercises 11–34, solve the equation using the multiplication or division properties of equality. **(See Examples 1–2.)**

11. $14b = 42$ **12.** $6p = 12$ **13.** $-8k = 56$ **14.** $-5y = 25$

15. $-16 = -8z$ **16.** $-120 = -10p$ **17.** $-t = -13$ **18.** $-h = -17$

19. $5 = -x$ **20.** $30 = -a$ **21.** $\dfrac{b}{7} = -3$ **22.** $\dfrac{a}{4} = -12$

23. $\dfrac{u}{-2} = -15$ **24.** $\dfrac{v}{-10} = -4$ **25.** $-4 = \dfrac{p}{7}$ **26.** $-9 = \dfrac{w}{6}$

27. $-28 = -7t$ **28.** $-33 = -3r$ **29.** $5m = 0$ **30.** $6q = 0$

31. $\dfrac{x}{7} = 0$ **32.** $\dfrac{t}{8} = 0$ **33.** $-6 = -z$ **34.** $-9 = -n$

Objective 2: Comparing the Properties of Equality

35. In your own words, explain how to determine when to use the addition property of equality.

36. In your own words, explain how to determine when to use the subtraction property of equality.

37. Explain how to determine when to use the division property of equality.

38. Explain how to determine when to use the multiplication property of equality.

Mixed Exercises

For Exercises 39–74, solve the equation. **(See Example 3.)**

39. $4 + x = -12$ **40.** $6 + z = -18$ **41.** $4y = -12$ **42.** $6p = -18$

43. $q - 4 = -12$ **44.** $p - 6 = -18$ **45.** $\dfrac{h}{4} = -12$ **46.** $\dfrac{w}{6} = -18$

47. $-18 = -9a$ **48.** $-40 = -8x$ **49.** $7 = r - 23$ **50.** $11 = s - 4$

51. $5 = \dfrac{y}{-3}$ **52.** $1 = \dfrac{h}{-5}$ **53.** $-52 = 5 + y$ **54.** $-47 = 12 + z$

55. $-4a = 0$ **56.** $-7b = 0$ **57.** $100 = 5k$ **58.** $95 = 19h$

59. $31 = -p$ **60.** $11 = -q$ **61.** $-3x + 7 + 4x = 12$ **62.** $6x + 7 - 5x = 10$

63. $5(x - 2) - 4x = 3$ **64.** $3(y - 6) - 2y = 8$

65. $3p + 4p = 25 - 4$ **66.** $2q + 3q = 54 - 9$

67. $-5 + 7 = 5x - 4(x - 1)$ **68.** $-3 + 11 = -2z + 3(z - 2)$

69. $-10 - 4 = 6m - 5(3 + m)$ **70.** $-15 - 5 = 9n - 8(2 + n)$

71. $5x - 2x = -15$ **72.** $13y - 10y = -18$

73. $-2(a + 3) - 6a + 6 = 8$ **74.** $-(b - 11) - 3b - 11 = -16$

Section 3.4   Solving Equations with Multiple Steps

Objectives

1. Solving Equations with Multiple Steps
2. General Procedure to Solve a Linear Equation

1. Solving Equations with Multiple Steps

In Sections 3.2 and 3.3 we studied a one-step process to solve linear equations. We used the addition, subtraction, multiplication, and division properties of equality. In this section, we combine these properties to solve equations that require multiple steps. This is shown in Example 1.

Skill Practice

Solve.

1. $3x + 7 = 25$

Example 1   **Solving a Linear Equation**

Solve. $2x - 3 = 15$

Solution:

Remember that our goal is to isolate x. Therefore, in this equation, we will first isolate the *term* containing x. This can be done by adding 3 to both sides.

$2x - 3 + 3 = 15 + 3$ Add 3 to both sides, because $-3 + 3 = 0$.

$2x = 18$ The term containing x is now isolated (by itself). The resulting equation now requires only one step to solve.

$\dfrac{2x}{2} = \dfrac{18}{2}$ Divide both sides by 2 to make the x coefficient equal to 1.

$x = 9$ Simplify. The solution is 9.

Check: $2x - 3 = 15$ Original equation

$2(9) - 3 \stackrel{?}{=} 15$ Substitute 9 for x.

$18 - 3 \stackrel{?}{=} 15 \checkmark$ True

Answer

1. 6

As Example 1 shows, we will generally apply the addition (or subtraction) property of equality to isolate the variable term first. Then we will apply the multiplication (or division) property of equality to obtain a coefficient of 1 on the variable term.

Example 2   Solving a Linear Equation

Solve. $22 = -3c + 10$

Solution:

We first isolate the term containing the variable by subtracting 10 from both sides.

$22 - 10 = -3c + 10 - 10$ Subtract 10 from both sides because $10 - 10 = 0$.

$12 = -3c$ The term containing c is now isolated.

$\dfrac{12}{-3} = \dfrac{-3c}{-3}$ Divide both sides by -3 to make the c coefficient equal to 1.

$-4 = c$ Simplify. The solution is -4.

> Check: $22 = -3c + 10$ Original equation
>
> $22 = -3(-4) + 10$ Substitute -4 for c.
>
> $22 = 12 + 10 \checkmark$ True

Skill Practice

Solve.

2. $-12 = -5t + 13$

Example 3   Solving a Linear Equation

Solve. $14 = \dfrac{y}{2} + 8$

Solution:

$14 = \dfrac{y}{2} + 8$

$14 - 8 = \dfrac{y}{2} + 8 - 8$ Subtract 8 from both sides. This will isolate the term containing the variable, y.

$6 = \dfrac{y}{2}$ Simplify.

$2 \cdot 6 = 2 \cdot \dfrac{y}{2}$ Multiply both sides by 2 to make the y coefficient equal to 1.

$12 = y$ Simplify. The solution is 12.

> Check: $14 = \dfrac{y}{2} + 8$
>
> $14 \stackrel{?}{=} \dfrac{(12)}{2} + 8$ Substitute 12 for y.
>
> $14 \stackrel{?}{=} 6 + 8 \checkmark$ True

Skill Practice

Solve.

3. $-3 = \dfrac{x}{3} + 9$

Answers

2. 5   **3.** -36

In Example 4, the variable x appears on both sides of the equation. In this case, apply the addition or subtraction properties of equality to collect the variable terms on one side of the equation and the constant terms on the other side.

Example 4   **Solving a Linear Equation with Variables on Both Sides**

Solve. $4x + 5 = -2x - 13$

Solution:

To isolate x, we must first "move" all x terms to one side of the equation. For example, suppose we add $2x$ to both sides. This would "remove" the x term from the right-hand side because $-2x + 2x = 0$. The term $2x$ is then combined with $4x$ on the left-hand side.

$$4x + 5 = -2x - 13$$

$$4x + 2x + 5 = -2x + 2x - 13 \qquad \text{Add } 2x \text{ to both sides.}$$

$$6x + 5 = -13 \qquad \text{Simplify. Next, we want to isolate the } \textit{term} \text{ containing } x.$$

$$6x + 5 - 5 = -13 - 5 \qquad \text{Subtract 5 from both sides to isolate the } x \text{ term.}$$

$$6x = -18 \qquad \text{Simplify.}$$

$$\frac{6x}{6} = \frac{-18}{6} \qquad \text{Divide both sides by 6 to obtain an } x \text{ coefficient of 1.}$$

$$x = -3 \qquad \text{The solution is } -3 \text{ and checks in the original equation.}$$

TIP: It should be noted that the variable may be isolated on either side of the equation. In Example 4 for instance, we could have isolated the x term on the right-hand side of the equation.

$$4x + 5 = -2x - 13$$

$$4x - 4x + 5 = -2x - 4x - 13 \qquad \text{Subtract } 4x \text{ from both sides. This "removes" the } x \text{ term from the left-hand side.}$$

$$5 = -6x - 13$$

$$5 + 13 = -6x - 13 + 13 \qquad \text{Add 13 to both sides to isolate the } x \text{ term.}$$

$$18 = -6x \qquad \text{Simplify.}$$

$$\frac{18}{-6} = \frac{-6x}{-6} \qquad \text{Divide both sides by } -6.$$

$$-3 = x \qquad \text{This is the same solution as in Example 4.}$$

2. General Procedure to Solve a Linear Equation

In Examples 1–4, we used multiple steps to solve equations. We also learned how to collect the variable terms on one side of the equation so that the variable could be isolated. The following procedure summarizes the steps to solve a linear equation.

> **PROCEDURE Solving a Linear Equation in One Variable**
> **Step 1** Simplify both sides of the equation.
> - Clear parentheses if necessary.
> - Combine *like* terms if necessary.
> **Step 2** Use the addition or subtraction property of equality to collect the variable terms on one side of the equation.
> **Step 3** Use the addition or subtraction property of equality to collect the constant terms on the *other* side of the equation.
> **Step 4** Use the multiplication or division property of equality to make the coefficient of the variable term equal to 1.
> **Step 5** Check the answer in the original equation.

Example 5 Solving a Linear Equation

Solve. $2(y + 10) = 8 - 4y$

Solution:

$2(y + 10) = 8 - 4y$

$2y + 20 = 8 - 4y$ **Step 1:** Simplify both sides of the equation. Clear parentheses.

$2y + 4y + 20 = 8 - 4y + 4y$ **Step 2:** Add $4y$ to both sides to collect the variable terms on the left.

$6y + 20 = 8$ Simplify.

$6y + 20 - 20 = 8 - 20$ **Step 3:** Subtract 20 from both sides to collect the constants on the right.

$6y = -12$ Simplify.

$\dfrac{6y}{6} = \dfrac{-12}{6}$ **Step 4:** Divide both sides by 6 to obtain a coefficient of 1 on the y term

$y = -2$ The solution is -2.

Check: $2(y + 10) = 8 - 4y$ **Step 5:** Check the solution in the original equation.

$2(-2 + 10) \overset{?}{=} 8 - 4(-2)$ Substitute -2 for y.

$2(8) \overset{?}{=} 8 - (-8)$

$16 \overset{?}{=} 16$ ✓ The solution checks.

Skill Practice
Solve.
5. $6(z + 4) = -16 - 4z$

Skill Practice

Solve.

6. $-3y - y - 4 = -5(y - 8)$

Example 6 **Solving a Linear Equation**

Solve. $2x + 3x + 2 = -4(3 - x)$

Solution:

$2x + 3x + 2 = -4(3 - x)$

$5x + 2 = -12 + 4x$ **Step 1:** Simplify both sides of the equation. On the left, combine *like* terms. On the right, clear parentheses.

$5x - 4x + 2 = -12 + 4x - 4x$ **Step 2:** Subtract $4x$ from both sides to collect the variable terms on the left.

$x + 2 = -12$ Simplify.

$x + 2 - 2 = -12 - 2$ **Step 3:** Subtract 2 from both sides to collect the constants on the right.

$x = -14$ **Step 4:** The x coefficient is already 1. The solution is -14.

Check: $2x + 3x + 2 = -4(3 - x)$ **Step 5:** Check in the original equation.

$2(-14) + 3(-14) + 2 \overset{?}{=} -4[3 - (-14)]$ Substitute -14 for x.

$-28 - 42 + 2 \overset{?}{=} -4(17)$

$-70 + 2 \overset{?}{=} -68$

$-68 \overset{?}{=} -68$ ✓   The solution checks.

Answer

6. 44

Section 3.4 Practice Exercises

Study Skills Exercise

1. A good way to determine what will be on a test is to look at both your notes and the exercises assigned by your instructor. List five types of problems that you think will be on the test for this chapter.

Review Exercises

For Exercises 2–10, solve the equation.

2. $4c = 12$

3. $\dfrac{t}{3} = -4$

4. $9 + (-11) = 4x - 3x + 5$

5. $-2x + 3x - 6 = -8 + 3$

6. $4 - 5(y + 3) + 6y = 7$

7. $-8 = 3 - 2(z - 4) + 3z$

8. $8 + h = 0$

9. $-8h = 0$

10. $9p - 6p = -8 + 11$

Objective 1: Solving Equations with Multiple Steps

For Exercises 11–26, solve the equation. **(See Examples 1–3.)**

11. $3m - 2 = 16$

12. $2n - 5 = 3$

13. $8c - 12 = 36$

14. $5t - 1 = -11$

15. $1 = -4z + 21$

16. $-4 = -3p + 14$

17. $9 = 12x - 15$

18. $7 = 5y - 8$

19. $\dfrac{b}{3} - 12 = -9$

20. $\dfrac{c}{5} + 2 = 4$

21. $-9 = \dfrac{w}{2} - 3$

22. $-16 = \dfrac{t}{4} - 14$

23. $\dfrac{m}{-3} + 40 = 60$

24. $\dfrac{c}{-4} - 3 = 5$

25. $-y - 7 = 14$

26. $-p + 8 = 20$

For Exercises 27–38, solve the equation. **(See Example 4.)**

27. $8 + 4b = 2 + 2b$

28. $2w + 10 = 5w - 5$

29. $7 - 5t = 3t - 9$

30. $4 - 2p = -3 + 5p$

31. $4 - 3d = 5d - 4$

32. $-3k + 14 = -4 + 3k$

33. $12p = 3p + 36$

34. $2x + 10 = 4x$

35. $4 + 2a - 7 = 3a + a + 3$

36. $4b + 2b - 7 = 2 + 4b + 5$

37. $-8w + 8 + 3w = 2 - 6w + 2$

38. $-12 + 5m + 10 = -2m - 10 - m$

Objective 2: General Procedure to Solve a Linear Equation

For Exercises 39–56, solve the equation. **(See Examples 5–6.)**

39. $5(z + 7) = 9 + 3z$

40. $6(w + 2) = 20 + 2w$

41. $2(1 - m) = 5 - 3m$

42. $3(2 - g) = 12 - g$

43. $3n - 4(n - 1) = 16$

44. $4p - 3(p + 2) = 18$

45. $4x + 2x - 9 = -3(5 - x)$

46. $-3x + x - 8 = -2(6 - x)$

47. $-4 + 2x + 1 = 3(x - 1)$

48. $-2 + 5x + 8 = 6(x + 2) - 6$

49. $9q - 5(q - 3) = 5q$

50. $6h - 2(h + 6) = 10h$

51. $-4(k - 2) + 14 = 3k - 20$

52. $-3(x + 4) - 9 = -2x + 12$

53. $3z + 9 = 3(5z - 1)$

54. $4y + 4 = 8(y - 2)$

55. $6(u - 1) + 5u + 1 = 5(u + 6) - u$

56. $2(2v + 3) + 8v = 6(v - 1) + 3v$

Problem Recognition Exercises

Comparing Expressions and Equations

For Exercises 1–6, identify the problem as an expression or as an equation.

1. $-5 + 4x - 6x = 7$

2. $-8(4 - 7x) + 4$

3. $4 - 6(2x - 3) + 1$

4. $10 - x = 2x + 19$

5. $6 - 3(x + 4) = 6$

6. $9 - 6(x + 1)$

For Exercises 7–30, solve the equation or simplify the expression.

7. $5t = 20$

8. $6x = 36$

9. $5t - 20t$

10. $6x - 36x$

11. $5(w - 3)$

12. $6(x - 2)$

13. $5(w - 3) = 20$

14. $6(x - 2) = 36$

15. $5 + t = 20$

16. $6 + x = 36$

17. $5 + t + 20$

18. $6 + x + 36$

19. $5 + 3p - 2 = 0$

20. $16 - 2k + 2 = 0$

21. $23u + 2 = -12u + 72$

22. $75w - 27 = 14w + 156$

23. $23u + 2 - 12u + 72$

24. $75w - 27 - 14w + 156$

25. $-2(x - 3) + 14 + 10 - (x + 4)$ **26.** $26 - (3x + 12) + 11 - 4(x + 1)$ **27.** $-2(x - 3) + 14 = 10 - (x + 4)$

28. $26 - (3x + 12) = 11 - 4(x + 1)$ **29.** $2 - 3(y + 1) = -4y + 7$

30. $5(t + 5) - 3t = t - 9$

Section 3.5 Applications and Problem Solving

Objectives

1. **Problem-Solving Flowchart**
2. **Translating Verbal Statements into Equations**
3. **Applications of Linear Equations**

1. Problem-Solving Flowchart

Linear equations can be used to solve many real-world applications. In Section 1.8, we introduced guidelines for problem solving. In this section, we expand on these guidelines to write equations to solve applications. Consider the problem-solving flowchart.

Problem-Solving Flowchart for Word Problems

Step 1 | Read the problem completely. | • Familiarize yourself with the problem. Estimate the answer if possible.

Step 2 | Assign labels to unknown quantities. | • Identify the unknown quantity or quantities. Let a variable represent one of the unknowns. Draw a picture and write down relevant formulas.

Step 3 | Write an equation in words. | • Verbalize what quantities must be equal.

Step 4 | Write a mathematical equation. | • Replace the verbal equation with a mathematical equation using x or some other variable.

Step 5 | Solve the equation. | • Solve for the variable using the steps for solving linear equations.

Step 6 | Interpret the results and write the final answer in words. | • Once you have obtained a numerical value for the variable, recall what it represents in the context of the problem. Can this value be used to determine other unknowns in the problem? Write an answer to the word problem *in words*.

Avoiding Mistakes
It is always a good idea to check your answer in the context of the problem. This will help you determine if your answer is reasonable.

2. Translating Verbal Statements into Equations

We begin solving word problems with practice translating between an English sentence and an algebraic equation. First, spend a minute to recall some of the key words that represent addition, subtraction, multiplication, and division. See Table 3-4.

Table 3-4

Addition: $a + b$	**Subtraction:** $a - b$
The *sum* of a and b a plus b b added to a b more than a a increased by b The total of a and b	The *difference* of a and b a minus b b subtracted from a a decreased by b b less than a
Multiplication: $a \cdot b$	**Division:** $a \div b$
The *product* of a and b a times b a multiplied by b	The *quotient* of a and b a divided by b b divided into a The ratio of a and b a over b a per b

Example 1 **Translating Sentences to Mathematical Equations**

A number decreased by 7 is 12. Find the number.

Solution:

	Step 1:	Read the problem completely.
Let x represent the number.	**Step 2:**	Label the variable.
A number decreased by 7 is 12.	**Step 3:**	Write the equation in words
$x \quad - \quad 7 = 12$	**Step 4:**	Translate to a mathematical equation.
$x - 7 = 12$	**Step 5:**	Solve the equation.
$x - 7 + 7 = 12 + 7$		Add 7 to both sides.
$x = 19$		
The number is 19.	**Step 6:**	Interpret the answer in words.

Avoiding Mistakes

To check the answer to Example 1, we see that 19 decreased by 7 is 12.

Answer

1. The number is -16.

Skill Practice

2. 4 subtracted from 8 times a number is 36. Find the number.

Example 2 **Translating Sentences to Mathematical Equations**

Seven less than 3 times a number results in 11. Find the number.

Solution:

	Step 1:	Read the problem completely.
Let x represent the number.	**Step 2:**	Label the variable.
Seven less than 3 times a number results in 11.	**Step 3:**	Write the equation in words

$$\underbrace{3x}_{\text{three times a number}} \overbrace{-\ 7}^{\text{7 less than}} = \overbrace{11}^{\text{results in 11}}$$

	Step 4:	Translate to a mathematical equation.
$3x - 7 + 7 = 11 + 7$	**Step 5:**	Solve the equation. Add 7 to both sides.
$3x = 18$		Simplify.
$\dfrac{3x}{3} = \dfrac{18}{3}$		Divide both sides by 3.
$x = 6$		

Avoiding Mistakes

To check the answer to Example 2, we have:

The value 3 times 6 is 18, and 7 less than 18 is 11.

The number is 6. **Step 6:** Interpret the answer in words.

Skill Practice

3. 8 added to twice a number is 22. Find the number.

Example 3 **Translating Sentences to Mathematical Equations**

Two times the sum of a number and 8 equals 38.

Solution:

	Step 1:	Read the problem completely.
Let x represent the number.	**Step 2:**	Label the variable.
Two times the sum of a number and 8 equals 38.	**Step 3:**	Write the equation in words.

Avoiding Mistakes

The sum $(x + 8)$ must be enclosed in parentheses so that the entire sum is multiplied by 2.

$$\overbrace{2}^{\text{two times}} \cdot \underbrace{(x + 8)}_{\text{the sum of a number and 8}} = \overbrace{38}^{\text{equals 38}}$$

	Step 4:	Translate to a mathematical equation.
$2(x + 8) = 38$	**Step 5:**	Solve the equation.
$2x + 16 = 38$		Clear parentheses.
$2x + 16 - 16 = 38 - 16$		Subtract 16 from both sides.
$2x = 22$		Simplify.
$\dfrac{2x}{2} = \dfrac{22}{2}$		Divide both sides by 2.
$x = 11$		

Avoiding Mistakes

To check the answer to Example 3, we have:

The sum of 11 and 8 is 19. Twice this amount gives 38 as expected.

The number is 11. **Step 6:** Interpret the answer in words.

Answers

2. The number is 5.
3. The number is 7.

3. Applications of Linear Equations

In Example 4, we practice representing quantities within a word problem by using variables.

Example 4 **Representing Quantities Algebraically**

a. Kathleen works twice as many hours in one week as Kevin. If Kevin works for h hours, write an expression representing the number of hours that Kathleen works.

b. At a carnival, rides cost $3 each. If Alicia takes n rides during the day, write an expression for the total cost.

c. Josie made $430 less during one week than her friend Annie made. If Annie made D dollars, write an expression for the amount that Josie made.

Solution:

a. Let h represent the number of hours that Kevin works.

Kathleen works twice as many hours as Kevin.
↓
$\overbrace{2h}$ is the number of hours that Kathleen works.

b. Let n represent the number of rides Alicia takes during the day.

Rides cost $3 each.
↓
$\overbrace{3n}$ is the total cost.

c. Let D represent the amount of money that Annie made during the week.

Josie made $430 less than Annie.
↓
$\overbrace{D - 430}$ represents the amount that Josie made.

In Examples 5 and 6, we practice solving application problems using linear equations.

Answers
4. $3x$ **5.** $7d$ **6.** $x + 8$

Example 5   **Applying a Linear Equation to Carpentry**

A carpenter must cut a 10-ft board into two pieces to build a brace for a picnic table. If one piece is to be four times longer than the other piece, how long should each piece be?

Solution:

	Step 1:	Read the problem completely.

We can let x represent the length of either piece. However, if we choose x to be the length of the shorter piece, then the longer piece has to be $4x$ (4 times as long).

Step 2: Label the variables. Draw a picture.

Let x = the length of the shorter piece.

Then $4x$ = the length of the longer piece.

$$\left(\begin{array}{c}\text{length of}\\\text{one piece}\end{array}\right) + \left(\begin{array}{c}\text{length of the}\\\text{other piece}\end{array}\right) = \left(\begin{array}{c}\text{total}\\\text{length}\end{array}\right)$$

Step 3: Write an equation in words.

$$x \quad + \quad 4x \quad = \quad 10$$

Step 4: Write a mathematical equation.

$$x + 4x = 10$$

Step 5: Solve the equation.

$$5x = 10$$

Combine *like* terms.

$$\frac{5x}{5} = \frac{10}{5}$$

Divide both sides by 5.

$$x = 2$$

Step 6: Interpret the results in words.

Recall that x represents the length of the shorter piece. Therefore, the shorter piece is 2 ft. The longer piece is given by $4x$ or $4(2 \text{ ft}) = 8$ ft.

The pieces are 2 ft and 8 ft.

Example 6   **Applying a Linear Equation**

One model of a Panasonic high-definition plasma TV sold for \$1500 more than a certain model made by Planar. The combined cost for these two models is \$8500. Find the cost for each model.

(*Source: Consumer Reports*)

Solution:

	Step 1: Read the problem completely.
Let x represent the cost of the Planar TV.	**Step 2:** Label the variables
Then $x + 1500$ represents the cost of the Panasonic.	

$$\begin{pmatrix} \text{cost of} \\ \text{Planar} \end{pmatrix} + \begin{pmatrix} \text{cost of} \\ \text{Panasonic} \end{pmatrix} = \begin{pmatrix} \text{total} \\ \text{cost} \end{pmatrix}$$

Step 3: Write an equation in words.

$$x \quad + \quad x + 1500 \quad = \quad 8500$$

Step 4: Write a mathematical equation.

$$x + x + 1500 = 8500$$

Step 5: Solve the equation.

$$2x + 1500 = 8500$$

Combine *like* terms.

$$2x + 1500 - 1500 = 8500 - 1500$$

Subtract 1500 from both sides.

$$2x = 7000$$

$$\frac{2x}{2} = \frac{7000}{2}$$

Divide both sides by 2.

$$x = 3500$$

Step 6: Interpret the results in words.

Since $x = 3500$, the Planar model TV costs \$3500.

The Panasonic model is represented by $x + 1500 = \$3500 + \$1500 = \$5000$.

TIP: In Example 6, we could have let x represent *either* the cost of the Planar model TV or the Panasonic model.

Suppose we had let x represent the cost of the Panasonic model.
Then $x - 1500$ is the cost of the Planar model (the Planar model is *less* expensive).

$$\begin{pmatrix} \text{cost of} \\ \text{Planar} \end{pmatrix} + \begin{pmatrix} \text{cost of} \\ \text{Panasonic} \end{pmatrix} = \begin{pmatrix} \text{total} \\ \text{cost} \end{pmatrix}$$

$$x - 1500 + \quad x \quad = 8500$$

$$2x - 1500 = 8500$$

$$2x - 1500 + 1500 = 8500 + 1500$$

$$2x = 10{,}000$$

$$x = 5000$$

Therefore, the Panasonic model costs \$5000 as expected.
The Planar model costs $x - 1500$ or $\$5000 - \$1500 = \$3500$.

Section 3.5 Practice Exercises

Boost *your* GRADE at ALEKS.com!

ALEKS
VERSION 3.0

- Practice Problems
- Self-Tests
- NetTutor
- e-Professors
- Videos

Study Skills Exercise

1. In solving an application it is very important first to read and understand what is being asked in the problem. One way to do this is to read the problem several times. Another is to read it out loud so you can hear yourself. Another is to rewrite the problem in your own words. Which of these methods do you think will help you in understanding an application?

Review Exercises

2. Use substitution to determine if -4 is a solution to the equation $-3x + 9 = 21$.

For Exercises 3–8, solve the equation.

3. $3t - 15 = -24$

4. $-6x + 4 = 16$

5. $\dfrac{b}{5} - 5 = -14$

6. $\dfrac{w}{8} - 3 = 3$

7. $2x + 22 = 6x - 2$

8. $-5y - 34 = -3y + 12$

Objective 2: Translating Verbal Statements into Equations

For Exercises 9–40,

a. write an equation that represents the given statement.

b. solve the problem. **(See Examples 1–3.)**

9. The sum of a number and 6 is 19. Find the number.

10. The sum of 12 and a number is 49. Find the number.

11. The difference of a number and 14 is 20. Find the number.

12. The difference of a number and 10 is 18. Find the number.

13. The quotient of a number and 3 is -8. Find the number.

14. The quotient of a number and -2 is 10. Find the number.

15. The product of a number and -6 is -60. Find the number.

16. The product of a number and -5 is -20. Find the number.

17. The difference of -2 and a number is -14. Find the number.

18. A number subtracted from -30 results in 42. Find the number.

19. 13 increased by a number results in −100. Find the number.

20. The total of 30 and a number is 13. Find the number.

21. Sixty is −5 times a number. Find the number.

22. Sixty-four is −4 times a number. Find the number.

23. Nine more than 3 times a number is 15. Find the number.

24. Eight more than twice a number is 20. Find the number.

25. Five times a number when reduced by 12 equals −27. Find the number.

26. Negative four times a number when reduced by 6 equals 14. Find the number.

27. Five less than the quotient of a number and 4 is equal to −12. Find the number.

28. Ten less than the quotient of a number and −6 is −2. Find the number.

29. Eight decreased by the product of a number and 3 is equal to 5. Find the number.

30. Four decreased by the product of a number and 7 is equal to 11. Find the number.

31. Three times the sum of a number and 4 results in −24. Find the number.

32. Twice the sum of 9 and a number is 30. Find the number.

33. Negative four times the difference of 3 and a number is −20. Find the number.

34. Negative five times the difference of 8 and a number is −55. Find the number.

35. The product of −12 and a number is the same as the sum of the number and 26. Find the number.

36. The difference of a number and 16 is the same as the product of the number and −3. Find the number.

37. Ten times the total of a number and 5 is 80. Find the number.

38. Three times the difference of a number and 5 is 15. Find the number.

39. The product of 3 and a number is the same as 10 less than twice the number.

40. Six less than a number is the same as 3 more than twice the number.

Objective 3: Applications of Linear Equations

41. A metal rod is cut into two pieces. One piece is five times as long as the other. If x represents the length of the shorter piece, write an expression for the length of the longer piece. **(See Example 4a.)**

42. Jackson scored three times as many points in a basketball game as Tony did. If p represents the number of points that Tony scored, write an expression for the number of points that Jackson scored.

43. Tickets to a college baseball game cost $6 each. If Stan buys n tickets, write an expression for the total cost. **(See Example 4b.)**

44. At a concession stand, drinks cost $2 each. If Frank buys x drinks, write an expression for the total cost.

45. Bill's daughter is 30 years younger than he is. Write an expression for his daughter's age if Bill is A years old. **(See Example 4c.)**

46. Carlita spent $88 less on tuition and fees than her friend Carlo did. If Carlo spent d dollars, write an expression for the amount that Carlita spent.

47. The number of prisoners at the Fort Dix Federal Correctional Facility is 1481 more than the number at Big Spring in Texas. If p represents the number of prisoners at Big Spring, write an expression for the number at Fort Dix.

48. Race car driver A. J. Foyt won 15 more races than Mario Andretti. If Mario Andretti won r races, write an expression for the number of races won by A. J. Foyt.

49. Carol sells homemade candles. Write an expression for her total revenue if she sells five candles for r dollars each.

50. Sandy bought eight tomatoes for c cents each. Write an expression for the total cost.

51. The cost to rent space in a shopping center doubled over a 10-year period. If c represents the original cost 10 years ago, write an expression for the cost now.

52. Jacob scored three times as many points in his basketball game on Monday as he did in Wednesday's game. If p represents the number of points scored on Wednesday, write an expression for the number scored on Monday.

For Exercises 53–64, use the problem-solving flowchart to set up and solve an equation to solve each problem.

53. Felicia has an 8-ft piece of ribbon. She wants to cut the ribbon into two pieces so that one piece is three times the length of the other. Find the length of each piece. **(See Example 5.)**

54. Richard and Linda enjoy visiting Hilton Head Island, South Carolina. The distance from their home to Hilton Head is 954 mi, so the drive takes them 2 days. Richard and Linda travel twice as far the first day as they do the second. How many miles do they travel each day?

55. A motorist drives from Minneapolis, Minnesota, to Madison, Wisconsin, and then on to Chicago, Illinois. The total distance is 360 mi. The distance between Minneapolis and Madison is 120 mi more than the distance from Madison to Chicago. Find the distance between Minneapolis and Madison.

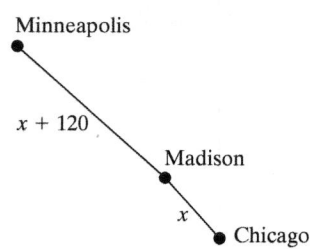

56. Two hikers on the Appalachian Trail hike from Hawk Mountain to Gooch Mountain. The next day, they hike from Gooch Mountain to Woods Hole. The total distance is 19 mi. If the distance between Gooch Mountain and Woods Hole is 5 mi more than the distance from Hawk Mountain to Gooch Mountain, find the distance they hiked each day.

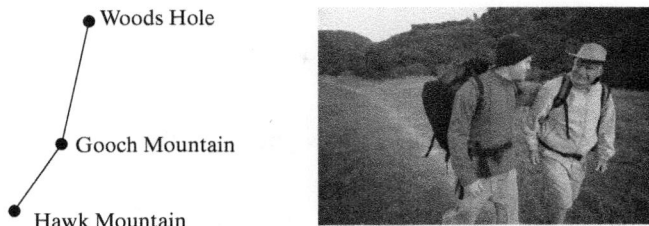

● Woods Hole

● Gooch Mountain

● Hawk Mountain

57. The Beatles had 9 more number one albums than Elvis Presley. Together, they had a total of 29 number one albums. How many number one albums did each have?
(See Example 6.)

58. A two-piece set of luggage costs $150. If sold individually, the larger bag costs $40 more than the smaller bag. What are the individual costs for each bag?

59. In the 2008 Super Bowl, the New England Patriots scored 3 points less than the New York Giants. A total of 31 points was scored in the game. How many points did each team score?

60. The most goals scored in a regular season NHL hockey game occurred during a game between the Edmonton Oilers and the Chicago Black Hawks. The total number of goals scored was 21. The Oilers scored 3 more goals than the Black Hawks. How many goals did each team score?

61. An apartment complex charges a refundable security deposit when renting an apartment. The deposit is $350 less than the monthly rent. If Charlene paid a total of $950 for her first month's rent and security deposit, how much is her monthly rent? How much is the security deposit?

62. Becca paid a total of $695 for tuition and lab fees for fall semester. Tuition for her courses cost $605 more than lab fees. How much did her tuition cost? What was the cost of the lab fees?

63. Stefan is paid a salary of $480 a week at his job. When he works overtime, he receives $18 an hour. If his weekly paycheck came to $588, how many hours of overtime did he put in that week?

64. Mercedes is paid a salary of $480 a week at her job. She worked 8 hr of overtime during the holidays and her weekly paycheck came to $672. What is her overtime pay per hour?

Constructing Linear Equations

Estimated time: 20 minutes

Group Size: 4

1. Construct a linear equation in which the solution is your age. The equation should require at least two operations. For example:

   "Solve the equation to guess my age:" $2(x + 4) = 106$

2. Pass your paper to the student sitting to your right. That student will solve the equation and verify that it is correct.

3. Next, each of you will construct another linear equation. The solution to this equation should be the number of pets that you have.

   "Solve the equation to guess the number of pets I have:"

   Equation _____

4. Pass your paper to the right. That student will solve the equation and verify that the solution is correct.

5. Each of you will construct another equation. This time, the solution should be the number of credit hours you are taking.

   "Solve the equation to guess the number of credit hours I am taking."

   Equation _____

6. Pass the papers to the right, solve the equation, and check the answer.

7. Construct an equation in which the solution is the number of sisters and brothers you have.

   "Solve the equation to guess the number of sisters and brothers I have."

   Equation _____

8. Pass the papers to the right again, solve the equation, and check the answer. The papers should now be back in the hands of their original owners.

Chapter 3 Summary

Section 3.1   Simplifying Expressions and Combining *Like* Terms

Key Concepts

An algebraic expression is the sum of one or more terms. A **term** is a constant or the product of a constant and one or more variables. If a term contains a variable it is called a **variable term**. A number multiplied by the variable is called a **coefficient**. A term with no variable is called a **constant term**.

Terms that have exactly the same variable factors with the same exponents are called *like* **terms**.

Properties

1. Commutative property of addition: $a + b = b + a$
2. Commutative property of multiplication:
   $a \cdot b = b \cdot a$
3. Associative property of addition:
   $(a + b) + c = a + (b + c)$
4. Associative property of multiplication:
   $(a \cdot b) \cdot c = a \cdot (b \cdot c)$
5. Distributive property of multiplication over addition: $a(b + c) = a \cdot b + a \cdot c$

Like terms can be combined by applying the distributive property.

To simplify an expression, first clear parentheses using the distributive property. Arrange *like* terms together. Then combine *like* terms.

Examples

Example 1

In the expression $12x + 3$,
   $12x$ is a variable term.
   12 is the coefficient of the term $12x$.
   The term 3 is a constant term.

Example 2

$5h$ and $-2h$ are *like* terms because the variable factor, h, is the same.

$6t$ and $6v$ are not *like* terms because the variable factors, t and v, are not the same.

Example 3

1. $5 + (-8) = -8 + 5$
2. $(3)(-9) = (-9)(3)$

3. $(-7 + 5) + 11 = -7 + (5 + 11)$

4. $(-3 \cdot 10) \cdot 2 = -3 \cdot (10 \cdot 2)$

5. $-3(4x + 12) = -3(4x) + (-3)(12)$
   $$= -12x - 36$$

Example 4

$3x + 15x - 7x = (3 + 15 - 7)x$
$$= 11x$$

Example 5

Simplify: $3(k - 4) - (6k + 10) + 14$

$3(k - 4) - (6k + 10) + 14$

$= 3k - 12 - 6k - 10 + 14$ Clear parentheses.

$= 3k - 6k - 12 - 10 + 14$

$= -3k - 8$

Section 3.2   Addition and Subtraction Properties of Equality

Key Concepts

An **equation** is a statement that indicates that two quantities are equal.

A **solution** to an equation is a value of the variable that makes the equation a true statement.

Definition of a Linear Equation in One Variable

Let a, b, and c be numbers such that $a \neq 0$. A **linear equation in one variable** is an equation that can be written in the form.

$$ax + b = c$$

Two equations that have the same solution are called **equivalent equations**.

The Addition and Subtraction Properties of Equality

Let $a, b,$ and c represent algebraic expressions.
1. The **addition property of equality:**
   If $a = b$, then $a + c = b + c$
2. The **subtraction property of equality:**
   If $a = b$, then $a - c = b - c$

Examples

Example 1

$3x + 4 = 6$ is an equation, compared to $3x + 4$, which is an expression.

Example 2

The number -4 is a solution to the equation $5x + 7 = -13$ because when we substitute -4 for x we get a true statement.

$$5(-4) + 7 \overset{?}{=} -13$$
$$-20 + 7 \overset{?}{=} -13$$
$$-13 \overset{?}{=} -13 \ \checkmark$$

Example 3

The equation $5x + 7 = -13$ is equivalent to the equation $x = -4$ because they both have the same solution, -4.

Example 4

To solve the equation $t - 12 = -3$, use the addition property of equality.

$$t - 12 = -3$$
$$t - 12 + 12 = -3 + 12$$
$$t = 9 \qquad \text{The solution is 9.}$$

Example 5

To solve the equation $-1 = p + 2$, use the subtraction property of equality.

$$-1 = p + 2$$
$$-1 - 2 = p + 2 - 2$$
$$-3 = p \qquad \text{The solution is } -3.$$

Section 3.3 Multiplication and Division Properties of Equality

Key Concepts

The Multiplication and Division Properties of Equality

Let a, b, and c represent algebraic expressions, $c \neq 0$.
1. The **multiplication property of equality:**
   If $a = b$, then $a \cdot c = b \cdot c$
2. The **division property of equality:**
   If $a = b$, then $\dfrac{a}{c} = \dfrac{b}{c}$

To determine which property to use to solve an equation, first identify the operation on the variable. Then use the property of equality that *reverses* the operation.

Examples

Example 1

Solve $\dfrac{w}{2} = -11$

$2\left(\dfrac{w}{2}\right) = 2(-11)$ Multiply both sides by 2.

$w = -22$ The solution is -22.

Example 2

Solve $3a = -18$

$\dfrac{3a}{3} = \dfrac{-18}{3}$ Divide both sides by 3.

$a = -6$ The solution is -6.

Example 3

Solve. $4x = 20$ and $4 + x = 20$

$\dfrac{4x}{4} = \dfrac{20}{4}$ $4 - 4 + x = 20 - 4$

$x = 5$ $x = 16$

The solution is 5.   The solution is 16.

Section 3.4 Solving Equations with Multiple Steps

Key Concepts

Steps to Solve a Linear Equation in One Variable

1. Simplify both sides of the equation.
   - Clear parentheses if necessary.
   - Combine *like* terms if necessary.
2. Use the addition or subtraction property of equality to collect the variable terms on one side of the equation.
3. Use the addition or subtraction property of equality to collect the constant terms on the *other* side of the equation.
4. Use the multiplication or division property of equality to make the coefficient of the variable term equal to 1.
5. Check the answer in the original equation.

Examples

Example 1

Solve: $4(x - 3) - 6 = -2x$

$4x - 12 - 6 = -2x$ **Step 1**

$4x - 18 = -2x$

$4x + 2x - 18 = -2x + 2x$ **Step 2**

$6x - 18 = 0$

$6x - 18 + 18 = 0 + 18$ **Step 3**

$6x = 18$

$\dfrac{6x}{6} = \dfrac{18}{6}$ **Step 4**

$x = 3$ The solution is 3.

Check: $4(x - 3) - 6 = -2x$ **Step 5**

$4(3 - 3) - 6 \stackrel{?}{=} -2(3)$

$4(0) - 6 \stackrel{?}{=} -6$

$-6 \stackrel{?}{=} -6$ ✓   True

| Section 3.5 | Applications and Problem Solving |

Key Concepts

Problem-Solving Flowchart for Word Problems

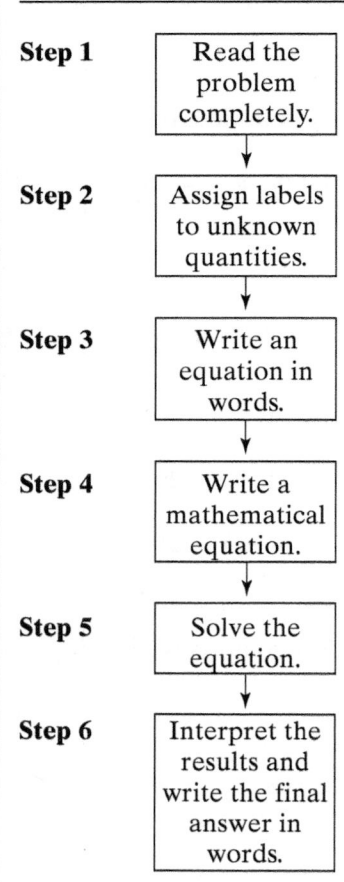

Step 1 — Read the problem completely.

Step 2 — Assign labels to unknown quantities.

Step 3 — Write an equation in words.

Step 4 — Write a mathematical equation.

Step 5 — Solve the equation.

Step 6 — Interpret the results and write the final answer in words.

Examples

Example 1

Subtract 5 times a number from 14. The result is -6. Find the number.

Step 1

Let n represent the unknown number.   **Step 2**

$$\underbrace{14}_{\text{from } 14} \quad \underbrace{-\quad 5n}_{\text{subtract } 5n} \quad \underbrace{=\ -6}_{\text{result is } -6}$$ **Step 3** **Step 4**

$$14 - 14 - 5n = -6 - 14$$ **Step 5**

$$-5n = -20$$

$$\frac{-5n}{-5} = \frac{-20}{-5}$$

$$n = 4$$

The number is 4.   **Step 6**

Example 2

An electrician needs to cut a 20-ft wire into two pieces so that one piece is four times as long as the other. How long should each piece be?   **Step 1**

Let x be the length of the shorter piece.   **Step 2**
Then $4x$ is the length of the longer piece.

The two pieces added together will be 20 ft.   **Step 3**

$$x + 4x = 20$$ **Step 4**

$$5x = 20$$ **Step 5**

$$\frac{5x}{5} = \frac{20}{5}$$

$$x = 4$$ **Step 6**

One piece of wire is 4 ft and the other is 4(4 ft), which is 16 ft.

Chapter 3 Review Exercises

Section 3.1

For Exercises 1–2, list the terms of the expression and identify the term as a variable term or a constant term. Then identify the coefficient.

1. $3a^2 - 5a + 12$ **2.** $-6xy - y + 2x$

For Exercises 3–6, determine if the two terms are *like* terms or unlike terms.

3. $5t^2, 5t$ **4.** $4h, -2h$

5. $21, -5$ **6.** $-8, -8k$

For Exercises 7–8, apply the commutative property of addition or multiplication to rewrite the expression.

7. $t - 5$ **8.** $h \cdot 3$

For Exercises 9–10, apply the associative property of addition or multiplication to rewrite the expression. Then simplify the expression.

9. $-4(2 \cdot p)$ **10.** $(m + 10) - 12$

For Exercises 11–14, apply the distributive property.

11. $3(2b + 5)$ **12.** $5(4x + 6y - 3z)$

13. $-(4c - 6d)$ **14.** $-(-4k + 8w - 12)$

For Exercises 15–22, combine *like* terms. Clear parentheses if necessary.

15. $-5x - x + 8x$

16. $-3y - 7y + y$

17. $6y + 8x - 2y - 2x + 10$

18. $12a - 5 + 9b - 5a + 14$

19. $5 - 3(x - 7) + x$

20. $6 - 4(z + 2) + 2z$

21. $4(u - 3v) - 5(u + v)$

22. $-5(p + 4) + 6(p + 1) - 2$

Section 3.2

For Exercises 23–24, determine if -3 is a solution to the equation.

23. $5x + 10 = -5$ **24.** $-3(x - 1) = -9 + x$

For Exercises 25–32, solve the equation using either the addition property of equality or the subtraction property of equality.

25. $r + 23 = -12$ **26.** $k - 3 = -15$

27. $10 = p - 4$ **28.** $21 = q + 3$

29. $5a + 7 - 4a = 20$ **30.** $-7t - 4 + 8t = 11$

31. $-4(m - 3) + 7 + 5m = 21$

32. $-2(w - 3) + 3w = -8$

Section 3.3

For Exercises 33–38, solve the equation using either the multiplication property of equality or the division property of equality.

33. $4d = -28$ **34.** $-3c = -12$

35. $\dfrac{t}{-2} = -13$ **36.** $\dfrac{p}{5} = 7$

37. $-42 = -7p$ **38.** $-12 = \dfrac{m}{4}$

Section 3.4

For Exercises 39–52, solve the equation.

39. $9x + 7 = -2$ **40.** $8y + 3 = 27$

41. $45 = 6m - 3$ **42.** $-25 = 2n - 1$

43. $\dfrac{p}{8} + 1 = 5$ **44.** $\dfrac{x}{-5} - 2 = -3$

45. $5x + 12 = 4x - 16$ **46.** $-4t - 2 = -3t + 5$

47. $-8 + 4y = 7y + 4$ **48.** $15 - 2c = 5c + 1$

49. $6(w - 2) + 15 = 3w$ **50.** $-4(h - 5) + h = 7h$

51. $-(5a + 3) - 3(a - 2) = 24 - a$

52. $-(4b - 7) = 2(b + 3) - 4b + 13$

Section 3.5

For Exercises 53–58,

  a. write an equation that represents the statement.

  b. solve the problem.

53. Four subtracted from a number is 13. Find the number.

54. The quotient of a number and -7 is -6. Find the number.

55. Three more than -4 times a number is -17. Find the number.

56. Seven less than 3 times a number is -22. Find the number.

57. Twice the sum of a number and 10 is 16. Find the number.

58. Three times the difference of 4 and a number is −9. Find the number.

59. A rack of discount CDs are on sale for $9 each. If Mario buys *n* CDs, write an expression for the total cost.

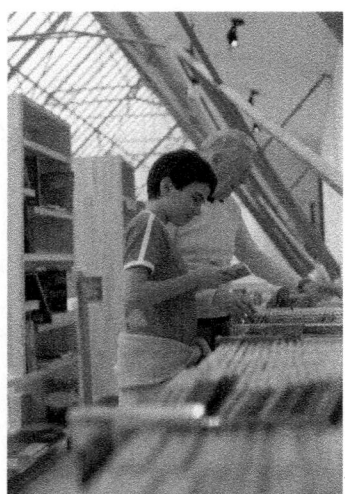

60. Henri bought four sandwiches for *x* dollars each. Write an expression that represents the total cost.

61. It took Winston 2 hr longer to finish his psychology paper than it did for Gus to finish. If Gus finished in *x* hours, write an expression for the amount of time it took Winston.

62. Gerard is 6 in. taller than his younger brother Dwayne. If Dwayne is *h* inches tall, write an expression for Gerard's height.

63. Monique and Michael drove from Ormond Beach, Florida, to Knoxville, Tennessee. Michael drove three times as far as Monique drove. If the total distance is 480 mi, how far did each person drive?

64. Joel ate twice as much pizza as Angela. Together, they finished off a 12-slice pizza. How many pieces did each person have?

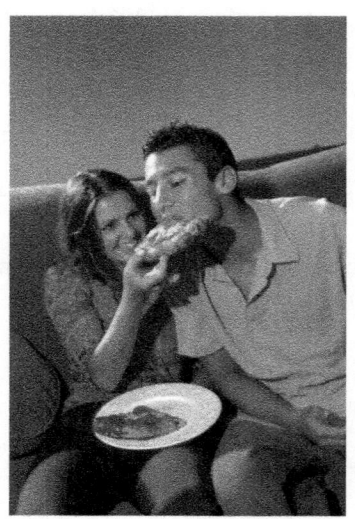

65. As of a recent year, Tom Cruise starred in 5 fewer films than Tom Hanks. If together they starred in 65 films, how many films did Tom Hanks and Tom Cruise star in individually?

66. Raul signed up for his classes for the spring semester. His load was 4 credit-hours less in the spring than in the fall. If he took a total of 28 hours in the two semesters combined, how many hours did he take in the fall? How many hours did he take in the spring?

Chapter 3   Test

For Exercises 1–5, state the property demonstrated. Choose from:

  a. commutative property of addition

  b. commutative property of multiplication

  c. associative property of addition

  d. associative property of multiplication

  e. distributive property of multiplication over addition.

1. $-5(9x) = (-5 \cdot 9)x$ **2.** $-5x + 9 = 9 + (-5x)$

3. $-3 + (u + v) = (-3 + u) + v$

4. $-4(b + 2) = -4b - 8$ **5.** $g(-6) = -6g$

For Exercises 6–11, simplify the expressions.

6. $-5x - 3x + x$

7. $-2a - 3b + 8a + 4b - a$

8. $4(a + 9) - 12$ **9.** $-3(6b) + 5b + 8$

10. $14y - 2(y - 9) + 21$

11. $2 - (5 - w) + 3(-2w)$

12. Explain the difference between an expression and an equation.

For Exercises 13–16, identify as either an expression or an equation.

13. $4x + 5$

14. $4x + 5 = 2$

15. $2(q - 3) = 6$

16. $2(q - 3) + 6$

For Exercises 17–36, solve the equation.

17. $a - 9 = 12$

18. $t - 6 = 12$

19. $7 = 10 + x$

20. $19 = 12 + y$

21. $-4p = 28$

22. $-3c = 30$

23. $-7 = \dfrac{d}{3}$

24. $8 = \dfrac{m}{4}$

25. $-6x = 12$

26. $-6 + x = 12$

27. $\dfrac{x}{-6} = 12$

28. $-6x = 12$

29. $4x - 5 = 23$

30. $-9x - 6 = 21$

31. $\dfrac{x}{7} + 1 = -11$

32. $\dfrac{z}{-2} - 3 = 4$

33. $5h - 2 = -h + 22$

34. $6p + 3 = 15 + 2p$

35. $-2(q - 5) = 6q + 10$

36. $-(4k - 2) - k = 2(k - 6)$

37. The product of -2 and a number is the same as the total of 15 and the number. Find the number.

38. Two times the sum of a number and 8 is 10. Find the number.

39. A high school student sells magazine subscriptions for $15 each. Write an expression that represents the total cost of m magazines.

40. Alberto is 5 years older than Juan. If Juan's age is represented by a, write an expression for Alberto's age.

41. Monica and Phil each have part-time jobs. Monica makes twice as much money in a week as Phil. If the total of their weekly earnings is $756, how much does each person make?

42. A computer with a monitor costs $899. If the computer costs $241 more than the monitor, what is the price of the computer? What is the price of the monitor?

Chapters 1–3   Cumulative Review Exercises

1. Identify the place value of the underlined digit.

   a. 34,9̱11   **b.** 20̱9,001   **c.** 5,9̱01,888

For Exercises 2–4, round the number to the indicated place value.

2. 45,921; thousands

3. 1,285,000; ten-thousands

4. 25,449; hundreds

5. Divide 39,190 by 46. Identify the dividend, divisor, quotient, and remainder.

6. Sarah cleans three apartments in a weekend. The apartments have five, six, and four rooms, respectively. If she earns $300 for the weekend, how much does she make per room?

7. The data represent the number of turkey subs sold between 11:00 A.M. and 12:00 P.M. at

Subs-R-Us over a 14-day period. Find the mean number of subs sold per day.

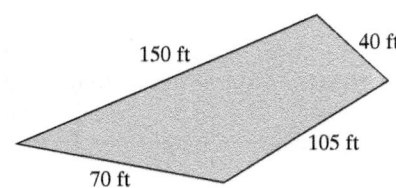

| 15 | 12 | 8 | 4 | 6 | 12 | 10 |
| 20 | 7 | 5 | 8 | 9 | 11 | 13 |

8. Find the perimeter of the lot.

150 ft   40 ft   105 ft   70 ft

For Exercises 9–14, perform the indicated operations.

9. $18 - (-5) + (-3)$

10. $-4 - (-7) - 8$

11. $4(5 - 11) + (-1)$

12. $5 - 23 + 12 - 3$

13. $-36 \div (0)$

14. $16 \div (-4) \cdot 3$

For Exercises 15–16, simplify the expression.

15. $-2x + 14 + 15 - 3x$

16. $3y - (5y + 6) - 12$

For Exercises 17–18, solve the equation.

17. $4p + 5 = -11$

18. $9(t - 1) - 7t + 2 = t - 15$

19. Evaluate the expression $a^2 - b$ for $a = -3$ and $b = 5$.

20. In a recent year, the recording artist Kanye West received 2 more Grammy nominations than Alicia Keys. Together they received 18 nominations. How many nominations did each receive?

Fractions and Mixed Numbers

4

Chapter 4

In this chapter, we study the concept of a fraction and a mixed number. We begin by learning how to simplify fractions to lowest terms. We follow with addition, subtraction, multiplication, and division of fractions and mixed numbers. At the end of the chapter, we solve equations with fractions.

Are You Prepared?

To review for this chapter, take a minute to practice the technique to solve linear equations. Use the solutions to complete the crossword. If you have trouble, see Section 3.4.

Across

3. $x + 489 = 23{,}949$

5. $\dfrac{x}{3} = 81$

6. $12{,}049 = -58{,}642 + y$

Down

1. $10x = 1000$

2. $2x - 4 = 254$

4. $-18{,}762 = -3z - 540$

5. $3x - 120 = 9920 - 2x$

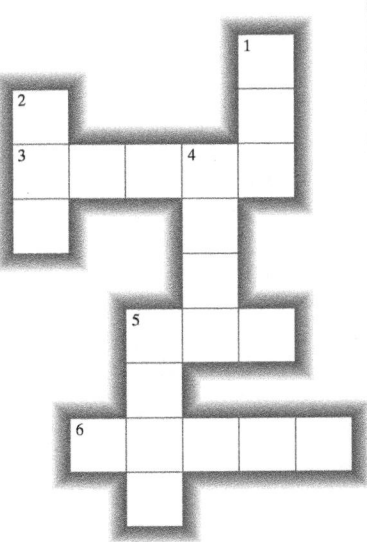

Section 4.1   Introduction to Fractions and Mixed Numbers

1. Definition of a Fraction

In Chapter 1, we studied operations on whole numbers. In this chapter, we work with numbers that represent part of a whole. When a whole unit is divided into equal parts, we call the parts **fractions** of a whole. For example, the pizza in Figure 4-1 is divided into 5 equal parts. One-fifth ($\frac{1}{5}$) of the pizza has been eaten, and four-fifths ($\frac{4}{5}$) of the pizza remains.

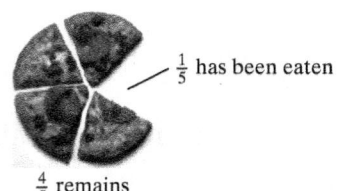

$\frac{1}{5}$ has been eaten

$\frac{4}{5}$ remains

Figure 4-1

A fraction is written in the form $\frac{a}{b}$, where a and b are whole numbers and $b \neq 0$. In the fraction $\frac{5}{8}$, the "top" number, 5, is called the **numerator**. The "bottom" number, 8, is called the **denominator**.

$$\text{numerator} \longrightarrow \frac{5}{8} \qquad \frac{2x^2}{3y} \longleftarrow \text{numerator}$$
$$\text{denominator} \longrightarrow \qquad \qquad \longleftarrow \text{denominator}$$

A fraction whose numerator is an integer and whose denominator is a nonzero integer is also called a **rational number**.

The denominator of a fraction denotes the number of equal pieces into which a whole unit is divided. The numerator denotes the number of pieces being considered. For example, the garden in Figure 4-2 is divided into 10 equal parts. Three sections contain tomato plants. Therefore, $\frac{3}{10}$ of the garden contains tomato plants.

$\frac{3}{10}$ tomato plants

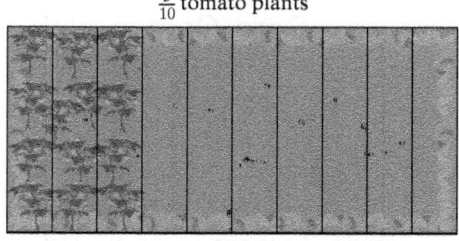

Figure 4-2

Avoiding Mistakes

The fraction $\frac{3}{10}$ can also be written as ³⁄₁₀. However, we discourage the use of the "slanted" fraction bar. In later applications of algebra, the slanted fraction bar can cause confusion.

Skill Practice

1. Write a fraction for the shaded portion and a fraction for the unshaded portion.

Example 1   Writing Fractions

Write a fraction for the shaded portion and a fraction for the unshaded portion of the figure.

Solution:

Shaded portion: $\dfrac{13}{16}$ ←——— 13 pieces are shaded.
←——— The triangle is divided into 16 equal pieces.

Unshaded portion: $\dfrac{3}{16}$ ←——— 3 pieces are not shaded.
←——— The triangle is divided into 16 equal pieces.

Answer

1. Shaded portion: $\frac{3}{8}$; unshaded portion: $\frac{5}{8}$

In Section 1.6, we learned that fractions represent division. For example, the fraction $\frac{5}{1} = 5 \div 1 = 5$. Interpreting fractions as division leads to the following important properties.

PROPERTY Properties of Fractions

Suppose that a and b represent nonzero numbers.

1. $\dfrac{a}{1} = a$ Example: $\dfrac{-8}{1} = -8$

2. $\dfrac{0}{a} = 0$ Example: $\dfrac{0}{-7} = 0$

3. $\dfrac{a}{0}$ is undefined   Example: $\dfrac{11}{0}$ is undefined

4. $\dfrac{a}{a} = 1$ Example: $\dfrac{-3}{-3} = 1$

5. $\dfrac{-a}{-b} = \dfrac{a}{b}$ Example: $\dfrac{-2}{-5} = \dfrac{2}{5}$

6. $-\dfrac{a}{b} = \dfrac{-a}{b} = \dfrac{a}{-b}$ Example: $-\dfrac{2}{3} = \dfrac{-2}{3} = \dfrac{2}{-3}$

Concept Connections

2. Which of the expressions is equivalent to $\frac{-6}{1}$?

   a. $\dfrac{6}{-1}$ b. $-\dfrac{6}{1}$

   c. -6 d. $\dfrac{-6}{-1}$

Property 6 tells us that a negative fraction can be written with the negative sign in the numerator, in the denominator, or out in front. This is because a quotient of two numbers with opposite signs is negative.

2. Proper and Improper Fractions

A positive fraction whose numerator is less than its denominator (or the opposite of such a fraction) is called a **proper fraction**. Furthermore, a positive proper fraction represents a number less than 1 whole unit. The following are proper fractions.

$\dfrac{1}{3}$
1 unit

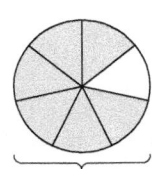
$\dfrac{6}{7}$
1 unit

A positive fraction whose numerator is greater than or equal to its denominator (or the opposite of such a fraction) is called an **improper fraction**. For example:

numerator greater → $\dfrac{4}{3}$ and $\dfrac{7}{7}$ ← numerator equal
than denominator   to denominator

A positive improper fraction represents a quantity greater than 1 whole unit or equal to 1 whole unit.

1 unit   1 unit
$\dfrac{4}{3}$

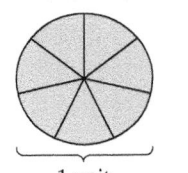
$\dfrac{7}{7}$
1 unit

Answer

2. a, b, c

Example 2 **Categorizing Fractions**

Identify each fraction as proper or improper.

a. $\frac{12}{5}$ **b.** $\frac{5}{12}$ **c.** $\frac{12}{12}$

Solution:

a. $\frac{12}{5}$ Improper fraction (numerator is greater than denominator)

b. $\frac{5}{12}$ Proper fraction (numerator is less than denominator)

c. $\frac{12}{12}$ Improper fraction (numerator is equal to denominator)

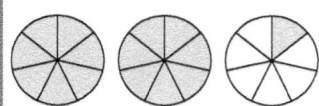

Example 3 **Writing Improper Fractions**

Write an improper fraction to represent the fractional part of an inch for the screw shown in the figure.

Avoiding Mistakes

Each whole unit is divided into 8 pieces. Therefore the screw is $\frac{11}{8}$ in., not $\frac{11}{16}$ in.

Solution:

Each 1-in. unit is divided into 8 parts, and the screw extends for 11 parts. Therefore, the screw is $\frac{11}{8}$ in.

3. Mixed Numbers

Sometimes a mixed number is used instead of an improper fraction to denote a quantity greater than one whole. For example, suppose a typist typed $\frac{9}{4}$ pages of a report. We would be more likely to say that the typist typed $2\frac{1}{4}$ pages (read as "two and one-fourth pages"). The number $2\frac{1}{4}$ is called a *mixed number* and represents 2 wholes plus $\frac{1}{4}$ of a whole.

$$\frac{9}{4} = 2\frac{1}{4}$$

In general, a **mixed number** is a sum of a whole number and a fractional part of a whole. However, by convention the plus sign is left out. For example,

$$3\frac{1}{2} \quad \text{means} \quad 3 + \frac{1}{2}$$

A negative mixed number implies that both the whole number part and the fraction part are negative. Therefore, we interpret the mixed number $-3\frac{1}{2}$ as

$$-3\frac{1}{2} = -\left(3 + \frac{1}{2}\right) = -3 + \left(-\frac{1}{2}\right)$$

Suppose we want to change a mixed number to an improper fraction. From Figure 4-3, we see that the mixed number $3\frac{1}{2}$ is the same as $\frac{7}{2}$.

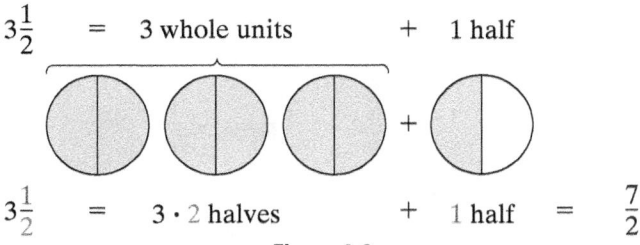

$3\frac{1}{2}$ = 3 whole units + 1 half

$3\frac{1}{2}$ = 3 · 2 halves + 1 half = $\frac{7}{2}$

Figure 4-3

The process to convert a mixed number to an improper fraction can be summarized as follows.

PROCEDURE **Changing a Mixed Number to an Improper Fraction**

Step 1 Multiply the whole number by the denominator.
Step 2 Add the result to the numerator.
Step 3 Write the result from step 2 over the denominator.

(whole number) · (denominator) + (numerator)

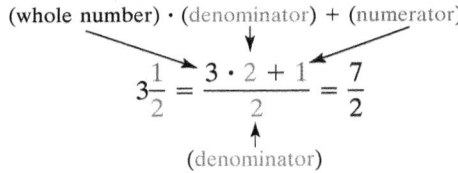

$$3\frac{1}{2} = \frac{3 \cdot 2 + 1}{2} = \frac{7}{2}$$

(denominator)

Example 4 **Converting Mixed Numbers to Improper Fractions**

Convert the mixed number to an improper fraction.

a. $7\frac{1}{4}$ **b.** $-8\frac{2}{5}$

Solution:

a. $7\frac{1}{4} = \frac{7 \cdot 4 + 1}{4}$

$= \frac{28 + 1}{4}$

$= \frac{29}{4}$

b. $-8\frac{2}{5} = -\left(8\frac{2}{5}\right)$ The entire mixed number is negative.

$= -\left(\frac{8 \cdot 5 + 2}{5}\right)$

$= -\left(\frac{40 + 2}{5}\right)$

$= -\frac{42}{5}$

Skill Practice

Convert the mixed number to an improper fraction.

7. $10\frac{5}{8}$ **8.** $-15\frac{1}{2}$

Avoiding Mistakes

The negative sign in the mixed number applies to both the whole number and the fraction.

Answers

7. $\frac{85}{8}$ **8.** $-\frac{31}{2}$

Now suppose we want to convert an improper fraction to a mixed number. In Figure 4-4, the improper fraction $\frac{13}{5}$ represents 13 slices of pizza where each slice is $\frac{1}{5}$ of a whole pizza. If we divide the 13 pieces into groups of 5, we make 2 whole pizzas with 3 pieces left over. Thus,

$$\frac{13}{5} = 2\frac{3}{5}$$

13 pieces = 2 groups of 5 + 3 left over

$$\frac{13}{5} = 2 + \frac{3}{5}$$

Figure 4-4

Avoiding Mistakes

When writing a mixed number, the + sign between the whole number and fraction should not be written.

This process can be accomplished by division.

$$\frac{13}{5} \longrightarrow \begin{array}{r} 2 \\ 5\overline{)13} \\ -10 \\ \hline 3 \end{array} \quad 2\frac{3}{5}$$

remainder

divisor

PROCEDURE Changing an Improper Fraction to a Mixed Number

Step 1 Divide the numerator by the denominator to obtain the quotient and remainder.

Step 2 The mixed number is then given by

$$\text{Quotient} + \frac{\text{remainder}}{\text{divisor}}$$

Skill Practice

Convert the improper fraction to a mixed number.

9. $\frac{14}{5}$ **10.** $-\frac{95}{22}$

Example 5 **Converting Improper Fractions to Mixed Numbers**

Convert to a mixed number.

a. $\frac{25}{6}$ **b.** $-\frac{39}{4}$

Solution:

a. $\frac{25}{6} \longrightarrow \begin{array}{r} 4 \\ 6\overline{)25} \\ -24 \\ \hline 1 \end{array} \quad 4\frac{1}{6}$

quotient remainder divisor

b. $-\frac{39}{4} = -\left(\frac{39}{4}\right)$ First perform division.

$$\begin{array}{r} 9 \\ 4\overline{)39} \\ -36 \\ \hline 3 \end{array} \quad 9\frac{3}{4}$$

quotient remainder divisor

$$= -9\frac{3}{4}$$ Then take the opposite of the result.

Answers

9. $2\frac{4}{5}$ **10.** $-4\frac{7}{22}$

The process to convert an improper fraction to a mixed number indicates that the result of a division problem can be written as a mixed number.

Example 6 Writing a Quotient as a Mixed Number

Divide. Write the quotient as a mixed number.

$$25\overline{)529}$$

Solution:

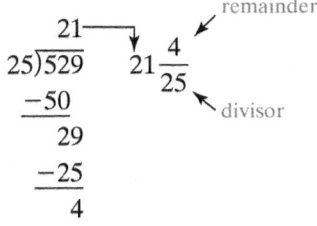

Skill Practice

Divide and write the quotient as a mixed number.

11. 5967 ÷ 41

4. Fractions and the Number Line

Fractions can be visualized on a number line. For example, to graph the fraction $\frac{3}{4}$, divide the distance between 0 and 1 into 4 equal parts. To plot the number $\frac{3}{4}$, start at 0 and count over 3 parts.

Example 7 Plotting Fractions on a Number Line

Plot the point on the number line corresponding to each fraction.

a. $\frac{1}{2}$ **b.** $\frac{5}{6}$ **c.** $-\frac{21}{5}$

Skill Practice

Plot the numbers on a number line.

12. $\frac{4}{5}$ **13.** $\frac{1}{3}$ **14.** $-\frac{13}{4}$

Solution:

a. $\frac{1}{2}$ Divide the distance between 0 and 1 into 2 equal parts.

b. $\frac{5}{6}$ Divide the distance between 0 and 1 into 6 equal parts.

c. $-\frac{21}{5} = -4\frac{1}{5}$ Write $-\frac{21}{5}$ as a mixed number.

The value $-4\frac{1}{5}$ is located one-fifth of the way between -4 and -5 on the number line. Divide the distance between -4 and -5 into 5 equal parts. Plot the point one-fifth of the way from -4 to -5.

Answers

11. $145\frac{22}{41}$

12.

13.

14.

In Section 2.1, we introduced absolute value and opposite. Now we apply these concepts to fractions.

Skill Practice

Simplify.

15. $\left|-\dfrac{12}{5}\right|$ **16.** $\left|\dfrac{3}{7}\right|$

17. $-\left|-\dfrac{3}{4}\right|$ **18.** $-\left(-\dfrac{3}{4}\right)$

Example 8 — **Determining the Absolute Value and Opposite of a Fraction**

Simplify. **a.** $\left|-\dfrac{2}{7}\right|$ **b.** $\left|\dfrac{1}{5}\right|$ **c.** $-\left|-\dfrac{4}{9}\right|$ **d.** $-\left(-\dfrac{4}{9}\right)$

Solution:

a. $\left|-\dfrac{2}{7}\right| = \dfrac{2}{7}$ The distance between $-\frac{2}{7}$ and 0 on the number line is $\frac{2}{7}$.

b. $\left|\dfrac{1}{5}\right| = \dfrac{1}{5}$ The distance between $\frac{1}{5}$ and 0 on the number line is $\frac{1}{5}$.

c. $-\left|-\dfrac{4}{9}\right| = -\left(\dfrac{4}{9}\right)$ Take the absolute value of $-\frac{4}{9}$ first. This gives $\frac{4}{9}$. Then take the opposite of $\frac{4}{9}$, which is $-\frac{4}{9}$.

$= -\dfrac{4}{9}$

d. $-\left(-\dfrac{4}{9}\right) = \dfrac{4}{9}$ Take the opposite of $-\frac{4}{9}$, which is $\frac{4}{9}$.

Answers

15. $\dfrac{12}{5}$ **16.** $\dfrac{3}{7}$

17. $-\dfrac{3}{4}$ **18.** $\dfrac{3}{4}$

Section 4.1 Practice Exercises

Study Skills Exercise

1. Define the key terms.

   a. Fraction   **b. Numerator**   **c. Denominator**   **d. Rational Number**

   e. Proper fraction   **f. Improper fraction**   **g. Mixed number**

Objective 1: Definition of a Fraction

For Exercises 2–5, identify the numerator and the denominator for each fraction.

2. $\dfrac{2}{3}$ **3.** $\dfrac{8}{9}$ **4.** $\dfrac{12x}{11y^2}$ **5.** $\dfrac{7p}{9q}$

For Exercises 6–11, write a fraction that represents the shaded area. **(See Example 1.)**

6.   **7.**   **8.**

9.

10.

11.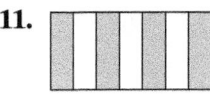

12. Write a fraction to represent the portion of gas in a gas tank represented by the gauge.

13. The scoreboard for a recent men's championship swim meet in Melbourne, Australia, shows the final standings in the event. What fraction of the finalists are from the USA?

14. Refer to the scoreboard from Exercise 13. What fraction of the finalists are from the Republic of South Africa (RSA)?

Name	Country	Time
Maginni, Filippo	ITA	48.43
Hayden, Brent	CAN	48.43
Sullivan, Eamon	AUS	48.47
Cielo Filho, Cesar	BRA	48.51
Lezak, Jason	USA	48.52
Van Den Hoogenband, Pieter	NED	48.63
Schoeman, Roland Mark	RSA	48.72
Neethling, Ryk	RSA	48.81

15. The graph categorizes a sample of people by blood type. What fraction of the sample represents people with type O blood?

16. Refer to the graph from Exercise 15. What fraction of the sample represents people with type A blood?

Sample by Blood Type

Type AB 7
Type O 41
Type B 12
Type A 43

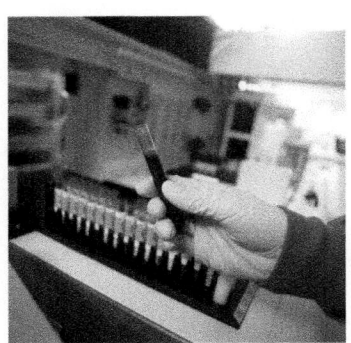

17. A class has 21 children—11 girls and 10 boys. What fraction of the class is made up of boys?

18. In a neighborhood in Ft. Lauderdale, Florida, 10 houses are for sale and 53 are not for sale. Write a fraction representing the portion of houses that are for sale.

For Exercises 19–28, simplify if possible.

19. $\dfrac{-13}{1}$ **20.** $\dfrac{-14}{1}$ **21.** $\dfrac{2}{2}$ **22.** $\dfrac{8}{8}$

23. $\dfrac{0}{-3}$ **24.** $\dfrac{0}{7}$ **25.** $\dfrac{-3}{0}$ **26.** $\dfrac{-11}{0}$

27. $\dfrac{-9}{-10}$ **28.** $\dfrac{-13}{-6}$

29. Which expressions are equivalent to $\dfrac{-9}{10}$?

    a. $\dfrac{9}{10}$ **b.** $-\dfrac{9}{10}$ **c.** $\dfrac{9}{-10}$ **d.** $\dfrac{-9}{-10}$

30. Which expressions are equivalent to $-\dfrac{4}{5}$?

    a. $\dfrac{-4}{5}$ **b.** $\dfrac{-4}{-5}$ **c.** $\dfrac{4}{-5}$ **d.** $-\dfrac{5}{4}$

31. Which expressions are equivalent to $\dfrac{-4}{1}$?

    a. $\dfrac{4}{-1}$ **b.** -4 **c.** $-\dfrac{4}{1}$ **d.** $\dfrac{1}{-4}$

32. Which expressions are equivalent to $\dfrac{-9}{1}$?

    a. $\dfrac{-9}{-1}$ **b.** $\dfrac{9}{-1}$ **c.** -9 **d.** $-\dfrac{9}{1}$

Objective 2: Proper and Improper Fractions

For Exercises 33–38, label the fraction as proper or improper. **(See Example 2.)**

33. $\dfrac{7}{8}$ **34.** $\dfrac{2}{3}$ **35.** $\dfrac{10}{10}$

36. $\dfrac{3}{3}$ **37.** $\dfrac{7}{2}$ **38.** $\dfrac{21}{20}$

For Exercises 39–42, write an improper fraction for the shaded portion of each group of figures. **(See Example 3.)**

39.

40.

41.

42.

Objective 3: Mixed Numbers

For Exercises 43–44, write an improper fraction and a mixed number for the shaded portion of each group of figures.

43.

44.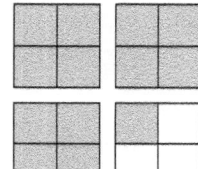

45. Write an improper fraction and a mixed number to represent the length of the nail.

1 in.   2 in.

46. Write an improper fraction and a mixed number that represent the number of cups of sugar needed for a batch of cookies, as indicated in the figure.

$\frac{1}{2}$

For Exercises 47–58, convert the mixed number to an improper fraction. **(See Example 4.)**

47. $1\frac{3}{4}$

48. $6\frac{1}{3}$

49. $-4\frac{2}{9}$

50. $-3\frac{1}{5}$

51. $-3\frac{3}{7}$

52. $-8\frac{2}{3}$

53. $6\frac{3}{4}$

54. $10\frac{3}{5}$

55. $11\frac{5}{12}$

56. $12\frac{1}{6}$

57. $-21\frac{3}{8}$

58. $-15\frac{1}{2}$

59. How many thirds are in 10?

60. How many sixths are in 2?

61. How many eighths are in $2\frac{3}{8}$?

62. How many fifths are in $2\frac{3}{5}$?

63. How many fourths are in $1\frac{3}{4}$?

64. How many thirds are in $5\frac{2}{3}$?

For Exercises 65–76, convert the improper fraction to a mixed number. **(See Example 5.)**

65. $\frac{37}{8}$

66. $\frac{13}{7}$

67. $-\frac{39}{5}$

68. $-\frac{19}{4}$

69. $-\frac{27}{10}$

70. $-\frac{43}{18}$

71. $\frac{52}{9}$

72. $\frac{67}{12}$

73. $\frac{133}{11}$

74. $\frac{51}{10}$

75. $-\frac{23}{6}$

76. $-\frac{115}{7}$

For Exercises 77–84, divide. Write the quotient as a mixed number. **(See Example 6.)**

77. $7\overline{)309}$

78. $4\overline{)921}$

79. $5281 \div 5$

80. $7213 \div 8$

81. $8913 \div 11$

82. $4257 \div 23$

83. $15\overline{)187}$

84. $34\overline{)695}$

Objective 4: Fractions and the Number Line

For Exercises 85–94, plot the fraction on the number line. **(See Example 7.)**

85. $\frac{3}{4}$ ⊢———————⊣——→
                    0   1

86. $\frac{1}{2}$ ⊢———————⊣——→
                    0   1

87. $\frac{1}{3}$ ⊢———————⊣——→
                    0   1

88. $\frac{1}{5}$ ⊢———————⊣——→
                    0   1

89. $-\frac{2}{3}$ ⊢———————⊣——→
                    −1   0

90. $-\frac{5}{6}$ ⊢———————⊣——→
                    −1   0

91. $\frac{7}{6}$ ⊢———————⊣———————⊣——→
                    0   1   2

92. $\frac{7}{5}$ ⊢———————⊣———————⊣——→
                    0   1   2

93. $-\frac{4}{3}$ ⊢———————⊣———————⊣——→
                    −2   −1   0

94. $-\frac{3}{2}$ ⊢———————⊣———————⊣——→
                    −2   −1   0

For Exercises 95–102, simplify. **(See Example 8.)**

95. $\left|-\frac{3}{4}\right|$

96. $\left|-\frac{8}{7}\right|$

97. $\left|\frac{1}{10}\right|$

98. $\left|\frac{3}{20}\right|$

99. $-\left|-\frac{7}{3}\right|$

100. $-\left|-\frac{1}{4}\right|$

101. $-\left(-\frac{7}{3}\right)$

102. $-\left(-\frac{1}{4}\right)$

Expanding Your Skills

103. True or false? Whole numbers can be written both as proper and improper fractions.

104. True or false? Suppose m and n are nonzero numbers, where $m > n$. Then $\frac{m}{n}$ is an improper fraction.

105. True or false? Suppose m and n are nonzero numbers, where $m > n$. Then $\frac{n}{m}$ is a proper fraction.

106. True or false? Suppose m and n are nonzero numbers, where $m > n$. Then $\frac{n}{3m}$ is a proper fraction.

Section 4.2   Simplifying Fractions

Objectives

1. Factorizations and Divisibility
2. Prime Factorization
3. Equivalent Fractions
4. Simplifying Fractions to Lowest Terms
5. Applications of Simplifying Fractions

1. Factorizations and Divisibility

Recall from Section 1.5 that two numbers multiplied to form a product are called factors. For example, $2 \cdot 3 = 6$ indicates that 2 and 3 are factors of 6. Likewise, because $1 \cdot 6 = 6$, the numbers 1 and 6 are factors of 6. In general, a **factor** of a number n is a nonzero whole number that divides evenly into n.

The products $2 \cdot 3$ and $1 \cdot 6$ are called factorizations of 6. In general, a **factorization** of a number n is a product of factors that equals n.

Example 1 Finding Factorizations of a Number

Find four different factorizations of 12.

Solution:

$$12 = \begin{cases} 1 \cdot 12 \\ 2 \cdot 6 \\ 3 \cdot 4 \\ 2 \cdot 2 \cdot 3 \end{cases}$$

TIP: Notice that a factorization may include more than two factors.

A factor of a number must divide evenly into the number. There are several rules by which we can quickly determine whether a number is divisible by 2, 3, 5, or 10. These are called divisibility rules.

PROCEDURE Divisibility Rules for 2, 3, 5, and 10

- *Divisibility by 2.* A whole number is divisible by 2 if it is an even number. That is, the ones-place digit is 0, 2, 4, 6, or 8.
  Examples:　26 and 384

- *Divisibility by 3.* A whole number is divisible by 3 if the sum of its digits is divisible by 3.
  Example:　312　(sum of digits is $3 + 1 + 2 = 6$, which is divisible by 3)

- *Divisibility by 5.* A whole number is divisible by 5 if its ones-place digit is 5 or 0.
  Examples:　45 and 260

- *Divisibility by 10.* A whole number is divisible by 10 if its ones-place digit is 0.
  Examples:　30 and 170

The divisibility rules for other numbers are harder to remember. In these cases, it is often easier simply to perform division to test for divisibility.

Example 2 Applying the Divisibility Rules

Determine whether the given number is divisible by 2, 3, 5, or 10.

a. 720　　**b.** 82

TIP: When in doubt about divisibility, you can check by division. When we divide 82 by 2, the remainder is zero. This means that 2 divides evenly into 82.

Solution:

Test for Divisibility

a. 720	By 2:	Yes.	The number 720 is even.
	By 3:	Yes.	The sum $7 + 2 + 0 = 9$ is divisible by 3.
	By 5:	Yes.	The ones-place digit is 0.
	By 10:	Yes.	The ones-place digit is 0.
b. 82	By 2:	Yes.	The number 82 is even.
	By 3:	No.	The sum $8 + 2 = 10$ is not divisible by 3.
	By 5:	No.	The ones-place digit is not 5 or 0.
	By 10:	No.	The ones-place digit is not 0.

2. Prime Factorization

Two important classifications of whole numbers are prime numbers and composite numbers.

> **DEFINITION** Prime and Composite Numbers
> - A **prime number** is a whole number greater than 1 that has only two factors (itself and 1).
> - A **composite number** is a whole number greater than 1 that is not prime. That is, a composite number will have at least one factor other than 1 and the number itself.
>
> *Note:* The whole numbers 0 and 1 are neither prime nor composite.

Skill Practice

Determine whether the number is prime, composite, or neither.
4. 39   **5.** 0   **6.** 41

Example 3 Identifying Prime and Composite Numbers

Determine whether the number is prime, composite, or neither.

a. 19   **b.** 51   **c.** 1

Solution:

a. The number 19 is prime because its only factors are 1 and 19.

b. The number 51 is composite because $3 \cdot 17 = 51$. That is, 51 has factors other than 1 and 51.

c. The number 1 is neither prime nor composite by definition.

TIP: The number 2 is the only even prime number.

Prime numbers are used in a variety of ways in mathematics. It is advisable to become familiar with the first several prime numbers: $2, 3, 5, 7, 11, 13, 17, 19, 23, 29, \ldots$

In Example 1 we found four factorizations of 12.

$$1 \cdot 12$$
$$2 \cdot 6$$
$$3 \cdot 4$$
$$2 \cdot 2 \cdot 3$$

The last factorization $2 \cdot 2 \cdot 3$ consists of only prime-number factors. Therefore, we say $2 \cdot 2 \cdot 3$ is the prime factorization of 12.

Concept Connections

7. Is the product $2 \cdot 3 \cdot 10$ the prime factorization of 60? Explain.

> **DEFINITION** Prime Factorization
>
> The **prime factorization** of a number is the factorization in which every factor is a prime number.
>
> *Note:* The order in which the factors are written does not affect the product.

Prime factorizations of numbers will be particularly helpful when we add, subtract, multiply, divide, and simplify fractions.

Answers

4. Composite   **5.** Neither   **6.** Prime
7. No. The factor 10 is not a prime number. The prime factorization of 60 is $2 \cdot 2 \cdot 3 \cdot 5$.

Example 4 **Determining the Prime Factorization of a Number**

Find the prime factorization of 220.

Solution:

One method to factor a whole number is to make a factor tree. Begin by determining *any* two numbers that when multiplied equal 220. Then continue factoring each factor until the branches "end" in prime numbers.

←Branches end in prime numbers.

> **TIP:** The prime factorization from Example 4 can also be expressed by using exponents as $2^2 \cdot 5 \cdot 11$.

Therefore, the prime factorization of 220 is $2 \cdot 2 \cdot 5 \cdot 11$.

> **TIP:** In creating a factor tree, you can begin with any two factors of the number. The result will be the same. In Example 4, we could have started with the factors of 4 and 55.
>
>
>
> The prime factorization is $2 \cdot 2 \cdot 5 \cdot 11$ as expected.

Another technique to find the prime factorization of a number is to divide the number by the smallest known prime factor of the number. Then divide the quotient by its smallest prime factor. Continue dividing in this fashion until the quotient is a prime number. The prime factorization is the product of divisors and the final quotient. This is demonstrated in Example 5.

Example 5 **Determining Prime Factorizations**

Find the prime factorization.

a. 198   **b.** 153

Solution:

a. 2 is the smallest prime factor of 198. ——→ 2)198
    3 is the smallest prime factor of 99. ——→ 3)99
    3 is the smallest prime factor of 33 ——→ 3)33
    The last quotient is prime. ——→ 11

The prime factorization of 198 is $2 \cdot 3 \cdot 3 \cdot 11$ or $2 \cdot 3^2 \cdot 11$.

b. 3)153
    3)51
    17

The prime factorization of 153 is $3 \cdot 3 \cdot 17$ or $3^2 \cdot 17$.

Skill Practice
8. Find the prime factorization of 90.

Skill Practice
Find the prime factorization of the given number.
9. 168   **10.** 990

Answers
8. $2 \cdot 3 \cdot 3 \cdot 5$ or $2 \cdot 3^2 \cdot 5$
9. $2 \cdot 2 \cdot 2 \cdot 3 \cdot 7$ or $2^3 \cdot 3 \cdot 7$
10. $2 \cdot 3 \cdot 3 \cdot 5 \cdot 11$ or $2 \cdot 3^2 \cdot 5 \cdot 11$

3. Equivalent Fractions

The fractions $\frac{3}{6}$, $\frac{2}{4}$, and $\frac{1}{2}$ all represent the same portion of a whole. See Figure 4-5. Therefore, we say that the fractions are *equivalent*.

$$\frac{3}{6} \quad = \quad \frac{2}{4} \quad = \quad \frac{1}{2}$$

Figure 4-5

Avoiding Mistakes

The test to determine whether two fractions are equivalent is not the same process as multiplying fractions. Multiplying fractions is covered in Section 4.3.

One method to show that two fractions are equivalent is to calculate their cross products. For example, to show that $\frac{3}{6} = \frac{2}{4}$, we have

$$\frac{3}{6} \quad \diagdown\!\!\!\diagup \quad \frac{2}{4}$$

$$3 \cdot 4 \overset{?}{=} 6 \cdot 2$$

$$12 = 12 \qquad \text{Yes. The fractions are equivalent.}$$

Skill Practice

Fill in the blank $\square$ with = or ≠.

11. $\frac{13}{24}\,\square\,\frac{6}{11}$ **12.** $\frac{9}{4}\,\square\,\frac{54}{24}$

Example 6   **Determining Whether Two Fractions Are Equivalent**

Fill in the blank $\square$ with = or ≠.

a. $\frac{18}{39}\,\square\,\frac{6}{13}$ **b.** $\frac{5}{7}\,\square\,\frac{7}{9}$

Solution:

a. $\frac{18}{39} \quad \overset{?}{\diagdown\!\!\!\diagup} \quad \frac{6}{13}$

$18 \cdot 13 \overset{?}{=} 39 \cdot 6$

$234 = 234$

Therefore, $\frac{18}{39} \boxed{=} \frac{6}{13}$.

b. $\frac{5}{7} \quad \overset{?}{\diagdown\!\!\!\diagup} \quad \frac{7}{9}$

$5 \cdot 9 \overset{?}{=} 7 \cdot 7$

$45 \neq 49$

Therefore, $\frac{5}{7} \boxed{\neq} \frac{7}{9}$.

4. Simplifying Fractions to Lowest Terms

In Figure 4-5, we see that $\frac{3}{6}$, $\frac{2}{4}$, and $\frac{1}{2}$ all represent equal quantities. However, the fraction $\frac{1}{2}$ is said to be in **lowest terms** because the numerator and denominator share no common factors other than 1.

To simplify a fraction to lowest terms, we apply the following important principle.

PROPERTY **Fundamental Principle of Fractions**

Suppose that a number, c, is a common factor in the numerator and denominator of a fraction. Then

$$\frac{a \cdot c}{b \cdot c} = \frac{a}{b} \cdot \frac{c}{c} = \frac{a}{b} \cdot 1 = \frac{a}{b} \qquad \text{provided } b \neq 0.$$

Answers

11. ≠   **12.** =

To simplify a fraction, we begin by factoring the numerator and denominator into prime factors. This will help identify the common factors.

Example 7 **Simplifying a Fraction to Lowest Terms**

Simplify to lowest terms.

a. $\dfrac{6}{10}$ **b.** $-\dfrac{170}{102}$ **c.** $\dfrac{20}{24}$

Solution:

a. $\dfrac{6}{10} = \dfrac{3 \cdot 2}{5 \cdot 2}$ Factor the numerator and denominator. Notice that 2 is a common factor.

$= \dfrac{3}{5} \cdot \dfrac{2}{2}$ Apply the fundamental principle of fractions.

$= \dfrac{3}{5} \cdot 1$ Any nonzero number divided by itself is 1.

$= \dfrac{3}{5}$

b. $-\dfrac{170}{102} = -\dfrac{5 \cdot 2 \cdot 17}{3 \cdot 2 \cdot 17}$ Factor the numerator and denominator.

$= -\dfrac{5}{3} \cdot \dfrac{2}{2} \cdot \dfrac{17}{17}$ Apply the fundamental principle of fractions.

$= -\dfrac{5}{3} \cdot 1 \cdot 1$ Any nonzero number divided by itself is 1.

$= -\dfrac{5}{3}$

c. $\dfrac{20}{24} = \dfrac{5 \cdot 2 \cdot 2}{3 \cdot 2 \cdot 2 \cdot 2}$ Factor the numerator and denominator.

$= \dfrac{5}{3 \cdot 2} \cdot \dfrac{2}{2} \cdot \dfrac{2}{2}$ Apply the fundamental principle of fractions.

$= \dfrac{5}{6} \cdot 1 \cdot 1$

$= \dfrac{5}{6}$

Skill Practice

Simplify to lowest terms.

13. $\dfrac{15}{35}$ **14.** $-\dfrac{26}{195}$

15. $\dfrac{150}{105}$

TIP: To check that you have simplified a fraction correctly, verify that the cross products are equal.

$$\dfrac{6}{10} \quad \dfrac{3}{5}$$

$$6 \cdot 5 \stackrel{?}{=} 10 \cdot 3$$

$$30 = 30 \checkmark$$

In Example 7, we show numerous steps to simplify fractions to lowest terms. However, the process is often made easier. For instance, we sometimes divide common factors, and replace them with the new common factor of 1.

$$\frac{20}{24} = \frac{5 \cdot \overset{1}{2} \cdot \overset{1}{2}}{3 \cdot 2 \cdot \underset{1}{2} \cdot \underset{1}{2}} = \frac{5}{6}$$

Answers

13. $\dfrac{3}{7}$ **14.** $-\dfrac{2}{15}$ **15.** $\dfrac{10}{7}$

The largest number that divides evenly into the numerator and denominator is called their **greatest common factor**. By identifying the greatest common factor you can simplify the process even more. For example, the greatest common factor of 20 and 24 is 4.

$$\frac{20}{24} = \frac{5 \cdot \overset{1}{4}}{6 \cdot \underset{1}{4}} = \frac{5}{6}$$

Notice that "dividing out" the common factor of 4 has the same effect as dividing the numerator and denominator by 4. This is often done mentally.

$$\frac{\overset{5}{20}}{\underset{6}{24}} = \frac{5}{6} \longleftarrow \text{20 divided by 4 equals 5.} \\ \longleftarrow \text{24 divided by 4 equals 6.}$$

TIP: Simplifying a fraction is also called reducing a fraction to lowest terms. For example, the simplified (or reduced) form of $\frac{20}{24}$ is $\frac{5}{6}$.

Example 8   **Simplifying Fractions to Lowest Terms**

Simplify the fraction. Write the answer as a fraction or an integer.

a. $\frac{75}{25}$ **b.** $\frac{12}{60}$

Solution:

a. $\frac{75}{25} = \frac{3 \cdot \overset{1}{25}}{1 \cdot \underset{1}{25}} = \frac{3}{1} = 3$ The greatest common factor in the numerator and denominator is 25.

Or alternatively: $\frac{\overset{3}{75}}{\underset{1}{25}} = \frac{3}{1} \longleftarrow$ 75 divided by 25 equals 3.
$\longleftarrow$ 25 divided by 25 equals 1.

$= 3$ **TIP:** Recall that any fraction of the form $\frac{n}{1} = n$. Therefore, $\frac{3}{1} = 3$.

b. $\frac{12}{60} = \frac{1 \cdot \overset{1}{12}}{5 \cdot \underset{1}{12}} = \frac{1}{5}$ The greatest common factor in the numerator and denominator is 12.

Or alternatively: $= \frac{\overset{1}{12}}{\underset{5}{60}} = \frac{1}{5} \longleftarrow$ 12 divided by 12 equals 1.
$\longleftarrow$ 60 divided by 12 equals 5.

Example 9 **Simplifying Fractions by 10, 100, and 1000**

Simplify each fraction to lowest terms by first reducing by 10, 100, or 1000. Write the answer as a fraction.

a. $\dfrac{170}{30}$ **b.** $\dfrac{2500}{75,000}$

Solution:

a. $\dfrac{170}{30} = \dfrac{17\cancel{0}}{3\cancel{0}}$ Both 170 and 30 are divisible by 10. "Strike through" one zero. This is equivalent to dividing by 10.

$= \dfrac{17}{3}$ The fraction $\frac{17}{3}$ is simplified completely.

b. $\dfrac{2500}{75,000} = \dfrac{25\cancel{00}}{75,0\cancel{00}}$ Both 2500 and 75,000 are divisible by 100. "Strike through" two zeros. This is equivalent to dividing by 100.

$= \dfrac{\overset{1}{\cancel{25}}}{\underset{30}{\cancel{750}}}$ Simplify further. Both 25 and 750 have a common factor of 25.

$= \dfrac{1}{30}$

The process to simplify a fraction is the same for fractions that contain variables. This is shown in Example 10.

Example 10 **Simplifying a Fraction Containing Variables**

Simplify. **a.** $\dfrac{10xy}{6x}$ **b.** $\dfrac{2a^3}{4a^4}$

Solution:

a. $\dfrac{10xy}{6x} = \dfrac{2 \cdot 5 \cdot x \cdot y}{2 \cdot 3 \cdot x}$ Factor the numerator and denominator. Common factors are shown in red.

$= \dfrac{\overset{1}{\cancel{2}} \cdot 5 \cdot \overset{1}{\cancel{x}} \cdot y}{\underset{1}{\cancel{2}} \cdot 3 \cdot \underset{1}{\cancel{x}}}$ Simplify.

$= \dfrac{5y}{3}$

b. $\dfrac{2a^3}{4a^4} = \dfrac{2 \cdot a \cdot a \cdot a}{2 \cdot 2 \cdot a \cdot a \cdot a \cdot a}$ Factor the numerator and denominator. Common factors are shown in red.

$= \dfrac{\overset{1}{\cancel{2}} \cdot \overset{1}{\cancel{a}} \cdot \overset{1}{\cancel{a}} \cdot \overset{1}{\cancel{a}}}{\underset{1}{\cancel{2}} \cdot 2 \cdot \underset{1}{\cancel{a}} \cdot \underset{1}{\cancel{a}} \cdot \underset{1}{\cancel{a}} \cdot a}$ Simplify.

$= \dfrac{1}{2a}$

Skill Practice

Simplify to lowest terms by first reducing by 10, 100, or 1000.

18. $\dfrac{630}{190}$ **19.** $\dfrac{1300}{52,000}$

Avoiding Mistakes

The "strike through" method only works for the digit 0 at the *end* of the numerator and denominator.

Concept Connections

20. How many zeros may be eliminated from the numerator and denominator of the fraction $\frac{430,000}{154,000,000}$?

Skill Practice

Simplify.

21. $\dfrac{18d}{15cd}$ **22.** $\dfrac{9w^2}{36w^3}$

Avoiding Mistakes

Since division by 0 is undefined, we know that the value of the variable cannot make the denominator equal 0. In Example 10, $x \neq 0$ and $a \neq 0$.

Answers

18. $\dfrac{63}{19}$ **19.** $\dfrac{1}{40}$
20. Four zeros; the numerator and denominator are both divisible by 10,000.
21. $\dfrac{6}{5c}$ **22.** $\dfrac{1}{4w}$

5. Applications of Simplifying Fractions

Example 11 **Simplifying Fractions in an Application**

Madeleine got 28 out of 35 problems correct on an algebra exam. David got 27 out of 45 questions correct on a different algebra exam.

a. What fractional part of the exam did each student answer correctly?

b. Which student performed better?

Solution:

a. Fractional part correct for Madeleine:

$$\frac{28}{35} \quad \text{or equivalently} \quad \frac{28}{35} = \frac{4 \cdot \overset{1}{7}}{5 \cdot \underset{1}{7}} = \frac{4}{5}$$

Fractional part correct for David:

$$\frac{27}{45} \quad \text{or equivalently} \quad \frac{27}{45} = \frac{3 \cdot \overset{1}{9}}{5 \cdot \underset{1}{9}} = \frac{3}{5}$$

b. From the simplified form of each fraction, we see that Madeleine performed better because $\frac{4}{5} > \frac{3}{5}$. That is, 4 parts out of 5 is greater than 3 parts out of 5. This is also easily verified on a number line.

Section 4.2 Practice Exercises

Study Skills Exercise

1. Define the key terms.

    a. Factor   **b. Factorization**   **c. Prime number**   **d. Composite number**

    e. Prime factorization   **f. Lowest terms**   **g. Greatest common factor**

Review Exercises

For Exercises 2–3, write two fractions, one representing the shaded area and one representing the unshaded area.

2. ⊢┼┼┼┼┼┼┼┼┼┼┼⊢→
    0   1

3.

4. Write a fraction with numerator 6 and denominator 5. Is this fraction proper or improper?

5. Write the fraction $\frac{23}{5}$ as a mixed number.

6. Write the mixed number $6\frac{2}{7}$ as a fraction.

Objective 1: Factorizations and Divisibility

For Exercises 7–10, find two different factorizations of each number. (Answers may vary.) **(See Example 1.)**

7. 8   **8.** 20   ● **9.** 24   **10.** 14

11. State the divisibility rule for dividing by 2.   **12.** State the divisibility rule for dividing by 10.

13. State the divisibility rule for dividing by 3.   **14.** State the divisibility rule for dividing by 5.

For Exercises 15–22, determine if the number is divisible by   **a.** 2   **b.** 3   **c.** 5   **d.** 10
(See Example 2.)

15. 45   **16.** 100   **17.** 137   **18.** 241

● **19.** 108   **20.** 1040   **21.** 3140   **22.** 2115

23. Ms. Berglund has 28 students in her class. Can she distribute a package of 84 candies evenly to her students?

24. Mr. Blankenship has 22 students in an algebra class. He has 110 sheets of graph paper. Can he distribute the graph paper evenly among his students?

Objective 2: Prime Factorization

For Exercises 25–32, determine whether the number is prime, composite, or neither. **(See Example 3.)**

25. 7   **26.** 17   **27.** 10   **28.** 21

29. 1   **30.** 0   **31.** 97   **32.** 57

● **33.** One method for finding prime numbers is the *sieve of Eratosthenes*. The natural numbers from 2 to 50 are shown in the table. Start at the number 2 (the smallest prime number). Leave the number 2 and cross out every second number after the number 2. This will eliminate all numbers that are multiples of 2. Then go back to the beginning of the chart and leave the number 3, but cross out every third number after the number 3 (thus eliminating the multiples of 3). Begin at the next open number and continue this process. The numbers that remain are prime numbers. Use this process to find the prime numbers less than 50.

	2	3	4	5	6	7	8	9	10
11	12	13	14	15	16	17	18	19	20
21	22	23	24	25	26	27	28	29	30
31	32	33	34	35	36	37	38	39	40
41	42	43	44	45	46	47	48	49	50

34. True or false? The square of any prime number is also a prime number.

35. True or false? All odd numbers are prime.   **36.** True or false? All even numbers are composite.

For Exercises 37–40, determine whether the factorization represents the prime factorization. If not, explain why.

● **37.** $36 = 2 \cdot 2 \cdot 9$ **38.** $48 = 2 \cdot 3 \cdot 8$ **39.** $210 = 5 \cdot 2 \cdot 7 \cdot 3$ **40.** $126 = 3 \cdot 7 \cdot 3 \cdot 2$

For Exercises 41–48, find the prime factorization. **(See Examples 4 and 5.)**

41. 70   **42.** 495   **43.** 260   **44.** 175

45. 147   **46.** 231   ● **47.** 616   **48.** 364

Objective 3: Equivalent Fractions

For Exercises 49–50, shade the second figure so that it expresses a fraction equivalent to the first figure.

● **49.**   **50.**

51. True or false? The fractions $\frac{4}{5}$ and $\frac{5}{4}$ are equivalent.

52. True or false? The fractions $\frac{3}{1}$ and $\frac{1}{3}$ are equivalent.

For Exercises 53–60, determine if the fractions are equivalent. Then fill in the blank with either = or ≠.
(See Example 6.)

53. $\frac{2}{3} \square \frac{3}{5}$ **54.** $\frac{1}{4} \square \frac{2}{9}$ **55.** $\frac{1}{2} \square \frac{3}{6}$ ● **56.** $\frac{6}{16} \square \frac{3}{8}$

57. $\frac{12}{16} \square \frac{3}{4}$ **58.** $\frac{4}{5} \square \frac{12}{15}$ **59.** $\frac{8}{9} \square \frac{20}{27}$ **60.** $\frac{5}{6} \square \frac{12}{18}$

Objective 4: Simplifying Fractions to Lowest Terms

For Exercises 61–80, simplify the fraction to lowest terms. Write the answer as a fraction or an integer.
(See Examples 7–8.)

61. $\frac{12}{24}$ **62.** $\frac{15}{18}$ **63.** $\frac{6}{18}$ **64.** $\frac{21}{24}$

65. $-\frac{36}{20}$ **66.** $-\frac{49}{42}$ **67.** $-\frac{15}{12}$ **68.** $-\frac{30}{25}$

69. $\frac{9}{9}$ **70.** $\frac{2}{2}$ ● **71.** $\frac{105}{140}$ **72.** $\frac{84}{126}$

73. $-\frac{33}{11}$ **74.** $-\frac{65}{5}$ **75.** $\frac{77}{110}$ **76.** $\frac{85}{153}$

77. $\frac{385}{195}$ **78.** $\frac{39}{130}$ **79.** $\frac{34}{85}$ **80.** $\frac{69}{92}$

For Exercises 81–88, simplify to lowest terms by first reducing the powers of 10. **(See Example 9.)**

81. $\frac{120}{160}$ **82.** $\frac{720}{800}$ **83.** $-\frac{3000}{1800}$ **84.** $-\frac{2000}{1500}$

● **85.** $\frac{42,000}{22,000}$ **86.** $\frac{50,000}{65,000}$ **87.** $\frac{5100}{30,000}$ **88.** $\frac{9800}{28,000}$

For Exercises 89–96, simplify the expression. **(See Example 10.)**

89. $\dfrac{16ab}{10a}$ **90.** $\dfrac{25mn}{10n}$ **91.** $\dfrac{14xyz}{7z}$ **92.** $\dfrac{18pqr}{6q}$

93. $\dfrac{5x^4}{15x^3}$ **94.** $\dfrac{4y^3}{20y}$ **95.** $-\dfrac{6ac^2}{12ac^4}$ **96.** $-\dfrac{3m^2n}{9m^2n^4}$

Objective 5: Applications of Simplifying Fractions

97. André tossed a coin 48 times and heads came up 20 times. What fractional part of the tosses came up heads? What fractional part came up tails?

98. At Pizza Company, Lee made 70 pizzas one day. There were 105 pizzas sold that day. What fraction of the pizzas did Lee make?

99. a. What fraction of the alphabet is made up of vowels? (Include the letter y as a vowel, not a consonant.)

   b. What fraction of the alphabet is made up of consonants?

100. Of the 88 constellations that can be seen in the night sky, 12 are associated with astrological horoscopes. The names of as many as 36 constellations are associated with animals or mythical creatures.

   a. Of the 88 constellations, what fraction is associated with horoscopes?

   b. What fraction of the constellations have names associated with animals or mythical creatures?

101. Jonathan and Jared both sold candy bars for a fundraiser. Jonathan sold 25 of his 35 candy bars, and Jared sold 24 of his 28 candy bars. **(See Example 11.)**

   a. What fractional part of his total number of candy bars did each person sell?

   b. Which person sold the greater fractional part?

102. Lisa and Lynette are taking online courses. Lisa has completed 14 out of 16 assignments in her course while Lynette has completed 15 out of 24 assignments.

   a. What fractional part of her total number of assignments did each woman complete?

   b. Which woman has completed more of her course?

 103. Raymond read 720 pages of a 792-page book. His roommate, Travis, read 540 pages from a 660-page book.

   a. What fractional part of the book did each person read?

   b. Which of the roommates read a greater fraction of his book?

104. Mr. Bishop and Ms. Waymire both gave exams today. By mid-afternoon, Mr. Bishop had finished grading 16 out of 36 exams, and Ms. Waymire had finished grading 15 out of 27 exams.

   a. What fractional part of her total has Ms. Waymire completed?

   b. What fractional part of his total has Mr. Bishop completed?

105. For a recent year, the population of the United States was reported to be 296,000,000. During the same year, the population of California was 36,458,000.

    a. Round the U.S. population to the nearest hundred million.

    b. Round the population of California to the nearest million.

    c. Using the results from parts (a) and (b), write a simplified fraction showing the portion of the U.S. population represented by California.

106. For a recent year, the population of the United States was reported to be 296,000,000. During the same year, the population of Ethiopia was 75,067,000.

    a. Round the U.S. population to the nearest hundred million.

    b. Round the population of Ethiopia to the nearest million.

    c. Using the results from parts (a) and (b), write a simplified fraction comparing the population of the United States to the population of Ethiopia.

    d. Based on the result from part (c), how many times greater is the U.S. population than the population of Ethiopia?

Expanding Your Skills

107. Write three fractions equivalent to $\frac{3}{4}$.

108. Write three fractions equivalent to $\frac{1}{3}$.

109. Write three fractions equivalent to $-\frac{12}{18}$.

110. Write three fractions equivalent to $-\frac{80}{100}$.

Calculator Connections

Topic: Simplifying Fractions on a Calculator

Some calculators have a fraction key, $\boxed{a\%}$. To enter a fraction, follow this example.

Expression: $\dfrac{3}{4}$

Keystrokes: $3 \boxed{a\%} 4 \boxed{=}$

Result: $\boxed{\qquad 3 \lrcorner 4 \qquad}$

       ↑   ↑

   numerator   denominator

To simplify a fraction to lowest terms, follow this example.

Expression: $\dfrac{22}{10}$

Keystrokes: $22 \boxed{a\%} 10 \boxed{=}$

Result: $\boxed{\quad 2 \lrcorner 1 \lrcorner 5 \quad} = 2\frac{1}{5}$

     ↑   ↑

 whole number fraction

To convert to an improper fraction, press $\boxed{2^{nd}}\ \boxed{d/e}$ $\qquad \boxed{\quad 11 \lrcorner 5 \quad} = \dfrac{11}{5}$

Calculator Exercises

For Exercises 111–118, use a calculator to simplify the fractions. Write the answer as a proper or improper fraction.

111. $\dfrac{792}{891}$

112. $\dfrac{728}{784}$

113. $\dfrac{779}{969}$

114. $\dfrac{462}{220}$

115. $\dfrac{493}{510}$

116. $\dfrac{871}{469}$

117. $\dfrac{969}{646}$

118. $\dfrac{713}{437}$

| **Multiplication and Division of Fractions** | **Section 4.3** |

1. Multiplication of Fractions

Suppose Elija takes $\frac{1}{3}$ of a cake and then gives $\frac{1}{2}$ of this portion to his friend Max. Max gets $\frac{1}{2}$ of $\frac{1}{3}$ of the cake. This is equivalent to the expression $\frac{1}{2} \cdot \frac{1}{3}$. See Figure 4-6.

Elija takes $\frac{1}{3}$

Max gets
$\frac{1}{2}$ of $\frac{1}{3} = \frac{1}{6}$

Figure 4-6

From the illustration, the product $\frac{1}{2} \cdot \frac{1}{3} = \frac{1}{6}$. Notice that the product $\frac{1}{6}$ is found by multiplying the numerators and multiplying the denominators. This is true in general to multiply fractions.

> **PROCEDURE Multiplying Fractions**
>
> To multiply fractions, write the product of the numerators over the product of the denominators. Then simplify the resulting fraction, if possible.
>
> $$\frac{a}{b} \cdot \frac{c}{d} = \frac{a \cdot c}{b \cdot d} \qquad \text{provided } b \text{ and } d \text{ are not equal to 0.}$$

Concept Connections

1. What fraction is $\frac{1}{2}$ of $\frac{1}{4}$ of a whole?

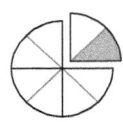

Example 1 Multiplying Fractions

Multiply.

a. $\dfrac{2}{5} \cdot \dfrac{4}{7}$ **b.** $-\dfrac{8}{3} \cdot 5$

Solution:

a. $\dfrac{2}{5} \cdot \dfrac{4}{7} = \dfrac{2 \cdot 4}{5 \cdot 7} = \dfrac{8}{35}$ ⟵ Multiply the numerators.
⟵ Multiply the denominators.

Notice that the product $\frac{8}{35}$ is simplified completely because there are no common factors shared by 8 and 35.

b. $-\dfrac{8}{3} \cdot 5 = -\dfrac{8}{3} \cdot \dfrac{5}{1}$ First write the whole number as a fraction.

$= -\dfrac{8 \cdot 5}{3 \cdot 1}$ Multiply the numerators. Multiply the denominators.
The product of two numbers of different signs is negative.

$= -\dfrac{40}{3}$ The product cannot be simplified because there are no common factors shared by 40 and 3.

Skill Practice

Multiply. Write the answer as a fraction.

2. $\dfrac{2}{3} \cdot \dfrac{5}{9}$ **3.** $-\dfrac{7}{12} \cdot 11$

Answers

1. $\dfrac{1}{8}$ **2.** $\dfrac{10}{27}$ **3.** $-\dfrac{77}{12}$

Example 2 illustrates a case where the product of fractions must be simplified.

Example 2 **Multiplying and Simplifying Fractions**

Multiply the fractions and simplify if possible. $\quad \dfrac{4}{30} \cdot \dfrac{5}{14}$

Solution:

$$\frac{4}{30} \cdot \frac{5}{14} = \frac{4 \cdot 5}{30 \cdot 14} \qquad \text{Multiply the numerators. Multiply the denominators.}$$

$$= \frac{20}{420} \qquad \text{Simplify by first dividing 20 and 420 by 10.}$$

$$= \frac{\overset{1}{2}}{\underset{21}{42}} \qquad \text{Simplify further by dividing 2 and 42 by 2.}$$

$$= \frac{1}{21}$$

It is often easier to simplify *before* multiplying. Consider the product from Example 2.

$$\frac{4}{30} \cdot \frac{5}{14} = \frac{\overset{2}{4}}{\underset{6}{30}} \cdot \frac{\overset{1}{5}}{\underset{7}{14}} \qquad \begin{array}{l} \text{4 and 14 share a common factor of 2.} \\ \text{30 and 5 share a common factor of 5.} \end{array}$$

$$= \frac{\overset{\overset{1}{2}}{4}}{\underset{\underset{3}{6}}{30}} \cdot \frac{\overset{1}{5}}{\underset{7}{14}} \qquad \text{2 and 6 share a common factor of 2.}$$

$$= \frac{1}{21}$$

Example 3 **Multiplying and Simplifying Fractions**

Multiply and simplify. $\quad \left(-\dfrac{10}{18}\right)\left(-\dfrac{21}{55}\right)$

Solution:

$$\left(-\frac{10}{18}\right)\left(-\frac{21}{55}\right) = +\left(\frac{10}{18} \cdot \frac{21}{55}\right) \qquad \begin{array}{l} \text{First note that the product will be} \\ \text{positive. The product of two numbers} \\ \text{with the same sign is positive.} \end{array}$$

$$\frac{10}{18} \cdot \frac{21}{55} = \frac{\overset{2}{10}}{\underset{6}{18}} \cdot \frac{\overset{7}{21}}{\underset{11}{55}} \qquad \begin{array}{l} \text{10 and 55 share a common factor of 5.} \\ \text{18 and 21 share a common factor of 3.} \end{array}$$

$$= \frac{\overset{\overset{1}{2}}{10}}{\underset{\underset{3}{6}}{18}} \cdot \frac{\overset{7}{21}}{\underset{11}{55}} \qquad \begin{array}{l} \text{We can simplify further because 2} \\ \text{and 6 share a common factor of 2.} \end{array}$$

$$= \frac{7}{33}$$

Example 4 **Multiplying Fractions Containing Variables**

Multiply and simplify.

a. $\dfrac{5x}{7} \cdot \dfrac{2}{15x}$ **b.** $\dfrac{2a^2}{3b} \cdot \dfrac{b^3}{a}$

> **Avoiding Mistakes**
>
> In Example 4, $x \neq 0$, $a \neq 0$, and $b \neq 0$. The denominator of a fraction cannot equal 0.

Solution:

a. $\dfrac{5x}{7} \cdot \dfrac{2}{15x} = \dfrac{5 \cdot x \cdot 2}{7 \cdot 3 \cdot 5 \cdot x}$ Multiply fractions and factor.

$= \dfrac{\overset{1}{\cancel{5}} \cdot \overset{1}{\cancel{x}} \cdot 2}{7 \cdot 3 \cdot \underset{1}{\cancel{5}} \cdot \underset{1}{\cancel{x}}}$ Simplify. The common factors are in red.

$= \dfrac{2}{21}$

b. $\dfrac{2a^2}{3b} \cdot \dfrac{b^3}{a} = \dfrac{2 \cdot a \cdot a \cdot b \cdot b \cdot b}{3 \cdot b \cdot a}$ Multiply fractions and factor.

$= \dfrac{2 \cdot a \cdot \overset{1}{\cancel{a}} \cdot \overset{1}{\cancel{b}} \cdot b \cdot b}{3 \cdot \underset{1}{\cancel{b}} \cdot \underset{1}{\cancel{a}}}$ Simplify. The common factors are in red.

$= \dfrac{2ab^2}{3}$

Skill Practice

Multiply and simplify.

6. $\dfrac{3w}{11} \cdot \dfrac{5}{6w}$

7. $\dfrac{5x^3}{6y} \cdot \dfrac{y^2}{x}$

2. Area of a Triangle

Recall that the area of a rectangle with length l and width w is given by

$$A = l \cdot w$$

> **FORMULA** **Area of a Triangle**
>
> The formula for the area of a triangle is given by $A = \frac{1}{2}bh$, read "one-half base times height."
>
>

The value of b is the measure of the base of the triangle. The value of h is the measure of the height of the triangle. The base b can be chosen as the length of any of the sides of the triangle. However, once you have chosen the base, the height must be measured as the shortest distance from the base to the opposite vertex (or point) of the triangle.

Figure 4-7 shows the same triangle with different choices for the base. Figure 4-8 shows a situation in which the height must be drawn "outside" the triangle. In such a case, notice that the height is drawn down to an imaginary extension of the base line.

Animation

Answers

6. $\dfrac{5}{22}$ **7.** $\dfrac{5x^2y}{6}$

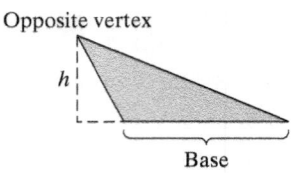

Figure 4-7

Figure 4-8

Find the area of the triangle.

8.

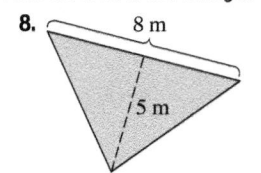

Example 5   **Finding the Area of a Triangle**

Find the area of the triangle.

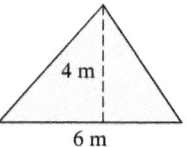

Solution:

$b = 6 \text{ m}$ and $h = 4 \text{ m}$ Identify the measure of the base and the height.

$A = \dfrac{1}{2} bh$

$= \dfrac{1}{2}(6 \text{ m})(4 \text{ m})$ Apply the formula for the area of a triangle.

$= \dfrac{1}{2}\left(\dfrac{6}{1} \text{ m}\right)\left(\dfrac{4}{1} \text{ m}\right)$ Write the whole numbers as fractions.

$= \dfrac{1}{2}\left(\dfrac{\overset{3}{6}}{1} \text{ m}\right)\left(\dfrac{4}{1} \text{ m}\right)$ Simplify.

$= \dfrac{12}{1} \text{ m}^2$ Multiply numerators. Multiply denominators.

$= 12 \text{ m}^2$ The area of the triangle is 12 square meters (m^2).

Find the area of the triangle.

9.

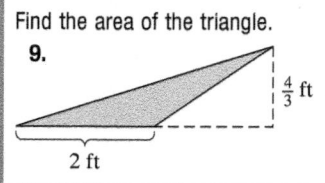

Example 6   **Finding the Area of a Triangle**

Find the area of the triangle.

Solution:

$b = \dfrac{5}{3} \text{ ft}$ and $h = \dfrac{3}{4} \text{ ft}$ Identify the measure of the base and the height.

$A = \dfrac{1}{2} bh$

$= \dfrac{1}{2}\left(\dfrac{5}{3} \text{ ft}\right)\left(\dfrac{3}{4} \text{ ft}\right)$ Apply the formula for the area of a triangle.

$= \dfrac{1}{2}\left(\dfrac{5}{\underset{1}{3}} \text{ ft}\right)\left(\dfrac{\overset{1}{3}}{4} \text{ ft}\right)$ Simplify.

Answers

8. 20 m²   **9.** $\dfrac{4}{3}$ ft² or $1\dfrac{1}{3}$ ft²

$= \dfrac{5}{8} \text{ ft}^2$ The area of the triangle is $\dfrac{5}{8}$ square feet (ft^2).

3. Reciprocal

Two numbers whose product is 1 are *reciprocals* of each other. For example, consider the product of $\frac{3}{8}$ and $\frac{8}{3}$.

$$\frac{3}{8}\cdot\frac{8}{3}=\frac{\overset{1}{\cancel{3}}}{\underset{1}{\cancel{8}}}\cdot\frac{\overset{1}{\cancel{8}}}{\underset{1}{\cancel{3}}}=1$$

Because the product equals 1, we say that $\frac{3}{8}$ is the reciprocal of $\frac{8}{3}$ and vice versa.

To divide fractions, first we need to learn how to find the reciprocal of a fraction.

Concept Connections

Fill in the blank.

10. The product of a number and its reciprocal is ____.

> **PROCEDURE** Finding the Reciprocal of a Fraction
>
> To find the **reciprocal** of a nonzero fraction, interchange the numerator and denominator of the fraction. If a and b are nonzero numbers, then the reciprocal of $\frac{a}{b}$ is $\frac{b}{a}$. This is because $\frac{a}{b}\cdot\frac{b}{a}=1$.

Example 7 Finding Reciprocals

Find the reciprocal.

a. $\frac{2}{5}$ **b.** $\frac{1}{9}$ **c.** 5 **d.** 0 **e.** $-\frac{3}{7}$

Solution:

a. The reciprocal of $\frac{2}{5}$ is $\frac{5}{2}$.

b. The reciprocal of $\frac{1}{9}$ is $\frac{9}{1}$, or 9.

c. First write the whole number 5 as the improper fraction $\frac{5}{1}$. The reciprocal of $\frac{5}{1}$ is $\frac{1}{5}$.

d. The number 0 has no reciprocal because $\frac{1}{0}$ is undefined.

e. The reciprocal of $-\frac{3}{7}$ is $-\frac{7}{3}$.   This is because $-\frac{3}{7}\cdot\left(-\frac{7}{3}\right)=1$.

Skill Practice

Find the reciprocal.

11. $\frac{7}{10}$ **12.** $\frac{1}{4}$
13. 7 **14.** 1
15. $-\frac{9}{8}$

TIP: From Example 7(e) we see that a negative number will have a negative reciprocal.

4. Division of Fractions

To understand the division of fractions, we compare it to the division of whole numbers. The statement $6\div2$ asks, "How many groups of 2 can be found among 6 wholes?" The answer is 3.

$$6\div2=3 \qquad \square\,\square \;\; \square\,\square \;\; \square\,\square$$

In fractional form, the statement $6\div2=3$ can be written as $\frac{6}{2}=3$. This result can also be found by multiplying.

$$6\cdot\frac{1}{2}=\frac{6}{1}\cdot\frac{1}{2}=\frac{6}{2}=3$$

That is, to divide by 2 is equivalent to multiplying by the reciprocal $\frac{1}{2}$.

Answers
10. 1 **11.** $\frac{10}{7}$ **12.** 4
13. $\frac{1}{7}$ **14.** 1 **15.** $-\frac{8}{9}$

In general, to divide two nonzero numbers we can multiply the dividend by the reciprocal of the divisor. This is how we divide by a fraction.

Concept Connections

Fill in the box to make the right- and left-hand sides equal.

16. $\dfrac{4}{7} \div \dfrac{3}{5} = \dfrac{4}{7} \cdot \square$

17. $\dfrac{2}{3} \div \dfrac{1}{5} = \square \cdot \dfrac{5}{1}$

> **PROCEDURE Dividing Fractions**
>
> To divide two fractions, multiply the dividend (the "first" fraction) by the reciprocal of the divisor (the "second" fraction).

The process to divide fractions can be written symbolically as

Change division to multiplication.

$$\dfrac{a}{b} \div \dfrac{c}{d} = \dfrac{a}{b} \cdot \dfrac{d}{c} \qquad \text{provided } b, c, \text{ and } d \text{ are not } 0.$$

Take the reciprocal of the divisor.

Skill Practice

Divide and simplify.

18. $\dfrac{1}{4} \div \dfrac{2}{5}$

19. $\dfrac{3}{8} \div \left(-\dfrac{9}{10}\right)$

Example 8 **Dividing Fractions**

Divide and simplify, if possible.

a. $\dfrac{2}{5} \div \dfrac{7}{4}$ **b.** $\dfrac{2}{27} \div \left(-\dfrac{8}{15}\right)$

Solution:

a. $\dfrac{2}{5} \div \dfrac{7}{4} = \dfrac{2}{5} \cdot \dfrac{4}{7}$ Multiply by the reciprocal of the divisor ("second" fraction).

$= \dfrac{2 \cdot 4}{5 \cdot 7}$ Multiply numerators. Multiply denominators.

$= \dfrac{8}{35}$

b. $\dfrac{2}{27} \div \left(-\dfrac{8}{15}\right) = \dfrac{2}{27} \cdot \left(-\dfrac{15}{8}\right)$ Multiply by the reciprocal of the divisor.

$= -\left(\dfrac{2}{27} \cdot \dfrac{15}{8}\right)$ The product will be negative.

$= -\left(\dfrac{\overset{1}{2}}{\underset{9}{27}} \cdot \dfrac{\overset{5}{15}}{\underset{4}{8}}\right)$ Simplify.

$= -\dfrac{5}{36}$ Multiply.

Avoiding Mistakes

Do not try to simplify until after taking the reciprocal of the divisor. In Example 8(a) it would be incorrect to "cancel" the 2 and the 4 in the expression $\frac{2}{5} \div \frac{7}{4}$.

Answers

16. $\dfrac{5}{3}$ **17.** $\dfrac{2}{3}$

18. $\dfrac{5}{8}$ **19.** $-\dfrac{5}{12}$

Example 9 Dividing Fractions

Divide and simplify. Write the answer as a fraction.

a. $\dfrac{35}{14} \div 7$ **b.** $-12 \div \left(-\dfrac{8}{3}\right)$

Solution:

a. $\dfrac{35}{14} \div 7 = \dfrac{35}{14} \div \dfrac{7}{1}$ Write the whole number 7 as an improper fraction *before* multiplying by the reciprocal.

$= \dfrac{35}{14} \cdot \dfrac{1}{7}$ Multiply by the reciprocal of the divisor.

$= \dfrac{\overset{5}{35}}{14} \cdot \dfrac{1}{\underset{1}{7}}$ Simplify.

$= \dfrac{5}{14}$ Multiply.

b. $-12 \div \left(-\dfrac{8}{3}\right) = +\left(12 \div \dfrac{8}{3}\right)$ First note that the quotient will be positive. The quotient of two numbers with the same sign is positive.

$12 \div \dfrac{8}{3} = \dfrac{12}{1} \div \dfrac{8}{3}$ Write the whole number 12 as an improper fraction.

$= \dfrac{12}{1} \cdot \dfrac{3}{8}$ Multiply by the reciprocal of the divisor.

$= \dfrac{\overset{3}{12}}{1} \cdot \dfrac{3}{\underset{2}{8}}$ Simplify.

$= \dfrac{9}{2}$ Multiply.

Example 10 Dividing Fractions Containing Variables

Divide and simplify. $-\dfrac{10x^2}{y^2} \div \dfrac{5}{y}$

Solution:

$-\dfrac{10x^2}{y^2} \div \dfrac{5}{y} = -\dfrac{10x^2}{y^2} \cdot \dfrac{y}{5}$ Multiply by the reciprocal of the divisor.

$= -\dfrac{2 \cdot 5 \cdot x \cdot x \cdot y}{y \cdot y \cdot 5}$ Multiply fractions and factor.

$= -\dfrac{2 \cdot \overset{1}{5} \cdot x \cdot x \cdot \overset{1}{y}}{y \cdot \underset{1}{y} \cdot \underset{1}{5}}$ Simplify. The common factors are in red.

$= -\dfrac{2x^2}{y}$

Skill Practice

Divide and simplify. Write the quotient as a fraction.

20. $\dfrac{15}{4} \div 10$

21. $-20 \div \left(-\dfrac{12}{5}\right)$

Skill Practice

Divide and simplify.

22. $-\dfrac{8y^3}{7} \div \dfrac{4y}{5}$

Answers

20. $\dfrac{3}{8}$ **21.** $\dfrac{25}{3}$ **22.** $-\dfrac{10y^2}{7}$

5. Applications of Multiplication and Division of Fractions

Sometimes it is difficult to determine whether multiplication or division is appropriate to solve an application problem. Division is generally used for a problem that requires you to separate or "split up" a quantity into pieces. Multiplication is generally used if it is necessary to take a fractional part of a quantity.

Example 11 Using Division in an Application

A road crew must mow the grassy median along a stretch of highway I-95. If they can mow $\frac{5}{8}$ mile (mi) in 1 hr, how long will it take them to mow a 15-mi stretch?

Solution:

Read and familiarize.

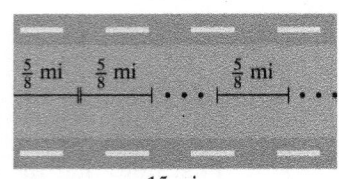

Strategy/operation: From the figure, we must separate or "split up" a 15-mi stretch of highway into pieces that are $\frac{5}{8}$ mi in length. Therefore, we must divide 15 by $\frac{5}{8}$.

$$15 \div \frac{5}{8} = \frac{15}{1} \cdot \frac{8}{5} \qquad \text{Write the whole number as a fraction. Multiply by the reciprocal of the divisor.}$$

$$= \frac{\overset{3}{15}}{1} \cdot \frac{8}{\underset{1}{5}}$$

$$= 24$$

The 15-mi stretch of highway will take 24 hr to mow.

Example 12 Using Division in an Application

A $\frac{9}{4}$-ft length of wire must be cut into pieces of equal length that are $\frac{3}{8}$ ft long. How many pieces can be cut?

Solution:

Read and familiarize.
Operation: Here we divide the total length of wire into pieces of equal length.

$$\frac{9}{4} \div \frac{3}{8} = \frac{9}{4} \cdot \frac{8}{3} \qquad \text{Multiply by the reciprocal of the divisor.}$$

$$= \frac{\overset{3}{9}}{\underset{1}{4}} \cdot \frac{\overset{2}{8}}{\underset{1}{3}} \qquad \text{Simplify.}$$

$$= 6$$

Six pieces of wire can be cut.

Example 13 **Using Multiplication in an Application**

Carson estimates that his total cost for college for 1 year is $12,600. He has financial aid to pay $\frac{2}{3}$ of the cost.

a. How much money will be paid by financial aid?

b. How much money will Carson have to pay?

c. If Carson's parents help him by paying $\frac{1}{2}$ of the amount not paid by financial aid, how much money will be paid by Carson's parents?

Solution:

a. Carson's financial aid will pay $\frac{2}{3}$ of $12,600. Because we are looking for a fraction of a quantity, we multiply.

$$\frac{2}{3} \cdot 12{,}600 = \frac{2}{3} \cdot \frac{12{,}600}{1}$$

$$= \frac{2}{\underset{1}{3}} \cdot \frac{\overset{4200}{\cancel{12{,}600}}}{1}$$

$$= 8400$$

Financial aid will pay $8400.

b. Carson will have to pay the remaining portion of the cost. This can be found by subtraction.

$$\$12{,}600 - \$8400 = \$4200$$

Carson will have to pay $4200.

> **TIP:** The answer to Example 13(b) could also have been found by noting that financial aid paid $\frac{2}{3}$ of the cost. This means that Carson must pay $\frac{1}{3}$ of the cost, or
>
> $$\frac{1}{3} \cdot \frac{\$12{,}600}{1} = \frac{1}{\underset{1}{3}} \cdot \frac{\overset{4200}{\$12{,}600}}{1}$$
>
> $$= \$4200$$

c. Carson's parents will pay $\frac{1}{2}$ of $4200.

$$\frac{1}{\underset{1}{2}} \cdot \frac{\overset{2100}{4200}}{1}$$

Carson's parents will pay $2100.

Answer
25. a. $12,000,000
     b. $8,000,000
     c. $6,400,000

Section 4.3 Practice Exercises

Boost *your* GRADE at
ALEKS.com!

ALEKS
version 3.0

• Practice Problems
• Self-Tests
• NetTutor

• e-Professors
• Videos

Study Skills Exercise

1. Define the key term **reciprocal**.

Review Exercises

2. The number 126 is divisible by which of the following?

   a. 2   **b.** 3   **c.** 5   **d.** 10

3. Identify the numerator and denominator. Then simplify the fraction. $\dfrac{2100}{7000}$

4. Simplify. $\dfrac{12x^2}{15x}$

5. Convert $2\dfrac{7}{8}$ to an improper fraction.

6. Convert $\dfrac{32}{9}$ to a mixed number.

Objective 1: Multiplication of Fractions

7. Shade the portion of the figure that represents $\frac{1}{4}$ of $\frac{1}{4}$.

8. Shade the portion of the figure that represents $\frac{1}{3}$ of $\frac{1}{4}$.

For Exercises 9–36, multiply the fractions and simplify to lowest terms. Write the answer as an improper fraction when necessary. **(See Examples 1–4.)**

9. $\dfrac{1}{2} \cdot \dfrac{3}{8}$

10. $\dfrac{2}{3} \cdot \dfrac{1}{3}$

11. $\left(-\dfrac{12}{7}\right)\left(-\dfrac{2}{5}\right)$

12. $\left(-\dfrac{9}{10}\right)\left(-\dfrac{7}{4}\right)$

13. $8 \cdot \left(\dfrac{1}{11}\right)$

14. $3 \cdot \left(\dfrac{2}{7}\right)$

15. $-\dfrac{4}{5} \cdot 6$

16. $-\dfrac{5}{8} \cdot 5$

17. $\dfrac{2}{9} \cdot \dfrac{3}{5}$

18. $\dfrac{1}{8} \cdot \dfrac{4}{7}$

19. $\dfrac{5}{6} \cdot \dfrac{3}{4}$

20. $\dfrac{7}{12} \cdot \dfrac{18}{5}$

21. $\dfrac{21}{5} \cdot \dfrac{25}{12}$

22. $\dfrac{16}{25} \cdot \dfrac{15}{32}$

23. $\dfrac{24}{15} \cdot \left(-\dfrac{5}{3}\right)$

24. $\dfrac{49}{24} \cdot \left(-\dfrac{6}{7}\right)$

25. $\left(\dfrac{6}{11}\right)\left(\dfrac{22}{15}\right)$

26. $\left(\dfrac{12}{45}\right)\left(\dfrac{5}{4}\right)$

27. $-12 \cdot \left(-\dfrac{15}{42}\right)$

28. $-4 \cdot \left(-\dfrac{8}{92}\right)$

29. $\dfrac{3y}{10} \cdot \dfrac{5}{y}$

30. $\dfrac{7z}{12} \cdot \dfrac{4}{z}$

31. $-\dfrac{4ab}{5} \cdot \dfrac{1}{8b}$

32. $-\dfrac{6cd}{7} \cdot \dfrac{1}{18d}$

33. $\dfrac{5x}{4y^2} \cdot \dfrac{y}{25x}$

34. $\dfrac{14w}{3z^4} \cdot \dfrac{z^2}{28w}$

35. $\left(-\dfrac{12m^3}{n}\right)\left(-\dfrac{n}{3m}\right)$

36. $\left(-\dfrac{15p^4}{t^2}\right)\left(-\dfrac{t^3}{3p}\right)$

Objective 2: Area of a Triangle

For Exercises 37–40, label the height with *h* and the base with *b*, as shown in the figure.

37.   **38.**   **39.**   **40.**

For Exercises 41–46, find the area of the triangle. **(See Examples 5–6.)**

41.   **42.**   **43.**   **44.**

45.   **46.**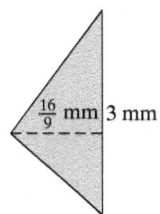

Objective 3: Reciprocal

For Exercises 47–54, find the reciprocal of the number, if it exists. **(See Example 7.)**

47. $\dfrac{7}{8}$ **48.** $\dfrac{5}{6}$ **49.** $-\dfrac{10}{9}$ **50.** $-\dfrac{14}{5}$

51. -4 **52.** -9 **53.** 0 **54.** $\dfrac{0}{4}$

Objective 4: Division of Fractions

For Exercises 55–58, fill in the blank.

55. Dividing by 3 is the same as multiplying by_____.   **56.** Dividing by 5 is the same as multiplying by_____.

57. Dividing by -8 is the same as _____ by $-\dfrac{1}{8}$.   **58.** Dividing by -12 is the same as _____ by $-\dfrac{1}{12}$.

For Exercises 59–78, divide and simplify the answer to lowest terms. Write the answer as a fraction or an integer. **(See Examples 8–10.)**

59. $\dfrac{2}{15} \div \dfrac{5}{12}$ **60.** $\dfrac{11}{3} \div \dfrac{6}{5}$ **61.** $\left(-\dfrac{7}{13}\right) \div \left(-\dfrac{2}{5}\right)$ **62.** $\left(-\dfrac{8}{7}\right) \div \left(-\dfrac{3}{10}\right)$

63. $\dfrac{14}{3} \div \dfrac{6}{5}$ **64.** $\dfrac{11}{2} \div \dfrac{3}{4}$ **65.** $\dfrac{15}{2} \div \left(-\dfrac{3}{2}\right)$ **66.** $\dfrac{9}{10} \div \left(-\dfrac{9}{2}\right)$

67. $\dfrac{3}{4} \div \dfrac{3}{4}$ **68.** $\dfrac{6}{5} \div \dfrac{6}{5}$ **69.** $-7 \div \dfrac{2}{3}$ **70.** $-4 \div \dfrac{3}{5}$

71. $\dfrac{12}{5} \div 4$ **72.** $\dfrac{20}{6} \div 2$ **73.** $-\dfrac{9}{100} \div \dfrac{13}{1000}$ **74.** $-\dfrac{1000}{17} \div \dfrac{10}{3}$

75. $\dfrac{4xy}{3} \div \dfrac{14x}{9}$ **76.** $\dfrac{3ab}{7} \div \dfrac{15a}{14}$ **77.** $-\dfrac{20c^3}{d^2} \div \dfrac{5c}{d^3}$ **78.** $-\dfrac{24w^2}{z} \div \dfrac{3w}{z^3}$

Mixed Exercises

For Exercises 79–94, multiply or divide as indicated. Write the answer as a fraction or an integer.

79. $\dfrac{7}{8} \div \dfrac{1}{4}$ **80.** $\dfrac{7}{12} \div \dfrac{5}{3}$ **81.** $\dfrac{5}{8} \cdot \dfrac{2}{9}$ **82.** $\dfrac{1}{16} \cdot \dfrac{4}{3}$

83. $6 \cdot \left(-\dfrac{4}{3}\right)$ **84.** $-12 \cdot \dfrac{5}{6}$ **85.** $\left(-\dfrac{16}{5}\right) \div (-8)$ **86.** $\left(-\dfrac{42}{11}\right) \div (-7)$

87. $\dfrac{1}{8} \cdot 16$ **88.** $\dfrac{2}{3} \cdot 9$ **89.** $8 \div \dfrac{16}{3}$ **90.** $5 \div \dfrac{15}{4}$

91. $\dfrac{13x^2}{y^2} \div \left(-\dfrac{26x}{y^3}\right)$ **92.** $\dfrac{11z}{w^3} \div \left(-\dfrac{33}{w}\right)$ **93.** $\left(-\dfrac{ad}{3}\right) \div \left(-\dfrac{ad^2}{6}\right)$ **94.** $\left(-\dfrac{c^2}{5}\right) \div \left(-\dfrac{c^3}{25}\right)$

Objective 5: Applications of Multiplication and Division of Fractions

95. During the month of December, a department store wraps packages free of charge. Each package requires $\frac{2}{3}$ yd of ribbon. If Li used up a 36-yd roll of ribbon, how many packages were wrapped? **(See Example 11.)**

96. A developer sells lots of land in increments of $\frac{3}{4}$ acre. If the developer has 60 acres, how many lots can be sold?

97. If one cup is $\frac{1}{16}$ gal, how many cups of orange juice can be filled from $\frac{3}{2}$ gal? **(See Example 12.)**

98. If 1 centimeter (cm) is $\frac{1}{100}$ meter (m), how many centimeters are in a $\frac{5}{4}$-m piece of rope?

99. Dorci buys 16 sheets of plywood, each $\frac{3}{4}$ in. thick, to cover her windows in the event of a hurricane. She stacks the wood in the garage. How high will the stack be?

100. Davey built a bookshelf 36 in. long. Can the shelf hold a set of encyclopedias if there are 24 books and each book averages $\frac{5}{4}$ in. thick? Explain your answer.

101. A radio station allows 18 minutes (min) of advertising each hour. How many 40-second ($\frac{2}{3}$-min) commercials can be run in

    a. 1 hr   **b.** 1 day

102. A television station has 20 min of advertising each hour. How many 30-second ($\frac{1}{2}$-min) commercials can be run in

    a. 1 hr   **b.** 1 day

103. Ricardo wants to buy a new house for $240,000. The bank requires $\frac{1}{10}$ of the cost of the house as a down payment. As a gift, Ricardo's mother will pay $\frac{2}{3}$ of the down payment. **(See Example 13.)**

    a. How much money will Ricardo's mother pay toward the down payment?

    b. How much money will Ricardo have to pay toward the down payment?

    c. How much is left over for Ricardo to finance?

104. Althea wants to buy a Toyota Camry for a total cost of $18,000. The dealer requires $\frac{1}{12}$ of the money as a down payment. Althea's parents have agreed to pay one-half of the down payment for her.

   a. How much money will Althea's parents pay toward the down payment?

   b. How much will Althea pay toward the down payment?

   c. How much will Althea have to finance?

105. Frankie's lawn measures 40 yd by 36 yd. In the morning he mowed $\frac{2}{3}$ of the lawn. How many square yards of lawn did he already mow? How much is left to be mowed?

106. Bob laid brick to make a rectangular patio in the back of his house. The patio measures 20 yd by 12 yd. On Saturday, he put down bricks for $\frac{3}{8}$ of the patio area. How many square yards is this?

107. In a certain sample of individuals, $\frac{2}{5}$ are known to have blood type O. Of the individuals with blood type O, $\frac{1}{4}$ are Rh-negative. What fraction of the individuals in the sample have O negative blood?

108. Jim has half a pizza left over from dinner. If he eats $\frac{1}{4}$ of this for breakfast, what fractional part did he eat for breakfast?

109. A lab technician has $\frac{7}{4}$ liters (L) of alcohol. If she needs samples of $\frac{1}{8}$ L, how many samples can she prepare?

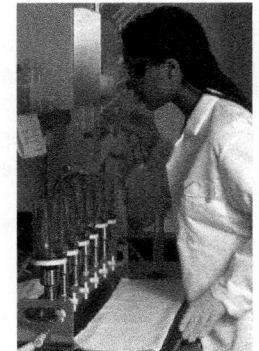

110. Troy has a $\frac{7}{8}$-in. nail that he must hammer into a board. Each strike of the hammer moves the nail $\frac{1}{16}$ in. into the board. How many strikes of the hammer must he make?

111. In the summer at the South Pole, heavy equipment is used 24 hr a day. For every gallon of fuel actually used at the South Pole, it takes $3\frac{1}{2}$ gal ($\frac{7}{2}$ gal) to get it there.

   a. If in one day 130 gal of fuel was used, how many gallons of fuel did it take to transport the 130 gal?

   b. How much fuel was used in all?

112. The Bishop Gaming Center hosts a football pool. There is $1200 in prize money. The first-place winner receives $\frac{2}{3}$ of the prize money. The second-place winner receives $\frac{1}{4}$ of the prize money, and the third-place winner receives $\frac{1}{12}$ of the prize money. How much money does each person get?

113. How many eighths are in $\frac{9}{4}$?

114. How many sixths are in $\frac{4}{3}$?

115. Find $\frac{2}{5}$ of $\frac{1}{5}$.

116. Find $\frac{2}{3}$ of $\frac{1}{3}$.

Expanding Your Skills

117. The rectangle shown here has an area of 30 ft². Find the length.

$\frac{5}{2}$ ft

?

118. The rectangle shown here has an area of 8 m². Find the width.

?

14 m

119. Find the next number in the sequence: $\frac{1}{2}, \frac{1}{4}, \frac{1}{8}, \frac{1}{16},$ _____

120. Find the next number in the sequence: $\frac{2}{3}, \frac{2}{9}, \frac{2}{27},$ _____

121. Which is greater, $\frac{1}{2}$ of $\frac{1}{8}$ or $\frac{1}{8}$ of $\frac{1}{2}$?

122. Which is greater, $\frac{2}{3}$ of $\frac{1}{4}$ or $\frac{1}{4}$ of $\frac{2}{3}$?

Section 4.4   Least Common Multiple and Equivalent Fractions

1. Least Common Multiple

In Section 4.5, we will learn how to add and subtract fractions. To add or subtract fractions with different denominators, we must learn how to convert unlike fractions into like fractions. An essential concept in this process is the idea of a least common multiple of two or more numbers.

When we multiply a number by the whole numbers 1, 2, 3, and so on, we form the **multiples** of the number. For example, some of the multiples of 6 and 9 are shown below.

Multiples of 6	Multiples of 9
$6 \cdot 1 = 6$	$9 \cdot 1 = 9$
$6 \cdot 2 = 12$	$9 \cdot 2 = 18$
$6 \cdot 3 = 18$	$9 \cdot 3 = 27$
$6 \cdot 4 = 24$	$9 \cdot 4 = 36$
$6 \cdot 5 = 30$	$9 \cdot 5 = 45$
$6 \cdot 6 = 36$	$9 \cdot 6 = 54$
$6 \cdot 7 = 42$	$9 \cdot 7 = 63$
$6 \cdot 8 = 48$	$9 \cdot 8 = 72$
$6 \cdot 9 = 54$	$9 \cdot 9 = 81$

In red, we have indicated several multiples that are common to both 6 and 9.

Concept Connections

1. Explain the difference between a multiple of a number and a factor of a number.

The **least common multiple (LCM)** of two given numbers is the smallest whole number that is a multiple of each given number. For example, the LCM of 6 and 9 is 18.

Multiples of 6:   6, 12, 18, 24, 30, 36, 42, . . .

Multiples of 9:   9, 18, 27, 36, 45, 54, 63, . . .

TIP: There are infinitely many numbers that are common multiples of both 6 and 9. These include 18, 36, 54, 72, and so on. However, 18 is the smallest and is therefore the *least* common multiple.

If one number is a multiple of another number, then the LCM is the larger of the two numbers. For example, the LCM of 4 and 8 is 8.

Multiples of 4:   4, 8, 12, 16, . . .

Multiples of 8:   8, 16, 24, 32, . . .

Skill Practice

Find the LCM by listing several multiples of each number.

   2. 15 and 25   **3.** 4, 6, and 10

Example 1   Finding the LCM by Listing Multiples

Find the LCM of the given numbers by listing several multiples of each number.

   a. 15 and 12   **b.** 10, 15, and 8

Solution:

   a. Multiples of 15:   15, 30, 45, 60
        Multiples of 12:   12, 24, 36, 48, 60

      The LCM of 15 and 12 is 60.

Answers

1. A multiple of a number is the product of the number and a whole number 1 or greater. A factor of a number is a value that divides evenly into the number.
2. 75   **3.** 60

b. Multiples of 10:   10, 20, 30, 40, 50, 60, 70, 80, 90, 100, 110, 120
   Multiples of 15:   15, 30, 45, 60, 75, 90, 105, 120
   Multiples of 8:   8, 16, 24, 32, 40, 48, 56, 64, 72, 80, 88, 96, 104, 112, 120

The LCM of 10, 15, and 8 is 120.

In Example 1 we used the method of listing multiples to find the LCM of two or more numbers. As you can see, the solution to Example 1(b) required several long lists of multiples. Here we offer another method to find the LCM of two given numbers by using their prime factors.

PROCEDURE   Using Prime Factors to Find the LCM of Two Numbers

Step 1 Write each number as a product of prime factors.
Step 2 The LCM is the product of unique prime factors from both numbers. Use repeated factors the maximum number of times they appear in either factorization.

This process is demonstrated in Example 2.

Example 2   **Finding the LCM by Using Prime Factors**

Find the LCM.

   a. 14 and 12   **b.** 50 and 24   **c.** 45, 54, and 50

Solution:

a. Find the prime factorization for 14 and 12.

	2's	3's	7's
14 =	2 ·		⑦
12 =	②·②·	③	

LCM = 2 · 2 · 3 · 7 = 84

For the factors of 2, 3, and 7, we circle the greatest number of times each occurs. The LCM is the product.

b. Find the prime factorization for 50 and 24.

	2's	3's	5's
50 =	2 ·		⑤·⑤
24 =	②·②·②·	③	

LCM = 2 · 2 · 2 · 3 · 5 · 5 = 600

The factor 5 is repeated twice. The factor 2 is repeated 3 times. The factor 3 is used only once.

(The LCM can also be written as $2^3 \cdot 3 \cdot 5^2$.)

c. Find the prime factorization for 45, 54, and 50.

	2's	3's	5's
45 =		3 · 3 ·	5
54 =	2 ·	③·③·③	
50 =	②·		⑤·⑤

LCM = 2 · 3 · 3 · 3 · 5 · 5 = 1350

(The LCM can also be written as $2 \cdot 3^3 \cdot 5^2$.)

Skill Practice

Find the LCM by using prime factors.

   4. 9 and 24
   5. 16 and 9
   6. 36, 42, and 30

TIP: The product 2 · 2 · 3 · 7 can also be written as $2^2 \cdot 3 \cdot 7$.

Answers
4. 72   **5.** 144   **6.** 1260

2. Applications of the Least Common Multiple

Example 3   Using the LCM in an Application

A tile wall is to be made from 6-in., 8-in., and 12-in. square tiles. A design is made by alternating rows with different-size tiles. The first row uses only 6-in. tiles, the second row uses only 8-in. tiles, and the third row uses only 12-in. tiles. Neglecting the grout seams, what is the shortest length of wall space that can be covered using only whole tiles?

Solution:

The length of the first row must be a multiple of 6 in., the length of the second row must be a multiple of 8 in., and the length of the third row must be a multiple of 12 in. Therefore, the shortest-length wall that can be covered is given by the LCM of 6, 8, and 12.

$$6 = 2 \cdot \boxed{3}$$
$$8 = \boxed{2 \cdot 2 \cdot 2}$$
$$12 = 2 \cdot 2 \cdot 3$$

The LCM is $2 \cdot 2 \cdot 2 \cdot 3 = 24$. The shortest-length wall is 24 in.

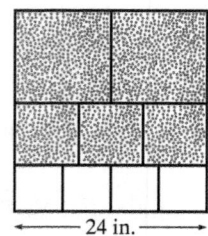

This means that four 6-in. tiles can be placed on the first row, three 8-in. tiles can be placed on the second row, and two 12-in. tiles can be placed in the third row. See Figure 4-9.

← 24 in. →

Figure 4-9

3. Writing Equivalent Fractions

A fractional amount of a whole may be represented by many fractions. For example, the fractions $\frac{1}{2}, \frac{2}{4}, \frac{3}{6}$, and $\frac{4}{8}$ all represent the same portion of a whole. See Figure 4-10.

$$\frac{1}{2} \quad = \quad \frac{2}{4} \quad = \quad \frac{3}{6} \quad = \quad \frac{4}{8}$$

Figure 4-10

Expressing a fraction in an equivalent form is important for several reasons. We need this skill to order fractions and to add and subtract fractions.

Writing a fraction as an equivalent fraction is an application of the fundamental principle of fractions given in Section 4.2.

Example 4   Writing Equivalent Fractions

Write the fraction with the indicated denominator. $\dfrac{2}{9} = \dfrac{}{36}$

Solution:

$$\frac{2}{9} = \frac{}{36}$$

What number must we multiply 9 by to get 36?

$$\frac{2 \cdot 4}{9 \cdot 4} = \frac{8}{36}$$

Multiply numerator and denominator by 4.

Therefore, $\dfrac{2}{9}$ is equivalent to $\dfrac{8}{36}$.

TIP: In Example 4, we multiplied numerator and denominator of the fraction by 4. This is the same as multiplying the fraction by a convenient form of 1.

$$\frac{2}{9} = \frac{2}{9} \cdot 1 = \frac{2}{9} \cdot \frac{4}{4} = \frac{2 \cdot 4}{9 \cdot 4} = \frac{8}{36}$$

This is the same as multiplying numerator and denominator by 4.

Example 5 Writing Equivalent Fractions

Write the fraction with the indicated denominator. $\frac{11}{8} = \frac{}{56}$

Solution:

$\frac{11}{8} = \frac{}{56}$

What number must we multiply 8 by to get 56?

$\frac{11 \cdot 7}{8 \cdot 7} = \frac{77}{56}$ Therefore, $\frac{11}{8}$ is equivalent to $\frac{77}{56}$.

Multiply numerator and denominator by 7.

Skill Practice
Write the fraction with the indicated denominator.
9. $\frac{5}{6} = \frac{}{54}$

Example 6 Writing Equivalent Fractions

Write the fractions with the indicated denominator.

a. $-\frac{5}{6} = -\frac{}{30}$ **b.** $\frac{9}{-4} = \frac{}{8}$

Solution:

a. $-\frac{5}{6} = -\frac{}{30}$

$-\frac{5 \cdot 5}{6 \cdot 5} = -\frac{25}{30}$ We must multiply by 5 to get a denominator of 30. Multiply numerator and denominator by 5.

Therefore, $-\frac{5}{6}$ is equivalent to $-\frac{25}{30}$.

b. $\frac{9 \cdot (-2)}{-4 \cdot (-2)} = \frac{-18}{8}$ We must multiply by -2 to get a denominator of 8. Multiply numerator and denominator by -2.

Therefore, $\frac{9}{-4}$ is equivalent to $\frac{-18}{8}$.

TIP: Recall that $\frac{-18}{8} = \frac{18}{-8} = -\frac{18}{8}$. All are equivalent to $\frac{9}{-4}$.

Skill Practice
Write the fractions with the indicated denominator.
10. $-\frac{10}{3} = -\frac{}{12}$
11. $\frac{3}{-8} = \frac{}{16}$

Answers
9. $\frac{45}{54}$ 10. $-\frac{40}{12}$ 11. $\frac{-6}{16}$

Skill Practice

Write the fractions with the indicated denominator.

12. $\dfrac{7}{9} = \dfrac{}{18y}$

13. $\dfrac{10}{w} = \dfrac{}{w^2}$

Example 7 **Writing Equivalent Fractions**

Write the fractions with the indicated denominator.

a. $\dfrac{2}{3} = \dfrac{}{9x}$ **b.** $\dfrac{4}{y} = \dfrac{}{y^2}$

Solution:

a. $\dfrac{2}{3} = \dfrac{}{9x}$

What must we multiply 3 by to get $9x$?

$\dfrac{2 \cdot 3x}{3 \cdot 3x} = \dfrac{6x}{9x}$ Therefore, $\dfrac{2}{3}$ is equivalent to $\dfrac{6x}{9x}$.

Multiply numerator and denominator by $3x$.

b. $\dfrac{4}{y} = \dfrac{}{y^2}$

What must we multiply y by to get y^2?

$\dfrac{4 \cdot y}{y \cdot y} = \dfrac{4y}{y^2}$ Therefore, $\dfrac{4}{y}$ is equivalent to $\dfrac{4y}{y^2}$.

Multiply numerator and denominator by y.

4. Ordering Fractions

Suppose we want to determine which of two fractions is larger. Comparing fractions with the same denominator, such as $\frac{3}{5}$ and $\frac{2}{5}$ is relatively easy. Clearly 3 parts out of 5 is greater than 2 parts out of 5.

$\frac{3}{5}$

$\frac{2}{5}$

Thus, $\dfrac{3}{5} > \dfrac{2}{5}$.

So how would we compare the relative size of two fractions with *different* denominators such as $\frac{3}{5}$ and $\frac{4}{7}$? Our first step is to write the fractions as equivalent fractions with the same denominator, called a common denominator. The **least common denominator (LCD)** of two fractions is the LCM of the denominators of the fractions. The LCD of $\frac{3}{5}$ and $\frac{4}{7}$ is 35, because this is the least common multiple of 5 and 7. In Example 8, we convert the fractions $\frac{3}{5}$ and $\frac{4}{7}$ to equivalent fractions having 35 as the denominator.

Skill Practice

Fill in the blank with $<$, $>$, or $=$.

14. $\dfrac{3}{8} \ \square \ \dfrac{4}{9}$

Example 8 **Comparing Two Fractions**

Fill in the blank with $<$, $>$, or $=$. $\dfrac{3}{5} \ \square \ \dfrac{4}{7}$

Solution:

The fractions have different denominators and cannot be compared by inspection. The LCD is 35. We need to convert each fraction to an equivalent fraction with a denominator of 35.

$\dfrac{3}{5} = \dfrac{3 \cdot 7}{5 \cdot 7} = \dfrac{21}{35}$ Multiply numerator and denominator by 7 because $5 \cdot 7 = 35$.

$\dfrac{4}{7} = \dfrac{4 \cdot 5}{7 \cdot 5} = \dfrac{20}{35}$ Multiply numerator and denominator by 5 because $7 \cdot 5 = 35$.

Because $\dfrac{21}{35} > \dfrac{20}{35}$, then $\dfrac{3}{5} \ \boxed{>} \ \dfrac{4}{7}$.

Answers

12. $\dfrac{14y}{18y}$ **13.** $\dfrac{10w}{w^2}$ **14.** $<$

The relationship between $\frac{3}{5}$ and $\frac{4}{7}$ is shown in Figure 4-11. The position of the two fractions is also illustrated on the number line. See Figure 4-12.

Figure 4-11

Figure 4-12

Example 9 **Ranking Fractions in Order from Least to Greatest**

Rank the fractions from least to greatest. $-\dfrac{9}{20}, \ -\dfrac{7}{15}, \ -\dfrac{4}{9}$

Solution:

We want to convert each fraction to an equivalent fraction with a common denominator. The least common denominator is the LCM of 20, 15, and 9.

$$
\left.
\begin{array}{l}
20 = \boxed{2 \cdot 2} \cdot \boxed{5} \\[4pt]
15 = 3 \cdot 5 \\[4pt]
9 = \boxed{3 \cdot 3}
\end{array}
\right\}
\quad \text{The least common denominator is } 2 \cdot 2 \cdot 3 \cdot 3 \cdot 5 = 180.
$$

Now convert each fraction to an equivalent fraction with a denominator of 180.

$-\dfrac{9}{20} = -\dfrac{9 \cdot 9}{20 \cdot 9} = -\dfrac{81}{180}$ Multiply numerator and denominator by 9 because $20 \cdot 9 = 180$.

$-\dfrac{7}{15} = -\dfrac{7 \cdot 12}{15 \cdot 12} = -\dfrac{84}{180}$ Multiply numerator and denominator by 12 because $15 \cdot 12 = 180$.

$-\dfrac{4}{9} = -\dfrac{4 \cdot 20}{9 \cdot 20} = -\dfrac{80}{180}$ Multiply numerator and denominator by 20 because $9 \cdot 20 = 180$.

The relative position of these fractions is shown on the number line.

Ranking the fractions from least to greatest we have $-\frac{84}{180}, -\frac{81}{180},$ and $-\frac{80}{180}$. This is equivalent to $-\frac{7}{15}, -\frac{9}{20},$ and $-\frac{4}{9}$.

Section 4.4 Practice Exercises

Boost *your* GRADE at ALEKS.com!

ALEKS® version 3.0

• Practice Problems
• Self-Tests
• NetTutor

• e-Professors
• Videos

Study Skills Exercise

1. Define the key terms.

    a. Multiple   **b. Least common multiple (LCM)**   **c. Least common denominator (LCD)**

Review Exercises

For Exercises 2–3, simplify the fraction.

2. $-\dfrac{104}{36}$

3. $\dfrac{30xy}{20x^3}$

For Exercises 4–6, multiply or divide as indicated. Write the answers as fractions.

4. $\left(-\dfrac{22}{5}\right)\left(-\dfrac{15}{4}\right)$

5. $\dfrac{60}{7} \div (-6)$

6. $\dfrac{4w}{9x^2} \div \dfrac{2w}{3x}$

7. Convert $-5\dfrac{3}{4}$ to an improper fraction.

8. Convert $-\dfrac{16}{7}$ to a mixed number.

Objective 1: Least Common Multiple

9. a. Circle the multiples of 24: 4, 8, 48, 72, 12, 240

   b. Circle the factors of 24: 4, 8, 48, 72, 12, 240

10. a. Circle the multiples of 30: 15, 90, 120, 3, 5, 60

   b. Circle the factors of 30: 15, 90, 120, 3, 5, 60

11. a. Circle the multiples of 36: 72, 6, 360, 12, 9, 108

   b. Circle the factors of 36: 72, 6, 360, 12, 9, 108

12. a. Circle the multiples of 28: 7, 4, 2, 56, 140, 280

   b. Circle the factors of 28: 7, 4, 2, 56, 140, 280

For Exercises 13–32, find the LCM. **(See Examples 1–2.)**

13. 10 and 25

14. 21 and 14

15. 16 and 12

16. 20 and 12

17. 18 and 24

18. 9 and 30

19. 12 and 15

20. 27 and 45

21. 42 and 70

22. 6 and 21

23. 8, 10, and 12

24. 4, 6, and 14

25. 12, 15, and 20

26. 20, 30, and 40

27. 16, 24, and 30

28. 20, 42, and 35

29. 6, 12, 18, and 20

30. 21, 35, 50, and 75

31. 5, 15, 18, and 20

32. 28, 10, 21, and 35

Objective 2: Applications of the Least Common Multiple

33. A tile floor is to be made from 10-in., 12-in., and 15-in. square tiles. A design is made by alternating rows with different-size tiles. The first row uses only 10-in. tiles, the second row uses only 12-in. tiles, and the third row uses only 15-in. tiles. Neglecting the grout seams, what is the shortest length of floor space that can be covered evenly by each row? **(See Example 3.)**

34. A patient admitted to the hospital was prescribed a pain medication to be given every 4 hr and an antibiotic to be given every 5 hr. Bandages applied to the patient's external injuries needed changing every 12 hr. The nurse changed the bandages and gave the patient both medications at 6:00 A.M. Monday morning.

   a. How many hours will pass before the patient is given both medications and has his bandages changed at the same time?

   b. What day and time will this be?

35. Four satellites revolve around the earth once every 6, 8, 10, and 15 hr, respectively. If the satellites are initially "lined up," how many hours must pass before they will again be lined up?

36. Mercury, Venus, and Earth revolve around the Sun approximately once every 3 months, 7 months, and 12 months, respectively (see the figure). If the planets begin "lined up," what is the minimum number of months required for them to be aligned again? (Assume that the planets lie roughly in the same plane.)

Objective 3: Writing Equivalent Fractions

For Exercises 37–66, rewrite each fraction with the indicated denominators. **(See Examples 4–7.)**

37. $\dfrac{2}{3} = \dfrac{}{21}$

38. $\dfrac{7}{4} = \dfrac{}{32}$

39. $\dfrac{5}{8} = \dfrac{}{16}$

40. $\dfrac{2}{9} = \dfrac{}{27}$

41. $-\dfrac{3}{4} = -\dfrac{}{16}$

42. $-\dfrac{3}{10} = -\dfrac{}{50}$

43. $\dfrac{4}{-5} = \dfrac{}{15}$

44. $\dfrac{3}{-7} = \dfrac{}{70}$

45. $\dfrac{7}{6} = \dfrac{}{42}$

46. $\dfrac{10}{3} = \dfrac{}{18}$

47. $\dfrac{11}{9} = \dfrac{}{99}$

48. $\dfrac{7}{5} = \dfrac{}{35}$

49. $5 = \dfrac{}{4}$ (*Hint:* $5 = \frac{5}{1}$)

50. $3 = \dfrac{}{12}$ (*Hint:* $3 = \frac{3}{1}$)

51. $\dfrac{11}{4} = \dfrac{}{4000}$

52. $\dfrac{18}{7} = \dfrac{}{700}$

53. $-\dfrac{11}{3} = -\dfrac{}{15}$

54. $-\dfrac{1}{6} = -\dfrac{}{60}$

55. $\dfrac{-5}{8} = \dfrac{}{24}$

56. $\dfrac{-20}{7} = \dfrac{}{35}$

57. $\dfrac{4y}{7} = \dfrac{}{28}$

58. $\dfrac{3v}{13} = \dfrac{}{26}$

59. $\dfrac{3}{8} = \dfrac{}{8y}$

60. $\dfrac{7}{13} = \dfrac{}{13u}$

61. $\dfrac{3}{5} = \dfrac{}{25p}$

62. $\dfrac{4}{9} = \dfrac{}{18v}$

63. $\dfrac{2}{x} = \dfrac{}{x^2}$

64. $\dfrac{6}{w} = \dfrac{}{w^2}$

65. $\dfrac{8}{ab} = \dfrac{}{ab^3}$

66. $\dfrac{9}{cd} = \dfrac{}{c^3d}$

Objective 4: Ordering Fractions

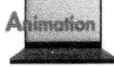

For Exercises 67–74, fill in the blanks with $<$, $>$, or $=$. **(See Example 8.)**

67. $\dfrac{7}{8} \,\square\, \dfrac{3}{4}$

68. $\dfrac{7}{15} \,\square\, \dfrac{11}{20}$

69. $\dfrac{13}{10} \,\square\, \dfrac{22}{15}$

70. $\dfrac{15}{4} \,\square\, \dfrac{21}{6}$

71. $-\dfrac{3}{12} \,\square\, -\dfrac{2}{8}$

72. $-\dfrac{4}{20} \,\square\, -\dfrac{6}{30}$

73. $-\dfrac{5}{18} \,\square\, -\dfrac{8}{27}$

74. $-\dfrac{9}{24} \,\square\, -\dfrac{8}{21}$

75. Which of the following fractions has the greatest value? $\dfrac{2}{3}, \dfrac{7}{8}, \dfrac{5}{6}, \dfrac{1}{2}$

76. Which of the following fractions has the least value? $\dfrac{1}{6}, \dfrac{1}{4}, \dfrac{2}{15}, \dfrac{2}{9}$

For Exercises 77–82, rank the fractions from least to greatest. **(See Example 9.)**

77. $\frac{7}{8}, \frac{2}{3}, \frac{3}{4}$

78. $\frac{5}{12}, \frac{3}{8}, \frac{2}{3}$

79. $-\frac{5}{16}, -\frac{3}{8}, -\frac{1}{4}$

80. $-\frac{2}{5}, -\frac{3}{10}, -\frac{5}{6}$

81. $-\frac{4}{3}, -\frac{13}{12}, \frac{17}{15}$

82. $-\frac{5}{7}, \frac{11}{21}, -\frac{18}{35}$

83. A patient had three cuts that needed stitches. A nurse recorded the lengths of the cuts. Where did the patient have the longest cut? Where did the patient have the shortest cut?

> *upper right arm* ³/₄ *in.*
> *Right hand* ¹¹/₁₆ *in.*
> *above left eye* ⁷/₈ *in.*

84. Three screws have lengths equal to $\frac{3}{4}$ in., $\frac{5}{8}$ in., and $\frac{11}{16}$ in. Which screw is the longest? Which is the shortest?

85. For a party, Aman had $\frac{3}{4}$ lb of cheddar cheese, $\frac{7}{8}$ lb of Swiss cheese, and $\frac{4}{5}$ lb of pepper jack cheese. Which type of cheese is in the least amount? Which type is in the greatest amount?

86. Susan buys $\frac{2}{3}$ lb of smoked turkey, $\frac{3}{5}$ lb of ham, and $\frac{5}{8}$ lb of roast beef. Which type of meat did she buy in the greatest amount? Which type did she buy in the least amount?

Expanding Your Skills

87. Which of the following fractions is between $\frac{1}{4}$ and $\frac{5}{6}$? Identify all that apply.

   a. $\frac{5}{12}$ **b.** $\frac{2}{3}$ **c.** $\frac{1}{8}$

88. Which of the following fractions is between $\frac{1}{3}$ and $\frac{11}{15}$? Identify all that apply.

   a. $\frac{2}{3}$ **b.** $\frac{4}{5}$ **c.** $\frac{2}{5}$

The LCM of two or more numbers can also be found with a method called "division of primes." For example, consider the numbers 32, 48, and 30. To find the LCM, first divide by any prime number that divides evenly into any of the numbers. Then divide and write the quotient as shown.

$$\begin{array}{r} 2\overline{)32 \quad 48 \quad 30} \\ 16 \quad 24 \quad 15 \end{array}$$

Repeat this process and bring down any number that is not divisible by the chosen prime.

$$\begin{array}{r} 2\overline{)32 \quad 48 \quad 30} \\ 2\overline{)16 \quad 24 \quad 15} \\ )8 \quad 12 \quad 15 \end{array} \quad \text{Bring down the 15.}$$

Continue until all quotients are 1. The LCM is the product of the prime factors on the left.

$$\begin{array}{r} 2\overline{)32 \quad 48 \quad 30} \\ 2\overline{)16 \quad 24 \quad 15} \\ 2\overline{)8 \quad 12 \quad 15} \\ 2\overline{)4 \quad 6 \quad 15} \\ 2\overline{)2 \quad 3 \quad 15} \\ 3\overline{)1 \quad 3 \quad 15} \\ 5\overline{)1 \quad 1 \quad 5} \\ 1 \quad 1 \quad 1 \end{array}$$ At this point, the prime number 2 does not divide evenly into any of the quotients. We try the next-greater prime number, 3.

The LCM is $2 \cdot 2 \cdot 2 \cdot 2 \cdot 2 \cdot 3 \cdot 5 = 480$.

For Exercises 89–92, use "division of primes" to determine the LCM of the given numbers.

89. 16, 24, and 28   **90.** 15, 25, and 35   **91.** 20, 18, and 27   **92.** 9, 15, and 42

Addition and Subtraction of Fractions

1. Addition and Subtraction of Like Fractions

In Section 4.3 we learned how to multiply and divide fractions. The main focus of this section is to add and subtract fractions. The operation of addition can be thought of as combining like groups of objects. For example:

3 apples $+ 1$ apple $= 4$ apples

three-fifths $+$ one-fifth $=$ four-fifths

$$\frac{3}{5} + \frac{1}{5} = \frac{4}{5}$$

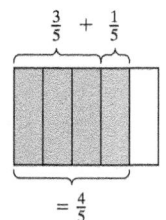

$$\frac{3}{5} + \frac{1}{5}$$

$$= \frac{4}{5}$$

Objectives

1. Addition and Subtraction of Like Fractions
2. Addition and Subtraction of Unlike Fractions
3. Applications of Addition and Subtraction of Fractions

The fractions $\frac{3}{5}$ and $\frac{1}{5}$ are **like fractions** because their denominators are the same. That is, the fractions have a **common denominator**.

The following property leads to the procedure to add and subtract like fractions.

> **PROPERTY Addition and Subtraction of Like Fractions**
>
> Suppose a, b, and c represent numbers, and $c \neq 0$, then
>
> $$\frac{a}{c} + \frac{b}{c} = \frac{a+b}{c} \quad \text{and} \quad \frac{a}{c} - \frac{b}{c} = \frac{a-b}{c}$$

> **PROCEDURE Adding and Subtracting Like Fractions**
>
> **Step 1** Add or subtract the numerators.
> **Step 2** Write the result over the common denominator.
> **Step 3** Simplify to lowest terms, if possible.

Example 1 **Adding and Subtracting Like Fractions**

Add. Write the answer as a fraction or an integer.

a. $\dfrac{1}{4} + \dfrac{5}{4}$ **b.** $\dfrac{2}{15} + \dfrac{1}{15} - \dfrac{13}{15}$

Solution:

a. $\dfrac{1}{4} + \dfrac{5}{4} = \dfrac{1+5}{4}$ .... Add the numerators.

$= \dfrac{6}{4}$ Write the sum over the common denominator.

$= \dfrac{\overset{3}{\cancel{6}}}{\underset{2}{\cancel{4}}}$ Simplify to lowest terms.

$= \dfrac{3}{2}$

> **Avoiding Mistakes**
>
> Notice that when adding fractions, we do not add the denominators. We add *only* the numerators.

Skill Practice

Add. Write the answer as a fraction or an integer.

1. $\dfrac{2}{9} + \dfrac{4}{9}$

2. $\dfrac{7}{12} - \dfrac{5}{12} - \dfrac{11}{12}$

Answers

1. $\dfrac{2}{3}$ **2.** $-\dfrac{3}{4}$

b. $\dfrac{2}{15} + \dfrac{1}{15} - \dfrac{13}{15} = \dfrac{2 + 1 - 13}{15}$ Add and subtract terms in the numerator. Write the result over the common denominator.

$= \dfrac{-10}{15}$ Simplify. The answer will be a negative fraction.

$= -\dfrac{\overset{2}{10}}{\underset{3}{15}}$ Simplify to lowest terms.

$= -\dfrac{2}{3}$

Example 2 **Subtracting Fractions**

Subtract. $\dfrac{3x}{5y} - \dfrac{2}{5y}$

Solution:

The fractions $\frac{3x}{5y}$ and $\frac{2}{5y}$ are like fractions because they have the same denominator.

$\dfrac{3x}{5y} - \dfrac{2}{5y} = \dfrac{3x - 2}{5y}$ Subtract the numerators. Write the result over the common denominator.

$= \dfrac{3x - 2}{5y}$ Notice that the numerator cannot be simplified further because $3x$ and 2 are not like terms.

2. Addition and Subtraction of Unlike Fractions

Adding fractions can be visualized by using a diagram. For example, the sum $\frac{1}{2} + \frac{1}{3}$ is illustrated in Figure 4-13.

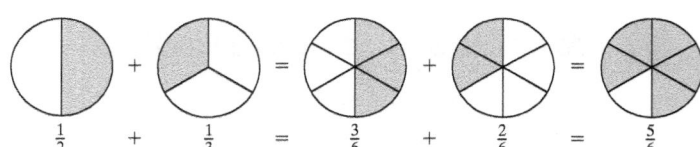

Figure 4-13

In Example 3, we use the concept of the LCD to help us add and subtract unlike fractions. The first step in adding or subtracting unlike fractions is to identify the LCD. Then we change the unlike fractions to like fractions having the LCD as the denominator.

Example 3 **Adding Unlike Fractions**

Add. $\dfrac{1}{6} + \dfrac{3}{4}$

Solution:

The LCD of $\frac{1}{6}$ and $\frac{3}{4}$ is 12. We can convert each individual fraction to an equivalent fraction with 12 as the denominator.

$$\frac{1}{6} = \frac{1 \cdot 2}{6 \cdot 2} = \frac{2}{12} \qquad \text{Multiply numerator and denominator by 2 because } 6 \cdot 2 = 12.$$

$$\frac{3}{4} = \frac{3 \cdot 3}{4 \cdot 3} = \frac{9}{12} \qquad \text{Multiply numerator and denominator by 3 because } 4 \cdot 3 = 12.$$

Thus, $\frac{1}{6} + \frac{3}{4}$ becomes $\frac{2}{12} + \frac{9}{12} = \frac{11}{12}.$

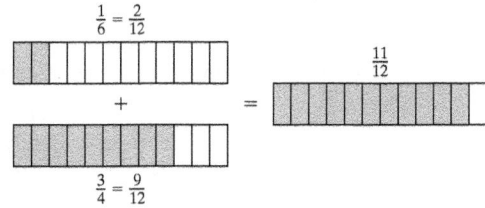

The general procedure to add or subtract unlike fractions is outlined as follows.

> **PROCEDURE Adding and Subtracting Unlike Fractions**
> **Step 1** Identify the LCD.
> **Step 2** Write each individual fraction as an equivalent fraction with the LCD.
> **Step 3** Add or subtract the numerators and write the result over the common denominator.
> **Step 4** Simplify to lowest terms, if possible.

Example 4 **Subtracting Unlike Fractions**

Subtract. $\dfrac{7}{10} - \dfrac{1}{5}$

Solution:

$$\frac{7}{10} - \frac{1}{5} \qquad \text{The LCD is 10. We must convert } \tfrac{1}{5} \text{ to an equivalent fraction with 10 as the denominator.}$$

$$= \frac{7}{10} - \frac{1 \cdot 2}{5 \cdot 2} \qquad \text{Multiply numerator and denominator by 2 because } 5 \cdot 2 = 10.$$

$$= \frac{7}{10} - \frac{2}{10} \qquad \text{The fractions are now like fractions.}$$

$$= \frac{7 - 2}{10} \qquad \text{Subtract the numerators.}$$

$$= \frac{5}{10}$$

$$= \frac{\overset{1}{\cancel{5}}}{\underset{2}{\cancel{10}}} \qquad \text{Simplify to lowest terms.}$$

$$= \frac{1}{2}$$

Avoiding Mistakes

When adding or subtracting fractions, we do not add or subtract the denominators.

Skill Practice

Subtract.

7. $-\dfrac{7}{12} - \dfrac{1}{8}$

Example 5 **Subtracting Unlike Fractions**

Subtract. $-\dfrac{4}{15} - \dfrac{1}{10}$

Solution:

$-\dfrac{4}{15} - \dfrac{1}{10}$ — The LCD is 30.

$= -\dfrac{4\cdot 2}{15\cdot 2} - \dfrac{1\cdot 3}{10\cdot 3}$ — Write the fractions as equivalent fractions with the denominators equal to the LCD.

$= -\dfrac{8}{30} - \dfrac{3}{30}$ — The fractions are now like fractions.

$= \dfrac{-8-3}{30}$ — The fraction $-\frac{8}{30}$ can be written as $\frac{-8}{30}$.

$= \dfrac{-11}{30}$ — Subtract the numerators.

$= -\dfrac{11}{30}$ — The fraction $-\frac{11}{30}$ is in lowest terms because the only common factor of 11 and 30 is 1.

Skill Practice

Add. Write the answer as a fraction.

8. $-3 + \dfrac{4}{5}$

Example 6 **Adding Unlike Fractions**

Add. Write the answer as a fraction. $-5 + \dfrac{3}{4}$

Solution:

$-5 + \dfrac{3}{4} = -\dfrac{5}{1} + \dfrac{3}{4}$ — Write the whole number as a fraction.

$= -\dfrac{5\cdot 4}{1\cdot 4} + \dfrac{3}{4}$ — The LCD is 4.

$= -\dfrac{20}{4} + \dfrac{3}{4}$ — The fractions are now like fractions.

$= \dfrac{-20+3}{4}$ — Add the terms in the numerator.

$= \dfrac{-17}{4}$ — Simplify.

$= -\dfrac{17}{4}$

Example 7 **Adding and Subtracting Unlike Fractions**

Add and subtract as indicated. $-\dfrac{7}{12} - \dfrac{2}{15} + \dfrac{7}{24}$

Answers

7. $-\dfrac{17}{24}$ **8.** $-\dfrac{11}{5}$

Solution:

$$-\frac{7}{12} - \frac{2}{15} + \frac{7}{24}$$ To find the LCD, factor each denominator.

$$= -\frac{7}{2 \cdot 2 \cdot 3} - \frac{2}{3 \cdot 5} + \frac{7}{2 \cdot 2 \cdot 2 \cdot 3}$$

$$\left.\begin{array}{l} 12 = 2 \cdot 2 \cdot \textcircled{3} \\ 15 = 3 \cdot \textcircled{5} \\ 24 = \textcircled{2 \cdot 2 \cdot 2} \cdot 3 \end{array}\right\}$$ The LCD is $2 \cdot 2 \cdot 2 \cdot 3 \cdot 5 = 120$.

We want to convert each fraction to an equivalent fraction having a denominator of $2 \cdot 2 \cdot 2 \cdot 3 \cdot 5 = 120$. Multiply numerator and denominator of each fraction by the factors missing from the denominator.

$$-\frac{7 \cdot (2 \cdot 5)}{2 \cdot 2 \cdot 3 \cdot (2 \cdot 5)} - \frac{2 \cdot (2 \cdot 2 \cdot 2)}{3 \cdot 5 \cdot (2 \cdot 2 \cdot 2)} + \frac{7 \cdot (5)}{2 \cdot 2 \cdot 2 \cdot 3 \cdot (5)}$$

$$= -\frac{70}{120} - \frac{16}{120} + \frac{35}{120}$$ The fractions are now like fractions.

$$= \frac{-70 - 16 + 35}{120}$$ Add and subtract terms in the numerator.

$$= \frac{-51}{120}$$

$$= -\frac{\overset{17}{\cancel{51}}}{\underset{40}{\cancel{120}}}$$ Simplify to lowest terms. The numerator and denominator share a common factor of 3.

$$= -\frac{17}{40}$$

Example 8   **Adding and Subtracting Fractions with Variables**

Add or subtract as indicated.   **a.** $\dfrac{4}{5} + \dfrac{3}{x}$ **b.** $\dfrac{7}{x} - \dfrac{3}{x^2}$

Solution:

a. $\dfrac{4}{5} + \dfrac{3}{x} = \dfrac{4 \cdot x}{5 \cdot x} + \dfrac{3 \cdot 5}{x \cdot 5}$ The LCD is $5x$. Multiply by the missing factor from each denominator.

$$= \frac{4x}{5x} + \frac{15}{5x}$$ Simplify each fraction.

$$= \frac{4x + 15}{5x}$$ The numerator cannot be simplified further because $4x$ and 15 are not like terms.

b. $\dfrac{7}{x} - \dfrac{3}{x^2} = \dfrac{7 \cdot x}{x \cdot x} - \dfrac{3}{x^2}$ The LCD is x^2.

$$= \frac{7x}{x^2} - \frac{3}{x^2}$$ Simplify each fraction.

$$= \frac{7x - 3}{x^2}$$

3. Applications of Addition and Subtraction of Fractions

Example 9 Applying Operations on Unlike Fractions

A new Kelly Safari SUV tire has $\frac{7}{16}$-in. tread. After being driven 50,000 mi, the tread depth has worn down to $\frac{7}{32}$ in. By how much has the tread depth worn away?

Tread

Solution:

In this case, we are looking for the difference in the tread depth.

$$\begin{array}{l}\text{Difference in} \\ \text{tread depth}\end{array} = \left(\begin{array}{c}\text{original} \\ \text{tread depth}\end{array}\right) - \left(\begin{array}{c}\text{final} \\ \text{tread depth}\end{array}\right)$$

$$= \frac{7}{16} - \frac{7}{32} \qquad \text{The LCD is 32.}$$

$$= \frac{7 \cdot 2}{16 \cdot 2} - \frac{7}{32} \qquad \begin{array}{l}\text{Multiply numerator and denominator} \\ \text{by 2 because } 16 \cdot 2 = 32.\end{array}$$

$$= \frac{14}{32} - \frac{7}{32} \qquad \text{The fractions are now like.}$$

$$= \frac{7}{32} \qquad \text{Subtract.}$$

The tire lost $\frac{7}{32}$ in. in tread depth after 50,000 mi of driving.

TIP: You can check your result by adding the final tread depth to the difference in tread depth to get the original tread depth.

$$\frac{7}{32} + \frac{7}{32} = \frac{14}{32} = \frac{7}{16}$$

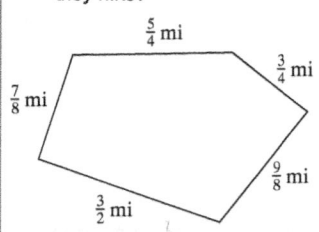

Example 10 Finding Perimeter

A parcel of land has the following dimensions. Find the perimeter.

Solution:

To find the perimeter, add the lengths of the sides.

$$\frac{1}{8} + \frac{1}{4} + \frac{5}{12} + \frac{1}{3} \qquad \text{The LCD is 24.}$$

$$= \frac{1 \cdot 3}{8 \cdot 3} + \frac{1 \cdot 6}{4 \cdot 6} + \frac{5 \cdot 2}{12 \cdot 2} + \frac{1 \cdot 8}{3 \cdot 8} \qquad \begin{array}{l}\text{Convert to like} \\ \text{fractions.}\end{array}$$

$$= \frac{3}{24} + \frac{6}{24} + \frac{10}{24} + \frac{8}{24}$$

$$= \frac{27}{24} \qquad \text{Add the fractions.}$$

$$= \frac{9}{8} \qquad \text{Simplify to lowest terms.}$$

The perimeter is $\frac{9}{8}$ mi or $1\frac{1}{8}$ mi.

Answers

12. $\frac{7}{15}$ in.

13. They hiked $\frac{11}{2}$ mi. or equivalently $5\frac{1}{2}$ mi.

Section 4.5 Practice Exercises

Study Skills Exercise

1. Define the key terms.

   a. Like fractions   **b. Common denominator**

Review Exercises

For Exercises 2–7, write the fraction as an equivalent fraction with the indicated denominator.

2. $\dfrac{3}{5} = \dfrac{}{15}$

3. $-\dfrac{6}{7} = -\dfrac{}{14}$

4. $\dfrac{3}{1} = \dfrac{}{10}$

5. $\dfrac{5}{1} = \dfrac{}{5}$

6. $\dfrac{3}{4x} = \dfrac{}{12x^2}$

7. $\dfrac{4}{t} = \dfrac{}{t^3}$

Objective 1: Addition and Subtraction of Like Fractions

For Exercises 8–9, shade in the portion of the third figure that represents the addition of the first two figures.

8.

9.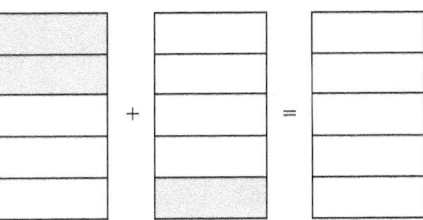

For Exercises 10–11, shade in the portion of the third figure that represents the subtraction of the first two figures.

10.

11.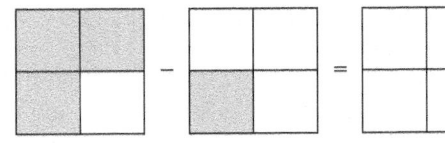

12. Explain the difference between evaluating the two expressions $\frac{2}{5} \cdot \frac{7}{5}$ and $\frac{2}{5} + \frac{7}{5}$.

For Exercises 13–28, add or subtract as indicated. Write the answer as a fraction or an integer. **(See Examples 1–2.)**

13. $\dfrac{7}{8} + \dfrac{5}{8}$

14. $\dfrac{1}{21} + \dfrac{13}{21}$

💿 **15.** $\dfrac{23}{12} - \dfrac{15}{12}$

16. $\dfrac{13}{6} - \dfrac{5}{6}$

💿 **17.** $\dfrac{18}{14} + \dfrac{11}{14} + \dfrac{6}{14}$

18. $\dfrac{7}{18} + \dfrac{22}{18} + \dfrac{10}{18}$

19. $\dfrac{14}{15} + \dfrac{2}{15} - \dfrac{4}{15}$

20. $\dfrac{19}{6} - \dfrac{11}{6} + \dfrac{5}{6}$

21. $-\dfrac{7}{2} + \dfrac{3}{2} - \dfrac{1}{2}$

22. $-\dfrac{8}{3} - \dfrac{2}{3} + \dfrac{1}{3}$

23. $\dfrac{5}{12} - \dfrac{19}{12} - \dfrac{7}{12}$

24. $\dfrac{5}{18} - \dfrac{7}{18} - \dfrac{13}{18}$

25. $\dfrac{3y}{2w} + \dfrac{5}{2w}$

26. $\dfrac{11a}{4b} + \dfrac{7}{4b}$

27. $\dfrac{x}{5y} - \dfrac{3x}{5y}$

28. $\dfrac{a}{9x} - \dfrac{5a}{9x}$

Objective 2: Addition and Subtraction of Unlike Fractions

For Exercises 29–64, add or subtract. Write the answer as a fraction simplified to lowest terms. **(See Examples 3–8.)**

29. $\dfrac{7}{8} + \dfrac{5}{16}$

30. $\dfrac{2}{9} + \dfrac{1}{18}$

31. $\dfrac{1}{15} + \dfrac{1}{10}$

32. $\dfrac{5}{6} + \dfrac{3}{8}$

33. $\dfrac{5}{6} + \dfrac{8}{7}$

34. $\dfrac{2}{11} + \dfrac{4}{5}$

35. $\dfrac{7}{8} - \dfrac{1}{2}$

36. $\dfrac{9}{10} - \dfrac{4}{5}$

37. $\dfrac{13}{12} - \dfrac{3}{4}$

38. $\dfrac{29}{30} - \dfrac{7}{10}$

39. $-\dfrac{10}{9} - \dfrac{5}{12}$

40. $-\dfrac{7}{6} - \dfrac{1}{15}$

41. $\dfrac{9}{8} - 2$

42. $\dfrac{11}{9} - 3$

43. $4 - \dfrac{4}{3}$

44. $2 - \dfrac{3}{8}$

45. $-\dfrac{16}{7} + 2$

46. $-\dfrac{15}{4} + 3$

47. $-\dfrac{1}{10} - \left(-\dfrac{9}{100}\right)$

48. $-\dfrac{3}{100} - \left(-\dfrac{21}{1000}\right)$

49. $\dfrac{3}{10} + \dfrac{9}{100} + \dfrac{1}{1000}$

50. $\dfrac{1}{10} + \dfrac{3}{100} + \dfrac{7}{1000}$

51. $\dfrac{5}{3} - \dfrac{7}{6} + \dfrac{5}{8}$

52. $\dfrac{7}{12} - \dfrac{2}{15} + \dfrac{5}{18}$

53. $-\dfrac{7}{10} - \dfrac{1}{20} - \left(-\dfrac{5}{8}\right)$

54. $\dfrac{1}{12} - \dfrac{3}{5} - \left(-\dfrac{3}{10}\right)$

55. $\dfrac{1}{2} + \dfrac{1}{4} - \dfrac{1}{8} - \dfrac{1}{16}$

56. $\dfrac{1}{3} - \dfrac{1}{9} + \dfrac{1}{27} - \dfrac{1}{81}$

57. $\dfrac{3}{4} + \dfrac{2}{x}$

58. $\dfrac{9}{5} + \dfrac{3}{y}$

59. $\dfrac{10}{x} + \dfrac{7}{y}$

60. $\dfrac{7}{a} + \dfrac{8}{b}$

61. $\dfrac{10}{x} - \dfrac{2}{x^2}$

62. $\dfrac{11}{z} - \dfrac{8}{z^2}$

63. $\dfrac{5}{3x} - \dfrac{2}{3}$

64. $\dfrac{13}{5t} - \dfrac{4}{5}$

Objective 3: Applications of Addition and Subtraction of Fractions

65. When doing her laundry, Inez added $\frac{3}{4}$ cup of bleach to $\frac{3}{8}$ cup of liquid detergent. How much total liquid is added to her wash?

66. What is the smallest possible length of screw needed to pass through two pieces of wood, one that is $\frac{7}{8}$ in. thick and one that is $\frac{1}{2}$ in. thick?

67. Before a storm, a rain gauge has $\frac{1}{8}$ in. of water. After the storm, the gauge has $\frac{9}{32}$ in. How many inches of rain did the storm deliver? **(See Example 9.)**

68. In one week it rained $\frac{5}{16}$ in. If a garden needs $\frac{9}{8}$ in. of water per week, how much more water does it need?

69. The information in the graph shows the distribution of a college student body by class.

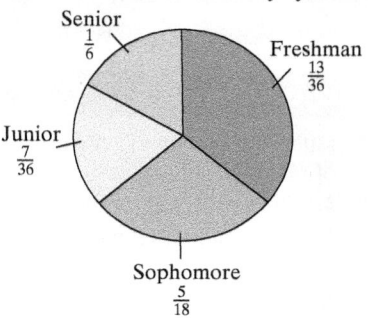

Distribution of Student Body by Class

a. What fraction of the student body consists of upper classmen (juniors and seniors)?

b. What fraction of the student body consists of freshmen and sophomores?

70. A group of college students took part in a survey. One of the survey questions read:

"Do you think the government should spend more money on research to produce alternative forms of fuel?"

The results of the survey are shown in the figure.

Survey Results

a. What fraction of the survey participants chose to strongly agree or agree?

b. What fraction of the survey participants chose to strongly disagree or disagree?

For Exercises 71–72, find the perimeter. **(See Example 10.)**

71.

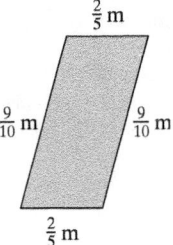

$\frac{2}{5}$ m

$\frac{9}{10}$ m $\frac{9}{10}$ m

$\frac{2}{5}$ m

72.

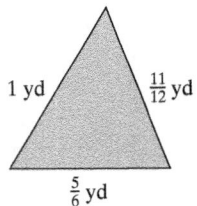

1 yd $\frac{11}{12}$ yd

$\frac{5}{6}$ yd

For Exercises 73–74, find the missing dimensions. Then calculate the perimeter.

73.

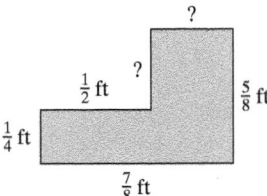

?

$\frac{1}{2}$ ft   ? $\frac{5}{8}$ ft

$\frac{1}{4}$ ft

$\frac{7}{8}$ ft

74.

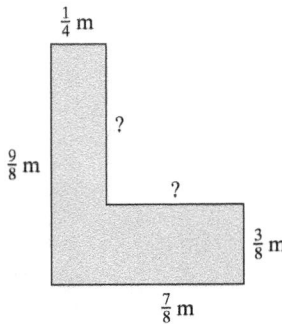

$\frac{1}{4}$ m

$\frac{9}{8}$ m   ?

?

$\frac{3}{8}$ m

$\frac{7}{8}$ m

Expanding Your Skills

75. Which fraction is closest to $\frac{1}{2}$?

a. $\frac{3}{4}$ b. $\frac{7}{10}$ c. $\frac{5}{6}$

76. Which fraction is closest to $\frac{3}{4}$?

a. $\frac{5}{8}$ b. $\frac{7}{12}$ c. $\frac{5}{6}$

Section 4.6	Estimation and Operations on Mixed Numbers

1. Multiplication and Division of Mixed Numbers

To multiply mixed numbers, we follow these steps.

> **PROCEDURE** Multiplying Mixed Numbers
>
> **Step 1** Change each mixed number to an improper fraction.
> **Step 2** Multiply the improper fractions and simplify to lowest terms, if possible (see Section 4.3).
>
> Answers greater than or equal to 1 may be written as an improper fraction or as a mixed number, depending on the directions of the problem.

Example 1 demonstrates this process.

Skill Practice

Multiply and write the answer as a mixed number or whole number.

1. $16\dfrac{1}{2} \cdot 3\dfrac{7}{11}$

2. $-10 \cdot \left(7\dfrac{1}{6}\right)$

Example 1	Multiplying Mixed Numbers

Multiply and write the answer as a mixed number or integer.

a. $7\dfrac{1}{2} \cdot 4\dfrac{2}{3}$ **b.** $-12 \cdot \left(1\dfrac{7}{9}\right)$

Solution:

a. $7\dfrac{1}{2} \cdot 4\dfrac{2}{3} = \dfrac{15}{2} \cdot \dfrac{14}{3}$ Write each mixed number as an improper fraction.

$= \dfrac{\overset{5}{\cancel{15}}}{\underset{1}{2}} \cdot \dfrac{\overset{7}{\cancel{14}}}{\underset{1}{3}}$ Simplify.

$= \dfrac{35}{1}$ Multiply.

$= 35$

> **Avoiding Mistakes**
>
> Do not try to multiply mixed numbers by multiplying the whole-number parts and multiplying the fractional parts. You will not get the correct answer.
> For the expression $7\frac{1}{2} \cdot 4\frac{2}{3}$, it would be incorrect to multiply $(7)(4)$ and $\frac{1}{2} \cdot \frac{2}{3}$. Notice that these values do not equal 35.

b. $-12 \cdot \left(1\dfrac{7}{9}\right) = -\dfrac{12}{1} \cdot \dfrac{16}{9}$ Write the whole number and mixed number as improper fractions.

$= -\dfrac{\overset{4}{\cancel{12}}}{1} \cdot \dfrac{16}{\underset{3}{\cancel{9}}}$ Simplify.

$= -\dfrac{64}{3}$ Multiply.

$= -21\dfrac{1}{3}$ Write the improper fraction as a mixed number.

$$\begin{array}{r} 21 \\ 3\overline{)64} \\ -6 \\ \hline 4 \\ -3 \\ \hline 1 \end{array}$$

Answers

1. 60   **2.** $-71\dfrac{2}{3}$

To divide mixed numbers, we use the following steps.

> **PROCEDURE** Dividing Mixed Numbers
> **Step 1** Change each mixed number to an improper fraction.
> **Step 2** Divide the improper fractions and simplify to lowest terms, if possible. Recall that to divide fractions, we multiply the dividend by the reciprocal of the divisor (see Section 4.3).
> Answers greater than or equal to 1 may be written as an improper fraction or as a mixed number, depending on the directions of the problem.

Example 2 **Dividing Mixed Numbers**

Divide and write the answer as a mixed number.

$$7\frac{1}{2} \div 4\frac{2}{3}$$

Solution:

$$7\frac{1}{2} \div 4\frac{2}{3} = \frac{15}{2} \div \frac{14}{3} \qquad \text{Write the mixed numbers as improper fractions.}$$

$$= \frac{15}{2} \cdot \frac{3}{14} \qquad \text{Multiply by the reciprocal of the divisor.}$$

$$= \frac{45}{28} \qquad \text{Multiply.}$$

$$= 1\frac{17}{28} \qquad \text{Write the improper fraction as a mixed number.}$$

Skill Practice
Divide and write the answer as a mixed number.

3. $10\frac{1}{3} \div 2\frac{5}{6}$

> **Avoiding Mistakes**
> Be sure to take the reciprocal of the divisor *after* the mixed number is changed to an improper fraction.

Example 3 **Dividing Mixed Numbers**

Divide and write the answers as mixed numbers.

a. $-6 \div \left(-5\frac{1}{7}\right)$ **b.** $13\frac{5}{6} \div (-7)$

Solution:

a. $-6 \div \left(-5\frac{1}{7}\right) = -\frac{6}{1} \div \left(-\frac{36}{7}\right)$ Write the whole number and mixed number as improper fractions.

$$= -\frac{6}{1} \cdot \left(-\frac{7}{36}\right) \qquad \text{Multiply by the reciprocal of the divisor.}$$

$$= -\frac{\overset{1}{6}}{1} \cdot \left(-\frac{7}{\underset{6}{36}}\right) \qquad \text{Simplify.}$$

$$= \frac{7}{6} \qquad \text{Multiply.}$$

$$= 1\frac{1}{6} \qquad \text{Write the improper fraction as a mixed number.}$$

Skill Practice
Divide and write the answers as mixed numbers.

4. $-8 \div \left(-4\frac{4}{5}\right)$

5. $12\frac{4}{9} \div (-8)$

Answers
3. $3\frac{11}{17}$ **4.** $1\frac{2}{3}$ **5.** $-1\frac{5}{9}$

b. $13\frac{5}{6} \div (-7) = \frac{83}{6} \div \left(-\frac{7}{1}\right)$ Write the integer, -7, and the mixed number as improper fractions.

$$= \frac{83}{6} \cdot \left(-\frac{1}{7}\right)$$ Multiply by the reciprocal of the divisor.

$$= -\frac{83}{42}$$ Multiply. The product is negative.

$$= -1\frac{41}{42}$$ Write the improper fraction as a mixed number.

2. Addition of Mixed Numbers

Now we will learn to add and subtract mixed numbers. To find the sum of two or more mixed numbers, add the whole-number parts and add the fractional parts.

Skill Practice

Add.

6. $7\frac{2}{15} + 2\frac{1}{15}$

Example 4   Adding Mixed Numbers

Add. $1\frac{5}{9} + 2\frac{1}{9}$

Solution:

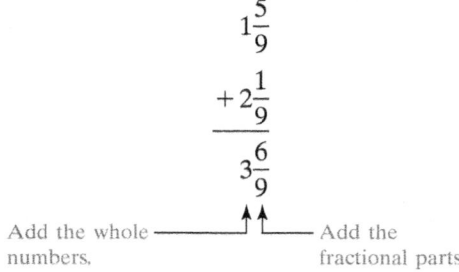

$$1\frac{5}{9}$$
$$+2\frac{1}{9}$$
$$\overline{3\frac{6}{9}}$$

Add the whole ———⤒⤒——— Add the
numbers.   fractional parts.

The sum is $3\frac{6}{9}$ which simplifies to $3\frac{2}{3}$.

> **TIP:** To understand why mixed numbers can be added in this way, recall that $1\frac{5}{9} = 1 + \frac{5}{9}$ and $2\frac{1}{9} = 2 + \frac{1}{9}$. Therefore,
>
> $$1\frac{5}{9} + 2\frac{1}{9} = 1 + \frac{5}{9} + 2 + \frac{1}{9}$$
> $$= 3 + \frac{6}{9}$$
> $$= 3\frac{6}{9}$$
> $$= 3\frac{2}{3}$$

When we perform operations on mixed numbers, it is often desirable to estimate the answer first. When rounding a mixed number, we offer the following convention.

1. If the fractional part of a mixed number is greater than or equal to $\frac{1}{2}$ (that is, if the numerator is half the denominator or greater), round to the next-greater whole number.
2. If the fractional part of the mixed number is less than $\frac{1}{2}$ (that is, if the numerator is less than half the denominator), the mixed number rounds down to the whole number.

Example 5   Adding Mixed Numbers

Estimate the sum and then find the actual sum.

$$42\frac{1}{12} + 17\frac{7}{8}$$

Answer

6. $9\frac{1}{5}$

Solution:

To estimate the sum, first round the addends.

$42\dfrac{1}{12}$　　rounds to　　　42

$+\ 17\dfrac{7}{8}$　　rounds to　　$\underline{+\ 18}$

　　　　　　　　　　　　　60　　　The estimated value is 60.

To find the actual sum, we must first write the fractional parts as like fractions. The LCD is 24.

$$42\dfrac{1}{12} = \quad 42\dfrac{1\cdot 2}{12\cdot 2} = \quad 42\dfrac{2}{24}$$

$$+\ 17\dfrac{7}{8} = +\ 17\dfrac{7\cdot 3}{8\cdot 3} = +\ 17\dfrac{21}{24}$$

$$\rule{3cm}{0.4pt}$$

$$59\dfrac{23}{24}$$

The actual sum is $59\frac{23}{24}$. This is close to our estimate of 60.

Skill Practice
Estimate the sum and then find the actual sum.

7. $6\dfrac{1}{11} + 3\dfrac{1}{2}$

Example 6　**Adding Mixed Numbers with Carrying**

Estimate the sum and then find the actual sum.

$$7\dfrac{5}{6} + 3\dfrac{3}{5}$$

Solution:

$7\dfrac{5}{6}$　　rounds to　　　8

$+\ 3\dfrac{3}{5}$　　rounds to　　$\underline{+\ 4}$

　　　　　　　　　　　　　12　　The estimated value is 12.

To find the actual sum, first write the fractional parts as like fractions. The LCD is 30.

$$7\dfrac{5}{6} = \quad 7\dfrac{5\cdot 5}{6\cdot 5} = \quad 7\dfrac{25}{30}$$

$$+\ 3\dfrac{3}{5} = +\ 3\dfrac{3\cdot 6}{5\cdot 6} = +\ 3\dfrac{18}{30}$$

$$\rule{3cm}{0.4pt}$$

$$10\dfrac{43}{30}$$

Notice that the number $\frac{43}{30}$ is an improper fraction. By convention, a mixed number is written as a whole number and a *proper* fraction. We have $\frac{43}{30} = 1\frac{13}{30}$. Therefore,

$$10\dfrac{43}{30} = 10 + 1\dfrac{13}{30} = 11\dfrac{13}{30}$$

The sum is $11\frac{13}{30}$. This is close to our estimate of 12.

Skill Practice
Estimate the sum and then find the actual sum.

8. $5\dfrac{2}{5} + 7\dfrac{8}{9}$

Concept Connections

9. Explain how you would rewrite $2\frac{9}{8}$ as a mixed number containing a proper fraction.

Answers

7. Estimate: 10; actual sum: $9\frac{13}{22}$

8. Estimate: 13; actual sum: $13\frac{13}{45}$

9. Write the improper fraction $\frac{9}{8}$ as $1\frac{1}{8}$ and add the result to 2. The result is $3\frac{1}{8}$.

We have shown how to add mixed numbers by writing the numbers in columns. Another approach to add or subtract mixed numbers is to write the numbers first as improper fractions. Then add or subtract the fractions, as you learned in Section 4.5. To demonstrate this process, we add the mixed numbers from Example 6.

Example 7 **Adding Mixed Numbers by Using Improper Fractions**

Add. $7\frac{5}{6} + 3\frac{3}{5}$

Solution:

$$7\frac{5}{6} + 3\frac{3}{5} = \frac{47}{6} + \frac{18}{5}$$ Write each mixed number as an improper fraction.

$$= \frac{47 \cdot 5}{6 \cdot 5} + \frac{18 \cdot 6}{5 \cdot 6}$$ Convert the fractions to like fractions. The LCD is 30.

$$= \frac{235}{30} + \frac{108}{30}$$ The fractions are now like fractions.

$$= \frac{343}{30}$$ Add the like fractions.

$$= 11\frac{13}{30}$$ Convert the improper fraction to a mixed number.

$$\begin{array}{r} 11 \\ 30\overline{)343} \\ -30 \\ \hline 43 \\ -30 \\ \hline 13 \end{array} \quad 11\frac{13}{30}$$

The mixed number $11\frac{13}{30}$ is the same as the value obtained in Example 6.

3. Subtraction of Mixed Numbers

To subtract mixed numbers, we subtract the fractional parts and subtract the whole-number parts.

Example 8 **Subtracting Mixed Numbers**

Subtract. $15\frac{2}{3} - 4\frac{1}{6}$

Answers

10. $17\frac{1}{12}$ **11.** $4\frac{5}{12}$

Solution:

To subtract the fractional parts, we need a common denominator. The LCD is 6.

$$15\frac{2}{3} = 15\frac{2\cdot 2}{3\cdot 2} = 15\frac{4}{6}$$
$$-4\frac{1}{6} = -4\frac{1}{6} = -4\frac{1}{6}$$
$$11\frac{3}{6}$$

Subtract the whole numbers. ⟶ ⟵ Subtract the fractional parts.

The difference is $11\frac{3}{6}$, which simplifies to $11\frac{1}{2}$.

Borrowing is sometimes necessary when subtracting mixed numbers.

Example 9 **Subtracting Mixed Numbers with Borrowing**

Subtract.

a. $17\frac{2}{7} - 11\frac{5}{7}$ **b.** $14\frac{2}{9} - 9\frac{3}{5}$

— Skill Practice —

Subtract.

12. $24\frac{2}{7} - 8\frac{5}{7}$

13. $9\frac{2}{3} - 8\frac{3}{4}$

Solution:

a. We will subtract $\frac{5}{7}$ from $\frac{2}{7}$ by borrowing 1 from the whole number 17. The borrowed 1 is written as $\frac{7}{7}$ because the common denominator is 7.

$$17\frac{2}{7} = \overset{16}{1\!\!7}\frac{2}{7} + \frac{7}{7} = 16\frac{9}{7}$$
$$-11\frac{5}{7} = -11\frac{5}{7} = -11\frac{5}{7}$$
$$5\frac{4}{7}$$

The difference is $5\frac{4}{7}$.

b. To subtract the fractional parts, we need a common denominator. The LCD is 45.

$$14\frac{2}{9} = 14\frac{2\cdot 5}{9\cdot 5} = 14\frac{10}{45}$$
$$-9\frac{3}{5} = -9\frac{3\cdot 9}{5\cdot 9} = -9\frac{27}{45}$$

We will subtract $\frac{27}{45}$ from $\frac{10}{45}$ by borrowing. Therefore, borrow 1 (or equivalently $\frac{45}{45}$) from 14.

$$= \overset{13}{1\!\!4}\frac{10}{45} + \frac{45}{45} = 13\frac{55}{45}$$
$$= -9\frac{27}{45} = -9\frac{27}{45}$$
$$4\frac{28}{45}$$

The difference is $4\frac{28}{45}$.

Answers

12. $15\frac{4}{7}$ **13.** $\frac{11}{12}$

Example 10 **Subtracting Mixed Numbers with Borrowing**

Subtract. $4 - 2\frac{5}{8}$

Solution:

$$\begin{array}{r} 4 \\ -2\dfrac{5}{8} \\ \hline \end{array}$$ In this case, we have no fractional part from which to subtract.

$$\begin{array}{r} 4\overset{\frac{3}{8}}{}\dfrac{8}{8} \\ -2\dfrac{5}{8} \\ \hline 1\dfrac{3}{8} \end{array}$$ We can borrow 1 or equivalently $\frac{8}{8}$ from the whole number 4.

> **TIP:** The borrowed 1 is written as $\frac{8}{8}$ because the common denominator is 8.

The difference is $1\frac{3}{8}$.

> **TIP:** The subtraction problem $4 - 2\frac{5}{8} = 1\frac{3}{8}$ can be checked by adding:
>
> $$1\frac{3}{8} + 2\frac{5}{8} = 3\frac{8}{8} = 3 + 1 = 4 \checkmark$$

In Example 11, we show the alternative approach to subtract mixed numbers by first writing each mixed number as an improper fraction.

Example 11 **Subtracting Mixed Numbers by Using Improper Fractions**

Subtract by first converting to improper fractions. Write the answer as a mixed number.

$$10\frac{2}{5} - 4\frac{3}{4}$$

Solution:

$$10\frac{2}{5} - 4\frac{3}{4} = \frac{52}{5} - \frac{19}{4}$$ Write each mixed number as an improper fraction.

$$= \frac{52 \cdot 4}{5 \cdot 4} - \frac{19 \cdot 5}{4 \cdot 5}$$ Convert the fractions to like fractions. The LCD is 20.

$$= \frac{208}{20} - \frac{95}{20}$$ Subtract the like fractions.

$$= \frac{113}{20}$$

$$= 5\frac{13}{20}$$ Write the result as a mixed number. $\begin{array}{r} 5 \\ 20\overline{)113} \\ -100 \\ \hline 13 \end{array}$

As you can see from Examples 7 and 11, when we convert mixed numbers to improper fractions, the numerators of the fractions become larger numbers. Thus, we must add (or subtract) larger numerators than if we had used the method involving columns. This is one drawback. However, an advantage of converting to improper fractions first is that there is no need for carrying or borrowing.

4. Addition and Subtraction of Negative Mixed Numbers

In Examples 4–11, we have shown two methods for adding and subtracting mixed numbers. The method of changing mixed numbers to improper fractions is preferable when adding or subtracting negative mixed numbers.

Example 12 **Adding and Subtracting Signed Mixed Numbers**

Add or subtract as indicated. Write the answer as a fraction.

a. $-3\frac{1}{2} - \left(-6\frac{2}{3}\right)$ **b.** $-4\frac{2}{3} - 1\frac{1}{6} + 2\frac{3}{4}$

Solution:

a. $-3\frac{1}{2} - \left(-6\frac{2}{3}\right) = -3\frac{1}{2} + 6\frac{2}{3}$ Rewrite subtraction in terms of addition.

$= -\frac{7}{2} + \frac{20}{3}$ Change the mixed numbers to improper fractions.

$= -\frac{7 \cdot 3}{2 \cdot 3} + \frac{20 \cdot 2}{3 \cdot 2}$ The LCD is 6.

$= -\frac{21}{6} + \frac{40}{6}$ Simplify.

$= \frac{-21 + 40}{6}$ Add the numerators. Note that the fraction $-\frac{21}{6}$ can be written as $\frac{-21}{6}$.

$= \frac{19}{6}$ Simplify.

b. $-4\frac{2}{3} - 1\frac{1}{6} + 2\frac{3}{4} = -\frac{14}{3} - \frac{7}{6} + \frac{11}{4}$ Change the mixed numbers to improper fractions.

$= -\frac{14 \cdot 4}{3 \cdot 4} - \frac{7 \cdot 2}{6 \cdot 2} + \frac{11 \cdot 3}{4 \cdot 3}$ The LCD is 12.

$= -\frac{56}{12} - \frac{14}{12} + \frac{33}{12}$ Change each fraction to an equivalent fraction with denominator 12.

$= \frac{-56 - 14 + 33}{12}$ Add and subtract the numerators.

$= \frac{-37}{12}$ or $-\frac{37}{12}$ Simplify.

Skill Practice

Add or subtract as indicated. Write the answers as fractions.

16. $-5\frac{3}{4} - \left(-1\frac{1}{2}\right)$

17. $-2\frac{5}{8} + 4\frac{3}{4} - 3\frac{1}{2}$

Answers

16. $-\frac{17}{4}$ **17.** $-\frac{11}{8}$

5. Applications of Mixed Numbers

Example 13 Subtracting Mixed Numbers in an Application

The average height of a 3-year-old girl is $38\frac{1}{3}$ in. The average height of a 4-year-old girl is $41\frac{3}{4}$ in. On average, by how much does a girl grow between the ages of 3 and 4?

Solution:

We use subtraction to find the difference in heights.

$$41\frac{3}{4} = \quad 41\frac{3 \cdot 3}{4 \cdot 3} = \quad 41\frac{9}{12}$$
$$-38\frac{1}{3} = -38\frac{1 \cdot 4}{3 \cdot 4} = -38\frac{4}{12}$$
$$\overline{\qquad\qquad\qquad\qquad\qquad 3\frac{5}{12}}$$

The average amount of growth is $3\frac{5}{12}$ in.

Example 14 Dividing Mixed Numbers in an Application

A construction site brings in $6\frac{2}{3}$ tons of soil. Each truck holds $\frac{2}{3}$ ton. How many truckloads are necessary?

Solution:

The $6\frac{2}{3}$ tons of soil must be distributed in $\frac{2}{3}$-ton increments. This will require division.

$6\frac{2}{3}$ tons

$\frac{2}{3}$ ton $\frac{2}{3}$ ton $\frac{2}{3}$ ton

$$6\frac{2}{3} \div \frac{2}{3} = \frac{20}{3} \div \frac{2}{3} \qquad \text{Write the mixed number as an improper fraction.}$$

$$= \frac{20}{3} \cdot \frac{3}{2} \qquad \text{Multiply by the reciprocal of the divisor.}$$

$$= \frac{\overset{10}{\cancel{20}}}{\underset{1}{\cancel{3}}} \cdot \frac{\overset{1}{\cancel{3}}}{\underset{1}{\cancel{2}}} \qquad \text{Simplify.}$$

$$= \frac{10}{1} \qquad \text{Multiply.}$$

$$= 10$$

A total of 10 truckloads of soil will be required.

Section 4.6 Practice Exercises

Review Exercises

For Exercises 1–8, perform the indicated operations. Write the answers as fractions.

1. $\dfrac{9}{5} + 3$

2. $\dfrac{3}{16} + \dfrac{7}{12}$

3. $\dfrac{25}{8} - \dfrac{23}{24}$

4. $-\dfrac{20}{9} \div \left(-\dfrac{10}{3}\right)$

5. $-\dfrac{42}{11} \div \left(-\dfrac{7}{2}\right)$

6. $\dfrac{52}{18} \div (-13)$

7. $\dfrac{125}{32} - \dfrac{51}{32} - \dfrac{58}{32}$

8. $\dfrac{17}{10} - \dfrac{23}{100} + \dfrac{321}{1000}$

For Exercises 9–10, write the mixed number as an improper fraction.

9. $3\dfrac{2}{5}$

10. $2\dfrac{7}{10}$

For Exercises 11–12, write the improper fraction as a mixed number.

11. $-\dfrac{77}{6}$

12. $-\dfrac{57}{11}$

Objective 1: Multiplication and Division of Mixed Numbers

For Exercises 13–32, multiply or divide the mixed numbers. Write the answer as a mixed number or an integer. **(See Examples 1–3.)**

13. $\left(2\dfrac{2}{5}\right)\left(3\dfrac{1}{12}\right)$

14. $\left(5\dfrac{1}{5}\right)\left(3\dfrac{3}{4}\right)$

15. $-2\dfrac{1}{3} \cdot \left(-6\dfrac{3}{5}\right)$

16. $-6\dfrac{1}{8} \cdot \left(-2\dfrac{3}{4}\right)$

17. $(-9) \cdot 4\dfrac{2}{9}$

18. $(-6) \cdot 3\dfrac{1}{3}$

19. $\left(5\dfrac{3}{16}\right)\left(5\dfrac{1}{3}\right)$

20. $\left(8\dfrac{2}{3}\right)\left(2\dfrac{1}{13}\right)$

21. $\left(7\dfrac{1}{4}\right) \cdot 10$

22. $\left(2\dfrac{2}{3}\right) \cdot 3$

23. $4\dfrac{1}{2} \div 2\dfrac{1}{4}$

24. $5\dfrac{5}{6} \div 2\dfrac{1}{3}$

25. $5\dfrac{8}{9} \div \left(-1\dfrac{1}{3}\right)$

26. $12\dfrac{4}{5} \div \left(-2\dfrac{3}{5}\right)$

27. $-2\dfrac{1}{2} \div \left(-1\dfrac{1}{16}\right)$

28. $-7\dfrac{3}{5} \div \left(-1\dfrac{7}{12}\right)$

29. $2 \div 3\dfrac{1}{3}$

30. $6 \div 4\dfrac{2}{5}$

31. $8\dfrac{1}{4} \div (-3)$

32. $6\dfrac{2}{5} \div (-2)$

Objective 2: Addition of Mixed Numbers

For Exercises 33–40, add the mixed numbers. **(See Examples 4–5.)**

33. $2\dfrac{1}{11}$
$+ 5\dfrac{3}{11}$

34. $5\dfrac{2}{7}$
$+ 4\dfrac{3}{7}$

35. $12\dfrac{1}{14}$
$+ 3\dfrac{5}{14}$

36. $1\dfrac{3}{20}$
$+ 17\dfrac{7}{20}$

37. $4\dfrac{5}{16}$ **38.** $21\dfrac{2}{9}$ **39.** $6\dfrac{2}{3}$ **40.** $7\dfrac{1}{6}$

  $+\,11\dfrac{1}{4}$ $+\,10\dfrac{1}{3}$ $+\,4\dfrac{1}{5}$ $+\,3\dfrac{5}{8}$

For Exercises 41–44, round the mixed number to the nearest whole number.

41. $5\dfrac{1}{3}$ **42.** $2\dfrac{7}{8}$ **43.** $1\dfrac{3}{5}$ **44.** $6\dfrac{3}{7}$

For Exercises 45–48, write the mixed number in proper form (that is, as a whole number with a proper fraction that is simplified to lowest terms).

45. $2\dfrac{6}{5}$ **46.** $4\dfrac{8}{7}$ **47.** $7\dfrac{5}{3}$ **48.** $1\dfrac{9}{5}$

For Exercises 49–54, round the numbers to estimate the answer. Then find the exact sum. In Exercise 49, the estimate is done for you. **(See Examples 6–7.)**

	Estimate	Exact		Estimate	Exact		Estimate	Exact
49.	7	$6\dfrac{3}{4}$	**50.**		$8\dfrac{3}{5}$	**51.**		$14\dfrac{7}{8}$
	$+\,8$	$+\,7\dfrac{3}{4}$		$+$	$+\,13\dfrac{4}{5}$		$+$	$+\,8\dfrac{1}{4}$
	15							

	Estimate	Exact		Estimate	Exact		Estimate	Exact
52.		$21\dfrac{3}{5}$	**53.**		$3\dfrac{7}{16}$	**54.**		$7\dfrac{7}{9}$
	$+$	$+\,24\dfrac{9}{10}$		$+$	$+\,15\dfrac{11}{12}$		$+$	$+\,8\dfrac{5}{6}$

For Exercises 55–62, add the mixed numbers. Write the answer as a mixed number or an integer. **(See Examples 6–7.)**

55. $3\dfrac{3}{4}+5\dfrac{2}{3}$ **56.** $6\dfrac{5}{7}+10\dfrac{3}{5}$ **57.** $11\dfrac{5}{8}+\dfrac{7}{6}$ **58.** $9\dfrac{5}{6}+\dfrac{3}{4}$

59. $3+6\dfrac{7}{8}$ **60.** $5+11\dfrac{1}{13}$ **61.** $124\dfrac{2}{3}+46\dfrac{5}{6}$ **62.** $345\dfrac{3}{5}+84\dfrac{7}{10}$

Objective 3: Subtraction of Mixed Numbers

For Exercises 63–66, subtract the mixed numbers. **(See Example 8.)**

63. $21\dfrac{9}{10}$ **64.** $19\dfrac{2}{3}$ **65.** $18\dfrac{5}{6}$ **66.** $21\dfrac{17}{20}$

  $-\,10\dfrac{3}{10}$ $-\,4\dfrac{1}{3}$ $-\,6\dfrac{2}{3}$ $-\,20\dfrac{1}{10}$

For Exercises 67–72, round the numbers to estimate the answer. Then find the exact difference. In Exercise 67, the estimate is done for you. **(See Examples 9–11.)**

	Estimate	Exact		Estimate	Exact		Estimate	Exact
67.	25	$25\frac{1}{4}$	**68.**		$36\frac{1}{5}$	**69.**		$17\frac{1}{6}$
	$-\ 14$	$-\ 13\frac{3}{4}$	$-$		$-\ 12\frac{3}{5}$	$-$		$-\ 15\frac{5}{12}$
	$\overline{11}$							

	Estimate	Exact		Estimate	Exact		Estimate	Exact
70.		$22\frac{5}{18}$	**71.**		$46\frac{3}{7}$	**72.**		$23\frac{1}{2}$
	$-$	$-\ 10\frac{7}{9}$	$-$		$-\ 38\frac{1}{2}$	$-$		$-\ 18\frac{10}{13}$

For Exercises 73–80, subtract the mixed numbers. Write the answer as a proper fraction or a mixed number. **(See Examples 9–11.)**

73. $6 - 2\frac{5}{6}$ **74.** $9 - 4\frac{1}{2}$ **75.** $12 - 9\frac{2}{9}$ **76.** $10 - 9\frac{1}{3}$

77. $3\frac{7}{8} - 3\frac{3}{16}$ **78.** $3\frac{1}{6} - 1\frac{23}{24}$ **79.** $12\frac{1}{5} - 11\frac{2}{7}$ **80.** $10\frac{1}{8} - 2\frac{17}{18}$

Objective 4: Addition and Subtraction of Negative Mixed Numbers

For Exercises 81–88, add or subtract the mixed numbers. Write the answer as a mixed number. **(See Example 12.)**

81. $-4\frac{2}{7} - 3\frac{1}{2}$ **82.** $-9\frac{1}{5} - 2\frac{1}{10}$ **83.** $-4\frac{3}{8} + 7\frac{1}{4}$ **84.** $-5\frac{2}{11} + 8\frac{1}{2}$

85. $3\frac{1}{2} - \left(-2\frac{1}{4}\right)$ **86.** $6\frac{1}{6} - \left(-4\frac{1}{3}\right)$ **87.** $5 + \left(-7\frac{5}{6}\right)$ **88.** $6 + \left(-10\frac{3}{4}\right)$

Mixed Exercises

For Exercises 89–96, perform the indicated operations. Write the answers as fractions or integers.

89. $\left(3\frac{1}{5}\right)\left(-2\frac{1}{4}\right)$ **90.** $(-10)\left(-3\frac{2}{5}\right)$ **91.** $4\frac{1}{8} - 3\frac{5}{6}$ **92.** $-5\frac{5}{6} - 3\frac{1}{3}$

93. $-8\frac{1}{3} \div \left(-2\frac{1}{6}\right)$ **94.** $10\frac{2}{3} \div (-8)$ **95.** $-6\frac{3}{10} + 4\frac{5}{6} - \left(-3\frac{1}{2}\right)$ **96.** $4\frac{4}{5} - \left(-2\frac{1}{4}\right) - 1\frac{3}{10}$

Objective 5: Applications of Mixed Numbers

For Exercises 97–100, use the table to find the lengths of several common birds.

Bird	Length
Cuban Bee Hummingbird	$2\frac{1}{4}$ in.
Sedge Wren	$3\frac{1}{2}$ in.
Great Carolina Wren	$5\frac{1}{2}$ in.
Belted Kingfisher	$11\frac{1}{4}$ in.

97. How much longer is the Belted Kingfisher than the Sedge Wren? **(See Example 13.)**

98. How much longer is the Great Carolina Wren than the Cuban Bee Hummingbird?

99. Estimate or measure the length of your index finger. Which is longer, your index finger or a Cuban Bee Hummingbird?

100. For a recent year, the smallest living dog in the United States was Brandy, a female Chihuahua, who measures 6 in. in length. How much longer is a Belted Kingfisher than Brandy?

101. Tabitha charges $8 per hour for baby sitting. If she works for $4\frac{3}{4}$ hr, how much should she be paid?

102. Kurt bought $2\frac{2}{3}$ acres of land. If land costs $10,500 per acre, how much will the land cost him?

103. According to the U.S. Census Bureau's Valentine's Day Press Release, the average American consumes $25\frac{7}{10}$ lb of chocolate in a year. Over the course of 25 years, how many pounds of chocolate would the average American consume?

104. Florida voters approved an amendment to the state constitution to set Florida's minimum wage at $6\frac{2}{3}$ per hour. Kayla earns minimum wage while working at the campus bookstore. If she works for $15\frac{3}{4}$ hr, how much should she be paid?

105. A student has three part-time jobs. She tutors, delivers newspapers, and takes notes for a blind student. During a typical week she works $8\frac{2}{3}$ hr delivering newspapers, $4\frac{1}{2}$ hr tutoring, and $3\frac{3}{4}$ hr note-taking. What is the total number of hours worked in a typical week?

106. A contractor ordered three loads of gravel. The orders were for $2\frac{1}{2}$ tons, $3\frac{1}{8}$ tons, and $4\frac{1}{3}$ tons. What is the total amount of gravel ordered?

107. The age of a small kitten can be approximated by the following rule. The kitten's age is given as 1 week for every quarter pound of weight. **(See Example 14.)**

  a. Approximately how old is a $1\frac{3}{4}$-lb kitten?

  b. Approximately how old is a $2\frac{1}{8}$-lb kitten?

108. Richard's estate is to be split equally among his three children. If his estate is worth $1\frac{3}{4}$ million, how much will each child inherit?

109. Lucy earns $14 per hour and Ricky earns $10 per hour. Suppose Lucy worked $35\frac{1}{2}$ hr last week and Ricky worked $42\frac{1}{2}$ hr.

   a. Who earned more money and by how much?

   b. How much did they earn altogether?

110. A roll of wallpaper covers an area of 28 ft². If the roll is $1\frac{17}{24}$ ft wide, how long is the roll?

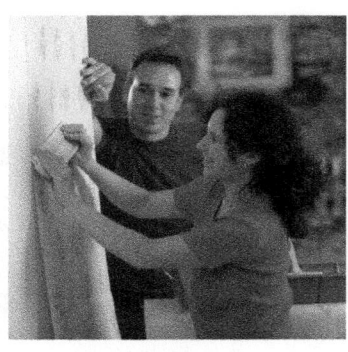

Figure for Exercise 110

111. A plumber fits together two pipes. Find the length of the larger piece.

$5\frac{3}{4}$ ft

$2\frac{1}{3}$ ft

112. Find the thickness of the carpeting and pad.

$\frac{3}{8}$ in.

$\frac{7}{16}$ in.

113. When using the word processor, Microsoft Word, the default margins are $1\frac{1}{4}$ in. for the left and right margins. If an $8\frac{1}{2}$ in. by 11 in. piece of paper is used, what is the width of the printing area?

114. A water gauge in a pond measured $25\frac{7}{8}$ in. on Monday. After 2 days of rain and runoff, the gauge read $32\frac{1}{2}$ in. By how much did the water level rise?

115. A patient admitted to the hospital was dehydrated. In addition to intravenous (IV) fluids, the doctor told the patient that she must drink at least 4 L of an electrolyte solution within the next 12 hr. A nurse recorded the amounts the patient drank in the patient's chart.

   a. How many L of electrolyte solution did the patient drink?

   b. How much more would the patient need to drink to reach 4 L?

Time	Amount
7 A.M.–10 A.M.	$1\frac{1}{4}$ L
10 A.M.–1 P.M.	$\frac{7}{8}$ L
1 P.M.–4 P.M.	$\frac{3}{4}$ L
4 P.M.–7 P.M.	$\frac{1}{2}$ L

116. Benjamin loves to hike in the White Mountains of New Hampshire. It takes him $4\frac{1}{2}$ hr to hike from the Pinkham Notch Visitor Center to the summit of Mt. Washington. If the round trip usually takes 8 hr, how long does it take for the return trip?

Expanding Your Skills

For Exercises 117–120, fill in the blank to complete the pattern.

117. $1, 1\frac{1}{3}, 1\frac{2}{3}, 2, 2\frac{1}{3}, \square$ **118.** $\frac{1}{4}, 1, 1\frac{3}{4}, 2\frac{1}{2}, 3\frac{1}{4}, \square$ **119.** $\frac{5}{6}, 1\frac{1}{6}, 1\frac{1}{2}, 1\frac{5}{6}, \square$ **120.** $\frac{1}{2}, 1\frac{1}{4}, 2, 2\frac{3}{4}, 3\frac{1}{2}, \square$

Calculator Connections

Topic: Multiplying and Dividing Fractions and Mixed Numbers on a Scientific Calculator

Expression	Keystrokes	Result
$\dfrac{8}{15} \cdot \dfrac{25}{28}$	8 $a\%$ 15 $\times$ 25 $a\%$ 28 $=$	$\boxed{10 \lrcorner 21} = \dfrac{10}{21}$
$2\dfrac{3}{4} \div \dfrac{1}{6}$	2 $a\%$ 3 $a\%$ 4 $\div$ 1 $a\%$ 6 $=$	$\boxed{16\_1\lrcorner 2} = 16\dfrac{1}{2}$

This is how you enter the mixed number $2\frac{3}{4}$.

To convert the result to an improper fraction, press 2nd d/e $\boxed{33\lrcorner 2} = \dfrac{33}{2}$

Topic: Adding and Subtracting Fractions and Mixed Numbers on a Calculator

Expression	Keystrokes	Result
$\dfrac{7}{18} + \dfrac{1}{3}$	7 $a\%$ 18 $+$ 1 $a\%$ 3 $=$	$\boxed{13 \lrcorner 18} = \dfrac{13}{18}$
$7\dfrac{5}{8} - 4\dfrac{2}{3}$	7 $a\%$ 5 $a\%$ 8 $-$ 4 $a\%$ 2 $a\%$ 3 $=$	$\boxed{2\_23 \lrcorner 24} = 2\dfrac{23}{24}$

$7\frac{5}{8}$ $4\frac{2}{3}$

To convert the result to an improper fraction, press 2nd d/e $\boxed{71 \lrcorner 24} = \dfrac{71}{24}$

Calculator Exercises

For Exercises 121–132, use a calculator to perform the indicated operations and simplify. Write the answer as a mixed number.

121. $12\dfrac{2}{3} \cdot 25\dfrac{1}{8}$

122. $38\dfrac{1}{3} \div 12\dfrac{1}{2}$

123. $56\dfrac{5}{6} \div 3\dfrac{1}{6}$

124. $25\dfrac{1}{5} \cdot 18\dfrac{1}{2}$

125. $\dfrac{23}{42} + \dfrac{17}{24}$

126. $\dfrac{14}{75} + \dfrac{9}{50}$

127. $\dfrac{31}{44} - \dfrac{14}{33}$

128. $\dfrac{29}{68} - \dfrac{7}{92}$

129. $32\dfrac{7}{18} + 14\dfrac{2}{27}$

130. $21\dfrac{3}{28} + 4\dfrac{31}{42}$

131. $7\dfrac{11}{21} - 2\dfrac{10}{33}$

132. $5\dfrac{14}{17} - 2\dfrac{47}{68}$

Problem Recognition Exercises

Operations on Fractions and Mixed Numbers

For Exercises 1–10, perform the indicated operations. Check the reasonableness of your answers by estimating.

1. a. $-\dfrac{7}{5} + \dfrac{2}{5}$ b. $-\dfrac{7}{5} \cdot \dfrac{2}{5}$ c. $-\dfrac{7}{5} \div \dfrac{2}{5}$ d. $-\dfrac{7}{5} - \dfrac{2}{5}$

2. a. $\dfrac{4}{3} \cdot \dfrac{5}{6}$ b. $\dfrac{4}{3} \div \dfrac{5}{6}$ c. $\dfrac{4}{3} + \dfrac{5}{6}$ d. $\dfrac{4}{3} - \dfrac{5}{6}$

3. a. $2\dfrac{3}{4} + \left(-1\dfrac{1}{2}\right)$ b. $2\dfrac{3}{4} - \left(-1\dfrac{1}{2}\right)$ c. $2\dfrac{3}{4} \div \left(-1\dfrac{1}{2}\right)$ d. $2\dfrac{3}{4} \cdot \left(-1\dfrac{1}{2}\right)$

4. a. $\left(4\dfrac{1}{3}\right) \cdot \left(2\dfrac{5}{6}\right)$ b. $\left(4\dfrac{1}{3}\right) \div \left(2\dfrac{5}{6}\right)$ c. $\left(4\dfrac{1}{3}\right) - \left(2\dfrac{5}{6}\right)$ d. $\left(4\dfrac{1}{3}\right) + \left(2\dfrac{5}{6}\right)$

5. a. $-4 - \dfrac{3}{8}$ b. $-4 \cdot \dfrac{3}{8}$ c. $-4 \div \dfrac{3}{8}$ d. $-4 + \dfrac{3}{8}$

6. a. $3\dfrac{2}{3} \div 2$ b. $3\dfrac{2}{3} - 2$ c. $3\dfrac{2}{3} + 2$ d. $3\dfrac{2}{3} \cdot 2$

7. a. $-4\dfrac{1}{5} - \left(-\dfrac{2}{3}\right)$ b. $-4\dfrac{1}{5} + \left(-\dfrac{2}{3}\right)$ c. $\left(-4\dfrac{1}{5}\right) \cdot \left(-\dfrac{2}{3}\right)$ d. $\left(-4\dfrac{1}{5}\right) \div \left(-\dfrac{2}{3}\right)$

8. a. $\dfrac{25}{9} \div 2$ b. $\dfrac{25}{9} \cdot 2$ c. $\dfrac{25}{9} - 2$ d. $\dfrac{25}{9} + 2$

9. a. $-1\dfrac{4}{5} \cdot \dfrac{5}{9}$ b. $-1\dfrac{4}{5} + \dfrac{5}{9}$ c. $-1\dfrac{4}{5} \div \dfrac{5}{9}$ d. $-1\dfrac{4}{5} - \dfrac{5}{9}$

10. a. $8 \cdot \dfrac{1}{8}$ b. $\dfrac{1}{9} \cdot 9$ c. $-\dfrac{3}{7} \cdot \left(-\dfrac{7}{3}\right)$ d. $-\dfrac{5}{13} \cdot \left(-\dfrac{13}{5}\right)$

Order of Operations and Complex Fractions   Section 4.7

1. Order of Operations

We will begin this section with a review of expressions containing exponents. Recall that to square a number, multiply the number times itself. For example: $5^2 = 5 \cdot 5 = 25$. The same process is used to square a fraction.

$$\left(\frac{3}{7}\right)^2 = \frac{3}{7} \cdot \frac{3}{7} = \frac{9}{49}$$

Objectives

1. Order of Operations
2. Complex Fractions
3. Simplifying Algebraic Expressions

Example 1   **Simplifying Expressions with Exponents**

Simplify.   **a.** $\left(\dfrac{2}{5}\right)^2$ **b.** $\left(-\dfrac{2}{5}\right)^2$ **c.** $-\left(\dfrac{2}{5}\right)^2$ **d.** $\left(-\dfrac{1}{4}\right)^3$

Solution:

a. $\left(\dfrac{2}{5}\right)^2 = \dfrac{2}{5} \cdot \dfrac{2}{5} = \dfrac{4}{25}$

b. $\left(-\dfrac{2}{5}\right)^2 = \left(-\dfrac{2}{5}\right)\left(-\dfrac{2}{5}\right) = \dfrac{4}{25}$ The base is negative. The product of two negatives is positive.

c. $-\left(\dfrac{2}{5}\right)^2 = -\left(\dfrac{2}{5}\right)\left(\dfrac{2}{5}\right) = -\dfrac{4}{25}$ First square the base. Then take the opposite.

d. $\left(-\dfrac{1}{4}\right)^3 = \left(-\dfrac{1}{4}\right)\left(-\dfrac{1}{4}\right)\left(-\dfrac{1}{4}\right) = -\dfrac{1}{64}$ The base is negative. The product of *three* negatives is negative.

In Section 1.7 we learned to recognize powers of 10. These are $10^1 = 10$, $10^2 = 100$, and so on. In this section, we learn to recognize the **powers of one-tenth**. That is, $\frac{1}{10}$ raised to a whole number power.

$$\left(\dfrac{1}{10}\right)^1 = \dfrac{1}{10}$$

$$\left(\dfrac{1}{10}\right)^2 = \dfrac{1}{10} \cdot \dfrac{1}{10} = \dfrac{1}{100}$$

$$\left(\dfrac{1}{10}\right)^3 = \dfrac{1}{10} \cdot \dfrac{1}{10} \cdot \dfrac{1}{10} = \dfrac{1}{1000}$$

$$\left(\dfrac{1}{10}\right)^4 = \dfrac{1}{10} \cdot \dfrac{1}{10} \cdot \dfrac{1}{10} \cdot \dfrac{1}{10} = \dfrac{1}{10,000}$$

$$\left(\dfrac{1}{10}\right)^5 = \dfrac{1}{10} \cdot \dfrac{1}{10} \cdot \dfrac{1}{10} \cdot \dfrac{1}{10} \cdot \dfrac{1}{10} = \dfrac{1}{100,000}$$

$$\left(\dfrac{1}{10}\right)^6 = \dfrac{1}{10} \cdot \dfrac{1}{10} \cdot \dfrac{1}{10} \cdot \dfrac{1}{10} \cdot \dfrac{1}{10} \cdot \dfrac{1}{10} = \dfrac{1}{1,000,000}$$

TIP: The instruction "simplify" means to perform all indicated operations. Fractional answers should always be written in lowest terms.

From these examples, we see that a power of one-tenth results in a fraction with a 1 in the numerator. The denominator has a 1 followed by the same number of zeros as the exponent.

Example 2   **Applying the Order of Operations**

Simplify. $\left(-\dfrac{2}{15} \cdot \dfrac{3}{4}\right)^2$

Solution:

$\left(-\dfrac{2}{15} \cdot \dfrac{3}{4}\right)^2 = \left(-\dfrac{\overset{1}{2}}{\underset{5}{15}} \cdot \dfrac{\overset{1}{3}}{\underset{2}{4}}\right)^2 = \left(-\dfrac{1}{10}\right)^2$ Multiply fractions within parentheses.

$\qquad\qquad = \left(-\dfrac{1}{10}\right)\left(-\dfrac{1}{10}\right)$ Square the fraction $-\dfrac{1}{10}$.

$\qquad\qquad = \dfrac{1}{100}$

Example 3 **Applying the Order of Operations**

Simplify. Write the answer as a fraction. $\frac{1}{2} + \left(3\frac{3}{5}\right) \cdot \left(-\frac{10}{9}\right)$

Solution:

$\frac{1}{2} + \left(3\frac{3}{5}\right) \cdot \left(-\frac{10}{9}\right)$ We must perform multiplication before addition.

$= \frac{1}{2} + \left(\frac{18}{5}\right) \cdot \left(-\frac{10}{9}\right)$ Write the mixed number $3\frac{3}{5}$ as $\frac{18}{5}$.

$= \frac{1}{2} + \left(\frac{\overset{2}{\cancel{18}}}{\cancel{5}_{1}}\right) \cdot \left(-\frac{\overset{2}{\cancel{10}}}{\cancel{9}_{1}}\right)$ Multiply fractions. The product will be negative.

$= \frac{1}{2} - \frac{4}{1}$

$= \frac{1}{2} - \frac{4 \cdot 2}{1 \cdot 2}$ Write the whole number over 1 and obtain a common denominator.

$= \frac{1}{2} - \frac{8}{2}$

$= \frac{1 - 8}{2}$ Subtract the fractions.

$= -\frac{7}{2}$ Simplify.

Skill Practice

Simplify. Write the answer as a fraction.

6. $\frac{2}{3} + \left(3\frac{3}{4}\right) \cdot \left(-\frac{8}{5}\right)$

Example 4 **Evaluating an Algebraic Expression**

Evaluate the expression. $2 \div y \cdot z$ for $y = -\frac{14}{3}$ and $z = -\frac{1}{3}$

Solution:

$2 \div y \cdot z$

$= 2 \div \left(-\frac{14}{3}\right) \cdot \left(-\frac{1}{3}\right)$ Substitute $-\frac{14}{3}$ for y and $-\frac{1}{3}$ for z.

$= \frac{2}{1} \cdot \left(-\frac{3}{14}\right) \cdot \left(-\frac{1}{3}\right)$ Write the whole number over 1. Multiply by the reciprocal of $-\frac{14}{3}$.

$= \frac{\overset{1}{\cancel{2}}}{1} \cdot \left(-\frac{\overset{1}{\cancel{3}}}{\cancel{14}_{7}}\right) \cdot \left(-\frac{1}{\cancel{3}_{1}}\right)$ Simplify by dividing out common factors. The product is positive.

$= \frac{1}{7}$

Skill Practice

Evaluate the expression for $a = -\frac{7}{15}$ and $b = \frac{21}{10}$.

7. $3 \cdot a \div b$

Avoiding Mistakes

Do not forget to write the "1" in the numerator of the fraction.

Answers

6. $-\frac{16}{3}$ **7.** $-\frac{2}{3}$

2. Complex Fractions

A **complex fraction** is a fraction in which the numerator and denominator contains one or more terms with fractions. We will simplify complex fractions in Examples 5 and 6.

Skill Practice

Simplify.

8. $\dfrac{\frac{5}{6}}{\frac{y}{21}}$

Example 5   Simplifying a Complex Fraction

Simplify. $\dfrac{\frac{3}{5}}{\frac{m}{10}}$

Solution:

a. $\dfrac{\frac{3}{5}}{\frac{m}{10}}$ ⟵—————— This fraction bar denotes division.

$= \dfrac{3}{5} \div \dfrac{m}{10}$ Write the expression as a division of fractions.

$= \dfrac{3}{5} \cdot \dfrac{10}{m}$ Multiply by the reciprocal of $\dfrac{m}{10}$.

$= \dfrac{3}{\overset{}{\underset{1}{5}}} \cdot \dfrac{\overset{2}{10}}{m}$ Reduce common factors.

$= \dfrac{6}{m}$ Simplify.

Skill Practice

Simplify.

9. $\dfrac{\frac{3}{10} - \frac{1}{2}}{2 + \frac{1}{5}}$

Example 6   Simplifying a Complex Fraction

Simplify. $\dfrac{\frac{2}{5} - \frac{1}{3}}{1 - \frac{3}{5}}$

Solution:

$\dfrac{\frac{2}{5} - \frac{1}{3}}{1 - \frac{3}{5}}$ This expression can be simplified using the order of operations. Subtract the fractions in the numerator and denominator separately. Then divide the results.

$= \dfrac{\frac{2 \cdot 3}{5 \cdot 3} - \frac{1 \cdot 5}{3 \cdot 5}}{\frac{1 \cdot 5}{1 \cdot 5} - \frac{3}{5}}$ The LCD in the numerator is 15.
In the denominator, the LCD is 5.

$= \dfrac{\frac{6}{15} - \frac{5}{15}}{\frac{5}{5} - \frac{3}{5}}$

Answers

8. $\dfrac{35}{2y}$ **9.** $-\dfrac{1}{11}$

$$= \frac{\dfrac{1}{15}}{\dfrac{2}{5}}$$ ⟵ This fraction bar represents division.

$$= \frac{1}{\overset{}{\underset{3}{15}}} \cdot \frac{\overset{1}{5}}{2}$$ Multiply by the reciprocal of $\dfrac{2}{5}$ and reduce common factors.

$$= \frac{1}{6}$$

As you can see from Example 6, simplifying a complex fraction can be a tedious process. For this reason, we offer an alternative approach, as demonstrated in Example 7.

Example 7 **Simplifying a Complex Fraction by Multiplying by the LCD**

Simplify. $\dfrac{\dfrac{2}{5} - \dfrac{1}{3}}{1 - \dfrac{3}{5}}$

Solution:

$$\frac{\dfrac{2}{5} - \dfrac{1}{3}}{1 - \dfrac{3}{5}}$$

First identify the LCD of all four terms in the expression. The LCD of $\frac{2}{5}, \frac{1}{3}, 1$, and $\frac{3}{5}$ is 15.

$$= \frac{15 \cdot \left(\dfrac{2}{5} - \dfrac{1}{3}\right)}{15 \cdot \left(1 - \dfrac{3}{5}\right)}$$

Group the terms in the numerator and denominator within parentheses. Then multiply each term in the numerator and denominator by the LCD, 15.

$$= \frac{\left(\overset{3}{15} \cdot \dfrac{2}{\underset{1}{5}}\right) - \left(\overset{5}{15} \cdot \dfrac{1}{\underset{1}{3}}\right)}{\left(15 \cdot 1\right) - \left(\overset{3}{15} \cdot \dfrac{3}{\underset{1}{5}}\right)}$$

Apply the distributive property to multiply each term by 15. Then simplify each product.

$$= \frac{6 - 5}{15 - 9} = \frac{1}{6}$$

Simplify the fraction.

3. Simplifying Algebraic Expressions

In Section 3.1, we simplified algebraic expressions by combining like terms. For example,

$$2x - 3x + 8x = (2 - 3 + 8)x \quad \text{Apply the distributive property.}$$

$$= 7x$$

In a similar way, we can combine like terms when the coefficients are fractions. This is demonstrated in Example 8.

Simplify.

11. $\frac{7}{4}y + \frac{2}{3}y$

Example 8 **Simplifying an Algebraic Expression**

Simplify. $\quad \frac{2}{5}x - \frac{1}{3}x$

Solution:

$\frac{2}{5}x - \frac{1}{3}x$ The two terms are like terms.

$= \left(\frac{2}{5} - \frac{1}{3}\right)x$ Combine like terms by applying the distributive property.

$= \left(\frac{2 \cdot 3}{5 \cdot 3} - \frac{1 \cdot 5}{3 \cdot 5}\right)x$ The LCD is 15.

$= \left(\frac{6}{15} - \frac{5}{15}\right)x$ Simplify.

$= \frac{1}{15}x$

TIP: $\frac{1}{15}x$ can also be written as $\frac{x}{15}$.

$$\frac{1}{15}x = \frac{1}{15} \cdot x = \frac{1}{15} \cdot \frac{x}{1} = \frac{x}{15}$$

Answer

11. $\frac{29}{12}y$

Section 4.7   Practice Exercises

Boost *your* GRADE at ALEKS.com!

ALEKS version 3.0

- Practice Problems
- Self-Tests
- NetTutor
- e-Professors
- Videos

Study Skills Exercise

1. Define the key terms.

     a. Powers of one-tenth   **b. Complex fraction**

Review Exercises

For Exercises 2–8, simplify.

2. $-\frac{2}{5} + \frac{7}{6}$ **3.** $-\frac{2}{5} - \frac{7}{6}$ **4.** $\left(-\frac{2}{5}\right)\left(\frac{7}{6}\right)$ **5.** $-\frac{2}{5} \div \frac{7}{6}$

6. $3\frac{1}{4} + \left(-2\frac{5}{6}\right)$ **7.** $\left(3\frac{1}{4}\right) \cdot \left(-2\frac{5}{6}\right)$ **8.** $3\frac{1}{4} \div \left(-2\frac{5}{6}\right)$

Objective 1: Order of Operations

For Exercises 9–44, simplify. **(See Examples 1–3.)**

9. $\left(\frac{1}{9}\right)^2$ **10.** $\left(\frac{1}{4}\right)^2$ **11.** $\left(-\frac{1}{9}\right)^2$ **12.** $\left(-\frac{1}{4}\right)^2$

13. $-\left(\frac{3}{2}\right)^3$ **14.** $-\left(\frac{4}{3}\right)^3$ **15.** $\left(-\frac{3}{2}\right)^3$ **16.** $\left(-\frac{4}{3}\right)^3$

17. $\left(\dfrac{1}{10}\right)^3$ **18.** $\left(\dfrac{1}{10}\right)^4$ **19.** $\left(-\dfrac{1}{10}\right)^6$ **20.** $\left(-\dfrac{1}{10}\right)^5$

21. $\left(-\dfrac{10}{3}\cdot\dfrac{3}{100}\right)^3$ **22.** $\left(-\dfrac{1}{6}\cdot\dfrac{3}{5}\right)^2$ **23.** $-\left(4\cdot\dfrac{3}{4}\right)^3$ **24.** $-\left(5\cdot\dfrac{2}{5}\right)^2$

25. $\dfrac{1}{6}+\left(2\dfrac{1}{3}\right)\cdot\left(1\dfrac{3}{4}\right)$ **26.** $\dfrac{7}{9}+\left(2\dfrac{1}{6}\right)\cdot\left(3\dfrac{1}{3}\right)$ **27.** $6-5\dfrac{1}{7}\div\left(-\dfrac{1}{7}\right)$ **28.** $11-6\dfrac{1}{3}\div\left(-1\dfrac{1}{6}\right)$

29. $-\dfrac{1}{3}\cdot\left|-\dfrac{21}{4}\cdot\dfrac{8}{7}\right|$ **30.** $-\dfrac{1}{6}\cdot\left|-\dfrac{24}{5}\cdot\dfrac{30}{8}\right|$ **31.** $\dfrac{16}{9}\cdot\left(\dfrac{1}{2}\right)^3$ **32.** $\dfrac{28}{6}\cdot\left(\dfrac{3}{2}\right)^2$

33. $\dfrac{54}{21}\div\dfrac{2}{3}\cdot\dfrac{7}{9}$ **34.** $\dfrac{48}{56}\div\dfrac{3}{8}\cdot\dfrac{7}{8}$ **35.** $7\dfrac{1}{8}\div\left(-1\dfrac{1}{3}\right)\div\left(-2\dfrac{1}{4}\right)$ **36.** $\left(-3\dfrac{1}{8}\right)\div5\dfrac{5}{7}\div1\dfrac{5}{16}$

37. $\dfrac{5}{4}\div\dfrac{3}{2}-\left(-\dfrac{5}{6}\right)$ **38.** $\dfrac{1}{7}\div\dfrac{2}{21}-\left(-\dfrac{5}{2}\right)$ **39.** $\left(\dfrac{1}{3}-\dfrac{1}{2}\right)^2$ **40.** $\left(-\dfrac{2}{3}+\dfrac{1}{6}\right)^2$

41. $\left(\dfrac{1}{4}\right)^2\div\left(\dfrac{5}{6}-\dfrac{2}{3}\right)+\dfrac{7}{12}$ **42.** $\left(\dfrac{1}{2}+\dfrac{1}{3}\right)\cdot\left(\dfrac{2}{5}\right)^2+\dfrac{3}{10}$ **43.** $\left(5-1\dfrac{7}{8}\right)\div\left(3-\dfrac{13}{16}\right)$ **44.** $\left(4+2\dfrac{1}{9}\right)\div\left(2-1\dfrac{11}{36}\right)$

For Exercises 45–52, evaluate the expression for the given values of the variables. **(See Example 4.)**

45. $-3\cdot a\div b$ for $a=-\dfrac{5}{6}$ and $b=\dfrac{3}{10}$ **46.** $4\div w\cdot z$ for $w=\dfrac{2}{7}$ and $z=-\dfrac{1}{5}$

47. xy^2 for $x=2\dfrac{1}{3}$ and $y=\dfrac{3}{2}$ **48.** c^3d for $c=-1\dfrac{1}{2}$ and $d=\dfrac{1}{3}$

49. $4x+6y$ for $x=\dfrac{1}{2}$ and $y=-\dfrac{3}{2}$ **50.** $2m-3n$ for $m=-\dfrac{3}{4}$ and $n=\dfrac{1}{6}$

51. $(4-w)(3+z)$ for $w=2\dfrac{1}{3}$ and $z=1\dfrac{2}{3}$ **52.** $(2+a)(7-b)$ for $a=-1\dfrac{1}{2}$ and $b=5\dfrac{1}{4}$

Objective 2: Complex Fractions

For Exercises 53–68, simplify the complex fractions. **(See Examples 5–7.)**

53. $\dfrac{\dfrac{5}{8}}{\dfrac{3}{4}}$ **54.** $\dfrac{\dfrac{8}{9}}{\dfrac{7}{12}}$ **55.** $\dfrac{-\dfrac{21}{10}}{\dfrac{6}{5}}$ **56.** $\dfrac{\dfrac{20}{3}}{-\dfrac{5}{8}}$

57. $\dfrac{\dfrac{3}{7}}{\dfrac{12}{x}}$ **58.** $\dfrac{\dfrac{5}{p}}{\dfrac{30}{11}}$ **59.** $\dfrac{\dfrac{-15}{w}}{\dfrac{25}{w}}$ **60.** $\dfrac{\dfrac{18}{t}}{\dfrac{15}{t}}$

61. $\dfrac{\dfrac{4}{3}-\dfrac{1}{6}}{1-\dfrac{1}{3}}$ **62.** $\dfrac{\dfrac{6}{5}+\dfrac{3}{10}}{2+\dfrac{1}{2}}$ **63.** $\dfrac{\dfrac{1}{2}+3}{\dfrac{9}{8}+\dfrac{1}{4}}$ **64.** $\dfrac{\dfrac{5}{2}+1}{\dfrac{3}{4}+\dfrac{1}{3}}$

65. $\dfrac{-\dfrac{5}{7} - \dfrac{1}{14}}{\dfrac{1}{2} - \dfrac{3}{7}}$

66. $\dfrac{-\dfrac{1}{4} + \dfrac{1}{6}}{\dfrac{4}{3} - \dfrac{5}{6}}$

67. $\dfrac{-\dfrac{7}{4} + \dfrac{3}{2}}{-\dfrac{7}{8} - \dfrac{1}{4}}$

68. $\dfrac{\dfrac{8}{3} - \dfrac{5}{6}}{\dfrac{1}{4} - \dfrac{4}{3}}$

Objective 3: Simplifying Algebraic Expressions

For Exercises 69–76, simplify the expressions. **(See Example 8.)**

69. $\dfrac{1}{2}y + \dfrac{3}{2}y$

70. $-\dfrac{4}{5}p + \dfrac{2}{5}p$

71. $\dfrac{3}{4}a - \dfrac{1}{8}a$

72. $\dfrac{1}{3}b + \dfrac{2}{9}b$

73. $\dfrac{4}{5}x - \dfrac{3}{10}x + \dfrac{1}{15}x$

74. $-\dfrac{3}{2}y - \dfrac{4}{3}y + \dfrac{3}{4}y$

75. $\dfrac{3}{2}y + \dfrac{1}{4}z - \dfrac{1}{6}y - 2z$

76. $-\dfrac{5}{8}a + 3b + \dfrac{1}{4}a - \dfrac{7}{2}b$

Expanding Your Skills

77. Evaluate

   a. $\left(\dfrac{1}{6}\right)^2$

   b. $\sqrt{\dfrac{1}{36}}$

78. Evaluate

   a. $\left(\dfrac{2}{7}\right)^2$

   b. $\sqrt{\dfrac{4}{49}}$

For Exercises 79–82, evaluate the square roots.

79. $\sqrt{\dfrac{1}{25}}$

80. $\sqrt{\dfrac{1}{100}}$

81. $\sqrt{\dfrac{64}{81}}$

82. $\sqrt{\dfrac{9}{4}}$

Section 4.8   Solving Equations Containing Fractions

Objectives

1. Solving Equations Containing Fractions
2. Solving Equations by Clearing Fractions

1. Solving Equations Containing Fractions

In this section we will solve linear equations that contain fractions. To begin, review the addition, subtraction, multiplication, and division properties of equality.

Property	Example
Addition Property of Equality If $a = b$, then $a + c = b + c$	Solve. $x - 4 = 6$ $x - 4 + 4 = 6 + 4$ $x = 10$
Subtraction Property of Equality If $a = b$, then $a - c = b - c$	Solve. $x + 3 = 5$ $x + 3 - 3 = 5 - 3$ $x = 2$
Multiplication Property of Equality If $a = b$, then $a \cdot c = b \cdot c$ (provided that $c \neq 0$)	Solve. $\dfrac{x}{5} = 3$ $\dfrac{x}{5} \cdot 5 = 3 \cdot 5$ $x = 15$
Division Property of Equality If $a = b$, then $\dfrac{a}{c} = \dfrac{b}{c}$ (provided that $c \neq 0$)	Solve. $9x = 27$ $\dfrac{9x}{9} = \dfrac{27}{9}$ $x = 3$

We will use the same properties to solve equations containing fractions. In Examples 1 and 2, we use the addition and subtraction properties of equality.

Example 1 **Using the Addition Property of Equality**

Solve. $x - \dfrac{3}{10} = \dfrac{9}{20}$

Solution:

$x - \dfrac{3}{10} = \dfrac{9}{20}$

$x - \dfrac{3}{10} + \dfrac{3}{10} = \dfrac{9}{20} + \dfrac{3}{10}$ Add $\dfrac{3}{10}$ to both sides to isolate x.

$x = \dfrac{9}{20} + \dfrac{3 \cdot 2}{10 \cdot 2}$ To add the fractions on the right, the LCD is 20.

$x = \dfrac{9}{20} + \dfrac{6}{20}$

$x = \dfrac{15}{20}$ Now simplify the fraction.

$x = \dfrac{3}{4}$ The solution is $\dfrac{3}{4}$.

Check: $x - \dfrac{3}{10} = \dfrac{9}{20}$

$\dfrac{3}{4} - \dfrac{3}{10} \overset{?}{=} \dfrac{9}{20}$ Substitute $\dfrac{3}{4}$ for x.

$\dfrac{3 \cdot 5}{4 \cdot 5} - \dfrac{3 \cdot 2}{10 \cdot 2} \overset{?}{=} \dfrac{9}{20}$

$\dfrac{15}{20} - \dfrac{6}{20} \overset{?}{=} \dfrac{9}{20}$ ✓ True

Example 2 **Using the Subtraction Property of Equality**

Solve. $-\dfrac{5}{4} = \dfrac{1}{2} + t$

Solution:

$-\dfrac{5}{4} = \dfrac{1}{2} + t$

$-\dfrac{5}{4} - \dfrac{1}{2} = \dfrac{1}{2} - \dfrac{1}{2} + t$ Subtract $\dfrac{1}{2}$ on both sides to isolate t.

$-\dfrac{5}{4} - \dfrac{1 \cdot 2}{2 \cdot 2} = t$ To subtract the fractions on the left, the LCD is 4.

$-\dfrac{5}{4} - \dfrac{2}{4} = t$

$-\dfrac{7}{4} = t$ The solution is $-\frac{7}{4}$ and checks in the original equation.

Recall that the product of a number and its reciprocal is 1. For example:

$$\frac{2}{7} \cdot \frac{7}{2} = 1, \qquad -\frac{3}{8} \cdot \left(-\frac{8}{3}\right) = 1, \qquad 5 \cdot \frac{1}{5} = 1$$

We will use this fact and the multiplication property of equality to solve the equations in Examples 3–5.

Skill Practice

Solve.

3. $\dfrac{3}{4}x = \dfrac{5}{6}$

Example 3 Using the Multiplication Property of Equality

Solve. $\dfrac{4}{5}x = \dfrac{2}{7}$

Solution:

$\dfrac{4}{5}x = \dfrac{2}{7}$ In this equation, we will apply the multiplication property of equality. Multiply both sides of the equation by the reciprocal of $\frac{4}{5}$. Do this because $\frac{5}{4} \cdot \frac{4}{5}x$ is equal to $1x$. This isolates the variable x.

$\dfrac{5}{4} \cdot \dfrac{4}{5}x = \dfrac{5}{4} \cdot \dfrac{2}{7}$ Multiply both sides of the equation by the reciprocal of $\frac{4}{5}$.

$1x = \dfrac{10}{28}$

$x = \dfrac{\overset{5}{\cancel{10}}}{\underset{14}{\cancel{28}}}$ Simplify.

$x = \dfrac{5}{14}$ The solution is $\frac{5}{14}$ and checks in the original equation.

Skill Practice

Solve.

4. $7 = -\dfrac{1}{4}y$

Example 4 Using the Multiplication Property of Equality

Solve. $8 = -\dfrac{1}{6}y$

Solution:

$8 = -\dfrac{1}{6}y$

$-6 \cdot (8) = -6 \cdot \left(-\dfrac{1}{6}y\right)$ Multiply both sides of the equation by the reciprocal of $-\frac{1}{6}$. Do this because $-6 \cdot (-\frac{1}{6}y)$ is equal to $1y$. This isolates the variable y.

$-48 = 1y$ The solution is -48 and checks in the original equation.

$-48 = y$

Answers

3. $\dfrac{10}{9}$ **4.** -28

Example 5	Using the Multiplication Property of Equality

Solve. $-\dfrac{2}{9} = -4w$

Solution:

$$-\frac{2}{9} = -4w$$

$$-\frac{1}{4}\left(-\frac{2}{9}\right) = -\frac{1}{4}(-4w)$$

Multiply both sides of the equation by the reciprocal of -4. Do this because $-\frac{1}{4} \cdot (-4w)$ is equal to $1w$. This isolates the variable w.

$$-\frac{1}{\overset{}{4}_2}\left(-\frac{\overset{1}{2}}{9}\right) = 1w$$

$$\frac{1}{18} = w$$

The solution is $\frac{1}{18}$ and checks in the original equation.

In Example 6, we solve an equation in which we must apply both the addition property of equality and the multiplication property of equality.

Example 6	Using Multiple Steps to Solve an Equation with Fractions

Solve. $\dfrac{3}{4}x - \dfrac{1}{3} = \dfrac{5}{6}$

Solution:

$$\frac{3}{4}x - \frac{1}{3} = \frac{5}{6}$$

$$\frac{3}{4}x - \frac{1}{3} + \frac{1}{3} = \frac{5}{6} + \frac{1}{3}$$

To isolate the x-term, add $\dfrac{1}{3}$ to both sides.

$$\frac{3}{4}x = \frac{5}{6} + \frac{1 \cdot 2}{3 \cdot 2}$$

To add the fractions on the right, the LCD is 6.

$$\frac{3}{4}x = \frac{5}{6} + \frac{2}{6}$$

$$\frac{3}{4}x = \frac{7}{6}$$

$$\frac{4}{3} \cdot \frac{3}{4}x = \frac{4}{3} \cdot \frac{7}{6}$$

Multiply both sides of the equation by the reciprocal of $\frac{3}{4}$. Do this because $\frac{4}{3} \cdot (\frac{3}{4}x)$ is equal to $1x$. This isolates the variable x.

$$x = \frac{\overset{2}{4}}{3} \cdot \frac{7}{\underset{3}{6}}$$

Simplify the product.

$$x = \frac{14}{9}$$

The solution is $\frac{14}{9}$ and checks in the original equation.

2. Solving Equations by Clearing Fractions

As you probably noticed, Example 6 required tedious manipulation of fractions to isolate the variable. Therefore, we will now show you an alternative technique that eliminates the fractions immediately. This technique is called **clearing fractions**. Its basis is to multiply both sides of the equation by the LCD of all terms in the equation. This is demonstrated in Examples 7–8.

Example 7   **Solving an Equation by First Clearing Fractions**

Solve. $\dfrac{y}{8} + \dfrac{3}{2} = \dfrac{y}{4}$

Solution:

$\dfrac{y}{8} + \dfrac{3}{2} = \dfrac{y}{4}$ The LCD of $\dfrac{y}{8}, \dfrac{3}{2},$ and $\dfrac{y}{4}$ is 8.

$8 \cdot \left(\dfrac{y}{8} + \dfrac{3}{2}\right) = 8 \cdot \left(\dfrac{y}{4}\right)$ Apply the multiplication property of equality. Multiply both sides of the equation by 8.

$8 \cdot \left(\dfrac{y}{8}\right) + 8 \cdot \left(\dfrac{3}{2}\right) = 8 \cdot \left(\dfrac{y}{4}\right)$ Use the distributive property to multiply each term by 8.

$\overset{1}{8} \cdot \left(\dfrac{y}{8_1}\right) + \overset{4}{8} \cdot \left(\dfrac{3}{2_1}\right) = \overset{2}{8} \cdot \left(\dfrac{y}{4_1}\right)$ Simplify each term.

$y + 12 = 2y$ The fractions have been "cleared." Now isolate the variable.

$y - y + 12 = 2y - y$ Subtract y from both sides to collect the variable terms on one side.

$12 = y$ Simplify.

The solution is 12 and checks in the original equation.

Clearing fractions is a technique that "removes" fractions from an equation and produces a simpler equation. Because this technique is so powerful, we will add it to step 1 of our procedure box for solving a linear equation in one variable.

PROCEDURE **Solving a Linear Equation in One Variable**

Step 1 Simplify both sides of the equation.
- Clear parentheses if necessary.
- Combine *like* terms if necessary.
- Consider clearing fractions if necessary.

Step 2 Use the addition or subtraction property of equality to collect the variable terms on one side of the equation.

Step 3 Use the addition or subtraction property of equality to collect the constant terms on the *other* side of the equation.

Step 4 Use the multiplication or division property of equality to make the coefficient of the variable term equal to 1.

Step 5 Check the answer in the original equation.

Example 8	**Solving an Equation by First Clearing Fractions**

Solve. $-\dfrac{4}{7}x - 2 = \dfrac{3}{14}$

Skill Practice

Solve.

8. $-\dfrac{3}{8}x - 3 = \dfrac{1}{4}$

Solution:

$$-\frac{4}{7}x - 2 = \frac{3}{14}$$ The LCD of $-\dfrac{4}{7}x$, -2, and $\dfrac{3}{14}$ is 14.

$$14 \cdot \left(-\frac{4}{7}x - 2\right) = 14 \cdot \left(\frac{3}{14}\right)$$ Multiply both sides by 14.

$$14 \cdot \left(-\frac{4}{7}x\right) + 14 \cdot (-2) = 14 \cdot \left(\frac{3}{14}\right)$$ Use the distributive property to multiply each term by 14.

$$\overset{2}{14} \cdot \left(-\frac{4}{7}x\right) + 14 \cdot (-2) = \overset{1}{14} \cdot \left(\frac{3}{14}\right)$$ Simplify each term.

$$-8x - 28 = 3$$ The fractions have been "cleared."

$$-8x - 28 + 28 = 3 + 28$$ Add 28 to both sides to isolate the x term.

$$-8x = 31$$

$$\frac{-8x}{-8} = \frac{31}{-8}$$ Apply the division property of equality to isolate x.

$$x = -\frac{31}{8}$$ The solution is $-\frac{31}{8}$ and checks in the original equation.

Avoiding Mistakes

Be sure to multiply each term by 14. This includes the constant term, -2.

Answer

8. $-\dfrac{26}{3}$

Section 4.8 Practice Exercises

Boost *your* GRADE at ALEKS.com!   ALEKS®   • Practice Problems   • e-Professors
version 3.0   • Self-Tests   • Videos
• NetTutor

Study Skills Exercises

1. When you solve equations involving several steps, it is recommended that you write an explanation for each step. In Example 8, an equation is solved with each step shown. Your job is to write an explanation for each step for the following equation.

$$\frac{3}{5}x - \frac{7}{10} = \frac{1}{2}$$ <u>**Explanation**</u>

$$10\left(\frac{3}{5}x - \frac{7}{10}\right) = 10\left(\frac{1}{2}\right)$$

$$6x - 7 = 5$$

$$6x - 7 + 7 = 5 + 7$$

$$6x = 12$$

$$\frac{6x}{6} = \frac{12}{6}$$

$$x = 2 \qquad \text{The solution is 2.}$$

2. Define the key terms.

    a. Addition property of equality   **b. Subtraction property of equality**

    c. Multiplication property of equality   **d. Division property of equality**   **e. Clearing fractions**

Review Exercises

For Exercises 3–8, simplify.

3. $\left(\dfrac{2}{3} - \dfrac{3}{2}\right)^2$

4. $\dfrac{3}{5} + \dfrac{9}{4} - 3\dfrac{1}{2}$

5. $\left(\dfrac{2}{3}\right)^2 - \left(\dfrac{3}{2}\right)^2$

6. $-\dfrac{3}{5} \div \dfrac{9}{4} \cdot \left(3\dfrac{1}{2}\right)$

7. $-5\dfrac{2}{3} - 4\dfrac{3}{8}$

8. $\left(3 - 1\dfrac{3}{4}\right)^2$

Objective 1: Solving Equations Containing Fractions

For Exercises 9–42, solve the equations. Write the answers as fractions or whole numbers. **(See Examples 1–6.)**

9. $p - \dfrac{5}{6} = \dfrac{1}{3}$

10. $q - \dfrac{3}{4} = \dfrac{3}{2}$

11. $-\dfrac{7}{10} = \dfrac{3}{5} + a$

12. $-\dfrac{3}{8} = \dfrac{1}{4} + b$

13. $\dfrac{2}{3} = y - \dfrac{5}{12}$

14. $\dfrac{7}{11} = z + \dfrac{3}{11}$

15. $t + \dfrac{3}{8} = 2$

16. $r - \dfrac{4}{7} = -1$

17. $\dfrac{1}{6} = -\dfrac{11}{6} + m$

18. $n + \dfrac{1}{2} = -\dfrac{2}{3}$

19. $\dfrac{3}{5}y = \dfrac{7}{10}$

20. $\dfrac{7}{2}x = \dfrac{5}{4}$

21. $\dfrac{5}{4}k = -\dfrac{1}{2}$

22. $-\dfrac{11}{12}h = -\dfrac{1}{6}$

23. $6 = -\dfrac{1}{4}x$

24. $3 = -\dfrac{1}{5}y$

25. $\dfrac{2}{3}m = 14$

26. $\dfrac{5}{9}n = 40$

27. $\dfrac{b}{7} = -3$

28. $\dfrac{a}{4} = 12$

29. $-\dfrac{u}{2} = -15$

30. $-\dfrac{v}{10} = -4$

31. $0 = \dfrac{3}{8}m$

32. $0 = \dfrac{1}{10}n$

33. $6x = \dfrac{12}{5}$

34. $7t = \dfrac{14}{3}$

35. $-\dfrac{5}{9} = -10x$

36. $-\dfrac{4}{3} = -6y$

37. $\dfrac{2}{5}x - \dfrac{1}{4} = \dfrac{3}{2}$

38. $\dfrac{5}{9}y - \dfrac{1}{3} = \dfrac{5}{6}$

39. $-\dfrac{4}{7} = \dfrac{1}{2} + \dfrac{3}{14}w$

40. $-\dfrac{1}{8} = \dfrac{3}{4} + \dfrac{5}{2}z$

41. $3p + \dfrac{1}{2} = \dfrac{5}{4}$

42. $2t - \dfrac{3}{8} = \dfrac{9}{16}$

Objective 2: Solving Equations by Clearing Fractions

For Exercises 43–54, solve the equations by first clearing fractions. **(See Examples 7–8.)**

43. $\dfrac{x}{5} + \dfrac{1}{2} = \dfrac{7}{10}$

44. $\dfrac{p}{4} + \dfrac{1}{2} = \dfrac{5}{8}$

45. $-\dfrac{5}{7}y - 1 = \dfrac{3}{2}$

46. $-\dfrac{2}{3}w - 3 = -\dfrac{1}{2}$

47. $\dfrac{2}{3} = \dfrac{5}{9} + \dfrac{1}{6}t$

48. $\dfrac{4}{5} = \dfrac{9}{15} + \dfrac{1}{3}n$

49. $\dfrac{m}{3} + \dfrac{m}{6} = \dfrac{5}{9}$

50. $\dfrac{4}{5} = \dfrac{n}{15} - \dfrac{n}{3}$

51. $\dfrac{x}{3} + \dfrac{7}{6} = \dfrac{x}{2}$

52. $\dfrac{p}{4} = \dfrac{p}{8} + \dfrac{1}{2}$

53. $\dfrac{3}{2}y + 3 = 2y + \dfrac{1}{2}$

54. $\dfrac{1}{4}x - 1 = 2 - \dfrac{1}{2}x$

Mixed Exercises

For Exercises 55–72, solve the equations.

55. $\dfrac{h}{4} = -12$

56. $\dfrac{w}{6} = -18$

57. $\dfrac{2}{3} + t = 1$

58. $\dfrac{3}{4} + q = 1$

59. $-\dfrac{3}{7}x = \dfrac{9}{10}$

60. $-\dfrac{2}{11}y = \dfrac{4}{15}$

61. $4c = -\dfrac{1}{3}$

62. $\dfrac{1}{3}b = -4$

63. $-p = -\dfrac{7}{10}$

64. $-8h = 0$

65. $-9 = \dfrac{w}{2} - 3$

66. $-16 = \dfrac{t}{4} - 14$

67. $2x - \dfrac{1}{2} = \dfrac{1}{6}$

68. $3z - \dfrac{3}{4} = \dfrac{1}{2}$

69. $\dfrac{5}{4}x = \dfrac{5}{6}x + \dfrac{2}{3}$

70. $\dfrac{3}{4}y = \dfrac{3}{2}y + \dfrac{1}{5}$

71. $-4 - \dfrac{3}{2}d = \dfrac{2}{5}$

72. $-2 - \dfrac{5}{4}z = \dfrac{5}{8}$

Expanding Your Skills

For Exercises 73–76, solve the equations by clearing fractions.

73. $p - 1 + \dfrac{1}{4}p = 2 + \dfrac{3}{4}p$

74. $\dfrac{4}{3} + \dfrac{2}{3}q = -\dfrac{5}{3} - q - \dfrac{1}{3}$

75. $\dfrac{5}{3}x - \dfrac{4}{5} = \dfrac{2}{3}x + 1$

76. $\dfrac{3}{4}y + \dfrac{9}{7} = -\dfrac{1}{4}y + 2$

Problem Recognition Exercises

Comparing Expressions and Equations

For Exercises 1–24, first identify the problem as an expression or as an equation. Then simplify the expression or solve the equation. Two examples are given for you.

Example: $\dfrac{1}{3} + \dfrac{1}{6} - \dfrac{5}{6}$

This is an expression. Combine like terms.

$$\dfrac{1}{3} + \dfrac{1}{6} - \dfrac{5}{6}$$

$$= \dfrac{2 \cdot 1}{2 \cdot 3} + \dfrac{1}{6} - \dfrac{5}{6}$$

$$= \dfrac{2}{6} + \dfrac{1}{6} - \dfrac{5}{6}$$

$$= \dfrac{-2}{6}$$

$$= -\dfrac{1}{3}$$

Example: $\dfrac{1}{3}x + \dfrac{1}{6} = \dfrac{5}{6}$

This is an equation. Solve the equation.

$$\dfrac{1}{3}x + \dfrac{1}{6} = \dfrac{5}{6}$$

$$6 \cdot \left(\dfrac{1}{3}x + \dfrac{1}{6}\right) = 6 \cdot \left(\dfrac{5}{6}\right)$$

$$2x + 1 = 5$$

$$2x + 1 - 1 = 5 - 1$$

$$2x = 4$$

$$\dfrac{2x}{2} = \dfrac{4}{2}$$

$$x = 2 \qquad \text{The solution is 2.}$$

1. $\dfrac{5}{3}x = \dfrac{1}{6}$

2. $\dfrac{7}{8}y = \dfrac{3}{4}$

3. $\dfrac{5}{3} - \dfrac{1}{6}$

4. $\dfrac{7}{8} - \dfrac{3}{4}$

5. $1 + \dfrac{2}{5}$

6. $1 + \dfrac{4}{5}$

7. $z + \dfrac{2}{5} = 0$

8. $w + \dfrac{4}{5} = 0$

9. $\dfrac{2}{9}x - \dfrac{1}{3} = \dfrac{5}{9}$

10. $\dfrac{3}{10}x - \dfrac{2}{5} = \dfrac{1}{10}$

11. $\dfrac{2}{9} - \dfrac{1}{3} + \dfrac{5}{9}$

12. $\dfrac{3}{10} - \dfrac{2}{5} + \dfrac{1}{10}$

13. $3(x - 4) + 2x = 12 + x$

14. $5(x + 4) - 2x = 10 - x$

15. $3(x - 4) + 2x - 12 + x$

16. $5(x + 4) - 2x + 10 - x$

17. $\dfrac{3}{4}x = 2$

18. $\dfrac{5}{7}y = 5$

19. $\dfrac{3}{4} \cdot 2$

20. $\dfrac{5}{7} \cdot 5$

21. $\dfrac{4}{7} = 2c$

22. $\dfrac{9}{4} = 3d$

23. $\dfrac{4}{7}c + 2c$

24. $\dfrac{9}{4}d + 3d$

Group Activity

Card Games with Fractions

Materials: A deck of fraction cards for each group. These can be made from index cards where one side of the card is blank, and the other side has a fraction written on it. The deck should consist of several cards of each of the following fractions.

$$\dfrac{1}{4}, \dfrac{1}{2}, \dfrac{3}{4}, \dfrac{1}{6}, \dfrac{1}{3}, \dfrac{2}{3}, \dfrac{5}{6}, \dfrac{1}{8}, \dfrac{3}{8}, \dfrac{5}{8}, \dfrac{7}{8}, \dfrac{1}{5}, \dfrac{2}{5}, \dfrac{3}{5}, \dfrac{4}{5}, \dfrac{1}{10}, \dfrac{3}{10}, \dfrac{4}{9}, \dfrac{2}{9}, \dfrac{3}{7}$$

Estimated time: Instructor discretion

In this activity, we outline three different games for students to play in their groups as a fun way to reinforce skills of adding fractions, recognizing equivalent fractions, and ordering fractions.

Game 1 "Blackjack"

Group Size: 3

1. In this game, one student in the group will be the dealer, and the other two will be players. The dealer will deal each player one card face down and one card face up. Then the players individually may elect to have more cards given to them (face up). The goal is to have the sum of the fractions get as close to "2" without going over.

2. Once the players have taken all the cards that they want, they will display their cards face up for the group to see. The player who has a sum closest to "2" without going over wins. The dealer will resolve any "disputes."

3. The members of the group should rotate after several games so that each person has the opportunity to be a player and to be the dealer.

Game 2 "War"

Group Size: 2

1. In this game, each player should start with half of the deck of cards. The players should shuffle the cards and then stack them neatly face down on the table. Then each player will select the top card from the deck, turn it over and place it on the table. The player who has the fraction with the greatest value "wins" that round and takes both cards.

2. Continue overturning cards and deciding who "wins" each round until all of the cards have been overturned. Then the players will count the number of cards they each collected. The player with the most cards wins.

Game 3 "Bingo"

Group Size: The whole class

1. Each student gets five fraction cards. The instructor will call out fractions that are not in lowest terms. The students must identify whether the fraction that was called is the same as one of the fractions on their cards. For example, if the instructor calls out "three-ninths," then students with the fraction card $\frac{1}{3}$ would have a match.

2. The student who first matches all five cards wins.

Chapter 4 Summary

Section 4.1   Introduction to Fractions and Mixed Numbers

Key Concepts

A **fraction** represents a part of a whole unit. For example, $\frac{1}{3}$ represents one part of a whole unit that is divided into 3 equal pieces. A fraction whose numerator is an integer and whose denominator is a nonzero integer is also called a **rational number**.

In the fraction $\frac{1}{3}$, the "top" number, 1, is the **numerator**, and the "bottom" number, 3, is the **denominator**.

A positive fraction in which the numerator is less than the denominator (or the opposite of such a fraction) is called a **proper fraction**. A positive fraction in which the numerator is greater than or equal to the denominator (or the opposite of such a fraction) is called an **improper fraction**.

The fraction $-\dfrac{a}{b}$ is equivalent to $\dfrac{-a}{b}$ or $\dfrac{a}{-b}$.

An improper fraction can be written as a **mixed number** by dividing the numerator by the denominator. Write the quotient as a whole number and write the remainder over the divisor.

A mixed number can be written as an improper fraction by multiplying the whole number by the denominator and adding the numerator. Then write that total over the denominator.

In a negative mixed number, both the whole number part and the fraction are negative.

Fractions can be represented on a number line. For example,

Examples

Example 1

$\frac{1}{3}$ of the pie is shaded.

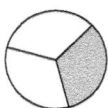

Example 2

For the fraction $\frac{7}{9}$, the numerator is 7 and the denominator is 9.

Example 3

$\frac{5}{3}$ is an improper fraction, $\frac{3}{5}$ is a proper fraction, and $\frac{3}{3}$ is an improper fraction.

Example 4

$$-\frac{5}{7} = \frac{-5}{7} = \frac{5}{-7}$$

Example 5

$\dfrac{10}{3}$ can be written as $3\dfrac{1}{3}$ because

$$\begin{array}{r} 3 \\ 3\overline{)10} \\ \underline{-9} \\ 1 \end{array}$$

Example 6

$2\dfrac{4}{5}$ can be written as $\dfrac{14}{5}$ because $\dfrac{2 \cdot 5 + 4}{5} = \dfrac{14}{5}$

Example 7

$$-5\frac{2}{3} = -\left(5 + \frac{2}{3}\right) = -5 - \frac{2}{3}$$

Example 8

Section 4.2 Simplifying Fractions

Key Concepts

A **factorization** of a number is a product of factors that equals the number.

Divisibility Rules for 2, 3, 5, and 10

A whole number is divisible by
- 2 if the ones-place digit is 0, 2, 4, 6, or 8.
- 3 if the sum of the digits is divisible by 3.
- 5 if the ones-place digit is 0 or 5.
- 10 if the ones-place digit is 0.

A **prime number** is a whole number greater than 1 that has exactly two factors, 1 and itself.

Composite numbers are whole numbers that have more than two factors. The numbers 0 and 1 are neither prime nor composite.

Prime Factorization

The **prime factorization** of a number is the factorization in which every factor is a prime number.

A factor of a number n is any number that divides evenly into n. For example, the factors of 80 are 1, 2, 4, 5, 8, 10, 16, 20, 40, and 80.

Equivalent fractions are fractions that represent the same portion of a whole unit.

To determine if two fractions are equivalent, calculate the cross products. If the cross products are equal, then the fractions are equivalent.

Examples

Example 1

$4 \cdot 4$ and $8 \cdot 2$ are two factorizations of 16.

Example 2

382 is divisible by 2.
640 is divisible by 2, 5, and 10.
735 is divisible by 3 and 5.

Example 3

9 is a composite number.
2 is a prime number.
1 is neither prime nor composite.

Example 4

$$
\begin{array}{r}
2)\overline{378} \\
3)\overline{189} \\
3)\overline{63} \\
3)\overline{21} \\
7
\end{array}
$$

The prime factorization of 378 is
$2 \cdot 3 \cdot 3 \cdot 3 \cdot 7$ or $2 \cdot 3^3 \cdot 7$

Example 5

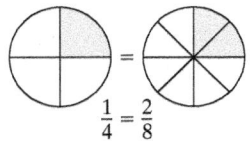

$$\frac{1}{4} = \frac{2}{8}$$

Example 6

a. Compare $\dfrac{5}{3}$ and $\dfrac{6}{4}$.

$$\frac{5}{3} \overset{?}{\underset{}{\times}} \frac{6}{4}$$

$20 \neq 18$

The fractions are not equivalent.

b. Compare $\dfrac{4}{5}$ and $\dfrac{8}{10}$.

$$\frac{4}{5} \overset{?}{\underset{}{\times}} \frac{8}{10}$$

$40 = 40$

The fractions are equivalent.

To simplify fractions to **lowest terms**, use the fundamental principle of fractions:

Given $\frac{a}{b}$ and the nonzero number c. Then

$$\frac{a \cdot c}{b \cdot c} = \frac{a}{b} \cdot \frac{c}{c} = \frac{a}{b} \cdot 1 = \frac{a}{b}$$

To simplify fractions with common powers of 10, "strike through" the common zeros first.

Example 7

$$\frac{25}{15} = \frac{5 \cdot 5}{3 \cdot 5} = \frac{5}{3} \cdot \frac{5}{5} = \frac{5}{3} \cdot 1 = \frac{5}{3}$$

$$\frac{3x^2}{5x^3} = \frac{3 \cdot \overset{1}{x} \cdot \overset{1}{x}}{5 \cdot \underset{1}{x} \cdot \underset{1}{x} \cdot x} = \frac{3}{5x}$$

Example 8

$$\frac{3,0\cancel{00}}{12,0\cancel{00}} = \frac{3}{12} = \frac{\overset{1}{3}}{\underset{4}{12}} = \frac{1}{4}$$

Section 4.3   Multiplication and Division of Fractions

Key Concepts

Multiplication of Fractions

To multiply fractions, write the product of the numerators over the product of the denominators. Then simplify the resulting fraction, if possible.

When multiplying a whole number and a fraction, first write the whole number as a fraction by writing the whole number over 1.

The formula for the area of a triangle is given by $A = \frac{1}{2}bh$.

Area is expressed in square units such as ft², in.², yd², m², and cm².

The **reciprocal** of $\frac{a}{b}$ is $\frac{b}{a}$ for $a, b \neq 0$. The product of a fraction and its reciprocal is 1. For example, $\frac{6}{11} \cdot \frac{11}{6} = 1$.

Examples

Example 1

$$\frac{4}{7} \cdot \frac{6}{5} = \frac{24}{35}$$

$$\left(\frac{15}{16}\right)\left(\frac{4}{5}\right) = \frac{\overset{3}{15}}{\underset{4}{16}} \cdot \frac{\overset{1}{4}}{\underset{1}{5}} = \frac{3}{4}$$

Example 2

$$-8 \cdot \left(\frac{5}{6}\right) = -\frac{\overset{4}{8}}{1} \cdot \frac{5}{\underset{3}{6}} = -\frac{20}{3}$$

Example 3

The area of the triangle is

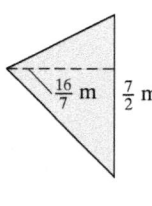

$$A = \frac{1}{2}bh$$

$$= \frac{1}{2}\left(\frac{7}{2}\text{m}\right)\left(\frac{16}{7}\text{m}\right)$$

$$= \frac{\overset{4}{112}}{\underset{1}{28}}\text{m}^2$$

$$= 4\text{ m}^2$$

The area is 4 m².

Example 4

The reciprocal of $-\frac{5}{8}$ is $-\frac{8}{5}$.
The reciprocal of 4 is $\frac{1}{4}$.

The number 0 does not have a reciprocal because $\frac{1}{0}$ is undefined.

Dividing Fractions

To divide two fractions, multiply the dividend (the "first" fraction) by the reciprocal of the divisor (the "second" fraction).

When dividing by a whole number, first write the whole number as a fraction by writing the whole number over 1. Then multiply by its reciprocal.

Example 5

$$\frac{18}{25} \div \frac{30}{35} = \frac{\overset{3}{\cancel{18}}}{\underset{5}{\cancel{25}}} \cdot \frac{\overset{7}{\cancel{35}}}{\underset{5}{\cancel{30}}} = \frac{21}{25}$$

Example 6

$$-\frac{9}{8} \div (-4) = -\frac{9}{8} \div \left(-\frac{4}{1}\right) = -\frac{9}{8} \cdot \left(-\frac{1}{4}\right) = \frac{9}{32}$$

Section 4.4   Least Common Multiple and Equivalent Fractions

Key Concepts

The numbers obtained by multiplying a number n by the whole numbers 1, 2, 3, and so on are called **multiples** of n.

The **least common multiple (LCM)** of two given numbers is the smallest whole number that is a multiple of each given number.

Examples

Example 1

The numbers 5, 10, 15, 20, 25, 30, 35, and 40 are several multiples of 5.

Example 2

Find the LCM of 8 and 10.
Some multiples of 8 are 8, 16, 24, 32, 40.
Some multiples of 10 are 10, 20, 30, 40.

40 is the least common multiple.

Using Prime Factors to Find the LCM of Two Numbers

1. Write each number as a product of prime factors.
2. The LCM is the product of unique prime factors from both numbers. Use repeated factors the maximum number of times they appear in either factorization.

Example 3

Find the LCM for the numbers 24 and 16.

$24 = 2 \cdot 2 \cdot 2 \cdot \boxed{3}$
$16 = \boxed{2 \cdot 2 \cdot 2 \cdot 2}$
$\text{LCM} = 2 \cdot 2 \cdot 2 \cdot 2 \cdot 3 = 48$

Writing Equivalent Fractions

Use the fundamental principle of fractions to convert a fraction to an equivalent fraction with a given denominator.

Example 4

Write the fraction with the indicated denominator.

$$\frac{3}{4} = \frac{}{36x}$$

$$\frac{3 \cdot 9x}{4 \cdot 9x} = \frac{27x}{36x}$$

The fraction $\dfrac{27x}{36x}$ is equivalent to $\dfrac{3}{4}$.

Ordering Fractions

Write the fractions with a common denominator. Then compare the numerators.

The **least common denominator (LCD)** of two fractions is the LCM of their denominators.

Example 5

Fill in the blank with the appropriate symbol, $<$ or $>$.

$$-\frac{5}{9} \,\square\, -\frac{7}{12} \quad \text{The LCD is 36.}$$

$$-\frac{5 \cdot 4}{9 \cdot 4} \,\square\, -\frac{7 \cdot 3}{12 \cdot 3}$$

$$-\frac{20}{36} \,\boxed{>}\, -\frac{21}{36}$$

Section 4.5 Addition and Subtraction of Fractions

Key Concepts

Adding or Subtracting Like Fractions

1. Add or subtract the numerators.
2. Write the sum or difference over the common denominator.
3. Simplify the fraction to lowest terms if possible.

Examples

Example 1

$$\frac{5}{8} + \frac{7}{8} = \frac{12}{8} = \frac{\overset{3}{\cancel{12}}}{\underset{2}{\cancel{8}}} = \frac{3}{2}$$

Example 2

A nail that is $\frac{13}{8}$ in. long is driven through a board that is $\frac{11}{8}$ in. thick. How much of the nail extends beyond the board?

$$\frac{13}{8} - \frac{11}{8} = \frac{2}{8} = \frac{1}{4}$$

The nail will extend $\frac{1}{4}$ in.

To add or subtract unlike fractions, first we must write each fraction as an equivalent fraction with a common denominator.

Adding or Subtracting Unlike Fractions

1. Identify the LCD.
2. Write each individual fraction as an equivalent fraction with the LCD.
3. Add or subtract the numerators and write the result over the common denominator.
4. Simplify to lowest terms, if possible.

Example 3

Simplify. $\dfrac{7}{5} - \dfrac{3}{10} + \dfrac{13}{15}$

$$\frac{7 \cdot 6}{5 \cdot 6} - \frac{3 \cdot 3}{10 \cdot 3} + \frac{13 \cdot 2}{15 \cdot 2} \qquad \text{The LCD is 30.}$$

$$= \frac{42}{30} - \frac{9}{30} + \frac{26}{30}$$

$$= \frac{42 - 9 + 26}{30}$$

$$= \frac{59}{30}$$

Section 4.6   Estimation and Operations on Mixed Numbers

Key Concepts

Multiplication of Mixed Numbers

Step 1 Change each mixed number to an improper fraction.

Step 2 Multiply the improper fractions and simplify to lowest terms, if possible.

Division of Mixed Numbers

Step 1 Change each mixed number to an improper fraction.

Step 2 Divide the improper fractions and simplify to lowest terms, if possible. Recall that to divide fractions, multiply the dividend by the reciprocal of the divisor.

Addition of Mixed Numbers

To find the sum of two or more mixed numbers, add the whole-number parts and add the fractional parts.

Subtraction of Mixed Numbers

To subtract mixed numbers, subtract the fractional parts and subtract the whole-number parts.
When the fractional part in the subtrahend is larger than the fractional part in the minuend, we borrow from the whole number part of the minuend.

We can also add or subtract mixed numbers by writing the numbers as improper fractions. Then add or subtract the fractions.

Examples

Example 1

$$4\frac{4}{5} \cdot 2\frac{1}{2} = \frac{\overset{12}{\cancel{24}}}{\cancel{5}} \cdot \frac{\overset{1}{\cancel{5}}}{\cancel{2}} = \frac{12}{1} = 12$$

Example 2

$$6\frac{2}{3} \div 2\frac{7}{9} = \frac{20}{3} \div \frac{25}{9} = \frac{\overset{4}{\cancel{20}}}{\cancel{3}} \cdot \frac{\overset{3}{\cancel{9}}}{\cancel{25}} = \frac{12}{5} = 2\frac{2}{5}$$

Example 3

$$
\begin{array}{r}
3\frac{5}{8} = 3\frac{10}{16} \\
+\, 1\frac{1}{16} = 1\frac{1}{16} \\
\hline
4\frac{11}{16}
\end{array}
$$

Example 4

$$
\begin{array}{r}
2\frac{9}{10} = 2\frac{27}{30} \\
+\, 6\frac{5}{6} = 6\frac{25}{30} \\
\hline
8\frac{52}{30} = 8 + 1\frac{22}{30} \\
= 9\frac{11}{15}
\end{array}
$$

Example 5

$$
\begin{array}{r}
5\frac{3}{4} = 5\frac{9}{12} \\
-\, 2\frac{2}{3} = 2\frac{8}{12} \\
\hline
3\frac{1}{12}
\end{array}
$$

Example 6

$$
\begin{array}{r}
7\frac{1}{2} = \overset{6}{\cancel{7}}\frac{\overset{5+10}{5}}{10} = 6\frac{15}{10} \\
-\, 3\frac{4}{5} = 3\frac{8}{10} = 3\frac{8}{10} \\
\hline
3\frac{7}{10}
\end{array}
$$

Example 7

$$-4\frac{7}{8} + 2\frac{1}{16} - 3\frac{1}{4} = -\frac{39}{8} + \frac{33}{16} - \frac{13}{4}$$

$$= -\frac{39 \cdot 2}{8 \cdot 2} + \frac{33}{16} - \frac{13 \cdot 4}{4 \cdot 4}$$

$$= -\frac{78}{16} + \frac{33}{16} - \frac{52}{16}$$

$$= \frac{-78 + 33 - 52}{16} = \frac{-97}{16} = -6\frac{1}{16}$$

Section 4.7 Order of Operations and Complex Fractions

Key Concepts

To simplify an expression with more than one operation, apply the order of operations.

Examples

Example 1

Simplify. $\left(\dfrac{2}{5} \cdot \dfrac{10}{7}\right)^2 + \dfrac{6}{7}$

$= \left(\dfrac{2}{\overset{}{\underset{1}{5}}} \cdot \dfrac{\overset{2}{10}}{7}\right)^2 + \dfrac{6}{7} = \left(\dfrac{4}{7}\right)^2 + \dfrac{6}{7}$

$= \dfrac{16}{49} + \dfrac{6}{7} = \dfrac{16}{49} + \dfrac{6 \cdot 7}{7 \cdot 7} = \dfrac{16}{49} + \dfrac{42}{49}$

$= \dfrac{58}{49}$ or $1\dfrac{9}{49}$

A complex fraction is a fraction with one or more fractions in the numerator or denominator.

Example 2

Simplify. $\dfrac{\dfrac{5}{m}}{\dfrac{15}{4}}$

$= \dfrac{5}{m} \cdot \dfrac{4}{15}$ Multiply by the reciprocal.

$= \dfrac{\overset{1}{5}}{m} \cdot \dfrac{4}{\underset{3}{15}} = \dfrac{4}{3m}$

To add or subtract like terms, apply the distributive property.

Example 3

Simplify. $\dfrac{3}{4}x - \dfrac{1}{8}x$

$= \left(\dfrac{3}{4} - \dfrac{1}{8}\right)x = \left(\dfrac{3 \cdot 2}{4 \cdot 2} - \dfrac{1}{8}\right)x$

$= \left(\dfrac{6}{8} - \dfrac{1}{8}\right)x = \dfrac{5}{8}x$

Section 4.8   Solving Equations Containing Fractions

Key Concepts

To solve equations containing fractions, we use the addition, subtraction, multiplication, and division properties of equality.

Example 1

Solve. $\dfrac{2}{3}x - \dfrac{1}{4} = \dfrac{1}{2}$

$\dfrac{2}{3}x - \dfrac{1}{4} + \dfrac{1}{4} = \dfrac{1}{2} + \dfrac{1}{4}$ Add $\dfrac{1}{4}$ to both sides.

$\dfrac{2}{3}x = \dfrac{1 \cdot 2}{2 \cdot 2} + \dfrac{1}{4}$ On the right-hand side, the LCD is 4.

$\dfrac{2}{3}x = \dfrac{2}{4} + \dfrac{1}{4}$

$\dfrac{2}{3}x = \dfrac{3}{4}$

$\dfrac{3}{2} \cdot \dfrac{2}{3}x = \dfrac{3}{2} \cdot \dfrac{3}{4}$ Multiply by the reciprocal of $\dfrac{2}{3}$.

$x = \dfrac{9}{8}$ The solution is $\dfrac{9}{8}$.

Examples

Another technique to solve equations with fractions is to multiply both sides of the equation by the LCD of all terms in the equation. This "clears" the fractions within the equation.

Example 2

Solve. $\dfrac{1}{9}x - 2 = \dfrac{5}{3}$ The LCD is 9.

$9 \cdot \left(\dfrac{1}{9}x - 2 \right) = 9 \cdot \left(\dfrac{5}{3} \right)$

$\overset{1}{9} \cdot \left(\dfrac{1}{9}x \right) - 9 \cdot (2) = \overset{3}{9} \cdot \left(\dfrac{5}{3} \right)$

$x - 18 = 15$

$x - 18 + 18 = 15 + 18$

$x = 33$ The solution is 33.

Chapter 4   Review Exercises

Section 4.1

For Exercises 1–2, write a fraction that represents the shaded area.

1.

2.

3. a. Write a fraction that has denominator 3 and numerator 5.

   b. Label this fraction as proper or improper.

4. a. Write a fraction that has numerator 1 and denominator 6.

   b. Label this fraction as proper or improper.

5. Simplify.

   a. $\left|-\dfrac{3}{8}\right|$ **b.** $\left|\dfrac{2}{3}\right|$ **c.** $-\left(-\dfrac{4}{9}\right)$

For Exercises 6–7, write a fraction and a mixed number that represent the shaded area.

6.   **7.**

For Exercises 8–9, convert the mixed number to a fraction.

8. $6\dfrac{1}{7}$ **9.** $11\dfrac{2}{5}$

For Exercises 10–11, convert the improper fraction to a mixed number.

10. $\dfrac{47}{9}$ **11.** $\dfrac{23}{21}$

For Exercises 12–15, locate the numbers on the number line.

12. $-\dfrac{10}{5}$ **13.** $-\dfrac{7}{8}$ **14.** $\dfrac{13}{8}$ **15.** $-1\dfrac{3}{8}$

```
 ──┼──────┼──────┼──────┼──────┼──
  -2     -1      0      1      2
```

For Exercises 16–17, divide. Write the answer as a mixed number.

16. $7\overline{)941}$ **17.** $26\overline{)1582}$

Section 4.2

For Exercises 18–19, refer to this list of numbers: 21, 43, 51, 55, 58, 124, 140, 260, 1200.

18. List all the numbers that are divisible by 3.

19. List all the numbers that are divisible by 5.

20. Identify the prime numbers in the following list. 2, 39, 53, 54, 81, 99, 112, 113

21. Identify the composite numbers in the following list. 1, 12, 27, 51, 63, 97, 130

For Exercises 22–23, find the prime factorization.

22. 330   **23.** 900

For Exercises 24–25, determine if the fractions are equivalent. Fill in the blank with = or ≠ .

24. $\dfrac{3}{6}\;\square\;\dfrac{5}{9}$ **25.** $\dfrac{15}{21}\;\square\;\dfrac{10}{14}$

For Exercises 26–33, simplify the fraction to lowest terms. Write the answer as a fraction.

26. $\dfrac{5}{20}$ **27.** $\dfrac{7}{35}$

28. $-\dfrac{24}{16}$ **29.** $-\dfrac{63}{27}$

30. $\dfrac{120}{1500}$ **31.** $\dfrac{140}{20,000}$

32. $\dfrac{4ac}{10c^2}$ **33.** $\dfrac{24t^3}{30t}$

34. On his final exam, Gareth got 42 out of 45 questions correct. What fraction of the test represents correct answers? What fraction represents incorrect answers?

35. Isaac proofread 6 pages of his 10-page term paper. Yulisa proofread 6 pages of her 15-page term paper.

   a. What fraction of his paper did Isaac proofread?

   b. What fraction of her paper did Yulisa proofread?

Section 4.3

For Exercises 36–41, multiply the fractions and simplify to lowest terms. Write the answer as a fraction or an integer.

36. $-\dfrac{2}{5} \cdot \dfrac{15}{14}$

37. $-\dfrac{4}{3} \cdot \dfrac{9}{8}$

38. $-14 \cdot \left(-\dfrac{9}{2}\right)$

39. $-33 \cdot \left(-\dfrac{5}{11}\right)$

40. $\dfrac{2x}{5} \cdot \dfrac{10}{x^2}$

41. $\dfrac{3y^3}{14} \cdot \dfrac{7}{y}$

42. Write the formula for the area of a triangle.

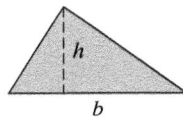

43. Find the area of the shaded region.

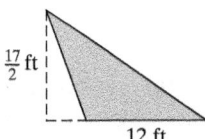

For Exercises 44–45, multiply.

44. $-\dfrac{3}{4} \cdot \left(-\dfrac{4}{3}\right)$

45. $\dfrac{1}{12} \cdot 12$

For Exercises 46–47, find the reciprocal of the number, if it exists.

46. $\dfrac{7}{2}$

47. -7

For Exercises 48–53, divide and simplify the answer to lowest terms. Write the answer as a fraction or an integer.

48. $\dfrac{28}{15} \div \dfrac{21}{20}$

49. $\dfrac{7}{9} \div \dfrac{35}{63}$

50. $-\dfrac{6}{7} \div 18$

51. $12 \div \left(-\dfrac{6}{7}\right)$

52. $\dfrac{4a^2}{7} \div \dfrac{a}{14}$

53. $\dfrac{11}{3y} \div \dfrac{22}{9y^3}$

54. How many $\frac{2}{3}$-lb bags of candy can be filled from a 24-lb sack of candy?

55. Chuck is an elementary school teacher and needs 22 pieces of wood, $\frac{3}{8}$ ft long, for a class project. If he has a 9-ft board from which to cut the pieces, will he have enough $\frac{3}{8}$-ft pieces for his class? Explain.

For Exercises 56–57, refer to the graph. The graph represents the distribution of the students at a college by race/ethnicity.

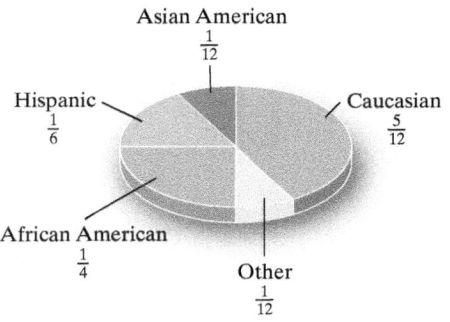

56. If the college has 3600 students, how many are African American?

57. If the college has 3600 students, how many are Asian American?

58. Amelia worked only $\frac{4}{5}$ of her normal 40-hr workweek. If she makes $18 per hour, how much money did she earn for the week?

Section 4.4

59. Find the prime factorization.

   a. 100   **b.** 65   **c.** 70

For Exercises 60–61, find the LCM by using any method.

60. 105 and 28   **61.** 16, 24, and 32

62. Sharon and Tony signed up at a gym on the same day. Sharon will be able to go to the gym every third day, and Tony will go to the gym every fourth day. In how many days will they meet again at the gym?

For Exercises 63–66, rewrite each fraction with the indicated denominator.

63. $\dfrac{5}{16} = \dfrac{}{48}$

64. $\dfrac{9}{5} = \dfrac{}{35}$

65. $\dfrac{7}{12} = \dfrac{}{60y}$

66. $\dfrac{-7}{x} = \dfrac{}{4x}$

For Exercises 67–69, fill in the blanks with $<$, $>$, or $=$.

67. $\dfrac{11}{24} \square \dfrac{7}{12}$

68. $\dfrac{5}{6} \square \dfrac{7}{9}$

69. $-\dfrac{5}{6} \square -\dfrac{15}{18}$

70. Rank the numbers from least to greatest.

$$-\dfrac{7}{10}, \ -\dfrac{72}{105}, \ -\dfrac{8}{15}, \ \dfrac{27}{35}$$

Section 4.5

For Exercises 71–80, add or subtract. Write the answer as a fraction simplified to lowest terms.

71. $\dfrac{5}{6} + \dfrac{4}{6}$

72. $\dfrac{4}{15} + \dfrac{6}{15}$

73. $\dfrac{9}{10} - \dfrac{61}{100}$

74. $\dfrac{11}{25} - \dfrac{2}{5}$

75. $-\dfrac{25}{11} - 2$

76. $-4 - \dfrac{37}{20}$

77. $\dfrac{2}{15} - \left(-\dfrac{5}{8}\right) - \dfrac{1}{3}$

78. $\dfrac{11}{14} - \dfrac{4}{7} - \left(-\dfrac{3}{2}\right)$

79. $\dfrac{7}{5w} + \dfrac{2}{w}$

80. $\dfrac{11}{a} + \dfrac{4}{b}$

For Exercises 81–82, find (a) the perimeter and (b) the area.

81.

$\frac{25}{16}$ m $\frac{5}{4}$ m $\frac{13}{4}$ m $\frac{63}{16}$ m

82.

$\frac{3}{2}$ yd

$\frac{7}{3}$ yd

Section 4.6

For Exercises 83–88, multiply or divide as indicated.

83. $\left(3\dfrac{2}{3}\right)\left(6\dfrac{2}{5}\right)$

84. $\left(11\dfrac{1}{3}\right)\left(2\dfrac{3}{34}\right)$

85. $-3\dfrac{5}{11} \div \left(-3\dfrac{4}{5}\right)$

86. $-7 \div \left(-1\dfrac{5}{9}\right)$

87. $-4\dfrac{6}{11} \div 2$

88. $10\dfrac{1}{5} \div (-17)$

For Exercises 89–90, round the numbers to estimate the answer. Then find the exact sum or difference.

89. $65\dfrac{1}{8} - 14\dfrac{9}{10}$

90. $43\dfrac{13}{15} - 20\dfrac{23}{25}$

Estimate: _____   Estimate: _____

Exact: _____   Exact: _____

For Exercises 91–100, add or subtract the mixed numbers.

91. $\begin{array}{r} 9\dfrac{8}{9} \\ + 1\dfrac{2}{7} \\ \hline \end{array}$

92. $\begin{array}{r} 10\dfrac{1}{2} \\ + 3\dfrac{15}{16} \\ \hline \end{array}$

93. $\begin{array}{r} 7\dfrac{5}{24} \\ - 4\dfrac{7}{12} \\ \hline \end{array}$

94. $\begin{array}{r} 5\dfrac{1}{6} \\ - 3\dfrac{1}{4} \\ \hline \end{array}$

95. $\begin{array}{r} 6 \\ - 2\dfrac{3}{5} \\ \hline \end{array}$

96. $\begin{array}{r} 8 \\ - 4\dfrac{11}{14} \\ \hline \end{array}$

97. $42\frac{1}{8} - \left(-21\frac{13}{16}\right)$ **98.** $38\frac{9}{10} - \left(-11\frac{3}{5}\right)$

99. $-4\frac{2}{3} + 1\frac{5}{6}$ **100.** $6\frac{3}{8} + \left(-10\frac{1}{4}\right)$

101. Corry drove for $4\frac{1}{2}$ hr in the morning and $3\frac{2}{3}$ hr in the afternoon. Find the total number of hours he drove.

102. Denise owned $2\frac{1}{8}$ acres of land. If she sells $1\frac{1}{4}$ acres, how much will she have left

103. It takes $1\frac{1}{4}$ gal of paint for Neva to paint her living room. If her great room is $2\frac{1}{2}$ times larger than the living room, how many gallons will it take to paint the great room?

104. A roll of ribbon contains $12\frac{1}{2}$ yd. How many pieces of length $1\frac{1}{4}$ yd can be cut from this roll?

Section 4.7

For Exercises 105–116, simplify.

105. $\left(\frac{3}{8}\right)^2$ **106.** $\left(-\frac{3}{8}\right)^2$

107. $\left(-\frac{3}{8} \cdot \frac{4}{15}\right)^5$ **108.** $\left(\frac{1}{25} \cdot \frac{15}{6}\right)^4$

109. $-\frac{2}{5} - \left(1\frac{2}{3}\right) \cdot \frac{3}{2}$ **110.** $\frac{7}{5} - \left(-2\frac{1}{3}\right) \div \frac{7}{2}$

111. $\left(\frac{2}{3} - \frac{5}{6}\right)^2 + \frac{5}{36}$ **112.** $\left(-\frac{1}{4} - \frac{1}{2}\right)^2 - \frac{1}{8}$

113. $\dfrac{\frac{8}{5}}{\frac{4}{7}}$ **114.** $\dfrac{\frac{14}{9}}{\frac{7}{x}}$

115. $\dfrac{-\frac{2}{3} - \frac{5}{6}}{3 + \frac{1}{2}}$ **116.** $\dfrac{\frac{3}{5} - 1}{-\frac{1}{2} - \frac{3}{10}}$

For Exercises 117–120, evaluate the expressions for the given values of the variables.

117. $x \div y \div z$ for $x = \frac{2}{3}$, $y = \frac{5}{6}$, and $z = -\frac{3}{5}$

118. a^2b for $a = -\frac{3}{5}$ and $b = 1\frac{2}{3}$

119. $t^2 + v^2$ for $t = \frac{1}{2}$ and $v = -\frac{1}{4}$

120. $2(w + z)$ for $w = 3\frac{1}{3}$ and $z = 2\frac{1}{2}$

For Exercises 121–124, simplify the expressions.

121. $-\frac{3}{4}x - \frac{2}{3}x$ **122.** $\frac{1}{5}y - \frac{3}{2}y$

123. $-\frac{4}{3}a + \frac{1}{2}c + 2a - \frac{1}{3}c$

124. $\frac{4}{5}w + \frac{2}{3}y + \frac{1}{10}w + y$

Section 4.8

For Exercises 125–134, solve the equations.

125. $x - \frac{3}{5} = \frac{2}{3}$ **126.** $y + \frac{4}{7} = \frac{3}{14}$

127. $\frac{3}{5}x = \frac{2}{3}$ **128.** $\frac{4}{7}y = \frac{3}{14}$

129. $-\frac{6}{5} = -2c$ **130.** $-\frac{9}{4} = -3d$

131. $-\frac{2}{5} + \frac{y}{10} = \frac{y}{2}$ **132.** $-\frac{3}{4} + \frac{w}{2} = \frac{w}{8}$

133. $2 = \frac{1}{2} - \frac{x}{10}$ **134.** $1 = \frac{7}{3} - \frac{t}{9}$

Chapter 4   Test

1. a. Write a fraction that represents the shaded portion of the figure.

b. Is the fraction proper or improper?

2. a. Write a fraction that represents the total shaded portion of the three figures.

b. Is the fraction proper or improper?

3. a. Write $\frac{11}{3}$ as a mixed number.

b. Write $3\frac{7}{9}$ as an improper fraction.

For Exercises 4–5, plot the fraction on the number line.

4. $\frac{13}{5}$

5. $-2\frac{3}{5}$

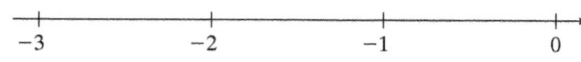

For Exercises 6–8, simplify.

6. $\left|-\frac{2}{11}\right|$

7. $-\left|-\frac{2}{11}\right|$

8. $-\left(-\frac{2}{11}\right)$

9. Label the following numbers as prime, composite, or neither.

a. 15   **b.** 0

c. 53   **d.** 1

e. 29   **f.** 39

10. Write the prime factorization of 45.

11. a. What is the divisibility rule for 3?

b. Is 1,981,011 divisible by 3?

12. Determine whether 1155 is divisible by

a. 2   **b.** 3

c. 5   **d.** 10

For Exercises 13–14, determine if the fractions are equivalent. Then fill in the blank with either = or ≠ .

13. $\frac{15}{12} \square \frac{5}{4}$

14. $-\frac{2}{5} \square -\frac{4}{25}$

For Exercises 15–16, simplify the fractions to lowest terms.

15. $\frac{150}{105}$

16. $\frac{100a}{350ab}$

17. Christine and Brad are putting their photographs in scrapbooks. Christine has placed 15 of her 25 photos, and Brad has placed 16 of his 20 photos.

a. What fractional part of the total photos has each person placed?

b. Which person has a greater fractional part completed?

For Exercises 18–23, multiply or divide as indicated. Simplify the fraction to lowest terms.

18. $\frac{2}{9} \cdot \frac{57}{46}$

19. $\left(-\frac{75}{24}\right)(-4)$

20. $\frac{28}{24} \div \frac{21}{8}$

21. $-\frac{105}{42} \div 5$

22. $\frac{4}{3y} \cdot \frac{y^2}{2}$

23. $-\frac{5ab}{c} \div \frac{a}{c^2}$

24. Find the area of the triangle.

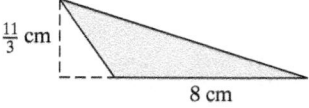

25. Which is greater, $20 \cdot \frac{1}{4}$ or $20 \div \frac{1}{4}$?

26. How many "quarter-pounders" can be made from 12 lb of ground beef?

27. A zoning requirement indicates that a house built on less than 1 acre of land may take up no more than one-half of the land. If Liz and George purchased a $\frac{4}{5}$-acre lot of land, what is the maximum land area that they can use to build the house?

28. **a.** List the first four multiples of 24.

   b. List all factors of 24.

   c. Write the prime factorization of 24.

29. Find the LCM for the numbers 16, 24, and 30.

For Exercises 30–31, write each fraction with the indicated denominator.

30. $\dfrac{5}{9} = \dfrac{}{63}$

31. $\dfrac{11}{21} = \dfrac{}{42w}$

32. Rank the fractions from least to greatest.

$$-\frac{5}{3}, \ -\frac{11}{21}, \ -\frac{4}{7}$$

33. Explain the difference between evaluating these two expressions:

$$\frac{5}{11} - \frac{3}{11} \quad \text{and} \quad \frac{5}{11} \cdot \frac{3}{11}$$

For Exercises 34–43, perform the indicated operations. Write the answer as a proper fraction or mixed number.

34. $\dfrac{3}{8} + \dfrac{3}{16}$

35. $\dfrac{7}{3} - 2$

36. $\dfrac{1}{4} - \dfrac{7}{12}$

37. $\dfrac{12}{y} - \dfrac{6}{y^2}$

38. $-7\dfrac{2}{3} \div 4\dfrac{1}{6}$

39. $-4\dfrac{4}{17} \cdot \left(-2\dfrac{4}{15}\right)$

40. $6\dfrac{3}{4} + 10\dfrac{5}{8}$

41. $12 - 9\dfrac{10}{11}$

42. $-3 - 4\dfrac{4}{9}$

43. $-2\dfrac{1}{5} - \left(-6\dfrac{1}{10}\right)$

44. A fudge recipe calls for $1\frac{1}{2}$ lb of chocolate. How many pounds are required for $\frac{2}{3}$ of the recipe?

45. Find the area and perimeter of this parking area.

$5\frac{7}{10}$ m

$4\frac{2}{5}$ m

For Exercises 46–50, simplify.

46. $\left(-\dfrac{6}{7}\right)^2$

47. $\left(\dfrac{1}{2} - \dfrac{3}{5}\right)^3$

48. $\dfrac{2}{5} - 3\dfrac{2}{3} \div \dfrac{11}{2}$

49. $\dfrac{\frac{24}{35}}{\frac{8}{15}}$

50. $\dfrac{\frac{2}{5} - \frac{1}{2}}{-\frac{3}{10} + 2}$

51. Evaluate the expression $x \div z + y$ for $x = -\frac{2}{3}$, $y = \frac{7}{4}$, and $z = 2\frac{2}{3}$.

52. Simplify the expression. $-\dfrac{4}{5}m - \dfrac{2}{3}m + 2m$

For Exercises 53–58, solve the equation.

53. $-\dfrac{5}{9} + k = \dfrac{2}{3}$

54. $-\dfrac{5}{9}k = \dfrac{2}{3}$

55. $\dfrac{6}{11} = -3t$

56. $-2 = -\dfrac{1}{8}p$

57. $\dfrac{3}{2} = -\dfrac{2}{3}x - \dfrac{5}{6}$

58. $\dfrac{3}{14}y - 1 = \dfrac{3}{7}$

Chapters 1–4   Cumulative Review Exercises

1. For the number 6,8$\underline{7}$3,129 identify the place value of the underlined digit.

2. Write the following inequality in words: $130 < 244$

3. Find the prime factorization of 360.

For Exercises 4–10, simplify.

4. $71 + (-4) + 81 + (-106)$

5. $-\dfrac{15}{16} \cdot \dfrac{2}{5}$

6. $368 \div (-4)$

7. $\dfrac{0}{-61}$

8. $-\dfrac{13}{8} + \dfrac{7}{4}$

9. $4 - \dfrac{18}{5}$

10. $2\dfrac{3}{5} \div 1\dfrac{7}{10}$

11. Simplify the expression. $\left(8\dfrac{1}{4} \div 2\dfrac{3}{4}\right)^2 \cdot \dfrac{5}{18} + \dfrac{5}{6}$

12. Simplify the fraction to lowest terms: $\dfrac{180}{900}$

13. Find the area of the rectangle.

28 m

5 m

14. Simplify the expressions.

    a. $-|-4|$ **b.** $-(-4)$ **c.** -4^2 **d.** $(-4)^2$

15. Simplify the expression. $-14 - 2(9 - 5^2)$

16. Combine *like* terms.
$$-6x - 4y - 9x + y + 4x - 5$$

17. Simplify. $-4(x - 5) - (3x + 2)$

18. Solve the equation. $-2(x - 3) + 4x = 3(x - 6)$

19. Solve the equation. $\dfrac{3}{4} = \dfrac{1}{2} + x$

20. Solve the equation. $\dfrac{x}{10} - 1 = \dfrac{2}{5}$

Decimals

5

Chapter 5

This chapter is devoted to the study of decimal numbers and their important applications in day-to-day life. We begin with a discussion of place value, and then we perform operations on signed decimal numbers. The chapter closes with applications and equations involving decimals.

Are You Prepared?

To prepare for your work with decimal numbers, take a minute to review place value, operations on integers, expressions, and equations. Write each answer in words and complete the crossword puzzle.

Across

2. Are $3x$ and 3 like terms?

3. Identify the place value of the underlined digit. 15,<u>4</u>27

5. Solve. $-5x + 4 = -21$

Down

1. Simplify. $(27 - 17)^2 - 80$

2. Simplify. $(-3)^2$

4. Simplify. $x - 3(x - 4) + 2x - 5$

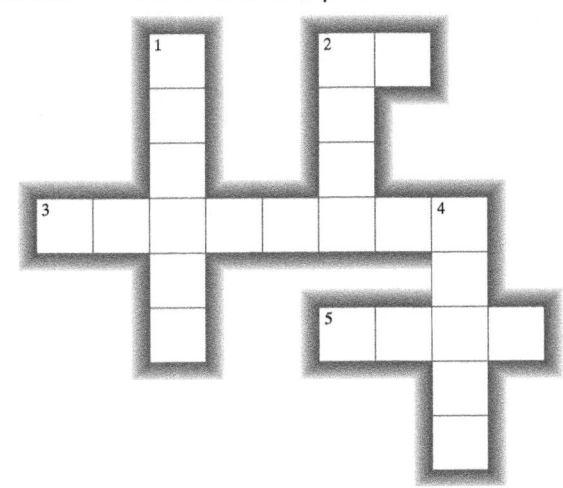

Section 5.1   Decimal Notation and Rounding

1. Decimal Notation

In Chapter 4, we studied fractional notation to denote equal parts of a whole. In this chapter, we introduce decimal notation to denote parts of a whole. We first introduce the concept of a decimal fraction. A **decimal fraction** is a fraction whose denominator is a power of 10. The following are examples of decimal fractions.

$$\frac{3}{10} \text{ is read as "three-tenths"}$$

$$\frac{7}{100} \text{ is read as "seven-hundredths"}$$

$$-\frac{9}{1000} \text{ is read as "negative nine-thousandths"}$$

We now want to write these fractions in **decimal notation**. This means that we will write the numbers by using place values, as we did with whole numbers. The place value chart from Section 1.2 can be extended as shown in Figure 5-1.

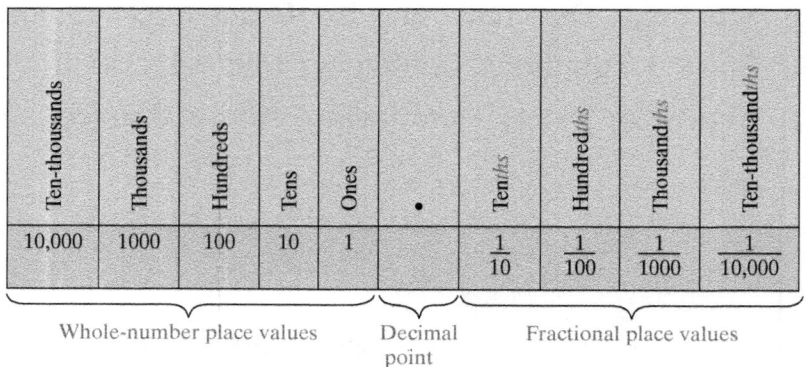

Ten-thousands	Thousands	Hundreds	Tens	Ones	.	Tenths	Hundredths	Thousandths	Ten-thousandths
10,000	1000	100	10	1		$\frac{1}{10}$	$\frac{1}{100}$	$\frac{1}{1000}$	$\frac{1}{10,000}$

Whole-number place values   Decimal point   Fractional place values

Figure 5-1

From Figure 5-1, we see that the decimal point separates the whole-number part from the fractional part. The place values for decimal fractions are located to the right of the decimal point. Their place value names are similar to those for whole numbers, but end in *ths*. Notice the correspondence between the tens place and the ten*ths* place. Similarly notice the hundreds place and the hundred*ths* place. Each place value on the left has a corresponding place value on the right, with the exception of the ones place. There is no "one*ths*" place.

Example 1 **Identifying Place Values**

Identify the place value of each underlined digit.

  a. 30,804.0<u>9</u>   **b.** −0.84692<u>0</u>   **c.** 2<u>9</u>3.604

Solution:

  a. 30,804.0<u>9</u>   The digit 9 is in the hundredths place.

  b. −0.84692<u>0</u>   The digit 2 is in the hundred-thousandths place.

  c. 2<u>9</u>3.604   The digit 9 is in the tens place.

For a whole number, the decimal point is understood to be after the ones place and is usually not written. For example:

$$42. = 42$$

Using Figure 5-1, we can write the numbers $\frac{3}{10}$, $\frac{7}{100}$, and $-\frac{9}{1000}$ in decimal notation.

Fraction	Word name	Decimal notation
$\dfrac{3}{10}$	Three-tenths	0.3 ↑ tenths place
$\dfrac{7}{100}$	Seven-hundredths	0.07 ↑ hundredths place
$-\dfrac{9}{1000}$	Negative nine-thousandths	−0.009 ↑ thousandths place

Now consider the number $15\frac{7}{10}$. This value represents 1 ten + 5 ones + 7 tenths. In decimal form we have 15.7.

The decimal point is interpreted as the word *and*. Thus, 15.7 is read as "fifteen *and* seven tenths." The number 356.29 can be represented as

$$356 + 2 \text{ tenths} + 9 \text{ hundredths} = 356 + \frac{2}{10} + \frac{9}{100}$$

$$= 356 + \frac{20}{100} + \frac{9}{100} \qquad \text{We can use the LCD of } 100 \text{ to add the fractions.}$$

$$= 356\frac{29}{100}$$

We can read the number 356.29 as "three hundred fifty-six *and* twenty-nine hundredths."

This discussion leads to a quicker method to read decimal numbers.

> **PROCEDURE** Reading a Decimal Number
> **Step 1** The part of the number to the left of the decimal point is read as a whole number. *Note:* If there is no whole-number part, skip to step 3.
> **Step 2** The decimal point is read *and*.
> **Step 3** The part of the number to the right of the decimal point is read as a whole number but is followed by the name of the place position of the digit farthest to the right.

> ── **Skill Practice** ──
>
> Write a word name for each number.
> **5.** 1004.6   **6.** 3.042
> **7.** −0.0063

Example 2 Reading Decimal Numbers

Write the word name for each number.

 a. 1028.4   **b.** 2.0736   **c.** −0.478

Solution:

 a. 1028.4   is written as "one thousand, twenty-eight and four-tenths."

 b. 2.0736   is written as "two and seven hundred thirty-six ten-thousandths."

 c. −0.478   is written as "negative four hundred seventy-eight thousandths."

> ── **Skill Practice** ──
>
> Write the word name as a numeral.
> **8.** Two hundred and two hundredths
> **9.** Negative seventy-nine and sixteen thousandths

Example 3 Writing a Numeral from a Word Name

Write the word name as a numeral.

 a. Four hundred eight and fifteen ten-thousandths

 b. Negative five thousand eight hundred and twenty-three hundredths

Solution:

 a. Four hundred eight and fifteen ten-thousandths: 408.0015

 b. Negative five thousand eight hundred and twenty-three hundredths: −5800.23

2. Writing Decimals as Mixed Numbers or Fractions

A fractional part of a whole may be written as a fraction or as a decimal. To convert a decimal to an equivalent fraction, it is helpful to think of the decimal in words. For example:

Decimal	Word Name	Fraction	
0.3	Three tenths	$\frac{3}{10}$	
0.67	Sixty-seven hundredths	$\frac{67}{100}$	
0.048	Forty-eight thousandths	$\frac{48}{1000} = \frac{6}{125}$	(simplified)
6.8	Six and eight-tenths	$6\frac{8}{10} = 6\frac{4}{5}$	(simplified)

From the list, we notice several patterns that can be summarized as follows.

Answers
5. One thousand, four and six-tenths
6. Three and forty-two thousandths
7. Negative sixty-three ten-thousandths
8. 200.02   **9.** −79.016

> **PROCEDURE** Converting a Decimal to a Mixed Number or Proper Fraction
>
> **Step 1** The digits to the right of the decimal point are written as the numerator of the fraction.
> **Step 2** The place value of the digit farthest to the right of the decimal point determines the denominator.
> **Step 3** The whole-number part of the number is left unchanged.
> **Step 4** Once the number is converted to a fraction or mixed number, simplify the fraction to lowest terms, if possible.

Example 4 Writing Decimals as Proper Fractions or Mixed Numbers

Write the decimals as proper fractions or mixed numbers and simplify.

a. 0.847 **b.** −0.0025 **c.** 4.16

Solution:

a. $0.847 = \dfrac{847}{1000}$

thousandths place

b. $-0.0025 = -\dfrac{25}{10{,}000} = -\dfrac{\overset{1}{25}}{\underset{400}{10{,}000}} = -\dfrac{1}{400}$

ten-thousandths place

c. $4.16 = 4\dfrac{16}{100} = 4\dfrac{\overset{4}{16}}{\underset{25}{100}} = 4\dfrac{4}{25}$

hundredths place

Skill Practice
Write the decimals as proper fractions or mixed numbers.
10. 0.034 **11.** −0.00086
12. 3.184

A decimal number greater than 1 can be written as a mixed number or as an improper fraction. The number 4.16 from Example 4(c) can be expressed as follows.

$$4.16 = 4\dfrac{16}{100} = 4\dfrac{4}{25} \quad \text{or} \quad \dfrac{104}{25}$$

A quick way to obtain an improper fraction for a decimal number greater than 1 is outlined here.

Concept Connections
13. Which is a correct representation of 3.17?
$3\dfrac{17}{100}$ or $\dfrac{317}{100}$

> **PROCEDURE** Writing a Decimal Number Greater Than 1 as an Improper Fraction
>
> **Step 1** The denominator is determined by the place position of the digit farthest to the right of the decimal point.
> **Step 2** The numerator is obtained by removing the decimal point of the original number. The resulting whole number is then written over the denominator.
> **Step 3** Simplify the improper fraction to lowest terms, if possible.

Answers
10. $\dfrac{17}{500}$ **11.** $-\dfrac{43}{50{,}000}$ **12.** $3\dfrac{23}{125}$
13. They are both correct representations.

For example:

Remove decimal point.

$$\overbrace{4.16}^{} = \frac{416}{100} = \frac{104}{25} \qquad \text{(simplified)}$$

hundredths ⎯
place

─ **Example 5**   **Writing Decimals as Improper Fractions** ─

Write the decimals as improper fractions and simplify.

a. 40.2   **b.** −2.113

Solution:

a. $40.2 = \dfrac{402}{10} = \dfrac{\overset{201}{\cancel{402}}}{\underset{5}{\cancel{10}}} = \dfrac{201}{5}$

b. $-2.113 = -\dfrac{2113}{1000}$ Note that the fraction is already in lowest terms.

3. Ordering Decimal Numbers

It is often necessary to compare the values of two decimal numbers.

> **PROCEDURE**   **Comparing Two Positive Decimal Numbers**
> **Step 1**   Starting at the left (and moving toward the right), compare the digits in each corresponding place position.
> **Step 2**   As we move from left to right, the first instance in which the digits differ determines the order of the numbers. The number having the greater digit is greater overall.

─ **Example 6**   **Ordering Decimals** ─

Fill in the blank with < or >.

a. 0.68 ☐ 0.7   **b.** 3.462 ☐ 3.4619

Solution:

different 6 < 7

a. 0.68 ⌐<⌐ 0.7

different 2 > 1

b. 3.462 ⌐>⌐ 3.4619

same

When ordering two negative numbers, you must be careful to visualize their relative positions on the number line. For example, $1.4 < 1.5$ but $-1.4 > -1.5$. See Figure 5-2.

Figure 5-2

Also note that when ordering two decimal numbers, sometimes it is necessary to insert additional zeros after the rightmost digit in a number. This does not change the value of the number. For example:

$$0.7 = 0.70 \quad \text{because} \quad \frac{7}{10} = \frac{70}{100}$$

Example 7 **Ordering Negative Decimals**

Fill in the blank with $<$ or $>$.

a. $-0.2 \ \square \ -0.05$ **b.** $-0.04591 \ \square \ -0.0459$

Solution:

a. Insert a zero in the hundredths place for the number on the left. The digits in the tenths place are different.

different

$-0.20 \ \boxed{<} \ -0.05$ $-0.2 < -0.05$

b. Insert a zero in the hundred-thousandths place for the number on the right. The digits in the hundred-thousandths place are different.

different

$-0.04591 \ \boxed{<} \ -0.04590$ $-0.04591 < -0.0459$

Skill Practice

Fill in the blank with $<$ or $>$.

18. $-0.32 \ \square \ -0.062$

19. $-0.873 \ \square \ -0.8731$

4. Rounding Decimals

The process to round the decimal part of a number is nearly the same as rounding whole numbers (see Section 1.4). The main difference is that the digits to the right of the rounding place position are dropped instead of being replaced by zeros.

> **PROCEDURE** **Rounding Decimals to a Place Value to the Right of the Decimal Point**
>
> **Step 1** Identify the digit one position to the right of the given place value.
> **Step 2** If the digit in step 1 is 5 or greater, add 1 to the digit in the given place value. Then discard the digits to its right.
> **Step 3** If the digit in step 1 is less than 5, discard it and any digits to its right.

Answers

18. $<$ **19.** $>$

Skill Practice

Round 187.26498 to the indicated place value.

20. Hundredths
21. Ten-thousandths

Example 8   **Rounding Decimal Numbers**

Round 14.795 to the indicated place value.

a. Tenths   **b.** Hundredths

Solution:

                                    remaining digits discarded
a. 1 4 . $\overset{+1}{7}$ 9 5 ≈ 14.8
          ↑ ↑
       tenths └──── This digit is 5 or greater. Add 1 to the tenths place.
       place

                                    remaining digit discarded
b. 1 4 . 7 $\overset{+1}{9}$ 5 ≈ 14.80
        ↑ ↑
   hundredths └──── This digit is 5 or greater. Add 1 to the hundredths place.
   place
         • Since the hundredths place digit is 9, adding 1 requires us
           to carry 1 to the tenths place digit.

In Example 8(b) the 0 in 14.80 indicates that the number was rounded to the hundredths place. It would be incorrect to drop the zero. Even though 14.8 has the same numerical value as 14.80, it implies a different level of accuracy. For example, when measurements are taken using some instrument such as a ruler or scale, the measured values are not exact. The place position to which a number is rounded reflects the accuracy of the measuring device. Thus, the value 14.8 lb indicates that the scale is accurate to the nearest tenth of a pound. The value 14.80 lb indicates that the scale is accurate to the nearest hundredth of a pound.

Skill Practice

22. Round 45.372 to the hundredths place.
23. Round 134.9996 to the thousandths place.

Example 9   **Rounding Decimal Numbers**

a. Round 4.81542 to the thousandths place.

b. Round 52.9999 to the hundredths place.

Solution:

                       remaining digits discarded
a. 4.81542 ≈ 4.815
           ↑↑
           │└──── This digit is less than 5. Discard it and all digits to the right.
       thousandths
       place

                       discard remaining digits
         $\overset{1}{}$ $\overset{1}{}\overset{+1}{}$
b. 5 2 . 9 9 9 9
          ↑ ↑
          │ └──── This digit is greater than 5. Add 1 to the hundredths place digit.
    hundredths
    place   • Since the hundredths place digit is 9, adding 1 requires us
                     to carry 1 to the tenths place digit.
                   • Since the tenths place digit is 9, adding 1 requires us to
                     carry 1 to the ones place digit.

         ≈ 53.00

Answers

20. 187.26   **21.** 187.2650
22. 45.37   **23.** 135.000

Section 5.1   Practice Exercises

Study Skills Exercise

1. Define the key terms.

   a. Decimal fraction   **b. Decimal notation**

Objective 1: Decimal Notation

2. State the first five place positions to the right of the decimal point in order from left to right.

For Exercises 3–10, expand the powers of 10 or $\frac{1}{10}$.

3. 10^2

4. 10^3

5. 10^4

6. 10^5

7. $\left(\dfrac{1}{10}\right)^2$

8. $\left(\dfrac{1}{10}\right)^3$

9. $\left(\dfrac{1}{10}\right)^4$

10. $\left(\dfrac{1}{10}\right)^5$

For Exercises 11–22, identify the place value of each underlined digit. **(See Example 1.)**

11. 3.9̲83

12. 34.8̲2̲

13. 440.39̲

14. 24̲8.94

15. 48̲9.02

16. 4.0928̲4

17. $-9.2834̲5$

18. $-0.321̲$

19. 0.489̲

20. 58̲.211

21. $-93̲.834$

22. $-5.000001̲$

For Exercises 23–30, write the word name for each decimal fraction.

23. $\dfrac{9}{10}$

24. $\dfrac{7}{10}$

25. $\dfrac{23}{100}$

26. $\dfrac{19}{100}$

27. $-\dfrac{33}{1000}$

28. $-\dfrac{51}{1000}$

29. $\dfrac{407}{10,000}$

30. $\dfrac{20}{10,000}$

For Exercises 31–38, write the word name for the decimal. **(See Example 2.)**

31. 3.24

32. 4.26

33. -5.9

34. -3.4

35. 52.3

36. 21.5

37. 6.219

38. 7.338

For Exercises 39–44, write the word name as a numeral. **(See Example 3.)**

39. Negative eight thousand, four hundred seventy-two and fourteen thousandths

40. Negative sixty thousand, twenty-five and four hundred one ten-thousandths

41. Seven hundred and seven hundredths

42. Nine thousand and nine thousandths

43. Negative two million, four hundred sixty-nine thousand and five hundred six thousandths

44. Negative eighty-two million, six hundred fourteen and ninety-seven ten-thousandths

Objective 2: Writing Decimals as Mixed Numbers or Fractions

For Exercises 45–56, write the decimal as a proper fraction or as a mixed number and simplify. **(See Example 4.)**

45. 3.7   **46.** 1.9   **47.** 2.8   **48.** 4.2

49. 0.25   **50.** 0.75   **51.** −0.55   **52.** −0.45

53. 20.812   **54.** 32.905   **55.** −15.0005   **56.** −4.0015

For Exercises 57–64, write the decimal as an improper fraction and simplify. **(See Example 5.)**

57. 8.4   **58.** 2.5   **59.** 3.14   **60.** 5.65

61. −23.5   **62.** −14.6   **63.** 11.91   **64.** 21.33

Objective 3: Ordering Decimal Numbers

For Exercises 65–72, fill in the blank with < or >. **(See Examples 6–7.)**

65. 6.312 ☐ 6.321   **66.** 8.503 ☐ 8.530   **67.** 11.21 ☐ 11.2099   **68.** 10.51 ☐ 10.5098

69. −0.762 ☐ −0.76   **70.** −0.1291 ☐ −0.129   **71.** −51.72 ☐ −51.721   **72.** −49.06 ☐ −49.062

73. Which number is between 3.12 and 3.13? Circle all that apply.

    a. 3.127   **b.** 3.129   **c.** 3.134   **d.** 3.139

74. Which number is between 42.73 and 42.86? Circle all that apply.

    a. 42.81   **b.** 42.64   **c.** 42.79   **d.** 42.85

75. The batting averages for five legends are given in the table. Rank the players' batting averages from lowest to highest. (*Source:* Baseball Almanac)

Player	Average
Joe Jackson	0.3558
Ty Cobb	0.3664
Lefty O'Doul	0.3493
Ted Williams	0.3444
Roger Hornsby	0.3585

76. The average speed, in miles per hour (mph), of the Daytona 500 for selected years is given in the table. Rank the speeds from slowest to fastest. (*Source:* NASCAR)

Year	Driver	Speed (mph)
1989	Darrell Waltrip	148.466
1991	Ernie Irvan	148.148
1997	Jeff Gordon	148.295
2007	Kevin Harvick	149.333

Objective 4: Rounding Decimals

77. The numbers given all have equivalent value. However, suppose they represent measured values from a scale. Explain the difference in the interpretation of these numbers.

$$0.25, \quad 0.250, \quad 0.2500, \quad 0.25000$$

78. Which number properly represents 3.499999 rounded to the thousandths place?

    a. 3.500   **b.** 3.5   **c.** 3.500000   **d.** 3.499

79. Which value is rounded to the nearest tenth, 7.1 or 7.10?

80. Which value is rounded to the nearest hundredth, 34.50 or 34.5?

For Exercises 81–92, round the decimals to the indicated place values. **(See Examples 8–9.)**

81. 49.943; tenths   **82.** 12.7483; tenths   **83.** 33.416; hundredths

84. 4.359; hundredths   **85.** −9.0955; thousandths   **86.** −2.9592; thousandths

87. 21.0239; tenths   **88.** 16.804; hundredths   **89.** 6.9995; thousandths

90. 21.9997; thousandths   **91.** 0.0079499; ten-thousandths   **92.** 0.00084985; ten-thousandths

93. A snail moves at a rate of about 0.00362005 miles per hour. Round the decimal value to the ten-thousandths place.

For Exercises 94–97, round the number to the indicated place value.

	Number	Hundreds	Tens	Tenths	Hundredths	Thousandths
94.	349.2395					
95.	971.0948					
96.	79.0046					
97.	21.9754					

Expanding Your Skills

98. What is the least number with three places to the right of the decimal that can be created with the digits 2, 9, and 7? Assume that the digits cannot be repeated.

99. What is the greatest number with three places to the right of the decimal that can be created from the digits 2, 9, and 7? Assume that the digits cannot be repeated.

Section 5.2	Addition and Subtraction of Decimals

Objectives

1. **Addition and Subtraction of Decimals**
2. **Applications of Addition and Subtraction of Decimals**
3. **Algebraic Expressions**

1. Addition and Subtraction of Decimals

In this section, we learn to add and subtract decimals. To begin, consider the sum $5.67 + 3.12$.

$$5.67 = \quad 5 + \frac{6}{10} + \frac{7}{100}$$

$$+\ 3.12 = +3 + \frac{1}{10} + \frac{2}{100}$$

$$8 + \frac{7}{10} + \frac{9}{100} = 8.79$$

Notice that the decimal points and place positions are lined up to add the numbers. In this way, we can add digits with the same place values because we are effectively adding decimal fractions with like denominators. The intermediate step of using fraction notation is often skipped. We can get the same result more quickly by adding digits in like place positions.

> **PROCEDURE Adding and Subtracting Decimals**
>
> **Step 1** Write the numbers in a column with the decimal points and corresponding place values lined up. (You may insert additional zeros as placeholders after the last digit to the right of the decimal point.)
>
> **Step 2** Add or subtract the digits in columns from right to left, as you would whole numbers. The decimal point in the answer should be lined up with the decimal points from the original numbers.

Example 1   Adding Decimals

Add. $27.486 + 6.37$

Solution:

$$\begin{array}{r} 27.486 \\ +\ 6.370 \\ \hline \end{array}$$ Line up the decimal points.
Insert an extra zero as a placeholder.

$$\begin{array}{r} \overset{1}{2}7.\overset{1}{4}86 \\ +\ 6.370 \\ \hline 33.856 \end{array}$$ Add digits with common place values.

Line up the decimal point in the answer.

With operations on decimals it is important to locate the correct position of the decimal point. A quick estimate can help you determine whether your answer is reasonable. From Example 1, we have

$$\begin{array}{lll} 27.486 & \text{rounds to} & 27 \\ 6.370 & \text{rounds to} & +6 \\ & & \hline \\ & & 33 \end{array}$$

The estimated value, 33, is close to the actual value of 33.856.

Example 2 **Adding Decimals**

Add.   3.7026 + 43 + 816.3

Solution:

$$
\begin{array}{r}
3.7026 \\
43.0000 \\
+\,816.3000 \\
\end{array}
$$

3.7026   Line up the decimal points.
43.0000   Insert a decimal point and four zeros after it.
+ 816.3000   Insert three zeros.

$$
\begin{array}{r}
\overset{1\ 1}{} \\
3.7026 \\
43.0000 \\
+\,816.3000 \\
\hline
863.0026
\end{array}
$$

3.7026   Add digits with common place values.
43.0000
+ 816.3000
863.0026   Line up the decimal point in the answer.

The sum is 863.0026.

TIP: To check that the answer is reasonable, round each addend.

3.7026	rounds to	4
43	rounds to	43
816.3	rounds to	+ 816
		863

(with small $\overset{1}{}$ above 43)

which is close to the actual sum, 863.0026.

Skill Practice
Add.
3. 2.90741 + 15.13 + 3

Example 3 **Subtracting Decimals**

Subtract.

a. 0.2868 − 0.056   **b.** 139 − 28.63   **c.** 192.4 − 89.387

Solution:

a.
$$
\begin{array}{r}
0.2868 \\
-\,0.0560 \\
\hline
0.2308
\end{array}
$$

0.2868   Line up the decimal points.
− 0.0560   Insert an extra zero as a placeholder.
0.2308   Subtract digits with common place values.
            Decimal point in the answer is lined up.

b.
$$
\begin{array}{r}
139.00 \\
-\,28.63 \\
\end{array}
$$

139.00   Insert extra zeros as placeholders.
− 28.63   Line up the decimal points.

$$
\begin{array}{r}
\overset{8\ \overset{9}{\cancel{10}}\ 10}{13\cancel{9}.\cancel{0}\,\cancel{0}} \\
-\,28.63 \\
\hline
110.37
\end{array}
$$

139.00   Subtract digits with common place values.
− 28.63   Borrow where necessary.
110.37   Line up the decimal point in the answer.

c.
$$
\begin{array}{r}
192.400 \\
-\,89.387 \\
\end{array}
$$

192.400   Insert extra zeros as placeholders.
− 89.387   Line up the decimal points.

$$
\begin{array}{r}
\overset{8\ 12\ \ 3\ \overset{9}{\cancel{10}}\ 10}{19\cancel{2}.\cancel{4}\,\cancel{0}\,\cancel{0}} \\
-\,89.387 \\
\hline
103.013
\end{array}
$$

192.400   Subtract digits with common place values.
− 89.387   Borrow where necessary.
103.013   Line up the decimal point in the answer.

Skill Practice
Subtract.
4. 3.194 − 0.512
5. 0.397 − 0.1584
6. 566.4 − 414.231

Answers
3. 21.03741   **4.** 2.682
5. 0.2386   **6.** 152.169

In Example 4, we will use the rules for adding and subtracting signed numbers.

Skill Practice

Simplify.

7. $-39.46 + 29.005$
8. $-0.345 - 6.51$
9. $-3.79 - (-6.2974)$

Example 4 **Adding and Subtracting Signed Decimal Numbers**

Simplify.

a. $-23.9 + 45.8$ **b.** $-0.694 - 0.482$ **c.** $2.61 - 3.79 - (-6.29)$

Solution:

a. $-23.9 + 45.8$ The sum will be *positive* because $|45.8|$ is greater than $|-23.9|$.

$= +(45.8 - 23.9)$ To add two numbers with different signs, subtract the smaller absolute value from the larger absolute value. Apply the sign from the number with the larger absolute value.

$$\begin{array}{r}\overset{4\ 18}{4\cancel{5}.8}\\ -\ 23.9\\ \hline 21.9\end{array}$$

$= 21.9$ The result is positive.

b. $-0.694 - 0.482$

$= -0.694 + (-0.482)$ Change subtraction to addition of the opposite.

$= -(0.694 + 0.482)$ To add two numbers with the same signs, add their absolute values and apply the common sign.

$$\begin{array}{r}\overset{1}{0.694}\\ +\ 0.482\\ \hline 1.176\end{array}$$

$= -1.176$ The result is negative.

c. $2.61 - 3.79 - (-6.29)$

$= \underbrace{2.61 + (-3.79)} + (6.29)$ Change subtraction to addition of the opposite. Add from left to right.

$= \quad -1.18 + 6.29$ $\begin{array}{r}3.79\\ -2.61\\ \hline 1.18\end{array}$ Subtract the smaller absolute value from the larger absolute value.

$= 5.11$ $\begin{array}{r}6.29\\ -1.18\\ \hline 5.11\end{array}$ Subtract the smaller absolute value from the larger absolute value.

2. Applications of Addition and Subtraction of Decimals

Decimals are used often in measurements and in day-to-day applications.

Answers

7. -10.455 **8.** -6.855
9. 2.5074

Example 5 Applying Addition and Subtraction of Decimals in a Checkbook

Fill in the balance for each line in the checkbook register, shown in Figure 5-3. What is the ending balance?

Check No.	Description	Debit	Credit	Balance
				$684.60
2409	Doctor	$ 75.50		
2410	Mechanic	215.19		
2411	Home Depot	94.56		
	Paycheck		$981.46	
2412	Veterinarian	49.90		

Figure 5-3

Solution:

We begin with $684.60 in the checking account. For each debit, we subtract. For each credit, we add.

Check No.	Description	Debit	Credit	Balance	
				$ 684.60	
2409	Doctor	$ 75.50		609.10	= $684.60 − $75.50
2410	Mechanic	215.19		393.91	= $609.10 − $215.19
2411	Home Depot	94.56		299.35	= $393.91 − $94.56
	Paycheck		$981.46	1280.81	= $299.35 + $981.46
2412	Veterinarian	49.90		1230.91	= $1280.81 − $49.90

The ending balance is $1230.91.

Skill Practice

10. Fill in the balance for each line in the checkbook register.

Check	Debit	Credit	Balance
			$437.80
1426	$82.50		
Pay		$514.02	
1427	26.04		

Example 6 Applying Decimals to Perimeter

a. Find the length of the side labeled x.

b. Find the length of the side labeled y.

c. Find the perimeter of the figure.

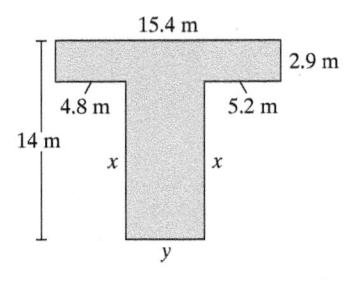

Solution:

a. If we extend the line segment labeled x with the dashed line as shown below, we see that the sum of side x and the dashed line must equal 14 m. Therefore, subtract $14 − 2.9$ to find the length of side x.

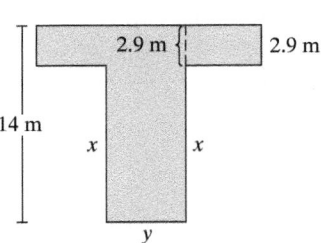

Length of side x:
$$\begin{array}{r} \overset{3\ 10}{1\cancel{4}.\cancel{0}} \\ -\ 2.9 \\ \hline 11.1 \end{array}$$

Side x is 11.1 m long.

Answer

10.

Check	Debit	Credit	Balance
			$ 437.80
1426	$82.50		355.30
Pay		$514.02	869.32
1427	26.04		843.28

Skill Practice

11. Consider the figure.

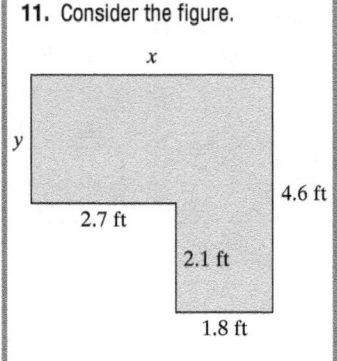

x

y

4.6 ft

2.7 ft

2.1 ft

1.8 ft

  a. Find the length of side *x*.
  b. Find the length of side *y*.
  c. Find the perimeter.

b. The dashed line in the figure below has the same length as side *y*. We also know that $4.8 + 5.2 + y$ must equal 15.4. Since $4.8 + 5.2 = 10.0,$

$$y = 15.4 - 10.0$$
$$= 5.4$$

The length of side *y* is 5.4 m.

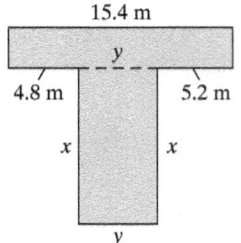

15.4 m

y

4.8 m   5.2 m

x   x

y

c. Now that we have the lengths of all sides, add them to get the perimeter.

```
  2 3
15.4
 2.9
 5.2
11.1
 5.4
11.1
 4.8
+ 2.9
-----
58.8
```

15.4 m

2.9 m   2.9 m

4.8 m   5.2 m

11.1 m   11.1 m

5.4 m

The perimeter is 58.8 m.

3. Algebraic Expressions

In Example 7, we practice combining *like* terms. In this case, the terms have decimal coefficients.

Skill Practice

Simplify by combining *like* terms.
12. $-9.15t - 2.34t$
13. $0.31w + 0.46z$
     $+ 0.45w - 0.2z$

Example 7   **Combining *Like* Terms**

Simplify by combining *like* terms.

  a. $-2.3x + 8.6x$ **b.** $0.042x + 0.539y + 0.65x - 0.21y$

Solution:

  a. $-2.3x + 8.6x = (-2.3 + 8.6)x$ Apply the distributive property.

                 $= (6.3)x$ 8.6   Subtract the smaller absolute

                 $= 6.3x$ $- 2.3$ value from the larger.

                                       6.3

TIP: To combine *like* terms, we can simply add or subtract the coefficients and leave the variable unchanged.

$$0.042x + 0.65x = 0.692x$$

  b. $0.042x + 0.539y + 0.65x - 0.21y$

     $= 0.042x + 0.65x + 0.539y - 0.21y$ Group *like* terms together.

     $= 0.692x - 0.329y$ Combine *like* terms by adding or subtracting the coefficients.

Answers

11. a. Side *x* is 4.5 ft.
   b. Side *y* is 2.5 ft.
   c. The perimeter is 18.2 ft.
12. $-11.49t$ **13.** $0.76w + 0.26z$

Section 5.2 Practice Exercises

Boost *your* GRADE at
ALEKS.com!

ALEKS
version 3.0

- Practice Problems
- Self-Tests
- NetTutor

- e-Professors
- Videos

Review Exercises

1. Which number is equal to 5.03? Circle all that apply.

    a. 5.030   **b.** 5.30   **c.** 5.0300   **d.** 5.3

2. Which number is equal to $\frac{7}{100}$? Circle all that apply.

    a. 0.7   **b.** 0.07   **c.** 0.070   **d.** 0.007

For Exercises 3–8, round the decimals to the indicated place values.

3. 23.489; tenths   **4.** 42.314; hundredths   **5.** 8.6025; thousandths

6. 0.981; tenths   **7.** 2.82998; ten-thousandths   **8.** 2.78999; thousandths

Objective 1: Addition and Subtraction of Decimals

For Exercises 9–14, add the decimal numbers. Then round the numbers and find the sum to determine if your answer is reasonable. The first estimate is done for you. **(See Examples 1–2.)**

Expression	Estimate		Expression	Estimate
9. 44.6 + 18.6	45 + 19 = 64	**10.** 28.2 + 23.2		
11. 5.306 + 3.645		**12.** 3.451 + 7.339		
13. 12.9 + 3.091		**14.** 4.125 + 5.9		

For Exercises 15–26, add the decimals. **(See Examples 1–2.)**

15. 78.9 + 0.9005   **16.** 44.2 + 0.7802   **17.** 23 + 8.0148   **18.** 7.9302 + 34

19. 34 + 23.0032 + 5.6   **20.** 23 + 8.01 + 1.0067   **21.** 68.394 + 32.02   **22.** 2.904 + 34.229

23. $\begin{array}{r} 103.94 \\ +\ \ 24.5 \\ \hline \end{array}$ **24.** $\begin{array}{r} 93.2 \\ +\ 43.336 \\ \hline \end{array}$ **25.** $\begin{array}{r} 54.2 \\ 23.993 \\ +\ \ 3.87 \\ \hline \end{array}$ **26.** $\begin{array}{r} 13.9001 \\ 72.4 \\ +\ 34.13 \\ \hline \end{array}$

For Exercises 27–32, subtract the decimal numbers. Then round the numbers and find the difference to determine if your answer is reasonable. The first estimate is done for you. **(See Example 3.)**

Expression	Estimate		Expression	Estimate
27. 35.36 − 21.12	35 − 21 = 14	**28.** 53.9 − 22.4		
29. 7.24 − 3.56		**30.** 23.3 − 20.8		
31. 45.02 − 32.7		**32.** 66.15 − 42.9		

For Exercises 33–44, subtract the decimals. **(See Example 3.)**

33. $14.5 - 8.823$

34. $33.2 - 21.932$

35. $2 - 0.123$

36. $4 - 0.42$

37. $55.9 - 34.2354$

38. $49.1 - 24.481$

39. $18.003 - 3.238$

40. $21.03 - 16.446$

41. $183.01 - 23.452$

42. $164.23 - 44.3893$

43. $1.001 - 0.0998$

44. $2.0007 - 0.0689$

Mixed Exercises: Addition and Subtraction of Signed Decimals

For Exercises 45–60, add or subtract as indicated. **(See Example 4.)**

45. $-506.34 + 83.4$

46. $-89.041 + 76.43$

47. $-0.489 - 0.87$

48. $-0.78 - 0.439$

49. $47.82 - (-3.159)$

50. $4.2 - (-9.8458)$

51. $55.3 - 68.4 - (-9.83)$

52. $3.45 - 8.7 - (-10.14)$

53. $5 - 9.432$

54. $7 - 11.468$

55. $-6.8 - (-8.2)$

56. $-10.3 - (-5.1)$

57. $-28.3 + (-82.9)$

58. $-92.6 + (-103.8)$

59. $2.6 - 2.06 - 2.006 + 2.0006$

60. $5.84 - 5.084 - 5.0084 + 58.4$

Objective 2: Applications of Addition and Subtraction of Decimals

61. Fill in the balance for each line in the checkbook register shown in the figure. What is the ending balance? **(See Example 5.)**

Check No.	Description	Debit	Credit	Balance
				$ 245.62
2409	Electric bill	$ 52.48		
2410	Groceries	72.44		
2411	Department store	108.34		
	Paycheck		$1084.90	
2412	Restaurant	23.87		
	Transfer from savings		200	

62. A section of a bank statement is shown in the figure. Find the mistake that was made by the bank.

Date	Action	Debit	Credit	Balance
				$1124.35
1/2/10	Check #4214	$749.32		375.03
1/3/10	Check #4215	37.29		337.74
1/4/10	Transfer from savings		$ 400.00	737.74
1/5/10	Paycheck		1451.21	2188.95
1/6/10	Cash withdrawal	150.00		688.95

63. A normal human red blood cell count is between 4.2 and 6.9 million cells per microliter (μL). A cancer patient undergoing chemotherapy has a red blood cell count of 2.85 million cells per microliter. How far below the lower normal limit is this?

64. A laptop computer was originally priced at $1299.99 and was discounted to $998.95. By how much was it marked down?

65. Water flows into a pool at a constant rate. The water level is recorded at several 1-hr intervals.

Time	Water Level
9:00 A.M.	4.2 in.
10:00 A.M.	5.9 in.
11:00 A.M.	7.6 in.
12:00 P.M.	9.3 in.

  a. From the table, how many inches is the water level rising each hour?

  b. At this rate, what will the water level be at 1:00 P.M.?

  c. At this rate, what will the water level be at 3:00 P.M.?

66. The amount of time that it takes Mercury, Venus, Earth, and Mars to revolve about the Sun is given in the graph.

  a. How much longer does it take Mars to complete a revolution around the Sun than the Earth?

  b. How much longer does it take Venus than Mercury to revolve around the Sun?

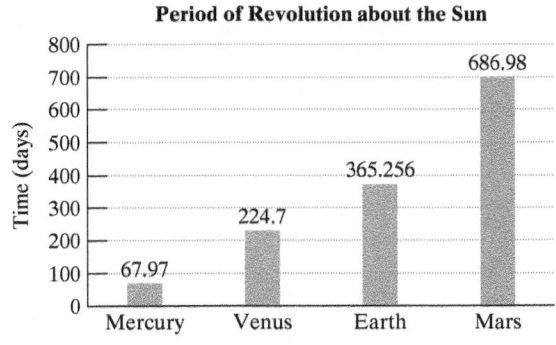

Period of Revolution about the Sun

Mercury 67.97, Venus 224.7, Earth 365.256, Mars 686.98 (Time in days)

Source: National Aeronautics and Space Administration

67. The table shows the thickness of four U.S. coins. If you stacked three quarters and a dime in one pile and two nickels and two pennies in another pile, which pile would be higher?

Coin	Thickness
Quarter	1.75 mm
Dime	1.35 mm
Nickel	1.95 mm
Penny	1.55 mm

Source: U.S. Department of the Treasury

68. How much thicker is a nickel than a quarter?

For Exercises 69–72, find the lengths of the sides labeled *x* and *y*. Then find the perimeter. **(See Example 6.)**

69.

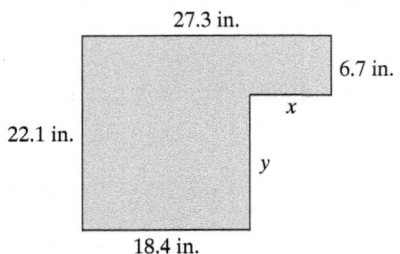

27.3 in.
6.7 in.
x
22.1 in.
y
18.4 in.

70.

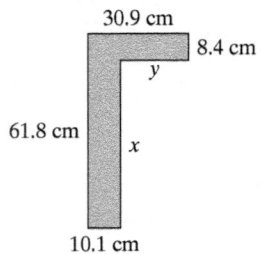

30.9 cm
8.4 cm
y
61.8 cm
x
10.1 cm

71.

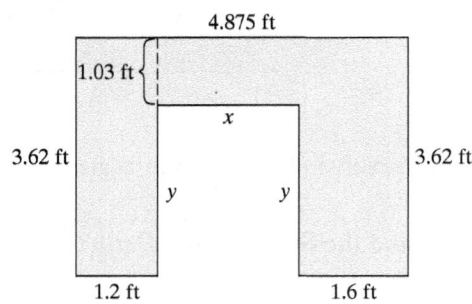

4.875 ft
1.03 ft
x
3.62 ft   3.62 ft
y   *y*
1.2 ft   1.6 ft

72.

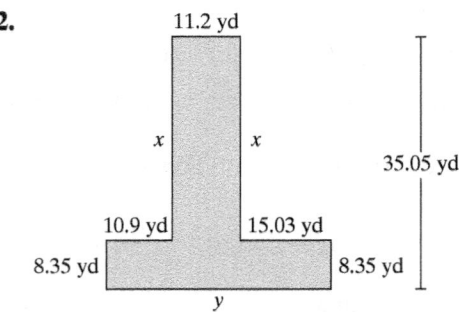

11.2 yd
x   *x*
35.05 yd
10.9 yd   15.03 yd
8.35 yd   8.35 yd
y

73. A city bus follows the route shown in the map. How far does it travel in one circuit?

7.25 mi
4.3 mi
5.9 mi
9.75 mi

74. Santos built a new deck and needs to put a railing around the sides. He does not need railing where the deck is against the house. How much railing should he purchase?

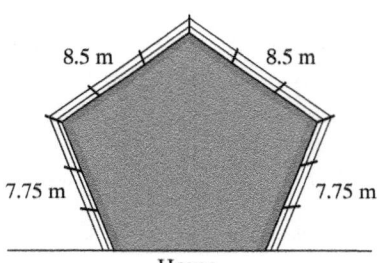

8.5 m   8.5 m
7.75 m   7.75 m
House

Objective 3: Algebraic Expressions

For Exercises 75–84, simplify by combining *like* terms. **(See Example 7.)**

75. $-5.83t + 9.7t$

76. $-2.158w + 10.4w$

77. $-4.5p - 8.7p$

78. $-98.46a - 12.04a$

79. $y - 0.6y$

80. $0.18x - x$

81. $0.025x + 0.83y + 0.82x - 0.31y$

82. $0.008m - 0.06n - 0.0043m + 0.092n$

83. $0.92c - 4.78d + 0.08c - 0.22d$

84. $3.62x - 80.09y - 0.62x + 10.09y$

Calculator Connections

Topic: Entering Decimals on a Calculator

To enter decimals on a calculator, use the [.] key.

Expression	Keystrokes	Result
984.126 + 37.11	984 [.] 126 [+] 37 [.] 11 **ENTER**	1021.236

Calculator Exercises

For Exercises 85–90, refer to the table. The table gives the closing stock prices (in dollars per share) for the first day of trading for the given month.

Stock	January	February	March	April	May
IBM	$97.27	$99.00	$92.27	$95.21	$103.17
FedEx	$109.77	$111.89	$114.16	$106.07	$106.11

85. By how much did the IBM stock increase between January and May?

86. By how much did the FedEx stock decrease between January and May?

87. Between which two consecutive months did the FedEx stock increase the most? What was the amount of increase?

88. Between which two consecutive months did the IBM stock increase the most? What was the amount of increase?

89. Between which two consecutive months did the FedEx stock decrease the most? What was the amount of decrease?

90. Between which two consecutive months did the IBM stock decrease the most? What was the amount of decrease?

Multiplication of Decimals and Applications with Circles

Section 5.3

1. Multiplication of Decimals

Multiplication of decimals is much like multiplication of whole numbers. However, we need to know where to place the decimal point in the product. Consider the product $(0.3)(0.41)$. One way to multiply these numbers is to write them first as decimal fractions.

$$(0.3)(0.41) = \frac{3}{10} \cdot \frac{41}{100} = \frac{123}{1000} \text{ or } 0.123$$

Objectives

1. **Multiplication of Decimals**
2. **Multiplication by a Power of 10 and by a Power of 0.1**
3. **Applications Involving Multiplication of Decimals**
4. **Circumference and Area of a Circle**

Another method multiplies the factors vertically. First we multiply the numbers as though they were whole numbers. We temporarily disregard the decimal point in the product because it will be placed later.

$$
\begin{array}{r}
0.41 \\
\times\ 0.3 \\
\hline
123
\end{array}
\quad \longleftarrow \quad \text{decimal point not yet placed}
$$

From the first method, we know that the correct answer to this problem is 0.123. Notice that 0.123 contains the same number of decimal places as the two factors combined. That is,

$$
\begin{array}{r}
0.41 \\
\times\ 0.3 \\
\hline
.123
\end{array}
$$

0.41   ←   2 decimal places
× 0.3   ←   1 decimal place
.123   ←   3 decimal places

The process to multiply decimals is summarized as follows.

Concept Connections

1. How many decimal places will be in the product (2.72)(1.4)?
2. Explain the difference between the process to multiply 123 × 51 and the process to multiply 1.23 × 5.1.

TIP: When multiplying decimals, it is *not* necessary to line up the decimal points as we do when we add or subtract decimals. Instead, we line up the right-most digits.

PROCEDURE Multiplying Two Decimals

Step 1 Multiply as you would integers.
Step 2 Place the decimal point in the product so that the number of decimal places equals the combined number of decimal places of both factors.

Note: You may need to insert zeros to the left of the whole-number product to get the correct number of decimal places in the answer.

In Example 1, we multiply decimals by using this process.

Skill Practice

Multiply.

3. (19.7)(4.1)

Example 1 Multiplying Decimals

Multiply.   11.914
           × 0.8

Solution:

$$
\begin{array}{r}
\overset{1\ 7}{}\overset{1\ 3}{} \\
11.914 \\
\times\ \ 0.8 \\
\hline
9.5312
\end{array}
\qquad
\begin{array}{l}
3 \text{ decimal places} \\
+\ 1 \text{ decimal place} \\
\hline
4 \text{ decimal places}
\end{array}
$$

The product is 9.5312.

Example 2 Multiplying Decimals

Multiply. Then use estimation to check the location of the decimal point.

$$(29.3)(2.8)$$

Solution:

$$
\begin{array}{r}
\overset{1}{} \\
\overset{7\ 2}{} \\
29.3 \\
\times\ 2.8 \\
\hline
2344 \\
5860 \\
\hline
82.04
\end{array}
\qquad
\begin{array}{l}
1 \text{ decimal place} \\
+\ 1 \text{ decimal place} \\
\\
\\
2 \text{ decimal places}
\end{array}
\qquad \text{The product is 82.04.}
$$

Answers

1. 3
2. The actual process of vertical multiplication is the same for both cases. However, for the product 1.23 × 5.1, the decimal point must be placed so that the product has the same number of decimal places as both factors combined (in this case, 3).
3. 80.77

To check the answer, we can round the factors and estimate the product. The purpose of the estimate is primarily to determine whether we have placed the decimal point correctly. Therefore, it is usually sufficient to round each factor to the left-most nonzero digit. This is called **front-end rounding**. Thus,

$$\begin{array}{rl} 29.3 & \text{rounds to} \quad 30 \\ 2.8 & \text{rounds to} \quad \underline{\times\ 3} \\ & \qquad\qquad\quad 90 \end{array}$$

The first digit for the actual product 82.04 and the first digit for the estimate 90 is the tens place. Therefore, we are reasonably sure that we have located the decimal point correctly. The estimate 90 is close to 82.04.

Skill Practice

4. Multiply (1.9)(29.1) and check your answer using estimation.

| Example 3 | **Multiplying Decimals** |

Multiply. Then use estimation to check the location of the decimal point.

$$-2.79 \times 0.0003$$

Solution:

The product will be *negative* because the factors have opposite signs.

Actual product:

$$\begin{array}{r} {\scriptstyle 2\ 2} \\ -2.79 \\ \underline{\times\ 0.0003} \\ -.000837 \end{array} \quad \begin{array}{l} 2 \text{ decimal places} \\ +\ 4 \text{ decimal places} \\ \hline 6 \text{ decimal places} \\ \text{(insert 3 zeros to the left)} \end{array}$$

Estimate:

$$\begin{array}{rl} -2.79 & \text{rounds to} \quad -3 \\ \times\ 0.0003 & \text{rounds to} \quad \underline{\times\ 0.0003} \\ & \qquad\qquad\qquad -0.0009 \end{array}$$

The first digit for both the actual product and the estimate is in the ten-thousandths place. We are reasonably sure the decimal point is positioned correctly.

The product is -0.000837.

Skill Practice

5. Multiply -4.6×0.00008, and check your answer using estimation.

2. Multiplication by a Power of 10 and by a Power of 0.1

Consider the number 2.7 multiplied by $10, 100, 1000\ldots$

$$\begin{array}{ccc} 10 & 100 & 1000 \\ \underline{\times\ 2.7} & \underline{\times\ 2.7} & \underline{\times\ 2.7} \\ 70 & 700 & 7000 \\ \underline{200} & \underline{2000} & \underline{20000} \\ 27.0 & 270.0 & 2700.0 \end{array}$$

Multiplying 2.7 by 10 moves the decimal point 1 place to the right.
Multiplying 2.7 by 100 moves the decimal point 2 places to the right.
Multiplying 2.7 by 1000 moves the decimal point 3 places to the right.

This leads us to the following generalization.

Answers

4. $55.29; \approx 2 \cdot 30 = 60$, which is close to 55.29.
5. $-0.000368; \approx -5 \times 0.00008 = -0.0004$, which is close to -0.000368.

> **PROCEDURE** **Multiplying a Decimal by a Power of 10**
>
> Move the decimal point to the right the same number of decimal places as the number of zeros in the power of 10.

Example 4 **Multiplying by Powers of 10**

Multiply.

a. $14.78 \times 10,000$ **b.** 0.0064×100 **c.** $-8.271 \times (-1,000,000)$

Solution:

a. $14.78 \times 10,000 = 147,800$ Move the decimal point 4 places to the right.

b. $0.0064 \times 100 = 0.64$ Move the decimal point 2 places to the right.

c. The product will be positive because the factors have the same sign.

    $-8.271 \times (-1,000,000) = 8,271,000$ Move the decimal point 6 places to the right.

Multiplying a positive decimal by $10, 100, 1000$, and so on increases its value. Therefore, it makes sense to move the decimal point to the *right*. Now suppose we multiply a decimal by $0.1, 0.01$, and 0.001. These numbers represent the decimal fractions $\frac{1}{10}$, $\frac{1}{100}$, and $\frac{1}{1000}$, respectively, and are easily recognized as powers of 0.1 (see Section 2.4). Taking one-tenth of a positive number or one-hundredth of a positive number makes the number smaller. To multiply by $0.1, 0.01, 0.001$, and so on (powers of 0.1), move the decimal point to the *left*.

$$
\begin{array}{ccc}
3.6 & 3.6 & 3.6 \\
\times \ 0.1 & \times \ 0.01 & \times \ 0.001 \\
\hline
.36 & .036 & .0036
\end{array}
$$

> **PROCEDURE** **Multiplying a Decimal by Powers of 0.1**
>
> Move the decimal point to the left the same number of places as there are decimal places in the power of 0.1.

Example 5 **Multiplying by Powers of 0.1**

Multiply.

a. 62.074×0.0001 **b.** 7965.3×0.1 **c.** -0.0057×0.00001

Solution:

a. $62.074 \times 0.0001 = 0.0062074$ Move the decimal point 4 places to the left. Insert extra zeros.

b. $7965.3 \times 0.1 = 796.53$ Move the decimal point 1 place to the left.

c. $-0.0057 \times 0.00001 = -0.000000057$ Move the decimal point 5 places to the left.

Sometimes people prefer to use number names to express very large numbers. For example, we might say that the U.S. population in a recent year was approximately 280 million. To write this in decimal form, we note that 1 million = 1,000,000. In this case, we have 280 of this quantity. Thus,

$$280 \text{ million} = 280 \times 1{,}000{,}000 \text{ or } 280{,}000{,}000$$

Example 6 Naming Large Numbers

Write the decimal number representing each word name.

a. The distance between the Earth and Sun is approximately 92.9 million miles.

b. The number of deaths in the United States due to heart disease in 2010 was projected to be 8 hundred thousand.

c. A recent estimate claimed that collectively Americans throw away 472 billion pounds of garbage each year.

Solution:

a. 92.9 million = 92.9 × 1,000,000 = 92,900,000

b. 8 hundred thousand = 8 × 100,000 = 800,000

c. 472 billion = 472 × 1,000,000,000 = 472,000,000,000

Skill Practice

Write a decimal number representing the word name.

13. The population in Bexar County, Texas, is approximately 1.6 million.

14. Light travels approximately 5.9 trillion miles in 1 year.

15. The legislative branch of the federal government employs approximately 31 thousand employees.

3. Applications Involving Multiplication of Decimals

Example 7 Applying Decimal Multiplication

Jane Marie bought eight cans of tennis balls for $1.98 each. She paid $1.03 in tax. What was the total bill?

Solution:

The cost of the tennis balls before tax is

$$8(\$1.98) = \$15.84$$

$$\begin{array}{r} {\scriptstyle 7\ 6} \\ 1.98 \\ \times\ \ \ 8 \\ \hline 15.84 \end{array}$$

Adding the tax to this value, we have

$$\begin{pmatrix} \text{Total} \\ \text{cost} \end{pmatrix} = \begin{pmatrix} \text{Cost of} \\ \text{tennis balls} \end{pmatrix} + (\text{Tax})$$

$$= \$15.84$$
$$\underline{+\ 1.03}$$
$$\$16.87 \qquad \text{The total cost is } \$16.87.$$

Skill Practice

16. A book club ordered 12 books on www.amazon.com for $8.99 each. The shipping cost was $4.95. What was the total bill?

Answers

13. 1,600,000
14. 5,900,000,000,000
15. 31,000
16. The total bill was $112.83.

Skill Practice

17. The IMAX movie screen at the Museum of Science and Discovery in Ft. Lauderdale, Florida, is 18 m by 24.4 m. What is the area of the screen?

Example 8 **Finding the Area of a Rectangle**

The *Mona Lisa* is perhaps the most famous painting in the world. It was painted by Leonardo da Vinci somewhere between 1503 and 1506 and now hangs in the Louvre in Paris, France. The dimensions of the painting are 30 in. by 20.875 in. What is the total area?

Solution:

Recall that the area of a rectangle is given by

$$A = l \cdot w$$

$$A = (30 \text{ in.})(20.875 \text{ in.})$$

$$= 626.25 \text{ in.}^2$$

$$\begin{array}{r} \overset{2\ 21}{20.875} \\ \times\ 30 \\ \hline 0 \\ 626250 \\ \hline 626.250 \end{array}$$

The area of the *Mona Lisa* is 626.25 in.².

4. Circumference and Area of a Circle

A **circle** is a figure consisting of all points in a flat surface located the same distance from a fixed point called the center. The **radius** of a circle is the length of any line segment from the center to a point on the circle. The **diameter** of a circle is the length of any line segment connecting two points on the circle and passing through the center. See Figure 5-4.

  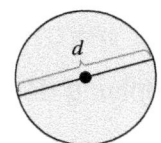

r is the length of the radius.   *d* is the length of the diameter.

Figure 5-4

Skill Practice

Find the length of a radius.
18.

104 m

Find the length of a diameter.
19.

$\frac{5}{8}$ yd

Notice that the length of a diameter is twice the radius. Therefore, we have

$$d = 2r \quad \text{or equivalently} \quad r = \frac{1}{2}d$$

Example 9 **Finding Diameter and Radius**

a. Find the length of a radius.   **b.** Find the length of a diameter.

46 cm $\frac{3}{4}$ ft

Solution:

a. $r = \frac{1}{2}d = \frac{1}{2}(46 \text{ cm}) = 23 \text{ cm}$ **b.** $d = 2r = \overset{1}{2}\left(\frac{3}{\underset{2}{4}} \text{ ft}\right) = \frac{3}{2} \text{ ft}$

Answers

17. The screen area is 439.2 m².

18. 52 m   **19.** $\frac{5}{4}$ yd

The distance around a circle is called the **circumference**. In any circle, if the circumference C is divided by the diameter, the result is equal to the number π (read "pi"). The number π in decimal form is 3.1415926535..., which goes on forever without a repeating pattern. We approximate π by 3.14 or $\frac{22}{7}$ to make it easier to use in calculations. The relationship between the circumference and the diameter of a circle is $\frac{C}{d} = \pi$. This gives us the following formulas.

FORMULA   Circumference of a Circle

The circumference C of a circle is given by

$$C = \pi d \qquad \text{or} \qquad C = 2\pi r$$

where π is approximately 3.14 or $\frac{22}{7}$.

Example 10   **Determining Circumference of a Circle**

Determine the circumference. Use 3.14 for π.

Solution:

The radius is given, $r = 4$ cm.

$$C = 2\pi r$$
$$= 2(\pi)(4 \text{ cm}) \qquad \text{Substitute 4 cm for } r.$$
$$= 8\pi \text{ cm}$$
$$\approx 8(3.14) \text{ cm} \qquad \text{Approximate } \pi \text{ by 3.14.}$$
$$\approx 25.12 \text{ cm} \qquad \text{The distance around the circle is approximately 25.12 cm.}$$

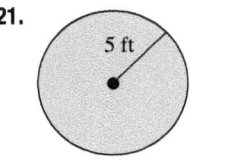

TIP: The circumference from Example 10 can also be found from the formula $C = \pi d$. In this case, the diameter is 8 cm.

$$C = \pi d$$
$$C = \pi(8 \text{ cm})$$
$$= 8\pi \text{ cm}$$
$$\approx 8(3.14) \text{ cm}$$
$$= 25.12 \text{ cm}$$

The formula for the area of a circle also involves the number π. In Chapter 8 we will provide the geometric basis for the formula given below.

FORMULA   Area of a Circle

The **area of a circle** is given by

$$A = \pi r^2$$

Skill Practice

22. Find the area of a circular clock having a radius of 6 in. Approximate the answer by using 3.14 for π. Round to the nearest whole unit.

Answer

22. ≈ 113 in.^{2}

Example 11 **Determining the Area of a Circle**

Determine the area of a circle that has radius 0.3 ft. Approximate the answer by using 3.14 for π. Round to two decimal places.

Solution:

$A = \pi r^2$

$\quad = \pi (0.3 \text{ ft})^2$ Substitute $r = 0.3$ ft.

$\quad = \pi (0.09 \text{ ft}^2)$ Square the radius. $(0.3 \text{ ft})^2 = (0.3 \text{ ft})(0.3 \text{ ft}) = 0.09 \text{ ft}^2$

$\quad = 0.09\pi \text{ ft}^2$

$\quad \approx 0.09(3.14) \text{ ft}^2$ Approximate π by 3.14.

$\quad = 0.2826 \text{ ft}^2$ Multiply decimals.

$\quad \approx 0.28 \text{ ft}^2$ The area is approximately 0.28 ft^2.

Avoiding Mistakes

$(0.3)^2 \neq (0.9)$. Be sure to count the number of places needed to the right of the decimal point. $(0.3)^2 = (0.3)(0.3) = 0.09$

TIP: Using the approximation 3.14 for π results in approximate answers for area and circumference. To express the exact answer, we must leave the result written in terms of π. In Example 11 the exact area is given by 0.09π ft^2.

Section 5.3   Practice Exercises

Boost *your* GRADE at ALEKS.com!

ALEKS version 3.0

- Practice Problems
- Self-Tests
- NetTutor
- e-Professors
- Videos

Study Skills Exercises

1. To help you remember the formulas for circumference and area of a circle, list them together and note the similarities and differences in the formulas.

     Circumference: _____   Area: _____

     Similarities: Differences:

2. Define the key terms.

     a. Front-end rounding   **b. Circle**   **c. Radius**

     d. Diameter   **e. Circumference**   **f. Area of a circle**

Review Exercises

For Exercises 3–5, round to the indicated place value.

     3. 49.997; tenths   **4.** -0.399; hundredths   **5.** -0.00298; thousandths

For Exercises 6–8, add or subtract as indicated.

     6. $-2.7914 + 5.03216$ **7.** $-33.072 - (-41.03)$ **8.** $-0.0723 - 0.514$

Objecitve 1: Multiplication of Decimals

For Exercises 9–16, multiply the decimals. (See Examples 1–3.)

9. $\begin{array}{r} 0.8 \\ \times\ 0.5 \\ \hline \end{array}$

10. $\begin{array}{r} 0.6 \\ \times\ 0.5 \\ \hline \end{array}$

11. (0.9)(4)

12. (0.2)(9)

13. (−60)(−0.003)

14. (−40)(−0.005)

15. $\begin{array}{r} 22.38 \\ \times\ 0.8 \\ \hline \end{array}$

16. $\begin{array}{r} 31.67 \\ \times\ 0.4 \\ \hline \end{array}$

For Exercises 17–30, multiply the decimals. Then estimate the answer by rounding. The first estimate is done for you. (See Examples 2–3.)

	Exact	Estimate		Exact	Estimate		Exact	Estimate

17. $\begin{array}{r} 8.3 \\ \times\ 4.5 \\ \hline \end{array}$ $\begin{array}{r} 8 \\ \times\ 5 \\ \hline 40 \end{array}$

18. $\begin{array}{r} 4.3 \\ \times\ 9.2 \\ \hline \end{array}$

19. $\begin{array}{r} 0.58 \\ \times\ 7.2 \\ \hline \end{array}$

20. 0.83(6.5)

21. 5.92(−0.8)

22. 9.14(−0.6)

23. (−0.413)(−7)

24. (−0.321)(−6)

25. 35.9 × 3.2

26. 41.7 × 6.1

27. (562)(0.004)

28. (984)(0.009)

29. −0.0004 × 3.6

30. −0.0008 × 6.5

Objective 2: Multiplication by a Power of 10 and by a Power of 0.1

31. Multiply.

a. 5.1 × 10   **b.** 5.1 × 100   **c.** 5.1 × 1000   **d.** 5.1 × 10,000

32. If 256.8 is multiplied by 0.001, will the decimal point move to the left or to the right? By how many places?

33. Multiply.

a. 5.1 × 0.1   **b.** 5.1 × 0.01   **c.** 5.1 × 0.001   **d.** 5.1 × 0.0001

34. Multiply.

a. −6.2 × 100   **b.** −6.2 × 0.01   **c.** −6.2 × 10,000   **d.** −6.2 × 0.0001

For Exercises 35–42, multiply the numbers by the powers of 10 and 0.1. (See Examples 4–5.)

35. 34.9 × 100

36. 2.163 × 100

37. 96.59 × 1000

38. 18.22 × 1000

39. −93.3 × 0.01

40. −80.2 × 0.01

41. −54.03 × (−0.001)

42. −23.11 × (−0.001)

For Exercises 43–48, write the decimal number representing each word name. (See Example 6.)

43. The number of beehives in the United States is 2.6 million. (*Source:* U.S. Department of Agriculture)

44. The people of France collectively consume 34.7 million gallons of champagne per year. (*Source*: Food and Agriculture Organization of the United Nations)

45. The most stolen make of car worldwide is Toyota. For a recent year, there were 4 hundred-thousand Toyota's stolen. (*Source:* Interpol)

46. The musical *Miss Saigon* ran for about 4 thousand performances in a 10-year period.

47. The people in the United States have spent over $20.549 billion on DVDs.

48. Coca-Cola Classic was the greatest selling brand of soft-drinks. For a recent year, over 4.8 billion gallons were sold in the United States. (*Source:* Beverage Marketing Corporation)

Objective 3: Applications Involving Multiplication of Decimals

49. One gallon of gasoline weighs about 6.3 lb. However, when burned, it produces 20 lb of carbon dioxide (CO_2). This is because most of the weight of the CO_2 comes from the oxygen in the air.

    a. How many pounds of gasoline does a Hummer H2 carry when its tank is full (the tank holds 32 gal).

    b. How many pounds of CO_2 does a Hummer H2 produce after burning an entire tankful of gasoline?

50. Corrugated boxes for shipping cost $2.27 each. How much will 10 boxes cost including tax of $1.59?

51. The Athletic Department at Broward College bought 20 pizzas for $10.95 each, 10 Greek salads for $3.95 each, and 60 soft drinks for $0.60 each. What was the total bill including a sales tax of $17.67? **(See Example 7.)**

52. A hotel gift shop ordered 40 T-shirts at $8.69 each, 10 hats at $3.95 each, and 20 beach towels at $4.99 each. What was the total cost of the merchandise, including the $29.21 sales tax?

53. Firestone tires cost $50.20 each. A set of four Lemans tires costs $197.99. How much can a person save by buying the set of four Lemans tires compared to four Firestone tires?

54. Certain DVD titles are on sale for 2 for $32. If they regularly sell for $19.99, how much can a person save by buying 4 DVDs?

For Exercises 55–56, find the area. **(See Example 8.)**

55.

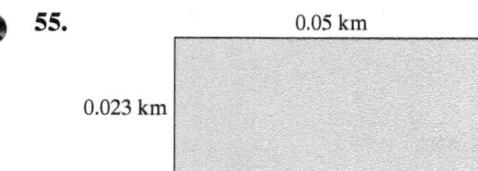

0.05 km

0.023 km

56.

4.5 yd

6.7 yd

57. Blake plans to build a rectangular patio that is 15 yd by 22.2 yd. What is the total area of the patio?

58. The front page of a newspaper is 56 cm by 31.5 cm. Find the area of the page.

For Exercises 59–66, simplify the expressions.

59. $(0.4)^2$

60. $(0.7)^2$

61. $(-1.3)^2$

62. $(-2.4)^2$

63. $(0.1)^3$

64. $(0.2)^3$

65. -0.2^2

66. -0.3^2

Objective 4: Circumference and Area of a Circle

67. How does the length of a radius of a circle compare to the length of a diameter?

68. Circumference is similar to which type of measure?

    a. Area   **b.** Volume   **c.** Perimeter   **d.** Weight

For Exercises 69–70, find the length of a diameter. **(See Example 9.)**

69.

70.

For Exercises 71–72, find the length of a radius. **(See Example 9.)**

71.

72.

For Exercises 73–76, find the circumference of the circle. Approximate the answer by using 3.14 for π. **(See Example 10.)**

73.

74.

75.

76.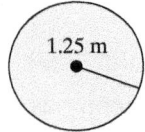

For Exercises 77–80, use 3.14 for π.

77. Find the circumference of the can of soda.

78. Find the circumference of a can of tuna.

79. Find the circumference of a compact disk.

80. Find the outer circumference of a pipe with 1.75-in. radius.

For Exercises 81–84, find the area. Approximate the answer by using 3.14 for π. Round to the nearest whole unit. **(See Example 11.)**

81.
20 mm

82.
10 ft

83.
6.2 ft

84.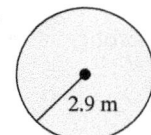
2.9 m

85. The Large Hadron Collider (LHC) is a particle accelerator and collider built to detect subatomic particles. The accelerator is in a huge circular tunnel that straddles the border between France and Switzerland. The diameter of the tunnel is 5.3 mi. Find the circumference of the tunnel. (*Source:* European Organization for Nuclear Research)

86. A ceiling fan blade rotates in a full circle. If the fan blades are 2 ft long, what is the area covered by the fan blades?

87. An outdoor torch lamp shines light a distance of 30 ft in all directions. What is the total ground area lighted?

88. Hurricane Katrina's eye was 32 mi wide. The eye of a storm of similar intensity is usually only 10 mi wide. (*Source:* Associated Press 10/8/05 "Mapping Katrina's Storm Surge")

   a. What area was covered by the eye of Katrina? Round to the nearest square mile.

   b. What is the usual area of the eye of a similar storm?

Expanding Your Skills

89. A hula hoop has a 20-in. diameter.

   a. Find the circumference. Use 3.14 for π.

   b. How many times will the hula hoop have to turn to roll down a 40-yd (1440 in.) driveway? Round to the nearest whole unit.

90. A bicycle wheel has a 26-in. diameter.

   a. Find the circumference. Use 3.14 for π.

   b. How many times will the wheel have to turn to go a distance of 1000 ft (12,000 in.)? Round to the nearest whole unit.

91. Latasha has a bicycle, and the wheel has a 22-in. diameter. If the wheels of the bike turned 1000 times, how far did she travel? Use 3.14 for π. Give the answer to the nearest inch and to the nearest foot (1 ft = 12 in.)

92. The exercise wheel for Al's dwarf hamster has a diameter of 6.75 in.

    a. Find the circumference. Use 3.14 for π and round to the nearest inch.

    b. How far does Al's hamster travel if he completes 25 revolutions? Write the answer in feet and round to the nearest foot.

Calculator Connections

Topic: Using the π Key

When finding the circumference or the area of a circle, we can use the ⬚π key on the calculator to lend more accuracy to our calculations. If you press the ⬚π key on the calculator, the display will show 3.141592654. This number is not the exact value of π (remember that in decimal form π is a nonterminating and nonrepeating decimal). However, using the ⬚π key provides more accuracy than by using 3.14. For example, suppose we want to find the area of a circle of radius 3 ft. Compare the values by using 3.14 for π versus using the ⬚π key.

Expression	Keystrokes	Result
$3.14 \cdot 3^2$	3.14 ×| 3 |x^2| =|	28.26
$\pi \cdot 3^2$	π| ×| 3 |x^2| =|	28.27433388

Again, it is important to note that neither of these answers is the exact area. The only way to write the exact value is to express the answer in terms of π. The exact area is 9π ft^2.

For Exercises 93–96, find the area and circumference rounded to four decimals places. Use the ⬚π key on your calculator.

93. 12.83 cm

94. 5.1 ft

95. 4.75 in.

96. 51.62 mm

Section 5.4 Division of Decimals

Objectives

1. Division of Decimals
2. Rounding a Quotient
3. Applications of Decimal Division

1. Division of Decimals

Dividing decimals is much the same as dividing whole numbers. However, we must determine where to place the decimal point in the quotient.

First consider the quotient 3.5 ÷ 7. We can write the numbers in fractional form and then divide.

$$3.5 \div 7 = \frac{35}{10} \div \frac{7}{1} = \frac{35}{10} \cdot \frac{1}{7} = \frac{35}{70} = \frac{5}{10} = 0.5$$

Now consider the same problem by using the efficient method of long division: $7\overline{)3.5}$.

When the divisor is a whole number, we place the decimal point directly above the decimal point in the dividend. Then we divide as we would whole numbers.

decimal point placed above
the decimal point in the dividend

$$7\overline{)3.5}^{.5}$$

> **PROCEDURE** Dividing a Decimal by a Whole Number
>
> To divide by a whole number:
> **Step 1** Place the decimal point in the quotient directly above the decimal point in the dividend.
> **Step 2** Divide as you would whole numbers.

Skill Practice

Divide. Check by using multiplication.
1. 502.96 ÷ 8

Example 1 Dividing by a Whole Number

Divide and check the answer by multiplying.

$$30.55 \div 13$$

Solution:

Locate the decimal point in the quotient.

$$13\overline{)30.55}$$

$$\begin{array}{r} 2.35 \\ 13\overline{)30.55} \\ -26 \\ \hline 45 \\ -39 \\ \hline 65 \\ -65 \\ \hline 0 \end{array}$$

Divide as you would whole numbers.

Check by multiplying:

$$\begin{array}{r} {\scriptstyle 1\;1} \\ 2.35 \\ \times\ 13 \\ \hline 705 \\ 2350 \\ \hline 30.55\ \checkmark \end{array}$$

Answer
1. 62.87

When dividing decimals, we do not use a remainder. Instead we insert zeros to the right of the dividend and continue dividing. This is demonstrated in Example 2.

Example 2 **Dividing by an Integer**

Divide and check the answer by multiplying.

$$\frac{-3.5}{-4}$$

Solution:

The quotient will be *positive* because the divisor and dividend have the same sign. We will perform the division without regard to sign and then write the quotient as a positive number.

Locate the decimal point in the quotient.

$$4\overline{)3.5}$$

$$\begin{array}{r} .8 \\ 4\overline{)3.5} \\ -32 \\ \hline 3 \end{array}$$ ← Rather than using a remainder, we insert zeros in the dividend and continue dividing.

$$\begin{array}{r} .875 \\ 4\overline{)3.500} \\ -32 \\ \hline 30 \\ -28 \\ \hline 20 \\ -20 \\ \hline 0 \end{array}$$

Check by multiplying:

$$\begin{array}{r} {\scriptstyle 3\ 2} \\ 0.875 \\ \times\ \ 4 \\ \hline 3.500\ \checkmark \end{array}$$

The quotient is 0.875.

Example 3 **Dividing by an Integer**

Divide and check the answer by multiplying. $40\overline{)5}$

Solution:

$$40\overline{)5.}$$ ← The dividend is a whole number, and the decimal point is understood to be to its right. Insert the decimal point above it in the quotient.

$$\begin{array}{r} .125 \\ 40\overline{)5.000} \\ -40 \\ \hline 100 \\ -80 \\ \hline 200 \\ -200 \\ \hline 0 \end{array}$$

Since 40 is greater than 5, we need to insert zeros to the right of the dividend.

Check by multiplying.

$$\begin{array}{r} {\scriptstyle 1\ 2} \\ 0.125 \\ \times\ 40 \\ \hline 000 \\ 5000 \\ \hline 5.000\ \checkmark \end{array}$$

The quotient is 0.125.

Sometimes when dividing decimals, the quotient follows a repeated pattern. The result is called a **repeating decimal**.

Skill Practice

Divide.
4. $2.4 \div 9$

Example 4 Dividing Where the Quotient Is a Repeating Decimal

Divide. $1.7 \div 30$

Solution:

$$
\begin{array}{r}
.05666\ldots \\
30\overline{)1.70000} \\
-150 \\
\hline
200 \\
-180 \\
\hline
200 \\
-180 \\
\hline
200
\end{array}
$$

Notice that as we continue to divide, we get the same values for each successive step. This causes a pattern of repeated digits in the quotient. Therefore, the quotient is a *repeating decimal*.

The quotient is 0.05666 . . . . To denote the repeated pattern, we often use a bar over the first occurrence of the repeat cycle to the right of the decimal point. That is,

$0.05666\ldots = 0.05\overline{6}$ ← ——— repeat bar

Avoiding Mistakes

In Example 4, notice that the repeat bar goes over only the 6. The 5 is not being repeated.

Skill Practice

Divide.
5. $11\overline{)57}$

Example 5 Dividing Where the Quotient Is a Repeating Decimal

Divide. $11\overline{)68}$

Solution:

$$
\begin{array}{r}
6.1818\ldots \\
11\overline{)68.0000} \\
-66 \\
\hline
20 \\
-11 \\
\hline
90 \\
-88 \\
\hline
20 \\
-11 \\
\hline
90 \\
-88 \\
\hline
20
\end{array}
$$

Could have stopped here →

Once again, we see a repeated pattern. The quotient is a repeating decimal. Notice that we could have stopped dividing when we obtained the second value of 20.

The quotient is $6.\overline{18}$.

Avoiding Mistakes

Be sure to put the repeating bar over the entire block of numbers that is being repeated. In Example 5, the bar extends over both the 1 and the 8. We have $6.\overline{18}$.

Answers
4. $0.2\overline{6}$ **5.** $5.\overline{18}$

The numbers $0.05\overline{6}$ and $6.\overline{18}$ are examples of repeating decimals. A decimal that "stops" is called a **terminating decimal**. For example, 6.18 is a terminating decimal, whereas $6.\overline{18}$ is a repeating decimal.

In Examples 1–5, we performed division where the divisor was an integer. Suppose now that we have a divisor that is *not* an integer, for example, $0.56 \div 0.7$. Because division can also be expressed in fraction notation, we have

$$0.56 \div 0.7 = \frac{0.56}{0.7}$$

If we multiply the numerator and denominator by 10, the denominator (divisor) becomes the whole number 7.

$$\frac{0.56}{0.7} = \frac{0.56 \times 10}{0.7 \times 10} = \frac{5.6}{7} \xrightarrow{\hspace{2cm}} 7\overline{)5.6}$$

Recall that multiplying decimal numbers by 10 (or any power of 10, such as 100, 1000, etc.) moves the decimal point to the right. We use this idea to divide decimal numbers when the divisor is not a whole number.

PROCEDURE   Dividing When the Divisor Is Not a Whole Number

Step 1 Move the decimal point in the divisor to the right to make it a whole number.

Step 2 Move the decimal point in the dividend to the right the same number of places as in step 1.

Step 3 Place the decimal point in the quotient directly above the decimal point in the dividend.

Step 4 Divide as you would whole numbers. Then apply the correct sign to the quotient.

Example 6 **Dividing Decimals**

Divide.

a. $0.56 \div (-0.7)$ **b.** $0.005\overline{)3.1}$

Solution:

a. The quotient will be *negative* because the divisor and dividend have different signs. We will perform the division without regard to sign and then apply the negative sign to the quotient.

$.7\overline{).56}$ Move the decimal point in the divisor and dividend one place to the right.

$7\overline{)5.6}$ ←——— Line up the decimal point in the quotient.

$$\begin{array}{r} 0.8 \\ 7\overline{)5.6} \\ \underline{-5\,6} \\ 0 \end{array}$$

The quotient is -0.8.

Skill Practice

Divide.
6. $0.64 \div (-0.4)$
7. $5.4 \div 0.03$

Answers
6. -1.6 **7.** 180

b. $.005\overline{)3.100}$ Move the decimal point in the divisor and dividend three places to the right. Insert additional zeros in the dividend if necessary. Line up the decimal point in the quotient.

$$
\begin{array}{r}
620. \\
5\overline{)3100.} \\
-30 \\
\hline
10 \\
-10 \\
\hline
00
\end{array}
$$

The quotient is 620.

Skill Practice

Divide.

8. $\dfrac{-70}{-0.6}$

Calculator Connections

Repeating decimals displayed on a calculator are rounded. This is because the display cannot show an infinite number of digits.

On a scientific calculator, the repeating decimal $45.\overline{45}$ might appear as

$$\boxed{45.45454545}$$

Example 7 **Dividing Decimals**

Divide. $\dfrac{-50}{-1.1}$

Solution:

The quotient will be *positive* because the divisor and dividend have the same sign. We will perform the division without regard to sign and then write the quotient as a positive number.

$1.1\overline{)50.0}$ Move the decimal point in the divisor and dividend one place to the right. Insert an additional zero in the dividend. Line up the decimal point in the quotient.

$$
\begin{array}{r}
45.45 \ldots \\
11\overline{)500.000} \\
-44 \\
\hline
60 \\
-55 \\
\hline
50 \\
-44 \\
\hline
60 \\
-55 \\
\hline
50
\end{array}
$$

The quotient is the repeating decimal, $45.\overline{45}$.

The quotient is $45.\overline{45}$.

> **Avoiding Mistakes**
>
> The quotient in Example 7 is a repeating decimal. The repeat cycle actually begins to the left of the decimal point. However, the repeat bar is placed on the first repeated block of digits to the *right* of the decimal point. Therefore, we write the quotient as $45.\overline{45}$.

When we multiply a number by 10, 100, 1000, and so on, we move the decimal point to the right. However, dividing a positive number by 10, 100, or 1000 decreases its value. Therefore, we move the decimal point to the *left*.

For example, suppose 3.6 is divided by 10, 100, and 1000.

$$
\begin{array}{r}
.36 \\
10\overline{)3.60} \\
-30 \\
\hline
60 \\
-60 \\
\hline
0
\end{array}
\qquad
\begin{array}{r}
.036 \\
100\overline{)3.600} \\
-300 \\
\hline
600 \\
-600 \\
\hline
0
\end{array}
\qquad
\begin{array}{r}
.0036 \\
1000\overline{)3.6000} \\
-3000 \\
\hline
6000 \\
-6000 \\
\hline
0
\end{array}
$$

Answer

8. $116.\overline{6}$

> **PROCEDURE** Dividing by a Power of 10
>
> To divide a number by a power of 10, move the decimal point to the *left* the same number of places as there are zeros in the power of 10.

Example 8 Dividing by a Power of 10

Divide.

a. $214.3 \div 10{,}000$ **b.** $0.03 \div 100$

Solution:

a. $214.3 \div 10{,}000 = 0.02143$ Move the decimal point four places to the left. Insert an additional zero.

b. $0.03 \div 100 = 0.0003$ Move the decimal point two places to the left. Insert two additional zeros.

Skill Practice

Divide.
9. $162.8 \div 1000$
10. $0.0039 \div 10$

2. Rounding a Quotient

In Example 7, we found that $50 \div 1.1 = 45.\overline{45}$. To check this result, we could multiply $45.\overline{45} \times 1.1$ and show that the product equals 50. However, at this point we do not have the tools to multiply repeating decimals. What we can do is round the quotient and then multiply to see if the product is *close* to 50.

Example 9 Rounding a Repeating Decimal

Round $45.\overline{45}$ to the hundredths place. Then use the rounded value to estimate whether the product $45.\overline{45} \times 1.1$ is close to 50. (This will serve as a check to the division problem in Example 7.)

Solution:

To round the number $45.\overline{45}$, we must write out enough of the repeated pattern so that we can view the digit to the right of the rounding place. In this case, we must write out the number to the thousandths place.

$$45.\overline{45} = 45.454 \cdots \approx 45.45$$

hundredths place   This digit is less than 5. Discard it and all others to its right.

Now multiply the rounded value by 1.1.

$$
\begin{array}{r}
45.45 \\
\times\ \ 1.1 \\
\hline
4545 \\
45450 \\
\hline
49.995
\end{array}
$$

This value is close to 50. We are reasonably sure that we divided correctly in Example 7.

Skill Practice

Round to the indicated place value.
11. $2.3\overline{15}$; thousandths

Sometimes we may want to round a quotient to a given place value. To do so, divide until you get a digit in the quotient one place value to the right of the rounding place. At this point, you can stop dividing and round the quotient.

Answers
9. 0.1628   **10.** 0.00039
11. 2.315

Skill Practice

Round the quotient to the indicated place value.

12. 42.68 ÷ 5.1; hundredths

Example 10   **Rounding a Quotient**

Round the quotient to the tenths place.

$$\frac{47.3}{5.4}$$

Solution:

$$5.4\overline{)47.3}$$

Move the decimal point in the divisor and dividend one place to the right. Line up the decimal point in the quotient.

tenths place

$$8.75 \leftarrow \text{hundredths place}$$
$$54\overline{)473.00}$$
$$\underline{-432}$$
$$410$$
$$\underline{-378}$$
$$320$$
$$\underline{-270}$$
$$50$$

To round the quotient to the tenths place, we must determine the hundredths-place digit and use it to base our decision on rounding. The hundredths-place digit is 5. Therefore, we round the quotient to the tenths place by increasing the tenths-place digit by 1 and discarding all digits to its right.

The quotient is approximately 8.8.

3. Applications of Decimal Division

Examples 11 and 12 show how decimal division can be used in applications. Remember that division is used when we need to distribute a quantity into equal parts.

Skill Practice

13. A 46.5-ft cable is to be cut into 6 pieces of equal length. How long is each piece?

Example 11   **Applying Division of Decimals**

A dinner costs $45.80, and the bill is to be split equally among 5 people. How much must each person pay?

Solution:

We want to distribute $45.80 equally among 5 people, so we must divide $45.80 ÷ 5.

$$9.16$$
$$5\overline{)45.80}$$
$$\underline{-45}$$
$$08$$
$$\underline{-5}$$
$$30$$
$$\underline{-30}$$
$$0$$

Each person must pay $9.16.

TIP: To check if your answer is reasonable, divide $45 among 5 people.

$$5\overline{)45}^{9}$$

The estimated value of $9 suggests that the answer to Example 11 is correct.

Division is also used in practical applications to express rates. In Example 12, we find the rate of speed in meters per second (m/sec) for the world record time in the men's 400-m run.

Example 12 **Using Division to Find a Rate of Speed**

In a recent year, the world-record time in the men's 400-m run was 43.2 sec. What is the speed in meters per second? Round to one decimal place. (*Source:* International Association of Athletics Federations)

Solution:

To find the rate of speed in meters per second, we must divide the distance in meters by the time in seconds.

$$43.2\overline{)400.0}$$

tenths place

9.25 ←——hundredths place

$$432\overline{)4000.00}$$
$$\underline{-3888}$$
$$1120$$
$$\underline{-864}$$
$$2560$$
$$\underline{-2160}$$
$$400$$

TIP: In Example 12, we had to find speed in meters per second. The units of measurement required in the answer give a hint as to the order of the division. The word *per* implies division. So to obtain meters *per* second implies 400 m ÷ 43.2 sec.

To round the quotient to the tenths place, determine the hundredths-place digit and use it to make the decision on rounding. The hundredths-place digit is 5, which is 5 or greater. Therefore, add 1 to the tenths-place digit and discard all digits to its right.

The speed is approximately 9.3 m/sec.

Skill Practice

14. For many years, the world-record time in the women's 200-m run was held by the late Florence Griffith-Joyner. She ran the race in 21.3 sec. Find the speed in meters per second. Round to the nearest tenth.

Answer

14. The speed was 9.4 m/sec.

Section 5.4 Practice Exercises

Boost *your* GRADE at ALEKS.com!

ALEKS version 3.0

- Practice Problems
- Self-Tests
- NetTutor
- e-Professors
- Videos

Study Skills Exercise

1. Define the key terms.

   a. Repeating decimal   **b. Terminating decimal**

Review Exercises

For Exercises 2–7, perform the indicated operation.

2. 5.28×1000 **3.** $-8.003 - 2.2$ **4.** $11.8(0.32)$

5. $-102.4 + 1.239$ **6.** $16.82 - 14.8$ **7.** -5.28×0.001

For Exercises 8–10, use 3.14 for π.

8. Determine the diameter of a circle whose radius is 2.75 yd.

9. Approximate the area of a circle whose diameter is 20 ft.

10. Approximate the circumference of a circle whose radius is 10 cm.

Objective 1: Division of Decimals

For Exercises 11–18, divide. Check the answer by using multiplication. (See Example 1.)

11. $\dfrac{8.1}{9}$ Check: _____ × 9 = 8.1   **12.** $\dfrac{4.8}{6}$ Check: _____ × 6 = 4.8

13. $6\overline{)1.08}$ Check: _____ × 6 = 1.08   **14.** $4\overline{)2.08}$ Check: _____ × 4 = 2.08

15. $-4.24 \div (-8)$ **16.** $-5.75 \div (-25)$ **17.** $5\overline{)105.5}$ **18.** $7\overline{)221.2}$

For Exercises 19–50, divide. (See Examples 2–7.)

19. $5\overline{)9.8}$ **20.** $3\overline{)2.07}$ **21.** $0.28 \div 8$ **22.** $0.54 \div 8$

23. $5\overline{)84.2}$ **24.** $2\overline{)89.1}$ **25.** $50\overline{)6}$ **26.** $80\overline{)6}$

27. $-4 \div 25$ **28.** $-12 \div 60$ **29.** $16 \div 3$ **30.** $52 \div 9$

31. $-19 \div (-6)$ **32.** $-9.1 \div (-3)$ **33.** $33\overline{)71}$ **34.** $11\overline{)42}$

35. $5.03 \div 0.01$ **36.** $3.2 \div 0.001$ **37.** $0.992 \div 0.1$ **38.** $123.4 \div 0.01$

39. $\dfrac{57.12}{-1.02}$ **40.** $\dfrac{95.89}{-2.23}$ **41.** $\dfrac{-2.38}{-0.8}$ **42.** $\dfrac{-5.51}{-0.2}$

43. $0.3\overline{)62.5}$ **44.** $1.05\overline{)22.4}$ **45.** $-6.305 \div (-0.13)$ **46.** $-42.9 \div (-0.25)$

47. $1.1 \div 0.001$ **48.** $4.44 \div 0.01$ **49.** $420.6 \div 0.01$ **50.** $0.31 \div 0.1$

51. If 45.62 is divided by 100, will the decimal point move to the right or to the left? By how many places?

52. If 5689.233 is divided by 100,000, will the decimal point move to the right or to the left? By how many places?

For Exercises 53–60, divide by the powers of 10. (See Example 8.)

53. $3.923 \div 100$ **54.** $5.32 \div 100$ **55.** $-98.02 \div 10$ **56.** $-11.033 \div 10$

57. $-0.027 \div (-100)$ **58.** $-0.665 \div (-100)$ **59.** $1.02 \div 1000$ **60.** $8.1 \div 1000$

Objective 2: Rounding a Quotient

For Exercises 61–66, round to the indicated place value. (See Example 9.)

61. Round $2.\overline{4}$ to the
  a. Tenths place
  b. Hundredths place
  c. Thousandths place

62. Round $5.\overline{2}$ to the
  a. Tenths place
  b. Hundredths place
  c. Thousandths place

63. Round $1.7\overline{8}$ to the
  a. Tenths place
  b. Hundredths place
  c. Thousandths place

64. Round $4.2\overline{7}$ to the

   a. Tenths place

   b. Hundredths place

   c. Thousandths place

65. Round $3.\overline{62}$ to the

   a. Tenths place

   b. Hundredths place

   c. Thousandths place

66. Round $9.\overline{38}$ to the

   a. Tenths place

   b. Hundredths place

   c. Thousandths place

For Exercises 67–75, divide. Round the answer to the indicated place value. Use the rounded quotient to check.
(See Example 10.)

67. $7\overline{)1.8}$ hundredths

68. $2.1\overline{)75.3}$ hundredths

69. $-54.9 \div 3.7$ tenths

70. $-94.3 \div 21$ tenths

71. $0.24\overline{)4.96}$ thousandths

72. $2.46\overline{)27.88}$ thousandths

73. $0.9\overline{)32.1}$ hundredths

74. $0.6\overline{)81.4}$ hundredths

75. $2.13\overline{)237.1}$ tenths

Objective 3: Applications of Decimal Division

When multiplying or dividing decimals, it is important to place the decimal point correctly. For Exercises 76–79, determine whether you think the number is reasonable or unreasonable. If the number is unreasonable, move the decimal point to a position that makes more sense.

76. Steve computed the gas mileage for his Honda Civic to be 3.2 miles per gallon.

77. The sale price of a new kitchen refrigerator is $96.0.

78. Mickey makes $8.50 per hour. He estimates his weekly paycheck to be $3400.

79. Jason works in a legal office. He computes the average annual income for the attorneys in his office to be $1400 per year.

For Exercises 80–88, solve the application. Check to see if your answers are reasonable.

80. Brooke owes $39,628.68 on the mortgage for her house. If her monthly payment is $695.24, how many months does she still need to pay? How many years is this?

81. A membership at a health club costs $560 per year. The club has a payment plan in which a member can pay $50 down and the rest in 12 equal payments. How much is each payment? **(See Example 11.)**

82. It is reported that on average 42,000 tennis balls are used and 650 matches are played at the Wimbledon tennis tournament each year. On average, how many tennis balls are used per match? Round to the nearest whole unit.

83. A standard 75-watt lightbulb costs $0.75 and lasts about 800 hr. An energy efficient fluorescent bulb that gives off the same amount of light costs $5.00 and lasts about 10,000 hr.

   a. How many standard lightbulbs would be needed to provide 10,000 hr of light?

   b. How much would it cost using standard lightbulbs to provide 10,000 hr of light?

   c. Which is more cost effective long term?

84. According to government tests, the 2009 Toyota Prius, a hybrid car, gets 45 miles per gallon of gas. If gasoline sells at \$3.20 per gallon, how many miles will a Prius travel on \$20.00 of gas?

85. In baseball, the batting average is found by dividing the number of hits by the number of times a batter was at bat. Babe Ruth had 2873 hits in 8399 times at bat. What was his batting average? Round to the thousandths place.

86. Ty Cobb was at bat 11,434 times and had 4189 hits, giving him the all-time best batting average. Find his average. Round to the thousandths place. (Refer to Exercise 85.)

87. Manny hikes 12 mi in 5.5 hr. What is his speed in miles per hour? Round to one decimal place. **(See Example 12.)**

88. Alicia rides her bike 33.2 mi in 2.5 hr. What is her speed in miles per hour? Round to one decimal place.

Expanding Your Skills

89. What number is halfway between -47.26 and -47.27?

90. What number is halfway between -22.4 and -22.5?

91. Which numbers when divided by 8.6 will produce a quotient less than 12.4? Circle all that apply.

     a. 111.8   **b.** 103.2   **c.** 107.5   **d.** 105.78

92. Which numbers when divided by 5.3 will produce a quotient greater than 15.8? Circle all that apply.

     a. 84.8   **b.** 84.27   **c.** 83.21   **d.** 79.5

Calculator Connections

Topic: Multiplying and Dividing Decimals on a Calculator

In some applications, the arithmetic on decimal numbers can be very tedious, and it is practical to use a calculator. To multiply or divide on a calculator, use the $\boxed{\times}$ and $\boxed{\div}$ keys, respectively. However, be aware that for repeating decimals, the calculator cannot give an exact value. For example, the quotient of $17 \div 3$ is the repeating decimal $5.\overline{6}$. The calculator returns the rounded value 5.666666667. This is *not* the exact value. Also, when performing division, be careful to enter the dividend and divisor into the calculator in the correct order. For example:

Expression	Keystrokes	Result
$17 \div 3$	17 $\div$ 3 $=$	5.666666667
$0.024\overline{)56.87}$	56.87 $\div$ 0.024 $=$	2369.583333
$\dfrac{82.9}{3.1}$	82.9 $\div$ 3.1 $=$	26.74193548

Calculator Exercises

For Exercises 93–98, multiply or divide as indicated.

93. $(2749.13)(418.2)$ **94.** $(139.241)(24.5)$

95. $(43.75)^2$ **96.** $(9.3)^5$

97. $21.5\overline{)2056.75}$ **98.** $14.2\overline{)4167.8}$

99. A Hummer H2 SUV uses 1260 gal of gas to travel 12,000 mi per year. A Honda Accord uses 375 gal of gas to go the same distance. Use the current cost of gasoline in your area, to determine the amount saved per year by driving a Honda Accord rather than a Hummer.

100. A Chevy Blazer gets 16.5 mpg and a Toyota Corolla averages 32 mpg. Suppose a driver drives 15,000 mi per year. Use the current cost of gasoline in your area to determine the amount saved per year by driving the Toyota rather than the Chevy.

101. As of June 2007, the U.S. capacity to generate wind power was 12,634 megawatts (MW). Texas generates approximately 3,352 MW of this power. (*Source:* American Wind Energy Association)

    a. What fraction of the U.S. wind power is generated in Texas? Express this fraction as a decimal number rounded to the nearest hundredth of a megawatt.

    b. Suppose there is a claim in a news article that Texas generates about one-fourth of all wind power in the United States. Is this claim accurate? Explain using your answer from part (a).

102. Population density is defined to be the number of people per square mile of land area. If California has 42,475,000 people with a land area of 155,959 square miles, what is the population density? Round to the nearest whole unit. (*Source:* U.S. Census Bureau)

103. The Earth travels approximately 584,000,000 mi around the Sun each year.

    a. How many miles does the Earth travel in one day?

    b. Find the speed of the Earth in miles per hour.

104. Although we say the time for the Earth to revolve about the Sun is 365 days, the actual time is 365.256 days. Multiply the fractional amount (0.256) by 4 to explain why we have a leap year every 4 years. (A leap year is a year in which February has an extra day, February 29.)

Problem Recognition Exercises

Operations on Decimals

For Exercises 1–24, perform the indicated operations.

1. a. $123.04 + 100$

    b. 123.04×100

    c. $123.04 - 100$

    d. $123.04 \div 100$

    e. $123.04 + 0.01$

    f. 123.04×0.01

    g. $123.04 \div 0.01$

    h. $123.04 - 0.01$

2. a. $5078.3 + 1000$

    b. 5078.3×1000

    c. $5078.3 - 1000$

    d. $5078.3 \div 1000$

    e. $5078.3 + 0.001$

    f. 5078.3×0.001

    g. $5078.3 \div 0.001$

    h. $5078.3 - 0.001$

3. a. $-4.8 + (-2.391)$

    b. $2.391 - (-4.8)$

4. a. $-632.46 + (-98.0034)$

    b. $98.0034 - (-632.46)$

5. a. $(32.9)(1.6)$

    b. $(-1.6)(-32.9)$

6. a. $(74.23)(0.8)$

    b. $(-0.8)(-74.23)$

7. a. 4(21.6)

   b. −0.25(21.6)

9. a. −448 ÷ 5.6

   b. (5.6)(−80)

11. 8(0.125)

13. 280 ÷ 0.07

15. $490\overline{)98{,}000{,}000}$

17. (−4500)(−300,000)

19.   83.4
   −78.9999
   $\overline{}$

21. −3.47 − (−9.2)

23. −3.47 − 9.2

8. a. 2(92.5)

   b. −0.5(92.5)

10. a. −496.8 ÷ 9.2

   b. (−54)(9.2)

12. 20(0.05)

14. 6400 ÷ 0.001

16. $2000\overline{)5{,}400{,}000}$

18. (−340)(−5000)

20.   124.7
   −47.9999
   $\overline{}$

22. −0.042 − (−0.097)

24. −0.042 − 0.097

Section 5.5   Fractions, Decimals, and the Order of Operations

Objectives

1. Writing Fractions as Decimals
2. Writing Decimals as Fractions
3. Decimals and the Number Line
4. Order of Operations Involving Decimals and Fractions
5. Applications of Decimals and Fractions

1. Writing Fractions as Decimals

Sometimes it is possible to convert a fraction to its equivalent decimal form by rewriting the fraction as a decimal fraction. That is, try to multiply the numerator and denominator by a number that will make the denominator a power of 10.

For example, the fraction $\frac{3}{5}$ can easily be written as an equivalent fraction with a denominator of 10.

$$\frac{3}{5} = \frac{3 \cdot 2}{5 \cdot 2} = \frac{6}{10} = 0.6$$

The fraction $\frac{3}{25}$ can easily be converted to a fraction with a denominator of 100.

$$\frac{3}{25} = \frac{3 \cdot 4}{25 \cdot 4} = \frac{12}{100} = 0.12$$

This technique is useful in some cases. However, some fractions such as $\frac{1}{3}$ cannot be converted to a fraction with a denominator that is a power of 10. This is because 3 is not a factor of any power of 10. For this reason, we recommend dividing the numerator by the denominator, as shown in Example 1.

Example 1 **Writing Fractions as Decimals**

Write each fraction or mixed number as a decimal.

a. $\dfrac{3}{5}$ **b.** $-\dfrac{68}{25}$ **c.** $3\dfrac{5}{8}$

Solution:

a. $\dfrac{3}{5}$ means $3 \div 5$.

$$\dfrac{3}{5} = 0.6$$

$$\begin{array}{r} .6 \\ 5\overline{)3.0} \\ -30 \\ \hline 0 \end{array}$$

Divide the numerator by the denominator.

b. $-\dfrac{68}{25}$ means $-(68 \div 25)$.

$$-\dfrac{68}{25} = -2.72$$

$$\begin{array}{r} 2.72 \\ 25\overline{)68.00} \\ -50 \\ \hline 180 \\ -175 \\ \hline 50 \\ -50 \\ \hline 0 \end{array}$$

Divide the numerator by the denominator.

c. $3\dfrac{5}{8} = 3 + \dfrac{5}{8} = 3 + (5 \div 8)$

$$= 3 + 0.625$$
$$= 3.625$$

$$\begin{array}{r} .625 \\ 8\overline{)5.000} \\ -48 \\ \hline 20 \\ -16 \\ \hline 40 \\ -40 \\ \hline 0 \end{array}$$

Divide the numerator by the denominator.

Skill Practice

Write each fraction or mixed number as a decimal.

1. $\dfrac{3}{8}$

2. $-\dfrac{43}{20}$

3. $12\dfrac{5}{16}$

The fractions in Example 1 are represented by terminating decimals. However, many fractions convert to repeating decimals.

Example 2 **Converting Fractions to Repeating Decimals**

Write each fraction as a decimal.

a. $\dfrac{4}{9}$ **b.** $-\dfrac{3}{22}$

Solution:

a. $\dfrac{4}{9}$ means $4 \div 9$.

$$\dfrac{4}{9} = 0.\overline{4}$$

$$\begin{array}{r} .44\ldots \\ 9\overline{)4.00} \\ -36 \\ \hline 40 \\ -36 \\ \hline 40 \end{array}$$

The quotient is a repeating decimal.

Skill Practice

Write each fraction as a decimal.

4. $\dfrac{8}{9}$ **5.** $-\dfrac{17}{11}$

Answers

1. 0.375 **2.** −2.15 **3.** 12.3125
4. $0.\overline{8}$ **5.** $-1.\overline{54}$

Calculator Connections

Repeating decimals displayed on a calculator must be rounded. For example, the repeating decimals from Example 2 might appear as follows.

| $0.\overline{4}$ | 0.444444444 |
| $-0.1\overline{36}$ | -0.136363636 |

b. $-\dfrac{3}{22}$ means $-(3 \div 22)$

$$
\begin{array}{r}
.1363\ldots \\
22\overline{)3.0000} \\
-22 \\
\hline
80 \\
-66 \\
\hline
140 \\
-132 \\
\hline
80
\end{array}
$$

The quotient is a repeating decimal.

$-\dfrac{3}{22} = -0.1\overline{36}$

Avoiding Mistakes

Be sure to carry out the division far enough to see the repeating digits. In Example 2(b), the next digit in the quotient is 3. The 1 does not repeat.

$$-\frac{3}{22} = -0.1363636\ldots$$

Several fractions are used quite often. Their decimal forms are worth memorizing and are presented in Table 5-1.

Concept Connections

6. Describe the pattern between the fractions $\frac{1}{9}$ and $\frac{2}{9}$ and their decimal forms.

Table 5-1

$\dfrac{1}{4} = 0.25$	$\dfrac{2}{4} = \dfrac{1}{2} = 0.5$	$\dfrac{3}{4} = 0.75$	
$\dfrac{1}{9} = 0.\overline{1}$	$\dfrac{2}{9} = 0.\overline{2}$	$\dfrac{3}{9} = \dfrac{1}{3} = 0.\overline{3}$	$\dfrac{4}{9} = 0.\overline{4}$
$\dfrac{5}{9} = 0.\overline{5}$	$\dfrac{6}{9} = \dfrac{2}{3} = 0.\overline{6}$	$\dfrac{7}{9} = 0.\overline{7}$	$\dfrac{8}{9} = 0.\overline{8}$

Skill Practice

Convert the fraction to a decimal rounded to the indicated place value.

7. $\dfrac{9}{7}$; tenths

8. $-\dfrac{17}{37}$; hundredths

Example 3 Converting Fractions to Decimals with Rounding

Convert the fraction to a decimal rounded to the indicated place value.

a. $\dfrac{162}{7}$; tenths place

b. $-\dfrac{21}{31}$; hundredths place

Solution:

a. $\dfrac{162}{7}$

$$
\begin{array}{r}
23.14 \\
7\overline{)162.00} \\
-14 \\
\hline
22 \\
-21 \\
\hline
10 \\
-7 \\
\hline
30 \\
-28 \\
\hline
2
\end{array}
$$

tenths place
hundredths place

To round to the tenths place, we must determine the hundredths-place digit and use it to base our decision on rounding.

$23.14 \approx 23.1$

The fraction $\dfrac{162}{7}$ is approximately 23.1.

Answers

6. The numerator of the fraction is the repeated digit in the decimal form.
7. 1.3   8. -0.46

$$\text{hundredths place}$$
$$\text{thousandths place}$$

b. $-\dfrac{21}{31}$

$$\begin{array}{r} .677 \\ 31\overline{)21.000} \\ -186 \\ \hline 240 \\ -217 \\ \hline 230 \\ -217 \\ \hline 13 \end{array}$$

To round to the hundredths-place, we must determine the thousandths-place digit and use it to base our decision on rounding.

$$0.67\overset{1}{7} \approx 0.68$$

The fraction $-\dfrac{21}{31}$ is approximately -0.68.

2. Writing Decimals as Fractions

In Section 5.1 we converted terminating decimals to fractions. We did this by writing the decimal as a decimal fraction and then reducing the fraction to lowest terms. For example:

$$0.46 = \frac{46}{100} = \frac{\overset{23}{\cancel{46}}}{\underset{50}{\cancel{100}}} = \frac{23}{50}$$

We do not yet have the tools to convert a repeating decimal to its equivalent fraction form. However, we can make use of our knowledge of the common fractions and their repeating decimal forms from Table 5-1.

Example 4 **Writing Decimals as Fractions**

Write the decimals as fractions.

a. 0.475   **b.** $0.\overline{6}$ **c.** -1.25

Solution:

a. $0.475 = \dfrac{475}{1000} = \dfrac{19 \cdot \overset{1}{\cancel{25}}}{40 \cdot \underset{1}{\cancel{25}}} = \dfrac{19}{40}$

b. From Table 5-1, the decimal $0.\overline{6} = \dfrac{2}{3}$.

c. $-1.25 = -\dfrac{125}{100} = -\dfrac{5 \cdot \overset{1}{\cancel{25}}}{4 \cdot \underset{1}{\cancel{25}}} = -\dfrac{5}{4}$

3. Decimals and the Number Line

Recall that a **rational number** is a fraction whose numerator is an integer and whose denominator is a nonzero integer. The following are all rational numbers.

$$\frac{2}{3}$$

$-\frac{5}{7}$ can be written as $\frac{-5}{7}$ or as $\frac{5}{-7}$.

6 can be written as $\frac{6}{1}$.

0.37 can be written as $\frac{37}{100}$.

$0.\overline{3}$ can be written as $\frac{1}{3}$.

Rational numbers consist of all numbers that can be expressed as terminating decimals or as repeating decimals.

- All numbers that can be expressed as *repeating decimals* are rational numbers.

  For example, $0.\overline{3} = 0.3333\ldots$ is a rational number.

- All numbers that can be expressed as *terminating decimals* are rational numbers.

  For example, 0.25 is a rational number.

- A number that *cannot* be expressed as a repeating or terminating decimal is not a rational number. These are called **irrational numbers**. An example of an irrational number is $\sqrt{2}$.

  For example, $\sqrt{2} \approx \underbrace{1.41421356237}\ldots$
  The digits never repeat and never terminate

TIP: In Section 5.3 we used another irrational number, π. Recall that we approximated π with 3.14 or $\frac{22}{7}$ when calculating area and circumference of a circle.

The rational numbers and the irrational numbers together make up the set of **real numbers**. Furthermore, every real number corresponds to a point on the number line.

In Example 5, we rank the numbers from least to greatest and visualize the position of the numbers on the number line.

Skill Practice

12. Rank the numbers from least to greatest. Then approximate the position of the points on the number line. $0.161, \frac{1}{6}, 0.16$

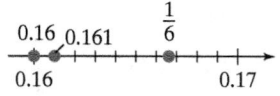
0.16   0.17

Answer
12. $0.16, 0.161, \frac{1}{6}$

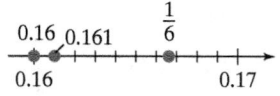
$\overset{0.16}{}\ \overset{0.161}{}\qquad \overset{\frac{1}{6}}{}$
0.16   0.17

Example 5   **Ordering Decimals and Fractions**

Rank the numbers from least to greatest. Then approximate the position of the points on the number line.

$$0.\overline{45}, \quad 0.45, \quad \frac{1}{2}$$

Solution:

First note that $\frac{1}{2} = 0.5$ and that $0.\overline{45} = 0.454545\ldots$. By writing each number in decimal form, we can compare the decimals as we did in Section 5.1.

	same		different	
0.454545 $\cdots$		0.450000	0.500000	This tells us that 0.5 is the greatest of the three values.
0.454545 $\cdots$		0.450000		This tells us that 0.454545 $\ldots$ > 0.450000.
	different			

Ranking the numbers from least to greatest we have: 0.45, $0.\overline{45}$,   0.5

The position of these numbers can be seen on the number line. Note that we have expanded the segment of the number line between 0.4 and 0.5 to see more place values to the right of the decimal point.

Recall that numbers that lie to the left on the number line have lesser value than numbers that lie to the right.

TIP: Be careful when ordering negative numbers. If the numbers in Example 5 had been negative, the order would be reversed. $-0.5 < -0.\overline{45} < -0.45$

4. Order of Operations Involving Decimals and Fractions

In Example 6, we perform the order of operations with an expression involving decimal numbers.

PROCEDURE Applying the Order of Operations

Step 1 First perform all operations inside parentheses or other grouping symbols.

Step 2 Simplify expressions containing exponents, square roots, or absolute values.

Step 3 Perform multiplication or division in the order that they appear from left to right.

Step 4 Perform addition or subtraction in the order that they appear from left to right.

Example 6 Applying the Order of Operations

Simplify. $16.4 - (6.7 - 3.5)^2$

Solution:

$16.4 - (6.7 - 3.5)^2$

$= 16.4 - (3.2)^2$ Perform the subtraction within parentheses first.

$$\begin{array}{r} 6.7 \\ -\ 3.5 \\ \hline 3.2 \end{array}$$

$= 16.4 - 10.24$ Perform the operation involving the exponent.

$$\begin{array}{r} 3.2 \\ \times\ 3.2 \\ \hline 64 \\ 960 \\ \hline 10.24 \end{array}$$

$= 6.16$ Subtract.

$$\begin{array}{r} {}^{3\ 10} \\ 16.\cancel{4}\,\cancel{0} \\ -\ 10.2\,4 \\ \hline 6.1\,6 \end{array}$$

Skill Practice

Simplify.

13. $(5.8 - 4.3)^2 - 2$

Answer

13. 0.25

In Example 7, we apply the order of operations on fractions and decimals combined.

─── **Skill Practice** ───

Simplify.

14. $(-2.6) \cdot \dfrac{3}{13} \div \left(1\dfrac{1}{2}\right)^2$

Example 7   **Applying the Order of Operations**

Simplify. $(-6.4) \cdot 2\dfrac{5}{8} \div \left(\dfrac{3}{5}\right)^2$

Solution:

Approach 1

Convert all numbers to fractional form.

$$(-6.4) \cdot 2\frac{5}{8} \div \left(\frac{3}{5}\right)^2 = -\frac{64}{10} \cdot \frac{21}{8} \div \left(\frac{3}{5}\right)^2$$

Convert the decimal and mixed number to fractions.

$$= -\frac{64}{10} \cdot \frac{21}{8} \div \frac{9}{25}$$

Square the quantity $\frac{3}{5}$.

$$= -\frac{64}{10} \cdot \frac{21}{8} \cdot \frac{25}{9}$$

Multiply by the reciprocal of $\frac{9}{25}$.

$$= -\frac{\overset{4}{\cancel{64}}}{\underset{1}{\underset{\cancel{2}}{\cancel{10}}}} \cdot \frac{\overset{7}{\cancel{21}}}{\underset{1}{\cancel{8}}} \cdot \frac{\overset{5}{\cancel{25}}}{\underset{3}{\cancel{9}}}$$

Simplify common factors.

$$= -\frac{140}{3} \text{ or } -46\frac{2}{3} \text{ or } -46.\overline{6}$$

Multiply.

Approach 2

Convert all numbers to decimal form.

$$(-6.4) \cdot 2\frac{5}{8} \div \left(\frac{3}{5}\right)^2 = (-6.4)(2.625) \div (0.6)^2$$

The fraction $\frac{5}{8} = 0.625$ and $\frac{3}{5} = 0.6$.

$$= (-6.4)(2.625) \div 0.36$$

Square the quantity 0.6. That is, $(0.6)(0.6) = 0.36$.

Multiply $(-6.4)(2.625)$.

$$\begin{array}{r} 2.625 \\ \times\ 6.4 \\ \hline 10500 \\ 157500 \\ \hline 16.8000 \end{array}$$

$$= -16.8 \div 0.36$$

Divide $-16.8 \div 0.36$.

$$= -46.\overline{6}$$

$$\begin{array}{r} 46.6\ldots \\ .36\overline{)16.80} \qquad 36\overline{)1680} \\ \underset{\uparrow}{} \underset{\uparrow}{} \quad -144 \\ \hline 240 \\ -216 \\ \hline 240 \end{array}$$

Answer

14. $-\dfrac{4}{15}$ or $-0.2\overline{6}$

When performing operations on fractions, sometimes it is desirable to write the answer as a decimal. For example, suppose that Sabina receives $\frac{1}{4}$ of a $6245 inheritance. She would want to express this answer as a decimal. Sabina should receive:

$$\frac{1}{4}(\$6245) = (0.25)(\$6245) = \$1561.25$$

If Sabina had received $\frac{1}{3}$ of the inheritance, then the decimal form of $\frac{1}{3}$ would have to be rounded to some desired place value. This would cause *round-off error*. Any calculation performed on a rounded number will compound the error. For this reason, we recommend that fractions be kept in fractional form as long as possible as you simplify an expression. Then perform division and rounding in the last step. This is demonstrated in Example 8.

Example 8 **Dividing a Fraction and Decimal**

Divide $\frac{4}{7} \div 3.6$. Round the answer to the nearest hundredth.

Solution:

If we attempt to write $\frac{4}{7}$ as a decimal, we find that it is the repeating decimal $0.\overline{571428}$. Rather than rounding this number, we choose to change 3.6 to fractional form: $3.6 = \frac{36}{10}$.

$$\frac{4}{7} \div 3.6 = \frac{4}{7} \div \frac{36}{10} \qquad \text{Write 3.6 as a fraction.}$$

$$= \frac{\overset{1}{4}}{7} \cdot \frac{10}{\underset{9}{36}} \qquad \text{Multiply by the reciprocal of the divisor.}$$

$$= \frac{10}{63} \qquad \text{Multiply and reduce to lowest terms.}$$

We must write the answer in decimal form, rounded to the nearest hundredth.

```
      .158
63)10.00
    -63
     370
    -315
     550
    -504
      46
```

Divide. To round to the hundredths place, divide until we find the thousandths-place digit in the quotient. Use that digit to make a decision for rounding.

≈ 0.16 Round to the nearest hundredth.

Skill Practice

Determine the area of the triangle.

16.

6.6 cm

8.4 cm

Example 9 Evaluating an Algebraic Expression

Determine the area of the triangle.

Solution:

In this triangle, the base is 6.8 ft. The height is 4.2 ft and is drawn outside the triangle.

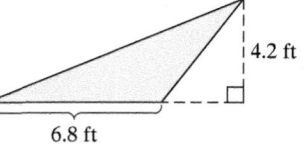

4.2 ft

6.8 ft

$$A = \frac{1}{2}bh \qquad\qquad \text{Formula for the area of a triangle}$$

$$A = \frac{1}{2}(6.8 \text{ ft})(4.2 \text{ ft}) \qquad \text{Substitute } b = 6.8 \text{ ft and } h = 4.2 \text{ ft.}$$

$$= 0.5\,(6.8 \text{ ft})(4.2 \text{ ft}) \qquad \text{Write } \tfrac{1}{2} \text{ as the terminating decimal, } 0.5.$$

$$= 14.28 \text{ ft}^2 \qquad\qquad \text{Multiply from left to right.}$$

The area is 14.28 ft².

5. Applications of Decimals and Fractions

Skill Practice

17. The odometer on a car read 46,125.9 mi. After a $13\frac{1}{4}$-hr trip, the odometer read 46,947.4 mi.

a. Find the total distance traveled on the trip.

b. Find the average speed in miles per hour (mph).

Example 10 Using Decimals and Fractions in a Consumer Application

Joanne filled the gas tank in her car and noted that the odometer read 22,341.9 mi. Ten days later she filled the tank again with $11\frac{1}{2}$ gal of gas. Her odometer reading at that time was 22,622.5 mi.

a. How many miles had she driven between fill-ups?

b. How many miles per gallon did she get?

Solution:

a. To find the number of miles driven, we need to subtract the initial odometer reading from the final reading.

$$
\begin{array}{r}
\overset{5\ \ 12\ \ 1\ \ 15}{2\,2\,,\,6\,2\,2\,.\,5} \\
-\ 2\,2\,,\,3\,4\,1\,.\,9 \\
\hline
2\,8\,0\,.\,6
\end{array}
$$

Recall that to add or subtract decimals, line up the decimal points.

Joanne had driven 280.6 mi between fill-ups.

b. To find the number of miles per gallon (mi/gal), we divide the number of miles driven by the number of gallons.

$$280.6 \div 11\frac{1}{2} = 280.6 \div 11.5$$

We convert to decimal form because the fraction $11\frac{1}{2}$ is recognized as 11.5.

$$= 24.4$$

Joanne got 24.4 mi/gal.

$$
\begin{array}{r}
24.4 \\
11.5\overline{)280.6}
\end{array}
$$

$$
\begin{array}{r}
24.4 \\
115\overline{)2806.0} \\
-230 \\
\hline
506 \\
-460 \\
\hline
460 \\
-460 \\
\hline
0
\end{array}
$$

Answers

16. 27.72 cm²

17. a. 821.5 mi   **b.** 62 mph

Section 5.5 Practice Exercises

Study Skills Exercise

1. Define the key terms.

   a. Rational number   **b. Irrational number**   **c. Real number**

Review Exercises

2. Round $0.7\overline{84}$ to the thousandths place.

For Exercises 3–8, perform the indicated operations.

3. $(-0.15)^2$ 4. $(-0.9)^2$ 5. $-4.48 \div (-0.7)$

6. $-2.43 \div (0.3)$ 7. $-4.67 - (-3.914)$ 8. $-8.365 - 0.9$

Objective 1: Writing Fractions as Decimals

For Exercises 9–12, write each fraction as a decimal fraction, that is, a fraction whose denominator is a power of 10. Then write the number in decimal form.

9. $\dfrac{2}{5}$ 10. $\dfrac{4}{5}$ 11. $\dfrac{49}{50}$ 12. $\dfrac{3}{50}$

For Exercises 13–24, write each fraction or mixed number as a decimal. **(See Example 1.)**

13. $\dfrac{7}{25}$ 14. $\dfrac{4}{25}$ 15. $-\dfrac{316}{500}$ 16. $-\dfrac{19}{500}$

17. $-\dfrac{16}{5}$ 18. $-\dfrac{68}{25}$ 19. $-5\dfrac{3}{12}$ 20. $-6\dfrac{5}{8}$

21. $\dfrac{18}{24}$ 22. $\dfrac{24}{40}$ ⊙ 23. $7\dfrac{9}{20}$ 24. $3\dfrac{11}{25}$

For Exercises 25–32, write each fraction or mixed number as a repeating decimal. **(See Example 2.)**

25. $3\dfrac{8}{9}$ 26. $4\dfrac{7}{9}$ ⊙ 27. $\dfrac{19}{36}$ 28. $\dfrac{7}{12}$

29. $-\dfrac{14}{111}$ 30. $-\dfrac{58}{111}$ 31. $\dfrac{25}{22}$ 32. $\dfrac{45}{22}$

For Exercises 33–40, convert the fraction to a decimal and round to the indicated place value. **(See Example 3.)**

33. $\dfrac{15}{16}$; tenths   34. $\dfrac{3}{11}$; tenths   35. $\dfrac{1}{7}$; thousandths   36. $\dfrac{2}{7}$; thousandths

37. $\dfrac{1}{13}$; hundredths   38. $\dfrac{9}{13}$; hundredths   39. $-\dfrac{5}{7}$; hundredths   40. $-\dfrac{1}{8}$; hundredths

41. Write the fractions as decimals. Explain how to memorize the decimal form for these fractions with a denominator of 9.

a. $\dfrac{1}{9}$ **b.** $\dfrac{2}{9}$ **c.** $\dfrac{4}{9}$ **d.** $\dfrac{5}{9}$

42. Write the fractions as decimals. Explain how to memorize the decimal forms for these fractions with a denominator of 3.

a. $\dfrac{1}{3}$ **b.** $\dfrac{2}{3}$

Objective 2: Writing Decimals as Fractions

For Exercises 43–46, complete the table. **(See Example 4.)**

43.

	Decimal Form	Fraction Form
a.	0.45	
b.		$1\dfrac{5}{8}$ or $\dfrac{13}{8}$
c.	$-0.\overline{7}$	
d.		$-\dfrac{5}{11}$

44.

	Decimal Form	Fraction Form
a.		$\dfrac{2}{3}$
b.	1.6	
c.		$-\dfrac{152}{25}$
d.	$-0.\overline{2}$	

45.

	Decimal Form	Fraction Form
a.	$0.\overline{3}$	
b.	-2.125	
c.		$-\dfrac{19}{22}$
d.		$\dfrac{42}{25}$

46.

	Decimal Form	Fraction Form
a.	0.75	
b.		$-\dfrac{7}{11}$
c.	$-1.\overline{8}$	
d.		$\dfrac{74}{25}$

Objective 3: Decimals and the Number Line

For Exercises 47–58, identify the number as rational or irrational.

47. $-\dfrac{2}{5}$ **48.** $-\dfrac{1}{9}$ **49.** 5   **50.** 3

51. 3.5   **52.** 1.1   **53.** $\sqrt{7}$ **54.** $\sqrt{11}$

55. π **56.** 2π **57.** $0.\overline{4}$ **58.** $0.\overline{9}$

For Exercises 59–66, insert the appropriate symbol. Choose from <, >, or =.

59. $0.2 \,\square\, \dfrac{1}{5}$

60. $1.5 \,\square\, \dfrac{3}{2}$

61. $0.2 \,\square\, 0.\overline{2}$

62. $\dfrac{3}{5} \,\square\, 0.\overline{6}$

63. $\dfrac{1}{3} \,\square\, 0.3$

64. $\dfrac{2}{3} \,\square\, 0.66$

65. $-4\dfrac{1}{4} \,\square\, -4.\overline{25}$

66. $-2.12 \,\square\, -2.\overline{12}$

For Exercises 67–70, rank the numbers from least to greatest. Then approximate the position of the points on the number line. **(See Example 5.)**

 67. $1.8,\ 1.75,\ 1.\overline{7}$

68. $5\dfrac{1}{6},\ 5.\overline{6},\ 5.0\overline{6}$

```
 ├──┼──┼──┼──┼──┼──►
1.5  1.6  1.7  1.8  1.9  2.0
```

```
 ├──┼──┼──┼──┼──┼──┼──►
5.0  5.1  5.2  5.3  5.4  5.5  5.6
```

69. $-0.\overline{1},\ -\dfrac{1}{10},\ -\dfrac{1}{5}$

70. $-3\dfrac{1}{4},\ -3\dfrac{1}{3},\ -3.3$

```
 ├────┼────┼────┼────┼────┼──►
-0.5  -0.4  -0.3  -0.2  -0.1   0
```

```
 ├────┼────┼────┼────┼────┼──►
-3.5  -3.4  -3.3  -3.2  -3.1   -3
```

Objective 4: Order of Operations Involving Decimals and Fractions

For Exercises 71–82, simplify by using the order of operations. **(See Example 6.)**

71. $(3.7 - 1.2)^2$

72. $(6.8 - 4.7)^2$

73. $16.25 - (18.2 - 15.7)^2$

74. $11.38 - (10.42 - 7.52)^2$

 75. $12.46 - 3.05 - 0.8^2$

76. $15.06 - 1.92 - 0.4^2$

77. $63.75 - 9.5(4)$

78. $6.84 + (3.6)(9)$

79. $-6.8 \div 2 \div 1.7$

80. $-8.4 \div 2 \div 2.1$

81. $2.2 - [9.34 + (1.2)^2]$

82. $4.2 \div 2.1 - (3.1)^2$

For Exercises 83–88, simplify by using the order of operations. Express the answer in decimal form. **(See Example 7.)**

83. $89.8 \div 1\dfrac{1}{3}$

84. $-30.12 \div \left(-1\dfrac{3}{5}\right)$

85. $-20.04 \div \left(-\dfrac{4}{5}\right)$

86. $(78.2 - 60.2) \div \dfrac{9}{13}$

87. $14.4\left(\dfrac{7}{4} - \dfrac{1}{8}\right)$

88. $6.5 + \dfrac{1}{8}\left(\dfrac{1}{5}\right)^2$

For Exercises 89–94, perform the indicated operations. Round the answer to the nearest hundredth when necessary. **(See Example 8.)**

89. $(2.3)\left(\dfrac{5}{9}\right)$

90. $(4.6)\left(\dfrac{7}{6}\right)$

91. $6.5 \div \left(-\dfrac{3}{5}\right)$

92. $\left(\dfrac{1}{12}\right)(6.24) \div (-2.1)$

93. $(42.81 - 30.01) \div \dfrac{9}{2}$

94. $\left(\dfrac{2}{7}\right)(5.1)\left(\dfrac{1}{10}\right)$

For Exercises 95–96, find the area of the triangle. **(See Example 9.)**

95.
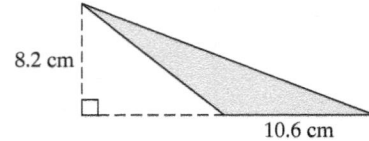
8.2 cm

10.6 cm

96.

7.4 m

9.6 m

For Exercises 97–100, evaluate the expression for the given value(s) of the variables. Use 3.14 for π.

97. $\frac{1}{3}\pi r^2$ for $r = 9$

98. $\frac{4}{3}\pi r^3$ for $r = 3$

99. $-\frac{1}{2}gt^2$ for $g = 9.8$ and $t = 4$

100. $\frac{1}{2}mv^2$ for $m = 2.5$ and $v = 6$

Objective 5: Applications of Decimals and Fractions

101. Oprah and Gayle traveled for $7\frac{1}{2}$ hr between Atlanta, Georgia, and Orlando, Florida. At the beginning of the trip, the car's odometer read 21,345.6 mi. When they arrived in Orlando, the odometer read 21,816.6 mi. **(See Example 10.)**

   a. How many miles had they driven on the trip?

   b. Find the average speed in miles per hour (mph).

102. Jennifer earns $720.00 per week. Alex earns $\frac{3}{4}$ of what Jennifer earns per week.

   a. How much does Alex earn per week?

   b. If they both work 40 hr per week, how much do they each make per hour?

103. A cell phone plan has a $39.95 monthly fee and includes 450 min. For time on the phone over 450 min, the charge is $0.40 per minute. How much is Jorge charged for a month in which he talks for 597 min?

104. A night at a hotel in Dallas costs $129.95 with a nightly room tax of $20.75. The hotel also charges $1.10 per phone call made from the phone in the room. If John stays for 5 nights and makes 3 phone calls, how much is his total bill?

105. Olivia's diet allows her 60 grams (g) of fat per day. If she has $\frac{1}{4}$ of her total fat grams for breakfast and a McDonald's Quarter Pounder (20.7 g of fat) for lunch, how many grams does she have left for dinner?

106. Todd is establishing his beneficiaries for his life insurance policy. The policy is for $150,000.00 and $\frac{1}{2}$ will go to his daughter, $\frac{3}{8}$ will go to his stepson, and the rest will go to his grandson. What dollar amount will go to the grandson?

107. Hannah bought three packages of printer paper for $4.79 each. The sales tax for the merchandise was $0.86. If Hannah paid with a $20 bill, how much change should she receive?

108. Mr. Timpson bought dinner for $28.42. He left a tip of $6.00. He paid the bill with two $20 bills. How much change should he receive?

Expanding Your Skills

For Exercises 109–112, perform the indicated operations.

109. $0.\overline{3} \cdot 0.3 + 3.375$

110. $0.\overline{5} \div 0.\overline{2} - 0.75$

111. $(0.\overline{8} + 0.\overline{4}) \cdot 0.39$

112. $(0.\overline{7} - 0.\overline{6}) \cdot 5.4$

Calculator Connections

Topic: Applications Using the Order of Operations with Decimals

Calculator Exercises

113. Suppose that Deanna owns 50 shares of stock in Company A, valued at $132.05 per share. She decides to sell these shares and use the money to buy stock in Company B, valued at $27.80 per share. Assume there are no fees for either transaction.

a. How many full shares of Company B stock can she buy?

b. How much money will be left after she buys the Company B stock?

114. One megawatt (MW) of wind power produces enough electricity to supply approximately 275 homes. For a recent year, the state of Texas produced 3352 MW of wind power. (*Source:* American Wind Energy Association)

a. About how many homes can be supplied with electricity using wind power produced in Texas?

b. The given table outlines new proposed wind power projects in Texas. If these projects are completed, approximately how many additional homes could be supplied with electricity?

Project	MW
JD Wind IV	79.8
Buffalo Gap, Phase II	232.5
Lone Star I (3Q)	128
Sand Bluff	90
Roscoe	209
Barton Chapel	120
Stanton Wind Energy Center	120
Whirlwind Energy Center	59.8
Sweetwater V	80.5
Champion	126.5

115. Health-care providers use the *body mass index* (BMI) as one way to assess a person's risk of developing diabetes and heart disease. BMI is calculated with the following equation:

$$BMI = \frac{703w}{h^2}$$

where w is the person's weight in pounds and h is the person's height in inches. A person whose BMI is between 18.5 to 24.9 has a lower risk of developing diabetes and heart disease. A BMI of 25.0 to 29.9 indicates moderate risk. A BMI above 30.0 indicates high risk.

a. What is the risk level for a person whose height is 67.5 in. and whose weight is 195 lb?

b. What is the risk level for a person whose height is 62.5 in. and whose weight is 110 lb?

116. Marty bought a home for $145,000. He paid $25,000 as a down payment and then financed the rest with a 30-yr mortgage. His monthly payments are $798.36 and go toward paying off the loan and interest on the loan.

a. How much money does Marty have to finance?

b. How many months are in a 30-yr period?

c. How much money will Marty pay over a 30-yr period to pay off the loan?

d. How much money did Marty pay in interest over the 30-yr period?

117. An inheritance for $80,460.60 is to be divided equally among four heirs. However, before the money can be distributed, approximately one-third of the money must go to the government for taxes. How much does each person get after the taxes have been taken?

Section 5.6 Solving Equations Containing Decimals

Objectives

1. Solving Equations Containing Decimals
2. Solving Equations by Clearing Decimals
3. Applications and Problem Solving

1. Solving Equations Containing Decimals

In this section, we will practice solving linear equations. In Example 1, we will apply the addition and subtraction properties of equality.

Skill Practice

Solve.
1. $t + 2.4 = 9.68$
2. $-97.5 = -31.2 + w$

Example 1 Applying the Addition and Subtraction Properties of Equality

Solve. **a.** $x + 3.7 = 5.42$ **b.** $-35.4 = -6.1 + y$

Solution:

a.
$$x + 3.7 = 5.42$$
$$x + 3.7 - 3.7 = 5.42 - 3.7$$
$$x = 1.72$$

The value 3.7 is added to x. To isolate x, we must reverse this process. Therefore, *subtract* 3.7 from both sides.

The solution is 1.72.

Check: $x + 3.7 = 5.42$
$(1.72) + 3.7 \stackrel{?}{=} 5.42$
$5.42 = 5.42$ ✓

b.
$$-35.4 = -6.1 + y$$
$$-35.4 + 6.1 = -6.1 + 6.1 + y$$
$$-29.3 = y$$

To isolate y, add 6.1 to both sides.

The solution is -29.3.

Check: $-35.4 = -6.1 + y$
$-35.4 \stackrel{?}{=} -6.1 + (-29.3)$
$-35.4 = -35.4$ ✓

In Example 2, we will apply the multiplication and division properties of equality.

Skill Practice

Solve.
3. $\dfrac{z}{11.5} = -6.8$
4. $-8.37 = -2.7p$

Example 2 Applying the Multiplication and Division Properties of Equality

Solve.   **a.** $\dfrac{t}{10.2} = -4.5$ **b.** $-25.2 = -4.2z$

Solution:

a.
$$\frac{t}{10.2} = -4.5$$
$$10.2\left(\frac{t}{10.2}\right) = 10.2(-4.5)$$
$$t = -45.9$$

The variable t is being divided by 10.2. To isolate t, *multiply* both sides by 10.2.

The solution is -45.9.

Check: $\dfrac{t}{10.2} = -4.5 \longrightarrow \dfrac{-45.9}{10.2} \stackrel{?}{=} -4.5$
$-4.5 = -4.5$ ✓

b. $-25.2 = -4.2z$

$$\frac{-25.2}{-4.2} = \frac{-4.2z}{-4.2}$$

The variable z is being multiplied by -4.2. To isolate z, *divide* by -4.2. The quotient will be positive.

Answers

1. 7.28   2. -66.3
3. -78.2 4. 3.1

$$6 = z$$

Check: $-25.2 = -4.2z$

$$-25.2 \stackrel{?}{=} -4.2(6)$$

$$-25.2 = -25.2 \checkmark$$

The solution is 6.

In Examples 3 and 4, multiple steps are required to solve the equation. As you read through Example 3, remember that we first isolate the variable term. Then we apply the multiplication or division property of equality to make the coefficient on the variable term equal to 1.

Example 3 Solving Equations Involving Multiple Steps

Solve. $2.4x - 3.85 = 8.63$

Solution:

$$2.4x - 3.85 = 8.63$$

$2.4x - 3.85 + 3.85 = 8.63 + 3.85$ To isolate the x term, add 3.85 to both sides.

$2.4x = 12.48$ Divide both sides by 2.4.

$\dfrac{2.4x}{2.4} = \dfrac{12.48}{2.4}$ This makes the coefficient on the x term equal to 1.

$x = 5.2$ The solution 5.2 checks in the original equation.

The solution is 5.2.

Skill Practice

Solve.
5. $5.8y - 14.4 = 55.2$

Example 4 Solving Equations Involving Multiple Steps

Solve. $0.03(x + 4) = 0.01x + 2.8$

Solution:

$$0.03(x + 4) = 0.01x + 2.8$$ Apply the distributive property to clear parentheses.

$$0.03x + 0.12 = 0.01x + 2.8$$

$0.03x - 0.01x + 0.12 = 0.01x - 0.01x + 2.8$ Subtract $0.01x$ from both sides. This places the variable terms all on one side.

$0.02x + 0.12 = 2.8$

$0.02x + 0.12 - 0.12 = 2.8 - 0.12$ Subtract 0.12 from both sides. This places the constant terms all on one side.

$0.02x = 2.68$

$\dfrac{0.02x}{0.02} = \dfrac{2.68}{0.02}$ Divide both sides by 0.02. This makes the coefficient on the x term equal to 1.

$x = 134$ The value 134 checks in the original equation.

The solution is 134.

Skill Practice

Solve.
6. $0.05(x + 6) = 0.02x - 0.18$

Answers
5. 12   **6.** −16

2. Solving Equations by Clearing Decimals

In Section 4.8 we learned that an equation containing fractions can be easier to solve if we clear the fractions. Similarly, when solving an equation with decimals, students may find it easier to clear the decimals first. To do this, we can multiply both sides of the equation by a power of 10 (10, 100, 1000, etc.). This will move the decimal point to the right in the coefficient on each term in the equation. This process is demonstrated in Example 5.

Example 5 Solving an Equation by Clearing Decimals

Solve. $0.05x - 1.45 = 2.8$

Solution:

To determine a power of 10 to use to clear fractions, identify the term with the most digits to the right of the decimal point. In this case, the terms $0.05x$ and 1.45 each have two digits to the right of the decimal point. Therefore, to clear decimals, we must multiply by 100. This will move the decimal point to the right two places.

$0.05x - 1.45 = 2.8$

$100(0.05x - 1.45) = 100(2.8)$ Multiply by 100 to clear decimals.

$100(0.05x) - 100(1.45) = 100(2.80)$ The decimal point will move to the right two places.

$5x - 145 = 280$

$5x - 145 + 145 = 280 + 145$ Add 145 to both sides.

$5x = 425$

$\dfrac{5x}{5} = \dfrac{425}{5}$ Divide both sides by 5.

$x = 85$ The value 85 checks in the original equation.

The solution is 85.

3. Applications and Problem Solving

In Examples 6–8, we will practice using linear equations to solve application problems.

Example 6 Translating to an Algebraic Expression

The sum of a number and 7.5 is three times the number. Find the number.

Solution:

Let x represent the number.   **Step 1:** Read the problem completely.

Step 2: Label the variable.

the sum of   3 times the number   **Step 3:** Write the equation in words.

$x + 7.5 = 3x$ **Step 4:** Translate to a mathematical equation.

a number 7.5

$$x - x + 7.5 = 3x - x$$

Step 5: Solve the equation.

Subtract x from both sides. This will bring all variable terms to one side.

$$7.5 = 2x$$

$$\frac{7.5}{2} = \frac{2x}{2}$$

Divide by 2.

$$3.75 = x$$

The number is 3.75.

Step 6: Interpret the answer in words.

Example 7   **Solving an Application Involving Geometry**

The perimeter of a triangle is 22.8 cm. The longest side is 8.4 cm more than the shortest side. The middle side is twice the shortest side. Find the lengths of the three sides.

Solution:

Let x represent the length of the shortest side.

Then the longest side is $(x + 8.4)$.

The middle side is $2x$.

Step 1: Read the problem completely.

Step 2: Label the variable and draw a figure.

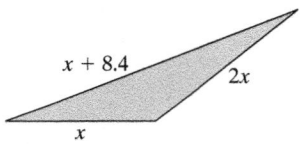

The sum of the lengths of the sides is 22.8 cm.

$$x + (x + 8.4) + 2x = 22.8$$

$$x + x + 8.4 + 2x = 22.8$$

$$4x + 8.4 = 22.8$$

$$4x + 8.4 - 8.4 = 22.8 - 8.4$$

$$4x = 14.4$$

$$\frac{4x}{4} = \frac{14.4}{4}$$

$$x = 3.6$$

Step 3: Write the equation in words.

Step 4: Write a mathematical equation.

Step 5: Solve the equation.

Combine *like* terms.

Subtract 8.4 from both sides.

Divide by 4 on both sides.

Step 6: Interpret the answer in words.

The shortest side is 3.6 cm.
The longest side is $(x + 8.4)$ cm $= (3.6 + 8.4)$ cm $= 12$ cm.
The middle side is $(2x)$ cm $= 2(3.6)$ cm $= 7.2$ cm.

The sides are 3.6 cm, 12 cm, and 7.2 cm.

Skill Practice

10. D.J. signs up for a new credit card that earns travel miles with a certain airline. She initially earns 15,000 travel miles by signing up for the new card. Then for each dollar spent she earns 2.5 travel miles. If at the end of one year she has 38,500 travel miles, how many dollars did she charge on the credit card?

Example 8 **Using a Linear Equation in a Consumer Application**

Joanne has a cellular phone plan in which she pays $39.95 per month for 450 min of air time. Additional minutes beyond 450 are charged at a rate of $0.40 per minute. If Joanne's bill comes to $87.95, how many minutes did she use beyond 450 min?

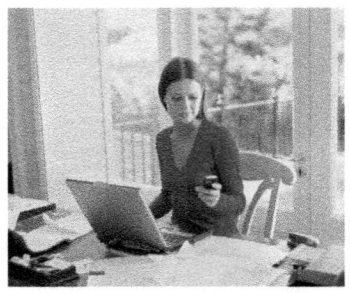

Solution:

| | **Step 1:** | Read the problem. |

Let x represent the number of minutes beyond 450.   **Step 2:** Label the variable.

Then $0.40x$ represents the cost for x additional minutes.

$$\begin{pmatrix}\text{Monthly}\\\text{fee}\end{pmatrix} + \begin{pmatrix}\text{Cost of}\\\text{additional minutes}\end{pmatrix} = \begin{pmatrix}\text{Total}\\\text{cost}\end{pmatrix}$$ **Step 3:** Write an equation in words.

$$39.95 \quad + \quad 0.40x \quad = \quad 87.95$$ **Step 4:** Write a mathematical equation.

$$39.95 + 0.40x = 87.95$$ **Step 5:** Solve the equation.

$$39.95 - 39.95 + 0.40x = 87.95 - 39.95$$ Subtract 39.95.

$$0.40x = 48.00$$

$$\frac{0.40x}{0.40} = \frac{48.00}{0.40}$$ Divide by 0.40.

$$x = 120$$

Answer

10. D.J. charged $9400.

Joanne talked for 120 min beyond 450 min.

Section 5.6   Practice Exercises

Boost *your* GRADE at ALEKS.com!   **ALEKS** version 3.0
- Practice Problems
- Self-Tests
- NetTutor
- e-Professors
- Videos

Review Exercises

For Exercises 1–2, find the area and circumference. Use 3.14 for π.

1.

0.1 m

2.

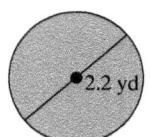

2.2 yd

For Exercises 3–6, simplify.

3. $(2.3 - 3.8)^2$ **4.** $(-1.6 + 0.4)^2$ **5.** $\frac{1}{2}(4.8 - 9.26)$ **6.** $-\frac{1}{4}[62.9 + (-4.8)]$

For Exercises 7–10, simplify by clearing parentheses and combining *like* terms.

7. $-1.8x + 2.31x$ **8.** $-6.9y + 4.23y$ **9.** $-2(8.4z - 3.1) - 5.3z$ **10.** $-3(9.2w - 4.1) + 3.62w$

Objective 1: Solving Equations Containing Decimals

For Exercises 11–34, solve the equations. **(See Examples 1–4.)**

11. $y + 8.4 = 9.26$ **12.** $z + 1.9 = 12.41$ **13.** $t - 3.92 = -8.7$ **14.** $w - 12.69 = -15.4$

15. $-141.2 = -91.3 + p$ **16.** $-413.7 = -210.6 + m$ **17.** $-0.07 + n = 0.025$ **18.** $-0.016 + k = 0.08$

19. $\dfrac{x}{-4.6} = -9.3$ **20.** $\dfrac{y}{-8.1} = -1.5$ **21.** $6 = \dfrac{z}{-0.02}$ **22.** $7 = \dfrac{a}{-0.05}$

23. $19.43 = -6.7n$ **24.** $94.08 = -8.4q$ **25.** $-6.2y = -117.8$ **26.** $-4.1w = -73.8$

27. $8.4x + 6 = 48$ **28.** $9.2n + 6.4 = 43.2$ **29.** $-3.1x - 2 = -29.9$ **30.** $-5.2y - 7 = -22.6$

31. $0.04(p - 2) = 0.05p + 0.16$ **32.** $0.06(t - 9) = 0.07t + 0.27$

33. $-2.5x + 5.76 = 0.4(6 - 5x)$ **34.** $-1.5m + 14.26 = 0.2(18 - m)$

Objective 2: Solving Equations by Clearing Decimals

For Exercises 35–42, solve by first clearing decimals. **(See Example 5.)**

35. $0.04x - 1.9 = 0.1$ **36.** $0.03y - 2.3 = 0.7$

37. $-4.4 = -2 + 0.6x$ **38.** $-3.7 = -4 + 0.5x$

39. $4.2 = 3 - 0.002m$ **40.** $3.8 = 7 - 0.016t$

41. $6.2x - 4.1 = 5.94x - 1.5$ **42.** $1.32x + 5.2 = 0.12x + 0.4$

Objective 3: Applications and Problem Solving

43. Nine times a number is equal to 36 more than the number. Find the number. **(See Example 6.)**

44. Six times a number is equal to 30.5 more than the number. Find the number.

45. The difference of 13 and a number is 2.2 more than three times the number. Find the number.

46. The difference of 8 and a number is 1.7 more than two times the number. Find the number.

47. The quotient of a number and 5 is -1.88. Find the number.

48. The quotient of a number and −2.5 is 2.72. Find the number.

49. The product of 2.1 and a number is 8.36 more than the number. Find the number.

50. The product of −3.6 and a number is 48.3 more than the number. Find the number.

51. The perimeter of a triangle is 21.5 yd. The longest side is twice the shortest side. The middle side is 3.1 yd longer than the shortest side. Find the lengths of the sides. **(See Example 7.)**

52. The perimeter of a triangle is 1.32 m. The longest side is 30 times the shortest side, and the middle side is 0.04 m more than the shortest side. Find the lengths of the sides.

53. Toni, Rafa, and Henri are all servers at the Chez Joëlle Restaurant. The tips collected for the night amount to $167.80. Toni made $22.05 less in tips than Rafa. Henri made $5.90 less than Rafa. How much did each person make?

54. Bob bought a popcorn, a soda, and a hotdog at the movies for $8.25. Popcorn costs $1 more than a hotdog. A soda costs $0.25 less than a hotdog. How much is each item?

55. The U-Rent-It home supply store rents pressure cleaners for $4.95, plus $4 per hour. A painter rents a pressure cleaner, and the bill comes to $18.95. For how many hours did he rent the pressure cleaner?
(See Example 8.)

56. A cellular phone company charges $59.95 each month and this includes 500 min. For minutes used beyond the first 500, the charge is $0.25 per minute. Jim's bill came to $90.70. How many minutes over 500 min did he use?

57. Karla's credit card bill is $420.90. Part of the bill is from the previous month's balance, part is in new charges, and part is from a late fee of $39. The previous balance is $172.40 less than the new charges. How much is the previous balance, and how much is in new charges?

58. Thayne's credit card bill is $879.10. This includes his charges and interest. If the new charges are $794.10 more than the interest, find the amount in charges and the amount in interest.

59. Madeline and Kim each rode 15 miles in a bicycle relay. Madeline's time was 8.25 min less than Kim's time. If the total time was 1 hr, 56.75 min, for how long did each person ride?

60. The two-night attendance for a Friday/Saturday basketball tournament at the University of Connecticut was 2570. There were 522 more people on Saturday for the finals than on Friday. How many people attended each night?

Group Activity

Purchasing from a Catalog

Materials: Catalog (such as Amazon, Sears, JC Penney, or the like) or a computer to access an online catalog

Estimated time: 15 min

Group Size: 4

1. Each person in the group will choose an item to add to the list of purchases. All members of the group will keep a list of all items ordered and the prices.

ORDER SHEET

Item	Price Each	Quantity	Total
		SUBTOTAL	
		SHIPPING	
		TOTAL	

2. When the order list is complete, each member will find the total cost of the items ordered (subtotal) and compare the answer with the other members of the group. When the correct subtotal has been determined, find the cost of shipping from the catalog. (This is usually found on the order page of the catalog.) Now find the total cost of this order.

Chapter 5 Summary

Section 5.1 — Decimal Notation and Rounding

Key Concepts

A **decimal fraction** is a fraction whose denominator is a power of 10.

Identify the place values of a decimal number.

$$1\ 2\ 3\ 4\ .\ 5\ 6\ 7\ 8$$

thousands, hundreds, tens, ones, decimal point, tenths, hundredths, thousandths, ten-thousandths

Reading a Decimal Number

1. The part of the number to the left of the decimal point is read as a whole number. *Note:* If there is not a whole-number part, skip to step 3.
2. The decimal point is read *and*.
3. The part of the number to the right of the decimal point is read as a whole number but is followed by the name of the place position of the digit farthest to the right.

Converting a Decimal to a Mixed Number or Proper Fraction

1. The digits to the right of the decimal point are written as the numerator of the fraction.
2. The place value of the digit farthest to the right of the decimal point determines the denominator.
3. The whole-number part of the number is left unchanged.
4. Once the number is converted to a fraction or mixed number, simplify the fraction to lowest terms, if possible.

Writing a Decimal Number Greater Than 1 as an Improper Fraction

1. The denominator is determined by the place position of the digit farthest to the right of the decimal point.
2. The numerator is obtained by removing the decimal point of the original number. The resulting whole number is then written over the denominator.
3. Simplify the improper fraction to lowest terms, if possible.

Examples

Example 1

$\frac{7}{10}$, $\frac{31}{100}$, and $\frac{191}{1000}$ are decimal fractions.

Example 2

In the number 34.914, the 1 is in the hundredths place.

Example 3

23.089 reads "twenty-three and eighty-nine thousandths."

Example 4

$$4.2 = 4\frac{2}{10} = 4\frac{1}{5}$$

Example 5

$$-5.24 = -\frac{524}{100} = -\frac{131}{25}$$

Comparing Two Decimal Numbers

1. Starting at the left (and moving toward the right), compare the digits in each corresponding place position.
2. As we move from left to right, the first instance in which the digits differ determines the order of the numbers. The number having the greater digit is greater overall.

Rounding Decimals to a Place Value to the Right of the Decimal Point

1. Identify the digit one position to the right of the given place value.
2. If the digit in step 1 is 5 or greater, add 1 to the digit in the given place value. Then discard the digits to its right.
3. If the digit in step 1 is less than 5, discard it and any digits to its right.

Example 6

$3.024 > 3.019$ because

different
$2 > 1$

$3.024 > 3.019$

same

Example 7

Round -4.8935 to the nearest hundredth.

remaining
digits discarded

$-4.89\overset{\frown}{35} \approx -4.89$

hundredths place

This digit is less than 5.

Section 5.2   Addition and Subtraction of Decimals

Key Concepts

Adding Decimals

1. Write the addends in a column with the decimal points and corresponding place values lined up.
2. Add the digits in columns from right to left as you would whole numbers. The decimal point in the answer should be lined up with the decimal points from the addends.

Subtracting Decimals

1. Write the numbers in a column with the decimal points and corresponding place values lined up.
2. Subtract the digits in columns from right to left as you would whole numbers. The decimal point in the answer should be lined up with the other decimal points.

Examples

Example 1

Add $6.92 + 12 + 0.001$.

$$
\begin{array}{r}
6.920 \\
12.000 \\
+\ 0.001 \\
\hline
18.921
\end{array}
$$

Add zeros to the right of the decimal point as placeholders.

Check by estimating:

6.92 rounds to 7 and 0.001 rounds to 0.

$7 + 12 + 0 = 19$, which is close to 18.921.

Example 2

Subtract $41.03 - 32.4$.

$$
\begin{array}{r}
\overset{\;\;\;10}{\overset{3\;\cancel{0}\;\;10}{\cancel{4}\,\cancel{1}.\cancel{0}\,3}} \\
-\ 32.40 \\
\hline
8.63
\end{array}
$$

Check by estimating:

41.03 rounds to 41 and 32.40 rounds to 32.

$41 - 32 = 9$, which is close to 8.63.

Section 5.3   Multiplication of Decimals and Applications with Circles

Key Concepts

Multiplying Two Decimals

1. Multiply as you would integers.
2. Place the decimal point in the product so that the number of decimal places equals the combined number of decimal places of both factors.

Multiplying a Decimal by Powers of 10

Move the decimal point to the right the same number of decimal places as the number of zeros in the power of 10.

Multiplying a Decimal by Powers of 0.1

Move the decimal point to the left the same number of places as there are decimal places in the power of 0.1.

Radius and Diameter of a Circle

$$d = 2r \quad \text{and} \quad r = \frac{1}{2}d$$

Circumference of a Circle

$$C = \pi d \quad \text{or} \quad C = 2\pi r$$

Area of a Circle

$$A = \pi r^2$$

Examples

Example 1

Multiply. 5.02×2.8

$$
\begin{array}{rl}
5.02 & \text{2 decimal places} \\
\times\ 2.8 & +\ 1\ \text{decimal place} \\
\hline
4016 & \\
10040 & \\
\hline
14.056 & \text{3 decimal places}
\end{array}
$$

Example 2

$$-83.251 \times 100 = -8325.1$$

Move 2 places
to the right.

Example 3

$$-149.02 \times (-0.001) = 0.14902$$

Move 3 places
to the left.

Example 4

Find the radius, circumference, and area. Use 3.14 for π.

$$r = \frac{20\ \text{ft}}{2} = 10\ \text{ft}$$

$$
\begin{aligned}
C &= 2\pi r \\
  &= 2\pi(10\ \text{ft}) \\
  &= 20\pi\ \text{ft} && \text{(exact circumference)} \\
  &\approx 20(3.14)\ \text{ft} \\
  &= 62.8\ \text{ft} && \text{(approximate value)}
\end{aligned}
$$

$$
\begin{aligned}
A &= \pi r^2 \\
  &= \pi(10\ \text{ft})^2 \\
  &= 100\pi\ \text{ft}^2 && \text{(exact area)} \\
  &\approx 100(3.14)\ \text{ft}^2 \\
  &= 314\ \text{ft}^2 && \text{(approximate value)}
\end{aligned}
$$

Section 5.4   Division of Decimals

Key Concepts

Dividing a Decimal by a Whole Number

1. Place the decimal point in the quotient directly above the decimal point in the dividend.
2. Divide as you would whole numbers.

Dividing When the Divisor Is Not a Whole Number

1. Move the decimal point in the divisor to the right to make it a whole number.
2. Move the decimal point in the dividend to the right the same number of places as in step 1.
3. Place the decimal point in the quotient directly above the decimal point in the dividend.
4. Divide as you would whole numbers. Then apply the correct sign to the quotient.

To round a repeating decimal, be sure to expand the repeating digits to one digit beyond the indicated rounding place.

Examples

Example 1

$62.6 \div 4$

$$
\begin{array}{r}
15.65 \\
4\overline{)62.60} \\
-4 \\
\hline
22 \\
-20 \\
\hline
26 \\
-24 \\
\hline
20 \\
-20 \\
\hline
0
\end{array}
$$

Example 2

$81.1 \div 0.9$ $.9\overline{)81.1}$

$$
\begin{array}{r}
90.11\ldots \\
9\overline{)811.00} \\
-81 \\
\hline
01 \\
00 \\
\hline
10 \\
-9 \\
\hline
10
\end{array}
$$

The pattern repeats.

The answer is the repeating decimal $90.\overline{1}$.

Example 3

Round $6.\overline{56}$ to the thousandths place.

6.5656

thousandths place

The digit 6 > 5 so increase the thousandths-place digit by 1.

$6.\overline{56} \approx 6.566$

Section 5.5   Fractions, Decimals, and the Order of Operations

Key Concepts

To write a fraction as a decimal, divide the numerator by the denominator.

These are some common fractions represented by decimals.

$\frac{1}{4} = 0.25$ $\frac{1}{2} = 0.5$ $\frac{3}{4} = 0.75$

$\frac{1}{9} = 0.\overline{1}$ $\frac{2}{9} = 0.\overline{2}$ $\frac{1}{3} = 0.\overline{3}$

$\frac{4}{9} = 0.\overline{4}$ $\frac{5}{9} = 0.\overline{5}$ $\frac{2}{3} = 0.\overline{6}$

$\frac{7}{9} = 0.\overline{7}$ $\frac{8}{9} = 0.\overline{8}$

To write a decimal as a fraction, first write the number as a decimal fraction and reduce.

A rational number can be expressed as a terminating or repeating decimal.

An **irrational number** cannot be expressed as a terminating or repeating decimal.

The rational numbers and the irrational numbers together make up the set of **real numbers.**

To rank decimals from least to greatest, compare corresponding digits from left to right.

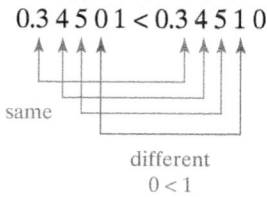

same

different
$0 < 1$

Examples

Example 1

$$\frac{17}{20} = 0.85 \qquad \begin{array}{r} .85 \\ 20\overline{)17.00} \\ -160 \\ \hline 100 \\ -100 \\ \hline 0 \end{array}$$

Example 2

$$\frac{14}{3} = 4.\overline{6} \qquad \begin{array}{r} 4.66\ldots \\ 3\overline{)14.00} \\ -12 \\ \hline 20 \\ -18 \\ \hline 20 \end{array}$$

The pattern repeats.

Example 3

$$-6.84 = -\frac{\overset{171}{684}}{\underset{25}{100}} = -\frac{171}{25} \quad \text{or} \quad -6\frac{21}{25}$$

Example 4

Rational: $-6, \frac{3}{4}, 3.78, -2.\overline{35}$

Irrational: $\sqrt{2} \approx 1.41421356237\ldots$

$\pi \approx 3.141592654\ldots$

Example 5

Plot the decimals $2.6, 2.\overline{6}$, and 2.58 on a number line.

Examples 6 and 7 apply the order of operations with fractions and decimals. There are two approaches for simplifying.

Option 1: Write the expressions as decimals.

Option 2: Write the expressions as fractions.

Example 6

$$\left(1.6 - \frac{13}{25}\right) \div 8 = (1.6 - 0.52) \div 8$$

$$= (1.08) \div 8$$

$$= 0.135$$

Example 7

$$\frac{2}{3}\left(2.2 + \frac{7}{5}\right) = \frac{2}{3}\left(\frac{22}{10} + \frac{7}{5}\right)$$

$$= \frac{2}{3}\left(\frac{11}{5} + \frac{7}{5}\right)$$

$$= \frac{2}{\overset{}{3}}\left(\frac{\overset{6}{18}}{5}\right) = \frac{12}{5} = 2.4$$

Section 5.6 Solving Equations Containing Decimals

Key Concepts

We solve equations containing decimals by using the addition, subtraction, multiplication, and division properties of equality.

Examples

Example 1

Solve. $6.24 = -2(10.53 - 2.1x)$

$$6.24 = -21.06 + 4.2x$$

$$6.24 + 21.06 = -21.06 + 21.06 + 4.2x$$

$$27.3 = 4.2x$$

$$\frac{27.3}{4.2} = \frac{4.2x}{4.2}$$

$$6.5 = x$$

The solution 6.5 checks in the original equation.

We can also solve decimal equations by first clearing decimals. Do this by multiplying both sides of the equation by a power of 10 (10, 100, 1000, etc.).

Example 2

Solve by clearing decimals.

$$0.02x + 1.3 = -0.025$$

$$1000(0.02x + 1.3) = 1000(-0.025)$$

$$1000(0.02x) + 1000(1.3) = 1000(-0.025)$$

$$20x + 1300 = -25$$

$$20x + 1300 - 1300 = -25 - 1300$$

$$20x = -1325$$

$$x = -66.25$$

The solution −66.25 checks in the original equation.

Chapter 5   Review Exercises

Section 5.1

1. Identify the place value for each digit in the number 32.16.

2. Identify the place value for each digit in the number 2.079.

For Exercises 3–6, write the word name for the decimal.

3. 5.7

4. 10.21

5. −51.008

6. −109.01

For Exercises 7–8, write the word name as a numeral.

7. Thirty-three thousand, fifteen and forty-seven thousandths.

8. Negative one hundred and one hundredth.

For Exercises 9–10, write the decimal as a proper fraction or mixed number.

9. −4.8

10. 0.025

For Exercises 11–12, write the decimal as an improper fraction.

11. 1.3

12. 6.75

For Exercises 13–14, fill in the blank with either < or >.

13. −15.032 ☐ −15.03

14. 7.209 ☐ 7.22

15. The earned run average (ERA) for five members of the American League for a recent season is given in the table. Rank the averages from least to greatest.

Player	ERA
Jon Garland	4.5142
Cliff Lee	4.3953
Gil Meche	4.4839
Jamie Moyer	4.3875
Vicente Padilla	4.5000

For Exercises 16–17, round the decimal to the indicated place value.

16. 89.9245;   hundredths

17. 34.8895;   thousandths

18. A quality control manager tests the amount of cereal in several brands of breakfast cereal against the amount advertised on the box. She selects one box at random. She measures the contents of one 12.5-oz box and finds that the box has 12.46 oz.

   a. Is the amount in the box less than or greater than the advertised amount?

   b. If the quality control manager rounds the measured value to the tenths place, what is the value?

19. Which number is equal to 571.24? Circle all that apply.

   a. 571.240   b. 571.2400

   c. 571.024   d. 571.0024

20. Which number is equal to 3.709? Circle all that apply.

   a. 3.7   b. 3.7090

   c. 3.709000   d. 3.907

Section 5.2

For Exercises 21–28, add or subtract as indicated.

21. 45.03 + 4.713

22. 239.3 + 33.92

23. 34.89 − 29.44

24. 5.002 − 3.1

25. −221 − 23.04

26. 34 + (−4.993)

27. 17.3 + 3.109 − 12.6

28. 189.22 − (−13.1) − 120.055

For Exercises 29–30, simplify by combining *like* terms.

29. $-5.1y - 4.6y + 10.2y$

30. $-2(12.5x - 3) + 11.5x$

31. The closing prices for a mutual fund are given in the graph for a 5-day period.

   a. Determine the difference in price between the two consecutive days for which the price increased the most.

   b. Determine the difference in price between the two consecutive days for which the price decreased the most.

Mutual Fund Price

Section 5.3

For Exercises 32–39, multiply the decimals.

32. 3.9
       $\times$ 2.1

33. 57.01
       $\times$ 1.3

34. $(60.1)(-4.4)$

35. $(-7.7)(45)$

36. 85.49×1000

37. 1.0034×100

38. $-92.01 \times (-0.01)$

39. $-104.22 \times (-0.01)$

For Exercises 40–41, write the decimal number representing each word name.

40. The population of Guadeloupe is approximately 4.32 hundred-thousand.

41. A recent season premier of *American Idol* had 33.8 million viewers.

42. A store advertises a package of two 9-volt batteries for sale at $3.99.

   a. What is the cost of buying 8 batteries?

   b. If another store has an 8-pack for the regular price of $17.99, how much can a customer save by buying batteries at the sale price?

43. If long-distance phone calls cost $0.07 per minute, how much will a 23-min long-distance call cost?

44. Find the area and perimeter of the rectangle.

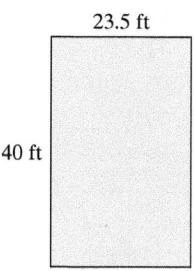

23.5 ft

40 ft

45. Population density gives the approximate number of people per square mile. The population density for Texas is given in the graph for selected years.

   a. Approximately how many people would have been located in a 200-mi^2 area in 1960?

   b. Approximately how many people would have been located in a 200-mi^2 area in 2006?

Population Density for Texas

Source: U.S. Census Bureau

46. Determine the diameter of a circle with radius 3.75 m.

47. Determine the radius of a circle with diameter 27.2 ft.

48. Find the area and circumference of a circular fountain with diameter 24 ft. Use 3.14 for π.

49. Find the area and circumference of a circular garden with radius 30 yd. Use 3.14 for π.

Section 5.4

For Exercises 50–59, divide. Write the answer in decimal form.

50. $8.55 \div 0.5$

51. $64.2 \div 1.5$

52. $0.06\overline{)0.248}$

53. $0.3\overline{)2.63}$

54. $-18.9 \div 0.7$

55. $-0.036 \div 1.2$

56. $493.93 \div 100$

57. $90.234 \div 10$

58. $-553.8 \div (-0.001)$

59. $-2.6 \div (-0.01)$

60. For each number, round to the indicated place.

	8.$\overline{6}$	52.$\overline{52}$	0.$\overline{409}$
Tenths			
Hundredths			
Thousandths			
Ten-thousandths			

For Exercises 61–62, divide and round the answer to the nearest hundredth.

61. $104.6 \div (-9)$

62. $71.8 \div (-6)$

63. a. A generic package of toilet paper costs $5.99 for 12 rolls. What is the cost per roll? (Round the answer to the nearest cent, that is, the nearest hundredth of a dollar.)

  b. A package of four rolls costs $2.29. What is the cost per roll?

  c. Which of the two packages offers the better buy?

Section 5.5

For Exercises 64–67, write the fraction or mixed number as a decimal.

64. $2\dfrac{2}{5}$

65. $3\dfrac{13}{25}$

66. $-\dfrac{24}{125}$

67. $-\dfrac{7}{16}$

For Exercises 68–70, write the fraction as a repeating decimal.

68. $\dfrac{7}{12}$

69. $\dfrac{55}{36}$

70. $-4\dfrac{7}{22}$

For Exercises 71–73, write the fraction as a decimal rounded to the indicated place value.

71. $\dfrac{5}{17}$; hundredths

72. $\dfrac{20}{23}$; tenths

73. $-\dfrac{11}{3}$; thousandths

74. Identify the numbers as rational or irrational.

  a. $6.\overline{4}$

  b. π

  c. $\sqrt{10}$

  d. $-\dfrac{8}{5}$

For Exercises 75–76, write a fraction or mixed number for the repeating decimal.

75. $0.\overline{2}$

76. $3.\overline{3}$

77. Complete the table, giving the closing value of stocks as reported in the *Wall Street Journal*.

Stock	Closing Price ($) (Decimal)	Closing Price ($) (Fraction)
Sun	5.20	
Sony	55.53	
Verizon		$41\dfrac{4}{25}$

For Exercises 78–79, insert the appropriate symbol. Choose from $<$, $>$, or $=$.

78. $1\dfrac{1}{3}$ ☐ 1.33

79. -0.14 ☐ $-\dfrac{1}{7}$

For Exercises 80–85, perform the indicated operations. Write the answers in decimal form.

80. $-7.5 \div \dfrac{3}{2}$

81. $\dfrac{1}{2}(4.6)(-2.4)$

82. $(-5.46 - 2.24)^2 - 0.29$

83. $[-3.46 - (-2.16)]^2 - 0.09$

84. $\left(\dfrac{1}{4}\right)^2\left(\dfrac{4}{5}\right) - 3.05$

85. $-1.25 - \dfrac{1}{3} \cdot \left(\dfrac{3}{2}\right)^2$

86. An audio Spanish course is available online at one website for the following prices. How much money is saved by buying the combo package versus the three levels individually?

Level	Price
Spanish I	$189.95
Spanish II	199.95
Spanish III	219.95
Combo (Spanish I, II, III combined)	519.95

87. Marvin drives the route shown in the figure each day, making deliveries. He completes one-third of the route before lunch. How many more miles does he still have to drive after lunch?

12.6 mi
5.4 mi
11.5 mi
14.2 mi
7.3 mi

Section 5.6

For Exercises 88–96, solve the equation.

88. $x + 4.78 = 2.2$

89. $6.2 + y = 4.67$

90. $11 = -10.4 + w$

91. $-20.4 = -9.08 + z$

92. $4.6 = 16.7 + 2.2m$

93. $21.8 = 12.05 + 3.9x$

94. $-0.2(x - 6) = 0.3x + 3.8$

95. $-0.5(9 + y) = -0.6y + 6.5$

96. $0.04z - 3.5 = 0.06z + 4.8$

For Exercises 97–98, determine a number that can be used to clear decimals in the equation. Then solve the equation.

97. $2p + 3.1 = 0.14$

98. $2.5w - 6 = 0.9$

99. Four times a number is equal to 19.5 more than the number. Find the number.

100. The sum of a number and 4.8 is three times the number. Find the number.

101. The product of a number and 0.05 is equal to 80. Find the number.

102. The quotient of a number and 0.05 is equal to 80. Find the number.

103. The perimeter of a triangle is 24.8 yd. The longest side is twice the shortest side. The middle side is 2.4 yd longer than the shortest side. Find the lengths of the sides.

104. Deanna rented a video game and a DVD for $12.98. DVDs cost $1 less to rent than video games. Find the cost to rent each item.

105. The U-Store-It Company rents a 10 ft by 12 ft storage space for $59, plus $89 per month. Mykeshia wrote a check for $593. How many months of storage will this cover?

Chapter 5 Test

1. Identify the place value of the underlined digit.

   a. 2$\underline{3}$4.17

   b. 234.1$\underline{7}$

2. Write the word name for -509.024.

3. Write the decimal 1.26 as a mixed number and as a fraction.

4. The field goal percentages for a recent basketball season are given in the table for four NBA teams. Rank the percentages from least to greatest.

Team	Percentage
LA Lakers	0.4419
Cleveland	0.4489
San Antonio	0.4495
Utah	0.4484

5. Which statement is correct?

   a. $0.043 > 0.430$

   b. $-0.692 > -0.926$

   c. $0.078 < 0.0780$

For Exercises 6–17, perform the indicated operation.

6. $-49.002 + 3.83$

7. $-34.09 - 12.8$

8. $28.1 \times (-4.5)$

9. $25.4 \div (-5)$

10. $4 - 2.78$

11. $12.03 + 0.1943$

12. $39.82 \div 0.33$

13. 42.7×10.3

14. $-45.92 \times (-0.1)$

15. $-579.23 \times (-100)$

16. $80.12 \div 0.01$

17. $2.931 \div 1000$

For Exercises 18–19, simplify by combining like terms.

18. $2.72x - 1.96x + 4.9x$

19. $2(4.1y - 3) + 6.4y + 2.7$

20. Determine the diameter of a circle with radius 12.2 ft.

21. Determine the circumference and area. Use 3.14 for π and round to the nearest whole unit.

16 cm

22. The temperature of a cake is recorded in 10-min intervals after it comes out of the oven. See the graph.

   a. What was the difference in temperature between 10 and 20 min?

   b. What was the difference in temperature between 40 and 50 min?

Temperature of Cake Versus Time

23. For a recent year, the United States consumed the most oil of any country in the world at 1.04 billion tons. China was second with 360 million tons.

a. Write a decimal number representing the amount of oil consumed by the United States.

b. Write a decimal number representing the amount of oil consumed by China.

c. What is the difference between the oil consumption in the United States and China?

24. A picture is framed and matted as shown in the figure.

   a. Find the area of the picture itself.

   b. Find the area of the matting *only*.

   c. Find the area of the frame *only*.

18.2 in.
13 in.
9 in.
7.5 in.
11 in.
16.5 in.

25. Jonas bought 200 shares of a stock for $36.625 per share and had to pay a commission of $4.25. Two years later he sold all of his shares at a price of $52.16 per share. If he paid $8 for selling the stock, how much money did he make overall?

26. Dalia purchased a new refrigerator for $1099.99. She paid $200 as a down payment and will finance the rest over a 2-year period. Approximately how much will her monthly payment be?

27. Kent determines that his Ford Ranger pickup truck gets 23 mpg in the city and 26 mpg on the highway. If he drives 110.4 mi in the city and 135.2 mi on the highway how much gas will he use?

28. Rank the numbers and plot them on a number line.

$$-3\frac{1}{2}, \; -3.\overline{5}, \; -3.2$$

-4.0   -3.5   -3.0

For Exercises 29–31, simplify.

29. $(8.7)\left(1.6 - \dfrac{1}{2}\right)$ **30.** $\dfrac{7}{3}\left(5.25 - \dfrac{3}{4}\right)^2$

31. $(0.2)^2 - \dfrac{5}{4}$

32. Identify the numbers as rational or irrational.

    a. $2\dfrac{1}{8}$ **b.** $\sqrt{5}$ **c.** 6π **d.** $-0.\overline{3}$

For Exercises 33–38, solve the equation.

33. $0.006 = 0.014 + p$ **34.** $0.04y = 7.1$

35. $-97.6 = -4.3 - 5w$ **36.** $3.9 + 6.2x = 24.98$

37. $-0.08z + 0.5 = 0.09(4 - z) + 0.12$

38. $0.9 + 0.4t = 1.6 + 0.6(t - 3)$

39. The difference of a number and 43.4 is equal to eight times the number. Find the number.

40. The quotient of a number and 0.004 is 60. Find the number.

Chapters 1–5 Cumulative Review Exercises

1. Simplify. $(17 + 12) - (8 - 3) \cdot 3$

2. Multiply and round the answer to the thousands place. $23{,}444 \cdot 103$

3. The chart shows the retail sales for several companies. Find the difference between the greatest and least sales in the chart.

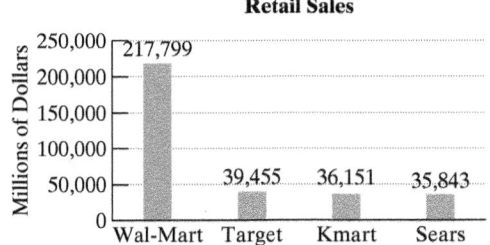

Retail Sales

For Exercises 4–7, multiply or divide as indicated. Write the answer as a fraction.

4. $-\dfrac{1}{5} \cdot \left(-\dfrac{6}{11}\right)$ **5.** $\left(\dfrac{6}{15}\right)\left(\dfrac{10}{7}\right)$

6. $\left(-\dfrac{7}{10}\right)^2$ **7.** $\dfrac{8}{3} \div 4$

8. A settlement for a lawsuit is made for \$15,000. The attorney gets $\frac{2}{5}$ of the settlement. How much is left?

9. Simplify.

    $\dfrac{8}{25} + \dfrac{1}{5} \div \dfrac{5}{6} - \left(\dfrac{2}{5}\right)^2$

For Exercises 10–11, add or subtract as indicated. Write the answers as fractions.

10. $\dfrac{5}{11} + 3$ **11.** $-\dfrac{12}{5} + \dfrac{9}{10}$

12. Find the area and perimeter.

$\dfrac{3}{8}$ ft

$\dfrac{5}{8}$ ft

For Exercises 13–16, perform the indicated operations.

13. $50.9 + (-123.23)$ **14.** $700.8 - 32.01$

15. -301.1×0.25 **16.** $51.2 \div 3.2$

17. Simplify by combining *like* terms.

    $-2.3x - 4.7 + 5.96x - 3.95$

18. Find the area and circumference of a circle with diameter 2 m. Use 3.14 for π.

For Exercises 19–20, solve the equations.

19. $-4.72 + 5x = -9.02$

20. $2(x - 5) + 7 = 3(4 + x) - 9$

Ratios, Proportions, and Percents

6

Chapter 6

In this chapter, we present rates, ratios, proportions, and the concept of percent. Percents are used to measure the number of parts per hundred of some whole amount.

Are You Prepared?

To prepare for your work with percents, take a minute to review multiplying and dividing by a power of 10. Work the problems on the left. Record the answers in the spaces on the right, according to the number of digits to the left and right of the decimal point. Then write the letter of each choice to complete the sentence below. If you need help, review Sections 5.3, 5.4, and 3.4.

1. 0.582×100

2. 0.002×100

3. $46 \times \dfrac{1}{100}$

4. 318×0.01

5. $0.5 \div 100$

6. Solve. $\dfrac{34}{160} = \dfrac{x}{100}$

7. Solve. $\dfrac{x}{4000} = \dfrac{36}{100}$

8. Solve. $0.3x = 16.2$

The mathematician's bakery was called

$\underline{}\ \underline{}\ \underline{}\ \underline{}\ \underline{}\ \ \underline{}\ \underline{}\ \ \underline{}\ \underline{}.$
1   2   3   4   5   2   6   7   8

S. $\underline{}\ \bullet\ \underline{}\ \underline{}$

F. $\underline{}\ \underline{}\ \bullet\ \underline{}\ \underline{}$

P. $\underline{}\ \underline{}\ \underline{}\ \underline{}\ \bullet$

O. $\bullet\ \underline{}$

I. $\underline{}\ \underline{}\ \bullet$

E. $\bullet\ \underline{}\ \underline{}\ \underline{}$

H. $\underline{}\ \underline{}\ \bullet\ \underline{}$

U. $\bullet\ \underline{}\ \underline{}$

Section 6.1   Ratios

Objectives

1. Writing a Ratio
2. Writing Ratios of Mixed Numbers and Decimals
3. Applications of Ratios

1. Writing a Ratio

Thus far we have seen two interpretations of fractions.

- The fraction $\frac{5}{8}$ represents 5 parts of a whole that has been divided evenly into 8 pieces.
- The fraction $\frac{5}{8}$ represents $5 \div 8$.

Now we consider a third interpretation.

- The fraction $\frac{5}{8}$ represents the ratio of 5 to 8.

A **ratio** is a comparison of two quantities. There are three different ways to write a ratio.

Concept Connections

1. When forming the ratio $\frac{a}{b}$, why must b not equal zero?

DEFINITION   Writing a Ratio

The ratio of a to b can be written as follows, provided $b \neq 0$.

   1. a to b **2.** $a : b$ **3.** $\dfrac{a}{b}$

                The colon means "to."   The fraction bar means "to."

Although there are three ways to write a ratio, we primarily use the fraction form.

Skill Practice

2. For a recent flight from Atlanta to San Diego, 291 seats were occupied and 29 were unoccupied. Write the ratio of:
   a. The number of occupied seats to unoccupied seats
   b. The number of unoccupied seats to occupied seats
   c. The number of occupied seats to the total number of seats

---

Example 1   **Writing a Ratio**

In an algebra class there are 15 women and 17 men.

  a. Write the ratio of women to men.

  b. Write the ratio of men to women.

  c. Write the ratio of women to the total number of people in the class.

Solution:

It is important to observe the *order* of the quantities mentioned in a ratio. The first quantity mentioned is the numerator. The second quantity is the denominator.

  a. The ratio of women to men is   **b.** The ratio of men to women is

$$\frac{15}{17} \qquad\qquad\qquad \frac{17}{15}$$

  c. First find the total number of people in the class.

     Total = number of women + number of men

           = 15 + 17

           = 32

Therefore the ratio of women to the total number of people in the class is

$$\frac{15}{32}$$

Answers

1. The value b must not be zero because division by zero is undefined.

2. **a.** $\dfrac{291}{29}$ **b.** $\dfrac{29}{291}$ **c.** $\dfrac{291}{320}$

It is often desirable to write a ratio in lowest terms. The process is similar to simplifying fractions to lowest terms.

Example 2   Writing Ratios in Lowest Terms

Write each ratio in lowest terms.

a. 15 ft to 10 ft   **b.** $20 to $10

Solution:

In part (a) we are comparing feet to feet. In part (b) we are comparing dollars to dollars. We can "cancel" the like units in the numerator and denominator as we would common factors.

a. $\dfrac{15\text{ ft}}{10\text{ ft}} = \dfrac{3 \cdot 5\text{ ft}}{2 \cdot 5\text{ ft}}$

$\qquad = \dfrac{3 \cdot \overset{1}{\cancel{5}}\text{ f\!t}}{2 \cdot \underset{1}{\cancel{5}}\text{ f\!t}}$ Simplify common factors. "Cancel" common units.

$\qquad = \dfrac{3}{2}$

Even though the number $\frac{3}{2}$ is equivalent to $1\frac{1}{2}$, we do not write the ratio as a mixed number. Remember that a ratio is a comparison of *two* quantities. If you did convert $\frac{3}{2}$ to the mixed number $1\frac{1}{2}$, you would write the ratio as $\dfrac{1\frac{1}{2}}{1}$. This would imply that the numerator is one and one-half times as large as the denominator.

b. $\dfrac{\$20}{\$10} = \dfrac{\overset{2}{\cancel{\$20}}}{\underset{1}{\cancel{\$10}}}$ Simplify common factors. "Cancel" common units.

$\qquad = \dfrac{2}{1}$

Although the fraction $\frac{2}{1}$ is equivalent to 2, we do not generally write ratios as whole numbers. Again, a ratio compares *two* quantities. In this case, we say that there is a 2-to-1 ratio between the original dollar amounts.

2. Writing Ratios of Mixed Numbers and Decimals

It is often desirable to express a ratio in lowest terms by using whole numbers in the numerator and denominator. This is demonstrated in Examples 3 and 4.

Example 3   Writing a Ratio in Terms of Whole Numbers

The length of a rectangular picture frame is 7.5 in., and the width is 6.25 in. Express the ratio of the length to the width. Then rewrite the ratio in terms of whole numbers simplified to lowest terms.

Solution:

The ratio of length to width is $\frac{7.5}{6.25}$. We now want to rewrite the ratio, using whole numbers in the numerator and denominator. If we multiply 7.5 by 10, the decimal point will move to the right one place, resulting in a whole number. If we multiply 6.25 by 100, the decimal point will move to the right two places, resulting in a whole number. Because we want to multiply the numerator and denominator by the *same* number, we choose the greater number, 100.

$$\frac{7.5}{6.25} = \frac{7.5 \times 100}{6.25 \times 100}$$ Multiply numerator and denominator by 100.

$$= \frac{750}{625}$$ Because the numerator and denominator are large numbers, we write the prime factorization of each. The common factors are now easy to identify.

$$= \frac{2 \cdot 3 \cdot \overset{1}{\cancel{5}} \cdot \overset{1}{\cancel{5}} \cdot \overset{1}{\cancel{5}}}{5 \cdot \underset{1}{\cancel{5}} \cdot \underset{1}{\cancel{5}} \cdot \underset{1}{\cancel{5}}}$$ Simplify common factors to lowest terms.

$$= \frac{6}{5}$$ The ratio of length to width is $\frac{6}{5}$.

In Example 3, we multiplied by 100 to move the decimal point *two* places to the right. Multiplying by 10 would not have been sufficient, because $6.25 \times 10 = 62.5$, which is not a whole number.

Skill Practice

7. A recipe calls for $2\frac{1}{2}$ cups of flour and $\frac{3}{4}$ cup of sugar. Write the ratio of flour to sugar. Then rewrite the ratio in terms of whole numbers in lowest terms.

Example 4 **Writing a Ratio in Terms of Whole Numbers**

Ling walked $2\frac{1}{4}$ mi on Monday and $3\frac{1}{2}$ mi on Tuesday. Write the ratio of miles walked Monday to miles walked Tuesday. Then rewrite the ratio in terms of whole numbers reduced to lowest terms.

Solution:

The ratio of miles walked on Monday to miles walked on Tuesday is $\frac{2\frac{1}{4}}{3\frac{1}{2}}$.

To convert this to a ratio of whole numbers, first we rewrite each mixed number as an improper fraction. Then we can divide the fractions and simplify.

$$\frac{2\frac{1}{4}}{3\frac{1}{2}} = \frac{\frac{9}{4}}{\frac{7}{2}} \longleftarrow \text{Write the mixed numbers as improper fractions.}$$
Recall that a fraction bar also implies division.

$$= \frac{9}{4} \div \frac{7}{2}$$

$$= \frac{9}{4} \cdot \frac{2}{7}$$ Multiply by the reciprocal of the divisor.

$$= \frac{9}{\underset{2}{\cancel{4}}} \cdot \frac{\overset{1}{\cancel{2}}}{7}$$ Simplify common factors to lowest terms.

$$= \frac{9}{14}$$ This is a ratio of whole numbers in lowest terms.

Answer

7. $\frac{2\frac{1}{2}}{\frac{3}{4}}, \frac{10}{3}$

3. Applications of Ratios

Ratios are used in a number of applications.

Example 5   Using Ratios to Express Population Increase

After the tragedy of Hurricane Katrina, New Orleans showed signs of recovery as more people moved back into the city. Three years after the storm, New Orleans had the fastest growth rate of any city in the United States. During a 1-year period, its population rose from 210,000 to 239,000. (*Source:* U.S. Census Bureau) Write a ratio expressing the increase in population to the original population for that year.

Solution:

To write this ratio, we need to know the increase in population.

$$\text{Increase} = 239{,}000 - 210{,}000 = 29{,}000$$

The ratio of the increase in population to the original number is

increase in population $\longrightarrow$ $\dfrac{29{,}000}{210{,}000}$ $\longleftarrow$ original population

$= \dfrac{29}{210}$ Simplify to lowest terms.

- **Skill Practice**

8. The U.S. Department of Transportation reported that more airports will have to expand to meet the growing demand of air travel. During a 5-year period, the Phoenix Sky Harbor Airport went from servicing 20 million passengers to 26 million passengers. Write a ratio of the increase in passengers to the original number.

Example 6   Applying Ratios to Unit Conversion

A fence is 12 yd long and 1 ft high.

a. Write the ratio of length to height with all units measured in yards.

b. Write the ratio of length to height with all units measured in feet.

1 ft = $\frac{1}{3}$ yd

12 yd

- **Skill Practice**

9. A painting is 2 yd in length by 2 ft wide.
  a. Write the ratio of length to width with all units measured in feet.
  b. Write the ratio of length to width with all units measured in yards.

Solution:

a. 3 ft = 1 yd, therefore, 1 ft = $\frac{1}{3}$ yd.

Measuring in yards, we see that the ratio of length to height is

$$\frac{12 \text{ yd}}{\frac{1}{3}\text{ yd}} = \frac{12}{1} \cdot \frac{3}{1} = \frac{36}{1}$$

b. The length is 12 yd = 36 ft. (Since 1 yd = 3 ft, then 12 yd = 12 · 3 ft = 36 ft.)

Measuring in feet, we see that the ratio of length to height is

$$\frac{36 \text{ ft}}{1 \text{ ft}} = \frac{36}{1}$$

Notice that regardless of the units used, the ratio is the same, 36 to 1. This means that the length is 36 times the height.

Answers

8. $\dfrac{3}{10}$ **9. a.** $\dfrac{3}{1}$ **b.** $\dfrac{3}{1}$

Study Skills Exercise

1. Define the key term **ratio**.

Objective 1: Writing a Ratio

2. Write a ratio of the number of females to males in your class.

For Exercises 3–8, write the ratio in two other ways.

3. 5 to 6

4. 3 to 7

5. 11 : 4

6. 8 : 13

7. $\frac{1}{2}$

8. $\frac{1}{8}$

For Exercises 9–14, write the ratios in fraction form. **(See Examples 1–2.)**

9. For a recent year, there were 10 named tropical storms and 6 hurricanes in the Atlantic. (*Source:* NOAA)

a. Write a ratio of the number of tropical storms to the number of hurricanes.

b. Write a ratio of the number of hurricanes to the number of tropical storms.

c. Write a ratio of the number of hurricanes to the total number of named storms.

11. In a certain neighborhood, 60 houses were on the market to be sold. During a 1-year period during a housing crisis, only 8 of these houses actually sold.

a. Write a ratio of the number of houses that sold to the total number that had been on the market.

b. Write a ratio of the number of houses that sold to the number that did not sell.

10. For a recent year, 250 million persons were covered by health insurance in the United States and 45 million were not covered. (*Source:* U.S. Census Bureau)

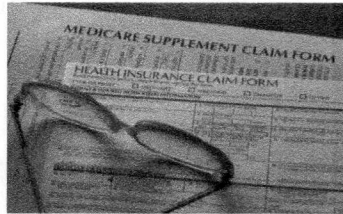

a. Write a ratio of the number of insured persons to the number of uninsured persons.

b. Write a ratio of the number of uninsured persons to the number of insured persons.

c. Write a ratio of the number of uninsured persons to the total number of persons.

12. There are 52 cars in the parking lot, of which 21 are silver.

a. Write a ratio of the number of silver cars to the total number of cars.

b. Write a ratio of the number of silver cars to the number of cars that are not silver.

13. In a recent survey of a group of computer users, 21 were MAC users and 54 were PC users.

   a. Write a ratio of the number of MAC users to PC users.

   b. Write a ratio for the number of MAC users to the total number of people surveyed.

14. At a school sporting event, the concession stand sold 450 bottles of water, 200 cans of soda, and 125 cans of iced tea.

   a. Write a ratio of the number of bottles of water sold to the number of cans of soda sold.

   b. Write a ratio of the number of cans of iced tea sold to the total number of drinks sold.

For Exercises 15–26, write the ratio in lowest terms. **(See Example 2.)**

15. 4 yr to 6 yr

16. 10 lb to 14 lb

17. 5 mi to 25 mi

18. 20 ft to 12 ft

19. 8 m to 2 m

20. 14 oz to 7 oz

21. 33 cm to 15 cm

22. 21 days to 30 days

23. \$60 to \$50

24. 75¢ to 100¢

25. 18 in. to 36 in.

26. 3 cups to 9 cups

Objective 2: Writing Ratios of Mixed Numbers and Decimals

For Exercises 27–38, write the ratio in lowest terms with whole numbers in the numerator and denominator. **(See Examples 3 and 4.)**

27. 3.6 ft to 2.4 ft

28. 10.15 hr to 8.12 hr

29. 8 gal to $9\frac{1}{3}$ gal

30. 24 yd to $13\frac{1}{3}$ yd

31. $16\frac{4}{5}$ m to $18\frac{9}{10}$ m

32. $1\frac{1}{4}$ in. to $1\frac{3}{8}$ in.

33. \$16.80 to \$2.40

34. \$18.50 to \$3.70

35. $\frac{1}{2}$ day to 4 days

36. $\frac{1}{4}$ mi to $1\frac{1}{2}$ mi

37. 10.25 L to 8.2 L

38. 11.55 km to 6.6 km

Objective 3: Applications of Ratios

39. In 1981, a giant sinkhole in Winter Park, Florida, "swallowed" a home, a public pool, and a car dealership (including five Porsches). One witness said that in a single day, the hole widened from 5 ft in diameter to 320 ft.

   a. Find the increase in the diameter of the sinkhole.

   b. Write a ratio representing the increase in diameter to the original diameter of 5 ft. **(See Example 5.)**

40. The temperature at 8:00 A.M. in Los Angeles was 66°F. By 2:00 P.M., the temperature had risen to 90°F.

   a. Find the increase in temperature from 8:00 A.M. to 2:00 P.M.

   b. Write a ratio representing the increase in temperature to the temperature at 8:00 A.M.

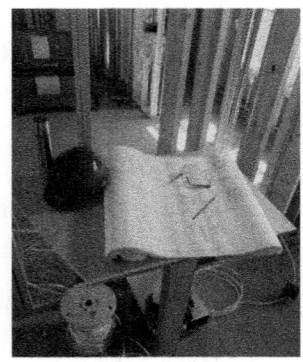

41. A window is 2 ft wide and 3 yd in length (2 ft is $\frac{2}{3}$ yd). **(See Example 6.)**

   a. Find the ratio of width to length with all units in yards.

   b. Find the ratio of width to length with all units in feet.

42. A construction company needs 2 weeks to construct a family room and 3 days to add a porch.

   a. Find the ratio of the time it takes for constructing the porch to the time for constructing the family room, with all units in weeks.

   b. Find the ratio of the time it takes for constructing the porch to the time for constructing the family room, with all units in days.

For Exercises 43–46, refer to the table showing Alex Rodriguez's salary (rounded to the nearest $100,000) for selected years during his career. Write each ratio in lowest terms.

Year	Team	Salary	Position
2007	New York Yankees	$22,700,000	Third baseman
2004	New York Yankees	$22,000,000	Third baseman
2000	Seattle Mariners	$4,400,000	Shortstop
1996	Seattle Mariners	$400,000	Shortstop

Source: USA TODAY

43. Write the ratio of Alex's salary for the year 1996 to the year 2000.

44. Write a ratio of Alex's salary for the year 2004 to the year 1996.

45. Write a ratio of the increase in Alex's salary between the years 1996 and the year 2000 to his salary in 1996.

46. Write a ratio of the increase in Alex's salary between the years 2004 and 2007 to his salary in 2004.

For Exercises 47–50, refer to the table that shows the average spending per person for reading (books, newspapers, magazines, etc.) by age group. Write each ratio in lowest terms.

Age Group	Annual Average ($)
Under 25 years	60
25 to 34 years	111
35 to 44 years	136
45 to 54 years	172
55 to 64 years	183
65 to 74 years	159
75 years and over	128

Source: Mediamark Research Inc.

47. Find the ratio of spending for the under-25 group to the spending for the group 75 years and over.

48. Find the ratio of spending for the group 25 to 34 years old to the spending for the group of 65 to 74 years old.

49. Find the ratio of spending for the group under 25 years old to the spending for the group of 55 to 64 years old.

50. Find the ratio of spending for the group 35 to 44 years old to the spending for the group 45 to 54 years old.

For Exercises 51–54, find the ratio of the shortest side to the longest side. Write each ratio in lowest terms with whole numbers in the numerator and denominator.

51.

52.

53.

54.

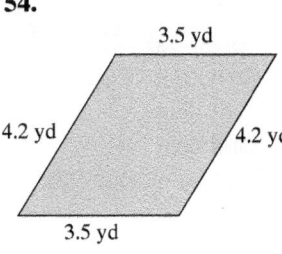

Expanding Your Skills

For Exercises 55–57, refer to the figure. The lengths of the sides for squares A, B, C, and D are given.

55. What are the lengths of the sides of square E?

56. Find the ratio of the lengths of the sides for the given pairs of squares.

   a. Square B to square A

   b. Square C to square B

   c. Square D to square C

   d. Square E to square D

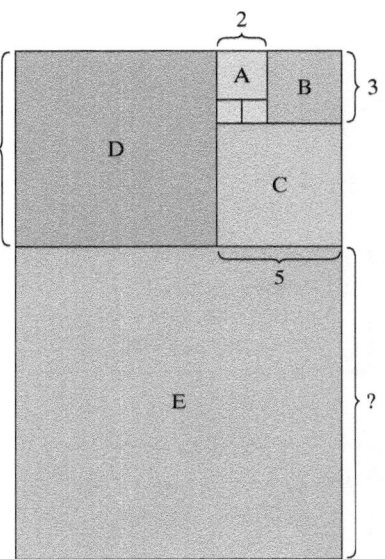

57. Write the decimal equivalents for each ratio in Exercise 56. Do these values seem to be approaching a number close to 1.618 (this is an approximation for the *golden ratio*, which is equal to $\frac{1 + \sqrt{5}}{2}$)? Applications of the golden ratio are found throughout nature. In particular, as a result of the geometrically pleasing pattern, artists and architects have proportioned their work to approximate the golden ratio.

58. The ratio of a person's height to the length of the person's lower arm (from elbow to wrist) is approximately 6.5 to 1. Measure your own height and lower arm length. Is the ratio you get close to the average of 6.5 to 1?

59. The ratio of a person's height to the person's shoulder width (measured from outside shoulder to outside shoulder) is approximately 4 to 1. Measure your own height and shoulder width. Is the ratio you get close to the average of 4 to 1?

Section 6.2   Rates

Objectives

1. **Definition of a Rate**
2. **Unit Rates**
3. **Unit Cost**
4. **Applications of Rates**

1. Definition of a Rate

A **rate** is a type of ratio used to compare different types of quantities, for example:

$$\frac{270 \text{ mi}}{13 \text{ gal}} \quad \text{and} \quad \frac{\$8.55}{1 \text{ hr}}$$

Several key words imply rates. These are given in Table 6-1.

Table 6-1

Key Word	Example	Rate
Per	117 miles per 2 hours	$\dfrac{117 \text{ mi}}{2 \text{ hr}}$
For	\$12 for 3 lb	$\dfrac{\$12}{3 \text{ lb}}$
In	400 meters in 43.5 seconds	$\dfrac{400 \text{ m}}{43.5 \text{ sec}}$
On	270 miles on 12 gallons of gas	$\dfrac{270 \text{ mi}}{12 \text{ gal}}$

Because a rate compares two different quantities it is important to include the units in both the numerator and the denominator. It is also desirable to write rates in lowest terms.

Concept Connections

1. Why is it important to include units when you are expressing a rate?

Skill Practice

Write each rate in lowest terms.

2. Maria reads 15 pages in 10 min.
3. A Chevrolet Corvette Z06 gets 163.4 mi on 8.6 gal of gas.
4. Marty's balance in his investment account changed by −\$254 in 4 months.

Example 1   **Writing Rates in Lowest Terms**

Write each rate in lowest terms.

a. In one region, there are approximately 640 trees on 12 acres.

b. Latonya drove 138 mi on 6 gal of gas.

c. After a cold front, the temperature changed by −10°F in 4 hr.

Solution:

a. The rate of 640 trees on 12 acres can be expressed as $\dfrac{640 \text{ trees}}{12 \text{ acres}}$.

Now write this rate in lowest terms. $\dfrac{\overset{160}{\cancel{640}} \text{ trees}}{\underset{3}{\cancel{12}} \text{ acres}} = \dfrac{160 \text{ trees}}{3 \text{ acres}}$

b. The rate of 138 mi on 6 gal of gas can be expressed as $\dfrac{138 \text{ mi}}{6 \text{ gal}}$.

Now write this rate in lowest terms. $\dfrac{\overset{23}{\cancel{138}} \text{ mi}}{\underset{1}{\cancel{6}} \text{ gal}} = \dfrac{23 \text{ mi}}{1 \text{ gal}}$

Answers

1. The units are different in the numerator and denominator and will not "cancel."
2. $\dfrac{3 \text{ pages}}{2 \text{ min}}$
3. $\dfrac{19 \text{ mi}}{1 \text{ gal}}$ or 19 mi/gal
4. $-\dfrac{\$127}{2 \text{ months}}$

c. $-10°F$ in 4 hr can be represented by $\dfrac{-10°F}{4\text{ hr}}$.

Writing this in lowest terms, we have: $\dfrac{-\overset{5}{\cancel{10}}°F}{\underset{2}{\cancel{4}}\text{ hr}} = -\dfrac{5°F}{2\text{ hr}}$

2. Unit Rates

A rate having a denominator of 1 unit is called a **unit rate**. Furthermore, the number 1 is often omitted in the denominator.

$\dfrac{23\text{ mi}}{1\text{ gal}} = 23$ mi/gal   is read as "twenty-three miles per gallon."

$\dfrac{52\text{ ft}}{1\text{ sec}} = 52$ ft/sec   is read as "fifty-two feet per second."

$\dfrac{\$15}{1\text{ hr}} = \$15$/hr   is read as "fifteen dollars per hour."

Concept Connections

5. Which rate is a unit rate?

$\dfrac{240\text{ mi}}{4\text{ hr}}$ or $\dfrac{60\text{ mi}}{1\text{ hr}}$

6. Which rate is a unit rate?

$\$24/1$ hr   or $\$24$/hr

> **PROCEDURE   Converting a Rate to a Unit Rate**
>
> To convert a rate to a unit rate, divide the numerator by the denominator and maintain the units of measurement.

Example 2   **Finding Unit Rates**

Write each rate as a unit rate. Round to three decimal places if necessary.

a. A health club charges $125 for 20 visits. Find the unit rate in dollars per visit.

b. In 1960, Wilma Rudolph won the women's 200-m run in 24 sec. Find her speed in meters per second.

c. During one baseball season, Barry Bonds got 149 hits in 403 at bats. Find his batting average. (*Hint:* Batting average is defined as the number of hits per the number of at bats.)

Skill Practice

Write a unit rate.

7. It costs $3.90 for 12 oranges.
8. A flight from Dallas to Des Moines travels a distance of 646 mi in 1.4 hr. Round the unit rate to the nearest mile per hour.
9. Under normal conditions, 98 in. of snow is equivalent to about 10 in. of rain.

Solution:

a. The rate of $125 for 20 visits can be expressed as $\dfrac{\$125}{20\text{ visits}}$.

To convert this to a unit rate, divide $125 by 20 visits.

$\dfrac{\$125}{20\text{ visits}} = \dfrac{\$6.25}{1\text{ visit}}$ or $6.25/visit

$$
\begin{array}{r}
6.25 \\
20)\overline{125.00} \\
-120 \\
\hline
50 \\
-40 \\
\hline
100 \\
-100 \\
\hline
0
\end{array}
$$

Answers

5. $\dfrac{60\text{ mi}}{1\text{ hr}}$

6. They are both unit rates.
7. $0.325 per orange
8. 461 mi/hr
9. 9.8 in. snow per 1 in. of rain

b. The rate of 200 m per 24 sec can be expressed as $\dfrac{200 \text{ m}}{24 \text{ sec}}$.

To convert this to a unit rate, divide 200 m by 24 sec.

$$\frac{200 \text{ m}}{24 \text{ sec}} \approx \frac{8.333 \text{ m}}{1 \text{ sec}} \quad \text{or approximately } 8.333 \text{ m/sec}$$

$$\begin{array}{r} 8.\overline{3} \\ 24\overline{)200.00} \\ -192 \\ \hline 80 \\ -72 \\ \hline 80 \end{array}$$ The quotient repeats.

Wilma Rudolph's speed was approximately 8.333 m/sec.

> **Avoiding Mistakes**
>
> Units of measurement must be included for the answer to be complete.

c. The rate of 149 hits in 403 at bats can be expressed as $\dfrac{149 \text{ hits}}{403 \text{ at bats}}$.

To convert this to a unit rate, divide 149 hits by 403 at bats.

$$\frac{149 \text{ hits}}{403 \text{ at bats}} \approx \frac{0.370 \text{ hit}}{1 \text{ at bat}} \quad \text{or } 0.370 \text{ hit/at bat}$$

3. Unit Cost

A **unit cost** or unit price is the cost per 1 unit of something. At the grocery store, for example, you might purchase meat for $3.79/lb ($3.79 per 1 lb). Unit cost is useful in day-to-day life when we compare prices. Example 3 compares the prices of three different sizes of apple juice.

> **Skill Practice**
>
> **10.** Gatorade comes in several size packages. Compute the unit price per ounce for each option (round to the nearest thousandth of a dollar). Then determine which is the best buy.
> **a.** $2.99 for a 64-oz bottle
> **b.** $3.99 for four 24-oz bottles
> **c.** $3.79 for six 12-oz bottles

Example 3 **Finding Unit Costs**

Apple juice comes in a variety of sizes and packaging options. Find the unit price per ounce and determine which is the best buy.

a. $1.69

Apple Juice
48 oz

b. $2.39

Apple Juice
64 oz

c. $2.99

Apple Juice
10-pack 6 oz each

Solution:

When we compute a unit cost, the cost is always placed in the numerator of the rate. Furthermore, when we divide the cost by the amount, we need to obtain enough digits in the quotient to see the variation in unit price. In this example, we have rounded to the nearest thousandth of a dollar (nearest tenth of a cent). This means that we use the ten-thousandths-place digit in the quotient on which to base our decision on rounding.

Answer

10. a. $0.047/oz
  b. $0.042/oz
  c. $0.053/oz
  The 4-pack of 24-oz bottles is the best buy.

	Rate	Quotient	Unit Rate (Rounded)
a.	$\dfrac{\$1.69}{48\ oz}$	$\$1.69 \div 48\ oz \approx \$0.0352/oz$	$0.035/oz or 3.5¢/oz
b.	$\dfrac{\$2.39}{64\ oz}$	$\$2.39 \div 64\ oz \approx \$0.0373/oz$	$0.037/oz or 3.7¢/oz
c.	$\begin{array}{c}6\ oz \times 10 = 60\ oz\\[2pt]\dfrac{\$2.99}{60\ oz}\end{array}$	$\$2.99 \div 60\ oz \approx \$0.0498/oz$	$0.050/oz or 5.0¢/oz

From the table, we see that the most economical buy is the 48-oz size because its unit rate is the least expensive.

4. Applications of Rates

Example 4 uses a unit rate for comparison in an application.

Example 4 Computing Mortality Rates

Mortality rate is defined to be the total number of people who die due to some risk behavior divided by the total number of people who engage in the risk behavior. Based on the following statistics, compare the mortality rate for undergoing heart bypass surgery to the mortality rate of flying on the space shuttle.

a. Roughly 28 people will die for every 1000 who undergo heart bypass surgery. (*Source:* The Society of Thoracic Surgeons)

b. As of August 2007, there have been 14 astronauts killed in space shuttle missions out of 830 astronauts who have flown.

Solution:

a. Mortality rate for heart bypass surgery: $\frac{28}{1000} = 0.028$ death/surgery

b. Mortality rate for flying on the space shuttle: $\frac{14}{830} \approx 0.017$ deaths/flight

Comparing these rates shows that it is riskier to have heart bypass surgery than to fly on the space shuttle.

Skill Practice

11. In Ecuador roughly 450 out of 500 adults can read. In Brazil, approximately 1700 out of 2000 adults can read.
   a. Compute the unit rate for Ecuador. (This unit rate is called the *literacy rate*.)
   b. Compute the unit rate for Brazil.
   c. Which country has the greater literacy rate?

Answer

11. a. 0.9 reader per adult
   b. 0.85 reader per adult
   c. Ecuador

Section 6.2 Practice Exercises

Boost *your* GRADE at ALEKS.com!

• Practice Problems
• Self-Tests
• NetTutor
• e-Professors
• Videos

Study Skills Exercise

1. Define the key terms.

   a. Rate   **b. Unit rate**   **c. Unit cost**

Review Exercises

2. Write the ratio 3 to 5 in two other ways.   **3.** Write the ratio 4:1 in two other ways.

For Exercises 4–6, write the ratio in lowest terms.

4. $6\frac{3}{4}$ ft to $8\frac{1}{4}$ ft

5. 1.08 mi to 2.04 mi

6. $28.40 to $20.80

Objective 1: Definition of a Rate

For Exercises 7–18, write each rate in lowest terms. **(See Example 1.)**

7. A type of laminate flooring sells for $32 for 5 ft^2.

8. A remote control car can go up to 44 ft in 5 sec.

9. Elaine drives 234 mi in 4 hr.

10. Travis has 14 blooms on 6 of his plants.

11. Tyler earned $58 in 8 hr.

12. Neil can type only 336 words in 15 min.

13. A printer can print 13 pages in 26 sec.

14. During a bad storm there was 2 in. of rain in 6 hr.

15. There are 130 calories in 8 snack crackers.

16. There are 50 students assigned to 4 advisers.

17. The temperature changed by $-18°F$ in 8 hr.

18. Jill's portfolio changed by $-$2600$ in 6 months.

Objective 2: Unit Rates

19. Of the following rates, identify those that are unit rates.

a. $\dfrac{\$0.37}{1\text{ oz}}$ **b.** $\dfrac{333.2\text{ mi}}{14\text{ gal}}$ **c.** 16 ft/sec   **d.** $\dfrac{59\text{ mi}}{1\text{ hr}}$

20. Of the following rates, identify those that are unit rates.

a. $\dfrac{3\text{ lb}}{\$1.00}$ **b.** $\dfrac{21\text{ ft}}{1\text{ sec}}$ **c.** 50 mi/hr   **d.** $\dfrac{232\text{ words}}{2\text{ min}}$

For Exercises 21–32, write each rate as a unit rate and round to the nearest hundredth when necessary. **(See Example 2.)**

21. The Osborne family drove 452 mi in 4 days.

22. The book of poetry *The Prophet* by Kahlil Gibran has estimated sales of $6,000,000 over an 80-year period.

23. A submarine practicing evasive maneuvers descended 100 m in $\frac{1}{4}$ hr. Find a unit rate representing the change in "altitude" per hour.

24. The ground dropped 74.4 ft in 24 hr in the famous Winter Park sinkhole of 1981. Find the unit rate representing the change in "altitude" per hour.

25. If Oscar bought an easy chair for $660 and plans to make 12 payments, what is the amount per payment?

26. The jockey David Gall had 7396 wins in 43 years of riding.

27. At the market, bananas cost $2.76 for 4 lb.

28. Ceramic tile sell for $13.08 for a box of 12 tiles. Find the price per tile.

29. Lottery prize money of $1,792,000 is for seven people.

30. One WeightWatchers group lost 123 lb for its 11 members.

31. A male speed skater skated 500 m in 35 sec. Find the rate in meters per second.

32. A female speed skater skated 500 m in 38 sec. Find the rate in meters per second.

Objective 3: Unit Cost

For Exercises 33–42, find the unit costs (that is, dollars per unit). Round the answers to three decimal places when necessary. **(See Example 3.)**

33. Tide laundry detergent costs $14.99 for 100 oz.

34. Dove liquid body wash costs $3.49 for 12 oz.

35. Soda costs $1.99 for a 2-L bottle.

36. Four chairs cost $221.00.

37. A set of four tires costs $210.

38. A package of three shirts costs $64.80.

39. A package of six newborn bodysuits costs $32.50.

40. A package of eight AAA batteries costs $9.84.

41. **a.** 40 oz of shampoo for $3.00

 b. 28 oz of shampoo for $2.10

 c. Which is the best buy?

42. **a.** 10 lb of potting soil for $1.70

 b. 30 lb of potting soil for $5.10

 c. Which is the best buy?

43. Corn comes in two size cans, 29 oz and 15 oz. The larger can costs $1.59 and the smaller can costs $1.09. Find the unit cost of each can. Which is the better buy? (Round to three decimal places.)

44. Napkins come in a variety of packages. A package of 400 napkins sells for $2.99, and a package of 100 napkins sells for $1.50. Find the unit cost of each package. Which is the better buy? (Round to four decimal places.)

Objective 4: Applications of Rates

45. Carbonated beverages come in different sizes and contain different amounts of sugar. Compute the amount of sugar per fluid ounce for each soda. Then determine which has the greatest amount of sugar per fluid ounce. **(See Example 4.)**

Soda	Amount	Sugar
Coca-Cola	20 fl oz	65 g
Mello Yello	12 fl oz	47 g
Canada Dry Ginger Ale	8 fl oz	24 g

46. Compute the amount of carbohydrate per fluid ounce for each soda. Then determine which has the greatest amount of carbohydrate per fluid ounce.

Soda	Amount	Carbohydrates
Coca-Cola	20 fl oz	65 g
Mello Yello	12 fl oz	47 g
Canada Dry Ginger Ale	8 fl oz	25 g

47. Carbonated beverages come in different sizes and have a different number of calories. Compute the number of calories per fluid ounce for each soda. Then determine which has the least number of calories per fluid ounce.

Soda	Amount	Calories
Coca-Cola	20 fl oz	240
Mello Yello	12 fl oz	170
Canada Dry Ginger Ale	8 fl oz	90

48. According to the National Institutes of Health, a platelet count below 20,000 per microliter of blood is considered a life-threatening condition. Suppose a patient's test results yield a platelet count of 13,000,000 for 100 microliters. Write this as a unit rate (number of platelets per microliter). Does the patient have a life-threatening condition?

49. The number of motor vehicles produced in the United States increased steadily by a total of 5,310,000 in an 18-year period. Compute the rate representing the increase in the number of vehicles produced per year during this time period. (*Source:* American Automobile Manufacturers Association)

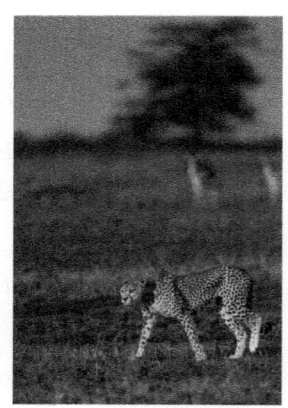

50. The total number of prisoners in the United States increased steadily by a total of 344,000 in an 8-year period. Compute the rate representing the increase in the number of prisoners per year.

51. a. The population of Mexico increased steadily by 22 million people in a 10-year period. Compute the rate representing the increase in the population per year.

b. The population of Brazil increased steadily by 10.2 million in a 5-year period. Compute the rate representing the increase in the population per year.

c. Which country has a greater rate of increase in population per year?

52. a. The price per share of Microsoft stock rose $18.24 in a 24-month period. Compute the rate representing the increase in the price per month.

b. The price per share of IBM stock rose $22.80 in a 12-month period. Compute the rate representing the increase in the price per month.

c. Which stock had a greater rate of increase per month?

53. A cheetah can run 120 m in 4.1 sec. An antelope can run 50 m in 2.1 sec. Compare their unit speeds to determine which animal is faster. Round to the nearest whole unit.

Calculator Connections

Topic: Applications of Unit Rates

Calculator Exercises

Don Shula coached football for 33 years. He had 328 wins and 156 losses. Tom Landry coached football for 29 years. He had 250 wins and 162 losses. Use this information to answer Exercises 54–55.

54. a. Compute a unit rate representing the average number of wins per year for Don Shula. Round to one decimal place.

b. Compute a unit rate representing the average number of wins per year for Tom Landry. Round to one decimal place.

c. Which coach had a better rate of wins per year?

55. a. Compute a unit rate representing the number of wins to the number of losses for Don Shula. Round to one decimal place.

    b. Compute a unit rate representing the number of wins to the number of losses for Tom Landry. Round to one decimal place.

    c. Which coach had a better win/loss rate?

56. Compare three brands of soap. Find the price per ounce and determine the best buy. (Round to two decimal places.)

    a. Dove: $7.89 for a 6-bar pack of 4.5-oz bars

    b. Dial: $2.89 for a 3-bar pack of 4.5-oz bars

    c. Irish Spring: $6.99 for an 8-bar pack of 4.5-oz bars

57. Mayonnaise comes in 32-, 16-, and 8-oz jars. They are priced at $5.59, $3.79, and $2.59, respectively. Find the unit cost of each size jar to find the best buy. (Round to three decimal places.)

58. Albacore tuna comes in different-size cans. Find the unit cost of each package to find the best buy. (Round to three decimal places.)

    a. $3.99 for a 12-oz can

    b. $6.29 for a 4-pack of 6-oz cans

    c. $3.39 for a 3-pack of 3-oz cans

59. Coca-Cola is sold in a variety of different packages. Find the unit cost of each package to find the better buy. (Round to three decimal places.)

    a. $4.99 for a case of 24 twelve-oz cans

    b. $5.00 for a 12-pack of 8-oz cans

Proportions and Applications of Proportions

Section 6.3

1. Definition of a Proportion

Objectives

Recall that a statement indicating that two quantities are equal is called an equation. In this section, we are interested in a special type of equation called a proportion. A **proportion** states that two ratios or rates are equal. For example:

$$\frac{1}{4} = \frac{10}{40} \text{ is a proportion.}$$

We know that the fractions $\frac{1}{4}$ and $\frac{10}{40}$ are equal because $\frac{10}{40}$ reduces to $\frac{1}{4}$.

We read the proportion $\frac{1}{4} = \frac{10}{40}$ as follows: "1 is to 4 as 10 is to 40."

We also say that the numbers 1 and 4 are *proportional to* the numbers 10 and 40.

1. Definition of a Proportion
2. Determining Whether Two Ratios Form a Proportion
3. Solving Proportions
4. Applications of Proportions

Skill Practice

Write a proportion for each statement.

1. 7 is to 28 as 13 is to 52.
2. $17 is to 2 hr as $102 is to 12 hr.
3. The numbers 5 and −11 are proportional to the numbers 15 and −33.

Example 1 **Writing Proportions**

Write a proportion for each statement.

a. 5 is to 12 as 30 is to 72.

b. 240 mi is to 4 hr as 300 mi is to 5 hr.

c. The numbers −3 and 7 are proportional to the numbers −12 and 28.

Solution:

a. $\dfrac{5}{12} = \dfrac{30}{72}$ 5 is to 12 as 30 is to 72.

b. $\dfrac{240 \text{ mi}}{4 \text{ hr}} = \dfrac{300 \text{ mi}}{5 \text{ hr}}$ 240 mi is to 4 hr as 300 mi is to 5 hr.

c. $\dfrac{-3}{7} = \dfrac{-12}{28}$ −3 and 7 are proportional to −12 and 28.

> **TIP:** A proportion is an equation and must have an equal sign.

2. Determining Whether Two Ratios Form a Proportion

To determine whether two ratios form a proportion, we must determine whether the ratios are equal. Recall from Section 4.2 that two fractions are equal whenever their cross products are equal. That is,

$$\frac{a}{b} = \frac{c}{d} \quad \text{implies} \quad a \cdot d \doteq b \cdot c \quad \text{(and vice versa).}$$

Skill Practice

Determine whether the ratios form a proportion.

4. $\dfrac{4}{9} \overset{?}{=} \dfrac{12}{27}$

5. $\dfrac{3\frac{1}{4}}{5} \overset{?}{=} \dfrac{8}{12}$

Example 2 **Determining Whether Two Ratios Form a Proportion**

Determine whether the ratios form a proportion.

a. $\dfrac{3}{5} \overset{?}{=} \dfrac{9}{15}$ **b.** $\dfrac{8}{4} \overset{?}{=} \dfrac{10}{5\frac{1}{2}}$

Solution:

a. $\dfrac{3}{5} \diagdown\!\!\!\!\diagup \dfrac{9}{15}$

$(3)(15) \overset{?}{=} (5)(9)$ Cross-multiply to form the cross products.

$45 = 45 \checkmark$

The cross products are equal. Therefore, the ratios form a proportion.

b. $\dfrac{8}{4} \diagdown\!\!\!\!\diagup \dfrac{10}{5\frac{1}{2}}$

$(8)\left(5\dfrac{1}{2}\right) \overset{?}{=} (4)(10)$ Cross-multiply to form the cross products.

$\dfrac{\overset{4}{8}}{1} \cdot \dfrac{11}{\underset{1}{2}} \overset{?}{=} 40$ Write the mixed number as an improper fraction.

$44 \neq 40$ Multiply fractions.

The cross products are not equal. The ratios do not form a proportion.

> **Avoiding Mistakes**
>
> Cross multiplication can be performed only when there are two fractions separated by an equal sign.

Answers

1. $\dfrac{7}{28} = \dfrac{13}{52}$ 2. $\dfrac{\$17}{2 \text{ hr}} = \dfrac{\$102}{12 \text{ hr}}$

3. $\dfrac{5}{-11} = \dfrac{15}{-33}$ 4. Yes   5. No

Example 3 **Determining Whether Pairs of Numbers Are Proportional**

Determine whether the numbers 2.7 and −5.3 are proportional to the numbers 8.1 and −15.9.

Solution:

Two pairs of numbers are proportional if their ratios are equal.

$$\dfrac{2.7}{-5.3} \times \dfrac{8.1}{-15.9}$$

$(2.7)(-15.9) \overset{?}{=} (-5.3)(8.1)$ Cross-multiply to form the cross products.

$-42.93 = -42.93$ ✓   Multiply decimals.

The cross products are equal. The ratios form a proportion.

Skill Practice

6. Determine whether the numbers −1.2 and 2.5 are proportional to the numbers −2 and 5.

3. Solving Proportions

A proportion is made up of four values. If three of the four values are known, we can solve for the fourth.

Consider the proportion $\frac{x}{20} = \frac{3}{4}$. We let the variable x represent the unknown value in the proportion. To solve for x, we can equate the cross products to form an equivalent equation.

$$\dfrac{x}{20} \times \dfrac{3}{4}$$

$4x = 3 \cdot 20$ Cross-multiply to form the cross products.

$4x = 60$ Simplify.

$\dfrac{4x}{4} = \dfrac{60}{4}$ Divide both sides by 4 to isolate x.

$x = 15$

We can check the value of x in the original proportion.

Check: $\dfrac{x}{20} = \dfrac{3}{4}$ $\xrightarrow{\text{substitute 15 for } x}$ $\dfrac{15}{20} \overset{?}{=} \dfrac{3}{4}$

$(15)(4) \overset{?}{=} (3)(20)$

$60 = 60$ ✓   The solution 15 checks.

The steps to solve a proportion are summarized next.

PROCEDURE Solving a Proportion

Step 1 Set the cross products equal to each other.
Step 2 Solve the equation.
Step 3 Check the solution in the original proportion.

Answer

6. No

Skill Practice

Solve the proportion. Be sure to check your answer.

7. $\dfrac{3}{w} = \dfrac{21}{77}$

Avoiding Mistakes

When solving a proportion, do not try to "cancel" like factors on opposite sides of the equal sign. The proportion, $\frac{4}{15} = \frac{9}{n}$ cannot be simplified.

Example 4 Solving a Proportion

Solve the proportion. $\qquad \dfrac{4}{15} = \dfrac{9}{n}$

Solution:

$$\dfrac{4}{15} = \dfrac{9}{n} \qquad \text{The variable can be represented by any letter.}$$

$$4n = (9)(15) \qquad \text{Set the cross products equal.}$$

$$4n = 135 \qquad \text{Simplify.}$$

$$\dfrac{4n}{4} = \dfrac{135}{4} \qquad \text{Divide both sides by 4 to isolate } n.$$

$$n = \dfrac{135}{4} \qquad \text{The fraction } \tfrac{135}{4} \text{ is in lowest terms.}$$

The solution may be written as $n = \frac{135}{4}$ or $n = 33\frac{3}{4}$ or $n = 33.75$.

To check the solution in the original proportion, we may use any of the three forms of the answer. We will use the decimal form.

$$\underline{\text{Check:}} \quad \dfrac{4}{15} = \dfrac{9}{n} \xrightarrow{\text{substitute } n = 33.75} \dfrac{4}{15} \overset{?}{=} \dfrac{9}{33.75}$$

$$(4)(33.75) \overset{?}{=} (9)(15)$$

$$135 = 135 \checkmark$$

The solution 33.75 checks in the original proportion.

Skill Practice

Solve the proportion. Be sure to check your answer.

8. $\dfrac{0.6}{x} = \dfrac{1.5}{-2}$

Example 5 Solving a Proportion

Solve the proportion. $\qquad \dfrac{0.8}{-3.1} = \dfrac{4}{p}$

Solution:

$$\dfrac{0.8}{-3.1} = \dfrac{4}{p}$$

$$0.8p = 4(-3.1) \qquad \text{Set the cross products equal.}$$

$$0.8p = -12.4 \qquad \text{Simplify.}$$

$$\dfrac{0.8p}{0.8} = \dfrac{-12.4}{0.8} \qquad \text{Divide both sides by 0.8.}$$

$$p = -15.5 \qquad \text{The value } -15.5 \text{ checks in the original equation.}$$

The solution is -15.5.

We chose to give the solution to Example 5 in decimal form because the values in the original proportion are decimal numbers. However, it would be correct to give the solution as a mixed number or fraction. The solution -15.5 is also equivalent to $-15\frac{1}{2}$ or $-\frac{31}{2}$.

Answers

7. 11 **8.** -0.8

4. Applications of Proportions

Proportions are used in a variety of applications. In Examples 6 through 9, we take information from the wording of a problem and form a proportion.

Example 6 **Using a Proportion in a Consumer Application**

Linda drove her Honda Accord 145 mi on 5 gal of gas. At this rate, how far can she drive on 12 gal?

Solution:

Let x represent the distance Linda can go on 12 gal.

This problem involves two rates. We can translate this to a proportion. Equate the two rates.

$$\text{distance} \longrightarrow \frac{145 \text{ mi}}{5 \text{ gal}} = \frac{x \text{ mi}}{12 \text{ gal}} \longleftarrow \text{distance}$$
$$\text{number of gallons} \longrightarrow \qquad\qquad \longleftarrow \text{number of gallons}$$

Solve the proportion.

$(145)(12) = (5) \cdot x$ Cross-multiply to form the cross products.

$1740 = 5x$

$\dfrac{1740}{5} = \dfrac{\overset{1}{\cancel{5}}x}{\underset{1}{\cancel{5}}}$ Divide both sides by 5.

$348 = x$ Divide. $1740 \div 5 = 348$

Linda can drive 348 mi on 12 gal of gas.

TIP: Notice that the two rates have the same units in the numerator (miles) and the same units in the denominator (gallons).

In Example 6 we could have set up a proportion in many different ways.

$$\frac{145 \text{ mi}}{5 \text{ gal}} = \frac{x \text{ mi}}{12 \text{ gal}} \quad \text{or} \quad \frac{5 \text{ gal}}{145 \text{ mi}} = \frac{12 \text{ gal}}{x \text{ mi}} \quad \text{or}$$

$$\frac{5 \text{ gal}}{12 \text{ gal}} = \frac{145 \text{ mi}}{x \text{ mi}} \quad \text{or} \quad \frac{12 \text{ gal}}{5 \text{ gal}} = \frac{x \text{ mi}}{145 \text{ mi}}$$

Notice that in each case, the cross products produce the same equation. We will generally set up the proportions so that the units in the numerators are the same and the units in the denominators are the same.

Example 7 **Using a Proportion in a Construction Application**

If a cable 25 ft long weighs 1.2 lb, how much will a 120-ft cable weigh?

Solution:

Let w represent the weight of the 120-ft cable.   Label the unknown.

length ⟶ $\dfrac{25 \text{ ft}}{1.2 \text{ lb}} = \dfrac{120 \text{ ft}}{w \text{ lb}}$ ⟵ length   Translate to a proportion.
weight ⟶   ⟵ weight

$(25) \cdot w = (1.2)(120)$ Equate the cross products.

$25w = 144$

$\dfrac{\overset{1}{25} w}{\underset{1}{25}} = \dfrac{144}{25}$ Divide both sides by 25.

$w = 5.76$ Divide. $144 \div 25 = 5.76$

The 120-ft cable weighs 5.76 lb.

Example 8 **Using a Proportion in a Geography Application**

The distance between Phoenix and Los Angeles is 348 mi. On a certain map, this is represented by 6 in. On the same map, the distance between San Antonio and Little Rock is $8\frac{1}{2}$ in. What is the actual distance between San Antonio and Little Rock?

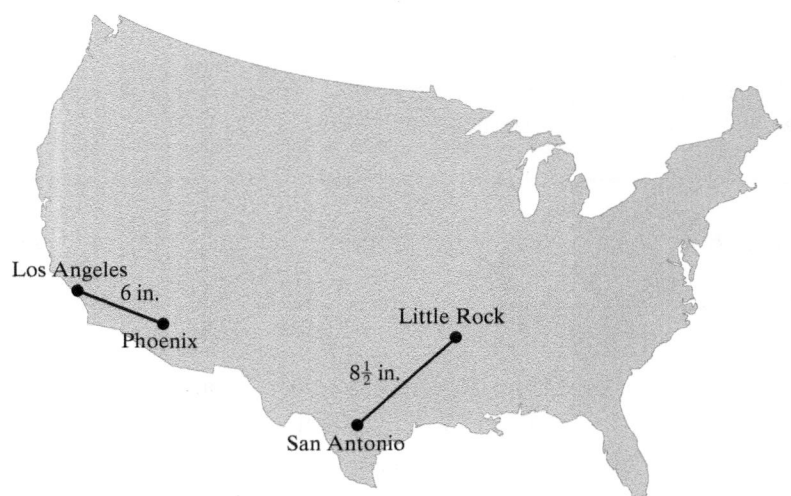

Solution:

Let d represent the distance between San Antonio and Little Rock.

actual distance ⟶ $\dfrac{348 \text{ mi}}{6 \text{ in.}} = \dfrac{d \text{ mi}}{8\frac{1}{2} \text{ in.}}$ ⟵ actual distance
distance on map ⟶   ⟵ distance on map

Translate to a proportion.

$(348)(8\frac{1}{2}) = (6) \cdot d$ Equate the cross products.

$(348)(8.5) = 6d$ Convert the values to decimal.

$$2958 = 6d$$

$$\frac{2958}{6} = \frac{\overset{1}{\cancel{6}}d}{\cancel{6}_1} \qquad \text{Divide both sides by 6.}$$

$$493 = d \qquad \text{Divide. } 2958 \div 6 = 493$$

The distance between San Antonio and Little Rock is 493 mi.

Example 9 **Applying a Proportion to Environmental Science**

A biologist wants to estimate the number of elk in a wildlife preserve. She sedates 25 elk and clips a small radio transmitter onto the ear of each animal. The elk return to the wild, and after 6 months, the biologist studies a sample of 120 elk in the preserve. Of the 120 elk sampled, 4 have radio transmitters. Approximately how many elk are in the whole preserve?

Solution:

Let n represent the number of elk in the whole preserve.

	Sample		Population	
number of elk in the sample with radio transmitters →	$\dfrac{4}{120}$	$=$	$\dfrac{25}{n}$	← number of elk in the population with radio transmitters
total elk in the sample →				← total elk in the population

$$4 \cdot n = (120)(25) \qquad \text{Equate the cross products.}$$

$$4n = 3000$$

$$\frac{\overset{1}{\cancel{4}}n}{\cancel{4}_1} = \frac{3000}{4} \qquad \text{Divide both sides by 4.}$$

$$n = 750 \qquad \text{Divide. } 3000 \div 4 = 750$$

There are approximately 750 elk in the wildlife preserve.

Skill Practice

12. To estimate the number of fish in a lake, the park service catches 50 fish and tags them. After several months the park service catches a sample of 100 fish and finds that 6 are tagged. Approximately how many fish are in the lake?

Answer

12. There are approximately 833 fish in the lake.

Section 6.3 Practice Exercises

Study Skills Exercise

1. Define the key term **proportion**.

Review Exercises

For Exercises 2–5, write as a reduced ratio or rate.

2. 3 ft to 45 ft

3. 3 teachers for 45 students

4. 6 apples for 2 pies

5. 6 days to 2 days

For Exercises 6–8, write as a unit rate.

6. 800 revolutions in 10 sec

7. 337.2 mi on 12 gal of gas

8. 13,516 passengers on 62 flights

Objective 1: Definition of a Proportion

For Exercises 9–20, write a proportion for each statement. **(See Example 1.)**

9. 4 is to 16 as 5 is to 20.

10. 3 is to 18 as 4 is to 24.

11. −25 is to 15 as −10 is to 6.

12. 35 is to −14 as 20 is to −8.

13. The numbers 2 and 3 are proportional to the numbers 4 and 6.

14. The numbers 2 and 1 are proportional to the numbers 26 and 13.

15. The numbers −30 and −25 are proportional to the numbers 12 and 10.

16. The numbers −24 and −18 are proportional to the numbers 8 and 6.

17. $6.25 per hour is proportional to $187.50 per 30 hr.

18. $115 per week is proportional to $460 per 4 weeks.

19. 1 in. is to 7 mi as 5 in. is to 35 mi.

20. 16 flowers is to 5 plants as 32 flowers is to 10 plants.

Objective 2: Determining Whether Two Ratios Form a Proportion

For Exercises 21–28, determine whether the ratios form a proportion. **(See Example 2.)**

21. $\dfrac{5}{18} \overset{?}{=} \dfrac{4}{16}$

22. $\dfrac{9}{10} \overset{?}{=} \dfrac{8}{9}$

23. $\dfrac{16}{24} \overset{?}{=} \dfrac{2}{3}$

24. $\dfrac{4}{5} \overset{?}{=} \dfrac{24}{30}$

25. $\dfrac{2\frac{1}{2}}{3\frac{2}{3}} \overset{?}{=} \dfrac{15}{22}$

26. $\dfrac{1\frac{3}{4}}{3} \overset{?}{=} \dfrac{7}{12}$

27. $\dfrac{2}{-3.2} \overset{?}{=} \dfrac{10}{-16}$

28. $\dfrac{4.7}{-7} \overset{?}{=} \dfrac{23.5}{-35}$

For Exercises 29–34, determine whether the pairs of numbers are proportional. **(See Example 3.)**

29. Are the numbers 48 and 18 proportional to the numbers 24 and 9?

30. Are the numbers 35 and 14 proportional to the numbers 5 and 2?

31. Are the numbers $2\frac{3}{8}$ and $1\frac{1}{2}$ proportional to the numbers $9\frac{1}{2}$ and 6?

32. Are the numbers $1\frac{2}{3}$ and $\frac{5}{6}$ proportional to the numbers 5 and $2\frac{1}{2}$?

33. Are the numbers −6.3 and 9 proportional to the numbers −12.6 and 16?

34. Are the numbers −7.1 and 2.4 proportional to the numbers −35.5 and 10?

Objective 3: Solving Proportions

For Exercises 35–38, determine whether the given value is a solution to the proportion.

35. $\dfrac{x}{40} = \dfrac{1}{-8};\quad x = -5$

36. $\dfrac{14}{x} = \dfrac{12}{-18};\quad x = -21$

37. $\dfrac{12.4}{31} = \dfrac{8.2}{y};\quad y = 20$

38. $\dfrac{4.2}{9.8} = \dfrac{z}{36.4};\quad z = 15.2$

For Exercises 39–58, solve the proportion. Be sure to check your answers. **(See Examples 4–5.)**

39. $\dfrac{12}{16} = \dfrac{3}{x}$

40. $\dfrac{20}{28} = \dfrac{5}{x}$

41. $\dfrac{9}{21} = \dfrac{x}{7}$

42. $\dfrac{15}{10} = \dfrac{3}{x}$

43. $\dfrac{p}{12} = \dfrac{-25}{4}$

44. $\dfrac{p}{8} = \dfrac{-30}{24}$

45. $\dfrac{3}{40} = \dfrac{w}{10}$

46. $\dfrac{5}{60} = \dfrac{z}{8}$

47. $\dfrac{16}{-13} = \dfrac{20}{t}$

48. $\dfrac{12}{b} = \dfrac{8}{-9}$

49. $\dfrac{m}{12} = \dfrac{5}{8}$

50. $\dfrac{16}{12} = \dfrac{21}{a}$

51. $\dfrac{17}{12} = \dfrac{4\frac{1}{4}}{x}$

52. $\dfrac{26}{30} = \dfrac{5\frac{1}{5}}{x}$

53. $\dfrac{0.5}{h} = \dfrac{1.8}{9}$

54. $\dfrac{2.6}{h} = \dfrac{1.3}{0.5}$

55. $\dfrac{\frac{3}{8}}{6.75} = \dfrac{x}{72}$

56. $\dfrac{12.5}{\frac{1}{4}} = \dfrac{120}{y}$

57. $\dfrac{4}{\frac{1}{10}} = \dfrac{-\frac{1}{2}}{z}$

58. $\dfrac{6}{\frac{1}{3}} = \dfrac{-\frac{1}{2}}{t}$

For Exercises 59–64, write a proportion for each statement. Then solve for the variable.

59. 25 is to 100 as 9 is to y.

60. 65 is to 15 as 26 is to y.

61. 15 is to 20 as t is to 10

62. 9 is to 12 as w is to 30.

63. The numbers -3.125 and 5 are proportional to the numbers -18.75 and k.

64. The numbers -4.75 and 8 are proportional to the numbers -9.5 and k.

Objective 4: Applications of Proportions

65. Pam drives her Toyota Prius 244 mi in city driving on 4 gal of gas. At this rate how many miles can she drive on 10 gal of gas? **(See Example 6.)**

66. Didi takes her pulse for 10 sec and counts 13 beats. How many beats per minute is this?

67. To cement a garden path, it takes crushed rock and cement in a ratio of 3.25 kg of rock to 1 kg of cement. If a 24 kg-bag of cement is purchased, how much crushed rock will be needed? **(See Example 7.)**

68. Suppose two adults produce 63.4 lb of garbage in one week. At this rate, how many pounds will 50 adults produce in one week?

69. On a map, the distance from Sacramento, California, to San Francisco, California, is 8 cm. The legend gives the actual distance at 91 mi. On the same map, Faythe measured 7 cm from Sacramento to Modesto, California. What is the actual distance? (Round to the nearest mile.) **(See Example 8.)**

70. On a map, the distance from Nashville, Tennessee, to Atlanta, Georgia, is 3.5 in., and the actual distance is 210 mi. If the map distance between Dallas, Texas, and Little Rock, Arkansas, is 4.75 in., what is the actual distance?

71. At Central Community College, the ratio of female students to male students is 31 to 19. If there are 6200 female students, how many male students are there?

72. Evelyn won an election by a ratio of 6 to 5. If she received 7230 votes, how many votes did her opponent receive?

73. If you flip a coin many times, the coin should come up heads about 1 time out of every 2 times it is flipped. If a coin is flipped 630 times, about how many heads do you expect to come up?

74. A die is a small cube used in games of chance. It has six sides, and each side has 1, 2, 3, 4, 5, or 6 dots painted on it. If you roll a die, the number 4 should come up about 1 time out of every 6 times the die is rolled. If you roll a die 366 times, about how many times do you expect the number 4 to come up?

75. A pitcher gave up 42 earned runs in 126 innings. Approximately how many earned runs will he give up in one game (9 innings)? This value is called the earned run average.

76. In one game Peyton Manning completed 34 passes for 357 yd. At this rate how many yards would be gained for 22 passes?

77. Pierre bought 480 Euros with $750 American. At this rate, how many Euros can he buy with $900 American?

78. Erik bought $624 Canadian with $600 American. At this rate, how many Canadian dollars can he buy with $250 American?

79. Each gram of fat consumed has 9 calories. If a $\frac{1}{2}$-cup serving of gelato has 81 calories from fat, how many grams of fat are in this serving?

80. Approximately 24 out of 100 Americans over the age of 12 smoke. How many smokers would you expect in a group of 850 Americans over the age of 12?

81. Park officials stocked a man-made lake with bass last year. To approximate the number of bass this year, a sample of 75 bass is taken out of the lake and tagged. Then later a different sample is taken, and it is found that 21 of 100 bass are tagged. Approximately how many bass are in the lake? Round to the nearest whole unit. **(See Example 9.)**

82. Laws have been instituted in Florida to help save the manatee. To establish the number in Florida, a sample of 150 manatees was marked and let free. A new sample was taken and found that there were 3 marked manatees out of 40 captured. What is the approximate population of manatees in Florida?

83. Yellowstone National Park in Wyoming has the largest population of free-roaming bison. To approximate the number of bison, 200 are captured and tagged and then let free to roam. Later, a sample of 120 bison is observed and 6 have tags. Approximate the population of bison in the park.

84. In Cass County, Michigan, there are about 20 white-tailed deer per square mile. If the county covers 492 mi^2, about how many white-tailed deer are in the county?

Expanding Your Skills

For Exercises 85–92, solve the proportions.

85. $\dfrac{x+1}{3} = \dfrac{5}{7}$

86. $\dfrac{2}{5} = \dfrac{x-2}{4}$

87. $\dfrac{x-3}{3x} = \dfrac{2}{3}$

88. $\dfrac{x-2}{4x} = \dfrac{3}{8}$

89. $\dfrac{x+3}{x} = \dfrac{5}{4}$

90. $\dfrac{x-5}{x} = \dfrac{3}{2}$

91. $\dfrac{x}{3} = \dfrac{x-2}{4}$

92. $\dfrac{x}{6} = \dfrac{x-1}{3}$

Calculator Connections

Topic: Solving Proportions

Calculator Exercises

93. In a recent year, the annual crime rate for Oklahoma was 4743 crimes per 100,000 people. If Oklahoma had approximately 3,500,000 people at that time, approximately how many crimes were committed? (*Source:* Oklahoma Department of Corrections)

94. To measure the height of the Washington Monument, a student 5.5 ft tall measures his shadow to be 3.25 ft. At the same time of day, he measured the shadow of the Washington Monument to be 328 ft long. Estimate the height of the monument to the nearest foot.

95. In a recent year, the rate of breast cancer in women was 110 cases per 100,000 women. At that time, the state of California had approximately 14,000,000 women. How many women in California would be expected to have breast cancer? (*Source:* Centers for Disease Control)

96. In a recent year, the rate of prostate disease in U.S. men was 118 cases per 1000 men. At that time, the state of Massachusetts had approximately 2,500,000 men. How many men in Massachusetts would be expected to have prostate disease? (*Source:* National Center for Health Statistics)

Problem Recognition Exercises

Operations on Fractions versus Solving Proportions

For Exercises 1–6, identify the problem as a proportion or as a product of fractions. Then solve the proportion or multiply the fractions.

1. a. $\dfrac{x}{4} = \dfrac{15}{8}$ **b.** $\dfrac{1}{4} \cdot \dfrac{15}{8}$

2. a. $\dfrac{2}{5} \cdot \dfrac{3}{10}$ **b.** $\dfrac{2}{5} = \dfrac{y}{10}$

3. a. $\dfrac{2}{7} \times \dfrac{3}{14}$ **b.** $\dfrac{2}{7} = \dfrac{n}{14}$

4. a. $\dfrac{m}{5} = \dfrac{6}{15}$ **b.** $\dfrac{3}{5} \times \dfrac{6}{15}$

5. a. $\dfrac{48}{p} = \dfrac{16}{3}$ **b.** $\dfrac{48}{8} \cdot \dfrac{16}{3}$

6. a. $\dfrac{10}{7} \cdot \dfrac{28}{5}$ **b.** $\dfrac{10}{7} = \dfrac{28}{t}$

For Exercises 7–10, solve the proportion or perform the indicated operation on fractions.

7. a. $\dfrac{3}{7} = \dfrac{6}{z}$ **b.** $\dfrac{3}{7} \div \dfrac{6}{35}$ **c.** $\dfrac{3}{7} + \dfrac{6}{35}$ **d.** $\dfrac{3}{7} \cdot \dfrac{6}{35}$

8. a. $\dfrac{4}{5} \div \dfrac{20}{3}$ **b.** $\dfrac{4}{v} = \dfrac{20}{3}$ **c.** $\dfrac{4}{5} \times \dfrac{20}{3}$ **d.** $\dfrac{4}{5} - \dfrac{20}{3}$

9. a. $\dfrac{14}{5} \cdot \dfrac{10}{7}$ **b.** $\dfrac{14}{5} = \dfrac{x}{7}$ **c.** $\dfrac{14}{5} - \dfrac{10}{7}$ **d.** $\dfrac{14}{5} \div \dfrac{10}{7}$

10. a. $\dfrac{11}{3} = \dfrac{66}{y}$ **b.** $\dfrac{11}{3} + \dfrac{66}{11}$ **c.** $\dfrac{11}{3} \div \dfrac{66}{11}$ **d.** $\dfrac{11}{3} \times \dfrac{66}{11}$

Section 6.4   Percents, Fractions, and Decimals

Objectives

1. Definition of Percent
2. Converting Percents to Fractions
3. Converting Percents to Decimals
4. Converting Fractions and Decimals to Percents
5. Percents, Fractions, and Decimals: A Summary

1. Definition of Percent

In this section we introduce the concept of percent. Literally, the word **percent** means *per one hundred*. To indicate percent, we use the percent symbol %. For example, 45% (read as "45 percent") of the land area in South America is rainforest (shaded in green). This means that if South America were divided into 100 squares of equal size, 45 of the 100 squares would cover rainforest. See Figures 6-1 and 6-2.

Figure 6-1   Figure 6-2

Consider another example. For a recent year, the population of Virginia could be described as follows.

21%	African American	21 out of 100 Virginians are African American
72%	Caucasian (non-Hispanic)	72 out of 100 Virginians are Caucasian (non-Hispanic)
3%	Asian American	3 out of 100 Virginians are Asian American
3%	Hispanic	3 out of 100 Virginians are Hispanic
1%	Other	1 out of 100 Virginians have other backgrounds

Figure 6-3 represents a sample of 100 residents of Virginia.

Concept Connections

1. Shade the portion of the figure represented by 18%.

Answer

1.

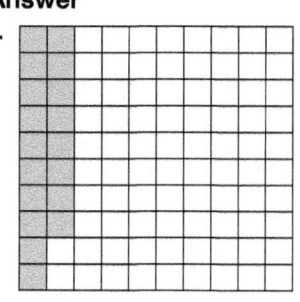

AA	AA	AA	C	C	C	C	C	C	C
AA	AA	C	C	C	C	C	C	C	C
AA	AA	C	C	C	C	C	C	C	C
AA	AA	C	C	C	C	C	C	C	H
AA	AA	C	C	C	C	C	C	C	H
AA	AA	C	C	C	C	C	C	C	H
AA	AA	C	C	C	C	C	C	C	A
AA	AA	C	C	C	C	C	C	C	A
AA	AA	C	C	C	C	C	C	C	A
AA	AA	C	C	C	C	C	C	C	O

AA African American
C   Caucasian (non-Hispanic)
A   Asian American
H   Hispanic
O   Other

Figure 6-3

2. Converting Percents to Fractions

By definition, a percent represents a ratio of parts per 100. Therefore, we can write percents as fractions.

Percent		Fraction	Example/Interpretation
7%	=	$\dfrac{7}{100}$	A sales tax of 7% means that 7 cents in tax is charged for every 100 cents spent.
35%	=	$\dfrac{35}{100}$	To say that 35% of households own a cat means that 35 per every 100 households own a cat.

Notice that $35\% = \dfrac{35}{100} = 35 \times \dfrac{1}{100} = 35 \div 100.$

From this discussion we have the following rule for converting percents to fractions.

> **PROCEDURE Converting Percents to Fractions**
> **Step 1** Replace the symbol % by $\times \frac{1}{100}$ (or by $\div 100$).
> **Step 2** Simplify the fraction to lowest terms, if possible.

Example 1 Converting Percents to Fractions

Convert each percent to a fraction.

a. 56%   **b.** 125%   **c.** 0.4%

Solution:

a. $56\% = 56 \times \dfrac{1}{100}$ Replace the % symbol by $\times \dfrac{1}{100}$.

$= \dfrac{56}{100}$ Multiply.

$= \dfrac{14}{25}$ Simplify to lowest terms.

b. $125\% = 125 \times \dfrac{1}{100}$ Replace the % symbol by $\times \dfrac{1}{100}$.

$= \dfrac{125}{100}$ Multiply.

$= \dfrac{5}{4}$ or $1\dfrac{1}{4}$ Simplify to lowest terms.

c. $0.4\% = 0.4 \times \dfrac{1}{100}$ Replace the % symbol by $\times \dfrac{1}{100}$.

$= \dfrac{4}{10} \times \dfrac{1}{100}$ Write 0.4 in fraction form.

$= \dfrac{4}{1000}$ Multiply.

$= \dfrac{1}{250}$ Simplify to lowest terms.

Skill Practice

Convert each percent to a fraction.
2. 55% **3.** 175%
4. 0.06%

Answers

2. $\dfrac{11}{20}$ **3.** $\dfrac{7}{4}$ **4.** $\dfrac{3}{5000}$

Note that $100\% = 100 \times \frac{1}{100} = 1$. That is, 100% represents 1 whole unit. In Example 1(b), $125\% = \frac{5}{4}$ or $1\frac{1}{4}$. This illustrates that any percent greater than 100% represents a quantity greater than 1 whole. Therefore, its fractional form may be expressed as an improper fraction or as a mixed number.

Note that $1\% = 1 \times \frac{1}{100} = \frac{1}{100}$. In Example 1(c), the value 0.4% represents a quantity less than 1%. Its fractional form is less than one-hundredth.

3. Converting Percents to Decimals

To express part of a whole unit, we can use a percent, a fraction, or a decimal. We would like to be able to convert from one form to another. The procedure for converting a percent to a decimal is the same as that for converting a percent to a fraction. We replace the % symbol by $\times \frac{1}{100}$. However, when converting to a decimal, it is usually more convenient to use the form $\times 0.01$.

> **PROCEDURE Converting Percents to Decimals**
>
> Replace the % symbol by $\times 0.01$. (This is equivalent to $\times \frac{1}{100}$ and $\div 100$.)
>
> *Note:* Multiplying a decimal by 0.01 (or dividing by 100) is the same as moving the decimal point 2 places to the left.

Example 2   **Converting Percents to Decimals**

Convert each percent to its decimal form.

a. 31%   **b.** 6.5%   **c.** 428%   **d.** $1\frac{3}{5}$%   **e.** 0.05%

Solution:

a. $31\% = 31 \times 0.01$ Replace the % symbol by $\times 0.01$.

$= 0.31$ Move the decimal point 2 places to the left.

b. $6.5\% = 6.5 \times 0.01$ Replace the % symbol by $\times 0.01$.

$= 0.065$ Move the decimal point 2 places to the left.

c. $428\% = 428 \times 0.01$ Because 428% is greater than 100% we expect the decimal form to be a number greater than 1.

$= 4.28$

d. $1\frac{3}{5}\% = 1.6 \times 0.01$ Convert the mixed number to decimal form.

$= 0.016$ Because the percent is just over 1%, we expect the decimal form to be just slightly greater than 0.01.

e. $0.05\% = 0.05 \times 0.01$ The value 0.05% is less than 1%. We expect the decimal form to be less than 0.01.

$= 0.0005$

4. Converting Fractions and Decimals to Percents

To convert a percent to a decimal or fraction, we replace the % symbol by $\times 0.01$ (or $\times \frac{1}{100}$). We will now reverse this process. To convert a decimal or fraction to a percent, multiply by 100 and apply the % symbol.

PROCEDURE Converting Fractions and Decimals to Percent Form

Multiply the fraction or decimal by 100%.

Note: Multiplying a decimal by 100 moves the decimal point 2 places to the right.

Example 3   Converting Decimals to Percents

Convert each decimal to its equivalent percent form.

a. 0.62   **b.** 1.75   **c.** 1   **d.** 0.004   **e.** 8.9

Solution:

a. $0.62 = 0.62 \times 100\%$ Multiply by 100%.

   $= 62\%$ Multiplying by 100 moves the decimal point 2 places to the right.

b. $1.75 = 1.75 \times 100\%$ Multiply by 100%.

   $= 175\%$ The decimal number 1.75 is greater than 1. Therefore, we expect a percent greater than 100%.

c. $1 = 1 \times 100\%$ Multiply by 100%.

   $= 100\%$ Recall that 1 whole is equal to 100%.

d. $0.004 = 0.004 \times 100\%$ Multiply by 100%.

   $= 0.4\%$ Move the decimal point to the right 2 places.

e. $8.9 = 8.90 \times 100\%$ Multiply by 100%.

   $= 890\%$

Skill Practice

Convert each decimal to its percent form.

13. 0.46
14. 3.25
15. 2
16. 0.0006
17. 2.5

TIP: Multiplying a number by 100% is equivalent to multiplying the number by 1. Thus, the value of the number is not changed.

Answers

13. 46%   **14.** 325%   **15.** 200%
16. 0.06%   **17.** 250%

Skill Practice

Convert the fraction to percent notation.

18. $\dfrac{7}{10}$

Example 4 **Converting a Fraction to Percent Notation**

Convert the fraction to percent notation. $\quad \dfrac{3}{5}$

Solution:

$$\dfrac{3}{5} = \dfrac{3}{5} \times 100\% \qquad \text{Multiply by 100\%.}$$

$$= \dfrac{3}{5} \times \dfrac{100}{1}\% \qquad \text{Convert the whole number to an improper fraction.}$$

$$= \dfrac{3}{\overset{}{\underset{1}{5}}} \times \dfrac{\overset{20}{\cancel{100}}}{1}\% \qquad \text{Multiply fractions and simplify to lowest terms.}$$

$$= 60\%$$

TIP: We could also have converted $\frac{3}{5}$ to decimal form first (by dividing the numerator by the denominator) and then converted the decimal to a percent.

convert to decimal   convert to percent

$$\dfrac{3}{5} = 0.60 \qquad = \qquad 0.60 \times 100\% = 60\%$$

Skill Practice

Convert the fraction to percent notation.

19. $\dfrac{1}{9}$

Example 5 **Converting a Fraction to Percent Notation**

Convert the fraction to percent notation. $\quad \dfrac{2}{3}$

Solution:

$$\dfrac{2}{3} = \dfrac{2}{3} \times 100\% \qquad \text{Multiply by 100\%.}$$

$$= \dfrac{2}{3} \times \dfrac{100}{1}\% \qquad \text{Convert the whole number to an improper fraction.}$$

$$= \dfrac{200}{3}\%$$

The number $\dfrac{200}{3}\%$ can be written as $66\dfrac{2}{3}\%$ or as $66.\overline{6}\%$.

TIP: First converting $\frac{2}{3}$ to a decimal before converting to percent notation is an alternative approach.

convert to decimal   convert to percent

$$\dfrac{2}{3} = 0.\overline{6} \qquad = \qquad 0.666\ldots \times 100\% = 66.\overline{6}\%$$

Answers

18. 70%

19. $\dfrac{100}{9}\%$ or $11\dfrac{1}{9}\%$ or $11.\overline{1}\%$

In Example 6, we convert an improper fraction and a mixed number to percent form.

Example 6 **Converting Improper Fractions and Mixed Numbers to Percents**

Convert to percent notation.

a. $2\frac{1}{4}$ **b.** $\frac{13}{10}$

Solution:

a. $2\frac{1}{4} = 2\frac{1}{4} \times 100\%$ Multiply by 100%.

$= \frac{9}{4} \times \frac{100}{1}\%$ Convert to improper fractions.

$= \frac{9}{4} \times \frac{\overset{25}{\cancel{100}}}{1}\%$ Multiply and simplify to lowest terms.

$= 225\%$

b. $\frac{13}{10} = \frac{13}{10} \times 100\%$ Multiply by 100%.

$= \frac{13}{10} \times \frac{100}{1}\%$ Convert the whole number to an improper fraction.

$= \frac{13}{\underset{1}{\cancel{10}}} \times \frac{\overset{10}{\cancel{100}}}{1}\%$ Multiply and simplify to lowest terms.

$= 130\%$

Skill Practice
Convert to percent notation.
20. $1\frac{7}{10}$
21. $\frac{11}{4}$

Notice that both answers in Example 6 are greater than 100%. This is reasonable because any number greater than 1 whole unit represents a percent greater than 100%.

In Example 7, we approximate a percent from its fraction form.

Example 7 **Approximating a Percent by Rounding**

Convert the fraction $\frac{5}{13}$ to percent notation rounded to the nearest tenth of a percent.

Solution:

$\frac{5}{13} = \frac{5}{13} \times 100\%$ Multiply by 100%.

$= \frac{5}{13} \times \frac{100}{1}\%$ Write the whole number as an improper fraction.

$= \frac{500}{13}\%$

To round to the nearest tenth of a percent, we must divide. We will obtain the hundredths-place digit in the quotient on which to base the decision on rounding.

$38.4\overset{1}{6} \approx 38.5$

Thus, $\frac{5}{13} \approx 38.5\%$.

$$
\begin{array}{r}
38.46 \\
13\overline{)500.00} \\
-39 \\
\hline
110 \\
-104 \\
\hline
60 \\
-52 \\
\hline
80 \\
-78 \\
\hline
2
\end{array}
$$

Skill Practice
22. Write the fraction $\frac{3}{7}$ in percent notation to the nearest tenth of a percent.

Avoiding Mistakes
In Example 7, we converted a fraction to a percent where rounding was necessary. We converted the fraction to percent form *before* dividing and rounding. If you try to convert to decimal form first, you might round too soon.

Answers
20. 170% **21.** 275% **22.** 42.9%

5. Percents, Fractions, and Decimals: A Summary

The diagram in Figure 6-4 summarizes the methods for converting fractions, decimals, and percents.

Converting a fraction or a decimal to a percent

• Multiply by 100%.
(Move decimal point 2 places right.)

Fraction or Decimal $\frac{2}{5}$ or 0.40   40%   Percent

• Replace % by $\times \frac{1}{100}$ (or $\times$ 0.01).
(Move decimal point 2 places left.)

Converting a percent to a fraction or a decimal

Figure 6-4

Table 6-2 shows some common percents and their equivalent fraction and decimal forms.

Table 6-2

Percent	Fraction	Decimal	Example/Interpretation
100%	1	1.00	Of people who give birth, 100% are female.
50%	$\frac{1}{2}$	0.50	Of the population, 50% is male. That is, one-half of the population is male.
25%	$\frac{1}{4}$	0.25	Approximately 25% of the U.S. population smokes. That is, one-quarter of the population smokes.
75%	$\frac{3}{4}$	0.75	Approximately 75% of homes have computers. That is, three-quarters of homes have computers.
10%	$\frac{1}{10}$	0.10	Of the population, 10% is left-handed. That is, one-tenth of the population is left-handed.
20%	$\frac{1}{5}$	0.20	Approximately 20% of computers sold in stores or online are Apple computers. That is, one-fifth of the computers are Apple computers.
1%	$\frac{1}{100}$	0.01	Approximately 1% of babies are born underweight. That is, about 1 in 100 babies is born underweight.
$33\frac{1}{3}$%	$\frac{1}{3}$	$0.\overline{3}$	A basketball player made $33\frac{1}{3}$% of her shots. That is, she made about 1 basket for every 3 shots attempted.
$66\frac{2}{3}$%	$\frac{2}{3}$	$0.\overline{6}$	Of the population, $66\frac{2}{3}$% prefers chocolate ice cream to other flavors. That is, 2 out of 3 people prefer chocolate ice cream.

Example 8 Converting Fractions, Decimals, and Percents

Complete the table.

	Fraction	Decimal	Percent
a.		0.55	
b.	$\frac{1}{200}$		
c.			160%
d.		2.4	
e.			$66\frac{2}{3}\%$
f.	$\frac{2}{9}$		

Skill Practice

Complete the table.

	Fraction	Decimal	Percent
25.		1.41	
26.	$\frac{1}{50}$		
27.			18%
28.		0.58	
29.			$33\frac{1}{3}\%$
30.	$\frac{7}{9}$		

Solution:

a. 0.55 to fraction: $\quad 0.55 = \dfrac{55}{100} = \dfrac{11}{20}$

0.55 to percent: $\quad 0.55 \times 100\% = 55\%$

b. $\dfrac{1}{200}$ to decimal: $\quad 1 \div 200 = 0.005$

$\dfrac{1}{200}$ to percent: $\quad \dfrac{1}{200} \times 100\% = \dfrac{100}{200}\% = 0.5\%$

c. 160% to fraction: $\quad 160 \times \dfrac{1}{100} = \dfrac{160}{100} = \dfrac{8}{5}$ or $1\dfrac{3}{5}$

160% to decimal: $\quad 160 \times 0.01 = 1.6$

d. 2.4 to fraction: $\quad \dfrac{24}{10} = \dfrac{12}{5}$ or $2\dfrac{2}{5}$

2.4 to percent: $\quad 2.4 \times 100\% = 240\%$

e. $66\dfrac{2}{3}\%$ to fraction: $\quad 66\dfrac{2}{3} \times \dfrac{1}{100} = \dfrac{\overset{2}{\cancel{200}}}{3} \times \dfrac{1}{\underset{1}{\cancel{100}}} = \dfrac{2}{3}$

$66\dfrac{2}{3}\%$ to decimal: $\quad 66\dfrac{2}{3} \times 0.01 = 66.\overline{6} \times 0.01 = 0.\overline{6}$

f. $\dfrac{2}{9}$ to decimal: $\quad 2 \div 9 = 0.\overline{2}$

$\dfrac{2}{9}$ to percent: $\quad \dfrac{2}{9} \times 100\% = \dfrac{2}{9} \times \dfrac{100}{1}\% = \dfrac{200}{9}\% = 22\dfrac{2}{9}\%$ or $22.\overline{2}\%$

The completed table is as follows.

	Fraction	Decimal	Percent
a.	$\frac{11}{20}$	0.55	55%
b.	$\frac{1}{200}$	0.005	0.5%
c.	$\frac{8}{5}$ or $1\frac{3}{5}$	1.6	160%
d.	$\frac{12}{5}$ or $2\frac{2}{5}$	2.4	240%
e.	$\frac{2}{3}$	$0.\overline{6}$	$66\frac{2}{3}\%$
f.	$\frac{2}{9}$	$0.\overline{2}$	$22\frac{2}{9}\%$ or $22.\overline{2}\%$

Answers

	Fraction	Decimal	Percent
25.	$\frac{141}{100}$ or $1\frac{41}{100}$	1.41	141%
26.	$\frac{1}{50}$	0.02	2%
27.	$\frac{9}{50}$	0.18	18%
28.	$\frac{29}{50}$	0.58	58%
29.	$\frac{1}{3}$	$0.\overline{3}$	$33\frac{1}{3}\%$
30.	$\frac{7}{9}$	$0.\overline{7}$	$77.\overline{7}\%$

Section 6.4 Practice Exercises

Boost *your* GRADE at
ALEKS.com!

• Practice Problems
• Self-Tests
• NetTutor
• e-Professors
• Videos

Study Skills Exercise

1. Define the key term **percent**.

Objective 1: Definition of Percent

For Exercises 2–6, use a percent to express the shaded portion of each drawing.

2.

3.

4.

5.

6.

For Exercises 7–10, write a percent for each statement.

7. A bank pays $2 in interest for every $100 deposited.

8. In South Dakota, 5 out of every 100 people work in construction.

9. Out of 100 acres, 70 acres were planted with corn.

10. On TV, 26 out of every 100 minutes are filled with commercials.

Objective 2: Converting Percents to Fractions

11. Explain the procedure to change a percent to a fraction.

12. What fraction represents 50%.

For Exercises 13–28, change the percent to a simplified fraction or mixed number. **(See Example 1.)**

13. 3%

14. 7%

15. 84%

16. 32%

17. 3.4%

18. 5.2%

19. 115%

20. 150%

21. 0.5% **22.** 0.2% **23.** 0.25% **24.** 0.75%

25. $5\frac{1}{6}\%$ **26.** $66\frac{2}{3}\%$ **27.** $124\frac{1}{2}\%$ **28.** $110\frac{1}{2}\%$

Objective 3: Converting Percents to Decimals

29. Explain the procedure to change a percent to a decimal.

30. To change 26.8% to decimal form, which direction would you move the decimal point, and by how many places?

For Exercises 31–42, change the percent to a decimal. **(See Example 2.)**

31. 58% **32.** 72% **33.** 8.5% **34.** 12.9%

35. 142% **36.** 201% **37.** 0.55% **38.** 0.75%

39. $26\frac{2}{5}\%$ **40.** $16\frac{1}{4}\%$ **41.** $55\frac{1}{20}\%$ **42.** $62\frac{1}{5}\%$

Objective 4: Converting Fractions and Decimals to Percents

For Exercises 43–54, convert the decimal to a percent. **(See Example 3.)**

43. 0.27 **44.** 0.51 **45.** 0.19 **46.** 0.33

47. 1.75 **48.** 2.8 **49.** 0.124 **50.** 0.277

51. 0.006 **52.** 0.0008 **53.** 1.014 **54.** 2.203

For Exercises 55–66, convert the fraction to a percent. **(See Examples 4–6.)**

55. $\frac{71}{100}$ **56.** $\frac{89}{100}$ **57.** $\frac{7}{8}$ **58.** $\frac{5}{8}$

59. $\frac{5}{6}$ **60.** $\frac{5}{12}$ **61.** $1\frac{3}{4}$ **62.** $2\frac{1}{8}$

63. $\frac{11}{9}$ **64.** $\frac{14}{9}$ **65.** $1\frac{2}{3}$ **66.** $1\frac{1}{6}$

For Exercises 67–74, write the fraction in percent notation to the nearest tenth of a percent. **(See Example 7.)**

67. $\frac{3}{7}$ **68.** $\frac{6}{7}$ **69.** $\frac{1}{13}$ **70.** $\frac{3}{13}$

71. $\frac{5}{11}$ **72.** $\frac{8}{11}$ **73.** $\frac{13}{15}$ **74.** $\frac{1}{15}$

Objective 5: Percents, Fractions, and Decimals: A Summary (Mixed Exercises)

For Exercises 75–80, match the percent with its fraction form.

75. $66\frac{2}{3}\%$ **76.** 10%   **a.** $\frac{3}{2}$ **b.** $\frac{3}{4}$

77. 90%   **78.** 75%   **c.** $\frac{2}{3}$ **d.** $\frac{1}{10}$

79. 25%   **80.** 150%   **e.** $\frac{9}{10}$ **f.** $\frac{1}{4}$

For Exercises 81–86, match the decimal with its percent form.

81. 0.30   **82.** $0.\overline{3}$ **a.** 5%   **b.** 50%

83. 5   **84.** 0.5   **c.** 80%   **d.** $33\frac{1}{3}\%$

85. 0.05   **86.** 0.8   **e.** 30%   **f.** 500%

For Exercises 87–90, complete the table. **(See Example 8.)**

87.

	Fraction	Decimal	Percent
a.	$\frac{1}{4}$		
b.		0.92	
c.			15%
d.		1.6	
e.	$\frac{1}{100}$		
f.			0.8%

88.

	Fraction	Decimal	Percent
a.			0.6%
b.	$\frac{2}{5}$		
c.		2	
d.	$\frac{1}{2}$		
e.		0.12	
f.			45%

89.

	Fraction	Decimal	Percent
a.			14%
b.		0.87	
c.		1	
d.	$\frac{1}{3}$		
e.			0.2%
f.	$\frac{19}{20}$		

90.

	Fraction	Decimal	Percent
a.		1.3	
b.			22%
c.	$\frac{3}{4}$		
d.		0.73	
e.			$22.\overline{2}\%$
f.	$\frac{1}{20}$		

For Exercises 91–94, write the fraction as a percent.

91. One-quarter of Americans say they entertain at home two or more times a month. (*Source: USA TODAY*)

92. According to the Centers for Disease Control (CDC), $\frac{37}{100}$ of U.S. teenage boys say they rarely or never wear their seatbelts.

93. According to the Centers for Disease Control, $\frac{1}{10}$ of teenage girls in the United States say they rarely or never wear their seatbelts.

94. In a recent year, $\frac{2}{3}$ of the beds in U.S. hospitals were occupied.

For Exercises 95–98, find the decimal and fraction equivalents of the percent given in the sentence.

95. For a recent year, the unemployment rate in the United States was 5.8%.

96. During a slow travel season, one airline cut its seating capacity by 15.8%.

97. During a period of a weak economy and rising fuel prices, low-fare airline, Southwest, raised its average fare during the second quarter by 8.4%. (*Source: USA TODAY*)

98. One year, the average U.S. income tax rate was 18.2%.

99. Explain the difference between $\frac{1}{2}$ and $\frac{1}{2}\%$.

100. Explain the difference between $\frac{3}{4}$ and $\frac{3}{4}\%$.

101. Explain the difference between 25% and 0.25%.

102. Explain the difference between 10% and 0.10%.

103. Which of the numbers represent 125%?

    a. 1.25   **b.** 0.125   **c.** $\frac{5}{4}$ **d.** $\frac{5}{4}\%$

104. Which of the numbers represent 60%?

    a. 6.0   **b.** 0.60%   **c.** 0.6   **d.** $\frac{3}{5}$

105. Which of the numbers represent 30%?

    a. $\frac{3}{10}$ **b.** $\frac{1}{3}$ **c.** 0.3   **d.** 0.03%

106. Which of the numbers represent 180%?

    a. 18   **b.** 1.8   **c.** $\frac{9}{5}$ **d.** $\frac{9}{5}\%$

Expanding Your Skills

107. Is the number 1.4 less than or greater than 100%?

108. Is the number 0.0087 less than or greater than 1%?

109. Is the number 0.052 less than or greater than 50%?

110. Is the number 25 less than or greater than 25%?

Percent Proportions and Applications

Section 6.5

1. Introduction to Percent Proportions

Recall that a percent is a ratio in parts per 100. For example, $50\% = \frac{50}{100}$. However, a percent can be represented by infinitely many equivalent fractions. Thus,

$$50\% = \frac{50}{100} = \frac{1}{2} = \frac{2}{4} = \frac{3}{6} \quad \text{and infinitely many more.}$$

Equating a percent to an equivalent ratio forms a proportion that we call a **percent proportion**. A percent proportion is a proportion in which one ratio is written with a denominator of 100. For example:

$$\frac{50}{100} = \frac{3}{6} \quad \text{is a percent proportion.}$$

Objectives

1. **Introduction to Percent Proportions**
2. **Solving Percent Proportions**
3. **Applications of Percent Proportions**

We will be using percent proportions to solve a variety of application problems. But first we need to identify and label the parts of a percent proportion.

A percent proportion can be written in the form:

$$\frac{\text{Amount}}{\text{Base}} = p\% \qquad \text{or} \qquad \frac{\text{Amount}}{\text{Base}} = \frac{p}{100}$$

For example:

$$4 \text{ L out of } 8 \text{ L is } 50\% \qquad\qquad \frac{4}{8} = 50\% \qquad \text{or} \qquad \frac{4}{8} = \frac{50}{100}$$

amount   base   p

In this example, 8 L is some total (or base) quantity and 4 L is some part (or amount) of that whole. The ratio $\frac{4}{8}$ represents a fraction of the whole equal to 50%. In general, we offer the following guidelines for identifying the parts of a percent proportion.

PROCEDURE   Identifying the Parts of a Percent Proportion

A percent proportion can be written as

$$\frac{\text{Amount}}{\text{Base}} = p\% \qquad \text{or} \qquad \frac{\text{Amount}}{\text{Base}} = \frac{p}{100}.$$

- The **base** is the total or whole amount being considered. It often appears after the word *of* within a word problem.
- The **amount** is the part being compared to the base. It sometimes appears with the word *is* within a word problem.

Skill Practice

Identify the amount, base, and *p* value. Then set up a percent proportion.

1. 12 mi is 20% of 60 mi.
2. 14% of $600 is $84.
3. 32 books out of 2000 books is 1.6%.

Example 1   Identifying Amount, Base, and *p* for a Percent Proportion

Identify the amount, base, and *p* value, and then set up a percent proportion.

a. 25% of 60 students is 15 students.   **b.** $32 is 50% of $64.

c. 5 of 1000 employees is 0.5%.

Solution:

For each problem, we recommend that you identify *p* first. It is the number in front of the symbol %. Then identify the base. In most cases it follows the word *of*. Then, by the process of elimination, find the amount.

a. 25% of 60 students is 15 students.

   p   base   amount
(before %   (after the
 symbol)   word *of*)

$$\text{amount} \rightarrow \frac{15}{60} = \frac{25}{100} \begin{matrix} \leftarrow p \\ \leftarrow 100 \end{matrix}$$
$$\text{base} \rightarrow$$

b. $32 is 50% of $64.

   amount   *p*   base

$$\text{amount} \rightarrow \frac{32}{64} = \frac{50}{100} \begin{matrix} \leftarrow p \\ \leftarrow 100 \end{matrix}$$
$$\text{base} \rightarrow$$

c. 5 of 1000 employees is 0.5%.

   amount   base   *p*

$$\text{amount} \rightarrow \frac{5}{1000} = \frac{0.5}{100} \begin{matrix} \leftarrow p \\ \leftarrow 100 \end{matrix}$$
$$\text{base} \rightarrow$$

2. Solving Percent Proportions

In Example 1, we practiced identifying the parts of a percent proportion. Now we consider percent proportions in which one of these numbers is unknown. Furthermore, we will see that the examples come in three types:

- Amount is unknown.
- Base is unknown.
- Value p is unknown.

However, the process for solving in each case is the same.

Example 2 **Solving Percent Proportions—Amount Unknown**

What is 30% of 180?

Solution:

What is 30% of 180? The base and value for p are known.

amount (x) p base   Let x represent the unknown amount.

$$\frac{x}{180} = \frac{30}{100}$$ Set up a percent proportion.

$100 \cdot x = (30)(180)$ Equate the cross products.

$100x = 5400$

$$\frac{\overset{1}{100}x}{\underset{1}{100}} = \frac{5400}{100}$$ Divide both sides of the equation by 100.

$x = 54$ Simplify to lowest terms.

Therefore, 54 is 30% of 180.

> **TIP:** We can check the answer to Example 2 as follows. Ten percent of a number is $\frac{1}{10}$ of the number. Furthermore, $\frac{1}{10}$ of 180 is 18. Thirty percent of 180 must be 3 times this amount.
>
> $3 \times 18 = 54$ ✔

Example 3 **Solving Percent Proportions—Base Unknown**

40% of what number is 25?

Solution:

40% of what number is 25? The amount and value of p are known.

p base (x) amount   Let x represent the unknown base.

$$\frac{25}{x} = \frac{40}{100}$$ Set up a percent proportion.

$(25)(100) = 40 \cdot x$ Equate the cross products.

$2500 = 40x$

$$\frac{2500}{40} = \frac{\overset{1}{40}x}{\underset{1}{40}}$$ Divide both sides by 40.

$62.5 = x$ Therefore, 40% of 62.5 is 25.

Skill Practice

6. What percent of $48 is $15?

Example 4 Solving Percent Proportions—*p* Unknown

12.4 mi is what percent of 80 mi?

Solution:

12.4 mi is what percent of 80 mi?   The amount and base are known.
  | | | The value of *p* is unknown.
amount   *p*   base

$$\frac{12.4}{80} = \frac{p}{100}$$ Set up a percent equation.

$$(12.4)(100) = 80 \cdot p$$ Equate the cross products.

$$1240 = 80p$$

$$\frac{1240}{80} = \frac{80p}{80}$$ Divide both sides by 80.

$$15.5 = p$$

Therefore, 12.4 mi is 15.5% of 80.

Avoiding Mistakes

Remember that *p* represents the number of *parts* per 100. However, Example 4 asked us to find the value of *p*%. Therefore, it was necessary to attach the % symbol to our value of *p*. For Example 4, we have *p* = 15.5. Therefore, *p*% is 15.5%.

3. Applications of Percent Proportions

We now use percent proportions to solve application problems involving percents.

Skill Practice

7. In a recent year it was estimated that 24.7% of U.S. adults smoked tobacco products regularly. In a group of 2000 adults, how many would be expected to be smokers?

Example 5 Using Percents in Meteorology

Buffalo, New York, receives an average of 94 in. of snow each year. This year it had 120% of the normal annual snowfall. How much snow did Buffalo get this year?

Solution:

This situation can be translated as:

"The amount of snow Buffalo received is 120% of 94 in."
        | | |
    amount (*x*)   *p*   base

$$\frac{x}{94} = \frac{120}{100}$$ Set up a percent proportion.

$$100 \cdot x = (120)(94)$$ Equate the cross products.

$$100x = 11{,}280$$

$$\frac{100x}{100} = \frac{11{,}280}{100}$$ Divide both sides by 100.

$$x = 112.8$$

This year, Buffalo had 112.8 in. of snow.

TIP: In a word problem, it is always helpful to check the reasonableness of your answer. In Example 5, the percent is greater than 100%. This means that the amount must be greater than the base. Therefore, we suspect that our solution is reasonable.

Answers

6. 31.25%   **7.** 494 people

| Example 6 | **Using Percents in Statistics** |

In a recent year, Harvard University's freshman class had 18% Asian American students. If this represented 380 students, how many students were admitted to the freshman class? Round to the nearest student.

Solution:

This situation can be translated as:

"380 **is** 18% **of** what number?"

amount $\quad$ p $\quad$ base (x)

$$\frac{380}{x} = \frac{18}{100} \qquad \text{Set up a percent proportion.}$$

$$(380)(100) = (18) \cdot x \qquad \text{Equate the cross products.}$$

$$38{,}000 = 18x$$

$$\frac{38{,}000}{18} = \frac{18x}{18} \qquad \begin{array}{l}\text{Note that } 38{,}000 \div 18 \approx 2111.1. \\ \text{Rounded to the nearest whole unit} \\ \text{(whole person), this is 2111.}\end{array}$$

$$2111 \approx x$$

The freshman class at Harvard had approximately 2111 students.

Skill Practice

8. Eight students in a statistics class received a grade of A in the class. If this represents about 19% of the class, how many students are in the class? Round to the nearest student.

TIP: We can check the answer to Example 6 by substituting $x = 2111$ back into the original proportion. The cross products will not be exactly the same because we had to round the value of x. However, the cross products should be *close*.

$$\frac{380}{2111} \stackrel{?}{=} \frac{18}{100} \qquad \text{Substitute } x = 2111 \text{ into the proportion.}$$

$$(380)(100) \stackrel{?}{=} (18)(2111)$$

$$38{,}000 \approx 37{,}998 \quad \checkmark \qquad \text{The values are very close.}$$

| Example 7 | **Using Percents in Finance** |

Suppose a tennis pro who is ranked 90th in the world on the men's professional tour earns $280,000 per year in tournament winnings and endorsements. He pays his coach $100,000 per year. What percent of his income goes toward his coach? Round to the nearest tenth of a percent.

Skill Practice

9. There were 425 donations made for various dollar amounts at an animal sanctuary. If 60 donations were made in the $100–$199 range, what percent does this represent? Round to the nearest tenth of a percent.

Answers
8. 42 students are in the class.
9. Of the donations, approximately 14.1% are in the $100–$199 range.

Solution:

This can be translated as:

"What percent of $280,000 is $100,000?"

The value of p is unknown.   base (x)   amount

$$\frac{100{,}000}{280{,}000} = \frac{p}{100}$$ Set up a percent proportion.

$$\frac{100{,}\cancel{000}}{280{,}\cancel{000}} = \frac{p}{100}$$ The ratio on the left side of the equation can be simplified by a factor of 10,000. "Strike through" four zeros in the numerator and denominator.

$$\frac{10}{28} = \frac{p}{100}$$

$(10)(100) = (28) \cdot p$ Equate the cross products.

$1000 = 28p$

$$\frac{1000}{28} = \frac{\overset{1}{\cancel{28}}p}{\underset{1}{\cancel{28}}}$$ Divide both sides by 28.

$$\frac{1000}{28} = p$$

$35.7 \approx p$ Dividing $1000 \div 28$, we get approximately 35.7.

The tennis pro spends about 35.7% of his income on his coach.

$$\begin{array}{r} 35.71 \\ 28\overline{)1000.00} \\ -84 \\ \hline 160 \\ -140 \\ \hline 200 \\ -196 \\ \hline 40 \\ -28 \\ \hline 12 \end{array}$$

Section 6.5   Practice Exercises

Study Skills Exercise

1. Define the key terms.

   a. Percent proportion   **b. Base**   **c. Amount**

Review Exercises

For Exercises 2–4, convert the decimal to a percent.

2. 0.55   **3.** 1.30   **4.** 0.0006

For Exercises 5–7, convert the fraction to a percent.

5. $\dfrac{3}{8}$ **6.** $\dfrac{5}{2}$ **7.** $\dfrac{1}{100}$

For Exercises 8–10, convert the percent to a fraction.

8. $62\frac{1}{2}\%$ **9.** 2% **10.** 77%

For Exercises 11–13, convert the percent to a decimal.

11. 82% **12.** 0.3% **13.** 100%

Objective 1: Introduction to Percent Proportions

14. Which of the proportions are percent proportions? Circle all that apply.

a. $\dfrac{7}{100} = \dfrac{x}{32}$ **b.** $\dfrac{42}{x} = \dfrac{15}{100}$ **c.** $\dfrac{2}{3} = \dfrac{x}{9}$ **d.** $\dfrac{7}{28} = \dfrac{10}{x}$

For Exercises 15–20, identify the amount, base, and p value. **(See Example 1.)**

15. 12 balloons is 60% of 20 balloons.

16. 25% of 400 cars is 100 cars.

17. $99 of $200 is 49.5%.

18. 45 of 50 children is 90%.

19. 50 hr is 125% of 40 hr.

20. 175% of 2 in. of rainfall is 3.5 in.

For Exercises 21–26, write the percent proportion.

21. 10% of 120 trees is 12 trees.

22. 15% of 20 pictures is 3 pictures.

23. 72 children is 80% of 90 children.

24. 21 dogs is 20% of 105 dogs.

25. 21,684 college students is 104% of 20,850 college students.

26. 103% of $40,000 is $41,200.

Objective 2: Solving Percent Proportions

For Exercises 27–36, solve the percent problems with an unknown amount. **(See Example 2.)**

27. Compute 54% of 200 employees.

28. Find 35% of 412.

29. What is $\frac{1}{2}\%$ of 40?

30. What is 1.8% of 900 g?

31. Find 112% of 500.

32. Compute 106% of 1050.

33. Pedro pays 28% of his salary in income tax. If he makes $72,000 in taxable income, how much income tax does he pay?

34. A car dealer sets the sticker price of a car by taking 115% of the wholesale price. If a car sells wholesale at $17,000, what is the sticker price?

35. Jesse Ventura became the 38th governor of Minnesota by receiving 37% of the votes. If approximately 2,060,000 votes were cast, how many did Mr. Ventura get?

36. In a psychology class, 61.9% of the class consists of freshmen. If there are 42 students, how many are freshmen? Round to the nearest whole unit.

For Exercises 37–46, solve the percent problems with an unknown base. **(See Example 3.)**

37. 18 is 50% of what number?

38. 22% of what length is 44 ft?

39. 30% of what weight is 69 lb?

40. 70% of what number is 28?

41. 9 is $\frac{2}{3}$% of what number?

42. 9.5 is 200% of what number?

43. Albert saves $120 per month. If this is 7.5% of his monthly income, how much does he make per month?

44. Janie and Don left their house in South Bend, Indiana, to visit friends in Chicago. They drove 80% of the distance before stopping for lunch. If they had driven 56 mi before lunch, what would be the total distance from their house to their friends' house in Chicago?

45. Aimee read 14 e-mails, which was only 40% of her total e-mails. What is her total number of e-mails?

46. A recent survey found that 5% of the population of the United States is unemployed. If Charlotte, North Carolina, has 32,000 unemployed, what is the population of Charlotte?

For Exercises 47–54, solve the percent problems with *p* unknown. **(See Example 4.)**

47. What percent of $120 is $42?

48. 112 is what percent of 400?

49. 84 is what percent of 70?

50. What percent of 12 letters is 4 letters?

51. What percent of 320 mi is 280 mi?

52. 54¢ is what percent of 48¢?

53. A student answered 29 problems correctly on a final exam of 40 problems. What percent of the questions did she answer correctly?

54. During his college basketball season, Jeff made 520 baskets out of 1280 attempts. What was his shooting percentage? Round to the nearest whole percent.

For Exercises 55–58, use the table given. The data represent 600 police officers broken down by gender and by the number of officers promoted.

	Promoted	Not Promoted	Total
Male	140	340	480
Female	20	100	120
Total	160	440	600

55. What percent of the officers are female?

56. What percent of the officers are male?

57. What percent of the officers were promoted? Round to the nearest tenth of a percent.

58. What percent of the officers were not promoted? Round to the nearest tenth of a percent.

Mixed Exercises

For Exercises 59–70, solve the problem using a percent proportion.

59. What is 15% of 50?

60. What is 28% of 70?

61. What percent of 240 is 96?

62. What percent of 600 is 432?

63. 85% of what number is 78.2?

64. 23% of what number is 27.6?

65. What is $3\frac{1}{2}$% of 2200?

66. What is $6\frac{3}{4}$% of 800?

67. 0.5% of what number is 44?

68. 0.8% of what number is 192?

69. 80 is what percent of 50?

70. 20 is what percent of 8?

Objective 3: Applications of Percent Proportions

71. The rainfall at Birmingham Airport in the United Kingdom averages 56 mm per month. In August the amount of rain that fell was 125% of the average monthly rainfall. How much rain fell in August? **(See Example 5.)**

72. In a recent survey, 38% of people in the United States say that gas prices have affected the type of vehicle they will buy. In a sample of 500 people who are in the market for a new vehicle, how many would you expect to be influenced by gas prices?

73. Harvard University reported that 232 African American students were admitted to the freshman class in a recent year. If this represents 11% of the total freshman class, how many freshmen were admitted? **(See Example 6.)**

74. Yellowstone National Park has 3366 mi^2 of undeveloped land. If this represents 99% of the total area, find the total area of the park.

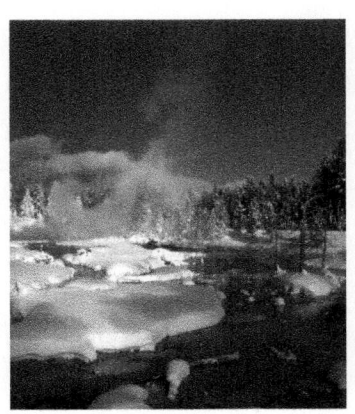

75. At the Albany Medical Center in Albany, New York, 546 beds out of 650 are occupied. What is the percent occupancy? **(See Example 7.)**

76. For a recent year, 6 hurricanes struck the United States coastline out of 16 named storms to make landfall. What percent does this represent?

77. The risk of breast cancer relapse after surviving 10 years is shown in the graph according to the stage of the cancer at the time of diagnosis. (*Source: Journal of the National Cancer Institute*)

  a. How many women out of 200 diagnosed with Stage II breast cancer would be expected to relapse after having survived 10 years?

  b. How many women out of 500 diagnosed with Stage I breast cancer would *not* be expected to relapse after having survived 10 years?

78. A computer has 74.4 GB (gigabytes) of memory available. If 7.56 GB is used, what percent of the memory is used? Round to the nearest percent.

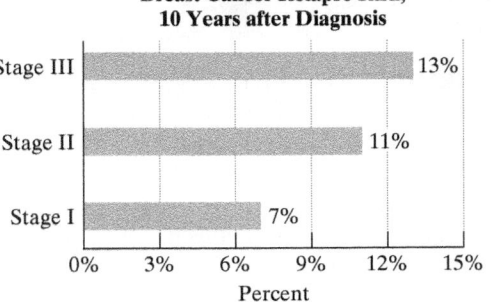

Breast Cancer Relapse Risk, 10 Years after Diagnosis

Figure for Exercise 77

A used car dealership sells several makes of vehicles. For Exercises 79–82, refer to the graph. Round the answers to the nearest whole unit.

79. If the dealership sold 215 vehicles in 1 month, how many were Chevys?

80. If the dealership sold 182 vehicles in 1 month, how many were Fords?

81. If the dealership sold 27 Hondas in 1 month, how many total vehicles were sold?

82. If the dealership sold 10 cars in the "Other" category, how many total vehicles were sold?

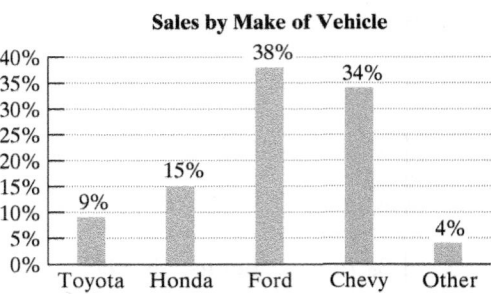

Sales by Make of Vehicle

Expanding Your Skills

83. Carson had $600 and spent 44% of it on clothes. Then he spent 20% of the remaining money on dinner. How much did he spend altogether?

84. Melissa took $52 to the mall and spent 24% on makeup. Then she spent one-half of the remaining money on lunch. How much did she spend altogether?

It is customary to leave a 15–20% tip for the server in a restaurant. However, when you are at a restaurant in a social setting, you probably do not want to take out a pencil and piece of paper to figure out the tip. It is more socially acceptable to compute the tip mentally. Try this method.

Step 1: First, if the bill is not a whole dollar amount, simplify the calculations by rounding the bill to the next-higher whole dollar.

Step 2: Take 10% of the bill. This is the same as taking one-tenth of the bill. Move the decimal point to the left 1 place.

Step 3: If you want to leave a 20% tip, double the value found in step 2.

Step 4: If you want to leave a 15% tip, first note that 15% is 5% + 10%. Therefore, add one-half of the value found in step 2 to the number in step 2.

85. Estimate a 20% tip on a bill of $57.65. (*Hint:* Round up to $58 first.)

86. Estimate a 20% tip on a bill of $18.79.

87. Estimate a 15% tip on a dinner bill of $42.00.

88. Estimate a 15% tip on a luncheon bill of $12.00.

Section 6.6 Percent Equations and Applications

Objectives

1. Solving Percent Equations— Amount Unknown
2. Solving Percent Equations—Base Unknown
3. Solving Percent Equations—Percent Unknown
4. Applications of Percent Equations

1. Solving Percent Equations—Amount Unknown

In this section, we investigate an alternative method to solve applications involving percents. We use percent equations. A **percent equation** represents a percent proportion in an alternative form. For example, recall that we can write a percent proportion as follows:

$$\frac{\text{amount}}{\text{base}} = p\% \qquad \text{percent proportion}$$

This is equivalent to writing   Amount = $(p\%) \cdot$ (base)   percent equation

To set up a percent equation, it is necessary to translate an English sentence into a mathematical equation. As you read through the examples in this section, you will notice several key words. In the phrase *percent of*, the word *of* implies multiplication. The verb *to be* (am, is, are, was, were, been) often implies = .

Example 1 Solving a Percent Equation—Amount Unknown

What is 30% of 60?

Solution:

We translate the words to mathematical symbols.

What is 30% of 60?

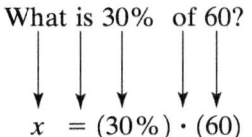

$x = (30\%) \cdot (60)$ 　　In this context, the word *of* means to multiply.

　　　　　　　　　　　Let x represent the unknown amount.

To find x, we must multiply 30% by 60. However, 30% means $\frac{30}{100}$ or 0.30. For the purpose of calculation, we *must* convert 30% to its equivalent decimal or fraction form. The equation becomes

$x = (0.30)(60)$

$\quad = 18$

The value 18 is 30% of 60.

> **TIP:** The solution to Example 1 can be checked by noting that 10% of 60 is 6. Therefore, 30% is equal to (3)(6) = 18.

Example 2 Solving a Percent Equation—Amount Unknown

142% of 75 amounts to what number?

Solution:

142% of 75 amounts to what number?

$(142\%) \cdot (75) \quad = \quad x$ 　　Let x represent the unknown amount.
The word *of* implies multiplication.
The phrase *amounts to* implies = .

$(1.42)(75) = x$ 　　Convert 142% to its decimal form (1.42).

$106.5 = x$ 　　Multiply.

Therefore, 142% of 75 amounts to 106.5.

Examples 1 and 2 illustrate that the percent equation gives us a quick way to find an unknown amount. For example, because $(p\%) \cdot (\text{base}) = \text{amount}$, we have

$$50\% \text{ of } 80 \ = 0.50(80) = 40$$

$$25\% \text{ of } 20 \ = 0.25(20) = 5$$

$$250\% \text{ of } 90 = 2.50(90) = 225$$

2. Solving Percent Equations—Base Unknown

Examples 3 and 4 illustrate the case in which the base is unknown.

Skill Practice

Use a percent equation to solve.
3. 80% of what number is 94?

| Example 3 | **Solving a Percent Equation—Base Unknown** |

40% of what number is 225?

Solution:

40% of what number is 225?   Let x represent the base number.

$(0.40) \cdot \quad x \quad = 225$ Notice that we immediately converted 40% to its decimal form 0.40 so that we would not forget.

$0.40x = 225$

$$\frac{0.40x}{0.40} = \frac{225}{0.40}$$ Divide both sides by 0.40.

$x = 562.5$ 40% of 562.5 is 225.

Skill Practice

Use a percent equation to solve.
4. 5.6 is 0.8% of what number?

| Example 4 | **Solving a Percent Equation—Base Unknown** |

0.19 is 0.2% of what number?

Solution:

0.19 is 0.2% of what number?   Let x represent the base number.

$0.19 = (0.002) \cdot x$ Convert 0.2% to its decimal form 0.002.

$0.19 = 0.002x$

$$\frac{0.19}{0.002} = \frac{0.002x}{0.002}$$ Divide both sides by 0.002.

$95 = x$ Therefore, 0.19 is 0.2% of 95.

3. Solving Percent Equations—Percent Unknown

Examples 5 and 6 demonstrate the process to find an unknown percent.

Skill Practice

Use a percent equation to solve.
5. 16.1 is what percent of 46?

| Example 5 | **Solving a Percent Equation—Percent Unknown** |

75 is what percent of 250?

Solution:

75 is what percent of 250?

$75 = \quad x \quad \cdot (250)$ Let x represent the unknown percent.

$75 = 250x$

$$\frac{75}{250} = \frac{250x}{250}$$ Divide both sides by 250.

$0.3 = x$

At this point, we have $x = 0.3$. To write the value of x in percent form, multiply by 100%.

$$x = 0.3$$
$$= 0.3 \times 100\%$$
$$= 30\%$$

Thus, 75 is 30% of 250.

Example 6 Solving a Percent Equation—Percent Unknown

What percent of $60 is $92? Round to the nearest tenth of a percent.

Solution:

What percent of $60 is $92?

$$x \cdot (60) = 92 \qquad \text{Let } x \text{ represent the unknown percent.}$$
$$60x = 92$$
$$\frac{60x}{60} = \frac{92}{60} \qquad \text{Divide both sides by 60.}$$
$$x = 1.5\overline{3} \qquad \textit{Note: } 92 \div 60 = 1.5\overline{3}.$$

At this point, we have $x = 1.5\overline{3}$. To convert x to its percent form, multiply by 100%.

$$x = 1.5\overline{3}$$
$$= 1.5\overline{3} \times 100\%$$
$$= (1.53333\ldots) \times 100\%$$
$$= 153.333\ldots\%$$

The hundredths-place digit is less than 5. Discard it and the digits to its right.

Round to the nearest tenth of a percent.

$$\approx 153.3\%$$

Therefore, $92 is approximately 153.3% of $60. (Notice that $92 is just over $1\frac{1}{2}$ times $60, so our answer seems reasonable.)

4. Applications of Percent Equations

In Examples 7, 8, and 9, we use percent equations in application problems. An important part of this process is to extract the base, amount, and percent from the wording of the problem.

Skill Practice

7. Brianna read 143 pages in a book. If this represents 22% of the book, how many pages are in the book?

Example 7 Using a Percent Equation in Ecology

Forty-six panthers are thought to live in Florida's Big Cypress National Preserve. This represents 53% of the panthers living in Florida. How many panthers are there in Florida? Round to the nearest whole unit. (*Source:* U.S. Fish and Wildlife Services)

Solution:

This problem translates to

"46 is 53% of the number of panthers living in Florida."

$$46 = (0.53) \cdot x$$ Let x represent the total number of panthers.

$$46 = 0.53x$$

$$\frac{46}{0.53} = \frac{\overset{1}{\cancel{0.53}}x}{\underset{1}{\cancel{0.53}}}$$ Divide both sides by 0.53.

$$87 \approx x$$ *Note:* $46 \div 0.53 \approx 87$ (rounded to the nearest whole number).

There are approximately 87 panthers in Florida.

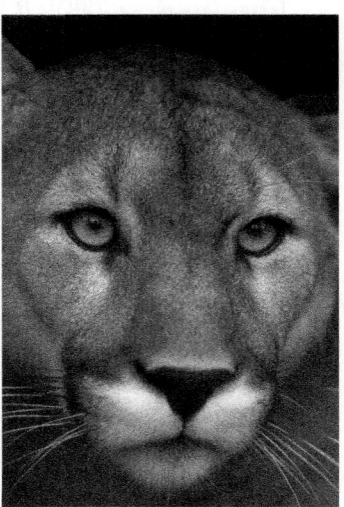

Skill Practice

8. Brandon had $60 in his wallet to take himself and a date to dinner and a movie. If he spent $28 on dinner and $19 on the movie and popcorn, what percent of his money did he spend? Round to the nearest tenth of a percent.

Example 8 Using a Percent Equation in Sports Statistics

Football player Tom Brady of the New England Patriots led his team to numerous Super Bowl victories. For one game during the season, Brady completed 23 of 30 passes. What percent of passes did he complete? Round to the nearest tenth of a percent.

Solution:

This problem translates to

"23 is what percent of 30?"

$$23 = \quad x \quad \cdot 30$$ Let x represent the unknown.

$$23 = 30x$$

$$\frac{23}{30} = \frac{\cancel{30}x}{\cancel{30}}$$ Divide both sides by 30.

$$0.767 \approx x$$ Divide. $23 \div 30 \approx 0.767$

The decimal value 0.767 has been rounded to 3 decimal places. We did this because the next step is to convert the decimal to a percent. Move the decimal point to the right 2 places and attach the % symbol. We have 76.7% which is rounded to the nearest tenth of a percent.

Answers

7. The book is 650 pages long.
8. Brandon spent about 78.3% of his money.

$$x \approx 0.767$$

$$= 0.767 \times 100\%$$

$$= 76.7\%$$

Tom Brady completed approximately 76.7% of his passes.

Example 9   Using a Percent Equation in Voting Statistics

Arnold Schwarzenegger received 50.5% of the votes in a California recall election for governor. If approximately 7.4 million votes were cast, how many votes did Schwarzenegger receive?

Solution:

This problem translates to

"What number is 50.5% of 7.4?"

↓	↓	↓	↓	↓

$x \quad = 0.505 \quad \cdot \ 7.4$ Write 50.5% in decimal form.

$x = (0.505)(7.4)$ Let x represent the number of votes for Schwarzenegger.

$x = 3.737$ Multiply.

Arnold Schwarzenegger received approximately 3.737 million votes.

Skill Practice

9. In a science class, 85% of the students passed the class. If there were 40 people in the class, how many passed?

Answer

9. 34 students passed the class.

Section 6.6   Practice Exercises

Boost *your* GRADE at ALEKS.com!

- Practice Problems
- Self-Tests
- NetTutor
- e-Professors
- Videos

Study Skills Exercise

1. Define the key term **percent equation**.

Review Exercises

For Exercises 2–3, convert the decimal to a percent.

2. 0.059

3. 1.46

For Exercises 4–5, convert the percent to a decimal and a fraction.

4. 124%

5. 0.02%

For Exercises 6–10, solve the equations.

6. $3x = 27$

7. $12x = 48$

8. $\dfrac{62}{100} = \dfrac{x}{47}$

9. $\dfrac{924}{x} = \dfrac{132}{100}$

10. $\dfrac{43}{80} = \dfrac{x}{100}$

Objective 1: Solving Percent Equations—Amount Unknown

For Exercises 11–16, write the percent equation. Then solve for the unknown amount. **(See Examples 1–2.)**

11. What is 35% of 700?

12. Find 12% of 625.

13. 0.55% of 900 is what number?

14. What is 0.4% of 75?

15. Find 133% of 600.

16. 120% of 40.4 is what number?

17. What is a quick way to find 50% of a number?

18. What is a quick way to find 10% of a number?

19. Compute 200% of 14 mentally.

20. Compute 75% of 80 mentally.

21. Compute 50% of 40 mentally.

22. Compute 10% of 32 mentally.

23. Household bleach is 6% sodium hypochlorite (active ingredient). In a 64-oz bottle, how much is active ingredient?

24. One antifreeze solution is 40% alcohol. How much alcohol is in a 12.5-L mixture?

25. Hall of Fame football player Dan Marino completed 60% of his passes. If he attempted 8358 passes, how many did he complete? Round to the nearest whole unit.

26. To pass an exit exam, a student must pass a 60-question test with a score of 80% or better. What is the minimum number of questions she must answer correctly?

Objective 2: Solving Percent Equations—Base Unknown

For Exercises 27–32, write the percent equation. Then solve for the unknown base. **(See Examples 3–4.)**

27. 18 is 40% of what number?

28. 72 is 30% of what number?

29. 92% of what number is 41.4?

30. 84% of what number is 100.8?

31. 3.09 is 103% of what number?

32. 189 is 105% of what number?

33. In tests of a new anti-inflammatory drug, it was found that 47 subjects experienced nausea. If this represents 4% of the sample, how many subjects were tested?

34. Ted typed 80% of his research paper before taking a break.

   a. If he typed 8 pages, how many total pages are in the paper?

   b. How many pages does he have left to type?

35. A recent report stated that approximately 61.6 million Americans had some form of heart and blood vessel disease. If this represents 22% of the population, approximate the total population of the United States.

36. A city has a population of 245,300 which is 110% of the population from the previous year. What was the population the previous year?

Objective 3: Solving Percent Equations—Percent Unknown

For Exercises 37–42 write the percent equation. Then solve for the unknown percent. Round to the nearest tenth of a percent if necessary. **(See Examples 5–6.)**

37. What percent of 480 is 120?   **38.** 180 is what percent of 2000?   **39.** 666 is what percent of 740?

40. What percent of 60 is 2.88?   **41.** What percent of 300 is 400?   **42.** 28 is what percent of 24?

43. Of the 8079 Americans serving in the Peace Corps for a recent year, 406 were over 50 years old. What percent is this? Round to the nearest whole percent.

44. At a softball game, the concession stand had 120 hot dogs and sold 84 of them. What percent was sold?

For Exercises 45–46, refer to the table that shows the 1-year absentee record for a business.

45. a. Determine the total number of employees.

    b. What percent missed exactly 3 days of work?

    c. What percent missed between 1 and 5 days, inclusive?

46. a. What percent missed at least 4 days?

    b. What percent did not miss any days?

Number of Days Missed	Number of Employees
0	4
1	2
2	14
3	10
4	16
5	18
6	10
7	6

Mixed Exercises

For Exercises 47–58, solve the problem using a percent equation.

47. What is 45% of 62?   **48.** What is 32% of 30?   **49.** What percent of 140 is 28?

50. What percent of 25 is 18?   **51.** 23% of what number is 34.5?   **52.** 12% of what number is 26.4?

53. What is $18\frac{1}{2}$% of 3000?   **54.** What is $\frac{1}{4}$% of 460?   **55.** 350% of what number is 2100?

56. 225% of what number is 18?   **57.** 1.2 is what percent of 600?   **58.** 10 is what percent of 2000?

Objective 4: Applications of Percent Equations

59. In a recent year, children and adolescents comprised 6.3 million hospital stays. If this represents 18% of all hospital stays, what was the total number of hospital stays? **(See Example 7.)**

60. One fruit drink advertised that it contained "10% real fruit juice." In one bottle, this was found to be 4.8 oz of real juice.

    a. How many ounces of drink does the bottle contain?

    b. How many ounces is something other than fruit juice?

61. Of the 87 panthers living in the wild in Florida, 11 are thought to live in Everglades National Park. To the nearest tenth of a percent, what percent is this? (*Source:* U.S. Fish and Wildlife Services) **(See Example 8.)**

62. Forty-four percent of Americans use online travel sites to book hotel or airline reservations. If 400 people need to make airline or hotel reservations, how many would be expected to use online travel sites?

63. Fifty-two percent of American parents have started to put money away for their children's college educations. In a survey of 800 parents, how many would be expected to have started saving for their children's education? (*Source: USA TODAY*) **(See Example 9.)**

64. Earth is covered by approximately 360 million km² of water. If the total surface area is 510 million km², what percent is water? (Round to the nearest tenth of a percent.)

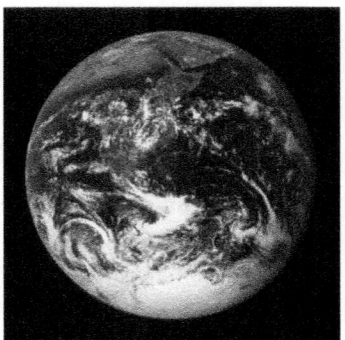

65. Brian has been saving money to buy a 61-in. Samsung Projection HDTV. He has saved $1440 so far, but this is only 60% of the total cost of the television. What is the total cost?

66. During a weak economy, milk prices increased during a 1-year period. The average price in 2008 was $3.90. If this value is 126% of the price from 2007, determine the price in 2007. Round to two decimal places. (*Source:* U.S. Department of Agriculture)

67. Mr. Asher made $49,000 as a teacher in Virginia in 2007, and he spent $8,800 on food that year. In 2008, he received a 4% increase in his salary, but his food costs increased by 6.2%.

    a. How much money was left from Mr. Asher's 2007 salary after subtracting the cost of food?

    b. How much money was left from his 2008 salary after subtracting the cost of food? Round to the nearest dollar.

68. The human body is 65% water. Mrs. Wright weighed 180 lb. After 1 year on a diet, her weight decreased by 15%.

    a. Before the diet, how much of Mrs. Wright's weight was water?

    b. After the diet, how much of Mrs. Wright's weight was water?

For Exercises 69–72, refer to the graph showing the distribution of fatal traffic accidents in the United States according to the age of the driver. (*Source:* National Safety Council)

Traffic Fatalities Distributed by Age of Driver

Bar graph. Vertical axis: 0% to 30%. Horizontal axis: Age (years). Values: 15–24: 27.4%; 25–34: 22.6%; 35–44: 20.4%; 45–54: 12.4%; 55–64: 7.1%; 65+: 10.1%.

69. If there were 60,000 fatal traffic accidents during a given year, how many would be expected to involve drivers in the 35–44 age group?

70. If there were 60,000 fatal traffic accidents, how many would be expected to involve drivers in the 15–24 age group?

71. If there were 9040 fatal accidents involving drivers in the 25–34 age group, how many total traffic fatalities were there for that year?

72. If there were 3550 traffic fatalities involving drivers in the 55–64 age group, how many total traffic fatalities were there for that year?

Expanding Your Skills

The maximum recommended heart rate (in beats per minute) is given by 220 minus a person's age. For aerobic activity, it is recommended that individuals exercise at 60%–85% of their maximum recommended heart rate. This is called the aerobic range. Use this information for Exercises 73–74.

73. **a.** Find the maximum recommended heart rate for a 20-year-old.

    b. Find the aerobic range for a 20-year-old.

74. **a.** Find the maximum recommended heart rate for a 42-year-old.

    b. Find the aerobic range for a 42-year-old.

Problem Recognition Exercises

Percents

For Exercises 1–4, determine the percent represented by the shaded portion of the figure.

1.   **2.**   **3.**   **4.**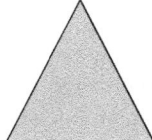

5. Is 104% of 80 less than or greater than 80?   **6.** Is 8% of 50 less than or greater than 5?

7. Is 11% of 90 less than or greater than 9?   **8.** Is 52% of 200 less than or greater than 100?

For Exercises 9–34, solve the problem by using a percent proportion or a percent equation.

9. 6 is 0.2% of what number?   **10.** What percent of 500 is 120?

11. 12% of 40 is what number?   **12.** 27 is what percent of 180?

13. 150% of what number is 105?   **14.** What number is 30% of 120?

15. What is 7% of 90?   **16.** 100 is 40% of what number?

17. 180 is what percent of 60?   **18.** 0.5% of 140 is what number?

19. 75 is 0.1% of what number?   **20.** 27 is what percent of 72?

21. What number is 50% of 50?   **22.** What number is 15% of 900?

23. 50 is 50% of what number?   **24.** 900 is 15% of what number?

25. What percent of 250 is 2?   **26.** 75 is what percent of 60?

27. 26 is 10% of what number?   **28.** 11 is 55% of what number?

29. What number is 10% of 26?   **30.** What number is 55% of 11?

31. 186 is what percent of 248?   **32.** 5 is what percent of 20?

33. 248 is what percent of 186?   **34.** 20 is what percent of 5?

For Exercises 35–40, perform the calculations mentally.

35. What is 10% of 82?   **36.** What is 5% of 82?

37. What is 20% of 82?   **38.** What is 50% of 82?

39. What is 200% of 82?   **40.** What is 15% of 82?

| Section 6.7 | Applications of Sales Tax, Commission, Discount, Markup, and Percent Increase and Decrease |

Objectives

1. Applications Involving Sales Tax
2. Applications Involving Commission
3. Applications Involving Discount and Markup
4. Applications Involving Percent Increase and Decrease

Percents are used in an abundance of applications in day-to-day life. In this section, we investigate six common applications of percents:

- Sales tax
- Commission
- Discount
- Markup
- Percent increase
- Percent decrease

1. Applications Involving Sales Tax

The first application involves computing sales tax. **Sales tax** is a tax based on a percent of the cost of merchandise.

> **FORMULA** Sales Tax Formula
>
> $$\begin{pmatrix} \text{Amount of} \\ \text{sales tax} \end{pmatrix} = \begin{pmatrix} \text{Tax} \\ \text{rate} \end{pmatrix} \cdot \begin{pmatrix} \text{Cost of} \\ \text{merchandise} \end{pmatrix}$$

In this formula, the tax rate is usually given by a percent. Also note that there are three parts to the formula, just as there are in the general percent equation (see Section 6.6). The sales tax formula is a special case of a percent equation.

Skill Practice

1. A graphing calculator costs $110. The sales tax rate is 4.5%.
   a. Compute the amount of sales tax.
   b. Compute the total cost.

Example 1 Computing Sales Tax

Suppose a Toyota Camry sells for $20,000.

a. Compute the sales tax for a tax rate of 5.5%.

b. What is the total price of the car?

Solution:

a. Let x represent the amount of sales tax.   Label the unknown.

Tax rate $= 5.5\%$ Identify the parts of the formula.

Cost of merchandise $= \$20,000$

$$\begin{pmatrix} \text{Amount of} \\ \text{sales tax} \end{pmatrix} = \begin{pmatrix} \text{Tax} \\ \text{rate} \end{pmatrix} \cdot \begin{pmatrix} \text{Cost of} \\ \text{merchandise} \end{pmatrix}$$
$$ x = (5.5\%) \cdot (\$20,000)$$

Substitute values into the sales tax formula.

$$x = (0.055)(\$20,000)$$

Convert the percent to its decimal form.

$$x = \$1100$$

The sales tax on the vehicle is $1100.

b. The total price is $20,000 + $1100 = $21,100.

Avoiding Mistakes

Notice that we must use the decimal form of the sales tax rate in the calculation.

TIP: Example 1(a) can also be solved by using a percent proportion.

$$\frac{5.5}{100} = \frac{x}{20,000} \quad \text{What is 5.5\% of 20,000?}$$

$$(5.5)(20,000) = 100x$$

$$110,000 = 100x$$

$$\frac{110,000}{100} = \frac{100x}{100} \quad \text{Divide both sides by 100.}$$

$$1100 = x \quad \text{The sales tax is \$1100.}$$

Example 2 **Computing a Sales Tax Rate**

Lindsay has just moved and must buy a new refrigerator for her home. The refrigerator costs $1200 and the sales tax is $48. Because she is new to the area, she does not know the sales tax rate. Use these figures to compute the tax rate.

Solution:

Let x represent the sales tax rate.   Label the unknown.

Cost of merchandise = $1200   Identify the parts of the formula.

Amount of sales tax = $48

$$\left(\begin{array}{c}\text{Amount of} \\ \text{sales tax}\end{array}\right) = \left(\begin{array}{c}\text{Tax} \\ \text{rate}\end{array}\right) \cdot \left(\begin{array}{c}\text{Cost of} \\ \text{merchandise}\end{array}\right)$$

$$48 = x \cdot (1200) \quad \begin{array}{l}\text{Substitute values into the sales} \\ \text{tax formula.}\end{array}$$

$$48 = 1200x$$

$$\frac{48}{1200} = \frac{\overset{1}{1200}x}{\underset{1}{1200}} \quad \text{Divide both sides by 1200.}$$

$$0.04 = x$$

The question asks for the tax rate, which is given in percent form.

$$x = 0.04$$

$$= 0.04 \times 100\%$$

$$= 4\% \quad \text{The sales tax rate is 4\%.}$$

Skill Practice

2. A DVD sells for $15. The sales tax is $0.90. What is the tax rate?

TIP: Example 2 can also be solved by using a percent proportion.

$$\frac{48}{1200} = \frac{p}{100}$$

Example 3 **Computing Cost of Merchandise**

The tax on a new CD comes to $1.05. If the tax rate is 6%, find the cost of the CD before tax.

Solution:

Let x represent the cost of the CD.   Label the unknown.

Tax rate = 6%   Identify the parts of the formula.

Amount of tax = $1.05

Skill Practice

3. Sales tax on a new lawn mower is $21.50. If the tax rate is 5%, compute the price of the lawn mower before tax.

Answers

2. The tax rate is 6%.
3. The mower costs $430 before tax.

$$\begin{pmatrix} \text{Amount of} \\ \text{sales tax} \end{pmatrix} = \begin{pmatrix} \text{Tax} \\ \text{rate} \end{pmatrix} \cdot \begin{pmatrix} \text{Cost of} \\ \text{merchandise} \end{pmatrix}$$

$$1.05 = (0.06) \cdot x$$ Notice that we immediately converted 6% to its decimal form.

$$1.05 = 0.06x$$

$$\frac{1.05}{0.06} = \frac{0.06x}{0.06}$$ Divide both sides by 0.06.

$$17.5 = x$$ The CD costs \$17.50.

2. Applications Involving Commission

Salespeople often receive all or part of their salary in commission. **Commission** is a form of income based on a percent of sales.

> **FORMULA** **Commission Formula**
>
> $$\begin{pmatrix} \text{Amount of} \\ \text{commission} \end{pmatrix} = \begin{pmatrix} \text{Commission} \\ \text{rate} \end{pmatrix} \cdot \begin{pmatrix} \text{Total} \\ \text{sales} \end{pmatrix}$$

For example, if a realtor gets a 6% commission on the sale of a \$200,000 home, then

$$\text{Commission} = (0.06)(\$200,000)$$
$$= \$12,000$$

Skill Practice

4. Trevor sold a home for \$160,000 and earned a \$6400 commission. What is his commission rate?

Example 4 **Computing Commission Rate**

Alexis works in real estate sales.

a. If she sells a \$150,000 house and earns a commission of \$10,500, what is her commission rate?

b. At this rate, how much will she earn by selling a \$200,000 house?

Solution:

a. Let x represent the commission rate.   Label the unknown.

Total sales = \$150,000   Identify the parts of the formula.

Amount of commission = \$10,500

$$\begin{pmatrix} \text{Amount of} \\ \text{commission} \end{pmatrix} = \begin{pmatrix} \text{Commission} \\ \text{rate} \end{pmatrix} \cdot \begin{pmatrix} \text{Total} \\ \text{sales} \end{pmatrix}$$

$$10,500 = x \cdot (150,000)$$ Substitute values into the commission formula.

$$10,500 = 150,000x$$

$$\frac{10,500}{150,000} = \frac{150,000x}{150,000}$$ Divide both sides by 150,000.

TIP: A percent proportion can be used to find the commission rate in Example 4.

$$\frac{10,500}{150,000} = \frac{p}{100}$$

Answer

4. His commission rate is 4%.

$$0.07 = x$$

$$x = 0.07 \times 100\% \qquad \text{Convert to percent form.}$$

$$= 7\%$$

The commission rate is 7%.

b. The commission on a $200,000 house is given by

Amount of commission = (0.07)($200,000) = $14,000

Alexis will earn $14,000 by selling a $200,000 house.

Example 5 **Computing Sales Base**

Tonya is a real estate agent. She makes $10,000 as her annual base salary for the work she does in the office. In addition, she makes 8% commission on her total sales. If her salary for the year amounts to $106,000, what was her total in sales?

Solution:

First note that her commission is her total salary minus the $10,000 for working in the office. Thus,

Amount of commission = $106,000 − $10,000 = $96,000

Let x represent Tonya's total sales.	Label the unknown.
Amount of commission = $96,000	Identify the parts of the formula.
Commission rate = 8%	

$$\begin{pmatrix} \text{Amount of} \\ \text{commission} \end{pmatrix} = \begin{pmatrix} \text{Commission} \\ \text{rate} \end{pmatrix} \cdot \begin{pmatrix} \text{Total} \\ \text{sales} \end{pmatrix}$$

$$96{,}000 = (0.08) \cdot x \qquad \text{Substitute values into the commission formula.}$$

$$96{,}000 = 0.08x$$

$$\frac{96{,}000}{0.08} = \frac{0.08x}{0.08} \qquad \text{Divide both sides by 0.08.}$$

$$1{,}200{,}000 = x$$

Tonya's sales totaled $1,200,000 ($1.2 million).

Skill Practice

5. A sales rep for a pharmaceutical firm makes $50,000 as his base salary. In addition, he makes 6% commission on sales. If his salary for the year amounts to $98,000, what were his total sales?

TIP: Example 5 can also be solved by using a percent proportion.

$$\frac{8}{100} = \frac{96{,}000}{x}$$

---

3. Applications Involving Discount and Markup

When we go to the store, we often find items discounted or on sale. For example, a printer might be discounted 20%, or a blouse might be on sale for 30% off. We compute the amount of the **discount** (the savings) as follows.

FORMULA Discount Formulas

$$\begin{pmatrix} \text{Amount of} \\ \text{discount} \end{pmatrix} = \begin{pmatrix} \text{Discount} \\ \text{rate} \end{pmatrix} \cdot \begin{pmatrix} \text{Original} \\ \text{price} \end{pmatrix}$$

Sale price = Original price − Amount of discount

Answer
5. He made $800,000 in sales.

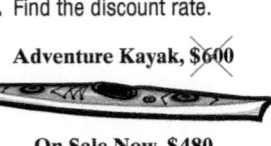
Example 6 **Computing Discount Rate**

A gold chain originally priced $500 is marked down to $375. What is the discount rate?

Solution:

First note that the amount of the discount is given by

$$\text{Discount} = \text{Original price} - \text{Sale price}$$
$$= \$500 - \$375$$
$$= \$125$$

Let x represent the discount rate.   Label the unknown.

Original price = $500   Identify the parts of the formula.

Amount of discount = $125

$$\binom{\text{Amount of}}{\text{discount}} = \binom{\text{Discount}}{\text{rate}} \cdot \binom{\text{Original}}{\text{price}}$$

$$125 \qquad = \qquad x \quad \cdot \quad 500 \qquad \text{Substitute values into discount formula.}$$

$$125 = 500x$$

$$\frac{125}{500} = \frac{500x}{500} \qquad \text{Divide both sides by 500.}$$

$$0.25 = x$$

Converting $x = 0.25$ to percent form, we have $x = 25\%$. The chain has been discounted 25%.

Retailers often buy goods from manufacturers or wholesalers. To make a profit, the retailer must increase the cost of the merchandise before reselling it. This is called **markup**.

FORMULA **Markup Formulas**

$$\binom{\text{Amount of}}{\text{markup}} = \binom{\text{Markup}}{\text{rate}} \cdot \binom{\text{Original}}{\text{price}}$$

$$\text{Retail price} = \text{Original price} + \text{Amount of markup}$$

Example 7 **Computing Markup**

A college bookstore marks up the price of books 40%.

   a. What is the markup for a math text that has a manufacturer price of $66?

   b. What is the retail price of the book?

   c. If there is a 6% sales tax, how much will the book cost to take home?

Solution:

a. Let x represent the amount of markup.   Label the unknown.

Markup rate = 40%   Identify parts of the formula.

Original price = $66

$$\left(\begin{array}{c}\text{Amount of}\\\text{markup}\end{array}\right) = \left(\begin{array}{c}\text{Markup}\\\text{rate}\end{array}\right) \cdot \left(\begin{array}{c}\text{Original}\\\text{price}\end{array}\right)$$

$$\begin{array}{ccc}\downarrow & \downarrow & \downarrow\\ x & = (0.40) \cdot & (\$66)\end{array}$$ Use the decimal form of 40%.

$$x = (0.40)(\$66)$$

$$= \$26.40$$

The amount of markup is $26.40.

b. Retail price = Original price + Markup

$$= \$66 + \$26.40$$

$$= \$92.40$$

The retail price is $92.40.

c. Next we must find the amount of the sales tax. This value is added to the cost of the book. The sales tax rate is 6%.

$$\left(\begin{array}{c}\text{Amount of}\\\text{sales tax}\end{array}\right) = \left(\begin{array}{c}\text{Tax}\\\text{rate}\end{array}\right) \cdot \left(\begin{array}{c}\text{Cost of}\\\text{merchandise}\end{array}\right)$$

$$\text{Tax} = (0.06) \cdot (\$92.40)$$

$$\approx \$5.54$$ Round the tax to the nearest cent.

The total cost of the book is $92.40 + $5.54 = $97.94.

It is important to note the similarities in the formulas presented in this section. To find the amount of sales tax, commission, discount, or markup, we multiply a rate (percent) by some original amount.

SUMMARY Formulas for Sales Tax, Commission, Discount, and Markup

$$\underline{\text{Amount}} = \underline{\text{Rate}} \times \underline{\text{Original amount}}$$

Sales tax:
$$\left(\begin{array}{c}\text{Amount of}\\\text{sales tax}\end{array}\right) = \left(\begin{array}{c}\text{Tax}\\\text{rate}\end{array}\right) \cdot \left(\begin{array}{c}\text{Cost of}\\\text{merchandise}\end{array}\right)$$

Commission:
$$\left(\begin{array}{c}\text{Amount of}\\\text{commission}\end{array}\right) = \left(\begin{array}{c}\text{Commission}\\\text{rate}\end{array}\right) \cdot \left(\begin{array}{c}\text{Total}\\\text{sales}\end{array}\right)$$

Discount:
$$\left(\begin{array}{c}\text{Amount of}\\\text{discount}\end{array}\right) = \left(\begin{array}{c}\text{Discount}\\\text{rate}\end{array}\right) \cdot \left(\begin{array}{c}\text{Original}\\\text{price}\end{array}\right)$$

Markup:
$$\left(\begin{array}{c}\text{Amount of}\\\text{markup}\end{array}\right) = \left(\begin{array}{c}\text{Markup}\\\text{rate}\end{array}\right) \cdot \left(\begin{array}{c}\text{Original}\\\text{price}\end{array}\right)$$

4. Applications Involving Percent Increase and Decrease

Two other important applications of percents are finding percent increase and percent decrease. For example:

- The price of gas increased 40% in 4 years.
- After taking a new drug for 3 months, a patient's cholesterol decreased by 35%.

When we compute **percent increase** or **percent decrease**, we are comparing the *change* between two given amounts to the *original amount*. The change (amount of increase or decrease) is found by subtraction. To compute the percent increase or decrease, we use the following formulas.

FORMULA Percent Increase or Percent Decrease

$$\left(\begin{matrix}\text{Percent}\\\text{increase}\end{matrix}\right) = \left(\frac{\text{Amount of increase}}{\text{Original amount}}\right) \times 100\%$$

$$\left(\begin{matrix}\text{Percent}\\\text{decrease}\end{matrix}\right) = \left(\frac{\text{Amount of decrease}}{\text{Original amount}}\right) \times 100\%$$

In Example 8, we apply the percent increase formula.

Skill Practice

8. After a raise, Denisha's salary increased from $42,500 to $44,200. What is the percent increase?

Example 8 Computing Percent Increase

The price of heating oil climbed from an average of $1.25 per gallon to $1.55 per gallon in a 3-year period. Compute the percent increase.

Solution:

The original price was $1.25 per gallon.   Identify the parts of the formula.

The final price after the increase is $1.55.

The amount of increase is given by subtraction.

Amount of increase = $1.55 − $1.25

= $0.30   There was a $0.30 increase in price.

$$\left(\begin{matrix}\text{Percent}\\\text{increase}\end{matrix}\right) = \left(\frac{\text{Amount of increase}}{\text{Original amount}}\right) \times 100\%$$

$$= \frac{0.30}{1.25} \times 100\%$$ Apply the percent increase formula.

$$= 0.24 \times 100\%$$

$$= 24\%$$

There was a 24% increase in the price of heating oil.

TIP: Example 8 could also have been solved by using a percent proportion.

$$\frac{p}{100} = \frac{\text{Amount of increase}}{\text{Original amount}}$$

$$\frac{p}{100} = \frac{0.30}{1.25}$$

Answer

8. Denisha's salary increased by 4%.

Example 9 Finding Percent Decrease in an Application

The graph in Figure 6-5 represents the closing price of Time Warner stock for a 5-day period. Compute the percent decrease between the first day and the fifth day.

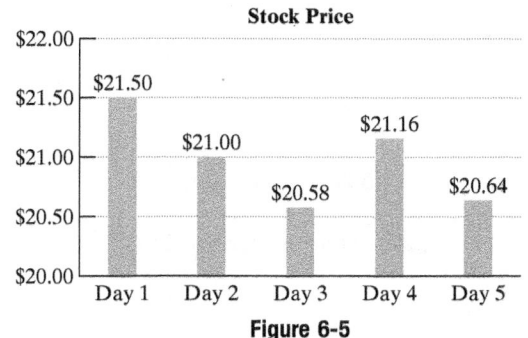

Figure 6-5

Solution:

The amount of decrease is given by: $21.50 − $20.64 = $0.86

The original amount is the closing price on Day 1: $21.50

$$\left(\begin{array}{c}\text{Percent}\\\text{decrease}\end{array}\right) = \left(\frac{\text{Amount of decrease}}{\text{Original amount}}\right) \times 100\%$$

$$= \left(\frac{\$0.86}{\$21.50}\right) \times 100\%$$

$$= (0.04) \times 100\%$$

$$= 4\%$$

The stock fell by 4%.

Skill Practice

9. Refer to the graph in Example 9. Compute the percent decrease between day 2 and day 3.

Answer

9. 2%

Section 6.7 Practice Exercises

Boost your GRADE at ALEKS.com!

ALEKS version 3.0

- Practice Problems
- Self-Tests
- NetTutor
- e-Professors
- Videos

Study Skills Exercises

1. You should not wait until the last minute to study for any test in math. It is particularly important for the final exam that you begin your review early. Check all the activities that will help you study for the final.

☐ Rework all old exams.

☐ Rework the chapter tests for the chapters you covered in class.

☐ Do the cumulative review exercises at the end of Chapters 2–6.

2. Define the key terms.

    a. Sales tax   **b. Commission**   **c. Discount**

    d. Markup   **e. Percent increase**   **f. Percent decrease**

Review Exercises

For Exercises 3–6, find the answer mentally.

3. What is 15% of 80?

4. 20 is what percent of 60?

5. 20 is 50% of what number?

6. What percent of 6 is 12?

For Exercises 7–12, solve the percent problem by using either method from Sections 7.2 or 7.3.

7. 52 is 0.2% of what number?

8. What is 225% of 36?

9. 6 is what percent of 25?

10. 18 is 75% of what number?

11. What is 1.6% of 550?

12. 32.2 is what percent of 28?

Objective 1: Applications Involving Sales Tax

For Exercises 13–14, complete the table.

13.	Cost of Item	Sales Tax Rate	Amount of Tax	Total Cost
a.	$20	5%		
b.	$12.50		$0.50	
c.		2.5%	$2.75	
d.	$55			$58.30

14.	Cost of Item	Sales Tax Rate	Amount of Tax	Total Cost
a.	$56	6%		
b.	$212		$14.84	
c.		3%	$18.00	
d.	$214			$220.42

15. A new coat costs $68.25. If the sales tax rate is 5%, what is the total bill? **(See Example 1.)**

16. Sales tax for a county in Wisconsin is 4.5%. Compute the amount of tax on a new personal MP3 player that sells for $64.

17. The sales tax on a set of luggage is $16.80. If the luggage cost before tax is $240.00, what is the sales tax rate? **(See Example 2.)**

18. A new shirt is labeled at $42.00. Jon purchased the shirt and paid $44.10.

    a. How much was the sales tax?

    b. What is the sales tax rate?

19. The 6% sales tax on a fruit basket came to $2.67. What is the price of the fruit basket? **(See Example 3.)**

20. The sales tax on a bag of groceries came to $1.50. If the sales tax rate is 6% what was the price of the groceries before tax?

Objective 2: Applications Involving Commission

For Exercises 21–22, complete the table.

21.	Total Sales	Commission Rate	Amount of Commission
a.	$20,000	5%	
b.	$125,000		$10,000
c.		10%	$540

22.	Total Sales	Commission Rate	Amount of Commission
a.	$540	16%	
b.	$800		$24
c.		15%	$159

23. Zach works in an insurance office. He receives a commission of 7% on new policies. How much did he make last month in commission if he sold $48,000 in new policies?

24. Marisa makes a commission of 15% on sales over $400. One day she sells $750 worth of merchandise.

    a. How much over $400 did Marisa sell?

    b. How much did she make in commission that day?

25. In one week, Rodney sold $2000 worth of sports equipment. He received $300 in commission. What is his commission rate? **(See Example 4.)**

26. A realtor sold a townhouse for $95,000. If he received a commission of $7600, what is his commission rate?

27. A realtor makes an annual salary of $25,000 plus a 3% commission on sales. If a realtor's salary is $67,000, what was the amount of her sales? **(See Example 5.)**

28. A salesperson receives a weekly salary of $100, plus a 5.5% commission on sales. Her salary last week was $1090. What were her sales that week?

Objective 3: Applications Involving Discount and Markup

For Exercises 29–32, complete the table.

29.	Original Price	Discount Rate	Amount of Discount	Sale Price
a.	$56	20%		
b.	$900			$600
c.			$8.50	$76.50
d.		50%	$38	

30.	Original Price	Discount Rate	Amount of Discount	Sale Price
a.	$175	15%		
b.	$900			$630
c.			$33	$77
d.		40%	$23.36	

31.	Original Price	Markup Rate	Amount of Markup	Retail Price
a.	$92	5%		
b.	$110			$118.80
c.			$97.50	$422.50
d.		20%	$9	

32.	Original Price	Markup Rate	Amount of Markup	Retail Price
a.	$25	10%		
b.	$50			$57.50
c.			$175	$875
d.		18%	$31.50	

33. Hospital employees get a 15% discount at the hospital cafeteria. If the lunch bill originally comes to $5.60, what is the price after the discount?

34. A health club membership costs $550 for 1 year. If a member pays up front in a lump sum, the member will receive a 10% discount.

    a. How much money is discounted?

    b. How much will the yearly membership cost with the discount?

35. A bathing suit is on sale for $45. If the regular price is $60, what is the discount rate? **(See Example 6.)**

36. A printer that sells for $229 is on sale for $183.20. What is the discount rate?

37. A business suit has a wholesale price of $150.00. A department store's markup rate is 18%. **(See Example 7.)**

   a. What is the markup for this suit?

   b. What is the retail price?

   c. If Antonio buys this suit including a 7% sales tax, how much will he pay?

38. An import/export business marks up imported merchandise by 110%. If a wicker chair imported from Singapore originally costs $84 from the manufacturer, what is the retail price?

39. A table is purchased from the manufacturer for $300 and is sold retail at $375. What is the markup rate?

40. A $60 hairdryer is sold for $69. What is the markup rate?

41. Find the discount and the sale price of the tent in the given advertisement.

**Explorer 4-person tent
On Sale** 30% OFF

Was $269

42. A set of dishes had an original price of $112. Then it was discounted 50%. A week later, the new sale price was discounted another 50%. At that time, was the set of dishes free? Explain why or why not.

43. A campus bookstore adds $43.20 to the cost of a science text. If the final cost is $123.20, what is the markup rate?

44. The retail price of a golf club is $420.00. If the golf store has marked up the price by $70, what is the markup rate?

45. Find the discount and the sale price of the bike in the given advertisement.

**Huffy Chopper Bike $109.99
Now 10% off.**

46. Find the discount and the discount rate of the chair from the given advertisement.

**Accent Chair was $235.00
and is now $188.00**

Objective 4: Applications Involving Percent Increase and Decrease

47. Select the correct percent increase for a price that is double the original amount. For example, a book that originally cost $30 now costs $60.

   a. 200%   **b.** 2%

   c. 100%   **d.** 150%

48. Select the correct percent increase for a price that is greater by $\frac{1}{2}$ of the original amount. For example, an employee made $20 per hour and now makes $30 per hour.

   a. 150%   **b.** 50%

   c. $\frac{1}{2}$%   **d.** 200%

49. The number of accidents from all-terrain vehicles that required emergency room visits for children under 16 increased from 21,000 to 42,000 in an 10-year period. What was the percent increase? **(See Example 8.)**

50. The number of deaths from alcohol-induced causes rose from approximately 20,200 to approximately 20,700 in a 10-year period. (*Source:* Centers for Disease Control) What is the percent increase? Round to the nearest tenth of a percent.

51. Robin's health-care premium increased from $5000 per year to $5500 per year. What is the percent increase?

52. The yearly deductible for Diane's health-care plan rose from $800 to $1000. What is the percent increase?

53. Joel's yearly salary went from $42,000 to $45,000. What is the percent increase? Round to the nearest percent.

54. For a recent year, 67.5 million people participated in recreational boating. Sixteen years later, that number increased to 72.6 million. Determine the percent increase. Round to one decimal place.

55. During a recent housing slump, the median price of homes decreased in the United States. If James bought his house for $360,000 and the value 1 year later was $253,800, compute the percent decrease in the value of the house.

56. The U.S. government classified 8 million documents as secret in 2001. By 2003 (2 years after the attacks on 9-11), this number had increased to 14 million. What is the percent increase?

57. A stock closed at $12.60 per share on Monday. By Friday, the closing price was $11.97 per share. What was the percent decrease? **(See Example 9.)**

58. During a 5-year period, the number of participants collecting food stamps went from 27 million to 17 million. What is the percent decrease? Round to the nearest whole percent. (*Source:* U.S. Department of Agriculture)

59. Julie bought a new water-efficient toilet for her house. Her old toilet used 5 gal of water per flush. The new toilet uses only 1.6 gal of water per flush. What is the percent decrease in water per flush?

60. Nancy put new insulation in her attic and discovered that her heating bill for December decreased from $160 to $140. What is the percent decrease?

61. Gus, the cat, originally weighed 12 lb. He was diagnosed with a thyroid disorder, and Dr. Smith the veterinarian found that his weight had decreased to 10.2 lb. What percent of his body weight did Gus lose?

62. To lose weight, Kelly reduced her Calories from 3000 per day to 1800 per day. What is the percent decrease in Calories?

Expanding Your Skills

63. The retail price of four tickets to the Alicia Keys "As I Am" tour is $648. The wholesale price of each ticket is $113.

  a. What is the markup amount per ticket?

  b. What is the markup rate? Round to one decimal place.

Calculator Connections

Topic: Using a Calculator to Compute Percent Increase and Percent Decrease

Calculator Exercises

For Exercises 64–67, determine the percent increase in the stock price for the given companies between 2000 and 2008. Round to the nearest tenth of a percent.

	Stock	Price Jan. 2000 ($ per share)	Price Jan. 2008 ($ per share)	Change ($)	Percent Increase
64.	eBay Inc.	$16.84	$26.15		
65.	Starbucks Corp.	$6.06	$16.92		
66.	Apple Inc.	$28.66	$178.85		
67.	IBM Corp.	$118.37	$127.52		

Section 6.8 | Simple and Compound Interest

Objectives

1. Simple Interest
2. Compound Interest
3. Using the Compound Interest Formula

1. Simple Interest

In this section, we use percents to compute simple and compound interest on an investment or a loan.

Banks hold large quantities of money for their customers. They keep some cash for day-to-day transactions, but invest the remaining portion of the money. As a result, banks often pay customers interest.

When making an investment, **simple interest** is the money that is earned on principal (**principal** is the original amount of money invested). When people take out a loan, the amount borrowed is the principal. The interest is a percent of the amount borrowed that you must pay back in addition to the principal.

The following formulas can be used to compute simple interest for an investment or a loan and to compute the total amount in the account.

Concept Connections

1. Consider this statement: "$8000 invested at 4% for 3 years yields $960." Identify the principal, interest, interest rate, and time.

FORMULA **Simple Interest Formulas**

Simple interest = Principal $\times$ Rate $\times$ Time $I = Prt$

   Total amount = Principal + Interest $A = P + I$

where I = amount of interest
   P = amount of principal
   r = annual interest rate (in decimal form)
   t = time (in years)
   A = total amount in an account

The time, t, is expressed in years because the rate, r, is an *annual* interest rate. If we were given a monthly interest rate, then the time, t, should be expressed in months.

Skill Practice

2. Suppose $1500 is invested in an account that earns 6% simple interest.
   a. How much interest is earned in 5 years?
   b. What is the total value of the account after 5 years?

Example 1 **Computing Simple Interest**

Suppose $2000 is invested in an account that earns 7% simple interest.

a. How much interest is earned after 3 years?

b. What is the total value of the account after 3 years?

Solution:

a. Principal: $P = \$2000$ Identify the parts of the formula.

   Annual interest rate: $r = 7\%$

   Time (in years): $t = 3$

   Let I represent the amount of interest.   Label the unknown.

   $I = Prt$

   $= (\$2000)(7\%)(3)$ Substitute values into the formula.

Answers

1. Principal = $8000; interest = $960; rate = 4% (or 0.04 in decimal form); time = 3 years
2. a. $450 in interest is earned.
   b. The total account value is $1950.

$$= (2000)(0.07)(3)$$ Convert 7% to decimal form.

$$= 420$$ Multiply from left to right.

The amount of interest earned is $420.

b. The total amount in the account is given by

$$A = P + I$$

$$= \$2000 + \$420$$

$$= \$2420$$

The total amount in the account is $2420.

Avoiding Mistakes

It is important to use the decimal form of the interest rate when calculating interest.

Concept Connections

3. To find the interest earned on $6000 at 5.5% for 6 years, what number should be substituted for r: 5.5 or 0.055?

When applying the simple interest formula, it is important that time be expressed in years. This is demonstrated in Example 2.

Example 2   **Computing Simple Interest**

Clyde takes out a loan for $3500. He pays simple interest at a rate of 6% for 4 years 3 months.

a. How much money does he pay in interest?

b. How much total money must he pay to pay off the loan?

Solution:

a. $P = \$3500$ Identify parts of the formula.

$r = 6\%$

$t = 4\frac{1}{4}$ years or 4.25 years   3 months $= \frac{3}{12}$ year $= \frac{1}{4}$ year

$I = Prt$

$= (\$3500)(0.06)(4.25)$ Substitute values into the interest formula. Convert 6% to decimal form 0.06.

$= \$892.50$ Multiply.

The interest paid is $892.50.

b. To find the total amount that must be paid, we have

$A = P + I$

$= \$3500 + \$892.50$

$= \$4392.50$ The total amount that must be paid is $4392.50.

Skill Practice

4. Morris takes out a loan for $10,000. He pays simple interest at 7% for 66 months.
  a. Write 66 months in terms of years.
  b. How much money does he pay in interest?
  c. How much total money must he repay to pay off the loan?

2. Compound Interest

Simple interest is based only on a percent of the original principal. However, many day-to-day applications involve compound interest. **Compound interest** is based on both the original principal and the interest earned.

To compare the difference between simple and compound interest, consider this scenario in Example 3.

Answers

3. 0.055
4. a. 66 months $=$ 5.5 years
  b. Morris pays $3850 in interest.
  c. Morris must pay a total of $13,850 to pay off the loan.

Example 3   **Comparing Simple Interest and Compound Interest**

Suppose $1000 is invested at 8% interest for 3 years.

a. Compute the total amount in the account after 3 years, using simple interest.

b. Compute the total amount in the account after 3 years of compounding interest annually.

Solution:

a. $P = \$1000$

   $r = 8\%$

   $t = 3$ years

   $I = Prt$

   $\quad = (\$1000)(0.08)(3)$

   $\quad = \$240$

The amount of simple interest earned is $240. The total amount in the account is $1000 + $240 = $1240.

b. To compute interest compounded annually over a period of 3 years, compute the interest earned in the first year. Then add the principal plus the interest earned in the first year. This value then becomes the principal on which to base the interest earned in the second year. We repeat this process, finding the interest for the second and third years based on the principal and interest earned in the preceding years. This process is outlined in a table.

Year	Interest Earned $I = Prt$	Total Amount in Account
First year	$I = (\$1000)(0.08)(1) = \$80$	$\$1000 + \$80 = \$1080$
Second year	$I = (\$1080)(0.08)(1) = \$86.40$	$\$1080 + \$86.40 = \$1166.40$
Third year	$I = (\$1166.40)(0.08)(1) = \$93.31$	$\$1166.40 + 93.31 = \mathbf{\$1259.71}$

The total amount in the account by compounding interest annually is $1259.71.

Notice that in Example 3 the final amount in the account is greater for the situation where interest is compounded. The difference is $1259.71 − $1240 = $19.71. By compounding interest we earn more money.

Interest may be compounded more than once per year.

Annually	1 time per year
Semiannually	2 times per year
Quarterly	4 times per year
Monthly	12 times per year
Daily	365 times per year

To compute compound interest, the calculations become very tedious. Banks use computers to perform the calculations quickly. You may want to use a calculator if calculators are allowed in your class.

3. Using the Compound Interest Formula

As you can see from Example 3, computing compound interest by hand is a cumbersome process. Can you imagine computing daily compound interest (365 times a year) by hand!

We now use a formula to compute compound interest. This formula requires the use of a scientific or graphing calculator. In particular, the calculator must have an exponent key $\boxed{y^x}$, $\boxed{x^y}$, or $\boxed{\wedge}$.

Let A = total amount in an account

$\quad P$ = principal

$\quad r$ = annual interest rate

$\quad t$ = time in years

$\quad n$ = number of compounding periods per year

Then $A = P \cdot \left(1 + \dfrac{r}{n}\right)^{n \cdot t}$ computes the total amount in an account.

To use this formula, note the following guidelines:

- Rate r must be expressed in decimal form.
- Time t must be the total time of the investment in *years*.
- Number n is the number of compounding periods per year.

Annual	$n = 1$
Semiannual	$n = 2$
Quarterly	$n = 4$
Monthly	$n = 12$
Daily	$n = 365$

Example 4 **Computing Compound Interest by Using the Compound Interest Formula**

Suppose $1000 is invested at 8% interest compounded annually for 3 years. Use the compound interest formula to find the total amount in the account after 3 years. Compare the result to the answer from Example 3(b).

Solution:

$P = \$1000$ 　　　　　Identify the parts of the formula.

$r = 8\%$ (0.08 in decimal form)

$t = 3$ years

$n = 1$ (annual compound interest is compounded 1 time per year)

$A = P \cdot \left(1 + \dfrac{r}{n}\right)^{n \cdot t}$

$\quad = 1000 \cdot \left(1 + \dfrac{0.08}{1}\right)^{1 \cdot 3}$ 　Substitute values into the formula.

$\quad = 1000(1 + 0.08)^3$ 　　Apply the order of operations. Divide within parentheses. Simplify the exponent.

Skill Practice

6. Suppose $2000 is invested at 5% interest compounded annually for 3 years. Use the formula.

$A = P \cdot \left(1 + \dfrac{r}{n}\right)^{n \cdot t}$

to find the total amount after 3 years. Compare the answer to Skill Practice exercise 5(b).

Answer

6. $2315.25; this is the same as the result in Skill Practice exercise 5(b).

$$= 1000(1.08)^3 \qquad \text{Add within parentheses.}$$
$$= 1000(1.259712) \qquad \text{Evaluate } (1.08)^3 = (1.08)(1.08)(1.08) = 1.259712.$$
$$= 1259.712 \qquad \text{Multiply.}$$
$$\approx 1259.71 \qquad \text{Round to the nearest cent.}$$

The total amount in the account after 3 years is \$1259.71. This is the same value obtained in Example 3(b).

Calculator Connections

Topic: Using a Calculator to Compute Compound Interest

To enter the expression from Example 4 into a calculator, follow these keystrokes.

Expression	Keystrokes	Result
$1000 \cdot (1 + 0.08)^3$	1000 × (1 + 0.08) y^x 3 =	1259.712
or	1000 × (1 + 0.08) ∧ 3 ENTER	1259.712

Example 5 Computing Compound Interest by Using the Compound Interest Formula

Suppose \$8000 is invested in an account that earns 5% interest compounded quarterly for $1\frac{1}{2}$ years. Use the compound interest formula to compute the total amount in the account after $1\frac{1}{2}$ years.

Solution:

$P = \$8000$ — Identify the parts of the formula.

$r = 5\%$ (0.05 in decimal form)

$t = 1.5$ years

$n = 4$ (quarterly interest is compounded 4 times per year)

$$A = P \cdot \left(1 + \frac{r}{n}\right)^{n \cdot t}$$

$$= 8000 \cdot \left(1 + \frac{0.05}{4}\right)^{(4)(1.5)} \qquad \text{Substitute values into the formula.}$$

$$= 8000(1 + 0.0125)^6 \qquad \text{Apply the order of operations. Divide within parentheses. Simplify the exponent.}$$

$$= 8000(1.0125)^6 \qquad \text{Add within parentheses.}$$

$$\approx 8000(1.077383181) \qquad \text{Evaluate } (1.0125)^6. \text{ If your teacher allows the use of a calculator, consider using the exponent key.}$$

$$\approx 8619.07 \qquad \text{Multiply and round to the nearest cent.}$$

The total amount in the account after $1\frac{1}{2}$ years is \$8619.07.

Answer

7. The account is worth \$73,652.88 after 30 years.

Section 6.8   Practice Exercises

Boost *your* GRADE at
ALEKS.com!

- Practice Problems
- Self-Tests
- NetTutor
- e-Professors
- Videos

Study Skills Exercise

1. Define the key terms.

   a. Simple interest   **b. Principal**   **c. Compound interest**

Review Exercises

For Exercises 2–3, write the percent in decimal form.

2. 3.5%

3. 2.25%

4. Jeff works as a pharmaceutical representative. He receives a 6% monthly commission on sales up to $60,000. He receives an 8.5% commission on all sales above $60,000. If he sold $86,000 worth of his product one month, how much did he receive in commission?

5. A paper shredder was marked down from $79 to $59. What is the percent decrease in price? Round to the nearest tenth of a percent.

6. A 19-in. computer monitor is marked down from $279 to $249. What is the percent decrease in price? Round to the nearest tenth of a percent.

Objective 1: Simple Interest

For Exercises 7–14, find the simple interest and the total amount including interest. **(See Example 1.)**

	Principal	Annual Interest Rate	Time, Years	Interest	Total Amount
7.	$6,000	5%	3	_____	_____
8.	$4,000	3%	2	_____	_____
9.	$5,050	6%	4	_____	_____
10.	$4,800	4%	3	_____	_____
11.	$12,000	4%	$4\frac{1}{2}$	_____	_____
12.	$6,230	7%	$6\frac{1}{3}$	_____	_____

13. $10,500   4.5%   4   _____   _____

14. $9,220   8%   4   _____   _____

15. Dale deposited $2500 in an account that pays $3\frac{1}{2}$% simple interest for 4 years. **(See Example 2.)**

  a. How much interest will he earn in 4 years?

  b. What will be the total value of the account after 4 years?

16. Charlene invested $3400 at 4% simple interest for 5 years.

  a. How much interest will she earn in 5 years?

  b. What will be the total value of the account after 5 years?

17. Gloria borrowed $400 for 18 months at 8% simple interest.

  a. How much interest will Gloria have to pay?

  b. What will be the total amount that she has to pay back?

18. Floyd borrowed $1000 for 2 years 3 months at 8% simple interest.

  a. How much interest will Floyd have to pay?

  b. What will be the total amount that he has to pay back?

19. Jozef deposited $10,300 into an account paying 4% simple interest 5 years ago. If he withdraws the entire amount of money, how much will he have?

20. Heather invested $20,000 in an account that pays 6% simple interest. If she invests the money for 10 years, how much will she have?

21. Anne borrowed $4500 from a bank that charges 10% simple interest. If she repays the loan in $2\frac{1}{2}$ years, how much will she have to pay back?

22. Dan borrowed $750 from his brother who is charging 8% simple interest. If Dan pays his brother back in 6 months, how much does he have to pay back?

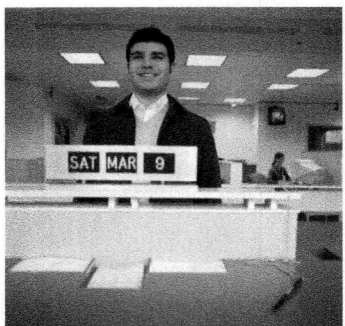

Objective 2: Compound Interest

23. If a bank compounds interest semiannually for 3 years, how many total compounding periods are there?

24. If a bank compounds interest quarterly for 2 years, how many total compounding periods are there?

25. If a bank compounds interest monthly for 2 years, how many total compounding periods are there?

26. If a bank compounds interest monthly for $1\frac{1}{2}$ years, how many total compounding periods are there?

27. Mary Ellen deposited $500 in a bank. **(See Example 3.)**

  a. If the bank offers 4% simple interest, compute the amount in the account after 3 years.

  b. Now suppose the bank offers 4% interest compounded annually. Complete the table to determine the amount in the account after 3 years.

Year	Interest Earned	Total Amount in Account
1		
2		
3		

28. The amount of $8000 is invested at 4% for 3 years.

  a. Compute the ending balance if the bank calculates simple interest.

  b. Compute the ending balance if the bank calculates interest compounded annually.

  c. How much more interest is earned in the account with compound interest?

Year	Interest Earned	Total Amount in Account
1		
2		
3		

29. Fatima deposited $24,000 in an account.

    a. If the bank offers 5% simple interest, compute the amount in the account after 2 years.

    b. Now suppose the bank offers 5% compounded semiannually (twice per year). Complete the table to determine the amount in the account after 2 years.

Period	Interest Earned	Total Amount in Account
1st		
2nd		
3rd		
4th		

30. The amount of $12,000 is invested at 8% for 1 year.

    a. Compute the ending balance if the bank calculates simple interest.

    b. Compute the ending balance if the bank calculates interest compounded quarterly.

    c. How much more interest is earned in the account with compound interest?

Period	Interest Earned	Total Amount in Account
1st		
2nd		
3rd		
4th		

Objective 3: Using the Compound Interest Formula

31. For the formula $A = P \cdot \left(1 + \dfrac{r}{n}\right)^{n \cdot t}$, identify what each variable means.

32. If $1000 is deposited in an account paying 8% interest compounded monthly for 3 years, label the following variables: P, r, n, and t.

Calculator Connections

Topic: Using a Calculator to Compute Compound Interest

Calculator Exercises

For Exercises 33–40, find the total amount in an account for an investment subject to the following conditions. **(See Examples 4–5.)**

	Principal	Annual Interest Rate	Time, Years	Compounded	Total Amount
33.	$5,000	4.5%	5	Annually	_____
34.	$12,000	5.25%	4	Annually	_____
35.	$6,000	5%	2	Semiannually	_____
36.	$4,000	3%	3	Semiannually	_____
37.	$10,000	6%	$1\frac{1}{2}$	Quarterly	_____
38.	$9,000	4%	$2\frac{1}{2}$	Quarterly	_____
39.	$14,000	4.5%	3	Monthly	_____
40.	$9,000	8%	2	Monthly	_____

Group Activity

Tracking Stocks

Materials: Computer with online access or the financial page of a newspaper.

Estimated time: 15 minutes

Group Size: 4

1. Each member of the group will choose a stock that is listed on the New York Stock Exchange. You can find prices in the newspaper or online at http://finance.yahoo.com/.

   Here are some possible stocks to track.

Apple Computer	Home Depot	Best Buy	Microsoft	Walgreens
Nike	Walmart	Hershey	Exxon Mobil	Coca-Cola

2. Beginning on a Monday, record the closing price of the stock. [The closing price is the price at the end of the day at 4:00 P.M. Eastern Standard Time (EST).] Then, each day for 2 weeks, record the closing price of the stock along with the difference in price from the previous day. Record an increase in price in green with an up arrow and a decrease in price in red with a down arrow as shown below. For example:

Date	Price ($)	Increase or Decrease ($)	Percent Increase/Decrease
April 5	34.67		
April 6	34.82	0.15 ⇑	0.4%
April 7	33.98	0.84 ⇓	2.4%

Date	Price ($)	Increase or Decrease ($)	Percent Increase/Decrease

3. For each stock, calculate the amount of increase or decrease in price from the previous day.

4. For each stock, calculate the *percent* increase or decrease in price from the previous day.

5. Which stock was the best investment during this 2-week period? (This is generally considered to be the stock with the greatest percent increase from the original day.)

Chapter 6   Summary

Section 6.1   Ratios

Key Concepts	**Examples**

Key Concepts

A **ratio** is a comparison of two quantities.

The ratio of a to b can be written as follows, provided $b \neq 0$.

   1. a to b 2. $a : b$ 3. $\dfrac{a}{b}$

When we write a ratio in fraction form, we generally simplify it to lowest terms.

Ratios that contain mixed numbers, fractions, or decimals can be simplified to lowest terms with whole numbers in the numerator and denominator.

Examples

Example 1

Three forms of a ratio:

4 to 6   4 : 6 $\dfrac{4}{6}$

Example 2

A hockey team won 4 games out of 6. Write a ratio of games won to total games played and simplify to lowest terms.

$$\frac{4 \text{ games won}}{6 \text{ games played}} = \frac{2}{3}$$

Example 3

$$\frac{2\frac{1}{6}}{\frac{2}{3}} = 2\frac{1}{6} \div \frac{2}{3} = \frac{13}{\overset{}{\underset{2}{6}}} \cdot \frac{\overset{1}{3}}{2} = \frac{13}{4}$$

Example 4

$$\frac{2.1}{2.8} = \frac{2.1}{2.8} \cdot \frac{10}{10} = \frac{21}{28} = \frac{\overset{3}{21}}{\underset{4}{28}} = \frac{3}{4}$$

Section 6.2   Rates

Key Concepts

A **rate** compares two different quantities.

Examples

Example 1

New Jersey has 8,470,000 people living in 21 counties. Write a reduced ratio of people per county.

$$\frac{8{,}470{,}000 \text{ people}}{21 \text{ counties}} = \frac{1{,}210{,}000 \text{ people}}{3 \text{ counties}}$$

A rate having a denominator of 1 unit is called a **unit rate**. To find a unit rate, divide the numerator by the denominator.

Example 2

If a race car traveled 1250 mi in 8 hr during a race, what is its speed in miles per hour?

$$\frac{1250 \text{ mi}}{8 \text{ hr}} = 156.25 \text{ mi/hr}$$

A **unit cost** or unit price is the cost per 1 unit, for example, $1.21/lb or 43¢/oz. Comparing unit prices can help determine the best buy.

Example 3

Tide laundry detergent is offered in two sizes: $18.99 for 150 oz and $13.59 for 100 oz. Find the unit prices to find the best buy.

$$\frac{\$18.99}{150 \text{ oz}} \approx \$0.1266/\text{oz}$$

$$\frac{\$13.59}{100 \text{ oz}} \approx \$0.1359/\text{oz}$$

The 150-oz package is the better buy because the unit cost is less.

Section 6.3   Proportions and Application of Proportions

Key Concepts

A **proportion** states that two ratios or rates are equal.

$\frac{14}{21} = \frac{2}{3}$ is a proportion.

Examples

Example 1

Write as a proportion.

56 mi is to 2 gal as 84 mi is to 3 gal.

$$\frac{56 \text{ mi}}{2 \text{ gal}} = \frac{84 \text{ mi}}{3 \text{ gal}}$$

To determine if two ratios form a proportion, check to see if the cross products are equal, that is,

$$\frac{a}{b} = \frac{c}{d} \quad \text{implies} \quad a \cdot d = b \cdot c \quad \text{(and vice versa)}$$

Example 2

$$\frac{3}{8} \stackrel{?}{=} \frac{2\frac{1}{2}}{6\frac{2}{3}}$$

$$3 \cdot 6\frac{2}{3} \stackrel{?}{=} 8 \cdot 2\frac{1}{2}$$

$$\frac{3}{1} \cdot \frac{20}{3} \stackrel{?}{=} \frac{8}{1} \cdot \frac{5}{2}$$

$$20 = 20 \ \checkmark$$

The ratios form a proportion.

To solve a proportion, solve the equation formed by the cross products.

Example 3

$$\frac{5}{-4} = \frac{18}{x} \qquad 5x = -4 \cdot 18$$

$$5x = -72$$

$$\frac{5x}{5} = \frac{-72}{5}$$

$$x = -\frac{72}{5}$$

The solution is $-\dfrac{72}{5}$ or $-14\dfrac{2}{5}$ or -14.4.

Example 4 demonstrates an application involving a proportion.

Example 4

According to the National Highway Traffic Safety Administration, 2 out of 5 traffic fatalities involve the use of alcohol. If there were 43,200 traffic fatalities in a recent year, how many involved the use of alcohol?

Let n represent the number of traffic fatalities involving alcohol.

Set up a proportion:

$$\frac{2 \text{ traffic fatalities w/alcohol}}{5 \text{ traffic fatalities}} = \frac{n}{43{,}200}$$

Solve the proportion:

$$2(43{,}200) = 5n$$

$$86{,}400 = 5n$$

$$\frac{86{,}400}{5} = \frac{\overset{1}{\cancel{5}}n}{\underset{1}{\cancel{5}}}$$

$$17{,}280 = n$$

17,280 traffic fatalities involved alcohol.

Section 6.4 Percents, Fractions, and Decimals

Key Concepts

The word **percent** means *per one hundred.*

Converting Percents to Fractions

1. Replace the % symbol by $\times \frac{1}{100}$ (or by $\div 100$).
2. Simplify the fraction to lowest terms, if possible.

Converting Percents to Decimals

Replace the % symbol by $\times 0.01$.
(This is equivalent to $\times \frac{1}{100}$ and $\div 100$.)

Note: Multiplying a decimal by 0.01 is the same as moving the decimal point 2 places to the left.

Converting Fractions and Decimals to Percent Form

Multiply the fraction or decimal by 100%.
(100% = 1)

Examples

Example 1

40% means 40 per 100 or $\frac{40}{100}$.

Example 2

$$84\% = 84 \times \frac{1}{100} = \frac{84}{100} = \frac{21}{25}$$

Example 3

$$24.5\% = 24.5 \times 0.01 = 0.245$$

Example 4

$$0.07\% = 0.07 \times 0.01 = 0.0007$$

(Move the decimal point 2 places to the left.)

Example 5

$$\frac{1}{5} = \frac{1}{5} \times 100\% = \frac{100}{5}\% = 20\%$$

Example 6

$$1.14 = 1.14 \times 100\% = 114\%$$

Example 7

$$\frac{2}{3} = 0.\overline{6} \times 100\% = 66.\overline{6}\% \text{ or } 66\tfrac{2}{3}\%$$

Section 6.5   Percent Proportions and Applications

Key Concepts

A **percent proportion** is a proportion that equates a percent to an equivalent ratio.

A percent proportion can be written in the form

$$\frac{\text{Amount}}{\text{Base}} = p\% \qquad \text{or} \qquad \frac{\text{Amount}}{\text{Base}} = \frac{p}{100}$$

The **base** is the total or whole amount being considered. The **amount** is the part being compared to the base.

To solve a percent proportion, equate the cross products and solve the resulting equation. The variable can represent the amount, base, or p. Examples 3–5 demonstrate each type of percent problem.

Example 4

Of a sample of 400 people, 85% found relief using a particular pain reliever. How many people found relief?

Solve the proportion: $\dfrac{x}{400} = \dfrac{85}{100}$

$$85 \cdot 400 = 100x$$

$$\frac{34{,}000}{100} = \frac{100x}{100}$$

$$340 = x$$

340 people found relief.

Examples

Example 1

$\dfrac{36}{100} = \dfrac{9}{25}$ is a percent proportion.

Example 2

For the percent proportion $\dfrac{12}{200} = \dfrac{6}{100}$, 12 is the amount, 200 is the base, and p is 6.

Example 3

44% of what number is 275?

Solve the proportion: $\dfrac{275}{x} = \dfrac{44}{100}$

$$44x = 275 \cdot 100$$

$$\frac{\overset{1}{\cancel{44}}x}{\cancel{44}} = \frac{27{,}500}{44}$$

$$x = 625$$

Example 5

There are approximately 750,000 career employees in the U.S. Postal Service. If 60,000 are mail handlers, what percent does this represent?

Solve the proportion: $\dfrac{60{,}000}{750{,}000} = \dfrac{p}{100}$

$$750{,}000p = 60{,}000 \cdot 100$$

$$\frac{\cancel{750{,}000}p}{\cancel{750{,}000}} = \frac{6{,}000{,}000}{750{,}000}$$

$$p = 8$$

Of career postal employees, 8% are mail handlers.

Section 6.6 Percent Equations and Applications

Key Concepts

A **percent equation** represents a percent proportion in an alternative form:

Amount = $(p\%) \cdot$ (base)

Examples 1–3 demonstrate three types of percent problems.

Example 2

Of the car repairs performed on a certain day, 21 were repairs on transmissions. If 60 cars were repaired, what percent involved transmissions?

Solve the equation: $21 = 60x$

$$\frac{21}{60} = \frac{\overset{1}{\cancel{60}}x}{\underset{1}{\cancel{60}}}$$

$$0.35 = x$$

Because the problem asks for a percent, we have $x = 0.35$

$\quad = 0.35 \times 100\%$

$\quad = 35\%$

Therefore, 35% of cars repaired involved transmissions.

Examples

Example 1

Of all breast cancer cases, 99% occur in women. Out of 2700 cases of breast cancer reported, how many are expected to occur in women?

Solve the equation: $x = (99\%)(2700)$

$$x = (0.99)(2700)$$

$$x = 2673$$

About 2673 cases are expected to occur in women.

Example 3

There are 599 endangered plants in the United States. This represents 60.7% of the total number of endangered species. Find the total number of endangered species. Round to the nearest whole number.

Solve the equation: $599 = 0.607x$

$$\frac{599}{0.607} = \frac{\overset{1}{\cancel{0.607}}x}{\underset{1}{\cancel{0.607}}}$$

$$987 \approx x$$

There is a total of approximately 987 endangered species in the United States.

Section 6.7 Applications of Sales Tax, Commission, Discount, Markup, and Percent Increase and Decrease

Key Concepts

To find **sales tax**, use the formula

$$\begin{pmatrix} \text{Amount of} \\ \text{sales tax} \end{pmatrix} = \begin{pmatrix} \text{Tax} \\ \text{rate} \end{pmatrix} \cdot \begin{pmatrix} \text{Cost of} \\ \text{merchandise} \end{pmatrix}$$

Examples

Example 1

A DVD is priced at $16.50, and the total amount paid is $17.82. To find the sales tax rate, first find the amount of tax.

$17.82 - $16.50 = $1.32

To compute the sales tax rate, solve: $1.32 = x \cdot 16.50$

$$\frac{1.32}{16.50} = \frac{x \cdot \overset{1}{\cancel{16.50}}}{\underset{1}{\cancel{16.50}}}$$

$$0.08 = x \qquad \text{The sales tax rate is 8\%.}$$

To find a **commission**, use the formula

$$\begin{pmatrix} \text{Amount of} \\ \text{commission} \end{pmatrix} = \begin{pmatrix} \text{Commission} \\ \text{rate} \end{pmatrix} \cdot \begin{pmatrix} \text{Total} \\ \text{sales} \end{pmatrix}$$

To find **discount** and sale price, use the formulas

$$\begin{pmatrix} \text{Amount of} \\ \text{discount} \end{pmatrix} = \begin{pmatrix} \text{Discount} \\ \text{rate} \end{pmatrix} \cdot \begin{pmatrix} \text{Original} \\ \text{price} \end{pmatrix}$$

Sale price = Original price − Amount of discount

To find **markup** and retail price, use the formulas

$$\begin{pmatrix} \text{Amount of} \\ \text{markup} \end{pmatrix} = \begin{pmatrix} \text{Markup} \\ \text{rate} \end{pmatrix} \cdot \begin{pmatrix} \text{Original} \\ \text{price} \end{pmatrix}$$

Retail price = Original price + Amount of markup

Percent increase or **percent decrease** compares the *change* between two given amounts to the *original amount*.

Computing Percent Increase or Decrease

$$\begin{pmatrix} \text{Percent} \\ \text{increase} \end{pmatrix} = \begin{pmatrix} \dfrac{\text{Amount of increase}}{\text{Original amount}} \end{pmatrix} \times 100\%$$

$$\begin{pmatrix} \text{Percent} \\ \text{decrease} \end{pmatrix} = \begin{pmatrix} \dfrac{\text{Amount of decrease}}{\text{Original amount}} \end{pmatrix} \times 100\%$$

Example 2

Fletcher makes 13% commission on the sale of all merchandise. If he sells $11,290 worth of merchandise, find how much Fletcher will earn.

$$x = (0.13)(11{,}290)$$
$$= 1467.7 \qquad \text{Fletcher will earn \$1467.70 in commission.}$$

Example 3

Margaret found a ring that was originally $425 but is on sale for 30% off. To find the sale price, first find the amount of discount.

$$a = (0.30) \cdot (425)$$
$$= 127.5$$

The sale price is $425 − $127.50 = $297.50.

Example 4

In 1 year a child grows from 35 in. to 42 in. The increase is $42 - 35 = 7$. The percent increase is

$$\frac{7}{35} \times 100\% = 0.20 \times 100\%$$
$$= 20\%$$

Section 6.8 Simple and Compound Interest

Key Concepts

To find the **simple interest** made on a certain **principal**, use the formula $I = Prt$

where I = amount of interest

         P = amount of principal

         r = annual interest rate

         t = time (in years)

The formula for the total amount in an account is $A = P + I$, where A = total amount in an account.

Examples

Example 1

Betsey deposited $2200 in her account, which pays 5.5% simple interest. To find the simple interest she will earn after 4 years, use the formula $I = Prt$ and solve for I.

$$I = (2200)(0.055)(4)$$
$$= 484 \qquad \text{She will earn \$484 interest.}$$

To find the balance or total amount of her account, apply the formula $A = P + I$.

$$A = 2200 + 484$$
$$= 2684 \qquad \text{Betsey's balance will be \$2684.}$$

Many day-to-day applications involve compound interest. **Compound interest** is based on both the original principal and the interest earned.

The formula $A = P \cdot \left(1 + \dfrac{r}{n}\right)^{n \cdot t}$ computes the total amount in an account that uses compound interest

where $\quad$ A = total amount in an account

$\qquad$ P = principal

$\qquad$ r = annual interest rate

$\qquad$ t = time (in years)

$\qquad$ n = number of compounding periods per year

Example 2

Gene borrows $1000 at 6% interest compounded semi-annually. If he pays off the loan in 3 years, how much will he have to pay?

We are given $P = 1000$, $r = 0.06$, $n = 2$ (semiannually means twice a year), and $t = 3$.

$$A = 1000\left(1 + \frac{0.06}{2}\right)^{2 \cdot 3}$$

$$= 1000(1.03)^6$$

$$\approx 1194.05$$

Gene will have to pay $1194.05 to pay off the loan with interest.

Chapter 6 Review Exercises

Section 6.1

For Exercises 1–3, write the ratios in two other ways.

1. $5 : 4$ $\qquad$ **2.** 3 to 1 $\qquad$ **3.** $\dfrac{8}{7}$

For Exercises 4–6, write the ratios in fraction form.

4. Saul had three daughters and two sons.

 a. Write a ratio of the number of sons to the number of daughters.

 b. Write a ratio of the number of daughters to the number of sons.

 c. Write a ratio of the number of daughters to the total number of children.

5. In his refrigerator, Jonathan has four bottles of soda and five bottles of juice.

 a. Write a ratio of the number of bottles of soda to the number of bottles of juice.

 b. Write a ratio of the number of bottles of juice to the number of bottles of soda.

 c. Write a ratio of the number of bottles of juice to the total number of bottles.

6. There are 12 face cards in a regular deck of 52 cards.

 a. Write a ratio of the number of face cards to the total number of cards.

 b. Write a ratio of the number of face cards to the number of cards that are not face cards.

For Exercises 7–10, write the ratio in lowest terms.

7. 52 cards to 13 cards $\qquad$ **8.** $21 to $15

9. 80 ft to 200 ft $\qquad$ **10.** 7 days to 28 days

For Exercises 11–14, write the ratio in lowest terms with whole numbers in the numerator and denominator.

11. $1\dfrac{1}{2}$ hr to $\dfrac{1}{3}$ hr $\qquad$ **12.** $\dfrac{2}{3}$ yd to $2\dfrac{1}{6}$ yd

13. $2.56 to $1.92 $\qquad$ **14.** 42.5 mi to 3.25 mi

15. This year a high school had an increase of 320 students. The enrollment last year was 1200 students.

   a. How many students will be attending this year?

   b. Write a ratio of the increase in the number of students to the total enrollment of students this year. Simplify to lowest terms.

16. A living room has dimensions of 3.8 m by 2.4 m. Find the ratio of length to width and reduce to lowest terms.

For Exercises 17–18, refer to the table that shows the number of personnel who smoke in a particular workplace.

	Smokers	Nonsmokers	Totals
Office personnel	12	20	32
Shop personnel	60	55	115

17. Find the ratio of the number of office personnel who smoke to the number of shop personnel who smoke.

18. Find the ratio of the total number of personnel who smoke to the total number of personnel.

Section 6.2

For Exercises 19–22, write each rate in lowest terms.

19. A concession stand sold 20 hot dogs in 45 min.

20. Mike can skate 4 mi in 34 min.

21. During a period in which the economy was weak, Evelyn's balance on her investment account changed by −$3400 in 6 months.

22. A submarine's "elevation" changed by −75 m in 45 min.

23. What is the difference between rates in lowest terms and unit rates?

For Exercises 24–27, write each rate as a unit rate.

24. A pheasant can fly 44 mi in $1\frac{1}{3}$ hr.

25. The temperature changed −14° in 3.5 hr.

26. A hummingbird can flap its wings 2700 times in 30 sec.

27. It takes David's lawn company 66 min to cut six lawns.

For Exercises 28–29, find the unit costs. Round the answers to three decimal places when necessary.

28. Body lotion costs $5.99 for 10 oz.

29. Three towels cost $10.00.

For Exercises 30–31, compute the unit cost (round to three decimal places). Then determine the best buy.

30. a. 48 oz of detergent for $5.99

   b. 60 oz of detergent for $7.19

   c. Which is the best buy?

31. a. 32 oz of spaghetti sauce for $2.49

   b. 48 oz of spaghetti sauce for $3.59

   c. Which is the best buy?

32. Suntan lotion costs $5.99 for 8 oz. If Sherri has a coupon for $2.00 off, what will be the unit cost of the lotion after the coupon has been applied?

33. A 24-roll pack of bathroom tissue costs $8.99 without a discount card. The package is advertised at 29¢ per roll if the buyer uses the discount card. What is the difference in price per roll when the buyer uses the discount card? Round to the nearest cent.

34. In Wilmington, North Carolina, Hurricane Floyd dropped 15.06 in. of rain during a 24-hr period. What was the average rainfall per hour? (*Source:* National Weather Service)

35. For a recent year, Toyota steadily increased the number of hybrid vehicles for sale in the United States from 130,000 to 250,000.

   a. What was the increase in the number of hybrid vehicles?

   b. How many additional hybrid vehicles will be available each month?

36. In 1990, Americans ate on average 386 lb of vegetables per year. By 2008, this value increased to 449 lb.

   a. What was the increase in the number of pounds of vegetables?

   b. How many additional pounds of vegetables did Americans add to their diet per year?

Section 6.3

For Exercises 37–42, write a proportion for each statement.

37. 16 is to 14 as 12 is to $10\frac{1}{2}$.

38. 8 is to 20 as 6 is to 15.

39. The numbers -5 and 3 are proportional to the numbers -10 and 6.

40. The numbers 4 and -3 are proportional to the numbers 20 and -15.

41. $11 is to 1 hr as $88 is to 8 hr.

42. 2 in. is to 5 mi as 6 in. is to 15 mi.

For Exercises 43–46, determine whether the ratios form a proportion.

43. $\dfrac{64}{81} \overset{?}{=} \dfrac{8}{9}$

44. $\dfrac{3\frac{1}{2}}{7} \overset{?}{=} \dfrac{7}{14}$

45. $\dfrac{5.2}{3} \overset{?}{=} \dfrac{15.6}{9}$

46. $\dfrac{6}{10} \overset{?}{=} \dfrac{6.3}{10.3}$

For Exercises 47–50, determine whether the pairs of numbers are proportional.

47. Are the numbers $2\frac{1}{8}$ and $4\frac{3}{4}$ proportional to the numbers $3\frac{2}{5}$ and $7\frac{3}{5}$?

48. Are the numbers $5\frac{1}{2}$ and 6 proportional to the numbers $6\frac{1}{2}$ and 7?

49. Are the numbers -4.25 and -8 proportional to the numbers 5.25 and 10?

50. Are the numbers 12.4 and 9.2 proportional to the numbers -3.1 and -2.3?

For Exercises 51–56, solve the proportion.

51. $\dfrac{100}{16} = \dfrac{25}{x}$

52. $\dfrac{y}{6} = \dfrac{45}{10}$

53. $\dfrac{1\frac{6}{7}}{b} = \dfrac{13}{21}$

54. $\dfrac{p}{6\frac{1}{3}} = \dfrac{3}{9\frac{1}{2}}$

55. $\dfrac{2.5}{-6.8} = \dfrac{5}{h}$

56. $\dfrac{0.3}{1.2} = \dfrac{k}{-3.6}$

57. One year of a dog's life is about the same as 7 years of a human life. If a dog is 12 years old in dog years, how does that equate to human years?

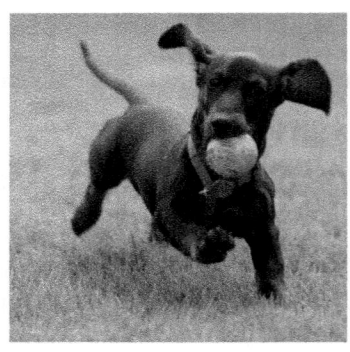

58. Lavu bought 17,120 Japanese yen with $160 American. At this rate, how many yen can he buy with $450 American?

59. The number of births in Alabama in a recent year was approximately 59,800. If the birthrate was about 13 per 1000, what was the approximate population of Alabama? (Round to the nearest person.)

60. If the tax on a $25.00 item is $1.20, what would be the tax on an item costing $145.00?

Section 6.4

For Exercises 61–64, use a percent to express the shaded portion of each drawing.

61.

62.

63.   **64.**

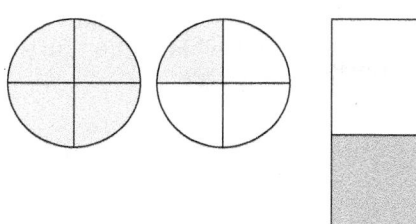

65. 68% can be expressed as which of the following forms? Identify all that apply.

a. $\dfrac{68}{1000}$ b. $\dfrac{68}{100}$

c. 0.68   d. 0.068

66. 0.4% can be expressed as which of the following forms? Identify all that apply.

a. $\dfrac{4}{100}$ b. 0.04

c. $\dfrac{0.4}{100}$ d. 0.004

For Exercises 67–74, write the percent as a fraction and as a decimal.

67. 30%   **68.** 95%

69. 135%   **70.** 212%

71. 0.2%   **72.** 0.6%

73. $66\frac{2}{3}\%$ **74.** $33\frac{1}{3}\%$

For Exercises 75–84, write the fraction or decimal as a percent. Round to the nearest tenth of a percent if necessary.

75. $\dfrac{5}{8}$ **76.** $\dfrac{7}{20}$

77. $\dfrac{7}{4}$ **78.** $\dfrac{11}{5}$

79. 0.006   **80.** 0.001

81. 4   **82.** 6

83. $\dfrac{3}{7}$ **84.** $\dfrac{9}{11}$

Section 6.5

For Exercises 85–88, write the percent proportion.

85. 6 books of 8 books is 75%

86. 15% of 180 lb is 27 lb.

87. 200% of $420 is $840.

88. 6 pine trees out of 2000 pine trees is 0.3%.

For Exercises 89–94, solve the percent problems, using proportions.

89. What is 12% of 50?

90. $5\frac{3}{4}\%$ of 64 is what number?

91. 11 is what percent of 88?

92. 8 is what percent of 2500?

93. 13 is $33\frac{1}{3}\%$ of what number?

94. 24 is 120% of what number?

95. Based on recent statistics, one airline expects that 4.2% of its customers will be "no-shows." If the airline sold 260 seats, how many people would the airline expect as no-shows? Round to the nearest whole unit.

96. In a survey of college students, 58% said that they wore their seatbelts regularly. If this represents 493 people, how many people were surveyed?

97. Victoria spends $720 per month on rent. If her monthly take-home pay is $1800, what percent does she pay in rent?.

98. Of the rental cars at the U-Rent-It company, 40% are compact cars. If this represents 26 cars, how many cars are on the lot?

Section 6.6

For Exercises 99–104, write as a percent equation and solve.

99. 18% of 900 is what number?

100. What number is 29% of 404?

101. 18.90 is what percent of 63?

102. What percent of 250 is 86?

103. 30 is 25% of what number?

104. 26 is 130% of what number?

105. A student buys a used book for $54.40. This is 80% of the original price. What was the original price?

106. Veronica has read 330 pages of a 600-page novel. What percent of the novel has she read?

107. Elaine tries to keep her fat intake to no more than 30% of her total calories. If she has a 2400-calorie diet, how many fat calories can she consume to stay within her goal?

108. It is predicted that by 2010, 13% of Americans will be over the age of 65. By 2050 that number could rise to 20%. Suppose that the U.S. population is 300,000,000 in 2010 and 404,000,000 in 2050.

    a. Find the number of Americans over 65 in the year 2010.

    b. Find the number of Americans over 65 in the year 2050.

Section 6.7

For Exercises 109–112, solve the problem involving sales tax.

109. A Plasma TV costs $1279. Find the sales tax if the rate is 6%.

110. The sales tax on a sofa is $47.95. If the sofa costs $685.00 before tax, what is the sales tax rate?

111. Kim has a digital camera. She decides to make prints for 40 photos. If the sales tax at a rate of 5% comes to $0.44, what was the price of the photos before tax? What is the cost per photo?

112. A resort hotel charges an 11% resort tax along with the 6% sales tax. If the hotel's one-night accommodation is $125.00, what will a tourist pay for 4 nights, including tax?

For Exercises 113–116, solve the problems involving commission.

113. At a recent auction, *Boy with a Pipe,* an early work by Pablo Picasso, sold for $104 million. The commission for the sale of the work was $11 million. What was the rate of commission? Round to the nearest tenth of a percent. (*Source:* The *New York Times*)

114. Andre earns a commission of 12% on sales of restaurant supplies. If he sells $4075 in one week, how much commission will he earn?

115. Sela sells sportswear at a department store. She earns an hourly wage of $8, and she gets a 5% commission on all merchandise that she sells over $200. If Sela works an 8-hr day and sells $420 of merchandise, how much will she earn that day?

116. A real estate agent earned $9600 for the sale of a house. If her commission rate is 6%, for how much did the house sell?

For Exercises 117–120, solve the problems involving discount and markup.

117. Find the discount and the sale price of the movie if the regular price is $28.95.

118. This notebook computer was originally priced at $1747. How much is the discount? After the $50 rebate, how much will a person pay for this computer?

119. A rug manufacturer sells a rug to a retail store for $160. The store then marks up the rug to $208. What is the markup rate?

120. Peg sold some homemade baskets to a store for $50 each. The store marks up all merchandise by 18%. What will be the retail price of the baskets after the markup?

For Exercises 121–122, solve the problem involving percent increase or decrease.

121. The number of species of animals on the endangered species list went from 263 in 1990 to 410 in 2006. Find the percent increase. Round to the nearest tenth of a percent. (*Source:* U.S. Fish and Wildlife Services)

122. During a weak period in the economy, the stock price for Hershey Foods fell from $50.62 per share to $32.68 per share. Compute the percent decrease. Round to the nearest tenth of a percent.

Section 6.8

For Exercises 123–124, find the simple interest and the total amount including interest.

	Principal	Annual Interest Rate	Time, Years	Interest	Total Amount
123.	$10,200	3%	4	_____	_____
124.	$7000	4%	5	_____	_____

125. Jean-Luc borrowed $2500 at 5% simple interest. What is the total amount that he will pay back at the end of 18 months (1.5 years)?

126. Kyle loaned his brother Win $800 and charged 2.5% simple interest. If Win pays all the money back (principal plus interest) at the end of 2 yr, how much will Win pay his brother.

127. Sydney deposited $6000 in a certificate of deposit that pays 4% interest compounded annually. Complete the table to determine her balance after 3 years.

Year	Interest	Total
1		
2		
3		

128. Nell deposited $10,000 in a money market account that pays 3% interest compounded semiannually. Complete the table to find her balance after 2 years.

Compound Periods	Interest	Total
Period 1 (end of first 6 months)		
Period 2 (end of year 1)		
Period 3 (end of 18 months)		
Period 4 (end of year 2)		

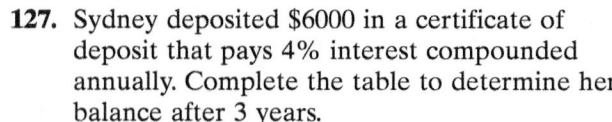 For Exercises 129–132, find the total amount for the investment, using compound interest. Use the formula

$$A = P \cdot \left(1 + \frac{r}{n}\right)^{n \cdot t}.$$

	Principal	Annual Interest Rate	Time in Years	Compounded	Total Amount
129.	$850	8%	2	Quarterly	_____
130.	$2050	5%	5	Semiannually	_____
131.	$11,000	7.5%	6	Annually	_____
132.	$8200	4.5%	4	Monthly	_____

Chapter 6   Test

1. An elementary school has 25 teachers and 521 students. Write a ratio of teachers to students in three different ways.

2. The months August and September bring the greatest number of hurricanes to the eastern seaboard and gulf coast states. As of this writing, 27 hurricanes had struck the U.S.

mainland in August and 44 had struck in September. (*Source:* NOAA)

a. Write a ratio of the number of hurricanes to strike in September to the number in August.

b. Write a ratio of the number of hurricanes to strike in August to the total number in these two peak months.

3. Find the ratio of the shortest side to the longest side. Write the ratio in lowest terms.

65 cm   87 cm

104 cm

4. **a.** In a recent year, the number of people in New Mexico whose income was below poverty level was 168 out of every 1000. Write this as a simplified ratio.

   b. The poverty level in Iowa was 72 people to 1000 people. Write this as a simplified ratio.

   c. Compare the ratios and comment.

5. Write as a simplified ratio in two ways: 30 sec to $1\frac{1}{2}$ min

   a. By converting 30 sec to minutes.

   b. By converting $1\frac{1}{2}$ min to seconds.

For Exercises 6–7, write as a rate, simplified to lowest terms.

6. 255 mi per 6 hr

7. 20 lb in 6 weeks

For Exercises 8–9, write as a unit rate. Round to the nearest hundredth.

8. The element platinum had density of 2145 g per 100 cm^3.

9. Approximately 104.8 oz of iron is present in 45.8 lb of rocks brought back from the moon.

10. What is the unit cost for Raid Ant and Roach spray valued at $6.72 for 30 oz? Round to the nearest cent.

11. A package containing 3 toe rings is on sale for 2 packs for $6.60. What is the cost of 1 toe ring?

For Exercises 12–14, write a proportion for each statement.

12. -42 is to 15 as -28 is to 10.

13. 20 pages is to 12 min as 30 pages is to 18 min.

14. $15 an hour is proportional to $75 for 5 hr.

For Exercises 15–18, solve the proportion.

15. $\dfrac{25}{p} = \dfrac{45}{-63}$

16. $\dfrac{32}{20} = \dfrac{20}{x}$

17. $\dfrac{n}{9} = \dfrac{3\frac{1}{3}}{6}$

18. $\dfrac{y}{-14} = \dfrac{7.2}{16.8}$

19. Cherise is an excellent student and studies 7.5 hr outside of class each week for a 3-credit-hour math class. At this rate, how many hours outside of class does she spend on homework if she is taking 12 credit-hours at school?

20. Ms. Ehrlich wants to approximate the number of goldfish in her backyard pond. She scooped out 8 and marked them. Later she scooped out 10 and found that 3 were marked. Estimate the number of goldfish in her pond. Round to the nearest whole unit.

21. Write a percent to express the shaded portion of the figure.

For Exercises 22–24, write the percent in decimal form and in fraction form.

22. For a recent year, the unemployment rate of Illinois was 5.4%.

23. The incidence of breast cancer increased by 0.15% between 2003 and 2005.

24. For a certain city, gas prices increased by 170% in 10 years.

25. Write the following percents in fraction form.

   a. 1%   **b.** 25%

   c. $33\frac{1}{3}$%   **d.** 50%

   e. $66\frac{2}{3}$%   **f.** 75%

   g. 100%   **h.** 150%

For Exercises 26–29, write the fraction as a percent. Round to the nearest tenth of a percent if necessary.

26. $\dfrac{3}{5}$

27. $\dfrac{1}{250}$

28. $\dfrac{7}{4}$

29. $\dfrac{5}{7}$

For Exercises 30–33, write the decimal as a percent.

30. 0.32

31. 0.052

32. 1.3

33. 0.006

For Exercises 34–36, solve the percent problems.

34. What is 120% of 16?

35. 21 is 6% of what number?

36. What percent of 220 is 198?

37. At McDonald's, a side salad without dressing has 10 mg of sodium. With a serving of Newman's Own Low-Fat Balsamic Dressing, the sodium content of the salad is 740 mg. (*Source:* www.mcdonalds.com)

    a. How much sodium is in the dressing itself?

    b. What percent of the sodium content in a side salad with dressing is from the dressing? Round to the nearest tenth of a percent.

The composition of the lower level of Earth's atmosphere is given in the figure. (Other gases are present in minute quantities.) For Exercises 38–39, use the information in the graph.

Composition of Earth's Atmosphere

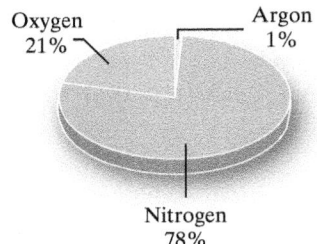

Oxygen 21%

Argon 1%

Nitrogen 78%

38. How much nitrogen would be expected in 500 m³ of atmosphere?

39. How much oxygen would be expected in 2000 m³ of atmosphere?

40. Natalia received an 8% raise in salary. If the amount of the raise is $4160, determine her salary before the raise. Determine her new salary.

41. Brad bought a pair of blue jeans that cost $30.00. He wrote his check for $32.10.

    a. What is the amount of sales tax that he paid?

    b. What is the sales tax rate?

42. Find the discount rate of the product in the advertisement.

End of Season Clearance Sale

Was $45.00

Now $18.00

Quantities are limited so... Shop Now!

43. A furniture store buys merchandise from the manufacturer and then marks it up by 30%.

    a. If the markup on a dining room set is $375, what was the price from the manufacturer?

    b. What is the retail price?

    c. If there is a 6% sales tax, what is the total cost to buy the dining room set?

44. Maury borrowed $5000 at 8% simple interest. He plans to pay back the loan in 3 years.

    a. How much interest will he have to pay?

    b. What is the total amount that he has to pay back?

45. Use the formula $A = P \cdot \left(1 + \dfrac{r}{n}\right)^{n \cdot t}$ to calculate the total amount in an account that began with $25,000 invested at 4.5% compounded quarterly for 5 years.

Chapters 1–6   Cumulative Review Exercises

1. What is the place value for the digit 6 in the number 26,009,235?

2. Multiply. $\begin{array}{r} 34{,}882 \\ \times\,100 \end{array}$

3. Divide. $9\overline{)783}$

4. Simplify. $\sqrt{16} - 6 \div 3 + 3^2$

For Exercises 5–6, multiply or divide as indicated. Simplify the fraction to lowest terms.

5. $\dfrac{3}{8} \cdot \dfrac{32}{9}$

6. $-\dfrac{21}{2} \div (-7)$

7. Find the perimeter of the figure.

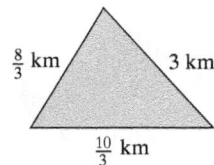

8. A sheet of paper has the dimensions $13\frac{1}{2}$ in. by 17 in. What is the area of the paper?

9. a. List four multiples of 18.

   b. List all factors of 18.

   c. Write the prime factorization of 18.

10. Write a fraction that represents the shaded portion of each figure.

a.   **b.**

11. Write the fraction as a decimal. $\dfrac{3}{8}$

12. Write the fraction as a percent. $\dfrac{7}{8}$

13. Simplify the expression. $-2x - 5(x - 6) + 9$

For Exercises 14–17, solve the equation.

14. $-3x + 5 = 17$

15. $4y - 9 = 3(y + 2)$

16. $\dfrac{3}{4} = \dfrac{15}{p}$

17. $\dfrac{4\frac{1}{3}}{p} = \dfrac{12}{18}$

18. A DC-10 aircraft flew 1799 mi in 3.5 hr. Find the unit rate in miles per hour.

19. Kevin deposited $13,000 in a certificate of deposit that pays 3.2% simple interest. How much will Kevin have if he keeps the certificate for 5 years?

20. A bank charges 8% interest that is compounded monthly. Use the formula
$$A = P \cdot \left(1 + \frac{r}{n}\right)^{n \cdot t}$$
to find the total amount of interest paid for a 10-year mortgage on $75,000.

Measurement and Geometry

7

Chapter 7

Measurement is used when collecting data (information) for virtually all scientific experiments. In this chapter, we study both the U.S. Customary units of measure and the metric system. Then we use both systems in applications of medicine and geometry.

Are You Prepared?

To prepare for this chapter, take a minute to review some of the geometry formulas presented earlier in the text. Match the formula on the left with the figure on the right.

1. $A = \pi r^2$ _____

2. $P = 4s$ _____

3. $C = 2\pi r$ _____

4. $A = s^2$ _____

5. $A = \dfrac{1}{2}bh$ _____

6. $P = 2l + 2w$ _____

7. $A = lw$ _____

8. $P = a + b + c$ _____

a. Area:

b. Circumference:

c. Area:

d. Perimeter:

e. Perimeter:

f. Area:

g. Area:

h. Perimeter:

Section 7.1 U.S. Customary Units of Measurement

1. U.S. Customary Units

In many applications in day-to-day life, we need to measure things. To measure an object means to assign it a number and a **unit of measure**. In this section, we present units of measure used in the United States for length, time, weight, and capacity. Table 7-1 gives several commonly used units and their equivalents.

Table 7-1 **Summary of U.S. Customary Units of Length, Time, Weight, and Capacity**

Length	Time
1 foot (ft) = 12 inches (in.)	1 year (yr) = 365 days
1 yard (yd) = 3 feet (ft)	1 week (wk) = 7 days
1 mile (mi) = 5280 feet (ft)	1 day = 24 hours (hr)
1 mile (mi) = 1760 yards (yd)	1 hour (hr) = 60 minutes (min)
	1 minute (min) = 60 seconds (sec)

Capacity	Weight
3 teaspoons (tsp) = 1 tablespoon (T)	1 pound (lb) = 16 ounces (oz)
1 cup (c) = 8 fluid ounces (fl oz)	1 ton = 2000 pounds (lb)
1 pint (pt) = 2 cups (c)	
1 quart (qt) = 2 pints (pt)	
1 quart (qt) = 4 cups (c)	
1 gallon (gal) = 4 quarts (qt)	

TIP: Sometimes units of feet are denoted with the ′ symbol. That is, 3 ft = 3′. Similarly, sometimes units of inches are denoted with the ″ symbol. That is, 4 in. = 4″.

2. U.S. Customary Units of Length

In Example 1, we will demonstrate how to convert between two units of measure by multiplying by a conversion factor. A **conversion factor** is a ratio of equivalent measures.

For example, note that 1 yd = 3 ft. Therefore, $\dfrac{1 \text{ yd}}{3 \text{ ft}} = 1$ and $\dfrac{3 \text{ ft}}{1 \text{ yd}} = 1$.

These ratios are called **unit ratios** (or **unit fractions**). In a unit ratio, the quotient is 1 because we are dividing measurements of equal length. To convert from one unit of measure to another, we can multiply by a unit ratio. We offer these guidelines to determine the proper unit ratio to use.

Concept Connections

Complete the unit ratio.

1. $\dfrac{1 \text{ ft}}{\square \text{ in.}}$ 2. $\dfrac{\square \text{ yd}}{3 \text{ ft}}$

PROCEDURE Choosing a Unit Ratio as a Conversion Factor

In a unit ratio,
- The unit of measure in the numerator should be the new unit you want to convert *to*.
- The unit of measure in the denominator should be the original unit you want to convert *from*.

Answers

1. $\dfrac{1 \text{ ft}}{12 \text{ in.}}$ 2. $\dfrac{1 \text{ yd}}{3 \text{ ft}}$

| **Example 1** | **Converting Units of Length by Using Unit Ratios** |

Convert the units of length.

a. 1500 ft = _____ yd   **b.** 9240 yd = _____ mi   **c.** 8.2 mi = _____ ft

Solution:

a. From Table 7-1, we have 1 yd = 3 ft.

$$1500 \text{ ft} = 1500 \text{ ft} \cdot \frac{1 \text{ yd}}{3 \text{ ft}}$$ ⟵ new unit to convert to
⟵ unit to convert from

$$= \frac{1500 \text{ ft}}{1} \cdot \frac{1 \text{ yd}}{3 \text{ ft}}$$

Notice that the original units of ft reduce or "cancel" in much the same way as simplifying fractions. The unit yd remains in the final answer.

$$= \frac{1500}{3} \text{ yd}$$

$$= 500 \text{ yd}$$

b. From Table 7-1, we have 1 mi = 1760 yd.

$$9240 \text{ yd} = 9240 \text{ yd} \cdot \frac{1 \text{ mi}}{1760 \text{ yd}}$$ ⟵ new unit to convert to
⟵ unit to convert from

$$= \frac{9240 \text{ yd}}{1} \cdot \frac{1 \text{ mi}}{1760 \text{ yd}}$$

The units of yd "cancel," leaving the answer in miles.

$$= \frac{9240}{1760} \text{ mi}$$

Multiply fractions.

$$= 5.25 \text{ mi}$$

Simplify.

c. From Table 7-1 we have 1 mi = 5280 ft.

$$8.2 \text{ mi} = 8.2 \text{ mi} \cdot \frac{5280 \text{ ft}}{1 \text{ mi}}$$ ⟵ new unit to convert to
⟵ unit to convert from

$$= \frac{8.2 \text{ mi}}{1} \cdot \frac{5280 \text{ ft}}{1 \text{ mi}}$$

The units of mi "cancel," leaving the answer in feet.

$$= 43,296 \text{ ft}$$

TIP: It is important to write the units associated with the numbers. The units can help you select the correct unit ratio.

Skill Practice

Convert, using unit ratios.
3. 720 in. = _____ ft
4. 4224 ft = _____ mi
5. 8 mi = _____ yd

Answers

3. 60 ft   **4.** 0.8 mi   **5.** 14,080 yd

Example 2 **Making Multiple Conversions of Length**

Convert the units of length.

a. 0.25 mi = _____ in.   **b.** 22 in. = _____ yd

Solution:

a. To convert miles to inches, we use two conversion factors. The first unit ratio converts miles to feet. The second unit ratio converts feet to inches.

$$0.25 \text{ mi} = 0.25 \text{ mi} \cdot \overset{\substack{\text{converts}\\\text{mi to ft}}}{\frac{5280 \text{ ft}}{1 \text{ mi}}} \cdot \overset{\substack{\text{converts}\\\text{ft to in.}}}{\frac{12 \text{ in.}}{1 \text{ ft}}}$$

$$= \frac{0.25 \, \cancel{\text{mi}}}{1} \cdot \frac{5280 \, \cancel{\text{ft}}}{1 \, \cancel{\text{mi}}} \cdot \frac{12 \text{ in.}}{1 \, \cancel{\text{ft}}}$$

The units mi and ft "cancel," leaving the answer in inches.

$$= 15,840 \text{ in.}$$

b. $22 \text{ in.} = 22 \text{ in.} \cdot \overset{\substack{\text{converts}\\\text{in. to ft}}}{\frac{1 \text{ ft}}{12 \text{ in.}}} \cdot \overset{\substack{\text{converts}\\\text{ft to yd}}}{\frac{1 \text{ yd}}{3 \text{ ft}}}$

Multiply by two conversion factors. The first converts inches to feet. The second converts feet to yards.

$$= \frac{22 \, \cancel{\text{in.}}}{1} \cdot \frac{1 \, \cancel{\text{ft}}}{12 \, \cancel{\text{in.}}} \cdot \frac{1 \text{ yd}}{3 \, \cancel{\text{ft}}}$$

The units in. and ft "cancel," leaving the answer in yards.

$$= \frac{22}{36} \text{ yd}$$

Multiply fractions.

$$= \frac{11}{18} \text{ yd} \quad \text{or} \quad 0.6\overline{1} \text{ yd}$$

Simplify.

To add and subtract measurements, we must have like units. For example:

$$3 \text{ ft} + 8 \text{ ft} = 11 \text{ ft}$$

Sometimes, however, measurements have mixed units. For example, a drainpipe might be 4 ft 6 in. long or symbolically 4′6″. Measurements and calculations with mixed units can be handled in much the same way as mixed numbers.

Example 3 **Adding and Subtracting Mixed Units of Measurement**

a. Add.   4′6″ + 2′9″   **b.** Subtract.   8′2″ − 3′6″

Solution:

a. 4′6″ + 2′9″ =
$$\begin{array}{r} 4 \text{ ft} + 6 \text{ in.} \\ +2 \text{ ft} + 9 \text{ in.} \\ \hline 6 \text{ ft} + 15 \text{ in.} \end{array}$$
Add like units.

$$= 6 \text{ ft} + 1 \text{ ft} + 3 \text{ in.}$$

Because 15 in. is more than 1 ft, we can write 15 in. = 12 in. + 3 in. = 1 ft + 3 in.

$$= 7 \text{ ft 3 in.} \quad \text{or} \quad 7′3″$$

b. $8'2'' - 3'6'' = \quad 8 \text{ ft} + 2 \text{ in.} = \quad \overset{7}{8} \text{ ft} + \overset{12 \text{ in.}}{2} \text{ in.} \qquad$ Borrow 1 ft = 12 in.
$\qquad\qquad\quad \underline{-(3 \text{ ft} + 6 \text{ in.})} \quad \underline{-(3 \text{ ft} + 6 \text{ in.})}$

$\qquad\qquad\qquad\qquad\qquad = \quad 7 \text{ ft} + 14 \text{ in.}$
$\qquad\qquad\qquad\qquad\qquad\quad \underline{-(3 \text{ ft} + \ 6 \text{ in.})}$
$\qquad\qquad\qquad\qquad\qquad\qquad 4 \text{ ft} + \ 8 \text{ in.} \quad \text{or} \quad 4'8''$

3. Units of Time

In Examples 4 and 5, we convert between two units of time.

Example 4   **Converting Units of Time**

Convert the units of time.

a. 32 hr = ___ days   **b.** 36 hr = ___ sec

Solution:

a. $32 \text{ hr} = \dfrac{32 \text{ hr}}{1} \cdot \dfrac{1 \text{ day}}{24 \text{ hr}}$ ⟵ new unit to convert to   Recall that
$\qquad\qquad\qquad\qquad\qquad$ ⟵ unit to convert from   1 day = 24 hr.

$\qquad\quad = \dfrac{32}{24} \text{ days}$ Multiply fractions.

$\qquad\quad = \dfrac{4}{3} \text{ days or } 1\dfrac{1}{3} \text{ days}$ Simplify.

$\qquad\qquad\qquad\qquad$ converts   converts
$\qquad\qquad\qquad\qquad$ hr to min   min to sec
$\qquad\qquad\qquad\qquad\quad\downarrow\qquad\quad\downarrow$

b. $36 \text{ hr} = \dfrac{36 \text{ hr}}{1} \cdot \dfrac{60 \text{ min}}{1 \text{ hr}} \cdot \dfrac{60 \text{ sec}}{1 \text{ min}}$ Multiply by two conversion factors.

$\qquad\quad = 129{,}600 \text{ sec}$ Simplify.

Example 5   **Converting Units of Time**

After running a marathon, Dave crossed the finish line and noticed that the race clock read 2:20:30. Convert this time to minutes.

Solution:

The notation 2:20:30 means 2 hr 20 min 30 sec. We must convert 2 hr to minutes and 30 sec to minutes. Then we add the total number of minutes.

$$2 \text{ hr} = \dfrac{2 \text{ hr}}{1} \cdot \dfrac{60 \text{ min}}{1 \text{ hr}} = 120 \text{ min}$$

$$30 \text{ sec} = \dfrac{30 \text{ sec}}{1} \cdot \dfrac{1 \text{ min}}{60 \text{ sec}} = \dfrac{30}{60} \text{ min} = \dfrac{1}{2} \text{ min} \quad \text{or} \quad 0.5 \text{ min}$$

The total number of minutes is 120 min + 20 min + 0.5 min = 140.5 min. Dave finished the race in 140.5 min.

Skill Practice

Convert.

10. 16 hr = _____ days

11. 24 hr = _____ sec

Skill Practice

12. When Ward Burton won the Daytona 500 his time was 2:22:45. Convert this time to minutes.

Answers

10. $\dfrac{2}{3}$ day   **11.** 86,400 sec

12. 142.75 min

4. U.S. Customary Units of Weight

Measurements of weight record the force of an object subject to gravity. In Example 6, we convert from one unit of weight to another.

Example 6 **Converting Units of Weight**

a. The average weight of an adult male African elephant is 12,400 lb. Convert this value to tons.

b. Convert the weight of a 7-lb 3-oz baby to ounces.

Solution:

a. Recall that 1 ton = 2000 lb.

$$12{,}400 \text{ lb} = \frac{12{,}400 \text{ lb}}{1} \cdot \frac{1 \text{ ton}}{2000 \text{ lb}}$$

$$= \frac{12{,}400}{2000} \text{ tons} \qquad \text{Multiply fractions.}$$

$$= \frac{31}{5} \text{ tons} \quad \text{or} \quad 6.2 \text{ tons}$$

An adult male African elephant weighs 6.2 tons.

b. To convert 7 lb 3 oz to ounces, we must convert 7 lb to ounces.

$$7 \text{ lb} = \frac{7 \text{ lb}}{1} \cdot \frac{16 \text{ oz}}{1 \text{ lb}} \qquad \text{Recall that 1 lb = 16 oz.}$$

$$= 112 \text{ oz}$$

The baby's total weight is 112 oz + 3 oz = 115 oz.

Example 7 **Applying U.S. Customary Units of Weight**

Jessica lifts four boxes of books. The boxes have the following weights: 16 lb 4 oz, 18 lb 8 oz, 12 lb 5 oz, and 22 lb 9 oz. How much weight did she lift altogether?

Solution:

```
   16 lb   4 oz                    Add like units in columns.
   18 lb   8 oz
   12 lb   5 oz
 + 22 lb   9 oz
   68 lb  26 oz = 68 lb + 26 oz
                = 68 lb + 1 lb + 10 oz    Recall that 1 lb = 16 oz.
                = 69 lb  10 oz
```

Jessica lifted 69 lb 10 oz of books.

5. U.S. Customary Units of Capacity

A typical can of soda contains 12 fl oz. This is a measure of capacity. Capacity is the volume or amount that a container can hold. The U.S. Customary units of capacity are fluid ounces (fl oz), cup (c), pint (pt), quart (qt), and gallon (gal).

One fluid ounce is approximately the amount of liquid that two large spoonfuls will hold. One cup is the amount in an average-size cup of tea. While Table 7-1 summarizes the relationships among units of capacity, we also offer an illustration (Figure 7-1).

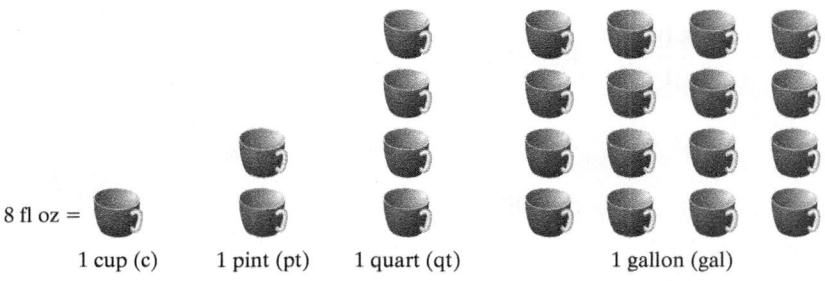

8 fl oz =   1 cup (c)   1 pint (pt)   1 quart (qt)   1 gallon (gal)

Figure 7-1

> **Concept Connections**
>
> **16.** From Figure 7-1, determine how many cups are in 1 gal.
> **17.** From Figure 7-1, determine how many pints are in 1 gal.

Example 8   **Converting Units of Capacity**

Convert the units of capacity.

a. 1.25 pt = _____ qt   **b.** 2 gal = _____ c   **c.** 48 fl oz = _____ gal

Solution:

a. $1.25 \text{ pt} = \dfrac{1.25 \text{ pt}}{1} \cdot \dfrac{1 \text{ qt}}{2 \text{ pt}}$ Recall that 1 qt = 2 pt.

$= \dfrac{1.25}{2} \text{ qt}$ Multiply fractions.

$= 0.625 \text{ qt}$ Simplify.

b. $2 \text{ gal} = 2 \text{ gal} \cdot \dfrac{4 \text{ qt}}{1 \text{ gal}} \cdot \dfrac{4 \text{ c}}{1 \text{ qt}}$ Use two conversion factors. The first unit ratio converts gallons to quarts. The second converts quarts to cups.

$= \dfrac{2 \text{ gal}}{1} \cdot \dfrac{4 \text{ qt}}{1 \text{ gal}} \cdot \dfrac{4 \text{ c}}{1 \text{ qt}}$

$= 32 \text{ c}$ Multiply.

c. $48 \text{ fl oz} = \dfrac{48 \text{ fl oz}}{1} \cdot \dfrac{1 \text{ c}}{8 \text{ fl oz}} \cdot \dfrac{1 \text{ qt}}{4 \text{ c}} \cdot \dfrac{1 \text{ gal}}{4 \text{ qt}}$ Convert from fluid ounces to cups, from cups to quarts, and from quarts to gallons.

$= \dfrac{48}{128} \text{ gal}$

$= \dfrac{3}{8} \text{ gal} \quad \text{or} \quad 0.375 \text{ gal}$

> **Skill Practice**
>
> Convert.
> **18.** 8.5 gal = _____ qt
> **19.** 2.25 qt = _____ c
> **20.** 40 fl oz = _____ qt

> **Avoiding Mistakes**
>
> It is important to note that ounces (oz) and fluid ounces (fl oz) are different quantities. An ounce (oz) is a measure of weight, and a fluid ounce (fl oz) is a measure of capacity. Furthermore,
>
> 16 oz = 1 lb
>
> 8 fl oz = 1 c

Answers
16. 16 c in 1 gal   **17.** 8 pt in 1 gal
18. 34 qt   **19.** 9 c
20. 1.25 qt

Skill Practice

21. A recipe calls for $3\frac{1}{2}$ c of tomato sauce. A jar of sauce holds 24 fl oz. Is there enough sauce in the jar for the recipe?

Answer

21. No, $3\frac{1}{2}$ c is equal to 28 fl oz. The jar only holds 24 fl oz.

Example 9 **Applying Units of Capacity**

A recipe calls for $1\frac{3}{4}$ c of chicken broth. A can of chicken broth holds 14.5 fl oz. Is there enough chicken broth in the can for the recipe?

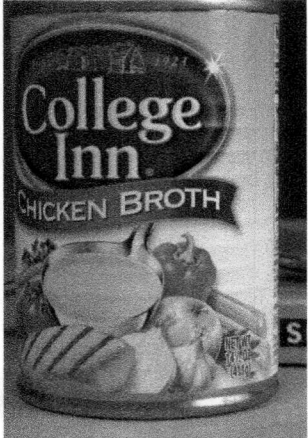

Solution:

We need to convert each measurement to the same unit of measure for comparison. Converting $1\frac{3}{4}$ c to fluid ounces, we have

$$1\frac{3}{4}\,c = \frac{7}{4}\,c \cdot \frac{8\text{ fl oz}}{1\,c} \quad \text{Recall that 1 c = 8 fl oz.}$$

$$= \frac{56}{4}\text{ fl oz} \quad \text{Multiply fractions.}$$

$$= 14\text{ fl oz} \quad \text{Simplify.}$$

The recipe calls for $1\frac{3}{4}$ c or 14 fl oz of chicken broth. The can of chicken broth holds 14.5 fl oz, which is enough.

Section 7.1 Practice Exercises

Boost *your* GRADE at ALEKS.com!

- Practice Problems
- Self-Tests
- NetTutor
- e-Professors
- Videos

Study Skills Exercise

1. Define the key terms.

    a. Unit of measure   **b. Conversion factor**   **c. Unit ratio (or unit fraction)**

Objective 2: U.S. Customary Units of Length

2. Identify an appropriate ratio to convert feet to inches by using multiplication.

    a. $\dfrac{12\text{ ft}}{1\text{ in.}}$ **b.** $\dfrac{12\text{ in.}}{1\text{ ft}}$ **c.** $\dfrac{1\text{ ft}}{12\text{ in.}}$ **d.** $\dfrac{1\text{ in.}}{12\text{ ft}}$

For Exercises 3–20, convert the units of length by using unit ratios. **(See Examples 1–2.)**

3. 9 ft = _____ yd

4. $2\frac{1}{3}$ yd = _____ ft

5. 3.5 ft = _____ in.

6. $4\frac{1}{2}$ in. = _____ ft

7. 11,880 ft = _____ mi

8. 0.75 mi = _____ ft

9. 14 ft = _____ yd

10. 75 in. = _____ ft

11. 320 mi = _____ yd

12. $3\frac{1}{4}$ ft = _____ in.

13. 171 in. = _____ yd

14. 0.3 mi = _____ in.

15. 2 yd = _____ in.

16. 12,672 in. = _____ mi

17. 0.8 mi = _____ in.

18. 900 in. = _____ yd

19. 31,680 in. = _____ mi

20. 6 yd = _____ in.

21. a. Convert 6′4″ to inches.

    b. Convert 6′4″ to feet.

22. a. Convert 10 ft 8 in. to inches.

    b. Convert 10 ft 8 in. to feet.

23. a. Convert 2 yd 2 ft to feet.

    b. Convert 2 yd 2 ft to yards.

24. a. Convert 3′6″ to feet.

    b. Convert 3′6″ to inches.

For Exercises 25–30, add or subtract as indicated. **(See Example 3.)**

25. 2 ft 8 in. + 3 ft 4 in.

26. 5 ft 2 in. + 6 ft 10 in.

27. 8 ft 8 in. − 5 ft 4 in.

28. 3 ft 2 in. − 1 ft 5 in.

29. 9′2″ − 4′10″

30. 4′10″ + 6′4″

Objective 3: Units of Time

For Exercises 31–42, convert the units of time. **(See Example 4.)**

31. 2 yr = _____ days

32. $1\frac{1}{2}$ days = _____ hr

33. 90 min = _____ hr

34. 3 wk = _____ days

35. 180 sec = _____ min

36. $3\frac{1}{2}$ hr = _____ min

37. 72 hr = _____ days

38. 28 days = _____ wk

39. 3600 sec = _____ hr

40. 168 hr = _____ wk

41. 9 wk = _____ hr

42. 1680 hr = _____ wk

For Exercises 43–46, convert the time given as hr:min:sec to minutes. **(See Example 5.)**

43. 1:20:30

44. 3:10:45

45. 2:55:15

46. 1:40:30

Objective 4: U.S. Customary Units of Weight

For Exercises 47–52, convert the units of weight. **(See Example 6.)**

47. 32 oz = _____ lb

48. 2500 lb = _____ tons

49. 2 tons = _____ lb

50. 4 lb = _____ oz

51. $3\frac{1}{4}$ tons = _____ lb

52. 3000 lb = _____ tons

For Exercises 53–58, add or subtract as indicated. **(See Example 7.)**

53. 6 lb 10 oz + 3 lb 14 oz

54. 12 lb 11 oz + 13 lb 7 oz

55. 30 lb 10 oz − 22 lb 8 oz

56. 5 lb − 2 lb 5 oz

57. 10 lb − 3 lb 8 oz

58. 20 lb 3 oz + 15 oz

Objective 5: U.S. Customary Units of Capacity

For Exercises 59–70, convert the units of capacity. **(See Example 8.)**

59. 16 fl oz = _____ c

60. 5 pt = _____ c

61. 6 gal = _____ qt

62. 8 pt = _____ qt

63. 1 gal = _____ c

64. 1 T = _____ tsp

65. 2 qt = _____ gal

66. 2 qt = _____ c

67. 1 pt = _____ fl oz

68. 32 fl oz = _____ qt

69. 2 T = _____ tsp

70. 2 gal = _____ pt

Mixed Exercises

71. A recipe for minestrone soup calls for 3 c of spaghetti sauce. If a jar of sauce has 48 fl oz, is there enough for the recipe? **(See Example 9.)**

72. A recipe for punch calls for 6 c of apple juice. A bottle of juice has 2 qt. Is there enough juice in the bottle for the recipe?

73. A plumber used two pieces of pipe for a job. One piece was 4′6″ and the other was 2′8″. How much pipe was used?

74. A carpenter needs to put wood molding around three sides of a room. Two sides are 6′8″ long, and the third side is 10′ long. How much molding should the carpenter purchase?

75. If you have 4 yd of rope and you use 5 ft, how much is left over? Express the answer in feet.

76. The Blaisdell Arena football field, home of the Hawaiian Islanders football team, did not have the proper dimensions required by the arena football league. The width was measured to be 82 ft 10 in. Regulation width is 85 ft. What is the difference between the widths of a regulation field and the field at Blaisdell Arena?

77. Find the perimeter in feet.

78. Find the perimeter in yards.

79. A 24-fl-oz jar of spaghetti sauce sells for $2.69. Another jar that holds 1 qt of sauce sells for $3.29. Which is a better buy? Explain.

80. Tatiana went to purchase bottled water. She found the following options: a 12-pack of 1-pt bottles; a 1-gal jug; and a 6-pack of 24-fl-oz bottles. Which option should Tatiana choose to get the most water? Explain.

81. A picnic table requires 5 boards that are 6′ long, 4 boards that are 3′3″ long, and 2 boards that are 18″ long. Find the total length of lumber required.

82. A roll of ribbon is 60 yd. If you wrap 12 packages that each use 2.5 ft of ribbon, how much ribbon is left over?

83. Byron lays sod in his backyard. Each piece of sod weighs 6 lb 4 oz. If he puts down 50 pieces, find the total weight.

84. A can of paint weighs 2 lb 4 oz. How much would 6 cans weigh?

85. The garden pictured needs a decorative border. The border comes in pieces that are 1.5 ft long. How many pieces of border are needed to surround the garden?

86. Monte fences all sides of a field with panels of fencing that are 2 yd long. How many panels of fencing does he need?

For Exercises 87–90, refer to the table.

Day	Time
Mon.	1 hr 10 min
Tues.	45 min
Wed.	1 hr 20 min
Thur.	30 min
Fri.	50 min
Sat.	Rest
Sun.	1 hr

87. Gil is a distance runner. The durations of his training runs for one week are given in the table. Find the total time that Gil ran that week and express the answer in mixed units.

88. Find the difference between the amount of time Gil trained on Monday and the amount of time he trained on Friday.

89. In a team triathlon, Torie swims $\frac{1}{2}$ mi in 15 min 30 sec. David rides his bicycle 20 mi in 50 min 20 sec. Emilie runs 4 mi in 28 min 10 sec. Find the total time for the team.

90. Joe competes in a biathlon. He runs 5 mi in 32 min 8 sec. He rides his bike 25 mi in 1 hr 2 min 40 sec. Find the total time for his race.

Expanding Your Skills

In Section 1.5 we learned that area is measured in square units such as in.^{2}, ft^2, yd^2, and mi^2. Converting square units involves a different set of conversion factors. For example, 1 yd = 3 ft, but 1 yd^2 = 9 ft^2. To understand why, recall that the formula for the area of a rectangle is $A = l \times w$. In a square, the length and the width are the same distance s. Therefore, the area of a square is given by the formula $A = s \times s$, where s is the length of a side.

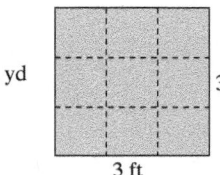

$$A = (1 \text{ yd})(1 \text{ yd}) \qquad A = (3 \text{ ft})(3 \text{ ft})$$
$$= 1 \text{ yd}^2 \qquad\qquad = 9 \text{ ft}^2$$

Instead of learning a new set of conversion factors, we can use multiples of the conversion factors that we mastered in this section.

Example: Converting Area

Convert 4 yd^2 to square feet.

Solution: We will use the unit ratio of $\dfrac{3 \text{ ft}}{1 \text{ yd}}$ twice.

$$\frac{4 \text{ yd}^2}{1} \cdot \underbrace{\frac{3 \text{ ft}}{1 \text{ yd}} \cdot \frac{3 \text{ ft}}{1 \text{ yd}}}_{\text{Multiply first.}} = \frac{4 \text{ yd}^2}{1} \cdot \frac{9 \text{ ft}^2}{1 \text{ yd}^2} = 36 \text{ ft}^2$$

> **TIP:** We use the unit ratio $\frac{3 \text{ ft}}{1 \text{ yd}}$ twice because there are two dimensions. Length and width must both be converted to feet.

For Exercises 91–98, convert the units of area by using multiple factors of the given unit ratio.

91. $54 \text{ ft}^2 = $ _____ yd^2 $\left(\text{Use two factors of the ratio } \dfrac{1 \text{ yd}}{3 \text{ ft}}.\right)$

92. $108 \text{ ft}^2 = $ _____ yd^2

93. $432 \text{ in.}^2 = $ _____ ft^2 $\left(\text{Use two factors of the ratio } \dfrac{1 \text{ ft}}{12 \text{ in.}}.\right)$

94. $720 \text{ in.}^2 = $ _____ ft^2

95. $5 \text{ ft}^2 = $ _____ in.^{2} $\left(\text{Use two factors of } \dfrac{12 \text{ in.}}{1 \text{ ft}}.\right)$

96. $7 \text{ ft}^2 = $ _____ in.^{2}

97. $3 \text{ yd}^2 = $ _____ ft^2 $\left(\text{Use two factors of } \dfrac{3 \text{ ft}}{1 \text{ yd}}.\right)$

98. $10 \text{ yd}^2 = $ _____ ft^2

Section 7.2 | Metric Units of Measurement

1. Introduction to the Metric System

Throughout history the lack of standard units of measure led to much confusion in trade between countries. In 1790 the French Academy of Sciences adopted a simple, decimal-based system of units. This system is known today as the **metric system**. The metric system is the predominant system of measurement used in science.

The simplicity of the metric system is a result of having one basic unit of measure for each type of quantity (length, mass, and capacity). The base units are the *meter* for length, the *gram* for mass, and the *liter* for capacity. Other units of length, mass, and capacity in the metric system are products of the base unit and a power of 10.

2. Metric Units of Length

The **meter** (m) is the basic unit of length in the metric system. A meter is slightly longer than a yard.

| 1 meter | 1 m ≈ 39 in. |
| 1 yard | 1 yd = 36 in. |

The meter was defined in the late 1700s as one ten-millionth of the distance along the Earth's surface from the North Pole to the Equator through Paris, France. Today the meter is defined as the distance traveled by light in a vacuum during $\frac{1}{299,792,458}$ sec.

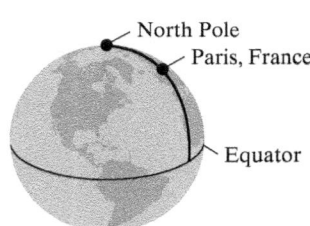

Six other common metric units of length are given in Table 7-2. Notice that each unit is related to the meter by a power of 10. This makes it particularly easy to convert from one unit to another.

TIP: The units of hectometer, dekameter, and decimeter are not frequently used.

Table 7-2 Metric Units of Length and Their Equivalents

1 kilometer (km) = 1000 m	
1 hectometer (hm) = 100 m	
1 dekameter (dam) = 10 m	
1 meter (m) = 1 m	
1 decimeter (dm) = 0.1 m	$\left(\frac{1}{10} \text{ m}\right)$
1 centimeter (cm) = 0.01 m	$\left(\frac{1}{100} \text{ m}\right)$
1 millimeter (mm) = 0.001 m	$\left(\frac{1}{1000} \text{ m}\right)$

TIP: In addition to the key facts presented in Table 7-2, the following equivalences are useful.

100 cm = 1 m
1000 mm = 1 m

Notice that each unit of length has a prefix followed by the word *meter* (kilometer, for example). You should memorize these prefixes along with their multiples of the basic unit, the meter. Furthermore, it is generally easiest to memorize the prefixes in order.

kilo-	hecto-	deka-	meter	deci-	centi-	milli-
× 1000	× 100	× 10	× 1	× 0.1	× 0.01	× 0.001

As you familiarize yourself with the metric units of length, it is helpful to have a sense of the distance represented by each unit (Figure 7-2).

Figure 7-2

- 1 *millimeter* is approximately the thickness of five sheets of paper.
- 1 *centimeter* is approximately the width of a key on a calculator.
- 1 *decimeter* is approximately 4 in.
- 1 *meter* is just over 1 yd.
- A *kilometer* is used to express longer distances in much the same way we use miles. The distance between Los Angeles and San Diego is about 193 km.

Example 1 **Measuring Distances in Metric Units**

Approximate the distance in centimeters and in millimeters.

Solution:

The numbered lines on the ruler are units of centimeters. Each centimeter is divided into 10 mm. We see that the width of the penny is not quite 2 cm. We can approximate this distance as 1.8 cm or equivalently 18 mm.

Concept Connections

Fill in the blank with < or >.

1. 1 km ☐ 1 m

2. 1 cm ☐ 1 m

3. 1 dam ☐ 1 dm

Select the most reasonable value.

4. The length of a fork is
   - **a.** 20 m
   - **b.** 20 km
   - **c.** 20 cm
   - **d.** 20 mm

5. The length of a city block is
   - **a.** $\frac{1}{2}$ km
   - **b.** $\frac{1}{2}$ cm
   - **c.** $\frac{1}{2}$ m
   - **d.** $\frac{1}{2}$ mm

Skill Practice

6. Approximate the length of the pin in centimeters and in millimeters.

Answers

1. >   2. <   3. >   4. c

5. a   6. 3.2 cm or 32 mm

In Example 2, we convert metric units of length by using unit ratios.

Skill Practice

Convert.

7. 8.4 km = _____ m

8. 64,000 cm = _____ m

Example 2 **Converting Metric Units of Length**

a. 10.4 km = _____ m   **b.** 88 mm = _____ m

Solution:

From Table 7-2, 1 km = 1000 m.

a. $10.4 \text{ km} = \dfrac{10.4 \text{ km}}{1} \cdot \dfrac{1000 \text{ m}}{1 \text{ km}}$ ◄——— new unit to convert to
◄——— unit to convert from

$= 10,400 \text{ m}$ Multiply.

b. $88 \text{ mm} = \dfrac{88 \text{ mm}}{1} \cdot \dfrac{1 \text{ m}}{1000 \text{ mm}}$ ◄——— new unit to convert to
◄——— unit to convert from

$= \dfrac{88}{1000} \text{ m}$

$= 0.088 \text{ m}$

Recall that the place positions in our numbering system are based on powers of 10. For this reason, when we multiply a number by 10, 100, or 1000, we move the decimal point 1, 2, or 3 places, respectively, to the right. Similarly, when we multiply by 0.1, 0.01, or 0.001, we move the decimal point to the left 1, 2, or 3 places, respectively.

Since the metric system is also based on powers of 10, we can convert between two metric units of length by moving the decimal point. The direction and number of place positions to move are based on the metric **prefix line**, shown in Figure 7-3.

Prefix Line

1000 m	100 m	10 m	1 m	0.1 m	0.01 m	0.001 m
km	hm	dam	m	dm	cm	mm
kilo-	hecto-	deka-		deci-	centi-	milli-

Figure 7-3

TIP: To use the prefix line effectively, you must know the order of the metric prefixes. Sometimes a mnemonic (memory device) can help. Consider the following sentence. The first letter of each word represents one of the metric prefixes.

kids	have	doughnuts	until	dad	calls	mom.
kilo-	hecto-	deka-	unit	deci-	centi-	milli-

↑
represents the main
unit of measurement
(meter, liter, or gram)

Answers

7. 8400 m   **8.** 640 m

> **PROCEDURE   Using the Prefix Line to Convert Metric Units**
>
> **Step 1** To use the prefix line, begin at the point on the line corresponding to the original unit you are given.
> **Step 2** Then count the number of positions you need to move to reach the new unit of measurement.
> **Step 3** Move the decimal point in the original measured value the same direction and same number of places as on the prefix line.
> **Step 4** Replace the original unit with the new unit of measure.

Example 3 **Using the Prefix Line to Convert Metric Units of Length**

Skill Practice

Convert.
9. 864 cm = _____ m
10. 8.2 km = _____ m

Use the prefix line for each conversion.

a. 0.0413 m = _____ cm   **b.** 4700 cm = _____ km

Solution:

a.

0.0413 m = 4.13 cm   From the prefix line, move the decimal point two places to the right.

b.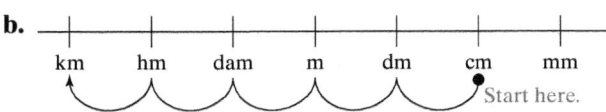

4700 cm = 0.04700 km = 0.047 km   From the prefix line, move the decimal point five places to the left.

---

3. Metric Units of Mass

In Section 7.1 we learned that the pound and ton are two measures of weight in the U.S. Customary System. Measurements of weight give the force of an object under the influence of gravity. The mass of an object is related to its weight. However, mass is not affected by gravity. Thus, the weight of an object will be different on Earth than on the Moon because the effect of gravity is different. The mass of the object will stay the same.

The fundamental unit of mass in the metric system is the **gram** (g). A penny is approximately 2.5 g (Figure 7-4). A paper clip is approximately 1 g (Figure 7-5).

Concept Connections

11. Which object could have a mass of 2 g?
  a. Rubber band
  b. Can of tuna fish
  c. Cell phone

≈ 2.5 g   ≈ 1 g
Figure 7-4   **Figure 7-5**

Answers
9. 8.64 m   **10.** 8200 m
11. a

Other common metric units of mass are given in Table 7-3. Once again, notice that the metric units of mass are related to the gram by powers of 10.

Table 7-3 **Metric Units of Mass and Their Equivalents**

1 kilogram (kg) = 1000 g		
1 hectogram (hg) = 100 g		
1 dekagram (dag) = 10 g		
1 gram (g) = 1 g		
1 decigram (dg) = 0.1 g	$(\frac{1}{10}$ g$)$	
1 centigram (cg) = 0.01 g	$(\frac{1}{100}$ g$)$	
1 milligram (mg) = 0.001 g	$(\frac{1}{1000}$ g$)$	

TIP: In addition to the key facts presented in Table 8-3, the following equivalences are useful.

100 cg = 1 g
1000 mg = 1 g

On the surface of Earth, 1 kg of mass is equivalent to approximately 2.2 lb of weight. Therefore, a 180-lb man has a mass of approximately 81.8 kg.

$$180 \text{ lb} \approx 81.8 \text{ kg}$$

The metric prefix line for mass is shown in Figure 7-6. This can be used to convert from one unit of mass to another.

Prefix Line

1000 g	100 g	10 g	1 g	0.1 g	0.01 g	0.001 g
kg	hg	dag	g	dg	cg	mg
kilo-	hecto-	deka-		deci-	centi-	milli-

Figure 7-6

Example 4   **Converting Metric Units of Mass**

a. 1.6 kg = _____ g   **b.** 1400 mg = _____ g

Solution:

a. $1.6 \text{ kg} = \dfrac{1.6 \text{ kg}}{1} \cdot \dfrac{1000 \text{ g}}{1 \text{ kg}}$ ← new unit to convert to
← unit to convert from

$= 1600 \text{ g}$

Start here.

$$1.6 \text{ kg} = 1.600 \text{ kg} = 1600 \text{ g}$$

b. $1400 \text{ mg} = \dfrac{1400 \text{ mg}}{1} \cdot \dfrac{1 \text{ g}}{1000 \text{ mg}}$ ← new unit to convert to
← unit to convert from

$= \dfrac{1400}{1000} \text{ g}$

$= 1.4 \text{ g}$

Start here.

$$1400 \text{ mg} = 1400 \text{ mg} = 1.4 \text{ g}$$

4. Metric Units of Capacity

The basic unit of capacity in the metric system is the **liter** (L). One liter is slightly more than 1 qt. Other common units of capacity are given in Table 7-4.

Table 7-4 **Metric Units of Capacity and Their Equivalents**

1 kiloliter (kL) = 1000 L
1 hectoliter (hL) = 100 L
1 dekaliter (daL) = 10 L
1 liter (L) = 1 L
1 deciliter (dL) = 0.1 L ($\frac{1}{10}$ L)
1 centiliter (cL) = 0.01 L ($\frac{1}{100}$ L)
1 milliliter (mL) = 0.001 L ($\frac{1}{1000}$ L)

TIP: In addition to the key facts presented in Table 7-4, the following equivalences are useful.

$$100 \text{ cL} = 1 \text{ L}$$
$$1000 \text{ mL} = 1 \text{ L}$$

1 mL is also equivalent to a **cubic centimeter** (**cc** or **cm³**). The unit cc is often used to measure dosages of medicine. For example, after having an allergic reaction to a bee sting, a patient might be given 1 cc of adrenaline.

The metric prefix line for capacity is similar to that of length and mass (Figure 7-7). It can be used to convert between metric units of capacity.

$1 \text{ cc} = 1 \text{ ml}$

Concept Connections

Fill in the blank with $<$, $>$, or $=$.

16. 1 kL ☐ 1 cL

17. 1 cL ☐ 1 L

18. 1 mL ☐ 1 cc

Prefix Line

1000 L	100 L	10 L	1 L	0.1 L	0.01 L	0.001 L
kL	hL	daL	L	dL	cL	mL
kilo-	hecto-	deka-		deci-	centi-	milli-

Figure 7-7

Example 5 **Converting Metric Units of Capacity**

a. 5.5 L = _____ mL   **b.** 150 cL = _____ L

Solution:

a. $5.5 \text{ L} = \dfrac{5.5 \cancel{\text{L}}}{1} \cdot \dfrac{1000 \text{ mL}}{1 \cancel{\text{L}}}$ ← new unit to convert to
← unit to convert from

$= 5500 \text{ mL}$

| kL | hL | daL | L | dL | cL | mL |

Start here.

$5.5 \text{ L} = 5.500 \text{ L} = 5500 \text{ mL}$

b. $150 \text{ cL} = \dfrac{150 \cancel{\text{cL}}}{1} \cdot \dfrac{1 \text{ L}}{100 \cancel{\text{cL}}}$ ← new unit to convert to
← unit to convert from

$= \dfrac{150}{100} \text{ L}$

$= 1.5 \text{ L}$

| kL | hL | daL | L | dL | cL | mL |

Start here.

$150 \text{ cL} = 1.50 \text{ L} = 1.5 \text{ L}$

Skill Practice

Convert.

19. 10.2 L = _____ cL

20. 150,000 mL = _____ kL

Answers

16. $>$ **17.** $<$ **18.** $=$
19. 1020 cL   **20.** 0.15 kL

Example 6 **Converting Metric Units of Capacity**

a. $15 \, cc = \underline{\hspace{1cm}} \, mL$ **b.** $0.8 \, cL = \underline{\hspace{1cm}} \, cc$

Solution:

a. Recall that $1 \, cc = 1 \, mL$. Therefore $15 \, cc = 15 \, mL$.

b. We must convert from centiliters to milliliters, and then from milliliters to cubic centimeters.

$$0.8 \, cL = \frac{0.8 \, \cancel{cL}}{1} \cdot \frac{10 \, mL}{1 \, \cancel{cL}}$$

$$= 8 \, mL$$

$$= 8 \, cc \qquad \text{Recall that } 1 \, mL = 1 \, cc.$$

$$0.8 \, cL = 8 \, mL = 8 \, cc$$

5. Summary of Metric Conversions

The prefix line in Figure 7-8 summarizes the relationships learned thus far.

1000	100	10	1	0.1	0.01	0.001
kilo-	hecto-	deka-	meter gram liter	deci-	centi-	milli-

Figure 7-8

Example 7 **Converting Metric Units**

a. The distance between San Jose and Santa Clara is 26 km. Convert this to meters.

b. A bottle of canola oil holds 946 mL. Convert this to liters.

c. The mass of a bag of rice is 90,700 cg. Convert this to grams.

d. A dose of an antiviral medicine is 0.5 cc. Convert this to milliliters.

Solution:

a. $26 \, km = 26{,}000 \, m$

b. $946 \, mL = 0.946 \, L$

c. 90,700 cg = 907.00 g = 907 g

| kilo- | hecto- | deka- | meter | deci- | centi- | milli- |

gram
liter

Start
here.

d. Recall that 1 cc = 1 mL. Therefore, 0.5 cc = 0.5 mL.

Section 7.2 Practice Exercises

Study Skills Exercise

1. Define the key terms.

   a. Metric system   **b. Meter**   **c. Prefix line**

   d. Gram   **e. Liter**   **f. Cubic centimeter**

Review Exercises

For Exercises 2–7, convert the units of measurement.

   2. 2200 yd = _____ mi   **3.** 8 c = _____ pt   **4.** 48 oz = _____ lb

   5. 1 day = _____ min   **6.** 160 fl oz = _____ gal   **7.** 3.5 lb = _____ oz

Objective 1: Introduction to the Metric System

   8. Identify the units that apply to length. Circle all that apply.

| **a.** Yard | **b.** Ounce | **c.** Fluid ounce | **d.** Meter | **e.** Quart |
| **f.** Gram | **g.** Pound | **h.** Liter | **i.** Mile | **j.** Inch |

   9. Identify the units that apply to weight or mass. Circle all that apply.

| **a.** Yard | **b.** Ounce | **c.** Fluid ounce | **d.** Meter | **e.** Quart |
| **f.** Gram | **g.** Pound | **h.** Liter | **i.** Mile | **j.** Inch |

   10. Identify the units that apply to capacity. Circle all that apply.

| **a.** Yard | **b.** Ounce | **c.** Fluid ounce | **d.** Meter | **e.** Quart |
| **f.** Gram | **g.** Pound | **h.** Liter | **i.** Mile | **j.** Inch |

Objective 2: Metric Units of Length

For Exercises 11–12, approximate each distance in centimeters and millimeters. **(See Example 1.)**

11.

12.

For Exercises 13–18, select the most reasonable measurement.

13. A table is _____ long.

   a. 2 m   **b.** 2 cm

   c. 2 km   **d.** 2 hm

14. A picture frame is _____ wide.

   a. 22 cm   **b.** 22 mm

   c. 22 m   **d.** 22 km

15. The distance between Albany, New York, and Buffalo, New York, is _____.

   a. 210 m   **b.** 2100 cm

   c. 2.1 km   **d.** 210 km

16. The distance between Denver and Colorado Springs is _____.

   a. 110 cm   **b.** 110 km

   c. 11,000 km   **d.** 1100 mm

17. The height of a full-grown giraffe is approximately _____.

   a. 50 m   **b.** 0.05 m

   c. 0.5 m   **d.** 5 m

18. The length of a canoe is _____.

   a. 5 m   **b.** 0.5 m

   c. 0.05 m   **d.** 500 m

For Exercises 19–30, convert metric units of length by using unit ratios or the prefix line. **(See Examples 2–3.)**

Prefix Line for Length

1000 m	100 m	10 m	1 m	0.1 m	0.01 m	0.001 m
km	hm	dam	m	dm	cm	mm
kilo-	hecto-	deka-		deci-	centi-	milli-

19. 2430 m = _____ km

20. 1251 mm = _____ m

21. 50 m = _____ mm

22. 1.3 m = _____ mm

23. 4 km = _____ m

24. 5 m = _____ cm

25. 4.31 cm = _____ mm

26. 18 cm = _____ mm

27. 3328 dm = _____ km

28. 128 hm = _____ km

29. 3 hm = _____ m

30. 450 mm = _____ dm

Objective 3: Metric Units of Mass

For Exercises 31–38, convert the units of mass. **(See Example 4.)**

31. 539 g = _____ kg

32. 328 mg = _____ g

33. 2.5 kg = _____ g

34. 2011 g = _____ kg

35. 0.0334 g = _____ mg

36. 0.38 dag = _____ dg

37. 409 cg = _____ g

38. 0.003 kg = _____ g

Objective 4: Metric Units of Capacity

For Exercises 39–42, fill in the blank with >, <, or =.

39. 1 cL _____ 1 L

40. 1 L _____ 1 mL

41. 1 mL _____ 1 cc

42. 1 L _____ 1 cc

43. What does the abbreviation cc represent?

44. Which of the following are measures of capacity? Circle all that apply.

a. cm   **b.** cc   **c.** cL   **d.** cg

For Exercises 45–54, convert the units of capacity. **(See Examples 5–6.)**

45. 3200 mL = _____ L

46. 280 L = _____ kL

47. 7 L = _____ cL

48. 0.52 L = _____ mL

49. 42 mL = _____ dL

50. 0.88 L = _____ hL

51. 64 cc = _____ mL

52. 125 mL = _____ cc

53. 0.04 L = _____ cc

54. 38 cc = _____ L

Objective 5: Summary of Metric Conversions (Mixed Exercises)

55. Identify the units that apply to length.

a. mL   **b.** mm   **c.** hg   **d.** cc   **e.** kg   **f.** hm   **g.** cL

56. Identify the units that apply to capacity.

a. kg   **b.** km   **c.** cL   **d.** cc   **e.** hm   **f.** dag   **g.** mm

57. Identify the units that apply to mass.

a. dg   **b.** hm   **c.** kL   **d.** cc   **e.** dm   **f.** kg   **g.** cL

For Exercises 58–69, complete the table.

	Object	mm	cm	m	km
58.	Distance between Orlando and Miami				402
59.	Length of the Mississippi River				3766
60.	Thickness of a dime	1.35			
61.	Diameter of a quarter	24.3			

	Object	mg	cg	g	kg
62.	Can of tuna			170	
63.	Bag of rice			907	
64.	Box of raisins		42,500		
65.	Hockey puck		17,000		

	Object	mL	cL	L	kL
66.	1 Tablespoon	15			
67.	Bottle of vanilla extract	59			
68.	Capacity of a cooler				0.0377
69.	Capacity of a gasoline tank				0.0757

For Exercises 70–75, convert the metric units as indicated. **(See Example 7.)**

70. The height of the tallest living tree is 112.014 m. Convert this to dekameters.

71. The Congo River is 4669 km long. Convert this to meters.

72. A One-A-Day Weight Smart Multivitamin tablet contains 60 mg of vitamin C. How many tablets must be taken to consume a total of 3 g of vitamin C?

73. A can contains 305 g of soup. Convert this to milligrams.

74. A gasoline can has a capacity of 19 L. Convert this to kiloliters.

75. The capacity of a coffee cup is 0.25 L. Convert this to milliliters.

76. In one day, Stacy gets 600 mg of calcium in her daily vitamin, 500 mg in her calcium supplement, and 250 mg in the dairy products she eats. How many grams of calcium will she get in one week?

77. Cliff drives his children to their sports activities outside of school. When he drives his son to baseball practice, it is a 6-km round trip. When he drives his daughter to basketball practice, it is a 1800-m round trip. If basketball practice is 3 times a week and baseball practice is twice a week, how many kilometers does Cliff drive?

78. A gas tank holds 45 L. If it costs $74.25 to fill up the tank, what is the price per liter?

79. A can of paint holds 120 L. How many kiloliters are contained in 8 cans?

80. A bottle of water holds 710 mL. How many liters are in a 6-pack?

81. A bottle of olive oil has 33 servings of 15 mL each. How many centiliters of oil does the bottle contain?

82. A quart of milk has 130 mg of sodium per cup. How much sodium is in the whole bottle?

83. A ½-c serving of cereal has 180 mg of potassium. This is 5% of the recommended daily allowance of potassium. How many grams is the recommended daily allowance?

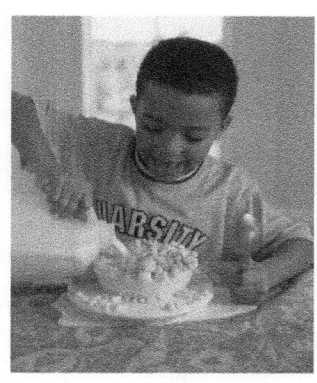

84. Rosanna has material 1.5 m long for a window curtain. If the window is 90 cm and she needs 10 cm for a hem at the bottom and 12 cm for finishing the top, does Rosanna have enough material?

85. Veronique has a piece of molding 1 m long. Does she have enough to cut four pieces to frame the picture shown in the figure?

86. A square tile is 110 mm in length. If they are placed side by side, how many tiles will it take to cover a length of wall 1.43 m long?

12 cm

40 cm

87. Two Olympic speed skating races for women are 500 m and 5 km. What is the difference (in meters) between the lengths of these races?

Expanding Your Skills

In the Expanding Your Skills of Section 7.1, we converted U.S. Customary units of area. We use the same procedure to convert metric units of area. This procedure involves multiplying by two unit ratios of length.

Example: Converting area

Convert 1000 mm² to square centimeters.

Solution: $\dfrac{1000\text{ mm}^2}{1} \cdot \underbrace{\dfrac{1\text{ cm}}{10\text{ mm}} \cdot \dfrac{1\text{ cm}}{10\text{ mm}}}_{\text{Multiply first.}} = \dfrac{1000\text{ mm}^2}{1} \cdot \dfrac{1\text{ cm}^2}{100\text{ mm}^2} = \dfrac{1000\text{ cm}^2}{100} = 10\text{ cm}^2$

For Exercises 88–91, convert the units of area, using two factors of the given unit ratio.

88. $30{,}000\text{ mm}^2 = \underline{\hspace{1cm}}\text{ cm}^2 \quad \left(\text{Use } \dfrac{1\text{ cm}}{10\text{ mm}}.\right)$
89. $65{,}000{,}000\text{ m}^2 = \underline{\hspace{1cm}}\text{ km}^2 \quad \left(\text{Use } \dfrac{1\text{ km}}{1000\text{ m}}.\right)$

90. $4.1\text{ m}^2 = \underline{\hspace{1cm}}\text{ cm}^2 \quad \left(\text{Use } \dfrac{100\text{ cm}}{1\text{ m}}.\right)$
91. $5600\text{ cm}^2 = \underline{\hspace{1cm}}\text{ m}^2 \quad \left(\text{Use } \dfrac{1\text{ m}}{100\text{ cm}}.\right)$

In the U.S. Customary System of measurement, 1 ton = 2000 lb. In the metric system, 1 metric ton = 1000 kg. Use this information to answer Exercises 92–95.

92. Convert 3300 kg to metric tons.

93. Convert 5780 kg to metric tons.

94. Convert 10.9 metric tons to kilograms.

95. Convert 8.5 metric tons to kilograms.

Objectives

1. Summary of U.S. Customary and Metric Unit Equivalents
2. Converting U.S. Customary and Metric Units
3. Applications
4. Units of Temperature

1. Summary of U.S. Customary and Metric Unit Equivalents

In this section, we learn how to convert between U.S. Customary and metric units of measure. Suppose, for example, that you take a trip to Europe. A street sign indicates that the distance to Paris is 45 km (Figure 7-9). This distance may be unfamiliar to you until you convert to miles.

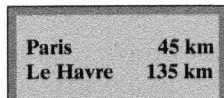

| Paris | 45 km |
| Le Havre | 135 km |

Figure 7-9

Skill Practice

1. Use the fact that 1 mi ≈ 1.61 km to convert 184 km to miles. Round to the nearest mile.

Example 1 **Converting Metric Units to U.S. Customary Units**

Use the fact that 1 mi ≈ 1.61 km to convert 45 km to miles. Round to the nearest mile.

Solution:

$$45 \text{ km} \approx \frac{45 \text{ km}}{1} \cdot \frac{1 \text{ mi}}{1.61 \text{ km}}$$ Set up a unit ratio to convert kilometers to miles.

$$= \frac{45}{1.61} \text{ mi}$$ Multiply fractions.

$$\approx 28 \text{ mi}$$ Divide and round to the nearest mile.

The distance of 45 km to Paris is approximately 28 mi.

Table 7-5 summarizes some common metric and U.S. Customary equivalents.

Table 7-5

Length	Weight/Mass (on Earth)	Capacity
1 in. = 2.54 cm	1 lb ≈ 0.45 kg	1 qt ≈ 0.95 L
1 ft ≈ 0.305 m	1 oz ≈ 28 g	1 fl oz ≈ 30 mL = 30 cc
1 yd ≈ 0.914 m		
1 mi ≈ 1.61 km		

2. Converting U.S. Customary and Metric Units

Using the U.S. Customary and metric equivalents given in Table 7-5, we can create unit ratios to convert between units.

Answer

1. 114 mi

Example 2 **Converting Units of Length**

Fill in the blank. Round to two decimal places, if necessary.

a. 18 cm = _____ in. **b.** 15 yd ≈ _____ m **c.** 8.2 m ≈ _____ ft

Solution:

a. $18 \text{ cm} = \dfrac{18 \text{ cm}}{1} \cdot \dfrac{1 \text{ in.}}{2.54 \text{ cm}}$ From Table 7-5, we know 1 in. = 2.54 cm.

$\quad = \dfrac{18}{2.54} \text{ in.}$ Multiply fractions.

$\quad \approx 7.09 \text{ in.}$ Divide and round to two decimal places.

b. $15 \text{ yd} \approx \dfrac{15 \text{ yd}}{1} \cdot \dfrac{0.914 \text{ m}}{1 \text{ yd}}$ From Table 7-5, we know 1 yd ≈ 0.914 m.

$\quad = 13.71 \text{ m}$ Multiply.

c. $8.2 \text{ m} \approx \dfrac{8.2 \text{ m}}{1} \cdot \dfrac{1 \text{ ft}}{0.305 \text{ m}}$ From Table 7-5, we know 1 ft ≈ 0.305 m.

$\quad = \dfrac{8.2}{0.305} \text{ ft}$ Multiply.

$\quad \approx 26.89 \text{ ft}$ Divide and round to two decimal places.

Skill Practice
Convert. Round to one decimal place.
2. 4 m ≈ _____ ft
3. 3 in. ≈ _____ cm
4. 6500 yd ≈ _____ m

Example 3 **Converting Units of Weight and Mass**

Fill in the blank. Round to one decimal place, if necessary.

a. 180 g ≈ _____ oz **b.** 5.25 tons ≈ _____ kg

Solution:

a. $180 \text{ g} \approx \dfrac{180 \text{ g}}{1} \cdot \dfrac{1 \text{ oz}}{28 \text{ g}}$ From Table 7-5, we know 1 oz ≈ 28 g.

$\quad = \dfrac{180}{28} \text{ oz}$

$\quad \approx 6.4 \text{ oz}$ Divide and round to one decimal place.

b. We can first convert 5.25 tons to pounds. Then we can use the fact that 1 lb ≈ 0.45 kg.

$5.25 \text{ tons} = \dfrac{5.25 \text{ tons}}{1} \cdot \dfrac{2000 \text{ lb}}{1 \text{ ton}}$ Convert tons to pounds.

$\quad = 10{,}500 \text{ lb}$

$\quad \approx 10{,}500 \text{ lb} \cdot \dfrac{0.45 \text{ kg}}{1 \text{ lb}}$ Convert pounds to kilograms.

$\quad = 4725 \text{ kg}$

Skill Practice
Convert. Round to one decimal place, if necessary.
5. 8 kg ≈ _____ lb
6. 4 tons ≈ _____ kg

Answers
2. 13.1 ft **3.** 7.6 cm **4.** 5941 m
5. 17.8 lb **6.** 3600 kg

Skill Practice

Convert. Round to one decimal place, if necessary.

7. 120 mL ≈ _____ fl oz

8. 4 qt ≈ _____ L

Example 4 **Converting Units of Capacity**

Fill in the blank. Round to two decimal places, if necessary.

a. 75 mL ≈ _____ fl oz   **b.** 3 qt ≈ _____ L

Solution:

a. $75 \text{ mL} \approx \dfrac{75 \text{ mL}}{1} \cdot \dfrac{1 \text{ fl oz}}{30 \text{ mL}}$ From Table 7-5, we know 1 fl oz ≈ 30 mL.

$= \dfrac{75}{30} \text{ fl oz}$ Multiply fractions.

$= 2.5 \text{ fl oz}$ Divide.

b. $3 \text{ qt} \approx \dfrac{3 \text{ qt}}{1} \cdot \dfrac{0.95 \text{ L}}{1 \text{ qt}}$ From Table 7-5, we know 1 qt ≈ 0.95 L.

$= 2.85 \text{ L}$ Multiply.

3. Applications

Example 5 **Converting Units in an Application**

A 2-L bottle of soda sells for $2.19. A 32-oz bottle of soda sells for $1.59. Compare the price per quart of each bottle to determine the better buy.

Solution:

Note that 1 qt = 2 pt = 4 c = 32 fl oz. So a 32-oz bottle of soda costs $1.59 per quart. Next, if we can convert 2 L to quarts, we can compute the unit cost per quart and compare the results.

$2 \text{ L} \approx \dfrac{2 \text{ L}}{1} \cdot \dfrac{1 \text{ qt}}{0.95 \text{ L}}$ Recall that 1 qt = 0.95 L.

$\approx \dfrac{2}{0.95} \text{ qt}$ Multiply fractions.

$\approx 2.11 \text{ qt}$ Divide and round to two decimal places.

Now find the cost per quart. $\dfrac{\$2.19}{2.11 \text{ qt}} \approx \$1.04 \text{ per quart}$

The cost for the 2-L bottle is $1.04 per quart, whereas the cost for 32 oz is $1.59 per quart. Therefore, the 2-L bottle is the better buy.

Skill Practice

9. A 720-mL bottle of water sells for $0.79. A 32-oz bottle of water sells for $1.29. Compare the price per ounce to determine the better buy.

Answers

7. 4 fl oz   **8.** 3.8 L

9. 720 mL is 24 oz. The cost per ounce is $0.033. The unit price for the 32-oz bottle is $0.040 per ounce. The 720-mL bottle is the better buy.

Example 6 **Converting Units in an Application**

In track and field, the 1500-m race is slightly less than 1 mi. How many yards less is it? Round to the nearest yard.

Solution:

We know that 1 mi = 1760 yd. If we can convert 1500 m to yards, then we can subtract the results.

$$1500 \text{ m} \approx \frac{1500 \text{ m}}{1} \cdot \frac{1 \text{ yd}}{0.914 \text{ m}}$$ Recall that 1 yd = 0.914 m.

$$\approx \frac{1500}{0.914} \text{ yd}$$ Multiply fractions.

$$\approx 1641 \text{ yd}$$ Divide and round to the nearest yard.

1 mi = 1760 yd

1500 m = ? yd

Therefore, the difference between 1 mi and 1500 m is:

(1 mi) − (1500 m)

1760 yd − 1641 yd = 119 yd

Skill Practice

10. In track and field, the 800-m race is slightly shorter than a half-mile race. How many yards less is it? Round to the nearest yard.

4. Units of Temperature

In the United States, the **Fahrenheit** scale is used most often to measure temperature. On this scale, water freezes at 32°F and boils at 212°F. The symbol ° stands for "degrees," and °F means "degrees Fahrenheit."

Another scale used to measure temperature is the **Celsius** temperature scale. On this scale, water freezes at 0°C and boils at 100°C. The symbol °C stands for "degrees Celsius."

Figure 7-10 shows the relationship between the Celsius scale and the Fahrenheit scale.

Concept Connections

Use Figure 7-10 to select the best choice.

11. The high temperature in Dallas for a day in July is
a. 34°C **b.** 34°F
12. The high temperature in Minneapolis for a day in March is
a. 34°C **b.** 34°F

Figure 7-10

Answers
10. 5 yd **11.** a **12.** b

To convert back and forth between the Fahrenheit and Celsius scales, we use the following formulas.

> **FORMULA** **Conversions for Temperature Scale**
>
> To convert from °C to °F: To convert from °F to °C:
>
> $$F = \frac{9}{5}C + 32 \qquad\qquad C = \frac{5}{9}(F - 32)$$
>
> *Note:* Using decimal notation we can write the formulas as
>
> $$F = 1.8C + 32 \qquad\qquad C = \frac{F - 32}{1.8}$$

Skill Practice

13. The ocean temperature in the Caribbean in August averages 84°F. Convert this to degrees Celsius and round to one decimal place.

Example 7   **Converting Units of Temperature**

Convert a body temperature of 98.6°F to degrees Celsius.

Solution:

Because we want to convert degrees Fahrenheit to degrees Celsius, we use the formula $C = \frac{5}{9}(F - 32)$.

$$C = \frac{5}{9}(F - 32)$$

$$= \frac{5}{9}(98.6 - 32) \qquad \text{Substitute } F = 98.6.$$

$$= \frac{5}{9}(66.6) \qquad \text{Perform the operation inside parentheses first.}$$

$$= \frac{(5)(66.6)}{9}$$

$$= 37 \qquad \text{Body temperature is 37°C.}$$

Skill Practice

14. The high temperature on a day in March for Raleigh, North Carolina, was 10°C. Convert this to degrees Fahrenheit.

Example 8   **Converting Units of Temperature**

Convert the temperature inside a refrigerator, 5°C, to degrees Fahrenheit.

Solution:

Because we want to convert degrees Celsius to degrees Fahrenheit, we use the formula $F = \frac{9}{5}C + 32$

$$F = \frac{9}{5}C + 32$$

$$= \frac{9}{5} \cdot 5 + 32 \qquad \text{Substitute } C = 5.$$

$$= \frac{9}{\cancel{5}} \cdot \frac{\cancel{5}}{1} + 32$$

$$= 9 + 32$$

$$= 41 \qquad \text{The temperature inside the refrigerator is 41°F.}$$

Answers

13. 28.9°C   14. 50°F

Section 7.3 Practice Exercises

Study Skills Exercises

1. Make a list of all the section titles in the chapter that you are studying. Write each section title on a separate sheet of paper or index card. Go back and fill in the list of objectives under each section title. When you are studying for the test, try to make up an exercise that corresponds to each objective and then work the exercise. To get started, write a problem for the objective of converting metric units of capacity from Section 7.2.

2. Define the key terms.

   a. Celsius   b. Fahrenheit

Review Exercises

For Exercises 3–6, select the equivalent amounts of mass. (*Hint:* There may be more than one answer for each exercise.)

3. 500 g   a. 500,000 g

                                   b. 5 g

4. 500 mg   c. 500,000,000 mg

                                   d. 0.5 kg

5. 500 cg   e. 5000 mg

                                   f. 50,000 cg

6. 500 kg   g. 0.5 g

                                   h. 50 cg

For Exercises 7–10, select the equivalent amounts of capacity.

7. 200 L   a. 2000 mL

                                   b. 200 cc

8. 200 kL   c. 0.2 kL

                                   d. 20,000,000 cL

9. 200 mL   e. 200,000 L

                                   f. 200,000 mL

10. 200 cL   g. 0.2 L

                                   h. 2 L

Objective 1: Summary of U.S. Customary and Metric Unit Equivalents

11. Identify an appropriate ratio to convert 5 yards to meters by using multiplication.

   a. $\dfrac{1 \text{ yd}}{0.914 \text{ m}}$ b. $\dfrac{0.914 \text{ m}}{1 \text{ yd}}$ c. $\dfrac{0.914 \text{ yd}}{1 \text{ m}}$ d. $\dfrac{1 \text{ m}}{0.914 \text{ yd}}$

12. Identify an appropriate ratio to convert 3 pounds to kilograms by using multiplication.

a. $\dfrac{0.45\ \text{lb}}{1\ \text{kg}}$ **b.** $\dfrac{1\ \text{kg}}{0.45\ \text{lb}}$ **c.** $\dfrac{1\ \text{lb}}{0.45\ \text{kg}}$ **d.** $\dfrac{0.45\ \text{kg}}{1\ \text{lb}}$

13. Identify an appropriate ratio to convert 2 quarts to liters by using multiplication.

a. $\dfrac{0.95\ \text{L}}{1\ \text{qt}}$ **b.** $\dfrac{1\ \text{qt}}{0.95\ \text{L}}$ **c.** $\dfrac{0.95\ \text{qt}}{1\ \text{L}}$ **d.** $\dfrac{1\ \text{L}}{0.95\ \text{qt}}$

14. Identify an appropriate ratio to convert 10 miles to kilometers by using multiplication.

a. $\dfrac{1\ \text{mi}}{1.61\ \text{km}}$ **b.** $\dfrac{1\ \text{km}}{1.61\ \text{mi}}$ **c.** $\dfrac{1.61\ \text{km}}{1\ \text{mi}}$ **d.** $\dfrac{1.61\ \text{mi}}{1\ \text{km}}$

Objective 2: Converting U.S. Customary and Metric Units

For Exercises 15–23, convert the units of length. Round the answer to one decimal place, if necessary. **(See Examples 1–2.)**

15. 2 in. ≈ _____ cm   **16.** 120 km ≈ _____ mi   **17.** 8 m ≈ _____ yd

18. 4 ft ≈ _____ m   **19.** 400 ft ≈ _____ m   **20.** 0.75 m ≈ _____ yd

21. 45 in ≈ _____ m   **22.** 150 cm ≈ _____ ft   **23.** 0.5 ft ≈ _____ cm

For Exercises 24–32, convert the units of weight and mass. Round the answer to one decimal place, if necessary. **(See Example 3.)**

24. 6 oz ≈ _____ g   **25.** 6 lb ≈ _____ kg   **26.** 4 kg ≈ _____ lb

27. 10 g ≈ _____ oz   **28.** 14 g ≈ _____ oz   **29.** 0.54 kg ≈ _____ lb

30. 0.3 lb ≈ _____ kg   **31.** 2.2 tons ≈ _____ kg   **32.** 4500 kg ≈ _____ tons

For Exercises 33–38, convert the units of capacity. Round the answer to one decimal place, if necessary. **(See Example 4.)**

33. 6 qt ≈ _____ L   **34.** 5 fl oz ≈ _____ mL   **35.** 120 mL ≈ _____ fl oz

36. 19 L ≈ _____ qt   **37.** 960 cc ≈ _____ fl oz   **38.** 0.5 fl oz ≈ _____ cc

Objective 3: Applications (Mixed Exercises)

For Exercises 39–54, refer to Table 7-5 on page 476.

39. A 2-lb box of sugar costs $3.19. A box that contains single-serving packets contains 354 g and costs $1.49. Find the unit costs in dollars per ounce to determine the better buy. **(See Example 5.)**

40. At the grocery store, Debbie compares the prices of a 2-L bottle of water and a 6-pack of bottled water. The 2-L bottle is priced at $1.59. The 6-pack costs $3.60, and each bottle in the package contains 24 fl oz. Compare the cost of water per quart to determine which is a better buy.

41. A cross-country skiing race is 30 km long. Is this length more or less than 18 mi? **(See Example 6.)**

42. A can of cat food is 85 g. How many ounces is this? Round to the nearest ounce.

43. Carly Patterson of the U.S. Olympic gymnastic team weighed 97 lb when she was the Olympic All-Around champion. How many kilograms is this?

44. Warren's dad ran the 100-yd dash when he was in high school. Suppose Warren runs the 100-*meter* dash on his track team.

　　a. Who runs the longer race?

　　b. Find the difference between the lengths in meters.

45. In a recent year, the price of gas in Germany was $1.90 per liter. What is the price per gallon?

46. A jar of spaghetti sauce is 2 lb 8 oz. How many kilograms is this? Round to two decimal places.

47. The thickness of a hockey puck is 2.54 cm. How many inches is this?

48. A bottle of grape juice contains 1.9 L of juice. Is there enough juice to fill 10 glasses that hold 6 oz each? If yes, how many ounces will be left over?

49. Football player Tony Romo weighs 99,790 g. How many pounds is this? Round to the nearest pound.

50. The distance between two lightposts is 6 m. How many feet is this? Round to the nearest foot.

51. A nurse gives a patient 45 cc of saline solution. How many fluid ounces does this represent?

52. Cough syrup comes in a bottle that contains 4 fl oz. How many milliliters is this?

53. Suppose this figure is a drawing of a room where 1 cm represents 2 ft. If you were to install molding along the edge of the floor, how many feet would you need?

2.9 cm
2.2 cm
4.4 cm
2.9 cm
2.2 cm
5.8 cm

54. Suppose this figure is a drawing of a room where 1 cm represents 3 ft. If you were to install molding along the edge of the floor, how many feet would you need?

4.3 cm
3.2 cm

Objective 4: Units of Temperature

For Exercises 55–60, convert the temperatures by using the appropriate formula: $F = \frac{9}{5}C + 32$ or $C = \frac{5}{9}(F - 32)$.
(See Examples 7–8.)

55. 25°C = _____ °F

56. 113°F = _____ °C

57. 68°F = _____ °C

58. 15°C = _____ °F

59. 30°C = _____ °F

60. 104°F = _____ °C

61. The boiling point of the element boron is 4000°C. Find the boiling point in degrees Fahrenheit.

62. The melting point of the element copper is 1085°C. Find the melting point in degrees Fahrenheit.

63. If the outdoor temperature is 35°C, is it a hot day or a cold day?

64. The high temperature in London, England, on a typical September day was 18°C, and the low was 13°C. Convert these temperatures to degrees Fahrenheit.

65. Use the fact that water boils at 100°C to show that the boiling point is 212°F.

66. Use the fact that water freezes at 0°C to show that the temperature at which water freezes is 32°F.

Expanding Your Skills

The USDA recommends that an adult woman get 46 g of protein per day. Peanuts are 25% protein. Use this information to answer Exercises 67–68.

67. How many grams of peanuts would an adult woman need to satisfy a day's protein requirement?

68. How many ounces of peanuts would be required for a woman's daily protein need? Round to the nearest tenth.

In the U.S. Customary System of measurement, 1 ton = 2000 lb. In the metric system, 1 metric ton = 1000 kg. Use this information to answer Exercises 69–72.

69. A Lincoln Navigator weighs 5700 lb. How many metric tons is this?

70. An elevator has a maximum capacity of 1200 lb. How many metric tons is this?

71. The average mass of a blue whale (the largest mammal in the world) is approximately 108 metric tons. How many pounds is this?

72. The mass of a Mini-Cooper is 1.25 metric tons. How many pounds is this? Round to the nearest pound.

Problem Recognition Exercises

U.S. Customary and Metric Conversions

For Exercises 1–32, convert the units as indicated.

1. 36 c = _____ qt

2. 220 cm = _____ m

3. $\frac{3}{4}$ lb = _____ oz

4. 0.3 L = _____ mL

5. 12 ft = _____ yd

6. 6.03 kg = _____ g

7. 45 dm = _____ m

8. 9 in. = _____ ft

9. $\frac{1}{2}$ mi = _____ ft

10. 6000 lb = _____ tons

11. 8 pt = _____ qt

12. 1.5 tsp = _____ T

13. 21 m = _____ km

14. 68 mg = _____ cg

15. 36 mL = _____ cc

16. 64 oz = _____ lb

17. 4322 g = _____ kg

18. 5 m = _____ mm

19. 20 fl oz = _____ c

20. 510 sec = _____ min

21. 4 pt = _____ gal

22. 26 fl oz = _____ c

23. 5.46 kg = _____ g

24. 9.02 L = _____ cL

25. 9.1 mi = _____ yd

26. 48 oz = _____ lb

27. 1.62 tons = _____ lb

28. 4.6 km = _____ m

29. 60 hr = _____ days

30. 8 cc = _____ mL

31. 8:32:24 = _____ min

32. 2 wk = _____ hr

Medical Applications Involving Measurement — Section 7.4

1. Additional Metric Units of Mass

Scientists and people in the medical community almost exclusively use the metric system. For example:

- A patient's mass may be recorded in kilograms.
- A dosage of cough syrup may be measured in milliliters.
- The active ingredient in a pain reliever is given in grams.

Sometimes doctors prescribe medicines in very small amounts. In these cases, it is sometimes more convenient to use units of **micrograms**. The abbreviation for microgram is mcg or sometimes μg. Furthermore,

$1000 \text{ mcg} = 1 \text{ mg}$ It takes 1 thousand micrograms to equal 1 milligram.

$1{,}000{,}000 \text{ mcg} = 1 \text{ g}$ It takes 1 million micrograms to equal 1 gram.

Objectives

1. Additional Metric Units of Mass
2. Medical Applications

Example 1   **Converting Units of Micrograms**

a. Convert. $\quad 0.85 \text{ mg} = \underline{\hspace{1.5cm}} \text{ mcg}$

b. A doctor gives a heart patient an initial dose of 200 mcg of nitroglycerin. How many milligrams is this?

Solution:

a. $0.85 \text{ mg} = \dfrac{0.85 \text{ mg}}{1} \cdot \dfrac{1000 \text{ mcg}}{1 \text{ mg}}$ ←——— new unit to convert to
                                   ←——— unit to convert from

           $= 850 \text{ mcg}$

b. $200 \text{ mcg} = \dfrac{200 \text{ mcg}}{1} \cdot \dfrac{1 \text{ mg}}{1000 \text{ mcg}}$ ←——— new unit to convert to
                                   ←——— unit to convert from

           $= 0.2 \text{ mg}$

Skill Practice

Convert.

1. $0.04 \text{ mg} = \underline{\hspace{1cm}} \text{ mcg}$
2. $95{,}000 \text{ mcg} = \underline{\hspace{1cm}} \text{ mg}$

---

2. Medical Applications

Example 2   **Applying Metric Units of Measure to Medicine**

A doctor orders the antibiotic oxacillin for a child. The dosage is 12.5 mg of the drug per kilogram of the child's body mass. This dosage is given 4 times a day.

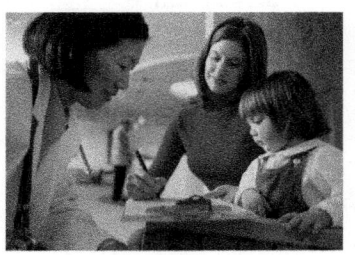

a. How much of the drug should a 24-kg child get in one dose?

b. How much of the drug would the child get if she were on a 10-day course of the antibiotic?

Solution:

a. We need to multiply the unit rate of 12.5 mg per kilogram times the child's body mass.

$$\text{Single dose} = (12.5 \text{ mg/kg})(24 \text{ kg})$$

$$= 300 \text{ mg}$$

Skill Practice

3. A child is to receive 0.5 mg of a drug per kilogram of the child's body mass. If the child is 27 kg, how much of the drug should the child receive?

Answers

1. 40 mcg   2. 95 mg   3. 13.5 mg

b. For a 10-day course, we need to multiply 300 g by the number of doses per day (4) and the total number of days (10).

Total amount of drug = (300 mg)(4)(10)

= 12,000 mg   or equivalently 12 g.

Skill Practice

4. A doctor orders amoxicillin (an antibiotic) in a liquid suspension form. The liquid contains 75 mg of amoxicillin per 5 mL of liquid. If the doctor orders 300 mg per day for a child, how much of the suspension should be given?

Answer

4. 20 mL

Example 3 **Applying Metric Units of Measure to Medicine**

The drug Aldomet (used for high blood pressure) comes in a concentration of 50 mg per milliliter of solution. If a doctor prescribes 225 mg per dose, how many milliliters should be administered for a single dose?

Solution:

The statement, 50 mg per milliliter, represents the ratio, $\dfrac{50\,\text{mg}}{1\,\text{mL}}$.

$$\dfrac{50\,\text{mg}}{1\,\text{mL}} = \dfrac{225\,\text{mg}}{x}$$ Use this ratio to set up a proportion.

$$50x = 225(1)$$ Equate the cross products.

$$\dfrac{50x}{50} = \dfrac{225}{50}$$ Divide by 50.

$$x = 4.5$$ A single dose is 4.5 mL.

Section 7.4 Practice Exercises

Study Skills Exercise

1. Define the key term **microgram**.

Review Exercises

For Exercises 2–10, perform the conversions.

2. 9.84 m = _____ mm

3. 4.28 km = _____ m

4. 42 cg = _____ g

5. 80 mg = _____ cg

6. 4 kL = _____ cL

7. 0.009 kL = _____ mL

8. 9 kg = _____ lb

9. 2800 g = _____ lb

10. 18 mL = _____ cc

Objective 1: Additional Metric Units of Mass

For Exercises 11–18, perform the conversions. **(See Example 1.)**

11. 0.01 mg = _____ mcg

12. 0.005 mg = _____ mcg

 13. 7500 mcg = _____ mg

14. 50 mcg = _____ mg

15. 500 mcg = _____ cg

16. 1000 mcg = _____ cg

17. 0.05 cg = _____ mcg

18. 0.001 cg = _____ mcg

Objective 2: Medical Applications

19. A doctor orders 0.2 mg of the drug atropine given by injection. How many micrograms is this?

20. The drug Synthroid is used to treat thyroid disease. A patient is sometimes started on a dose of 0.05 mg/day. How many micrograms is this?

21. The drug cyanocobalamin is prescribed by one doctor in the amount of 1000 mcg. How many milligrams is this?

22. An injection of naloxone is given in the amount of 800 mcg. How many milligrams is this?

23. The drug Zovirax is sometimes used to treat chicken pox in children. One doctor recommended 20 mg of the drug per kilogram of the child's body mass, 4 times daily.
(See Example 2.)

   a. How much of the drug should a 20-kg child receive for one dose?

   b. How much of the drug would be given over a 5-day period?

24. The drug Amoxil is sometimes used to treat children with bacterial infections. One doctor prescribed 40 mg of the drug per kilogram of the child's body mass, 3 times daily.

   a. How much of the drug should a 15-kg child receive for one dose?

   b. How much of the drug would be given to the child over a 10-day period?

25. A nurse must administer 45 mg of a drug. The drug is available in a liquid form with a concentration of 15 mg per milliliter of the solution. How many milliliters of the solution should the nurse give? **(See Example 3.)**

26. A patient must receive 500 mg of medication in a solution that has a strength of 250 mg per 5 milliliter of solution. How many milliliters of solution should be given?

27. The drug amoxicillin is an antibiotic used to treat bacterial infections. A doctor orders 250 mg every 8 hr. How many grams of the drug would be given in 1 wk?

28. A blood alcohol concentration of 0.08% is the upper legal limit for operating a motor vehicle. For a typical 175-lb man, each 12-oz can of beer consumed within 1 hr will raise his blood alcohol concentration by 0.028%. If he consumes three cans of beer within 1 hr, what is his blood alcohol concentration? Is he below the legal limit for driving home?

29. Dr. Boyd gives a patient 2 cc of Zantac. How many milliliters is this?

30. If a nurse mixed 11.5 mL of sterile water with 1.5 mL of oxacillin, how many cubic centimeters will this produce?

31. A tetanus vaccine was purchased by a group of family practice doctors. They purchased 1 L of the vaccine. How many patients can be vaccinated if the normal dose is 2 cc?

32. A pharmacist has a 1-L bottle of cough syrup. How many 20-cL bottles can she make?

33. A doctor orders 0.2 mg of a drug per kilogram of a patient's body mass. How much of the drug should be given to a patient who is 48 kg?

34. The dosage for a painkiller is 0.05 mg per kilogram of a patient's body mass. How much of the drug should be administered to a patient who is 90 kg?

Expanding Your Skills

35. A normal value of hemoglobin in the blood for an adult male is 18 gm/dL (that is, 18 grams per deciliter). How much hemoglobin would be expected in 20 mL of a males's blood?

36. A normal value of hemoglobin in the blood for an adult female is 15 gm/dL (that is, 15 grams per deciliter). How much hemoglobin would be expected in 40 mL of a female's blood?

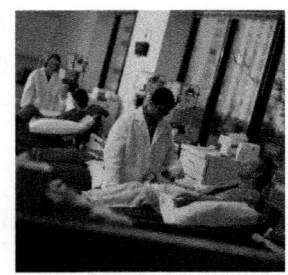

Section 7.5	Lines and Angles

1. Basic Definitions

In this chapter, we will introduce some basic concepts of geometry.

A **point** is a specific location in space. We often symbolize a point by a dot and label it with a capital letter such as *P*.

A **line** consists of infinitely many points that follow a straight path. A line extends forever in both directions. This is illustrated by arrowheads at both ends. Figure 7-11 shows a line through points *A* and *B*. The line can be represented as $\overleftrightarrow{AB}$ or as $\overleftrightarrow{BA}$.

Figure 7-11

A **line segment** is a part of a line between and including two distinct endpoints. A line segment with endpoints *P* and *Q* can be denoted $\overline{PQ}$ or $\overline{QP}$. See Figure 7-12.

Figure 7-12

A **ray** is the part of a line that includes an endpoint and all points on one side of the endpoint. In Figure 7-13, ray $\overrightarrow{PQ}$ is named by using the endpoint *P* and another point *Q* on the ray. Notice that the rays $\overrightarrow{PQ}$ and $\overrightarrow{QP}$ are different because they extend in different directions. See Figure 7-13.

Concept Connections

1. Are the rays $\overrightarrow{AB}$ and $\overrightarrow{BA}$ the same?
2. Are the lines $\overleftrightarrow{PQ}$ and $\overleftrightarrow{QP}$ the same?

Ray $\overrightarrow{PQ}$ Ray $\overrightarrow{QP}$

Figure 7-13

TIP: A ray has only one endpoint, which is always written first.

Skill Practice

Identify each as a point, line, line segment, or ray.

3. $\overline{RS}$ | 4. •*Q*
5. $\overrightarrow{XY}$ | 6. $\overleftrightarrow{TV}$

Example 1	Identifying Points, Lines, Line Segments, and Rays

Identify each as a point, line, line segment, or ray.

a. $\overleftrightarrow{MN}$ **b.** $\overrightarrow{NM}$ **c.** $\overline{MN}$ **d.** • *S*

Solution:

a. The double arrowheads indicate that $\overleftrightarrow{MN}$ is a line.

b. The single arrowhead indicates that $\overrightarrow{NM}$ is a ray with endpoint *N*.

c. The bar drawn above the letters $\overline{MN}$ indicates a line segment with endpoints *M* and *N*.

d. The dot represents a point.

Answers

1. No   2. Yes
3. Line segment
4. Point   5. Ray   6. Line

2. Naming and Measuring Angles

An **angle** is a geometric figure formed by two rays that share a common endpoint. The common endpoint is called the **vertex** of the angle. In Figure 7-14, the rays $\overrightarrow{PR}$ and $\overrightarrow{PQ}$ share the endpoint P. These rays form the sides of the angle and the angle is denoted $\angle QPR$ or $\angle RPQ$. Notice that when we name an angle, the vertex must be the middle letter. Sometimes a small arc ⟩ is drawn to illustrate the location of an angle. In such a case, the angle may be named by using the symbol $\angle$ along with the letter of the vertex.

$\angle QPR$ or $\angle RPQ$ or $\angle P$

Figure 7-14

TIP: Sometimes angles are named by a number or lowercase letter between the rays. See $\angle x$ shown here.

Avoiding Mistakes

The ° symbol can be used for temperature or for measuring angles. The context of the problem tells us whether temperature or angle measure is implied by the symbol.

The most common unit to measure an angle is the degree, denoted by °. To become familiar with the measure of angles, consider the following benchmarks. Two rays that form a quarter turn of a circle make a 90° angle. A 90° angle is called a **right angle** and is often depicted with a □ symbol. Two rays that form a half turn of a circle make a 180° angle. A 180° angle is called a **straight angle** because it appears as a straight line. A full circle has 360°. For example, the second hand of a clock sweeps out an angle of 360° in 1 minute. See Figure 7-15.

| 90° | 180° | 360° |
| Right angle | Straight angle | |

Figure 7-15

We can approximate the measure of an angle by using a tool called a *protractor*, shown in Figure 7-16. A protractor uses equally spaced tick marks around a semicircle to measure angles from 0° to 180°.

Animation

Figure 7-16

Example 2 shows how we can use a protractor to measure several angles. To denote the measure of an angle, we use the symbol m, written in front of the name of the angle. For example, if the measure of angle A is 30°, we write $m(\angle A) = 30°$.

| **Example 2** | **Measuring Angles** |

Read the protractor to determine the measure of each angle.

a. ∠*AOB*   **b.** ∠*AOC*   **c.** ∠*AOD*   **d.** ∠*AOE*

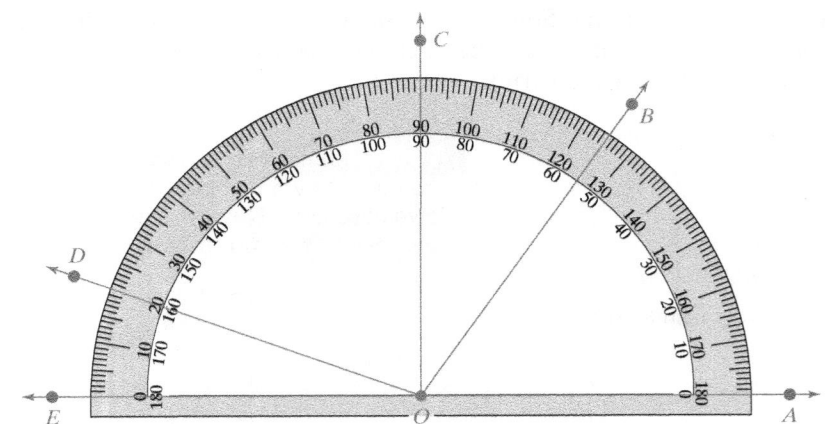

Solution:

We will use the inner scale on the protractor. This is done because we are measuring the angles in a counterclockwise direction, beginning at 0° along ray $\overrightarrow{OA}$.

a. $m(\angle AOB) = 55°$ On the inner scale, ray $\overrightarrow{OA}$ is aligned with 0° and ray $\overrightarrow{OB}$ passes through 55°. Therefore, $m(\angle AOB) = 55°$.

b. $m(\angle AOC) = 90°$ ∠*AOC* is a right angle.

c. $m(\angle AOD) = 160°$

d. $m(\angle AOE) = 180°$ ∠*AOE* is a straight angle.

An angle is said to be an **acute angle** if its measure is between 0° and 90°. An angle is said to be an **obtuse angle** if its measure is between 90° and 180°. See Figure 7-17.

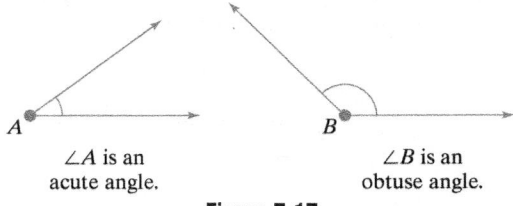

∠*A* is an   ∠*B* is an
acute angle.   obtuse angle.

Figure 7-17

3. Complementary and Supplementary Angles

- Two angles are said to be equal or **congruent** if they have the same measure.
- Two angles are said to be **complementary** if the sum of their measures is 90°. In Figure 7-18, the complement of a 60° angle is a 30° angle and vice versa.
- Two angles are said to be **supplementary** if the sum of their measures is 180°. In Figure 7-19, the supplement of a 60° angle is a 120° angle and vice versa.

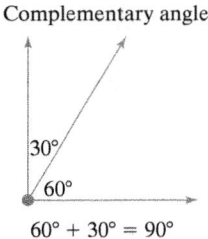

Complementary angles

$60° + 30° = 90°$

Figure 7-18

Supplementary angles

$60° + 120° = 180°$

Figure 7-19

Example 3 **Identifying Supplementary and Complementary Angles**

a. What is the supplement of a 105° angle?

b. What is the complement of a 12° angle?

Solution:

a. Let x represent the measure of the supplement of a 105° angle.

$x + 105 = 180$	The sum of a 105° angle and its supplement must equal 180°.
$x + 105 - 105 = 180 - 105$	Subtract 105 from both sides to solve for x.
$x = 75$	The supplement is a 75° angle.

b. Let y represent the measure of the complement of a 12° angle.

$y + 12 = 90$	The sum of a 12° angle and its complement must equal 90°.
$y + 12 - 12 = 90 - 12$	Subtract 12 from both sides to solve for y.
$y = 78$	The complement is a 78° angle.

4. Parallel and Perpendicular Lines

Two lines may intersect (cross) or may be parallel. **Parallel lines** lie on the same flat surface, but never intersect. See Figure 7-20.

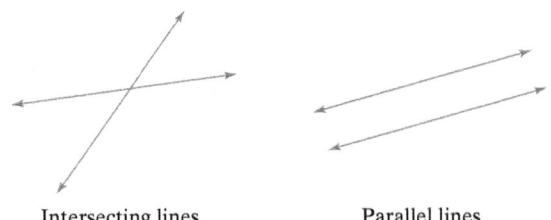

Intersecting lines   Parallel lines

Figure 7-20

Notice that two intersecting lines form four angles. In Figure 7-21, $\angle a$ and $\angle c$ are **vertical angles**. They appear on opposite sides of the vertex. Likewise, $\angle b$ and $\angle d$ are vertical angles. Vertical angles are equal in measure. That is $m(\angle a) = m(\angle c)$ and $m(\angle b) = m(\angle d)$.

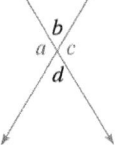

Figure 7-21

Angles that share a side are called *adjacent* angles. One pair of *adjacent* angles in Figure 7-21 is $\angle a$ and $\angle b$.

If two lines intersect at a right angle, they are **perpendicular lines**. See Figure 7-22.

TIP: Sometimes we use the symbol $\perp$ to denote perpendicular lines.

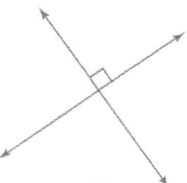

Figure 7-22

In Figure 7-23, lines L_1 and L_2 are parallel lines. If a third line m intersects the two parallel lines, eight angles are formed. Suppose we label the eight angles formed by lines L_1, L_2, and m with the numbers 1–8.

Figure 7-23

These angles have the special properties found in Table 7-6.

Table 7-6

Lines L_1 and L_2 are Parallel; Line m is an Intersecting Line	Name of Angles	Property
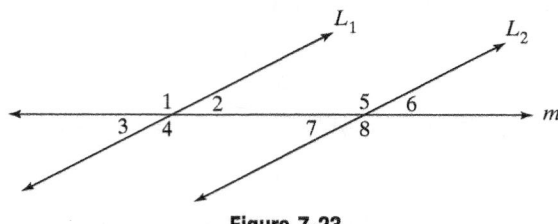	The following pairs of angles are called **alternate interior angles**: $\angle 2$ and $\angle 7$ $\angle 4$ and $\angle 5$	**Alternate interior angles are equal in measure.** $m(\angle 2) = m(\angle 7)$ $m(\angle 4) = m(\angle 5)$
	The following pairs of angles are called **alternate exterior angles**: $\angle 1$ and $\angle 8$ $\angle 3$ and $\angle 6$	**Alternate exterior angles are equal in measure.** $m(\angle 1) = m(\angle 8)$ $m(\angle 3) = m(\angle 6)$
	The following pairs of angles are called **corresponding angles**: $\angle 1$ and $\angle 5$ $\angle 2$ and $\angle 6$ $\angle 3$ and $\angle 7$ $\angle 4$ and $\angle 8$	**Corresponding angles are equal in measure.** $m(\angle 1) = m(\angle 5)$ $m(\angle 2) = m(\angle 6)$ $m(\angle 3) = m(\angle 7)$ $m(\angle 4) = m(\angle 8)$

Example 4 Finding the Measure of Angles in a Diagram

Assume that lines L_1 and L_2 are parallel. Find the measure of each angle, and explain how the angle is related to the given angle of 65°.

  a. $\angle a$

  b. $\angle b$

  c. $\angle c$

  d. $\angle d$

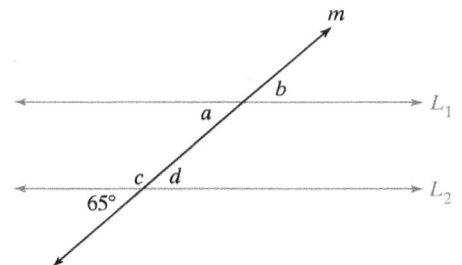

Skill Practice

Assume that lines L_1 and L_2 are parallel. Find the measure of each angle. Explain how the angle is related to the given angle.

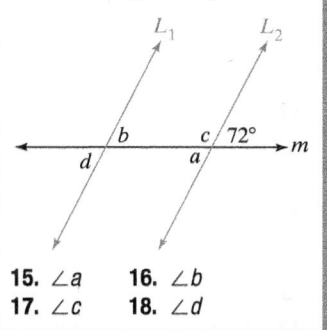

15. $\angle a$ **16.** $\angle b$
17. $\angle c$ **18.** $\angle d$

Solution:

  a. $m(\angle a) = 65°$ $\angle a$ is a corresponding angle to the given angle.

  b. $m(\angle b) = 65°$ $\angle b$ is an alternate exterior angle to the given angle.

  c. $m(\angle c) = 115°$ $\angle c$ is the supplement to the given angle.

  d. $m(\angle d) = 65°$ $\angle d$ and the given angle are vertical angles.

Answers
15. 72°; vertical angles
16. 72°; corresponding angles
17. 108°; supplementary angles
18. 72°; alternate exterior angles

Section 7.5   Practice Exercises

Boost *your* GRADE at ALEKS.com!   **ALEKS**   • Practice Problems   • e-Professors
   • Self-Tests   • Videos
   • NetTutor

Study Skills Exercise

  1. Define the key terms.

a. Point	**b. Line**	**c. Line segment**	**d. Ray**
e. Angle	**f. Vertex**	**g. Right angle**	**h. Straight angle**
i. Acute angle	**j. Obtuse angle**	**k. Congruent angles**	**l. Complementary angles**
m. Supplementary angles	**n. Parallel lines**	**o. Vertical angles**	**p. Perpendicular lines**
q. Alternate exterior angles	**r. Alternate interior angles**	**s. Corresponding angles**	

Objective 1: Basic Definitions

  2. Explain the difference between a line and a line segment.

  3. Explain the difference between a line and a ray.

  4. Is the ray $\overrightarrow{AB}$ the same as $\overrightarrow{BA}$? Explain.

For Exercises 5–10, identify each figure as a line, line segment, ray, or point. **(See Example 1.)**

5. K   H →

6. K   H

7. H

8. H   K →

9. ← H   K →

10. K

For Exercises 11–14, draw a figure that represents the expression.

11. $\overline{XY}$

12. A point named X

13. $\overleftrightarrow{YX}$

14. $\overrightarrow{XY}$

Objective 2: Naming and Measuring Angles

15. Sketch a right angle.

16. Sketch a straight angle.

17. Sketch an acute angle.

18. Sketch an obtuse angle.

For Exercises 19–24, use the protractor to determine the measure of each angle. **(See Example 2.)**

19. $m(\angle AOB)$

20. $m(\angle AOC)$

21. $m(\angle AOD)$

22. $m(\angle AOE)$

23. $m(\angle AOF)$

24. $m(\angle AOG)$

For Exercises 25–32, label each as an obtuse angle, acute angle, right angle, or straight angle.

25. $m(\angle A) = 90°$ **26.** $m(\angle E) = 91°$ **27.** $m(\angle B) = 98°$ **28.** $m(\angle F) = 30°$

29. $m(\angle C) = 2°$ **30.** $m(\angle G) = 130°$ **31.** $m(\angle D) = 180°$ **32.** $m(\angle H) = 45°$

Objective 3: Complementary and Supplementary Angles

For Exercises 33–40, the measure of an angle is given. Find the measure of the complement. **(See Example 3.)**

33. 80°   **34.** 5°   **35.** 27°   **36.** 64°

37. 29.5°   **38.** 13.2°   **39.** 89°   **40.** 1°

For Exercises 41–48, the measure of an angle is given. Find the measure of the supplement. **(See Example 3.)**

41. 80°   **42.** 5°   **43.** 127°   **44.** 124°

45. 37.4°   **46.** 173.9°   **47.** 179°   **48.** 1°

49. Can two supplementary angles both be obtuse? Why or why not?

50. Can two supplementary angles both be acute? Why or why not?

51. Can two complementary angles both be acute? Why or why not?

52. Can two complementary angles both be obtuse? Why or why not?

53. What angle is its own supplement?

54. What angle is its own complement?

Objective 4: Parallel and Perpendicular Lines

55. Sketch two lines that are parallel.

56. Sketch two lines that are *not* parallel.

57. Sketch two lines that are perpendicular.

58. Sketch two lines that are *not* perpendicular.

For Exercises 59–62, find the measure of angles *a*, *b*, *c*, and *d*.

59.

60.

61.

62.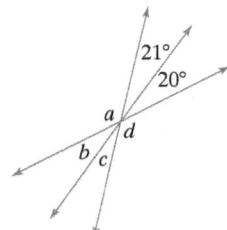

63. If two intersecting lines form vertical angles and each angle measures 90°, what can you say about the lines?

64. Can two adjacent angles formed by two intersecting lines be complementary, supplementary, or neither?

For Exercises 65–66, refer to the figure.

65. Describe the pair of angles, ∠*a* and ∠*c*, as complementary, vertical, or supplementary angles.

66. Describe the pair of angles, ∠*b* and ∠*c*, as complementary, vertical, or supplementary angles.

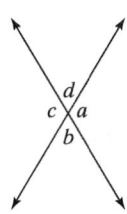

For Exercises 67–70, refer to the figure.

67. Identify a pair of vertical angles.

68. Identify a pair of alternate interior angles.

69. Identify a pair of alternate exterior angles.

70. Identify a pair of corresponding angles.

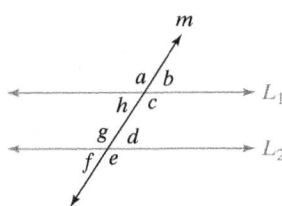

For Exercises 71–72, find the measure of angles *a*–*g* in the figure. Assume that L_1 and L_2 are parallel and that *m* is an intersecting line. (See Example 4.)

71.

72.

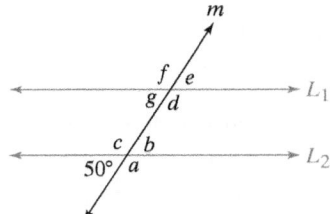

For Exercises 73–82, refer to the figure and answer true or false.

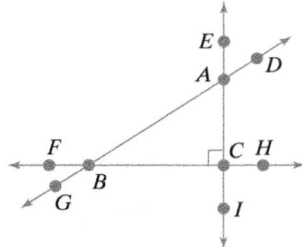

73. $\overleftrightarrow{AC}$ and $\overleftrightarrow{BC}$ are perpendicular lines.

74. $\overleftrightarrow{AB}$ and $\overleftrightarrow{AC}$ are perpendicular lines.

75. $\angle GBF$ is an acute angle.

76. $\angle EAD$ is an acute angle.

77. $\angle EAD$ and $\angle DAC$ are complementary angles.

78. $\angle GBF$ and $\angle FBA$ are complementary angles.

79. $\angle EAD$ and $\angle CAB$ are vertical angles.

80. $\angle ABC$ and $\angle FBG$ are vertical angles.

81. The point *B* is on $\overline{GA}$.

82. The point *C* is on $\overline{BH}$.

For Exercises 83–86, find the measure of $\angle XYZ$.

83.

84.

85.

86.

Expanding Your Skills

87. Use the figure to find the measure of each angle.

   a. $\angle AOB$

   b. $\angle EOD$

   c. $\angle AOE$

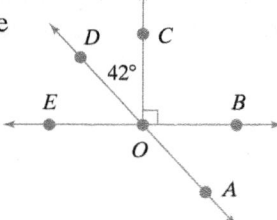

88. Use the figure to find the measure of each angle.

   a. $\angle AOB$

   b. $\angle EOD$

   c. $\angle AOE$

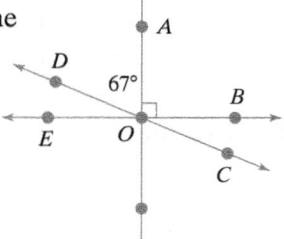

The second hand on a clock sweeps out a complete circle in 1 min. A circle forms a 360° arc. Use this information for Exercises 89–92.

89. How many degrees does a second hand on a clock move in 30 sec?

90. How many degrees does a second hand on a clock move in 15 sec?

91. How many degrees does a second hand on a clock move in 20 sec?

92. How many degrees does a second hand on a clock move in 45 sec?

Triangles, the Pythagorean Theorem, and Similar Triangles

1. Triangles

A triangle is a three-sided polygon. Furthermore, the sum of the measures of the angles within a triangle is 180°. Teachers often demonstrate this fact by tearing a triangular sheet of paper as shown in Figure 7-24. Then they align the **vertices** (points) of the triangle to form a straight angle.

1. **Triangles**
2. **Pythagorean Theorem**
3. **Similar Triangles**

Figure 7-24

PROPERTY   Angles of a Triangle

The sum of the measures of the angles of a triangle equals 180°.

Example 1   **Finding the Measure of Angles Within a Triangle**

Find the measure of angles a and b.

a.

b.

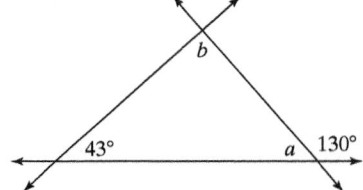

Find the measures of angles a and b.

1.

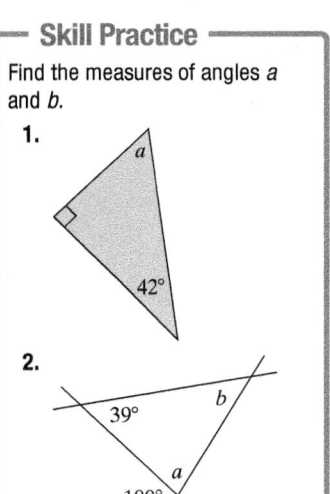

2.

Solution:

a. Recall that the □ symbol represents a 90° angle.

$38° + 90° + m(\angle a) = 180°$	The sum of the angles within a triangle is 180°.
$128° + m(\angle a) = 180°$	Add the measures of the two known angles.
$128° - 128° + m(\angle a) = 180° - 128°$	Solve for $m(\angle a)$.
$m(\angle a) = 52°$	

b. $\angle a$ is the supplement of the 130° angle. Thus $m(\angle a) = 50°$.

$43° + 50° + m(\angle b) = 180°$	The sum of the angles within a triangle is 180°.
$93° + m(\angle b) = 180°$	Add the measures of the two known angles.
$93° - 93° + m(\angle b) = 180° - 93°$	Solve for $m(\angle b)$.
$m(\angle b) = 87°$	

Answers

1. $m(\angle a) = 48°$
2. $m(\angle a) = 80°$
   $m(\angle b) = 61°$

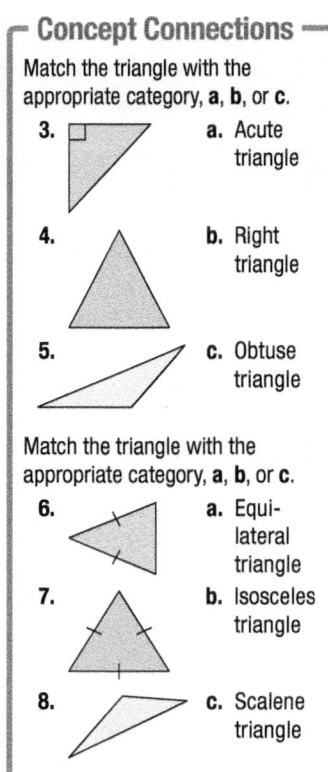
Triangles may be categorized by the measures of their angles and by the number of equal sides or angles (Figures 7-25 and 7-26).

- An **acute triangle** is a triangle in which all three angles are acute.
- A **right triangle** is a triangle in which one angle is a right angle.
- An **obtuse triangle** is a triangle in which one angle is obtuse.

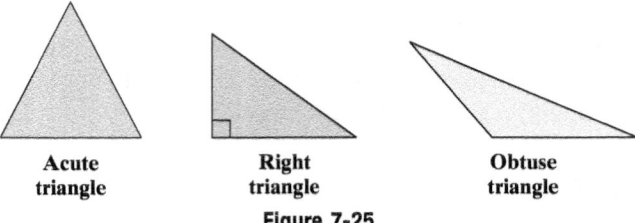

Acute triangle   Right triangle   Obtuse triangle

Figure 7-25

- An **equilateral triangle** is a triangle in which all three sides (and all three angles) are equal in measure.
- An **isosceles triangle** is a triangle in which two sides are equal in length (the angles opposite the equal sides are also equal in measure).
- A **scalene triangle** is a triangle in which no sides (or angles) are equal in measure.

Equilateral triangle   Isosceles triangle   Scalene triangle

Figure 7-26

TIP: Sometimes we use tick marks / to denote segments of equal length. Similarly, we sometimes use a small arc ⌒ to denote angles of equal measure.

2. Pythagorean Theorem

In a right triangle, the two sides forming the right angle are called the **legs**. The side opposite the right angle is called the **hypotenuse**. Note that the hypotenuse is always the longest side. See Figure 7-27. We often use the letters a and b to represent the legs of a right triangle. The letter c is used to label the hypotenuse.

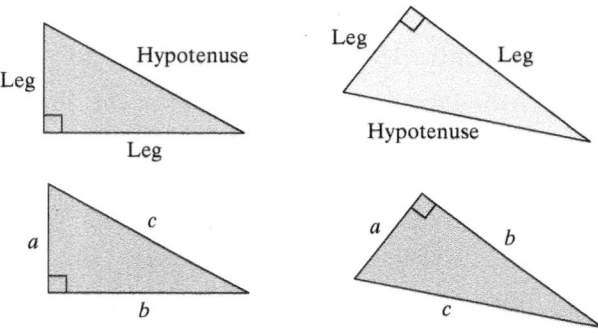

Leg   Hypotenuse   Leg   Leg
Leg   Hypotenuse

Figure 7-27

For any right triangle, the **Pythagorean theorem** gives us the following important relationship among the lengths of the sides.

Concept Connections

9. Label the triangle with the words *leg*, *leg*, and *hypotenuse*.

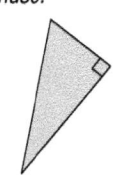

PROPERTY Pythagorean Theorem

For any right triangle,

$$(\text{Leg})^2 + (\text{Leg})^2 = (\text{Hypotenuse})^2$$

Using the letters a, b, and c to represent the legs and hypotenuse, respectively, we have

$$a^2 + b^2 = c^2$$

---

10. Label the triangle with the letters a, b, and c, where c represents the hypotenuse.

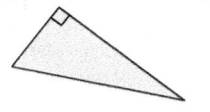

Applying the Pythagorean theorem requires the operations of *squaring* a number and *taking the square root* of a number. For example, recall from Section 1.7 that $6^2 = 6 \times 6 = 36$ and $\sqrt{36} = 6$ because $6^2 = 36$.

Example 2 **Finding the Length of the Hypotenuse of a Right Triangle**

Find the length of the hypotenuse of the right triangle.

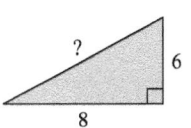

Skill Practice

11. Find the length of the hypotenuse.

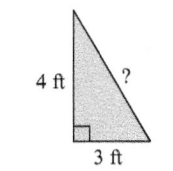

Solution:

The lengths of the legs are given.

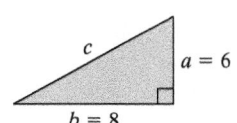

Label the triangle, using a, b, and c. It does not matter which leg is labeled a and which is labeled b.

$a^2 + b^2 = c^2$	Apply the Pythagorean theorem.
$(6)^2 + (8)^2 = c^2$	Substitute $a = 6$ and $b = 8$.
$36 + 64 = c^2$	Simplify.
$100 = c^2$	The solution to this equation is the positive number, c, that when squared equals 100.
$\sqrt{100} = c$	
$10 = c$	Simplify the square root of 100.

The solution may be checked using the Pythagorean theorem.

$$a^2 + b^2 = c^2$$
$$(6)^2 + (8)^2 \stackrel{?}{=} (10)^2$$
$$36 + 64 = 100 \checkmark$$

TIP: The value $\sqrt{100} = 10$ because $10^2 = 100$.

Answers

9.

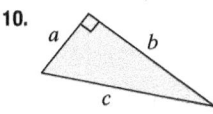

In Example 3, we solve for one of the legs of a right triangle when the other leg and the hypotenuse are known.

11. 5 ft

Skill Practice

12. Find the length of the unknown side.

Example 3 **Finding the Length of a Leg of a Right Triangle**

Find the length of the unknown side of the right triangle.

Solution:

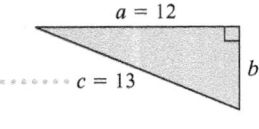

Label the triangle, using a, b, and c. One of the legs is unknown. It doesn't matter whether we call the unknown leg a or b.

$$a^2 + b^2 = c^2$$ Apply the Pythagorean theorem.

$$(12)^2 + b^2 = (13)^2$$ Substitute $a = 12$ and $c = 13$.

$$144 + b^2 = 169$$ Simplify.

$$144 - 144 + b^2 = 169 - 144$$ Solve for b^2.

$$b^2 = 25$$ The solution to this equation is the positive number, b, that when squared equals 25.

$$b = \sqrt{25}$$

$$b = 5$$ Simplify the square root of 25.

The solution may be checked by using the Pythagorean theorem.

$$a^2 + b^2 = c^2$$

$$(12)^2 + (5)^2 \stackrel{?}{=} (13)^2$$

$$144 + 25 = 169 ✔$$

Avoiding Mistakes

Always remember that the hypotenuse (longest side) is given the letter "c" when applying the Pythagorean theorem.

TIP: The value $\sqrt{25} = 5$ because $5^2 = 25$.

In Example 4 we use the Pythagorean theorem in an application.

Skill Practice

13. The bottom of a 17-ft ladder is placed 8 ft from the base of a building. How far up the building is the top of the ladder?

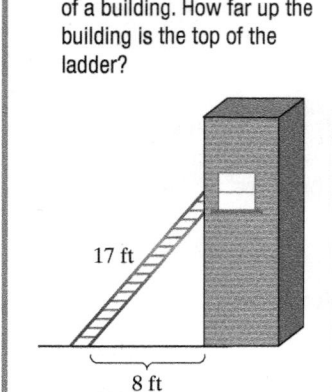

Example 4 **Using the Pythagorean Theorem in an Application**

When Barb swam across a river, the current carried her 300 yd downstream from her starting point. If the river is 400 yd wide, how far did Barb swim?

Solution:

We first familiarize ourselves with the problem and draw a diagram (Figure 7-28). The distance Barb actually swims is the hypotenuse of the right triangle. Therefore, we label this distance c.

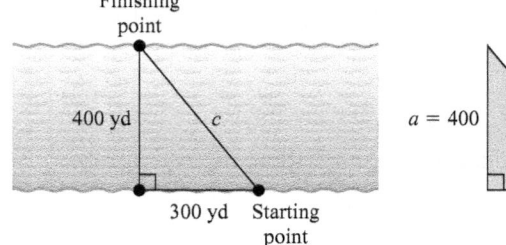

Figure 7-28

Answers

12. 10 in.   **13.** 15 ft

$$a^2 + b^2 = c^2 \quad \text{Apply the Pythagorean theorem.}$$

$$(400)^2 + (300)^2 = c^2 \quad \text{Substitute } a = 400 \text{ and } b = 300.$$

$$160,000 + 90,000 = c^2 \quad \text{Simplify.}$$

$$250,000 = c^2 \quad \text{Add. The solution to this equation is the positive number, } c, \text{ that when squared equals 250,000.}$$

$$\sqrt{250,000} = c$$

$$500 = c \quad \text{Simplify.}$$

Barb swam 500 yd.

3. Similar Triangles

Proportions are used in geometry with **similar triangles**. Two triangles are similar if their corresponding angles have equal measure. In such a case, the lengths of the corresponding sides are proportional. The triangles in Figure 7-29 are similar. Therefore, the following ratios are equivalent.

$$\frac{a}{x} = \frac{b}{y} = \frac{c}{z}$$

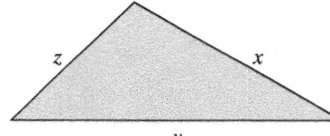

Figure 7-29

Example 5 **Using Similar Triangles to Find an Unknown Side in a Triangle**

The triangles in Figure 7-30 are similar.

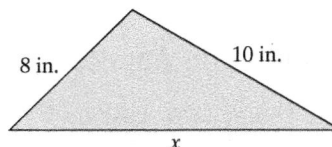

Figure 7-30

a. Solve for x. **b.** Solve for y.

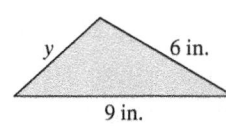

Solution:

a. The lengths of the upper right sides of the triangles are given. These form a known ratio of $\frac{10}{6}$. Because the triangles are similar, the ratio of the other corresponding sides must be equal to $\frac{10}{6}$. To solve for x, we have:

bottom side from large triangle $\longrightarrow \dfrac{x}{9 \text{ in.}} = \dfrac{10 \text{ in.}}{6 \text{ in.}}$ $\longleftarrow$ right side from large triangle
bottom side from small triangle $\hspace{4.5cm}$ $\longleftarrow$ right side from small triangle

$$\frac{x}{9} = \frac{10}{6}$$

$$x \cdot 6 = (9)(10) \qquad \text{Equate the cross products.}$$

$$6x = 90$$

$$\frac{\cancel{6}x}{\cancel{6}} = \frac{90}{6} \qquad \text{Divide both sides of the equation by 6.}$$

$$x = 15$$

The length of side x is 15 in.

b. To solve for y, the ratio of the upper left sides of the triangles must equal $\frac{10}{6}$.

left side from large triangle $\longrightarrow \dfrac{8 \text{ in.}}{y} = \dfrac{10 \text{ in.}}{6 \text{ in.}}$ $\longleftarrow$ right side from large triangle
left side from small triangle $\hspace{4.5cm}$ $\longleftarrow$ right side from small triangle

$$\frac{8}{y} = \frac{10}{6}$$

$$(8)(6) = y \cdot 10 \qquad \text{Equate the cross products.}$$

$$48 = 10y$$

$$\frac{48}{10} = \frac{\cancel{10}y}{\cancel{10}} \qquad \text{Divide both sides by 10.}$$

$$4.8 = y$$

The length of side y is 4.8 in.

Skill Practice

15. The Sun casts a 3.2-ft shadow of a 6 ft man. At the same time, the Sun casts a 80-ft shadow of a building. How tall is the building?

Example 6 **Using Similar Triangles in an Application**

The shadow cast by a yardstick is 2 ft long. The shadow cast by a tree is 11 ft long. Find the height of the tree.

Solution:

Let x represent the height of the tree.

We will assume that the measurements were taken at the same time of day. Therefore, the angle of the Sun is the same on both objects, and we can set up similar triangles (Figure 7-31).

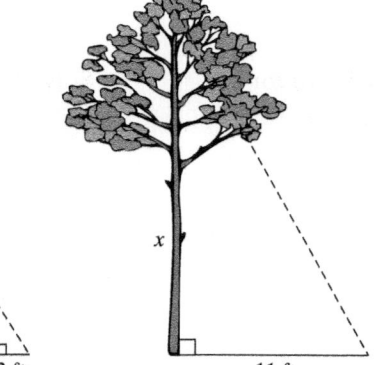

1 yd = 3 ft

2 ft

x

11 ft

Figure 7-31

Answer

15. The building is 150 ft tall.

height of yardstick → $\dfrac{3 \text{ ft}}{x}$ = $\dfrac{2 \text{ ft}}{11 \text{ ft}}$ ← length of yardstick's shadow

height of tree → $\dfrac{}{x}$ $\dfrac{}{11 \text{ ft}}$ ← length of tree's shadow

$$\frac{3}{x} = \frac{2}{11}$$

$(3)(11) = x \cdot 2$ Equate the cross products.

$33 = 2x$ Solve the equation.

$\dfrac{33}{2} = \dfrac{\overset{1}{2x}}{\underset{1}{2}}$ Divide both sides by 2.

$16.5 = x$

The tree is 16.5 ft high.

Section 7.6   Practice Exercises

Study Skills Exercises

1. When solving an application involving geometry, draw an appropriate figure and label the known quantities with numbers and the unknown quantities with variables. This will help you solve the problem. After reading this section, what geometric figure do you think you will be drawing most often in this section?

2. Define the key terms.

   a. **Vertices**

   d. **Obtuse triangle**

   g. **Scalene triangle**

   j. **Legs of a right triangle**

   b. **Acute triangle**

   e. **Equilateral triangle**

   h. **Pythagorean theorem**

   k. **Similar triangles**

   c. **Right triangle**

   f. **Isosceles triangle**

   i. **Hypotenuse**

Review Exercises

3. Do $\angle ACB$ and $\angle BCA$ represent the same angle?

4. Is line segment $\overline{MN}$ the same as the line segment $\overline{NM}$?

5. Is ray $\overrightarrow{AB}$ the same as ray $\overrightarrow{BA}$?

6. Is the line $\overleftrightarrow{PQ}$ the same as the line $\overleftrightarrow{QP}$?

7. Is a right angle an obtuse angle?

8. Can two acute angles be supplementary?

Objective 1: Triangles

For Exercises 9–16, find the measures of angles a and b. **(See Example 1.)**

9.

10.

11.

12.

13.

14.

15.

16.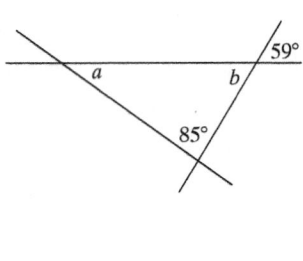

For Exercises 17–22, choose all figures that apply. The tick marks / denote segments of equal length, and small arcs ⟩ denote angles of equal measure.

17. Acute triangle

18. Obtuse triangle

19. Right triangle

20. Scalene triangle

21. Isosceles triangle

22. Equilateral triangle

a.

b.

c.

d.

e.

f.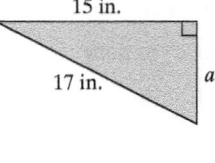

Objective 2: Pythagorean Theorem

For Exercises 23–26, find the length of the unknown side. **(See Examples 2–3.)**

23.

24.

25.

26.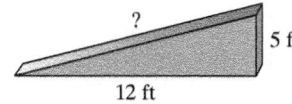

For Exercises 27–30, find the length of the unknown leg or hypotenuse.

27. Leg = 24 ft, hypotenuse = 26 ft

28. Leg = 9 km, hypotenuse = 41 km

29. Leg = 32 in., leg = 24 in.

30. Leg = 16 m, leg = 30 m

31. Find the length of the supporting brace. **(See Example 4.)**

32. Find the length of the ramp.

33. Find the height of the airplane above the ground.

34. A 25-in. television measures 25 in. across the diagonal. If the width is 20 in., find the height.

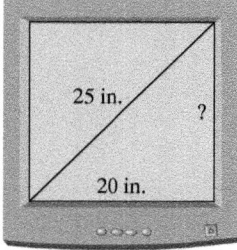

35. A car travels east 24 mi and then south 7 mi. How far is the car from its starting point?

36. A 26-ft-long wire is to be tied from a stake in the ground to the top of a 24-ft pole. How far from the bottom of the pole should the stake be placed?

For Exercises 37–40, the triangles are similar. Solve for x and y. **(See Example 5.)**

37.

38.

39.

40.

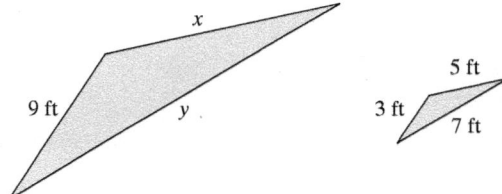

41. To estimate the height of a light pole, a mathematics student measures the length of a shadow cast by a meterstick and the length of the shadow cast by the light pole. Find the height of the light pole. **(See Example 6.)**

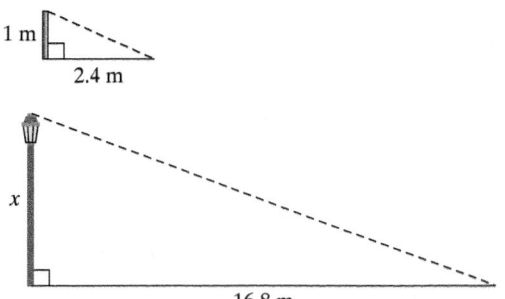

42. To estimate the height of a building, a student measures the length of a shadow cast by a yardstick and the length of the shadow cast by the building. Find the height of the building.

43. A 6-ft-tall man standing 54 ft from a light post casts an 18-ft shadow. What is the height of the light post?

44. For a science project at school, a student must measure the height of a tree. The student measures the length of the shadow of the tree and then measures the length of the shadow cast by a yardstick. Use similar triangles to find the height of the tree.

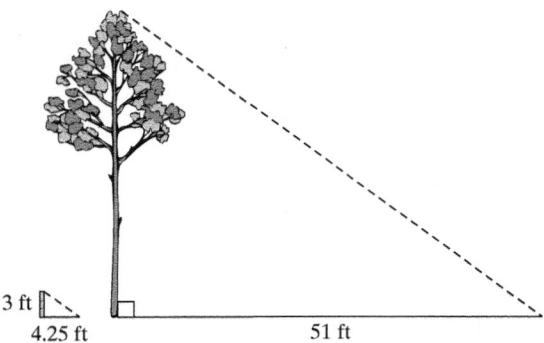

Expanding Your Skills

For Exercises 45–48, find the perimeter.

45.

46.

47.

48.

Calculator Connections

Topic: Entering Square Roots on a Calculator

In this section, we used the Pythagorean theorem to find the length of a side of a right triangle when the other two sides were given. In such problems, it is necessary to find the square root of a positive number. However, many square roots cannot be simplified to a whole number. For example, there is no whole number that when squared equals 26. However, we might speculate that $\sqrt{26}$ is a number slightly greater than 5 because $\sqrt{25} = 5$. A decimal approximation can be made by using a calculator.

$$\sqrt{26} \approx 5.099 \qquad \text{because } 5.099^2 = 25.999801 \approx 26$$

To enter a square root on a calculator, use the $\boxed{\sqrt{}}$ key. On some calculators, the $\boxed{\sqrt{}}$ function is associated with the x^2 key. In such a case, it is necessary to press $\boxed{\text{2}^{\text{nd}}}$ or $\boxed{\text{SHIFT}}$ first, followed by the $\boxed{x^2}$ key. Some calculators require the square root key to be entered first, before the number, while with others we enter the number first followed by $\boxed{\sqrt{}}$.

Expression	Keystrokes			Result
$\sqrt{26}$	26 $\boxed{\sqrt{}}$	or	$\boxed{\sqrt{}}$ 26 $\boxed{=}$	5.099019514
$\sqrt{9325}$	9325 $\boxed{\sqrt{}}$	or	$\boxed{\sqrt{}}$ 9325 $\boxed{=}$	96.56603958
$\sqrt{100}$	100 $\boxed{\sqrt{}}$	or	$\boxed{\sqrt{}}$ 100 $\boxed{=}$	10

For Exercises 49–54, complete the table. For the estimate, find two consecutive whole numbers between which the square root lies. The first row is done for you.

	Square Root	Estimate	Calculator Approximation (Round to 3 Decimal Places)
	$\sqrt{50}$	is between 7 and 8	7.071
49.	$\sqrt{10}$	is between ____ and ____	
50.	$\sqrt{90}$	is between ____ and ____	
51.	$\sqrt{116}$	is between ____ and ____	
52.	$\sqrt{65}$	is between ____ and ____	
53.	$\sqrt{5}$	is between ____ and ____	
54.	$\sqrt{48}$	is between ____ and ____	

For Exercises 55–62, use a calculator to approximate the square root to three decimal places.

55. $\sqrt{427.75}$ **56.** $\sqrt{3184.75}$ **57.** $\sqrt{1,246,000}$ **58.** $\sqrt{50,416,000}$

59. $\sqrt{0.49}$ **60.** $\sqrt{0.25}$ **61.** $\sqrt{0.56}$ **62.** $\sqrt{0.82}$

Topic: Pythagorean Theorem

For Exercises 63–68, find the length of the unknown side. Round to three decimal places if necessary.

63.

64.

65. Leg = 5 mi, leg = 10 mi   **66.** Leg = 2 m, leg = 8 m

67. Leg = 12 in., hypotenuse = 22 in.   **68.** Leg = 15 ft, hypotenuse = 18 ft

69. A square tile is 1 ft on each side. What is the length of the diagonal? Round to the nearest hundredth of a foot.

70. A tennis court is 120 ft long and 60 ft wide. What is the length of the diagonal? Round to the nearest hundredth of a foot.

71. A contractor plans to construct a cement patio for one of the houses that he is building. The patio will be a square, 25 ft by 25 ft. After the contractor builds the frame for the cement, he checks to make sure that it is square by measuring the diagonals. Use the Pythagorean theorem to determine what the length of the diagonals should be if the contractor has constructed the frame correctly. Round to the nearest hundredth of a foot.

| Section 7.7 | Perimeter, Circumference, and Area |

1. Quadrilaterals

At this point, you are familiar with several geometric figures. We have calculated perimeter and area of squares, rectangles, triangles and circles. In this section, we revisit these concepts and also define some additional geometric figures.

Recall that a **polygon** is a flat figure formed by line segments connected at their ends. A four-sided polygon is called a **quadrilateral**. Some quadrilaterals fall in the following categories.

A **parallelogram** is a quadrilateral with opposite sides parallel. It follows that opposite sides must be equal in length.

Parallelogram

A **rectangle** is a parallelogram with four right angles.

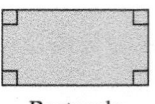

Rectangle

A **square** is a rectangle with sides of equal length.

Square

A **rhombus** is a parallelogram with sides of equal length. The angles are not necessarily equal.

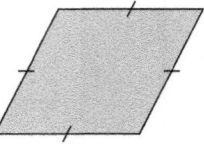

Rhombus

A **trapezoid** is a quadrilateral with one pair of parallel sides.

Trapezoid

Notice that some figures belong to more than one category. For example, a square is also a rectangle and a parallelogram.

2. Perimeter and Circumference

Recall that the **perimeter** of a polygon is the distance around the figure. For example, we use perimeter to find the amount of fencing needed to enclose a yard. The perimeter of a polygon is found by adding the lengths of the sides. Also recall that the "perimeter" of a circle is called the **circumference**.

We summarize some of the formulas presented earlier in the text.

FORMULA **Perimeter and Circumference**

Rectangle	Square	Triangle	Circle

   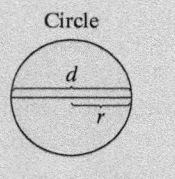

$$P = 2l + 2w \qquad P = 4s \qquad P = a + b + c \qquad C = 2\pi r \ \text{ or } \ C = \pi d$$

TIP: The approximate circumference of a circle can be calculated by using either 3.14 or $\frac{22}{7}$ for the value of π. To express the exact circumference, the answer must be written in terms of π.

Example 1 **Finding Perimeter and Circumference**

Use an appropriate formula to find the perimeter or circumference. Use 3.14 for π.

a.

b.

c.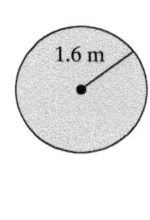

Solution:

a. To find the perimeter, add the lengths of the sides.

$P = a + b + c$

$P = 4'5'' + 2'8'' + 3'6''$ or

$\begin{array}{r} P = 4 \text{ ft } \ \ 5 \text{ in.} \\ 2 \text{ ft } \ \ 8 \text{ in.} \\ + \ 3 \text{ ft } \ \ 6 \text{ in.} \\ \hline 9 \text{ ft } 19 \text{ in.} = 9 \text{ ft} + (1 \text{ ft} + 7 \text{ in.}) \end{array}$

$\qquad\qquad\qquad\qquad = 10 \text{ ft } 7 \text{ in.} \quad \text{or} \quad 10'7''$

b. First note that to add the lengths of the sides, we must have like units.

$$9 \text{ in.} = \frac{9 \text{ in.}}{1} \cdot \frac{1 \text{ ft}}{12 \text{ in.}} = \frac{9}{12} \text{ ft} = \frac{3}{4} \text{ ft or } 0.75 \text{ ft}$$

$P = 2l + 2w$ \qquad\qquad The figure is a rectangle. Use $P = 2l + 2w$.

$= 2(6 \text{ ft}) + 2(0.75 \text{ ft})$ \qquad Substitute $l = 6$ ft and $w = 0.75$ ft.

$= 12 \text{ ft} + 1.5 \text{ ft}$ \qquad\qquad Simplify.

$= 13.5 \text{ ft}$

c. From the figure, $r = 1.6$ m.

$C = 2\pi(1.6 \text{ m})$ \qquad\qquad Use the formula, $C = 2\pi r$.

$= 3.2\pi \text{ m}$ \qquad\qquad\qquad This is the exact value of the circumference.

$\approx 3.2(3.14) \text{ m}$ \qquad\qquad Substitute 3.14 for π.

$= 10.048 \text{ m}$ \qquad\qquad The circumference is approximately 10.048 m.

Skill Practice

1. Find the perimeter.

4' 3''

2. Find the perimeter in feet.

3 yd

2 ft

3. Find the circumference. Use $\frac{22}{7}$ for π.

14 cm

Answers
1. 17'   **2.** 22 ft   **3.** 44 cm

3. Area

Recall that the **area** of a region is the number of square units that can be enclosed within the region. For example, the rectangle shown in Figure 7-32 encloses 6 square inches (in.²). We would compute area in such applications as finding the amount of sod needed to cover a yard or the amount of carpeting to cover a floor.

We have already presented the formulas to compute the area of a square, a rectangle, a triangle, and a circle. We summarize these along with the area formulas for a parallelogram and trapezoid. These should be memorized as common knowledge.

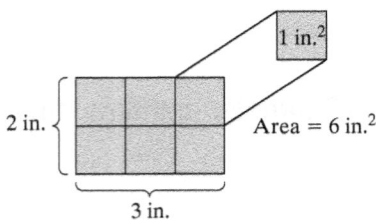

Figure 7-32

FORMULA Area Formulas

Animation

Rectangle

$A = lw$

Square

$A = s^2$

Parallelogram

$A = bh$

Triangle

$A = \frac{1}{2}bh$

Trapezoid

$A = \frac{1}{2}(a + b)h$

Circle

$A = \pi r^2$

TIP: Because the height of a parallelogram is perpendicular to the base, sometimes it must be drawn *outside* the parallelogram.

Example 2 Finding Area

a. Determine the area of the field.

b. Determine the area of the matting.

1.8 km

0.6 km

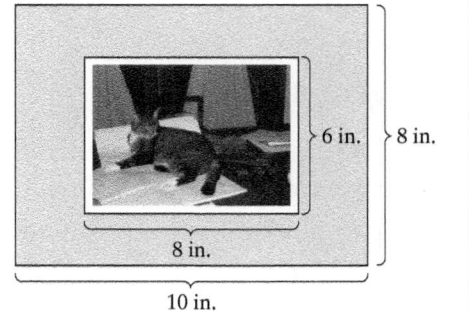

6 in. 8 in.

8 in.

10 in.

Answer

4. 8 cm²

Solution:

a. The field is in the shape of a parallelogram. The base is 0.6 km and the height is 1.8 km.

$A = bh$ Area formula for a parallelogram.

$\quad = (0.6 \text{ km})(1.8 \text{ km})$ Substitute $b = 0.6$ km and $h = 1.8$ km.

$\quad = 1.08 \text{ km}^2$

The field is 1.08 km^2.

> **TIP:** When two common units are multiplied, such as km · km, the resulting units are square units, such as km².

b. To find the area of the matting only, we can subtract the inner 6-in. by 8-in. area from the outer 8-in. by 10-in. area. In each case, apply the formula, $A = lw$

$$\underset{\downarrow}{\text{outer area}} \quad - \quad \underset{\downarrow}{\text{inner area}}$$

$$\text{Area of matting} = (10 \text{ in.})(8 \text{ in.}) - (8 \text{ in.})(6 \text{ in.})$$

$$= 80 \text{ in.}^2 - 48 \text{ in.}^2$$

$$= 32 \text{ in.}^2$$

The matting is 32 in.^2.

Example 3   **Finding Area**

Determine the area of each region.

a.

16 cm

7 cm

b.

5 ft

11 ft

9 ft

Solution:

a. $A = \dfrac{1}{2} bh$ Apply the formula for the area of a triangle.

$\quad = \dfrac{1}{2}(16 \text{ cm})(7 \text{ cm})$ Substitute $b = 16$ cm and $h = 7$ cm.

$\quad = \dfrac{1}{2}\left(\dfrac{\overset{8}{16}}{1} \text{ cm}\right)\left(\dfrac{7}{1} \text{ cm}\right)$ Multiply fractions.

$\quad = 56 \text{ cm}^2$

b. $A = \frac{1}{2}(a + b)h$ Apply the formula for the area of a trapezoid.

In this case, the two parallel sides are the left-hand side and the right-hand side. Therefore, these sides are the two bases, a and b.

The "height" is the distance between the two parallel sides.

$A = \frac{1}{2}(11 \text{ ft} + 9 \text{ ft})(5 \text{ ft})$ Substitute $a = 11$ ft, $b = 9$ ft, and $h = 5$ ft.

$= \frac{1}{2}(20 \text{ ft})(5 \text{ ft})$ Simplify within parentheses first.

$= \frac{1}{2}\left(\frac{\overset{10}{\cancel{20}}}{1} \text{ ft}\right)\left(\frac{5}{1}\text{ft}\right)$ Multiply fractions.

$= 50 \text{ ft}^2$

This is the "height" h.

5 ft

11 ft   9 ft

These sides are parallel. Therefore, they are the bases a and b.

The formula for the area of a circle was given in Section 5.3. Here we show the basis for the formula. The circumference of a circle is given by $C = 2\pi r$. The length of a *semicircle* (one-half of a circle) is one-half of this amount: $\frac{1}{2}2\pi r = \pi r$. To visualize the formula for the area of a circle, consider the bottom half and top half of a circle cut into pie-shaped wedges. Unfold the figure as shown (Figure 7-33).

πr $\approx \pi r$ $\approx r$

Figure 7-33

The resulting figure is nearly a parallelogram, with base approximately equal to πr and height approximately equal to the radius of the circle. The area is (base) $\cdot$ (height) $\approx (\pi r) \cdot r = \pi r^2$. This is the area formula for a circle.

Skill Practice

9. Determine the area of a 9-in. diameter plate. Use 3.14 for π and round to the nearest tenth.

Example 4   Computing the Area of a Circle

Determine the area of the gold medal.

Use $\frac{22}{7}$ for π.

7 cm

Answer

9. 63.6 in.^{2}

Solution:

First note that the radius is found by $r = \frac{1}{2}d$. Therefore, $r = \frac{1}{2}(7 \text{ cm}) = \frac{7}{2}$ cm.

$A = \pi \left(\dfrac{7}{2} \text{ cm} \right)^2$ Substitute $r = \dfrac{7}{2}$ cm into the formula $A = \pi r^2$.

$= \pi \left(\dfrac{49}{4} \text{ cm}^2 \right)$ Simplify the factor with the exponent.

$= \dfrac{49}{4} \pi \text{ cm}^2$ This is the exact area, which is written in terms of π.

$\approx \left(\dfrac{\overset{7}{\cancel{49}}}{\underset{2}{\cancel{4}}} \text{ cm}^2 \right) \left(\dfrac{\overset{11}{\cancel{22}}}{\underset{1}{\cancel{7}}} \right)$ Substitute $\dfrac{22}{7}$ for π.

$= \dfrac{77}{2} \text{ cm}^2$ The medal has an area of approximately $\dfrac{77}{2}$ cm^2 or $38\dfrac{1}{2}$ cm^2.

TIP: The approximate area of a circle can be calculated using either 3.14 or $\frac{22}{7}$ for π. In Example 4 we could have used $\pi = 3.14$ and $r = \frac{7}{2} = 3.5$ cm.

$$A = \pi r^2$$
$$A \approx (3.14)(3.5 \text{ cm})^2$$
$$A = 38.465 \text{ cm}^2$$

Example 5   **Finding Area for a Landscaping Application**

Sod can be purchased in palettes for $225. If a palette contains 240 ft^2 of sod, how much will it cost to cover the area in Figure 7-34?

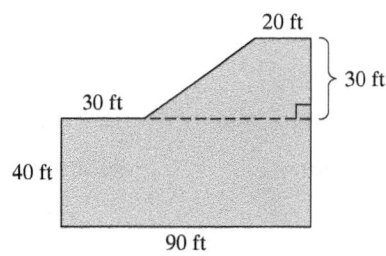

Figure 7-34

Solution:

To find the total cost, we need to know the total number of square feet. Then we can determine how many 240-ft^2 palettes are required.

20 ft

30 ft

60 ft

+

This distance is given by 90 ft − 30 ft = 60 ft.

40 ft

90 ft

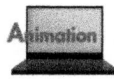

The total area is given by

$$\begin{array}{c} \underset{\substack{\text{area of}\\ \text{trapezoid}}}{\downarrow} \quad \underset{\substack{\text{area of}\\ \text{rectangle}}}{\downarrow} \\ A = \tfrac{1}{2}(a + b)h + lw \\ = \tfrac{1}{2}(60\text{ ft} + 20\text{ ft})(30\text{ ft}) + (90\text{ ft})(40\text{ ft}) \\ = \tfrac{1}{2}(80\text{ ft})(30\text{ ft}) + 3600\text{ ft}^2 \\ = 1200\text{ ft}^2 + 3600\text{ ft}^2 \\ = 4800\text{ ft}^2 \qquad \text{The total area is } 4800\text{ ft}^2. \end{array}$$

To determine how many 240-ft^2 palettes of sod are required, divide the total area by 240 ft^2.

Number of palettes: $4800\text{ ft}^2 \div 240\text{ ft}^2 = 20$

The total cost for 20 palettes is   ($225 per palette) $\times$ 20 palettes = $4500

The cost for the sod is $4500.

Section 7.7 Practice Exercises

Study Skills Exercises

1. It may help to remember formulas if you understand how they were derived. For example, the perimeter of a square has the formula $P = 4s$. It was derived from the fact that perimeter measures the distance around a figure.
   Explain how the formula for the perimeter of a rectangle ($P = 2l + 2w$) was derived.

$P = s + s + s + s$
$= 4s$

2. Define the key terms.

   a. Polygon   **b. Quadrilateral**   **c. Parallelogram**   **d. Rectangle**

   e. Square   **f. Rhombus**   **g. Trapezoid**   **h. Perimeter**

   i. Circumference   **j. Area**

Review Exercises

For Exercises 3–8, state the characteristics of each triangle.

3. Isosceles triangle   4. Right triangle

5. Acute triangle   6. Equilateral triangle

7. Obtuse triangle   8. Scalene triangle

Objective 1: Quadrilaterals

9. Write the definition of a quadrilateral.

For Exercises 10–14, state the characteristics of each quadrilateral.

10. Square

11. Trapezoid

12. Parallelogram

13. Rectangle

14. Rhombus

Objective 2: Perimeter and Circumference

For Exercises 15–24, determine the perimeter or circumference. Use 3.14 for π. **(See Example 1.)**

15. Rectangle

15 cm

25 cm

16. Square

32 in.

17. Square

65 mm

18. Rectangle

5.8 yd

3.4 yd

19. Trapezoid

2 m

3 m

1.8 m

3.9 m

20. Trapezoid

46 cm

46 cm

60 cm

85 cm

21.

8 ft

22.

$2\frac{1}{2}$ km

23.

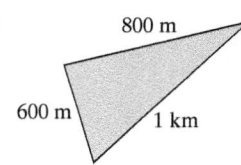

800 m

600 m

1 km

24.

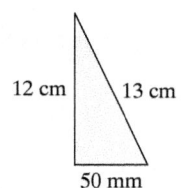

12 cm

13 cm

50 mm

25. Find the perimeter of a triangle with sides 3 ft 8 in., 2 ft 10 in., and 4 ft.

26. Find the perimeter of a triangle with sides 4 ft 2 in., 3 ft, and 2 ft 9 in.

27. Find the perimeter of a rectangle with length 2 ft and width 6 in.

28. Find the perimeter of a rectangle with length 4 m and width 85 cm.

29. Find the lengths of the two missing sides labeled x and y. Then find the perimeter of the figure.

y

300 mm

4.5 dm

x

250 mm

7.5 dm

30. Find the lengths of the two missing sides labeled a and b. Then find the perimeter of the figure.

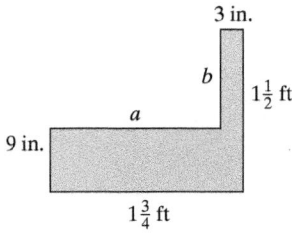

3 in.

b

$1\frac{1}{2}$ ft

a

9 in.

$1\frac{3}{4}$ ft

31. Rain gutters are going to be installed around the perimeter of a house. What is the total length needed?

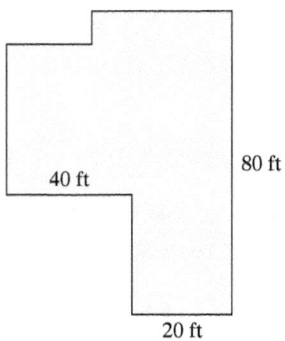

40 ft

80 ft

20 ft

32. Wood molding needs to be installed around the perimeter of a living room floor. With no molding needed in the doorway, how much molding is needed?

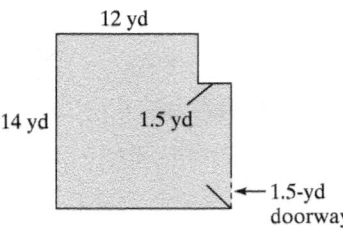

12 yd

14 yd

1.5 yd

←1.5-yd doorway

Objective 3: Area

For Exercises 33–44, determine the area of the shaded region. **(See Examples 2–3.)**

33.

24 yd

34.

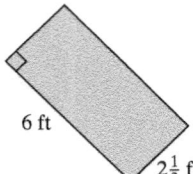

6 ft

$2\frac{1}{3}$ ft

35.

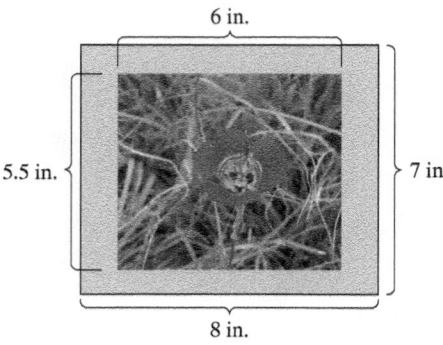

6 in.

5.5 in.

7 in.

8 in.

36.

6 ft

3.4 ft

2 ft

8 ft

37.

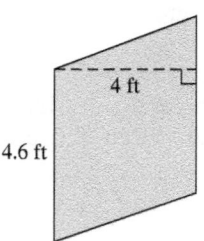

4 ft

4.6 ft

38.

70 cm

78 cm

39.

9 m

12 m

40.

3 km

1 km

41.

35 in.

16 in.

47 in.

42.
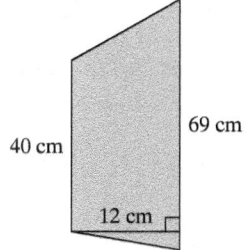
69 cm

40 cm

12 cm

43.

5.8 ft

12.8 ft

3.1 ft

18.4 ft

44.
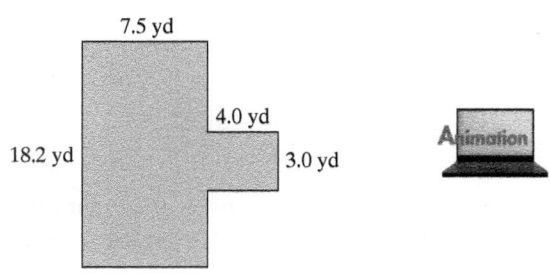
7.5 yd

4.0 yd

18.2 yd

3.0 yd

For Exercises 45–48, determine the area of the circle, using $\frac{22}{7}$ for π. **(See Example 4.)**

 45.

7 m

46.

$\frac{7}{4}$ km

47.

21 cm

48.
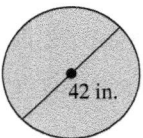
42 in.

For Exercises 49–52, determine the area of the circle, using 3.14 for π. Round to the nearest whole unit.

49.

12 mm

50.

25 mm

51.

1.2 ft

52.
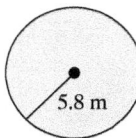
5.8 m

53. Determine the area of the sign.

4 yd

1.5 yd

A+
Lumber

3 yd

54. Determine the area of the kite.

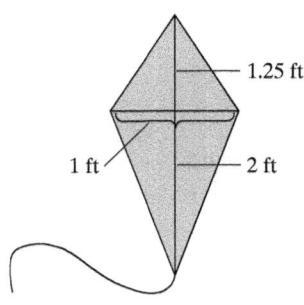
1.25 ft

1 ft

2 ft

55. A rectangular living room is all to be carpeted except for the tiled portion in front of the fireplace. If carpeting is $2.50 per square foot (including installation), how much will the carpeting cost? **(See Example 5.)**

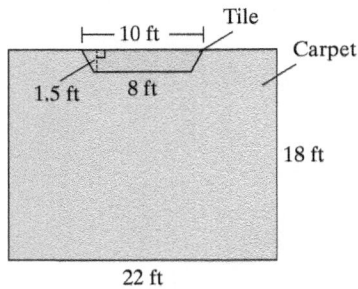

56. A patio area is to be covered with outdoor tile. If tile costs $8 per square foot (including installation), how much will it cost to tile the whole patio?

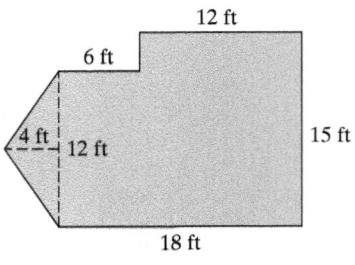

57. The Baker family plans to paint their garage floor with paint that resists gas, oil, and dirt from tires. The garage is 21 ft wide and 23 ft long. The paint kit they plan to use will cover approximately 250 square feet.

   a. What is the area of the garage floor?

   b. How many kits will be needed to paint the entire garage floor?

Expanding Your Skills

For Exercises 58–61, determine the area of the shaded region. Use 3.14 for π.

58.

59.

60.

61.

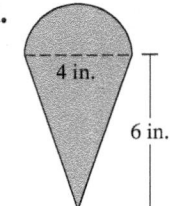

62. Find the length of side c by dividing this figure into a rectangle and a right triangle. Then find the perimeter of the figure.

63. Find the perimeter of the figure.

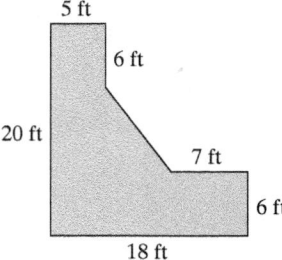

Problem Recognition Exercises

Area, Perimeter, and Circumference

For Exercises 1–14, determine the area and the perimeter or circumference for each figure.

1.

5 ft
5 ft

2.

12 m
12 m

3.

300 cm
4 m

4.

6 in.
2 ft

5.

1 ft
1.5 ft
1 yd

6.

520 m
430 m
1.1 km

7.

3 yd
4 yd

8.

5 cm
12 cm

9.

14 m
5 m   4 m   5 m
8 m

10.
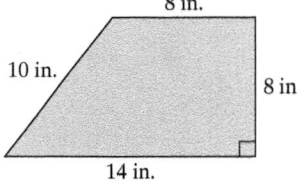
8 in.
10 in.
8 in.
14 in.

11. Use 3.14 for π.
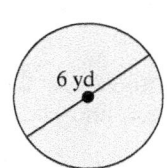
6 yd

12. Use 3.14 for π.

40 cm

13. Use $\dfrac{22}{7}$ for π.

28 cm

14. Use $\dfrac{22}{7}$ for π.
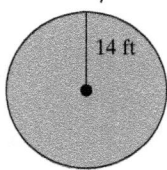
14 ft

For Exercises 15–18,

  a. Choose the type of formula needed to solve the problem: perimeter, circumference, or area.

  b. Solve the problem.

15. Find the amount of fencing needed to enclose a square field whose side measures 16 yd.

16. Find the amount of wood trim needed to frame a circular window with diameter $1\frac{3}{4}$ ft. Use $\frac{22}{7}$ for π.

17. Find the amount of carpeting needed to cover the floor of a rectangular room that is $12\frac{1}{2}$ ft by 10 ft.

18. Find the amount of sod needed to cover a circular garden with diameter 20 m. Use 3.14 for π.

Section 7.8 | Volume and Surface Area

Objectives

1. **Volume**
2. **Surface Area**

1. Volume

In this section, we learn how to compute volume. Volume is another word for capacity. We use volume, for example, to determine how much can be held in a moving van.

In addition to the units of capacity learned in Sections 7.1 and 7.2, volume can be measured in cubic units. For example, a cube that is 1 cm on a side has a volume of 1 cubic centimeter (1 cm^3 or cc). A cube that is 1 in. on a side has a volume of 1 cubic inch (1 in.^3). See Figure 7-35. Additional units of volume include cubic feet (ft^3), cubic yards (yd^3), cubic meters (m^3), and so on.

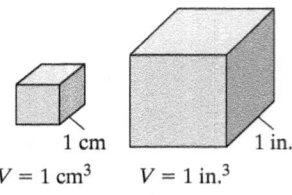

1 cm   1 in.
$V = 1 \text{ cm}^3$ $V = 1 \text{ in.}^3$

Figure 7-35

> **TIP:** Recall that 1 cubic centimeter can also be denoted as 1 cc. Furthermore, 1 cc = 1 mL.

The formulas used to compute the volume of several common solids are given.

FORMULA

Rectangular Solid	Cube	Right Circular Cylinder
$V = lwh$	$V = s^3$	$V = \pi r^2 h$

Notice that the volume formulas for these three figures are given by the product of the area of the base and the height of the figure:

$$V = lw\mathbf{h} \qquad V = s \cdot s \cdot \mathbf{s} \qquad V = \pi r^2 \mathbf{h}$$

area of rectangular base   area of square base   area of circular base

A right circular cone has the shape of a party hat. A sphere has the shape of a ball. To compute the volume of a cone and a sphere, we use the following formulas.

> **TIP:** Notice that the formula for the volume of a right circular cone is $\frac{1}{3}$ that of a right circular cylinder.
>
>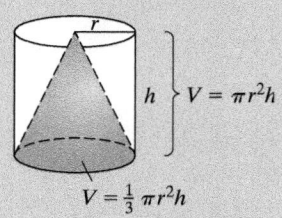
>
> $h \; \Big\} \; V = \pi r^2 h$
>
> $V = \frac{1}{3}\pi r^2 h$

FORMULA

Right Circular Cone	Sphere
$V = \frac{1}{3}\pi r^2 h$	$V = \frac{4}{3}\pi r^3$

Example 1 **Finding Volume**

Find the volume. Round to the nearest whole unit.

Solution:

$V = lwh$
Use the volume formula for a rectangular solid. Identify the length, width, and height.

$= (4 \text{ in.})(3 \text{ in.})(5 \text{ in.})$ $l = 4$ in., $w = 3$ in., and
$h = 5$ in.

$= 60 \text{ in.}^3$

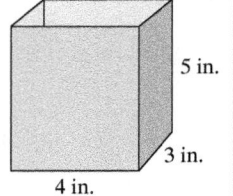

We can visualize the volume by "layering" cubes that are each 1 in. high (Figure 7-36). The number of cubes in each layer is equal to $4 \times 3 = 12$. Each layer has 12 cubes, and there are 5 layers. Thus, the total number of cubes is $12 \times 5 = 60$ for a volume of 60 in.^{3}

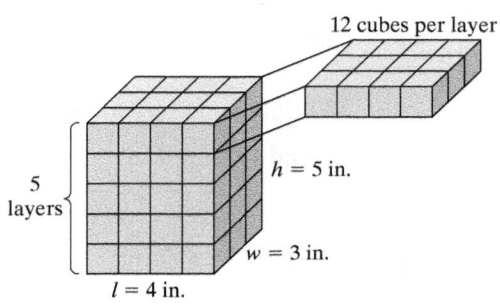

Figure 7-36

Skill Practice

Find the volume.

1.

Animation

Example 2 **Finding the Volume of a Cylinder**

Find the volume. Use 3.14 for π. Round to the nearest whole unit.

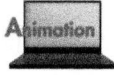

Solution:

$V = \pi r^2 h$
Use the formula for the volume of a right circular cylinder.

$\approx (3.14)(3.7 \text{ cm})^2(11.2 \text{ cm})$
Substitute 3.14 for π, $r = 3.7$ cm, and $h = 11.2$ cm.

$= (3.14)(13.69 \text{ cm}^2)(11.2 \text{ cm})$
Simplify exponents first.

$= 481.44992 \text{ cm}^3$
Multiply from left to right.

$\approx 481 \text{ cm}^3$
Round to the nearest whole unit.

Skill Practice

Find the volume. Use 3.14 for π.

2.

Answers
1. 176 in.^{3} **2.** ≈ 56.52 in.^{3}

Example 3 **Finding the Volume of a Sphere**

Find the volume. Use 3.14 for π. Round to one decimal place.

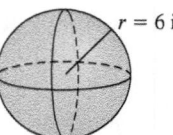
$r = 6$ in.

Solution:

$V = \dfrac{4}{3}\pi r^3$ Use the formula for the volume of a sphere.

$\approx \dfrac{4}{3}(3.14)(6 \text{ in.})^3$ Substitute 3.14 for π and $r = 6$ in.

$= \dfrac{4}{3}(3.14)(216 \text{ in.}^3)$ Simplify exponents first.
$(6 \text{ in.})^3 = (6 \text{ in.})(6 \text{ in.})(6 \text{ in.}) = 216 \text{ in.}^3$

$= \dfrac{4}{3}\left(\dfrac{3.14}{1}\right)\left(\dfrac{216 \text{ in.}^3}{1}\right)$ Multiply fractions.

$= \dfrac{4}{\underset{1}{\cancel{3}}}\left(\dfrac{3.14}{1}\right)\left(\dfrac{\overset{72}{\cancel{216}} \text{ in.}^3}{1}\right)$ Simplify to lowest terms.

$= 904.32 \text{ in.}^3$ Multiply from left to right.

$\approx 904.3 \text{ in.}^3$ Round to one decimal place.

Example 4 **Finding the Volume of a Cone**

Find the volume. Use 3.14 for π. Round to one decimal place.

8 in.
5 in.

Solution:

$V = \dfrac{1}{3}\pi r^2 h$ Use the formula for the volume of a right circular cone.

To find the radius we have $r = \dfrac{1}{2}d = \dfrac{1}{2}(5 \text{ in.}) = 2.5 \text{ in.}$

$V \approx \dfrac{1}{3}(3.14)(2.5 \text{ in.})^2(8 \text{ in.})$ Substitute 3.14 for π, $r = 2.5$ in., and $h = 8$ in.

$= \dfrac{1}{3}\left(\dfrac{3.14}{1}\right)\left(\dfrac{6.25 \text{ in.}^2}{1}\right)\left(\dfrac{8 \text{ in.}}{1}\right)$ Simplify exponents first.

$= \dfrac{157}{3} \text{ in.}^3$ Multiply fractions.

$\approx 52.3 \text{ in.}^3$ Round to one decimal place.

2. Surface Area

Surface area (often abbreviated SA) is the area of the surface of a three-dimensional object. To illustrate, consider the surface area of a soup can in the shape of a right circular cylinder.

If we peel off the label, we see that the label forms a rectangle whose length is the circumference of the base, $2\pi r$. The width of the rectangle is the height of the can, h. The area of the label is determined by multiplying the length and the width: $l \times w = 2\pi rh$. To determine the total surface area, add the areas of the top and bottom of the can to this rectangular area.

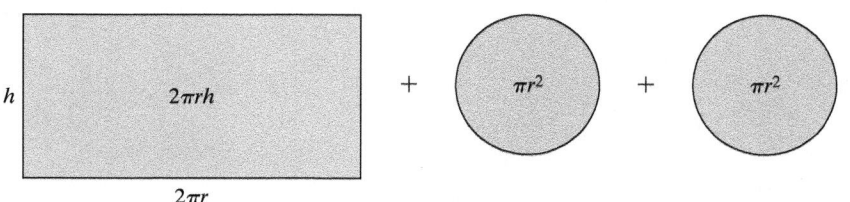

$$\text{Surface area} = 2\pi rh + \pi r^2 + \pi r^2 \text{ or}$$

$$\text{SA} = 2\pi rh + 2\pi r^2$$

Table 7-7 gives the formulas for the surface areas of four common solids.

Table 7-7 **Surface Area**

Cube	Rectangular Solid	Cylinder	Sphere
$\text{SA} = 6s^2$	$\text{SA} = 2lh + 2lw + 2hw$	$\text{SA} = 2\pi rh + 2\pi r^2$	$\text{SA} = 4\pi r^2$

Example 5 **Determining Surface Area**

Determine the surface area of the rectangular solid.

Solution:

Use the formula $\text{SA} = 2lh + 2lw + 2hw$, where $l = 5$ in., $w = 4$ in. and $h = 9$ in.

$\text{SA} = 2(5 \text{ in.})(9 \text{ in.}) + 2(5 \text{ in.})(4 \text{ in.}) + 2(9 \text{ in.})(4 \text{ in.})$

$\quad = 90 \text{ in.}^2 + 40 \text{ in.}^2 + 72 \text{ in.}^2 \qquad\qquad\qquad\qquad \text{Multiply.}$

$\quad = 202 \text{ in.}^2 \qquad\qquad\qquad\qquad\qquad\qquad\qquad\qquad \text{Add.}$

The surface area of the rectangular solid is 202 in.^{2}

Skill Practice

5. Determine the surface area of the cube with the side length of 3 ft.

Avoiding Mistakes

Although we are working with a three-dimensional figure, we are finding area. The answer will be in square units, not cubic units, as in calculating volume.

Answer

5. 54 ft^2

┌─────────────────────────────┐
│ **Skill Practice** │
│ **6.** Determine the surface area of │
│ a cylinder with radius 15 cm │
│ and height 20 cm. │
└─────────────────────────────┘

Example 6 **Determining Surface Area**

Determine the surface area of a sphere with radius 6 m. Use 3.14 for π.

Solution:

Use the formula $SA = 4\pi r^2$, where $r = 6$ m.

$$SA = 4\pi(6 \text{ m})^2$$
$$\approx 4(3.14)(36 \text{ m}^2) \qquad \text{Substitute 3.14 for } \pi.$$
$$\approx 452.16 \text{ m}^2$$

Answer

6. 3297 cm^2

Section 7.8 Practice Exercises

Study Skills Exercise

1. Define the key terms.

   a. **Rectangular solid**   b. **Cube**   c. **Right circular cylinder**

   d. **Right circular cone**   e. **Sphere**

Review Exercises

2. Determine the measure of the complement and supplement of 82°.

3. Determine the measure of the complement and supplement of 24°.

4. Determine the measure of the complement and supplement of 79°.

5. Determine the measures of angles *a–g*.
   Assume that lines l_1 and l_2 are parallel.

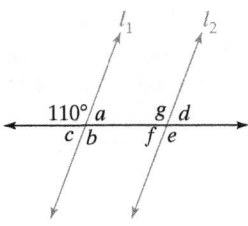

6. Determine the measures of angles *a–h*.

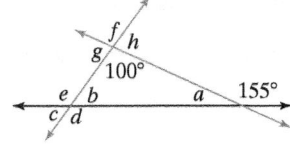

Objective 1: Volume

For Exercises 7–18, find the volume. Use 3.14 for π where necessary. **(See Examples 1–4.)**

7.

1.4 cm
1.4 cm
1.4 cm

8.
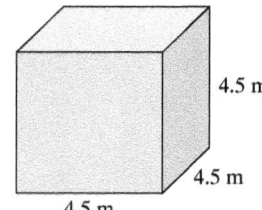
4.5 m
4.5 m
4.5 m

9.

6 in.
12 ft
8 ft

10.

0.8 ft
0.8 ft
2.5 yd

11.

$r = 2$ mm
$h = 1$ mm

12.

3 m
6 m

13.

$r = 9$ yd

14.
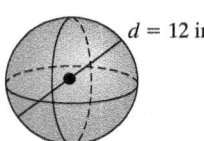
$d = 12$ in.

15.

9 cm
5 cm

16.
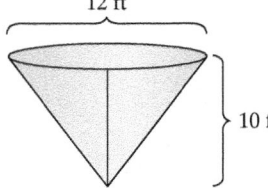
12 ft
10 ft

17.

12 ft

18.
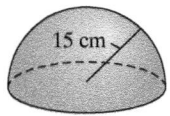
15 cm

For Exercises 19–26, use 3.14 for π. Round each value to the nearest whole unit.

19. The diameter of a volleyball is 8.2 in. Find the volume.

20. The diameter of a basketball is 9 in. Find the volume.

21. Find the volume of the sand pile.

12 ft

10 ft

22. In decorating cakes, many people use an icing bag that has the shape of a cone. Find the volume of the icing bag.

12 cm

20 cm

23. Find the volume of water (in cubic feet) that the pipe can hold.

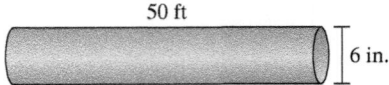

50 ft

6 in.

24. Find the volume of the wastebasket that has the shape of a cylinder with the height of 3 ft and diameter of 2 ft.

25. Sam bought an aboveground circular swimming pool with diameter 27 ft and height 54 in.

   a. Approximate the volume of the pool in cubic feet using 3.14 for π.

   b. How many gallons of water will it take to fill the pool? (*Hint:* 1 gal $\approx$ 0.1337 ft^3.)

3 ft

2 ft

26. Richard needs 3 in. of topsoil for his vegetable garden that is in the shape of a rectangle, 15 ft by 20 ft.

   a. Find the amount of topsoil needed in cubic feet.

   b. If topsoil can be purchased in bags containing 2 ft^3, how many bags must Richard purchase?

Objective 2: Surface Area

For Exercises 27–34, determine the surface area to the nearest tenth of a unit. Use 3.14 for π when necessary. **(See Examples 5–6.)**

27. Determine the amount of cardboard for the cereal box.

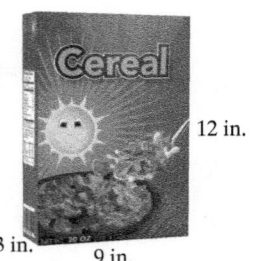

12 in.

3 in.

9 in.

28. Determine the amount of cardboard for the box of macaroni.

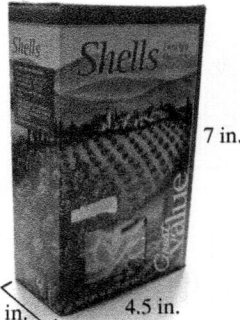

7 in.

1.75 in.

4.5 in.

29. Determine the surface area for the sugar cube.

1.5 cm

1.5 cm

1.5 cm

30. Determine the surface area of the Sudoku cube.

2.3 in.

2.3 in.

2.3 in.

31. Determine the amount of cardboard for the container of oatmeal.

2 in.

7 in.

32. Determine the amount of steel needed for the can of tomato paste.

1.2 in.

3.2 in.

33. Determine the surface area of the volleyball.

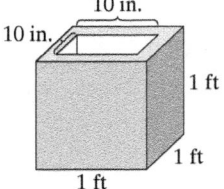

$r = 4.1$ in.

34. Determine the surface area of the golf ball.

4.2 cm

For Exercises 35–42, determine the surface area of the object described. Use 3.14 for π when necessary. (See Examples 5–6.)

35. A rectangular solid with dimensions 12 ft by 14 ft by 3 ft

36. A rectangular solid with dimensions 8 m by 7 m by 5 m

37. A cube with each side 4 cm long

38. A cube with each side 10 yd long

39. A cylinder with radius 9 in. and height 15 in.

40. A cylinder with radius 90 mm and height 75 mm

41. A sphere with radius 10 mm

42. A sphere with radius 9 m

Expanding Your Skills

For Exercises 43–46, find the volume of the shaded region. Use 3.14 for π if necessary.

43. The height of the interior portion is 1 ft.

10 in.
10 in.
1 ft
1 ft
1 ft
1 ft

44. The height of the interior portion is 1 ft.

2.75 ft
9 in.
1 ft
1 ft
3 ft

45.

$r = 1$ in.
5 in.
5 in.
5 in.

46.

1.5 in.
6 in.
2 in.
4.5 in.

47. A machine part is in the shape of a cylinder with a hole drilled through the center. Find the volume of the machine part.

20 mm

2 mm
(inner diameter)

6 mm
(outer diameter)

48. To insulate pipes, a cylinder of Styrofoam has a hole drilled through it to fit around a pipe. What is the volume of this piece of insulation?

4 in.

30 in.

6 in.

49. A silo is in the shape of a cylinder with a hemisphere on the top. Find the volume.

20 ft

6 ft

50. An ice cream cone is in the shape of a cone with a sphere on top. Assuming that ice cream is packed inside the cone, find the volume of the ice cream.

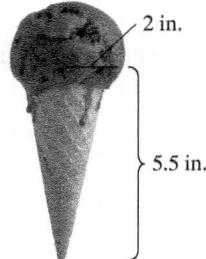

2 in.

5.5 in.

The volume formulas for right circular cylinders and right circular cones are the same for slanted cylinders and cones. For Exercises 51–54, find the volume. Use 3.14 for π.

51.

$h = 9$ in.

$r = 3$ in.

52.

$h = 12$ mm

$r = 5$ mm

53.

$h = 40$ cm

$r = 20$ cm

54.

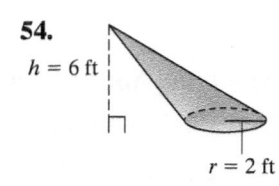

$h = 6$ ft

$r = 2$ ft

A square-based pyramid is a solid figure with a square base and triangular faces that meet at a common point called the apex. The formula for the volume is below.

$$V = \frac{1}{3} s^2 h$$

h

s

The length of the sides of the square base is s, and h is the perpendicular height from the apex to the base.

For Exercises 55–56, determine the volume of the pyramid.

55.

12 ft

10 ft

56.

6 m

$4\frac{1}{2}$ m

Group Activity

Remodeling the Classroom

Materials: A tape measure for measuring the size of the classroom.
Advertisements online or from the newspaper for carpet and paint.

Estimated time: 30 minutes

Group Size: 3–4

In this activity, your group will determine the cost for updating your classroom with new paint and new carpet.

1. Measure and record the dimensions of the room and also the height of the walls. You may want to sketch the floor and walls and then label their dimensions on the figure.

2. Calculate and record the area of the floor.

3. Calculate and record the total area of the walls. Subtract any area taken up by doors, windows, and chalkboards.

4. Look through advertisements for carpet that would be suitable for your classroom. You may have to look online for a better choice. Choose a carpet.

5. Calculate how much carpet is needed based on your measurements. To do this, take the area of the floor found in step 2 and add 10% of that figure to allow for waste.

6. Determine the cost to carpet the classroom. Do not forget to include carpet padding and labor to install the carpet. You may have to look online to find prices for padding and installation if they are not included in the price. Also include sales tax for your area.

7. Look through advertisements for paint that would be suitable for your classroom. You may have to look online for a better choice. Choose a paint.

8. Calculate the number of gallons of paint needed for your classroom. You may assume that 1 gal of paint will cover 400 ft^2. Calculate the cost of paint for the classroom. Include sales tax, but do not include labor costs for painting. You will do the painting yourself!

9. Calculate the total cost for carpeting and painting the classroom.

Chapter 7   Summary

Section 7.1   U.S. Customary Units of Measurement

Key Concepts

In the following lists, we give several units of measure common to the **U.S. Customary System**.

Length

$1 \text{ ft} = 12 \text{ in.}$ $1 \text{ in.} = \frac{1}{12} \text{ ft}$

$1 \text{ yd} = 3 \text{ ft}$ $1 \text{ ft} = \frac{1}{3} \text{ yd}$

$1 \text{ mi} = 5280 \text{ ft}$ $1 \text{ ft} = \frac{1}{5280} \text{ mi}$

$1 \text{ mi} = 1760 \text{ yd}$ $1 \text{ yd} = \frac{1}{1760} \text{ mi}$

Time

$1 \text{ year} = 365 \text{ days}$

$1 \text{ week} = 7 \text{ days}$

$1 \text{ day} = 24 \text{ hours (hr)}$

$1 \text{ hour (hr)} = 60 \text{ minutes (min)}$

$1 \text{ minute (min)} = 60 \text{ seconds (sec)}$

Weight

$1 \text{ pound (lb)} = 16 \text{ ounces (oz)}$

$1 \text{ ton} = 2000 \text{ pounds (lb)}$

Capacity

$1 \text{ cup (c)} = 8 \text{ fluid ounces (fl oz)}$

$1 \text{ pint (pt)} = 2 \text{ cups (c)}$

$1 \text{ quart (qt)} = 2 \text{ pints (pt)}$

$1 \text{ gallon (gal)} = 4 \text{ quarts (qt)}$

Examples

Example 1

To convert 8 yd to feet, multiply by the conversion factor.

$$8 \text{ yd} \cdot \frac{3 \text{ ft}}{1 \text{ yd}} = \frac{8 \text{ yd}}{1} \cdot \frac{3 \text{ ft}}{1 \text{ yd}} = 24 \text{ ft}$$

Example 2

To add 3 ft 9 in. + 2 ft 10 in., add like terms.

$$
\begin{array}{r}
3 \text{ ft} + 9 \text{ in.} \\
+ 2 \text{ ft} + 10 \text{ in.} \\
\hline
5 \text{ ft} + 19 \text{ in.} = 5 \text{ ft} + 1 \text{ ft} + 7 \text{ in.}
\end{array}
$$

$$= 6 \text{ ft } 7 \text{ in.}$$

Example 3

Convert. $200 \text{ min} = \underline{} \text{ hr}$

$$200 \text{ min} \cdot \frac{1 \text{ hr}}{60 \text{ min}} = \frac{200}{60} \text{ hr}$$

$$= \frac{10}{3} \text{ hr or } 3\frac{1}{3} \text{ hr}$$

Example 4

Convert. $6 \text{ lb} = \underline{} \text{ oz}$

$$6 \text{ lb} \cdot \frac{16 \text{ oz}}{1 \text{ lb}} = 96 \text{ oz}$$

Example 5

Convert. $40 \text{ c} = \underline{} \text{ gal}$

$$40 \text{ c} \cdot \frac{1 \text{ pt}}{2 \text{ c}} \cdot \frac{1 \text{ qt}}{2 \text{ pt}} \cdot \frac{1 \text{ gal}}{4 \text{ qt}}$$

$$= \frac{40 \text{ c}}{1} \cdot \frac{1 \text{ pt}}{2 \text{ c}} \cdot \frac{1 \text{ qt}}{2 \text{ pt}} \cdot \frac{1 \text{ gal}}{4 \text{ qt}}$$

$$= \frac{40}{16} \text{ gal} = \frac{5}{2} \text{ gal or } 2\frac{1}{2} \text{ gal}$$

Section 7.2   Metric Units of Measurement

Key Concepts

The **metric system** also offers units for measuring length, mass, and capacity. The base units are the **meter** for length, the **gram** for mass, and the **liter** for capacity. Other units of length, mass, and capacity in the metric system are powers of 10 of the base unit.

Metric units of length and their equivalents are given.

1 kilometer (km) = 1000 m

1 hectometer (hm) = 100 m

1 dekameter (dam) = 10 m

1 meter (m) = 1 m

1 decimeter (dm) = 0.1 m $\left(\frac{1}{10}\text{ m}\right)$

1 centimeter (cm) = 0.01 m $\left(\frac{1}{100}\text{ m}\right)$

1 millimeter (mm) = 0.001 m $\left(\frac{1}{1000}\text{ m}\right)$

The metric unit conversions for mass are given in **grams**.

1 kilogram (kg) = 1000 g

1 hectogram (hg) = 100 g

1 dekagram (dag) = 10 g

1 gram (g) = 1 g

1 decigram (dg) = 0.1 g $\left(\frac{1}{10}\text{ g}\right)$

1 centigram (cg) = 0.01 g $\left(\frac{1}{100}\text{ g}\right)$

1 milligram (mg) = 0.001 g $\left(\frac{1}{1000}\text{ g}\right)$

The metric unit conversions for capacity are given in **liters**.

1 kiloliter (kL) = 1000 L

1 hectoliter (hL) = 100 L

1 dekaliter (daL) = 10 L

1 liter (L) = 1 L

1 deciliter (dL) = 0.1 L $\left(\frac{1}{10}\text{ L}\right)$

1 centiliter (cL) = 0.01 L $\left(\frac{1}{100}\text{ L}\right)$

1 milliliter (mL) = 0.001 L $\left(\frac{1}{1000}\text{ L}\right)$

Note that 1 mL = 1 cc.

Example

Example 1

To convert 2 km to meters, we can use a unit ratio:

$$2\text{ km} = \frac{2\cancel{\text{ km}}}{1}\cdot\frac{1000\text{ m}}{1\cancel{\text{ km}}} \quad \longleftarrow \text{ new unit}$$
$$\phantom{2\text{ km} = } \longleftarrow \text{ original unit}$$

$$= 2000\text{ m}$$

Or we can use the prefix line.

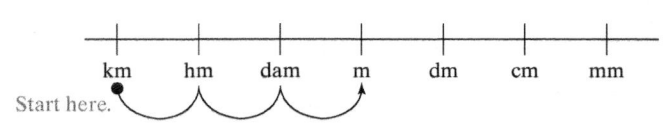

2 km = 2.000 km = 2000 m

Example 2

To convert 0.962 kg to grams, we can use a unit ratio:

$$0.962\text{ kg} = \frac{0.962\cancel{\text{ kg}}}{1}\cdot\frac{1000\text{ g}}{1\cancel{\text{ kg}}} \quad \longleftarrow \text{ new unit}$$
$$\phantom{0.962\text{ kg} = } \longleftarrow \text{ original unit}$$

$$= 962\text{ g}$$

Or we can use the prefix line.

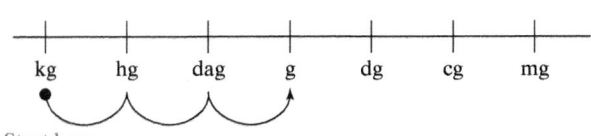

0.962 kg = 0.962 kg = 962 g

Example 3

To convert 59,000 cL to kL, we can use unit ratios:

$$59{,}000\text{ cL} = \frac{59{,}000\cancel{\text{ cL}}}{1}\cdot\frac{1\cancel{\text{ L}}}{100\cancel{\text{ cL}}}\cdot\frac{1\text{ kL}}{1000\cancel{\text{ L}}}$$

$$= 0.59\text{ kL}$$

Or we can use the prefix line.

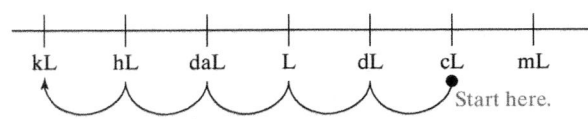

59,000 cL = 59,000 cL = 0.59 kL

Section 7.3   Converting Between U.S. Customary and Metric Units

Key Concepts

The common conversions between the U.S. Customary and metric systems are given.

Length

1 in. = 2.54 cm

1 ft ≈ 0.305 m

1 yd ≈ 0.914 m

1 mi ≈ 1.61 km

Weight/Mass (on Earth)

1 lb ≈ 0.45 kg

1 oz ≈ 28 g

Capacity

1 qt ≈ 0.95 L

1 fl oz ≈ 30 mL = 30 cc

To convert U.S. Customary units to metric or metric units to U.S. Customary units, use unit ratios.

The U.S. Customary System uses the **Fahrenheit** scale (°F) to measure temperature. The metric system uses the **Celsius** scale (°C). The conversions are given.

To convert from °C to °F: $F = \dfrac{9}{5}C + 32$

To convert from °F to °C: $C = \dfrac{5}{9}(F - 32)$

Examples

Example 1

Convert 1200 yd to meters by using a unit ratio.

$$1200 \text{ yd} \approx \frac{1200 \text{ yd}}{1} \cdot \frac{0.914 \text{ m}}{1 \text{ yd}} = 1096.8 \text{ m}$$

Example 2

To convert 900 cc to fluid ounces, recall that 1 cc = 1 mL. Therefore, 900 cc = 900 mL. Then use a unit ratio to convert to fluid ounces.

$$900 \text{ mL} \approx \frac{900 \text{ mL}}{1} \cdot \frac{1 \text{ fl oz}}{30 \text{ mL}} = 30 \text{ fl oz}$$

Example 3

The average January temperature in Havana, Cuba, is 21°C. The average January temperature in Johannesburg, South Africa, is 69°F. Which temperature is warmer?

Convert 21°C to degrees Fahrenheit:

$$F = \frac{9}{5}C + 32$$

$$= \frac{9}{5}(21) + 32$$

$$= 37.8 + 32 = 69.8$$

The value 21°C = 69.8°F, which is 0.8 degree warmer than the temperature in Johannesburg.

Section 7.4   Medical Applications Involving Measurement

Key Concepts

In medical applications, the **microgram** is often used.

1000 mcg = 1 mg

1,000,000 mcg = 1 g

Examples

Example 1

Convert.

575 mcg = _____ mg

$$575 \text{ mcg} = \frac{575 \text{ mcg}}{1} \cdot \frac{1 \text{ mg}}{1000 \text{ mcg}} = 0.575 \text{ mg}$$

The metric system is used in many applications in medicine.

Example 2

A doctor prescribes 25 mcg of a given drug per kilogram of body mass for a patient. If the patient's mass is 80 kg, determine the total amount of drug that the patient will get.

$$\text{Total amount} = \left(\frac{25 \text{ mcg}}{1 \text{ kg}}\right) \cdot (80 \text{ kg})$$

$$= 2000 \text{ mcg or } 2 \text{ mg}$$

Section 7.5   Lines and Angles

Key Concepts

An **angle** is a geometric figure formed by two rays that share a common endpoint. The common endpoint is called the **vertex** of the angle.

An angle is **acute** if its measure is between 0° and 90°. An angle is **obtuse** if its measure is between 90° and 180°.

Two angles are said to be **complementary** if the sum of their measures is 90°. Two angles are said to be **supplementary** if the sum of their measures is 180°.

Given two intersecting lines, **vertical angles** are angles that appear on opposite sides of the vertex.

When two parallel lines are crossed by another line eight angles are formed.

Examples

Example 1

$\angle DEF$

Example 2

Acute angle   Obtuse angle

Example 3

The complement of a 32° angle is a 58° angle. The supplement of a 32° angle is a 148° angle.

Example 4

Intersecting lines:

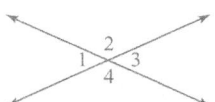

$\angle 1$ and $\angle 3$ are vertical angles and are congruent. Also, $\angle 2$ and $\angle 4$ are vertical angles and are congruent.

Example 5

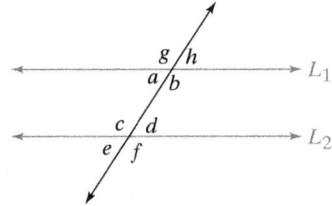

$m(\angle a) = m(\angle d)$ because they are **alternate interior angles**.
$m(\angle e) = m(\angle h)$ because they are **alternate exterior angles**.
$m(\angle c) = m(\angle g)$ because they are **corresponding angles**.

| Section 7.6 | **Triangles, the Pythagorean Theorem, and Similar Triangles** |

Key Concepts

The sum of the measures of the angles of any triangle is 180°.

An **acute triangle** is a triangle in which all three angles are acute.

A **right triangle** is a triangle in which one angle is a right angle.

An **obtuse triangle** is a triangle in which one angle is obtuse.

An **equilateral triangle** is a triangle in which all three sides (and all three angles) are equal in measure.

An **isosceles triangle** is a triangle in which two sides are equal in length (the angles opposite the equal sides are also equal in measure).

A **scalene triangle** is a triangle in which no sides (or angles) are equal in measure.

Pythagorean Theorem

The sum of the squares of the **legs of a right triangle** equals the square of the **hypotenuse**.

 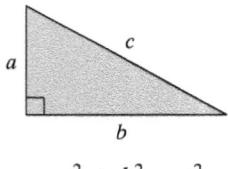

$$a^2 + b^2 = c^2$$

Similar Triangles

If two triangles are **similar triangles,** then the lengths of the corresponding sides are proportional.

Examples

Example 1

$22° + 120° + 38° = 180°$

Example 2

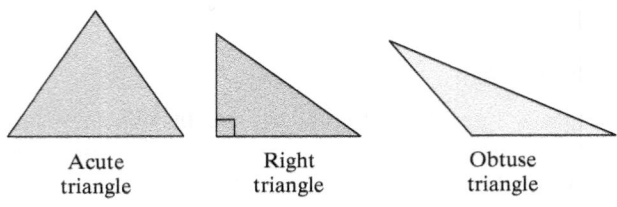

Acute triangle   Right triangle   Obtuse triangle

Example 3

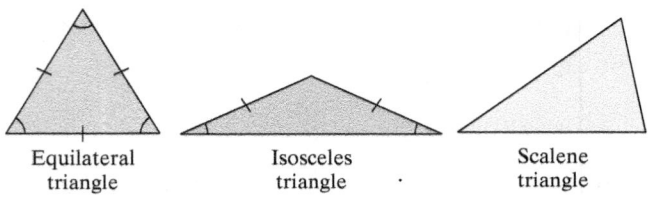

Equilateral triangle   Isosceles triangle   Scalene triangle

Example 4

To find the length of the hypotenuse, solve for c.

$$6^2 + 8^2 = c^2$$
$$36 + 64 = c^2$$
$$100 = c^2$$
$$\sqrt{100} = c$$
$$10 = c$$

c is the positive number that when squared equals 100.

The length of the hypotenuse is 10 cm.

Example 5

The triangles are similar. Solve for x.

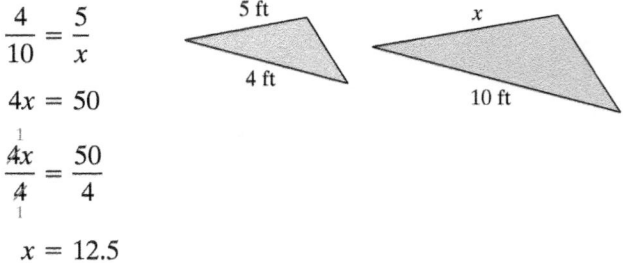

$$\frac{4}{10} = \frac{5}{x}$$
$$4x = 50$$
$$\frac{4x}{4} = \frac{50}{4}$$
$$x = 12.5$$

The length of the side x is 12.5 ft.

Section 7.7   Perimeter, Circumference, and Area

Key Concepts

A four-sided **polygon** is called a **quadrilateral**.

A **parallelogram** is a quadrilateral with opposite sides parallel.

A **rectangle** is a parallelogram with four right angles.

A **square** is a rectangle with sides equal in length.

A **rhombus** is a parallelogram with sides equal in length.

A **trapezoid** is a quadrilateral with one pair of parallel sides.

Perimeter is the distance around a figure.

Perimeter of a triangle: $P = a + b + c$

Perimeter of a square: $P = 4s$

Perimeter of a rectangle: $P = 2l + 2w$

Circumference of a circle: $C = 2\pi r$

Area is the number of square units that can be enclosed by a figure.

Area of a rectangle: $A = lw$

Area of a square: $A = s^2$

Area of a parallelogram: $A = bh$

Area of a triangle: $A = \frac{1}{2}bh$

Area of a trapezoid: $A = \frac{1}{2}(a + b)h$

Area of a circle: $A = \pi r^2$

Examples

Example 1

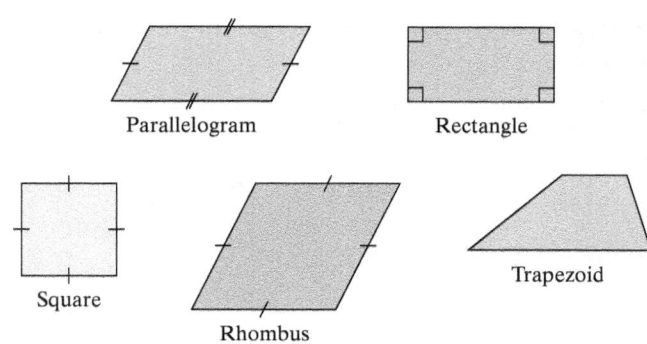

Parallelogram   Rectangle

Square   Rhombus   Trapezoid

Example 2

Determine the perimeter.

First convert the length and width to the same units of measurement.

80 mm

22 cm

For the width: 80 mm = 8 cm.

$P = 2l + 2w$ Perimeter formula (rectangle)

$P = 2(22 \text{ cm}) + 2(8 \text{ cm})$

$\quad = 44 \text{ cm} + 16 \text{ cm}$

$\quad = 60 \text{ cm}$ The perimeter is 60 cm.

Example 3

Determine the area.

5.5 m

4 m

6 m

$A = \frac{1}{2}(a + b)h$ Area of a trapezoid

$A = \frac{1}{2}(6 \text{ m} + 5.5 \text{ m})(4 \text{ m})$

$\quad = \frac{1}{2}(11.5 \text{ m})(4 \text{ m})$

$\quad = 23 \text{ m}^2$

The area is 23 m².

Section 7.8   Volume and Surface Area

Key Concepts

Volume (V) is another word for capacity.

Surface area (SA) is the sum of all the areas of a solid figure.

Formulas for selected solids are given.

Rectangular solid

$V = lwh$

$SA = 2lh + 2lw + 2hw$

Cube

$V = s^3$

$SA = 6s^2$

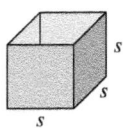

Right circular cylinder

$V = \pi r^2 h$

$SA = 2\pi rh + 2\pi r^2$

Right circular cone

$V = \dfrac{1}{3}\pi r^2 h$

Sphere

$V = \dfrac{4}{3}\pi r^3$

$SA = 4\pi r^2$

Examples

Example 1

Find the volume of the cone.

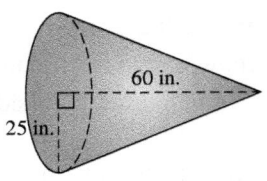

60 in.

25 in.

$V = \dfrac{1}{3}\pi r^2 h$

$\approx \dfrac{1}{3}(3.14)(25 \text{ in.})^2(60 \text{ in.})$

$= 39{,}250 \text{ in.}^3$

The volume is approximately 39,250 in.^{3}

Example 2

Determine the surface area.

$h = 4$ in.

$w = 3$ in.

$l = 10$ in.

$SA = 2lh + 2lw + 2hw$

$\quad = 2(10 \text{ in.})(4 \text{ in.}) + 2(10 \text{ in.})(3 \text{ in.}) + 2(4 \text{ in.})(3 \text{ in.})$

$\quad = 80 \text{ in.}^2 + 60 \text{ in.}^2 + 24 \text{ in.}^2$

$\quad = 164 \text{ in.}^2$

Chapter 7   Review Exercises

Section 7.1

For Exercises 1–6, convert the units of length.

1. 48 in. = _____ ft

2. $3\frac{1}{4}$ ft = _____ in.

3. 2 mi = _____ yd

4. 7040 ft = _____ mi

5. $\frac{1}{2}$ mi = _____ ft

6. 2 yd = _____ in.

For Exercises 7–10, perform the indicated operations.

7. 3 ft 9 in. + 5 ft 6 in.

8. 4′11″ + 1′5″

9. 5′3″ − 2′5″

10. 12 ft 7 in. − 8 ft 10 in.

11. Find the perimeter in feet.

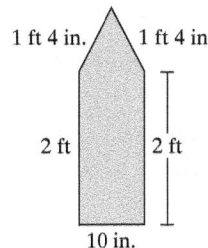

1 ft 4 in. 1 ft 4 in.

2 ft   2 ft

10 in.

12. A roll of wire contains 50 yd of wire. If Ivan uses 48 ft, how much wire is left?

For Exercises 13–22, convert the units of time, weight, and capacity.

13. 72 hr = _____ days

14. 6 min = _____ sec

15. 5 lb = _____ oz

16. 1 wk = _____ hr

17. 12 fl oz = _____ c

18. 0.25 ton = _____ lb

19. 3500 lb = _____ tons

20. 2 gal = _____ pt

21. 12 oz = _____ lb

22. 16 qt = _____ gal

23. A runner finished a race with a time of 2:24:30. Convert the time to minutes.

24. Margaret Johansson gave birth to triplets who weighed 3 lb 10 oz, 4 lb 2 oz, and 4 lb 1 oz. What was the total weight of the triplets?

Section 7.2

For Exercises 25–26, select the most reasonable measurement.

25. A pencil is _____ long.

   a. 16 mm   **b.** 16 cm

   c. 16 m   **d.** 16 km

26. The distance between Houston and Dallas is _____ .

   a. 362 mm   **b.** 362 cm

   c. 362 m   **d.** 362 km

For Exercises 27–32, convert the metric units of length.

27. 52 cm = _____ mm

28. 93 m = _____ km

29. 34 dm = _____ m

30. 2.1 m = _____ dam

31. 4 cm = _____ m

32. 1.2 m = _____ mm

For Exercises 33–36, convert the metric units of mass.

33. 6.1 g = _____ cg

34. 420 g = _____ kg

35. 3212 mg = _____ g

36. 0.7 hg = _____ g

For Exercises 37–40, convert the metric units of capacity.

37. 830 cL = _____ L

38. 124 mL = _____ cc

39. 225 cc = _____ cL

40. 0.49 kL = _____ L

41. The dimensions of a dining room table are 2 m by 125 cm. Convert the units to meters and find the perimeter and area of the tabletop.

42. A bottle of apple juice contains 1.2 L of juice. If a glass holds 24 cL, how many glasses can be filled from this bottle?

43. An adult has a mass of 68 kg. A baby has a mass of 3200 g. What is the difference in their masses, in kilograms?

44. From a wooden board 2 m long, Jesse needs to cut 3 pieces that are each 75 cm long. Is the 2-m length of board long enough for the 3 pieces?

Section 7.3

For Exercises 45–54, refer to page 476. Convert the units of length, capacity, mass, and weight. Round to the nearest hundredth, if necessary.

45. 6.2 in. ≈ _____ cm

46. 75 mL ≈ _____ fl oz

47. 140 g ≈ _____ oz

48. 5 L ≈ _____ qt

49. 3.4 ft ≈ _____ m

50. 100 lb ≈ _____ kg

51. 120 km ≈ _____ mi

52. 6 qt ≈ _____ L

53. 1.5 fl oz ≈ _____ cc

54. 12.5 tons ≈ _____ kg

55. The height of a computer desk is 30 in. The height of the chair is 38 cm. What is the difference in height between the desk and chair, in centimeters?

56. A bag of snack crackers contains 7.2 oz. If one serving is 30 g, approximately how many servings are in one bag?

57. The Boston Marathon is 42.195 km long. Convert this distance to miles. Round to the tenths place.

58. Write the formula to convert degrees Fahrenheit to degrees Celsius.

59. When roasting a turkey, the meat thermometer should register between 180°F and 185°F to indicate that the turkey is done. Convert these temperatures to degrees Celsius. Round to the nearest tenth, if necessary.

60. Write the formula to convert degrees Celsius to degrees Fahrenheit.

61. The average October temperature for Toronto, Ontario, Canada, is 8°C. Convert this temperature to degrees Fahrenheit.

Section 7.4

For Exercises 62–65, convert the metric units.

62. 0.45 mg = _____ mcg

63. 1.5 mg = _____ mcg

64. 400 mcg = _____ mg

65. 5000 mcg = _____ cg

66. A nasal spray delivers 2.5 mg of active ingredient per milliliter of solution. Determine the amount of active ingredient per cc.

67. A physician prescribes a drug based on a patient's mass. The dosage is given as 0.04 mg of the drug per kilogram of the patient's mass.

    a. How much would the physician prescribe for an 80-kg patient?

    b. If the dosage was to be given twice a day, how much of the drug would the patient take in a week?

68. A prescription for cough syrup indicates that 30 mL should be taken twice a day for 7 days. What is the total amount, in liters, of cough syrup to be taken?

69. A standard hypodermic syringe holds 3 cc of fluid. If a nurse uses 1.8 mL of the fluid, how much is left in the syringe?

70. A medication comes in 250-mg capsules. If Clayton took 3 capsules a day for 10 days, how many grams of the medication did he take?

Section 7.5

For Exercises 71–74, match the symbol with a description.

71. $\overleftrightarrow{AB}$ **a.** Ray AB

72. $\overrightarrow{AB}$ **b.** Line segment AB

73. $\overrightarrow{BA}$ **c.** Ray BA

74. $\overline{AB}$ **d.** Line AB

75. Describe the measure of an acute angle.

76. Describe the measure of an obtuse angle.

77. Describe the measure of a right angle.

78. Let $m(\angle X) = 33°$.

   a. Find the complement of $\angle X$.

   b. Find the supplement of $\angle X$.

79. Let $m(\angle T) = 20°$.

   a. Find the complement of $\angle T$.

   b. Find the supplement of $\angle T$.

For Exercises 80–84, refer to the figure. Find the measures of the angles.

80. $m(\angle a)$

81. $m(\angle b)$

82. $m(\angle c)$

83. $m(\angle d)$

84. $m(\angle e)$

Section 7.6

For Exercises 85–86, find the measures of the angles x and y.

85.

86.

For Exercises 87–88, describe the characteristics of each type of triangle.

87. Equilateral triangle

88. Isosceles triangle

For Exercises 89–90, simplify the square roots.

89. $\sqrt{25}$ **90.** $\sqrt{49}$

For Exercises 91–92, find the length of the unknown side.

91.

92.

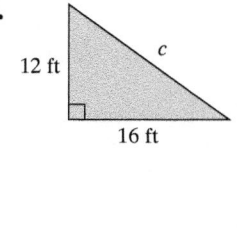

93. Kayla is flying a kite. At one point the kite is 5 m from Kayla horizontally and 12 m above her (see figure). How much string is extended? (Assume there is no slack.)

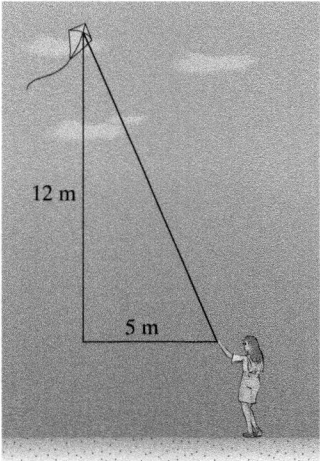

94. Consider the similar triangles shown here. Find the values of x and y.

Section 7.7

95. Find the perimeter of the figure.

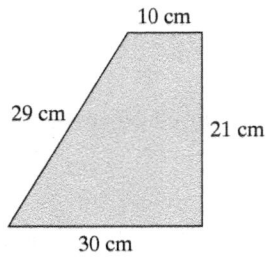

96. How much fencing is required to put up a chain link fence around a 120-yd by 80-yd playground?

97. The perimeter of a square is 62 ft. What is the length of each side?

98. Find the circumference of a circle with a 20-cm diameter. Use 3.14 for π.

99. Find the area of the triangle.

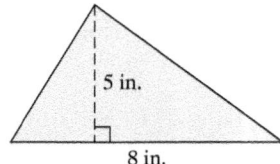

100. Fatima has a Persian rug 8.5 ft by 6 ft. What is the area?

101. A lot is 150 ft by 80 ft. Within the lot, there is a 12-ft easement along all edges. An easement is the portion of the lot on which nothing may be built. What is the area of the portion that may be used for building?

102. Find the area.

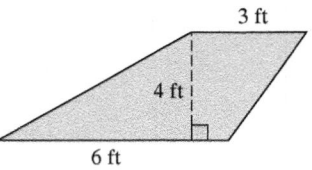

103. Find the area of a circle with a 20-cm diameter. Use 3.14 for π.

104. Find the area.

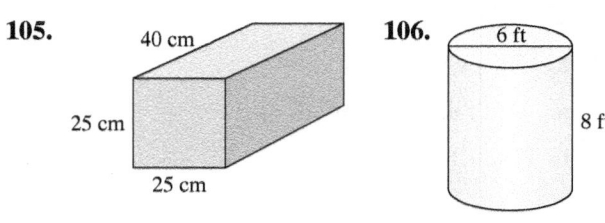

Section 7.8

For Exercises 105–108, find the volume and surface area. Use 3.14 for π.

105. **106.**

107. **108.**

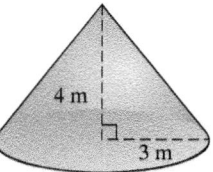

109. Find the volume. Use 3.14 for π.

110. Find the volume of a can of paint if the can is a cylinder with radius 6.5 in. and height 7.5 in. Round to the nearest whole unit.

111. Find the volume of a ball if the diameter of the ball is approximately 6 in. Round to the nearest whole unit.

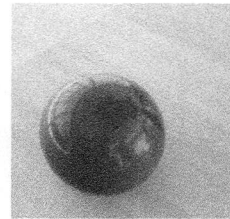

112. A microwave oven is a rectangular solid with dimensions 1 ft by 1 ft 9 in. by 1 ft 4 in. Find the volume in cubic feet.

For Exercises 113–114, find the volume of the shaded region. Use 3.14 for π if necessary. Round to the nearest whole unit.

113.

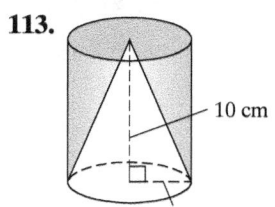

10 cm

4 cm

114. 15 in.

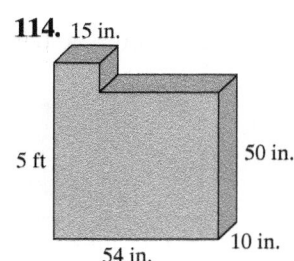

5 ft

50 in.

54 in.

10 in.

Chapter 7   Test

1. Identify the units that apply to measuring length. Circle all that apply.

   a. Pound   **b.** Ounce   **c.** Meter

   d. Mile   **e.** Gram   **f.** Pint

   g. Feet   **h.** Liter   **i.** Fluid ounce

   j. Kilometer

2. Identify the units that apply to measuring capacity. Circle all that apply.

   a. Pound   **b.** Ounce   **c.** Meter

   d. Mile   **e.** Gram   **f.** Pint

   g. Foot   **h.** Liter   **i.** Fluid ounce

   j. Kilometer

3. Identify the units that apply to measuring mass or weight. Circle all that apply.

   a. Pound   **b.** Ounce   **c.** Meter

   d. Mile   **e.** Gram   **f.** Pint

   g. Foot   **h.** Liter   **i.** Fluid ounce

   j. Kilometer

4. A backyard needs 25 ft of fencing. How many yards is this?

5. It's estimated that an adult *Tyrannosaurus Rex* weighed approximately 11,000 lb. How many tons is this?

6. Two exits on the highway are 52,800 ft apart. How many miles is this?

7. A recipe for brownies calls for $\frac{3}{4}$ c of milk and 4 oz of water. What is the total amount of liquid in ounces?

8. A television show has 1200 sec of commercials. How many minutes is this?

9. Find the perimeter of the rectangle in feet.

30"

2'

2'

30"

10. A decorator wraps a gift, using two pieces of ribbon. One is 1′10″ and the other is 2′4″. Find the total length of ribbon used.

11. When Stephen was born, he weighed 8 lb 1 oz. When he left the hospital, he weighed 7 lb 10 oz. How much weight did he lose after he was born?

12. A decorative pillow requires 3 ft 11 in. of fringe around the perimeter of the pillow. If five pillows are produced, how much fringe is required?

13. Josh ran a race and finished with the time of 1:15:15. Convert this time to minutes.

14. Approximate the width of the nut in centimeters and millimeters.

15. Select the most reasonable measurement for the length of a living room.

   a. 5 mm   **b.** 5 cm   **c.** 5 m   **d.** 5 km

16. The length of the Mackinac Bridge in Michigan is 1158 m. What is this length in kilometers?

17. A tablespoon (1 T) contains 0.015 L. How many milliliters is this?

18. a. What does the abbreviation cc stand for?

   b. Convert 235 mL to cubic centimeters.

   c. Convert 1 L to cubic centimeters.

19. A can of diced tomatoes is 411 g. Convert 411 g to centigrams.

20. A box of crackers is 210 g. If a serving of crackers is 30,000 mg, how many servings are in the box?

For Exercises 21–26, refer to Table 7-5 on page 476.

21. A bottle of Sprite contains 2 L. What is the capacity in quarts? Round to the nearest tenth.

22. Usain Bolt is one of the premier sprinters in track and field. His best race is the 100-m. How many yards is this? Round to the nearest yard.

23. The distance between two exits on a highway is 4.5 km. How far is this in miles? Round to the nearest tenth.

24. Breckenridge, Colorado, is 9603 ft above sea level. What is this height in meters? Round to the nearest meter.

25. A snowy egret stands about 20 in. tall and has a 38-in. wingspan. Convert both values to centimeters.

26. The mass of a laptop computer is 5000 g. What is the weight in pounds? Round to the nearest pound.

27. The oven temperature needed to bake cookies is 375°F. What is this temperature in degrees Celsius? Round to the nearest tenth.

28. The average January temperature in Albuquerque, New Mexico, is 2°C. Convert this temperature to degrees Fahrenheit.

29. A patient is supposed to get 0.1 mg of a drug for every kilogram of body mass, four times a day. How much of the drug would a 70-kg woman get each day?

30. Gus, the cat, had an overactive thyroid gland. The vet prescribed 0.125 mg of Methimazole every 12 hr. How many micrograms is this per week?

31. Which is a correct representation of the line shown?

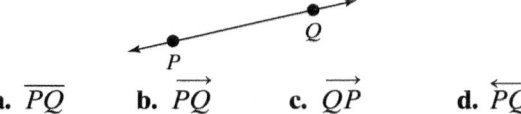

   a. $\overline{PQ}$ **b.** $\overrightarrow{PQ}$ **c.** $\overrightarrow{QP}$ **d.** $\overleftrightarrow{PQ}$

32. Which is a correct representation of the ray pictured?

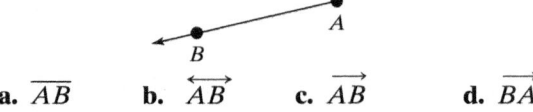

   a. $\overline{AB}$ **b.** $\overleftrightarrow{AB}$ **c.** $\overrightarrow{AB}$ **d.** $\overrightarrow{BA}$

33. What is the complement of a 16° angle?

34. What is the supplement of a 147° angle?

35. Find the missing angle.

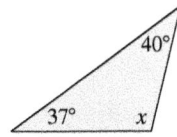

36. Consider the similar triangles shown here. Find the values of *a* and *b*.

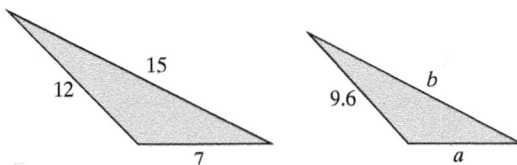

37. Determine the perimeter and area.

38. A farmer uses a rotating sprinkler to water his crops. If the spray of water extends 150 ft, find the area of one such region. Use 3.14 for π.

39. Find the area of the shaded region.

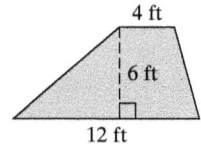

40. Determine the measure of angles *x* and *y*. Assume that line 1 is parallel to line 2.

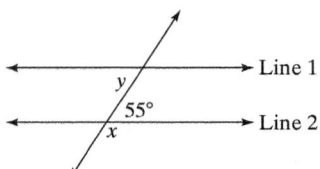

41. Given that the lengths of $\overline{AB}$ and $\overline{BC}$ are equal, what are the measures of $\angle A$ and $\angle C$?

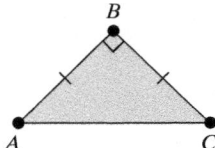

42. From the figure, determine $m(\angle S)$.

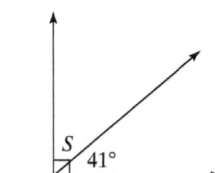

43. What is the measure of $\angle A$?

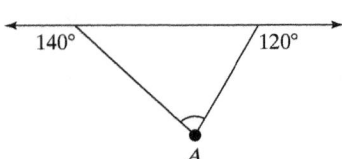

44. A firefighter places a 13-ft ladder against a wall of a burning building. If the bottom of the ladder is 5 ft from the base of the building, how far up the building will the ladder reach?

45. José is a landscaping artist and wants to make a walkway through a rectangular garden, as shown. What is the length of the walkway?

46. Jayne wants to put up a wallpaper border for the perimeter of a 12-ft by 15-ft room. The border comes in 6-yd rolls. How many rolls would be needed?

47. Find the area of the ceiling fan blade shown in the figure.

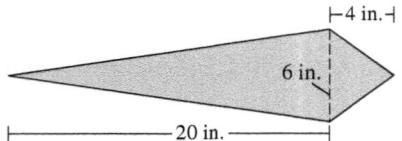

48. Find the volume of the child's wading pool shown in the figure. Use 3.14 for π and round the answer to the nearest whole unit.

49. Find the volume of the briefcase.

For Exercises 50–51, determine the volume. Use 3.14 for π.

50. **51.**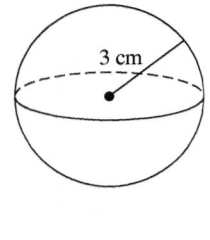

52. Determine the surface area for the sphere in Exercise 51.

53. Determine the surface area for the rectangular briefcase in Exercise 49, excluding the handle.

Chapters 1–7 Cumulative Review Exercises

For Exercises 1–4, perform the indicated operations with mixed numbers.

1. $6\frac{2}{3} + 2\frac{5}{6}$ **2.** $6\frac{2}{3} \cdot 2\frac{5}{6}$

3. $6\frac{2}{3} \div 2\frac{5}{6}$ **4.** $6\frac{2}{3} - 2\frac{5}{6}$

For Exercises 5–7, simplify the expression.

5. $-2 - 36 \div (5 - 8)^2$

6. -6^2

7. $-7(a - 2b) + 4a + 5b$

For Exercises 8–9, solve the equation.

8. $-18 = -4 + 2x$

9. $-\frac{2}{3}y = 12$

10. If a car dealership sells 18 cars in a 5-day period, how many cars can the dealership expect to sell in 25 days?

11. Four-fifths of the drinks sold at a movie theater were soda. What percent is this?

12. Of the trees in a forest, 62% were saved from a fire. If this represents 1420 trees, how many trees were originally in the forest? Round to the nearest whole tree.

13. The sales tax on a $21 meal is $1.26. What is the sales tax rate?

14. If $5000 is invested at 3.4% simple interest for 6 years, how much interest is earned?

For Exercises 15–16, convert the units of capacity, length, mass, and weight. Round to one decimal place, if necessary.

15. 72 in. ≈ _____ cm   **16.** 72 in. = _____ ft

17. A regular octagon has eight sides of equal length. A stop sign is in the shape of a regular octagon. Find the perimeter of the stop sign.

 12 in.

18. Determine the length of the missing side.

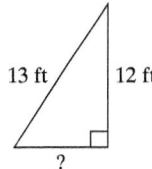

19. Determine the measure of the missing angle.

20. Find the volume and surface area.

Introduction to Statistics

8

CHAPTER OUTLINE

Chapter 8

This chapter introduces the study of statistics. This includes interpreting and constructing a variety of statistical graphs such as bar graphs, line graphs, circle graphs, pictographs, and histograms. We also learn how to compute the mean, median, and mode to measure the "center" of a set of values.

Are You Prepared?

Tables and graphs provide an efficient and easy way to analyze information. Fill in the table provided by using the information given in the paragraph. Then use the table to answer the questions.

The Agriculture Department of a university is collecting data regarding the number of animals on several ranches in Wyoming. Stevens Ranch has 125 horses and 200 cattle. Raven Ranch has 150 cattle. Summit Ranch has 12 horses, 125 cattle, and 32 bison. Yellowstone Ranch has 32 horses and 73 bison. Ellis Ranch has 6 horses, 225 cattle, and 20 llamas.

1. What is the total number of animals on all the ranches?
2. Which ranch has the most animals?
3. What percentage of the animals is horses?
4. What percentage of the ranches has bison?
5. What is the fewest number of animals on a ranch?

Ranch	Horses	Cattle	Bison	Llamas	Total
Stevens					
Raven					
Summit					
Yellowstone					
Ellis					
Total					

Section 8.1   Tables, Bar Graphs, Pictographs, and Line Graphs

1. Introduction to Data and Tables

Statistics is the branch of mathematics that involves collecting, organizing, and analyzing **data** (information). One method to organize data is by using tables. A **table** uses rows and columns to reference information. The individual entries within a table are called **cells**.

— Skill Practice ——

For Exercises 1–4, use the information in Table 8-1.

1. Which hurricane had the highest sustained wind speed at landfall?
2. Which hurricane was the most recent?
3. What was the difference in the death toll for Fran and Alicia?
4. How many times greater was the cost for Katrina than for Fran?

Example 1   Interpreting Data in a Table

Table 8-1 summarizes the maximum wind speed, number of reported deaths, and estimated cost for recent hurricanes that made landfall in the United States. (*Source:* National Oceanic and Atmospheric Administration)

Table 8-1

Hurricane	Date	Landfall	Maximum Sustained Winds at Landfall (mph)	Number of Reported Deaths	Estimated Cost ($ Billions)
Katrina	2005	Louisiana, Mississippi	125	1836	81.2
Fran	1996	North Carolina, Virginia	115	37	5.8
Andrew	1992	Florida, Louisiana	145	61	35.6
Hugo	1989	South Carolina	130	57	10.8
Alicia	1983	Texas	115	19	5.9

a. Which hurricane caused the greatest number of deaths?

b. Which hurricane was the most costly?

c. What was the difference in the maximum sustained winds for hurricane Andrew and hurricane Katrina?

d. How many times greater was the death toll for Hugo than for Alicia?

Solution:

a. The death toll is reported in the 5th column. The death toll for hurricane Katrina, 1836, is the greatest value.

b. The estimated cost is reported in the 6th column. Hurricane Katrina was also the costliest hurricane at $81.2 billion.

Answers

1. Andrew   2. Katrina
3. 18 deaths   4. 14 times greater

c. The wind speeds are given in the 4th column. The difference in the wind speed for hurricane Andrew and hurricane Katrina is 145 mph − 125 mph = 20 mph.

d. There were 57 deaths from Hugo and 19 from Alicia. The ratio of deaths from Hugo to deaths from Alicia is given by

$$\frac{57}{19} = 3$$

There were 3 times as many deaths from Hugo as from Alicia.

Example 2 **Constructing a Table from Observed Data**

The following data were taken by a student conducting a study for a statistics class. The student observed the type of vehicle and gender of the driver for 18 vehicles in the school parking lot. Complete the table.

Male–car	Female–truck	Male–truck
Male–truck	Female–car	Male–truck
Female–car	Male–truck	Male–motorcycle
Female–car	Male–car	Female–car
Male–motorcycle	Female–car	Female–car
Female–motorcycle	Male–car	Male–car

Driver \ Vehicle	Car	Truck	Motorcycle
Male			
Female			

Solution:

We need to count the number of data values that fall in each of the six cells. One method is to go through the list of data one by one. For each value place a tally mark | in the appropriate cell. For example, the first data value male–car would go in the cell in the first row, first column.

Driver \ Vehicle	Car	Truck	Motorcycle
Male	IIII	IIII	II
Female	IIII I	I	I

To form the completed table, count the number of tally marks in each cell. See Table 8-2.

Table 8-2

Driver \ Vehicle	Car	Truck	Motorcycle
Male	4	4	2
Female	6	1	1

5. A political poll was taken to determine the political party and gender of several registered voters. The following codes were used.

M = male
F = female
dem = Democrat
rep = Republican
ind = Independent

Complete the table given the following results.

F–dem	F–rep	M–dem
M–rep	M–ind	M–rep
F–dem	M–rep	F–dem
F–dem	M–dem	F–ind
M–dem	M–ind	M–rep
M–rep	F–rep	F–dem

	Male	Female
Democrat		
Republican		
Independent		

Answer

5.

	Male	Female
Democrat	3	5
Republican	5	2
Independent	2	1

2. Bar Graphs

In Table 8-1, we see that hurricane Andrew had the greatest wind speed of those listed. This can be visualized in a graph. Figure 8-1 shows a bar graph of the wind speed for the hurricanes listed in Table 8-1. Notice that the bar showing wind speed for Andrew is the highest.

Figure 8-1

Notice that the bar graph compares the data values through the height of each bar. The bars in a bar graph may also be presented horizontally. For example, the double bar graph in Figure 8-2 illustrates the data from Example 2.

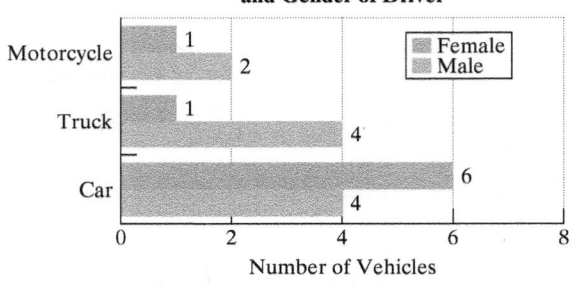

Figure 8-2

Example 3 **Constructing a Bar Graph**

The number of fat grams for five different ice cream brands and flavors is given in Table 8-3. Each value is based on a $\frac{1}{2}$-c serving. Construct a bar graph with vertical bars to depict this information.

Table 8-3

Brand/Flavor	Number of Fat Grams (g) per $\frac{1}{2}$-c Serving
Breyers Strawberry	6
Edy's Grand Light Mint Chocolate Chip	4.5
Healthy Choice Chocolate Fudge Brownie	2
Ben and Jerry's Chocolate Chip Cookie Dough	15
Häagen-Dazs Vanilla Swiss Almond	20

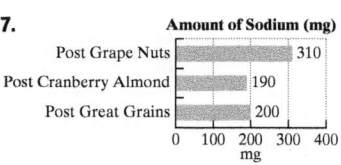

Solution:

First draw a horizontal line and label the different ice cream brands categories. Then draw a vertical line on the left-hand side of the graph as in Figure 8-3. The vertical line represents the number of grams of fat. The vertical scale must extend to at least 20 to accommodate the largest value in the table. In Figure 8-3, the vertical scale ranges from 0 to 24 in multiples (or steps) of 4.

Avoiding Mistakes

The scale on the y-axis should begin at 0 and increase by equal intervals.

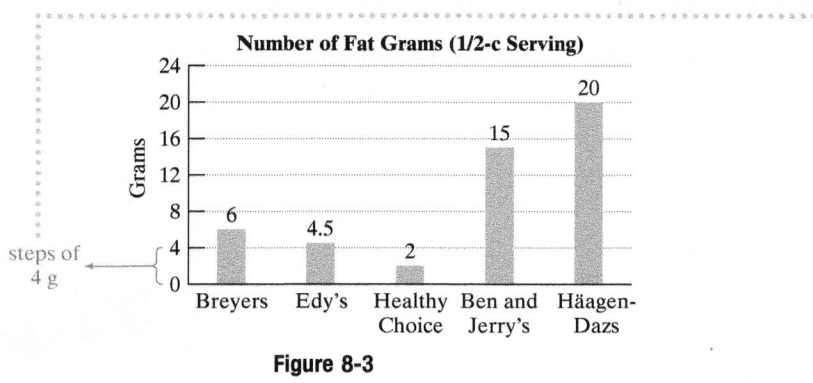

Figure 8-3

3. Pictographs

Sometimes a bar graph might use an icon or small image to convey a unit of measurement. This type of bar graph is called a **pictograph**.

Example 4 **Interpreting a Pictograph**

The number of music CDs sold in the United States is given in Figure 8-4 for selected years. (*Source:* Recording Industry Association of America)

a. What is the value of each CD icon in the graph?

b. From the graph, estimate the number of CDs sold in 1997.

c. For which year were there approximately 900 million CDs sold?

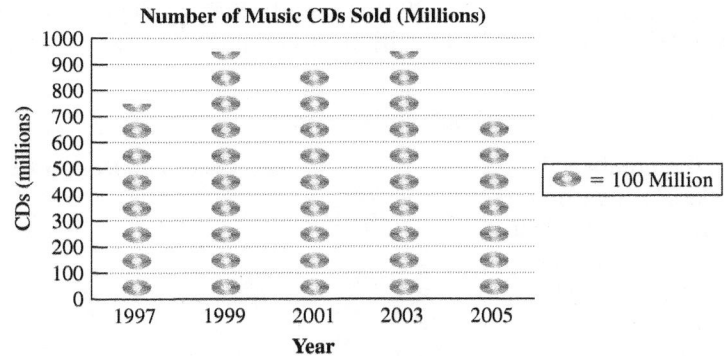

Figure 8-4

Skill Practice

For Exercises 8–10, refer to the pictograph showing the number of tigers living in the wild.

8. What is the value of each tiger icon?

9. From the graph, estimate the number of Sumatran tigers.

10. Estimate the number of Siberian tigers.

Solution:

a. The legend indicates that ⬭ = 100 million CDs sold.

b. The height of the "bar" in 1997 is given by $7\frac{1}{2}$ CDs. Therefore, there were approximately 750 million CDs sold in 1997.

c. The "bar" containing 9 CDs (900 million sold) corresponds to the year 2001.

Answers

8. 100 tigers   **9.** 400 Sumatran tigers
10. 150 Siberian tigers

4. Line Graphs

Line graphs are often used to track how one variable changes with respect to a second variable. For example, a line graph may illustrate a pattern or trend of a variable over time and allow us to make predictions.

Example 5 **Interpreting a Line Graph**

Figure 8-5 shows the number of bachelor's degrees earned by men and women for selected years. (*Source:* U.S. Census Bureau)

Figure 8-5

a. In 1950, who earned more bachelor's degrees, men or women?

b. In 2000, who earned more bachelor's degrees, men or women?

c. Use the trends in the graph to predict the number of bachelor's degrees earned by men and by women for the year 2010.

Solution:

a. The blue graph represents men, and the red graph represents women. In 1950, men earned approximately 320 thousand bachelor's degrees. Women earned approximately 100 thousand. Men earned more bachelor's degrees in 1950.

b. In 2000, women earned more bachelor's degrees.

c. To predict the number of bachelor's degrees earned by men and women in the year 2010, we need to extend both line graphs. See the dashed lines in Figure 8-6. The number of bachelor's degrees earned by women is predicted to be approximately 850 thousand. The number of degrees earned by men will be approximately 550 thousand.

Figure 8-6

| Example 6 | **Constructing a Line Graph** |

Table 8-4 gives the number of worldwide airline fatalities (excludes deaths caused by terrorism) for selected years. Use the data given in the table to create a line graph.

Table 8-4

Year	Number of Deaths
1986	641
1990	544
1994	1170
1998	904
2002	577
2006	773

Source: International Civil Aviation Administration

Solution:

First draw a horizontal line and label the year. Then draw a vertical line on the left-hand side of the graph, as in Figure 8-7. The vertical line represents the number of fatalities. In Figure 8-7, the vertical scale ranges from 0 to 1400 in multiples (or steps) of 200. For each year, plot a point corresponding to the number of deaths for that year. Then connect the points.

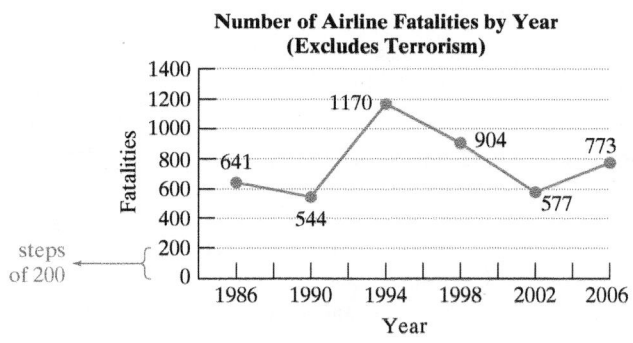

Figure 8-7

In Figure 8-7, we labeled the value at each data point because the exact values are difficult to read from the graph.

Skill Practice

14. The table gives the number of cars registered in the United States (in millions) for selected years. (*Source:* U.S. Department of Transportation) Create a line graph for this information.

Year	Number of Cars (Millions)
1960	62
1970	89
1980	122
1990	134
2000	134

Answer

14.

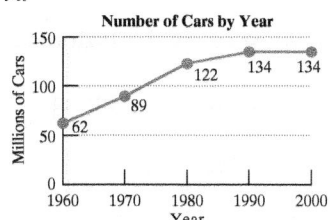

| Section 8.1 | **Practice Exercises** |

Boost *your* GRADE at ALEKS.com!

ALEKS® version 3.0

- Practice Problems
- Self-Tests
- NetTutor
- e-Professors
- Videos

Study Skills Exercise

1. Define the key terms.

   a. **Statistics**   b. **Data**   c. **Table**

   d. **Cells**   e. **Pictograph**   f. **Line graph**

Objective 1: Introduction to Data and Tables

For Exercises 2–6 refer to the table. The table represents the Seven Summits (the highest peaks from each continent). **(See Example 1.)**

Mountain	Continent	Height (ft)
Mt. Kilimanjaro	Africa	19,340
Elbrus	Europe	18,510
Aconcagua	South America	22,834
Denali	North America	20,320
Vinson Massif	Antarctica	16,864
Mt. Kosciusko	Australia	7,310
Mt. Everest	Asia	29,035

2. What is the difference in the heights of Elbrus and Vinson Massif?

3. In which continent does the highest mountain lie?

4. Which mountain among those listed is the lowest? In which continent does it lie?

5. How much higher is Aconcagua than Denali?

6. What is the difference between the heights of the highest mountain in Europe and the highest mountain in Australia?

For Exercises 7–12 refer to the table. The table gives the average ages (in years) for U.S. women and men married for the first time for selected years. (*Source:* U.S. Census Bureau)

	Men	Women
1940	24.3	21.5
1960	22.8	20.3
1980	24.7	22.0
2000	26.8	25.1

7. By how much has the average age for women increased between 1940 and 2000?

8. By how much has the average age for men increased between 1940 and 2000?

9. What is the difference between the men's and women's average age at first marriage in 1940?

10. What is the difference between the men's and women's average age at first marriage in 2000?

11. Which group, men or women, had the consistently higher age at first marriage?

12. Which group, men or women, had a greater increase in age between 1940 and 2000?

13. The following data were taken from a survey of a third-grade class. The survey denotes the gender of a student and whether the student owned a dog, a cat, or neither. Complete the table. Be sure to label the rows and columns. **(See Example 2.)**

	Dog	Cat	Neither
Boy			
Girl			

Boy–dog	Boy–dog	Boy–cat	Boy–neither
Girl–dog	Girl–neither	Boy–dog	Girl–cat
Girl–neither	Girl–neither	Girl–dog	Girl–cat
Boy–dog	Girl–cat	Boy–neither	Girl–dog
Boy–neither	Girl–neither	Girl–cat	Girl–neither

14. In a group of 20 women, 10 were given an experimental drug to lower cholesterol. The other 10 were given a placebo. The letter "D" indicates that the person got the drug, and the letter "P" indicates that the person received the placebo. The values "yes" or "no" indicate whether the person's cholesterol was lowered. Complete the table.

	Yes	No
Drug (D)		
Placebo (P)		

D–yes	D–yes	P–no	D–no	P–yes	D–yes	P–no	P–no	D–yes	D–no
P–yes	P–no	D–yes	P–yes	P–yes	D–no	D–yes	P–no	D–yes	P–no

Objective 2: Bar Graphs

15. The table shows the number of students per computer in U.S. public schools for selected years. (*Source:* National Center for Education Statistics) **(See Example 3.)**

    a. In which year did students have the best access to a computer?

    b. Draw a bar graph with vertical bars to illustrate these data.

Year	Students
1992	16
1995	10
1998	5.7
2001	4.9
2004	4.2
2007	4.0

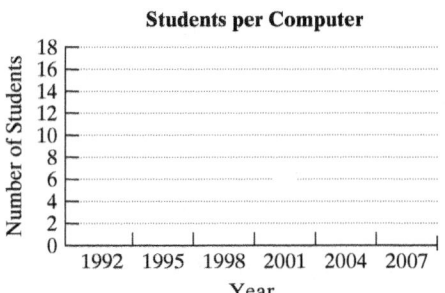

16. The number of new jobs for selected industries are given in the table. (*Source:* Bureau of Labor Statistics)

    a. Which category has the greatest number of new jobs? How many new jobs is this?

    b. Draw a bar graph with vertical bars to illustrate these data.

Industry	Number of New Jobs
Health care	219,400
Temporary help	212,000
Construction	173,000
Food service	167,600
Retail	78,600

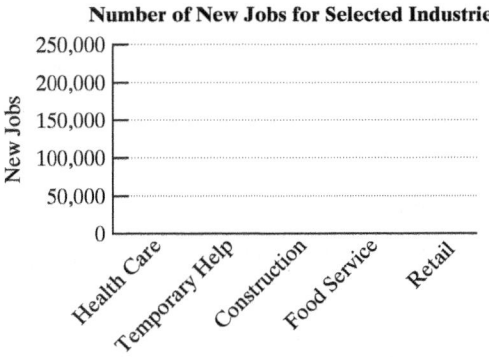

17. The table shows the number of cellular telephone subscriptions by year in the United States. (*Source:* U.S. Bureau of the Census) Construct a bar graph with horizontal bars. The length of each bar represents the number of cellular phone subscriptions for the given year.

Year	Number of Subscriptions (millions)
2002	141
2003	159
2004	182
2005	208
2006	238

18. The table represents the world's major consumers of primary energy for a recent year. All measurements are in quadrillions of Btu. *Note:* 1 quadrillion = 1,000,000,000,000,000. (*Source:* Energy Information Administration, U.S. Department of Energy) Construct a bar graph using horizontal bars. The length of each bar gives the amount of energy consumed for that country.

Country	Amount of Energy Consumed (Quadrillions of Btu)
Germany	14
Japan	22
Russia	28
China	37
United States	99

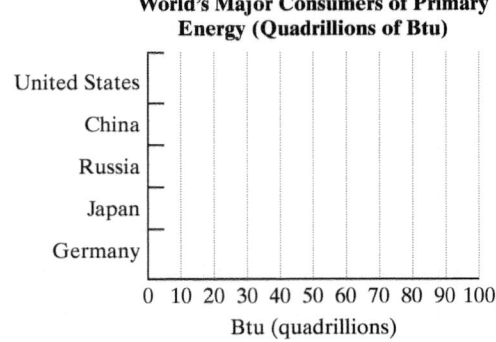

Objective 3: Pictographs

19. A local ice cream stand kept track of its ice cream sales for one weekend, as shown in the figure. **(See Example 4.)**

  a. What does each ice cream icon represent?

  b. From the graph, estimate the number of servings of ice cream sold on Saturday.

  c. Which day had approximately 275 servings of ice cream sold?

20. Adults access the Internet to see weather updates and check on current news. The pictograph displays the percent of adult Internet users who access these topics.

  a. What does each computer icon represent?

  b. From the graph, estimate the percent of adult users that access the Internet for weather.

  c. Which type of news is accessed about 45% of the time?

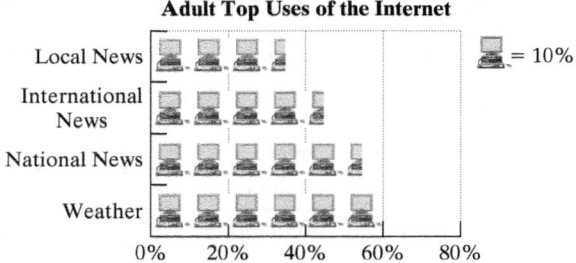

21. The figure displays the annual sales of books for three major companies as of 2010.

  a. Estimate the sales for the company with the greatest annual sales.

  b. Estimate the total sales for all three companies.

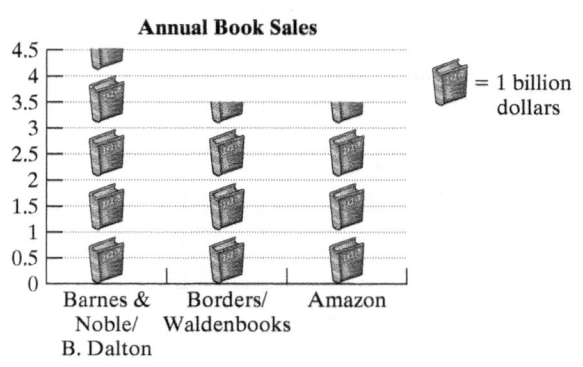

22. Recently the largest populations of senior citizens were in California, Florida, New York, Texas, and Pennsylvania, as shown in the figure. (*Source:* U.S. Bureau of the Census)

    a. Estimate the number of senior citizens living in Texas.

    b. How many more senior citizens are living in California than in Pennsylvania?

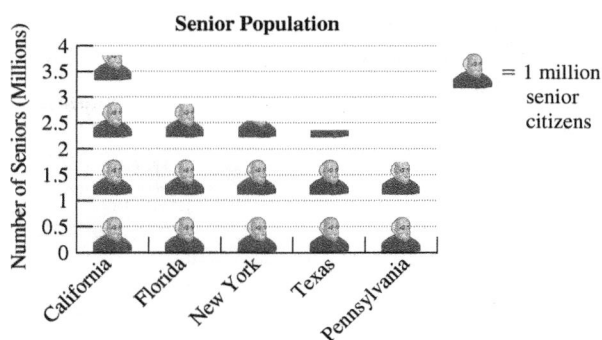

Objective 4: Line Graphs

For Exercises 23–28, use the graph provided. The graph shows the trend depicted by the percent of men and women over 65 years old in the labor force. (*Source:* Bureau of the Census) (See Example 5.)

23. What was the difference in the percent of men and the percent of women over 65 in the labor force in the year 1920?

24. What was the difference in the percent of men and the percent of women over 65 in the labor force in the year 2000?

25. What was the overall trend in the percent of women over 65 in the labor force for the years shown in the graph?

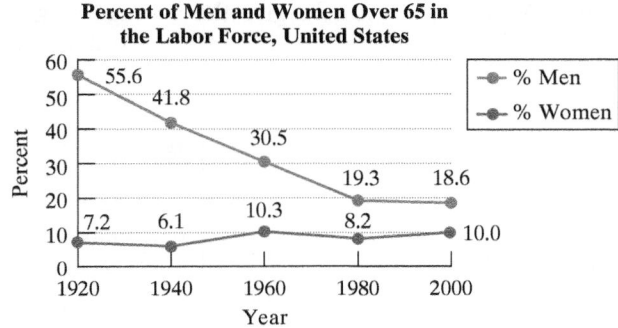

26. What was the overall trend in the percent of men over 65 in the labor force for the years shown in the graph?

27. Use the graph to predict the number of men over 65 in the labor force in the year 2020. Answers will vary.

28. Use the graph to predict the number of women over 65 in the labor force in the year 2020. Answers will vary.

For Exercises 29–34, refer to the graph representing the number of hybrid cars sold in January in the United States for the given years. (*Source:* U.S. Energy Information Administration)

29. In which year were the most hybrid cars sold in January? How many were sold?

30. In which year was the least number of hybrid cars sold in January? How many were sold?

31. What is the difference between the January sales in 2006 and 2005?

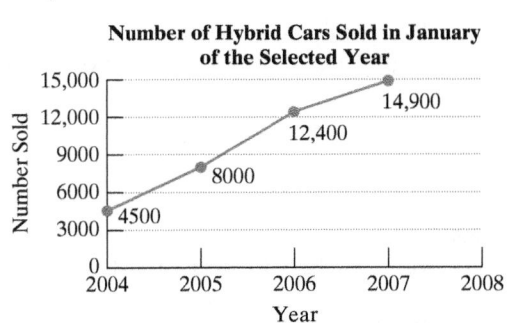

32. What is the difference between the January sales in 2007 and 2006?

33. Between which two years was the increase in January sales the greatest?

34. Between which two years was the increase in January sales the least?

35. The data shown here give the average height for girls based on age. (*Source:* National Parenting Council) Make a line graph to illustrate these data. For each age value, plot a point for the corresponding height. (See Example 6.)

Age	Height (in.)
2	35
3	38.5
4	41.5
5	44
6	46
7	48
8	50.5
9	53

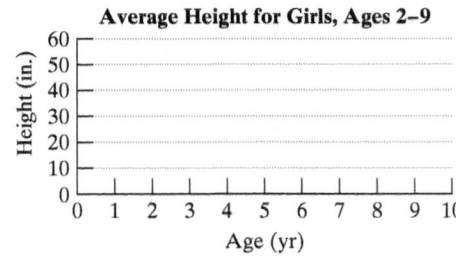

36. The data shown here give the average height for boys based on age. (*Source:* National Parenting Council) Make a line graph to illustrate these data. For each age value, plot a point for the corresponding height.

Age	Height (in.)
2	36
3	39
4	42
5	44
6	46.75
7	49
8	51
9	53.5

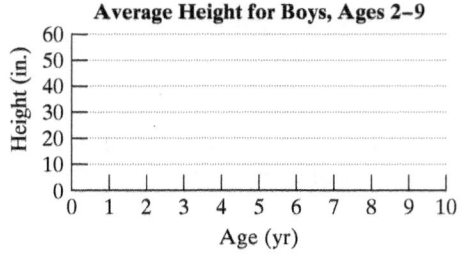

Expanding Your Skills

All packaged food items have to display nutritional facts so that the consumer can make informed choices. For Exercises 37–40, refer to the nutritional chart for Breyers French Vanilla ice cream.

37. How many servings are there per container? How much total fat is in one container of this ice cream?

38. How much total sodium is in one container of this ice cream?

39. If 8 g of fat is 13% of the daily value, what is the daily value of fat? Round to 1 decimal place.

40. If 50 mg of cholesterol is 17% of the daily value, what is the daily value of cholesterol? Round to the nearest whole unit.

Nutrition Facts		
Serving Size $\frac{1}{2}$ cup (68 g)		
Servings per Container 14		
Amount per Serving		
Calories 150		**Calories from Fat** 80
		% Daily Value
Total Fat	8 g	13%
Saturated fat	5 g	25%
Cholesterol	50 mg	17%
Sodium	45 mg	2%
Total Carbohydrate		
Dietary fiber	0 g	
Sugars	15 g	
Protein	3 g	

Frequency Distributions and Histograms

1. Frequency Distributions

The medical community agrees that sodium intake is one of the variables contributing to high blood pressure. The amount of sodium (in mg) for a 1-cup serving of processed breakfast cereals is given for 40 cereals.

146	143	316	269	243	249	213	160	269	288
299	234	267	275	263	171	202	120	146	139
241	210	150	197	359	238	249	200	178	219
204	203	253	165	207	362	250	223	255	224

Suppose we want to organize this information. One way is to create a frequency distribution. A **frequency distribution** is a table displaying the number of values that fall within categories called **class intervals**. This is demonstrated in Example 1.

Objectives

1. Frequency Distributions
2. Histograms

Example 1 Creating a Frequency Distribution

Complete the table to form a frequency distribution for the number of grams of sodium per 1-cup servings of forty breakfast cereals.

Class Intervals Amount of Sodium (mg)	Tally	Frequency Number of Cereals
100–149		
150–199		
200–249		
250–299		
300–349		
350–399		

Solution:

The classes in the first column represent different amounts of sodium. Go through the list of data and use tally marks to track the number of cereals that fall into each class. Tally marks are shown in red for the first six values in the first row: 146, 143, 316, 269, 243, and 249.

Table 8-5

Class Intervals Amount of Sodium (mg)	Tally	Frequency Number of Cereals
100–149	卌	5
150–199	卌 I	6
200–249	卌 卌 卌 I	16
250–299	卌 卌	10
300–349	I	1
350–399	II	2

The frequency is a count of the tally marks for each class. See Table 8-5.

Skill Practice

1. The ages (in years) of individuals arrested on a certain day in Galveston, Texas, are listed.

18	20	35	46
19	26	24	32
28	25	30	34
22	29	39	19
18	19	26	40

Complete the table to form a frequency distribution.

Class (Age)	Tally	Frequency
18–23		
24–29		
30–35		
36–41		
42–47		

Answer

1.

Class (Age)	Tally	Frequency
18–23	卌 II	7
24–29	卌 I	6
30–35	IIII	4
36–41	II	2
42–47	I	1

Example 2 **Interpreting a Frequency Distribution**

Consider the frequency distribution in Table 8-5.

a. Which class has the most values?

b. How many values are represented in the table?

c. What percent of cereals have 300 mg or more of sodium per 1-cup serving?

Solution:

a. The 200- to 249-mg class has 16 data values. This is the greatest frequency.

b. The number of data values is given by the sum of the frequencies.

$$\text{Total number of values} = 5 + 6 + 16 + 10 + 1 + 2$$

$$= 40$$

c. One cereal belongs to the 300 – 349 mg class, and two cereals belong to the 350- to 399-mg class. So there are 3 cereals among the group of 40 studied that have 300 mg or more of sodium. The percentage is given by

$$\frac{3}{40} = 0.075 \quad \text{or} \quad 7.5\%$$

Therefore, 7.5% of processed breakfast cereals have 300 mg or more of sodium per cup.

When creating a frequency distribution, keep these important guidelines in mind.

- The classes should be equally spaced. For instance in Example 1, we would not want one class to represent a 50-mg interval and another to represent a 100-mg interval.
- The classes should not overlap. That is, a data value should belong to one and only one class.
- In general, we create a frequency distribution with between 5 and 15 classes.

2. Histograms

A **histogram** is a special bar graph that illustrates data given in a frequency distribution. The class intervals are given on the horizontal scale. The height of each bar in a histogram represents the frequency for each class. Furthermore, the bars of a histogram touch with no space between the bars.

Example 3 **Constructing a Histogram**

Construct a histogram for the frequency distribution given in Example 1.

Solution:

Class Intervals Amount of Sodium (mg)	Frequency Number of Cereals
100–149	5
150–199	6
200–249	16
250–299	10
300–349	1
350–399	2

To create a histogram, list the classes (amount of sodium) on the horizontal scale. Then on the vertical scale, mark off units to represent the frequency (Figure 8-8).

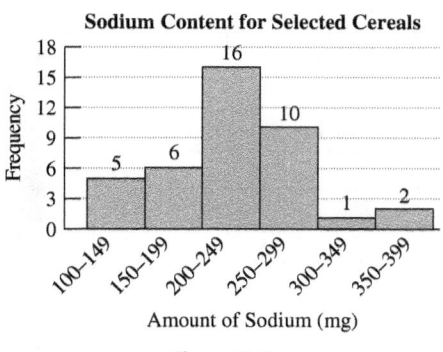

Sodium Content for Selected Cereals

Figure 8-8

Skill Practice

5. Construct a histogram for the frequency distribution in margin Exercise 1.

Answer

5.

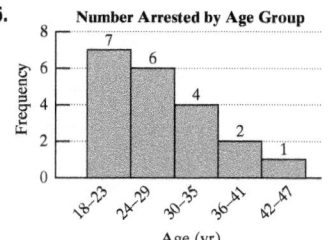

Number Arrested by Age Group

Section 8.2 Practice Exercises

Boost *your* GRADE at ALEKS.com!

- Practice Problems
- Self-Tests
- NetTutor
- e-Professors
- Videos

Study Skills Exercise

1. Define the key terms.

   a. **Frequency distribution**   b. **Class intervals**   c. **Histogram**

Objective 1: Frequency Distributions

2. For a frequency distribution, what is the recommended number of classes?

3. From the frequency distribution, determine the total number of data.

Class Intervals	Frequency
1–4	14
5–8	18
9–12	24
13–16	10
17–20	6

4. From the frequency distribution, determine the total number of data.

Class Intervals	Frequency
1–50	29
51–100	12
101–150	6
151–200	22
201–250	56
251–300	60

5. For the table in Exercise 3, which class contains the most data?

6. For the table in Exercise 4, which class contains the most data?

7. The retirement age (in years) for 20 college professors is given. Complete the frequency distribution. **(See Examples 1 and 2.)**

67	56	68	70	60	65	73	72	56	65
71	66	72	69	65	65	63	65	68	70

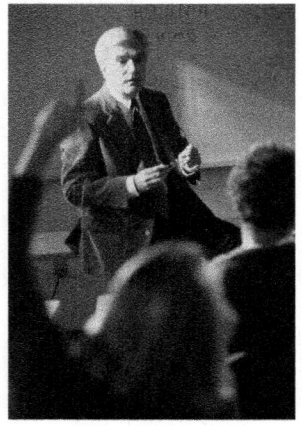

Class Intervals (Age in Years)	Tally	Frequency (Number of Professors)
56–58		
59–61		
62–64		
65–67		
68–70		
71–73		

a. Which class has the most values?

b. How many data values are represented in the table?

c. What percent of the professors retire when they are 68 to 70 yr old?

8. The number of miles run in one day by 16 selected runners is given. Complete the frequency distribution.

2	4	7	3	8	4	5	7
4	6	4	3	4	2	4	10

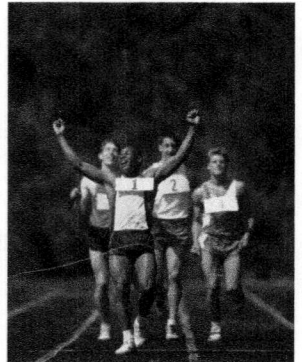

Class Intervals (Number of Miles)	Tally	Frequency (Number of Runners)
1–2		
3–4		
5–6		
7–8		
9–10		

a. Which class has the most values?

b. How many data values are represented in the table?

c. What percent of the runners run 3 to 4 mi/day?

9. The number of gallons of gas purchased by 16 customers at a certain gas station is given. Complete the frequency distribution.

12.7	13.1	9.8	12.0	10.4	9.8	14.2	8.6
19.2	8.1	14.0	15.4	12.8	18.2	15.1	13.0

Class Intervals (Amount in Gal)	Tally	Frequency (Number of Customers)
8.0–9.9		
10.0–11.9		
12.0–13.9		
14.0–15.9		
16.0–17.9		
18.0–19.9		

a. Which class has the most values?

b. How many data values are represented in the table?

c. What percent of the customers purchased 18 to 19.9 gal of gas?

10. The hourly salaries (in dollars) for 15 student employees at Miami-Dade College are given. Complete the frequency distribution.

7.95	8.00	9.20	8.15	7.85
7.95	8.50	9.00	8.25	8.95
9.25	9.50	10.05	10.00	8.30

Class Intervals (Hourly Wage, $)	Tally	Frequency (Number of Employees)
7.50–7.99		
8.00–8.49		
8.50–8.99		
9.00–9.49		
9.50–9.99		
10.00–10.49		

a. Which class has the most values?

b. How many data values are represented in the table?

c. What percent of the employees earn $9.00 or more?

11. Explain what is wrong with the following class intervals.

Class	Tally	Frequency
0–4		
5–10		
11–17		
18–25		
26–34		

12. Explain what is wrong with the following class intervals.

Class	Tally	Frequency
1–6		
7–11		
12–17		
18–23		
24–28		

13. Explain what is wrong with the following class intervals.

Class	Tally	Frequency
1–20		
21–40		

14. Explain what is wrong with the following class intervals.

Class	Tally	Frequency
1–33		
34–66		
67–99		

15. Explain what is wrong with the following class intervals.

Class	Tally	Frequency
10–12		
12–14		
14–16		
16–18		
18–20		

16. Explain what is wrong with the following class intervals.

Class	Tally	Frequency
1–5		
5–10		
10–15		
15–20		
20–25		
25–30		

17. The heights of 20 students at Valencia Community College are given. Complete the frequency distribution.

70	71	73	62	65	70	69	70
64	66	73	63	68	67	69	72
64	66	67	69				

Class Interval (Height, in.)	Frequency (Number of Students)
62–63	
64–65	
66–67	
68–69	
70–71	
72–73	

18. The amount withdrawn in dollars from a certain ATM is given for 20 customers. Construct a frequency distribution.

40	50	200	200	100	120	200
50	100	60	100	100	30	40
100	100	50	200	150	200	

Class Interval (Amount, $)	Frequency (Number of Customers)
0–49	
50–99	
100–149	
150–199	
200–249	

Objective 2: Histograms

19. Construct a histogram for the frequency table in Exercise 17. **(See Example 3.)**

Heights of Valencia Community College Students

20. Construct a histogram for the frequency table in Exercise 18.

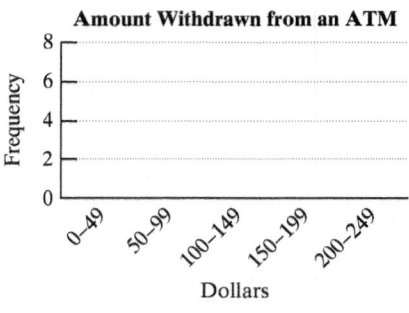

Amount Withdrawn from an ATM

21. Construct a histogram, using the given data. Each number represents the number of Calories in a 100-g serving for selected fruits.

59	65	48	49	161	47	92	43
52	59	56	49	35	55	72	30
67	44	32	32	61	29	30	

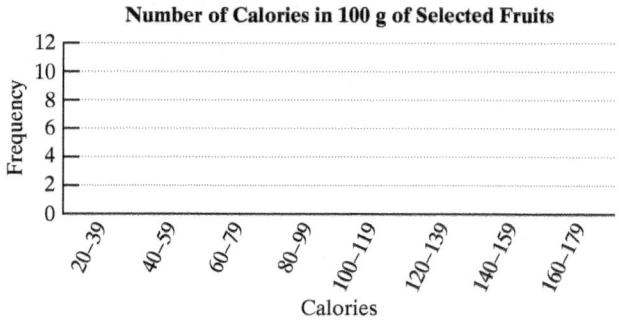

Number of Calories in 100 g of Selected Fruits

22. The list of data gives the number of children of the Presidents of the United States (in no particular order). Construct a histogram.

0	4	3	3	2	2	5	10	0	5	2
4	5	7	4	3	6	4	0	7	5	6
1	4	3	0	4	3	2	6	4	6	8
3	2	1	0	2	6	0	2	2		

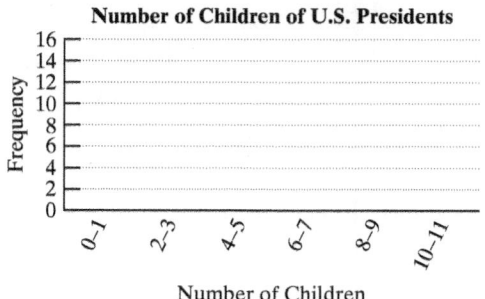

Number of Children of U.S. Presidents

Circle Graphs

1. Interpreting Circle Graphs

Thus far we have used bar graphs, line graphs, and histograms to visualize data. A **circle graph** (or pie graph) is another type of graph used to show how a whole amount is divided into parts. Each part of the circle, called a **sector**, is like a slice of pie. The size of each piece relates to the fraction of the whole it represents.

Objectives

1. **Interpreting Circle Graphs**
2. **Circle Graphs and Percents**
3. **Constructing Circle Graphs**

Example 1 **Interpreting a Circle Graph**

The grade distribution for a math test is shown in the circle graph (Figure 8-9).

Grade Distribution

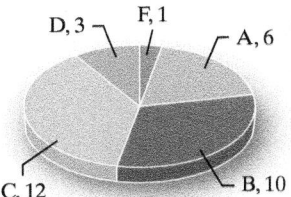

Figure 8-9

a. How many total grades are represented?

b. How many grades are B's?

c. How many times more C's are there than D's?

d. What percent of the grades were A's?

Skill Practice

A used car dealership sells cars and trucks. Use the circle graph to answer Exercises 1–4.

Vehicle Distribution by Make

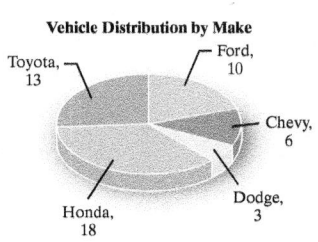

1. How many total vehicles are represented?
2. How many are Toyotas?
3. How many times more Hondas are there than Dodges?
4. What percent are Fords?

Solution:

a. The total number of grades is equal to the sum of the number of grades from each category.

$$\text{Total number of grades} = 6 + 10 + 12 + 3 + 1$$
$$= 32$$

b. The number of B's is represented by the red portion of the graph. There are 10 B's.

c. There are 12 C's and 3 D's. The ratio of C's to D's is $\frac{12}{3} = 4$. Therefore, there are 4 times as many C's as D's.

d. There are 6 A's. The percent of A's is given by

$$\frac{6}{32} = 0.1875$$

Therefore, the percent of A's is 18.75%.

Answers

1. 50   **2.** 13
3. There are 6 times more Hondas than Dodges.
4. 20% are Fords.

2. Circle Graphs and Percents

Sometimes circle graphs show data in percent form. This is illustrated in Example 2.

| Example 2 | **Calculating Amounts by Using a Circle Graph** |

A certain video rental store carries 2000 different videos. It groups its video collection by the categories shown in the graph (Figure 8-10).

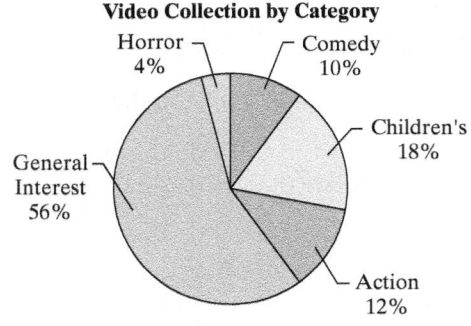

Video Collection by Category

Figure 8-10

a. How many videos are comedy?

b. How many videos are action or horror?

Solution:

a. First note that the store carries 2000 different videos. From the graph we know that 10% are comedies. Therefore, this question can be interpreted as

What is 10% of 2000?
$$\downarrow\ \downarrow\ \downarrow\quad \downarrow\ \downarrow$$
$$x = (0.10) \cdot (2000)$$

$$= 200 \qquad\qquad \text{There are 200 comedies.}$$

b. From the graph we know that 12% of the videos are action and 4% are horror. This accounts for 16% of the total video collection. Therefore, this question asks

What is 16% of 2000?
$$\downarrow\ \downarrow\ \downarrow\quad \downarrow\ \downarrow$$
$$x = (0.16) \cdot (2000)$$

$$= 320 \qquad\qquad \text{There are 320 videos that are action or horror.}$$

3. Constructing Circle Graphs

Recall that a full circle is a 360° arc. To draw a circle graph, we must compute the number of degrees of arc for each sector. In Example 2, 10% of the videos are comedies. To draw the sector for this category, we must determine 10% of 360°.

$$10\% \text{ of } 360° = 0.10(360°) = 36°$$

The sector representing comedies should be drawn with a 36° angle. To do this, we can use a protractor (Figure 8-11).

To draw a sector with a 36° arc, first draw a circle. Place the hole in the protractor over the center of the circle. Using the inner scale on the protractor, place a tick mark at 0° and at 36°. Use a straightedge to draw two line segments from the center of the circle to each tick mark. See Figure 8-11.

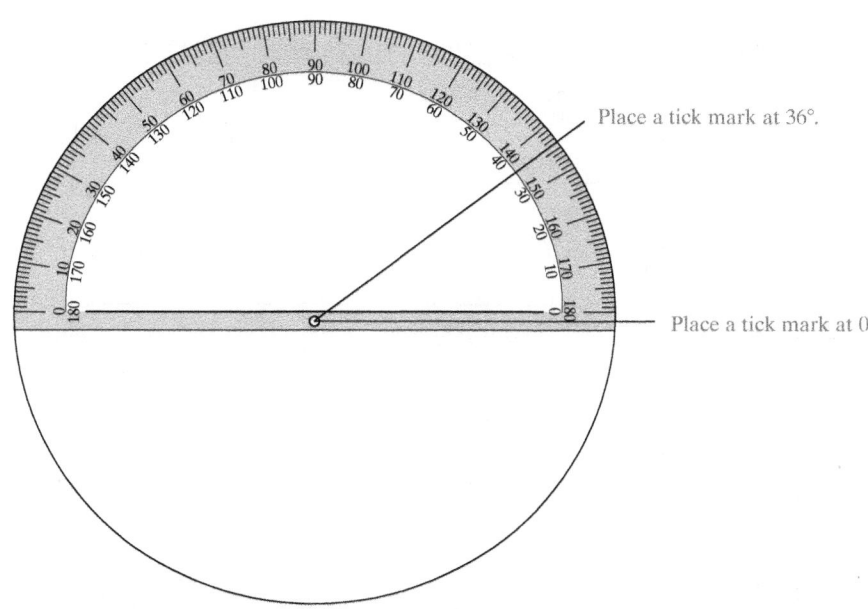

Place a tick mark at 36°.

Place a tick mark at 0°.

Figure 8-11

In Example 3, we use this technique to construct a circle graph.

Example 3 **Constructing a Circle Graph**

A teacher earns a monthly salary of $2400 after taxes. Her monthly budget is broken down in Table 8-6.

Table 8-6

Budget Item	Monthly Value ($)
Rent	840
Utilities	210
Car expenses	510
Groceries	360
Savings	300
Other	180

Construct a circle graph illustrating the information in this table. Label each sector of the graph with the percent that it represents.

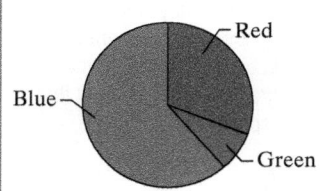

Concept Connections

For Exercises 7 and 8, refer to the circle graph.

Red

Blue

Green

7. Which value best represents the number of degrees in the red sector?
   a. 30°   **b.** 240°
   c. 120°

8. Which value best represents the number of degrees in the blue sector?
   a. 210°   **b.** 30°
   c. 300°

Answers

7. c

8. a

9. Voters in Oregon were asked to identify the political party to which they belonged. Construct a circle graph. Label each sector of the graph with the percent that it represents.

Political Affiliation	Number
Democrat	900
Republican	720
Libertarian	36
Green Party	144

Solution:

This problem calls for two types of calculations: (1) For each budget item, we must compute the percent of the whole that it represents. (2) We must determine the number of degrees for each category. We can use a table to help organize our calculations.

Budget Item	Monthly Value ($)	Percent	Number of Degrees
Rent	840	$=\dfrac{840}{2400}=0.35$ or 35%	35% of 360° $=0.35(360°)$ $=126°$
Utilities	210	$=\dfrac{210}{2400}=0.0875$ or 8.75%	8.75% of 360° $=0.0875(360°)$ $=31.5°$
Car	510	$=\dfrac{510}{2400}=0.2125$ or 21.25%	21.25% of 360° $=0.2125(360°)$ $=76.5°$
Groceries	360	$=\dfrac{360}{2400}=0.15$ or 15%	15% of 360° $=0.15(360°)$ $=54°$
Savings	300	$=\dfrac{300}{2400}=0.125$ or 12.5%	12.5% of 360° $=0.125(360°)$ $=45°$
Other	180	$=\dfrac{180}{2400}=0.075$ or 7.5%	7.5% of 360° $=0.075(360°)$ $=27°$

Now construct the circle graph. Use the degree measures found in the table for each sector. Label the graph with the percent for each sector (Figure 8-12).

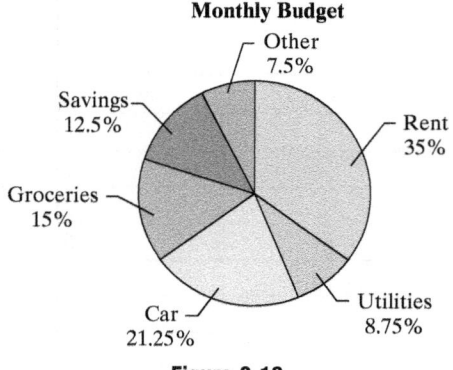

Monthly Budget

Figure 8-12

Answer

9.

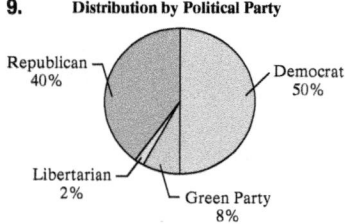

Distribution by Political Party

Section 8.3 Practice Exercises

Study Skills Exercise

1. Define the key terms.

   a. **Circle graph** b. **Sector**

Objective 1: Interpreting Circle Graphs

For Exercises 2–10, refer to the graph. The graph represents the number of traffic fatalities by age group in the U.S. (*Source:* U.S. Bureau of the Census) **(See Example 1.)**

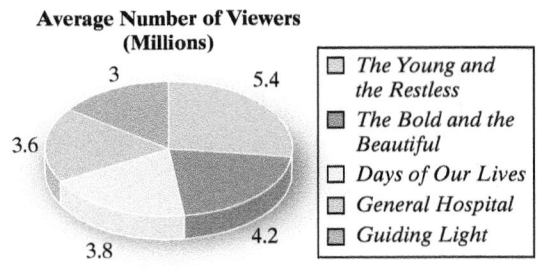

Number of U.S. Traffic Fatalities

65 yr and older (9600)
55–64 yr (6400)
15–24 yr (16,000)
45–54 yr (9600)
35–44 yr (10,880)
25–34 yr (11,520)

2. Which of the age groups has the least fatalities?

3. What is the total number of traffic fatalities?

4. Which of the age groups has the most fatalities?

5. How many more people died in the 25–34 age group than in the 35–44 age group?

6. How many more people died in the 45–54 age group than in the 55–64 group?

7. What percent of the deaths were from the 15–24 group?

8. What percent of the deaths were from the 65 and older age group?

9. How many times more deaths were from the 15–24 age group than the 55–64 age group?

10. How many times more deaths were from the 25–34 age group than from the 65 and older group?

For Exercises 11–16, refer to the figure. The figure represents the average daily number of viewers for five daytime dramas. (*Source:* Nielsen Media Research)

11. How many viewers are represented?

Average Number of Viewers (Millions)

3   5.4
3.6
3.8   4.2

☐ *The Young and the Restless*
■ *The Bold and the Beautiful*
☐ *Days of Our Lives*
☐ *General Hospital*
☐ *Guiding Light*

12. How many viewers does the most popular daytime drama have?

13. How many times more viewers does *The Young and the Restless* have than *Guiding Light*?

14. How many times more viewers does *The Young and the Restless* have than *General Hospital*?

15. What percent of the viewers watch *General Hospital*?

16. What percent of the viewers watch *The Bold and the Beautiful*?

Objective 2: Circle Graphs and Percents

For Exercises 17–20, use the graph representing the type of music CDs found in a store containing approximately 8000 CDs. **(See Example 2.)**

17. How many CDs are musica Latina?

18. How many CDs are rap?

19. How many CDs are jazz or classical?

20. How many CDs are *not* Pop/R&B?

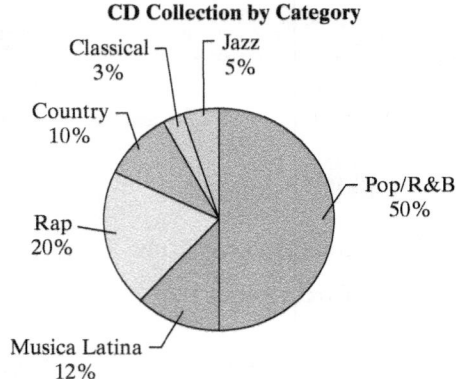

CD Collection by Category

For Exercises 21–24, use the graph representing the states that hosted Super Bowl I through Super Bowl XXXVI (a total of 36 Super Bowls).

21. How many Super Bowls were played in Louisiana?

22. How many Super Bowls were played in Florida? Round to the nearest whole number.

23. How many Super Bowls were played in Georgia? Round to the nearest whole number.

24. How many Super Bowls were played in Michigan? Round to the nearest whole number.

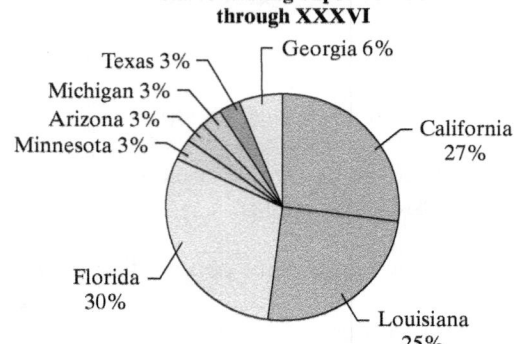

States Hosting Super Bowls I through XXXVI

Objective 3: Constructing Circle Graphs

For Exercises 25–32, use a protractor to construct an angle of the given measure.

25. $20°$

26. $70°$

27. $125°$

28. $270°$

29. $195°$

30. $5°$

31. $300°$

32. $90°$

33. Draw a circle and divide it into sectors of $30°$, $60°$, $100°$, and $170°$.

34. Draw a circle and divide it into sectors of $125°$, $180°$, and $55°$.

35. The table provided gives the expenses for one semester at college. **(See Example 3.)**

    a. Complete the table.

	Expenses	Percent	Number of Degrees
Tuition	$9000		
Books	600		
Housing	2400		

    b. Construct a circle graph to display the college expenses. Label the graph with percents.

College Expenses for a Semester

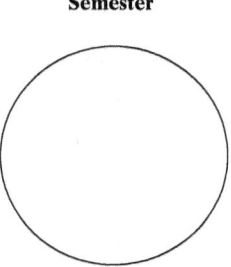

36. The table provided gives the number of establishments of the three largest pizza chains.

    a. Complete the table.

	Number of Stores	Percent	Number of Degrees
Pizza Hut	8100		
Domino's	7200		
Papa Johns	2700		

    b. Construct a circle graph. Label the graph with percents.

Percent of Pizza Establishments

37. The Sunshine Nursery sells flowering plants, shrubs, ground cover, trees, and assorted flower pots. Construct a pie graph to show the distribution of the types of purchases.

Types of Purchases	Percent of Distribution
Flowering plants	45%
Shrubs	13%
Ground cover	18%
Trees	20%
Flower pots	4%

Sunshine Nursery Distribution of Sales

38. The party affiliation of registered Latino voters for a recent year is as follows:

    45% Democrat   20% Republican

    13% Other   22% Independent

Construct a circle graph from this information.

Party Affiliation of Latino Voters

Section 8.4 Mean, Median, and Mode

1. Mean

When given a list of numerical data, it is often desirable to obtain a single number that represents the central value of the data. In this section, we introduce three such values called the mean, median, and mode. The first calculation we present is the mean (or average) of a list of data values.

DEFINITION Mean

The **mean** (or average) of a set of numbers is the sum of the values divided by the number of values. We can write this as a formula.

$$\text{Mean} = \frac{\text{sum of the values}}{\text{number of values}}$$

Skill Practice

Housing prices for five homes in one neighborhood are given.

$108,000 $149,000
$164,000 $118,000
$144,000

1. Find the mean of these five houses.
2. Suppose a new home is built in the neighborhood for $1.3 million ($1,300,000). Find the mean price of all six homes.

Avoiding Mistakes

When computing a mean remember that the data are added first before dividing.

Example 1 Finding the Mean of a Data Set

A small business employs five workers. Their yearly salaries are

$42,000 $36,000 $45,000 $35,000 $38,000

a. Find the mean yearly salary for the five employees.

b. Suppose the owner of the business makes $218,000 per year. Find the mean salary for all six individuals (that is, include the owner's salary).

Solution:

a. Mean salary of five employees

$$= \frac{42,000 + 36,000 + 45,000 + 35,000 + 38,000}{5}$$

$$= \frac{196,000}{5} \quad \text{Add the data values.}$$

$$= 39,200 \quad \text{Divide.}$$

The mean salary for employees is $39,200.

b. Mean of all six individuals

$$= \frac{42,000 + 36,000 + 45,000 + 35,000 + 38,000 + 218,000}{6}$$

$$= \frac{414,000}{6}$$

$$= 69,000$$

The mean salary with the owner's salary included is $69,000.

Answers

1. $136,600   **2.** $330,500

2. Median

In Example 1, you may have noticed that the mean salary was greatly affected by the unusually high value of $218,000. For this reason, you may want to use a different measure of "center" called the median. The **median** is the "middle" number in an ordered list of numbers.

PROCEDURE Finding the Median

To compute the median of a list of numbers, first arrange the numbers in order from least to greatest.

- If the number of data values in the list is *odd*, then the median is the middle number in the list.

- If the number of data values is *even*, there is no single middle number. Therefore, the median is the mean (average) of the two middle numbers in the list.

Example 2 Finding the Median of a Data Set

Consider the salaries of the five workers from Example 1.

$42,000 $36,000 $45,000 $35,000 $38,000

a. Find the median salary for the five workers.

b. Find the median salary including the owner's salary of $218,000.

Solution:

a. 35,000   36,000   38,000   42,000   45,000   Arrange the data in order.

Because there are five data values (an *odd* number), the median is the middle number.

The median is $38,000.

b. Now consider the scores of all six individuals (including the owner). Arrange the data in order.

35,000   36,000   38,000   42,000   45,000   218,000

There are six data values (an *even* number). The median is the average of the two middle numbers.

$$\frac{38,000 + 42,000}{2}$$

$$= \frac{80,000}{2}$$ Add the two middle numbers.

$$= 40,000$$ Divide.

The median of all six salaries is $40,000.

Skill Practice

3. Find the median of the five housing prices given in margin Exercise 1.

$108,000	$149,000
$164,000	$118,000
$144,000	

4. Find the median of the six housing prices given in margin Exercise 2.

$108,000	$149,000
$164,000	$118,000
$144,000	$1,300,000

Answers

3. $144,000   **4.** $146,500

In Examples 1 and 2, the mean of all six salaries is $69,000, whereas the median is $40,000. These examples show that the median is a better representation for a central value when the data list has an unusually high (or low) value.

Skill Practice

5. The monthly rainfall for Houston, Texas, is given in the table. Find the median rainfall amount.

Month	Rainfall (in.)
Jan.	4.5
Feb.	3.0
March	3.2
April	3.5
May	5.1
June	6.8
July	4.3
Aug.	4.5
Sept.	5.6
Oct.	5.3
Nov.	4.5
Dec.	3.8

Example 3 **Finding the Median of a Data Set**

For a recent year, the student-to-teacher ratio for elementary schools is shown in Table 8-7. Find the median student-to-teacher ratio.

Table 8-7

State	Student-to-Teacher Ratio
California	20.6
Illinois	16.1
Indiana	16.1
Maine	12.5
Mississippi	16.1
New Hampshire	14.5
North Dakota	13.4
Rhode Island	14.8
Utah	21.9
Wisconsin	14.1

Source: National Center for Education Statistics

Solution:

First arrange the numbers in order from least to greatest:

ME	ND	WI	NH	RI	IL	IN	MS	CA	UT
12.5	13.4	14.1	14.5	14.8	16.1	16.1	16.1	20.6	21.9

$$\text{Median} = \frac{14.8 + 16.1}{2} = 15.45$$

There are 10 data values (an *even* number). Therefore, the median is the average of the middle two numbers. The median student-to-teacher ratio is 15.45. This indicates that there are approximately 15 or 16 students per teacher.

Note: The median may not be one of the original data values. This was true in Example 3.

3. Mode

A third representative value for a list of data is called the mode.

DEFINITION **Mode**

The **mode** of a set of data is the value or values that occur most often.

- If two values occur most often we say the data are **bimodal**.
- If more than two values occur most often, we say there is no mode.

Answer

5. 4.5 in.

Example 4 **Finding the Mode of a Data Set**

Find the mode of the student-to-teacher ratios from Example 3.

Solution:

12.5   13.4   14.1   14.5   14.8   16.1   16.1   16.1   20.6   21.9

The data value 16.1 appears the most often. Therefore, the mode is 16.1.

Example 5 **Finding the Mode of a Data Set**

Find the mode of the list of average monthly temperatures for Albany, New York. Values are in °F.

Jan.	Feb.	March	April	May	June	July	Aug.	Sept.	Oct.	Nov.	Dec.
22	25	35	47	58	66	71	69	61	49	39	26

Solution:

No data value occurs most often. There is no mode for this set of data.

Example 6 **Finding the Mode of a Data Set**

The grades for a quiz in college algebra are as follows. The scores are out of a possible 10 points.

9	4	6	9	9	8	2	1	4	9
5	10	10	5	7	7	9	8	7	3
9	7	10	7	10	1	7	4	5	6

Solution:

Sometimes arranging the data in order makes it easier to find the repeated values.

1	1	2	3	4	4	4	5	5	5
6	6	7	7	7	7	7	7	8	8
9	9	9	9	9	9	10	10	10	10

The score of 9 occurs 6 times. The score of 7 occurs 6 times. There are two modes, 9 and 7, because these scores both occur more than any other score. We say that these data are *bimodal*.

TIP: To remember the difference between median and mode, think of the *median* of a highway that goes down the *middle*. Think of the word *mode* as sounding similar to the word *most*.

4. Weighted Mean

Sometimes data values in a list appear multiple times. In such a case, we can compute a **weighted mean**. In Example 7, each data value is "weighted" by the number of times it appears in the list.

Skill Practice

9. People throw coins in wishing wells, and often the money is used for charity. The number of coins collected from one wishing well is shown in the table. Compute the mean dollar amount per coin. Round to three decimal places.

Number of Coins

Quarter	182
Dime	359
Nickel	403
Penny	1056

0 200 400 600 800 1000 1200

Example 7 **Computing a Weighted Mean**

Donations are made to a certain charitable organization in increments of $25, $50, $75, and $100, as shown in Figure 8-13. Find the mean amount donated.

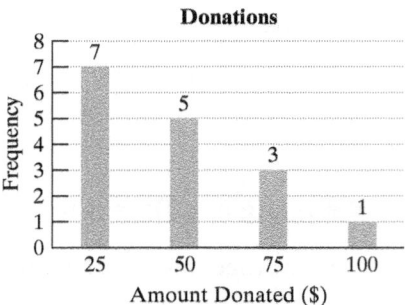

Figure 8-13

Solution:

Notice that there are 16 data values represented in the graph:

$$7 \text{ of these} \begin{cases} \$25 \\ \$25 \\ \$25 \\ \$25 \\ \$25 \\ \$25 \\ \$25 \end{cases} \quad 5 \text{ of these} \begin{cases} \$50 \\ \$50 \\ \$50 \\ \$50 \\ \$50 \end{cases} \quad 3 \text{ of these} \begin{cases} \$75 \\ \$75 \\ \$75 \end{cases} \quad 1 \text{ of these} \{\$100$$

The data value $25 occurs seven times. Rather than adding $25 seven times, we can find the sum by multiplying $25(7) = $175. Similarly, the value $50 occurs 5 times for a sum of $50(5) = $250, and so on. To find the sum of all the values, multiply each data value by the number of times it occurs (its frequency). Then add the results. This process can be organized easily in a table.

Amount Donated ($)	Frequency	Product ($)
25	7	(25)(7) = 175
50	5	(50)(5) = 250
75	3	(75)(3) = 225
100	1	(100)(1) = 100
Total:	**16**	**750** ← sum of all data values

total number of donations made

The mean is the sum of all donations divided by the total number of donations made (total frequency).

$$\text{Mean} = \frac{750}{16} = 46.875$$

The mean amount donated is $46.88.

Answer

9. $0.056

Section 8.4   Practice Exercises

Study Skills Exercise

1. Define the key terms.

    a. Mean   **b. Median**   **c. Mode**   **d. Bimodal**   **e. Weighted mean**

Objective 1: Mean

2. True or False: The mean is always the best measure of central value.

For Exercises 3–8, find the mean of each set of numbers. **(See Example 1.)**

3. $4, 6, 5, 10, 4, 5, 8$ **4.** $3, 8, 5, 7, 4, 2, 7, 4$ **5.** $0, 5, 7, 4, 7, 2, 4, 3$

6. $7, 6, 5, 10, 8, 4, 8, 6, 0$ **7.** $10, 13, 18, 20, 15$ **8.** $22, 14, 12, 16, 15$

9. The wingspan of five butterflies is given in the table. Find the mean wingspan.

Butterfly	Wingspan (in.)
Queen Alexandra's birdwing	11.0
African giant swallowtail	9.1
Goliath birdwing	8.3
Buru opalescent birdwing	7.9
Chimaera birdwing	7.5

10. The number of wins in the American Baseball League, Central Division, for a recent year is given in the table. Find the mean number of wins.

Team	Number of Wins
Minnesota Twins	96
Chicago White Sox	90
Kansas City Royals	62
Cleveland Indians	78
Detroit Tigers	95

11. The flight times in hours for six flights between New York and Los Angeles are given. Find the mean flight time. Round to the nearest tenth of an hour.

    5.5, 6.0, 5.8, 5.8, 6.0, 5.6

12. A nurse takes the temperature of a patient every 10 min and records the temperatures as follows: 98°F, 98.4°F, 98.9°F, 100.1°F, and 99.2°F. Find the patient's mean temperature.

13. The number of Calories for six different chicken sandwiches and chicken salads is given in the table.

    a. What is the mean number of Calories for a chicken sandwich? Round to the nearest whole unit.

    b. What is the mean number of Calories for a salad with chicken? Round to the nearest whole unit.

    c. What is the difference in the means?

Chicken Sandwiches	Salads with Chicken
360	310
370	325
380	350
400	390
400	440
470	500

14. The heights of the players from two NBA teams are given in the table. All heights are in inches.

Philadelphia 76ers' Height (in.)	Milwaukee Bucks' Height (in.)
83	70
83	83
72	82
79	72
77	82
84	85
75	75
76	75
82	78
79	77

    a. Find the mean height for the players on the Philadelphia 76ers.

    b. Find the mean height for the players on the Milwaukee Bucks.

    c. What is the difference in the mean heights?

15. Zach received the following scores for his first four tests: 98%, 80%, 78%, 90%.

    a. Find Zach's mean test score.

    b. Zach got a 59% on his fifth test. Find the mean of all five tests.

    c. How did the low score of 59% affect the overall mean of five tests?

16. The prices of four steam irons are $50, $30, $25, and $45.

    a. Find the mean of these prices.

    b. An iron that costs $140 is added to the list. What is the mean of all five irons?

    c. How does the expensive iron affect the mean?

Objective 2: Median

For Exercises 17–22, find the median for each set of numbers. (See Examples 2–3.)

17. 16, 14, 22, 13, 20, 19, 17

18. 32, 35, 22, 36, 30, 31, 38

19. 109, 118, 111, 110, 123, 100

20. 134, 132, 120, 135, 140, 118

21. 58, 55, 50, 40, 40, 55

22. 82, 90, 99, 82, 88, 87

23. The infant mortality rates for five countries are given in the table. Find the median.

Country	Infant Mortality Rate (Deaths per 1000)
Sweden	3.93
Japan	4.10
Finland	3.82
Andorra	4.09
Singapore	3.87

24. The inflation rates for five countries are given in the table. Find the median.

Country	Inflation Rate (%)
Angola	1700
Sudan	133
Turkey	80
Venezuela	103
Bulgaria	311

25. The ages (in years) of the last 10 Presidents at the time of their inauguration are given. Find the median age.

46, 64, 69, 52, 61, 56, 55, 43, 62, 60

26. A list of the number of commuter rail stations from eight systems is given. Find the median number of stations.

124, 227, 108, 167, 121, 177, 49, 18

27. The number of passengers (in millions) on 9 leading airlines for a recent year is listed. Find the median number of passengers. (*Source: International Airline Transport Association*)

48.3, 42.4, 91.6, 86.8, 46.5, 71.2, 45.4, 56.4, 51.7

28. For a recent year the number of albums sold (in millions) is listed for the 10 best sellers. Find the median number of albums sold.

2.7, 3.0, 4.8, 7.4, 3.4, 2.6, 3.0, 3.0, 3.9, 3.2

Objective 3: Mode

For Exercises 29–34, find the mode(s) for each set of numbers. **(See Examples 4–6.)**

29. 4, 5, 3, 8, 4, 9, 4, 2, 1, 4

30. 12, 14, 13, 17, 19, 18, 19, 17, 17

31. 90%, 89%, 91%, 77%, 88%

32. 132, 253, 553, 255, 552, 234

33. 28, 21, 24, 23, 24, 30, 21

34. 45, 42, 40, 41, 49, 49, 42

35. The table gives the price of seven "smart" cell phones. Find the mode.

Brand and Model	Price ($)
Samsung	600
Kyocera	400
Sony Ericsson	800
PalmOne	450
Motorola	300
Siemens	600

36. The table gives the number of hazardous waste sites for selected states. Find the mode.

State	Number of Sites
Florida	51
New Jersey	112
Michigan	67
Wisconsin	39
California	96
Pennsylvania	94
Illinois	39
New York	90

37. The unemployment rates in percent for nine countries are given. Find the mode.

6.3%, 7.0%, 5.8%, 9.1%, 5.2%, 8.8%, 8.4%, 5.4%, 5.2%

38. The list gives the number of children who were absent from class for a 10-day period. Find the mode.

1, 6, 2, 2, 4, 4, 2, 2, 3, 2

39. The prices for five different brands of paper towel are given in the list. Find the mode.

$2.49, $2.39, $2.51, $2.49, $2.51

40. The length of time (in minutes) of eight TV commercials is given. Find the mode.

1.00, 0.50, 1.00, 1.25, 2.00, 0.50, 1.00, 0.50

Mixed Exercises

41. Six test scores for Jonathan's history class are listed. Find the mean and median. Round to the nearest tenth if necessary. Did the mean or median give a better overall score for Jonathan's performance?

92%, 98%, 43%, 98%, 97%, 85%

42. Nora's math test results are listed. Find the mean and median. Round to the nearest tenth if necessary. Did the mean or median give a better overall score for Nora's performance?

52%, 85%, 89%, 90%, 83%, 89%

43. Listed below are monthly costs for seven health insurance companies for a self-employed person, 55 yr of age, and in good health. Find the mean, median, and mode (if one exists). Round to the nearest dollar. (*Source:* eHealth Insurance Company)

$312, $225, $221, $256, $308, $280, $147

44. The salaries for seven Associate Professors at the University of Michigan are listed. These are salaries for 9-month contracts. Find the mean, median, and mode (if one exists). Round to the nearest dollar. (*Source:* University of Michigan, University Library)

$104,000, $107,000, $67,750, $82,500, $73,500, $88,300, $104,000

45. The prices of 10 single-family, 3-bedroom homes for sale in Santa Rosa, California, are listed. Find the mean, median, and mode (if one exists).

$850,000, $835,000, $839,000, $829,000,

$850,000, $850,000, $850,000, $847,000,

$1,850,000, $825,000

46. The prices of 10 single-family, 3-bedroom homes for sale in Boston, Massachusetts, are listed. Find the mean, median, and mode (if one exists).

$300,000, $2,495,000, $2,120,000, $220,000,

$194,000, $391,000, $315,000, $330,000,

$435,000, $250,000

Objective 4: Weighted Mean

47. There are 20 students enrolled in a 12th-grade math class. The graph displays the number of students by age. First complete the table, and then find the mean. **(See Example 7.)**

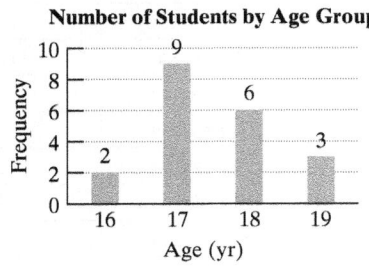

Age (yr)	Number of Students	Product
16		
17		
18		
19		
Total:		

48. A survey was made in a neighborhood of 37 houses. The graph represents the number of residents who live in each house. Complete the table and determine the mean number of residents per house.

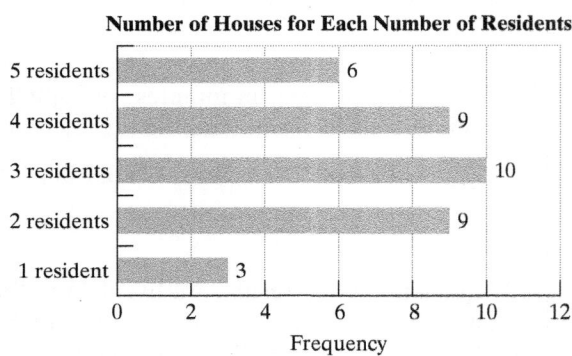

Number of Residents in Each House	Number of Houses	Product
1		
2		
3		
4		
5		
Total:		

49. Several instructors were asked the number of students who were initially enrolled in their classes. The results are represented in the graph. Find the weighted mean of the number of students initially enrolled in class. Round to the nearest whole unit.

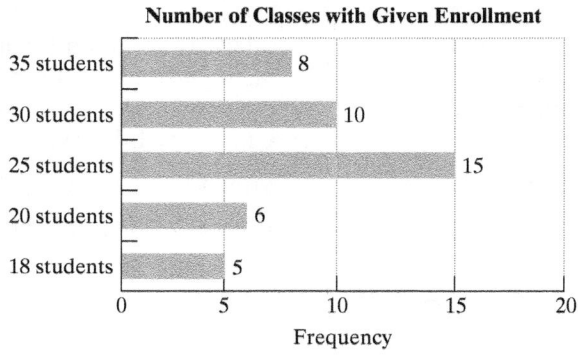

At most colleges and universities, weighted means are used to compute students' grade point averages (GPAs). At one college, the grades A–F are assigned numerical values as follows:

$$A = 4.0 \quad C = 2.0$$
$$B+ = 3.5 \quad D+ = 1.5$$
$$B = 3.0 \quad D = 1.0$$
$$C+ = 2.5 \quad F = 0.0$$

Grade point average is a weighted mean where the "weights" for each grade are the number of credit-hours for that class. Use this information to answer Exercises 50–53.

50. Compute the GPA for the following grades. Round to the nearest hundredth.

Course	Grade	Number of Credit-Hours (Weights)
Intermediate Algebra	B	4
Theater	C	1
Music Appreciation	A	3
World History	D	5

51. Compute the GPA for the following grades. Round to the nearest hundredth.

Course	Grade	Number of Credit-Hours (Weights)
General Psychology	B+	3
Beginning Algebra	A	4
Student Success	A	1
Freshman English	B	3

52. Compute the GPA for the following grades. Round to the nearest hundredth.

Course	Grade	Number of Credit-Hours (Weights)
Business Calculus	B+	3
Biology	C	4
Library Research	F	1
American Literature	A	3

53. Compute the GPA for the following grades. Round to the nearest hundredth.

Course	Grade	Number of Credit-Hours (Weights)
University Physics	C+	5
Calculus I	A	4
Computer Programming	D	3
Swimming	A	1

Group Activity

Creating a Statistical Report

Materials: A computer with Internet access or the local newspaper

Estimated time: 20–30 minutes

Group Size: 4

The group members will collect numerical data from the Internet or the newspaper. The data will be analyzed using the statistical techniques learned in this chapter. Here is one suggested project.

1. Record the age and gender of the individuals who were arrested in your town during the past week. This can often be found in the local section of the newspaper. For example, you can visit the website for the Daytona Beach *News-Journal* and select "local news" and then "news of record." Record 20 or 30 data values.

2. Compute the mean, median, and mode for the ages of men arrested. Compute the mean, median, and mode for the ages of women arrested. Do the statistics suggest a difference in the average age of arrest for men versus women?

3. Determine the percentage of men and the percentage of women in the sample. Does there appear to be a significant difference?

4. Organize the data by age group and construct a frequency distribution and histogram.

Note: The steps given in this project offer suggestions for organizing and analyzing the data you collect. These steps outline standard statistical techniques that apply to a variety of data sets. You might consider doing a different project that investigates a topic of interest to you. Here are some other ideas.

• Collect the weight and gender of babies born in the local hospital.

• Collect the age and gender of students who take classes at night versus those who take classes during the day.

• Collect stock prices for a 2- or 3-week period.

Can you think of other topics for a project?

Chapter 8 Summary

Section 8.1 Tables, Bar Graphs, Pictographs, and Line Graphs

Key Concepts and Examples

Statistics is the branch of mathematics that involves collecting, organizing, and analyzing **data** (information). Information can often be organized in tables and graphs. The individual entries within a table are called **cells**.

Example 1

The data in the table give the number of Calories for a 1-c serving of selected vegetables.

Vegetable (1 c)	Number of Calories
Corn	85
Green beans	35
Eggplant	25
Peas	125
Spinach	40

A **pictograph** uses an icon or small image to convey a unit of measurement.

Example 3

What is the value of each icon in the graph?

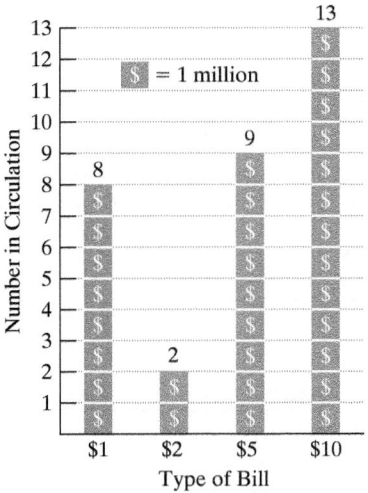

Each icon is worth 1,000,000 bills in circulation.

Examples

Example 2

Construct a bar graph for the data in Example 1.

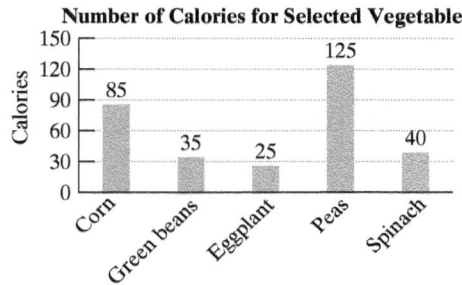

Line graphs are often used to track how one variable changes with respect to the change in a second variable.

Example 4

In what year were there 52.3 million married-couple households?

From the graph, the year 1990 corresponds to 52.3 million married-couple households.

Section 8.2 — Frequency Distributions and Histograms

Key Concepts

A **frequency distribution** is a table displaying the number of data values that fall within specified intervals called **class intervals**.

When constructing a frequency distribution, keep these important guidelines in mind.

- The classes should be equally spaced.
- The classes should not overlap.
- In general, use between 5 and 15 classes.

A **histogram** is a special bar graph that illustrates data given in a frequency distribution. The class intervals are given on the horizontal scale. The height of each bar in a histogram measures the frequency for each class.

Examples

Example 1

Create a frequency distribution for the following data.

50	53
54	51
50	40
50	47
53	36
44	34
52	32
42	30

Class Intervals	Tally	Frequency
30–34	III	3
35–39	I	1
40–44	III	3
45–49	I	1
50–54	IIII III	8

Example 2

Create a histogram for the data in Example 1.

Section 8.3 — Circle Graphs

Key Concepts

A **circle graph** (or pie graph) is a type of graph used to show how a whole amount is divided into parts. Each part of the circle, called a **sector**, is like a slice of pie.

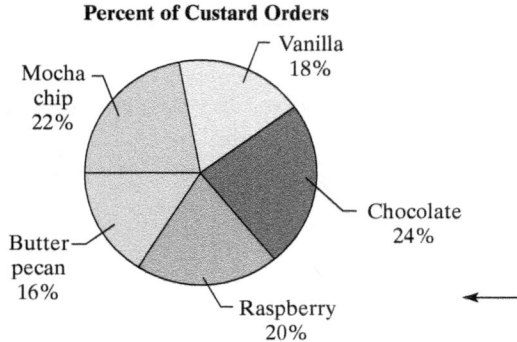

Percent of Custard Orders

Examples

Example 1

At Ritter's Frozen Custard, the flavors for the day are given with the number of orders for each flavor.

Flavor	Number of Orders
Vanilla	180
Chocolate	240
Raspberry	200
Butter pecan	160
Mocha chip	220

Construct a circle graph for the data given. Label the sectors with percents.

Section 8.4   Mean, Median, and Mode

Key Concepts

The **mean** (or average) of a set of numbers is the sum of the values divided by the number of values.

$$\text{Mean} = \frac{\text{sum of the values}}{\text{number of values}}$$

The **median** is the "middle" number in an ordered list of numbers. For an ordered list of numbers:

- If the number of data values is *odd*, then the median is the middle number in the list.
- If the number of data values is *even*, the median is the mean of the two middle numbers in the list.

The **mode** of a set of data is the value or values that occur most often.

When data values in a list appear multiple times, we can compute a **weighted mean**.

Examples

Example 1

Find the mean test score: 92, 100, 86, 60, 90

$$\text{Mean} = \frac{92 + 100 + 86 + 60 + 90}{5}$$

$$= \frac{428}{5} = 85.6$$

Example 2

Find the median: 12   18   6   10   5

First order the list: 5   6   10   12   18
The median is the middle number, 10.

Example 3

Find the median: 15   20   20   32   40   45

The median is the average of 20 and 32:

$$\frac{20 + 32}{2} = \frac{52}{2} = 26 \qquad \text{The median is 26.}$$

Example 4

Find the mode: 7   2   5   7   7   4   6   10

The value 7 is the mode because it occurs most often.

Example 5

The ages of children in a day-care center are given in the table. Find the mean age.

Age (yr)	Frequency	Product
3	5	$3 \cdot 5 = 15$
4	10	$4 \cdot 10 = 40$
5	3	$5 \cdot 3 = 15$
6	2	$6 \cdot 2 = 12$
Total	**20**	**82**

$$\text{Mean} = \frac{82}{20} = 4.1$$

The mean age is 4.1 yr.

Chapter 8   Review Exercises

Section 8.1

For Exercises 1–4, refer to the table. The table gives the number of Calories and the amount of fat, cholesterol, sodium, and carbohydrate for a single $\frac{1}{2}$-c serving of chocolate ice cream.

Ice Cream	Calories	Fat(g)	Cholesterol (mg)	Sodium (mg)	Carbohydrate (g)
Breyers	150	8	20	35	17
Häagen-Dazs	270	18	115	60	22
Edy's Grand	150	8	25	35	17
Blue Bell	160	8	35	70	18
Godiva	290	18	65	50	28

1. Which ice cream has the most calories?

2. Which ice cream has the least amount of cholesterol?

3. How many more times the sodium does Blue Bell have per serving than Edy's Grand?

4. What is the difference in the amount of carbohydrate for Godiva and Blue Bell?

Since 1940 the number of U.S. farms has decreased. However, the average size of the farms has increased. The graph shows the average size of U.S. farms for selected years. Refer to the graph for Exercises 5–8. (*Source:* U.S. Department of Agriculture)

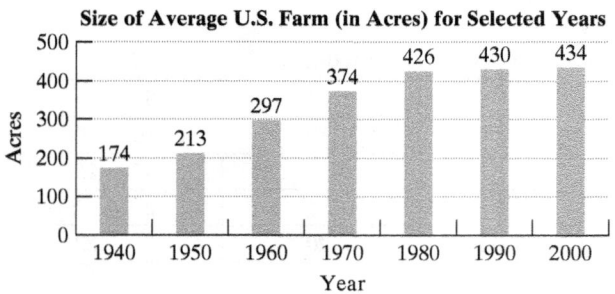

Size of Average U.S. Farm (in Acres) for Selected Years

5. What was the average size of the farms in 1970?

6. What is the difference between the average size farm in the year 2000 compared to 1940?

7. What is the difference between the average size farm in the year 1990 compared to 1980?

8. In which 10-year interval was the increase the greatest?

For Exercises 9–12, refer to the pictograph. The graph represents the number of tornadoes during four months with active weather.

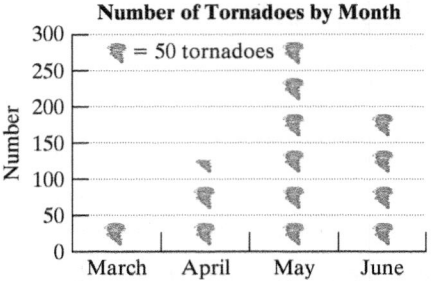

Number of Tornadoes by Month

9. What does each icon represent?

10. From the graph, estimate the number of tornadoes in May.

11. Which month had approximately 200 tornadoes?

12. Estimate the difference in the number of tornadoes in April and the number in March.

For Exercises 13–16, refer to the graph. The graph represents the number of liver transplants in the United States for selected years. (*Source:* U.S. Department of Health and Human Services)

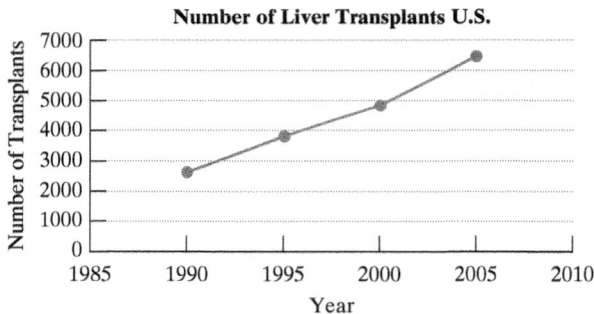

Number of Liver Transplants U.S.

13. In which year did the greatest number of liver transplants occur?

14. Approximate the number of liver transplants for the year 2000.

15. Does the trend appear to be increasing or decreasing?

16. Extend the graph to predict the number of liver transplants for the year 2007.

17. The table shows several movies that grossed over 100 million dollars in the United States. Construct a bar graph using horizontal bars. The length of each bar should represent the amount of money in millions that each movie grossed. (*Source: Washington Post*)

Movie Title	Gross (in millions)	Year
Titanic	601	1997
Star Wars	461	1977
Shrek 2	436	2004
Lord of the Rings: The Fellowship of the Ring	314	2001
Harry Potter and the Goblet of Fire	290	2005
Wedding Crashers	209	2005

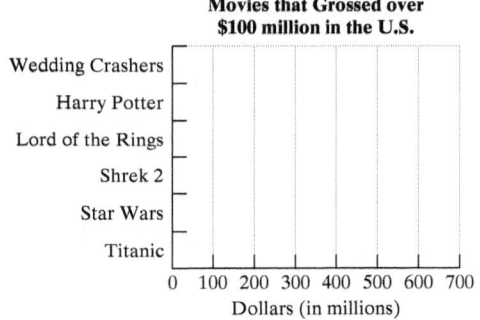

Movies that Grossed over $100 million in the U.S.

Section 8.2

The ages of students in a Spanish class are given.

18   22   19   26   31   20   40   24   43   22
29   28   35   42   29   30   24   31   23   21

Use these data for Exercises 18–19.

18. Complete the frequency table.

Class Intervals (Age)	Frequency
18–21	
22–25	
26–29	
30–33	
34–37	
38–41	
42–45	

19. Construct a histogram of the data in Exercise 18.

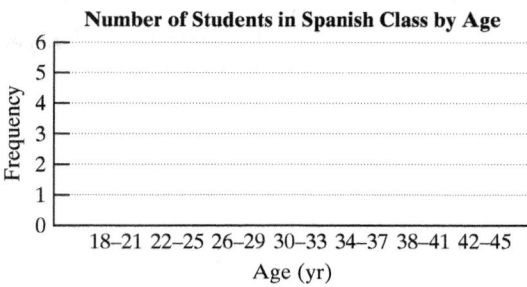

Number of Students in Spanish Class by Age

Section 8.3

The pie graph describes the types of subs offered at Larry's Sub Shop. Use the information in the graph for Exercises 20–22.

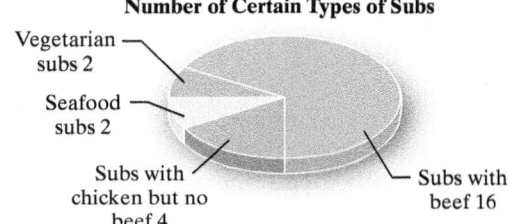

Number of Certain Types of Subs

20. How many types of subs are offered at Larry's?

21. What fraction of the subs at Larry's is made with beef?

22. What fraction of the subs at Larry's is not made with beef?

23. A survey was conducted with 200 people, and they were asked their highest level of education. The results of the survey are given in the table.

a. Complete the table.

Education Level	Number of People	Percent	Number of Degrees
Grade school	10		
High school	50		
Some college	60		
Four-year degree	40		
Post graduate	40		

b. Construct a circle graph using percents from the information in the table from part (a).

Percent by Education Level

Section 8.4

24. For the list of quiz scores, find the mean, median, and mode(s).

20, 20, 18, 16, 18, 17, 16, 10, 20, 20, 15, 20

25. Juanita kept track of how many milligrams of calcium she took each day through vitamins and dairy products. Determine the mean number of milligrams of calcium per day. Round to the nearest 10 (mg).

26. The seating capacity for five arenas used by the NBA is given in the table. Find the median number of seats.

Arena	Number of Seats
St. Louis Arena, St. Louis	20,000
TD Garden, Boston	18,624
Time Warner Arena, Charlotte	19,077
United Center, Chicago	20,917
Quicken Loans Arena, Cleveland	20,562

27. The manager of a restaurant had his customers fill out evaluations on the service that they received. A scale of 1 to 5 was used, where 1 represents very poor service and 5 represents excellent service. Given the list of responses, determine the mode(s).

4 5 3 4 4 3 2 5 5 1 4 3 4 4 5
2 5 4 4 3 2 5 5 1 4

28. There are 20 children participating in an afternoon fitness program. The graph displays the number of children by age. Complete the table and then find the mean age of the children.

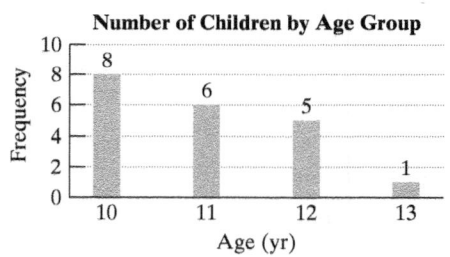

Age (yr)	Number of Children	Product
10		
11		
12		
13		

Chapter 8 Test

1. The table represents the world's major producers of primary energy for a recent year. All measurements are in quadrillions of Btu.

   Note: 1 quadrillion = 1,000,000,000,000,000. (*Source:* Energy Information Administration, U.S. Dept. of Energy)

Country	Amount of Energy Produced (quadrillions of BTUs)
United States	72
Russia	43
China	35
Saudi Arabia	43
Canada	18

   Construct a bar graph using horizontal bars. The length of each bar corresponds to the amount of energy produced for each country.

   World's Major Producers of Primary Energy (Quadrillions of Btu)

   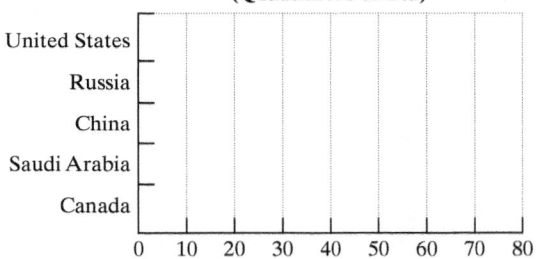

2. Of the approximately 2.9 million workers in 1820 in the United States, 71.8% were employed in farm occupations. Since then, the percent of U.S. workers in farm occupations has declined. The table shows the percent of total U.S. workers who worked in farm-related occupations for selected years. (*Source:* U.S. Department of Agriculture)

Year	Percent of U.S. Workers in Farm Occupations
1820	72%
1860	59%
1900	38%
1940	17%
1980	3%

   a. Which year had the greatest percent of U.S. workers employed in farm occupations? What is the value of the greatest percent?

   b. Make a line graph with the year on the horizontal scale and the percent on the vertical scale.

   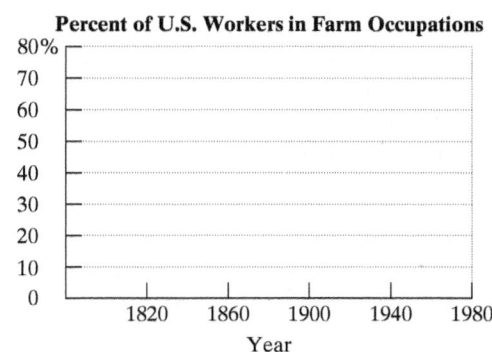

   c. Based on the graph, estimate the percent of U.S. workers employed in farm occupations for the year 1960.

For Exercises 3–5, refer to the pictograph. The pictograph shows the flower sales for the first 5 months of the year for a flower shop.

Flower Shop Sales ($)

3. What is the value of each flower icon?

4. From the graph, estimate the sales for the month of April.

5. Which month brought in sales of $5000?

For Exercises 6–8, refer to the table. The rainfall amounts for Salt Lake City, Utah, and Seattle, Washington, are given in the table for selected months. All values are in inches. (*Source:* National Oceanic and Atmospheric Administration)

	April	**May**	**June**	**July**
Salt Lake City	2.02	2.09	0.77	0.72
Seattle	2.75	2.03	2.5	0.92

6. Which city is generally wetter?

7. What is the difference in the amount of rainfall in Seattle and Salt Lake City during June?

8. Find the mean amount of rainfall for these months for each city.

9. A cellular phone company questioned 20 people at a mall, to determine approximately how many minutes each individual spent on the cell phone each month. Using the list of results, complete the frequency distribution and construct a histogram.

100   120   250   180   300   200   250   175
110   280   330   280   300   325   60   75
100   350   60   90

Number of Minutes Used Monthly	**Tally**	**Frequency**
51–100		
101–150		
151–200		
201–250		
251–300		
301–350		

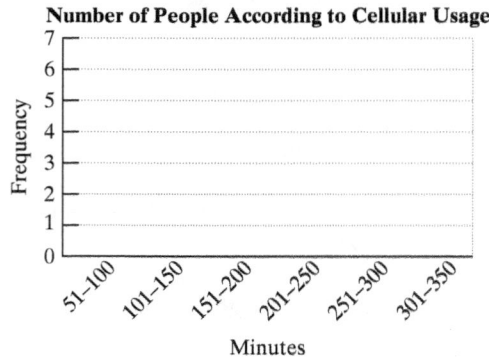

Number of People According to Cellular Usage

For Exercises 10–12, refer to the circle graph. The circle graph shows the percent of homes having different types of flooring in the living room area.

Percent of Types of Floor Covering

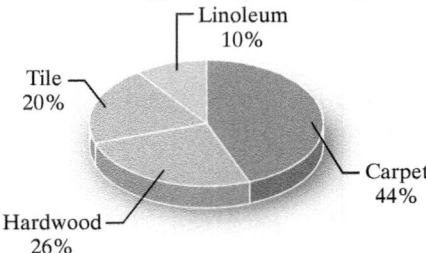

10. If 150 people were questioned, how many would be expected to have carpet on their living room floor?

11. If 200 people were questioned, how many would be expected to have tile on their living room floor?

12. If 300 people were questioned, how many would not be expected to have linoleum on their living room floor?

For Exercises 13–15, refer to the table. The table represents the heights of the Seven Summits (the highest peaks from each continent).

Mountain	**Continent**	**Height (ft)**
Mt. Kilimanjaro	Africa	19,340
Elbrus	Europe	18,510
Aconcagua	South America	22,834
Denali	North America	20,320
Vinson Massif	Antarctica	16,864
Mt. Kosciusko	Australia	7,310
Mt. Everest	Asia	29,035

13. What is the mean height of the Seven Summits? Round to the nearest whole unit.

14. What is the median height?

15. Is there a mode?

16. Mike and Darcy listed the amount of money paid for going to the movies for the past 3 months. This list contains the amount for 2 tickets. Find the mean, median, and mode.

$11 $14 $11 $16 $15 $16 $12 $16 $15 $20

Chapters 1–8 Cumulative Review Exercises

1. Identify the place value of the underlined digit.

   a. 23,990,192   **b.** 5,981,902   **c.** 3,019,226

2. Add.   2087 + 53 + 10,499 + 6

3. Estimate the product by first rounding each number to the nearest hundred.

$$687 \times 1243$$

4. What fraction of this circle is shaded?

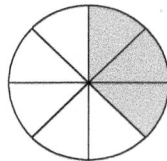

5. Simplify. $\dfrac{5}{8} \div \dfrac{6}{15} \cdot \dfrac{24}{25}$

6. The table gives the prices of certain stocks and their increase or decrease from one day to the next. Complete the table.

Stock	Yesterday's Closing Price ($)	Increase/ Decrease	Today's Closing Price ($)
RylGold	13.28	0.27	
NetSolve	9.51	−0.17	
Metals USA	14.35	0.10	
PAM Transpt	18.09	0.09	
Steel Tch	21.63	−0.37	

For Exercises 7–8, multiply or divide by powers of 10.

7. 68.412 × 100   **8.** 68.412 ÷ 0.001

9. The estimated forest cover in the Brazilian Amazon in 1970 was approximately 3.7 million square kilometers. By 2005, the amount dropped to 3.0 million km². (*Source:* National Geographic Society)

   a. By how many square kilometers had the Brazilian Amazon forest cover decreased?

   b. Compute the percent decrease in forest cover. Round to the nearest tenth of a percent.

10. Quick Cut Lawn Company can service 5 customers in $2\frac{3}{4}$ hr. Speedy Lawn Company can service 6 customers in 3 hr. Find the unit rate in time per customer for both lawn companies and decide which company is faster.

11. If Rosa can type a 4-page English paper in 50 min, how long will it take her to type a 10-page term paper?

12. Find the values of x and y, assuming that the two triangles are similar.

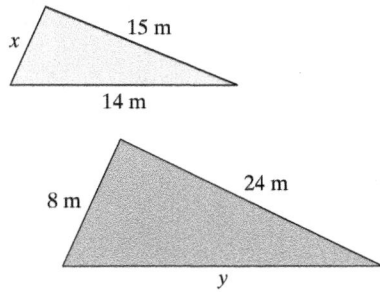

13. A savings account pays 3.4% simple interest. If $1200 is invested for 5 years, what will be the balance?

14. Convert 2 ft 5 in. to inches.

15. Add. 3 yd 2 ft + 5 yd 2 ft

16. Divide 16 lb 12 oz by 4.

For Exercises 17–18, identify the type of angle. Choose from acute, obtuse, right, or straight.

17.   **18.**

19. The monthly number of deaths resulting from tornados for a recent year are given. Find the mean and median. Round to the nearest whole unit.

   33, 10, 62, 132, 123, 316, 138,

   123, 133, 18, 150, 26

20. Simplify the expression.

$$30 - 3(5 - 2)^2$$

Linear Equations and Inequalities

9

Chapter 9

In Chapter 9, we learn how to solve linear equations and inequalities in one variable.

Are You Prepared?

One of the skills needed involves multiplication of fractions and decimals. The following set of problems will review that skill. For help with multiplying fractions, see Chapter 4. For help with multiplying decimals, see Chapter 5.

Simplify each expression and fill in the blank with the correct answer written as a word. Then fill the word into the puzzle. The words will fit in the puzzle according to the number of letters in each word.

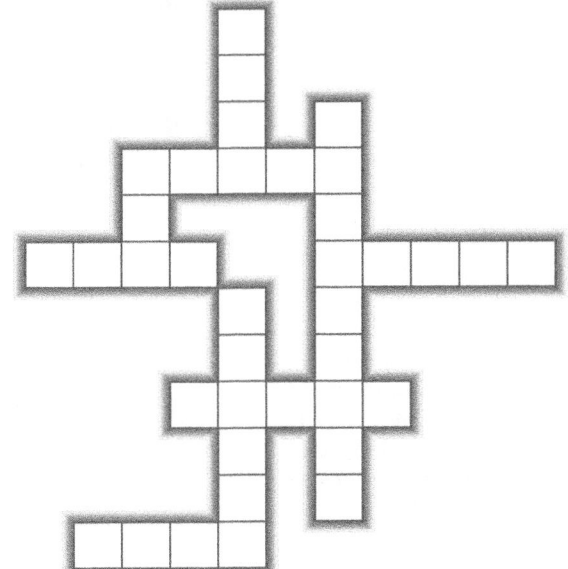

$8 \cdot \left(\dfrac{3}{8}\right) = $ _____

$6 \cdot \left(\dfrac{2}{3}\right) = $ _____

$100(0.17) = $ _____

$100(0.09) = $ _____

_____ $\cdot \left(\dfrac{2}{5}\right) = 2$

_____ $\cdot \left(\dfrac{6}{7}\right) = 6$

_____ $\cdot \left(\dfrac{3}{4}\right) = 6$

_____ $\cdot \left(\dfrac{5}{6}\right) = 10$

_____ $\cdot (0.4) = 4$

Section 9.1   Sets of Numbers and the Real Number Line

Objectives

1. The Set of Real Numbers
2. Inequalities
3. Absolute Value of a Real Number

1. The Set of Real Numbers

The numbers we work with on a day-to-day basis are all part of the set of **real numbers**. The real numbers encompass zero, all positive, and all negative numbers, including those represented by fractions and decimal numbers. The set of real numbers can be represented graphically on a horizontal number line with a point labeled as 0. Positive real numbers are graphed to the right of 0, and negative real numbers are graphed to the left of 0. Zero is neither positive nor negative. Each point on the number line corresponds to exactly one real number. For this reason, this number line is called the *real number line* (Figure 9-1).

Figure 9-1

Skill Practice

1. Plot the numbers on a real number line.
   $\{-1, \frac{3}{4}, -2.5, \frac{10}{3}\}$

Example 1   Plotting Points on the Real Number Line

Plot the points on the real number line that represent the following real numbers.

a. -3 **b.** $\dfrac{3}{2}$ **c.** -4.7 **d.** $\dfrac{16}{5}$

Solution:

a. Because -3 is negative, it lies three units to the left of 0.

b. The fraction $\frac{3}{2}$ can be expressed as the mixed number $1\frac{1}{2}$, which lies half-way between 1 and 2 on the number line.

c. The negative number -4.7 lies $\frac{7}{10}$ units to the left of -4 on the number line.

d. The fraction $\frac{16}{5}$ can be expressed as the mixed number $3\frac{1}{5}$, which lies $\frac{1}{5}$ unit to the right of 3 on the number line.

TIP: The natural numbers are used for counting. For this reason, they are sometimes called the "counting numbers."

In mathematics, a well-defined collection of elements is called a **set**. "Well-defined" means the set is described in such a way that it is clear whether an element is in the set. The symbols { } are used to enclose the elements of the set. For example, the set {A, B, C, D, E} represents the set of the first five letters of the alphabet.

Several sets of numbers are used extensively in algebra and are *subsets* (or part) of the set of real numbers.

DEFINITION   Natural Numbers, Whole Numbers, and Integers

The set of **natural numbers** is $\{1, 2, 3, \ldots\}$

The set of **whole numbers** is $\{0, 1, 2, 3, \ldots\}$

The set of **integers** is $\{\ldots -3, -2, -1, 0, 1, 2, 3, \ldots\}$

Answer

1.

Notice that the set of whole numbers includes the natural numbers. Therefore, every natural number is also a whole number. The set of integers includes the set of whole numbers. Therefore, every whole number is also an integer.

Fractions are also among the numbers we use frequently. A number that can be written as a fraction whose numerator is an integer and whose denominator is a nonzero integer is called a *rational number*.

DEFINITION Rational Numbers

The set of **rational numbers** is the set of numbers that can be expressed in the form $\frac{p}{q}$, where both p and q are integers and q does not equal 0.

We also say that a rational number $\frac{p}{q}$ is a *ratio* of two integers, p and q, where q is not equal to zero.

Example 2 **Identifying Rational Numbers**

Show that the following numbers are rational numbers by finding an equivalent ratio of two integers.

a. $\dfrac{-2}{3}$ **b.** -12 **c.** 0.5 **d.** $0.\overline{6}$

Solution:

a. The fraction $\frac{-2}{3}$ is a rational number because it can be expressed as the ratio of -2 and 3.

b. The number -12 is a rational number because it can be expressed as the ratio of -12 and 1, that is, $-12 = \frac{-12}{1}$. In this example, we see that an integer is also a rational number.

c. The terminating decimal 0.5 is a rational number because it can be expressed as the ratio of 5 and 10. That is, $0.5 = \frac{5}{10}$. In this example, we see that a terminating decimal is also a rational number.

d. The repeating decimal $0.\overline{6}$ is a rational number because it can be expressed as the ratio of 2 and 3. That is, $0.\overline{6} = \frac{2}{3}$. In this example, we see that a repeating decimal is also a rational number.

Skill Practice

Show that each number is rational by finding an equivalent ratio of two integers.

2. $\dfrac{3}{7}$ **3.** -5

4. 0.3 **5.** $0.\overline{3}$

Some real numbers, such as the number π, cannot be represented by the ratio of two integers. These numbers are called irrational numbers and in decimal form are nonterminating, nonrepeating decimals. The value of π, for example, can be approximated as $\pi \approx 3.1415926535897932$. However, the decimal digits continue forever with no repeated pattern. Another example of an irrational number is $\sqrt{3}$ (read as "the positive square root of 3"). The expression $\sqrt{3}$ is a number that when multiplied by itself is 3. There is no rational number that satisfies this condition. Thus, $\sqrt{3}$ is an irrational number.

TIP: Any rational number can be represented by a terminating decimal or by a repeating decimal.

DEFINITION Irrational Numbers

The set of **irrational numbers** is a subset of the real numbers whose elements cannot be written as a ratio of two integers.

Note: An irrational number cannot be written as a terminating decimal or as a repeating decimal.

Answers

2. ratio of 3 and 7
3. ratio of -5 and 1
4. ratio of 3 and 10
5. ratio of 1 and 3

The set of real numbers consists of both the rational and the irrational numbers. The relationship among these important sets of numbers is illustrated in Figure 9-2:

Figure 9-2

Skill Practice

Identify the sets to which each number belongs. Choose from: natural numbers, whole numbers, integers, rational numbers, irrational numbers, real numbers.

6. -4 **7.** $0.\overline{7}$
8. $\sqrt{13}$ **9.** 12   **10.** 0

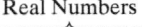 **Example 3** **Classifying Numbers by Set**

Check the set(s) to which each number belongs. The numbers may belong to more than one set.

	Natural Numbers	Whole Numbers	Integers	Rational Numbers	Irrational Numbers	Real Numbers
5						
$\dfrac{-47}{3}$						
1.48						
$\sqrt{7}$						
0						

Solution:

	Natural Numbers	Whole Numbers	Integers	Rational Numbers	Irrational Numbers	Real Numbers
5	✔	✔	✔	✔ (ratio of 5 and 1)		✔
$\dfrac{-47}{3}$				✔ (ratio of -47 and 3)		✔
1.48				✔ (ratio of 148 and 100)		✔
$\sqrt{7}$					✔	✔
0		✔	✔	✔ (ratio of 0 and 1)		✔

Answers

6. Integers, rational numbers, real numbers
7. Rational numbers, real numbers
8. Irrational numbers, real numbers
9. Natural numbers, whole numbers, integers, rational numbers, real numbers
10. Whole numbers, integers, rational numbers, real numbers

2. Inequalities

The relative size of two real numbers can be compared using the real number line. Suppose a and b represent two real numbers. We say that a is less than b, denoted $a < b$, if a lies to the left of b on the number line.

$a < b$

We say that a is greater than b, denoted $a > b$, if a lies to the right of b on the number line.

$a > b$

Table 9-1 summarizes the relational operators that compare two real numbers a and b.

Table 9-1

Mathematical Expression	Translation	Example
$a < b$	a is less than b.	$2 < 3$
$a > b$	a is greater than b.	$5 > 1$
$a \leq b$	a is less than or equal to b.	$4 \leq 4$
$a \geq b$	a is greater than or equal to b.	$10 \geq 9$
$a = b$	a is equal to b.	$6 = 6$
$a \neq b$	a is not equal to b.	$7 \neq 0$
$a \approx b$	a is approximately equal to b.	$2.3 \approx 2$

The symbols $<, >, \leq, \geq$, and $\neq$ are called *inequality signs*, and the expressions $a < b, a > b, a \leq b, a \geq b$, and $a \neq b$ are called **inequalities**.

Example 4 **Ordering Real Numbers**

The average temperatures (in degrees Celsius) for selected cities in the United States and Canada in January are shown in Table 9-2.

Table 9-2

City	Temp (°C)
Prince George, British Columbia	−12.5
Corpus Christi, Texas	13.4
Parkersburg, West Virginia	−0.9
San Jose, California	9.7
Juneau, Alaska	−5.7
New Bedford, Massachusetts	−0.2
Durham, North Carolina	4.2

Plot a point on the real number line representing the temperature of each city. Compare the temperatures between the following cities and fill in the blank with the appropriate inequality sign: $<$ or $>$.

Solution:

a. Temperature of San Jose $\boxed{<}$ temperature of Corpus Christi

b. Temperature of Juneau $\boxed{>}$ temperature of Prince George

c. Temperature of Parkersburg $\boxed{<}$ temperature of New Bedford

d. Temperature of Parkersburg $\boxed{>}$ temperature of Prince George

3. Absolute Value of a Real Number

Recall that the absolute value of a real number a, denoted $|a|$, is the distance between a and 0 on the number line. For example, $|3| = 3$ and $|-3| = 3$.

Example 5 **Finding the Absolute Value of a Real Number**

Evaluate the absolute value expressions.

a. $|-4|$ **b.** $\left|\frac{1}{2}\right|$ **c.** $|-6.2|$ **d.** $|0|$

Solution:

a. $|-4| = 4$ -4 is 4 units from 0 on the number line.

b. $\left|\frac{1}{2}\right| = \frac{1}{2}$ $\frac{1}{2}$ is $\frac{1}{2}$ unit from 0 on the number line.

c. $|-6.2| = 6.2$ -6.2 is 6.2 units from 0 on the number line.

d. $|0| = 0$ 0 is 0 units from 0 on the number line.

The definition of $|a|$ may be given symbolically depending on whether a is negative or nonnegative.

DEFINITION **Absolute Value of a Real Number**

Let a be a real number. Then

1. If a is nonnegative (that is, $a \geq 0$), then $|a| = a$.

2. If a is negative (that is, $a < 0$), then $|a| = -a$.

This definition states that if *a* is a nonnegative number, then $|a|$ equals *a* itself. If *a* is a negative number, then $|a|$ equals the opposite of *a*. For example:

$|9| = 9$ Because 9 is positive, then $|9|$ equals the number 9 itself.

$|-7| = 7$ Because -7 is negative, then $|-7|$ equals the opposite of -7, which is 7.

Example 6	**Comparing Absolute Value Expressions**

Determine if the statements are true or false.

a. $|3| \leq 3$ **b.** $-|5| = |-5|$

Solution:

a. $|3| \leq 3$ True. The symbol $\leq$ means "less than *or* equal to." Since $|3|$ is equal to 3, then $|3| \leq 3$ is a true statement.

b. $-|5| = |-5|$ False. On the left-hand side, $-|5|$ is the opposite of $|5|$. Hence $-|5| = -5$. On the right-hand side, $|-5| = 5$. Therefore, the original statement simplifies to $-5 = 5$, which is false.

Section 9.1   Practice Exercises

Boost *your* GRADE at
ALEKS.com!

ALEKS®
version 3.0

• Practice Problems   • e-Professors
• Self-Tests   • Videos
• NetTutor

Study Skills Exercises

1. It is always helpful to read the material in a section and make notes before it is presented in class. Writing notes ahead of time will free you to listen more in class and to pay special attention to the concepts that need clarification. Refer to your class syllabus and list the next two sections that will be covered in class and a time that you can read them beforehand.

2. Define the key terms:

   a. Real numbers   **b. Set**   **c. Natural numbers**   **d. Whole numbers**

   e. Integers   **f. Rational numbers**   **g. Irrational numbers**   **h. Inequality**

Objective 1: The Set of Real Numbers

3. Plot the numbers on a real number line: $\{1, -2, -\pi, 0, -\frac{5}{2}, 5.1\}$ (See Example 1.)

4. Plot the numbers on a real number line: $\{3, -4, \frac{1}{8}, -1.7, -\frac{4}{3}, 1.75\}$

For Exercises 5–20, describe each number as (a) a terminating decimal, (b) a repeating decimal, or (c) a nonterminating, nonrepeating decimal. Then classify the number as a rational number or as an irrational number. **(See Example 2.)**

5. 0.29

6. 3.8

7. $\frac{1}{9}$

8. $\frac{1}{3}$

9. $\frac{1}{8}$

10. $\frac{1}{5}$

11. 2π

12. 3π

13. -0.125

14. -3.24

15. -3

16. -6

17. $0.\overline{2}$

18. $0.\overline{6}$

19. $\sqrt{6}$

20. $\sqrt{10}$

21. List three numbers that are real numbers but not rational numbers.

22. List three numbers that are real numbers but not irrational numbers.

23. List three numbers that are integers but not natural numbers.

24. List three numbers that are integers but not whole numbers.

25. List three numbers that are rational numbers but not integers.

For Exercises 26–32, let $A = \{-\frac{3}{2}, \sqrt{11}, -4, 0.\overline{6}, 0, \sqrt{7}, 1\}$ **(See Example 3.)**

26. Are all of the numbers in set A real numbers?

27. List all of the rational numbers in set A.

28. List all of the whole numbers in set A.

29. List all of the natural numbers in set A.

30. List all of the irrational numbers in set A.

31. List all of the integers in set A.

32. Plot the real numbers from set A on a number line. (*Hint:* $\sqrt{11} \approx 3.3$ and $\sqrt{7} \approx 2.6$)

Objective 2: Inequalities

33. The LPGA Samsung World Championship of women's golf scores for selected players are given in the table. Compare the scores and fill in the blank with the appropriate inequality sign: $<$ or $>$. **(See Example 4.)**

a. Kane's score _____ Pak's score.

b. Sorenstam's score _____ Davies' score.

c. Pak's score _____ McCurdy's score.

d. Kane's score _____ Davies' score.

LPGA Golfers	Final Score with Respect to Par
Annika Sorenstam	7
Laura Davies	−4
Lorie Kane	0
Cindy McCurdy	3
Se Ri Pak	−8

34. The elevations of selected cities in the United States are shown in the figure. Compare the elevations and fill in the blank with the appropriate inequality sign: $<$ or $>$. (A negative number indicates that the city is below sea level.)

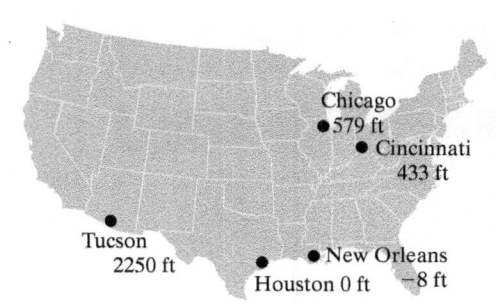

a. Elevation of Tucson _____ elevation of Cincinnati.

b. Elevation of New Orleans _____ elevation of Chicago.

c. Elevation of New Orleans _____ elevation of Houston.

d. Elevation of Chicago _____ elevation of Cincinnati.

Objective 3: Absolute Value of a Real Number

For Exercises 35–46, simplify. **(See Example 5.)**

35. $|-2|$

36. $|-7|$

37. $|-1.5|$

38. $|-3.7|$

39. $-|-1.5|$

40. $-|-3.7|$

41. $\left|\dfrac{3}{2}\right|$

42. $\left|\dfrac{7}{4}\right|$

43. $-|10|$

44. $-|20|$

45. $-\left|-\dfrac{1}{2}\right|$

46. $-\left|-\dfrac{11}{3}\right|$

For Exercises 47–48, answer true or false. If a statement is false, explain why.

47. If n is positive, then $|n|$ is negative.

48. If m is negative, then $|m|$ is negative.

For Exercises 49–72, determine if the statements are true or false. Use the real number line to justify the answer. **(See Example 6.)**

49. $5 > 2$

50. $8 < 10$

51. $6 < 6$

52. $19 > 19$

53. $-7 \geq -7$

54. $-1 \leq -1$

55. $\dfrac{3}{2} \leq \dfrac{1}{6}$

56. $-\dfrac{1}{4} \geq -\dfrac{7}{8}$

57. $-5 > -2$

58. $6 < -10$

59. $8 \neq 8$

60. $10 \neq 10$

61. $|-2| \geq |-1|$

62. $|3| \leq |-1|$

63. $\left|-\dfrac{1}{9}\right| = \left|\dfrac{1}{9}\right|$

64. $\left|-\dfrac{1}{3}\right| = \left|\dfrac{1}{3}\right|$

65. $|7| \neq |-7|$

66. $|-13| \neq |13|$

67. $-1 < |-1|$

68. $-6 < |-6|$

69. $|-8| \geq |8|$

70. $|-11| \geq |11|$

71. $|-2| \leq |2|$

72. $|-21| \leq |21|$

Expanding Your Skills

73. For what numbers, a, is $-a$ positive?

74. For what numbers, a, is $|a| = a$?

Section 9.2 | Solving Linear Equations

Objectives

1. Solving Linear Equations
2. Solving Linear Equations Involving Multiple Steps
3. Conditional Equations, Identities, and Contradictions

1. Solving Linear Equations

An *equation* is a statement that indicates that two quantities are equal. A **solution to an equation** is a value for the variable that makes the equation a true statement. Substituting a solution for the variable in an equation makes the right-hand side equal to the left-hand side.

Equation	Solution	Check	
$2y + 4 = 10$	3	$2(3) + 4 \stackrel{?}{=} 10$	Substitute 3 for y.
		$6 + 4 \stackrel{?}{=} 10$ ✔	

In this chapter, we will focus on solving linear equations in one variable. In Section 3.2, we introduced the following definition.

> **DEFINITION** Linear Equation in One Variable
>
> Let a, b, and c be real numbers such that $a \neq 0$. A **linear equation in one variable** is an equation that can be written in the form
>
> $$ax + b = c$$
>
> **Note:** A linear equation in one variable is often called a first-degree equation because the variable x has an implied exponent of 1.
>
> | Examples | Notes |
> |---|---|
> | $3x + 5 = 20$ | $a = 3, b = 5, c = 20$ |
> | $-9x - 4 = 6$ can be written as $-9x + (-4) = 6$ | $a = -9, b = -4, c = 6$ |
> | $6x + 7 - 5x = 11$ can be written as $x + 7 = 11$ | $a = 1, b = 7, c = 11$ |

To solve a linear equation in the variable x, the goal is to write the equation in the form $x =$ number. In particular, notice the x-term is isolated and that the coefficient of x is 1. The properties of equality enable us to rewrite an equation as an equivalent equation in the desired form.

> **SUMMARY** Properties of Equality
>
> Let a, b, and c represent algebraic expressions.
>
> 1. If $a = b$, then $a + c = b + c$ Addition property of equality
> 2. If $a = b$, then $a - c = b - c$ Subtraction property of equality
> 3. If $a = b$, then $ac = bc$ (for $c \neq 0$)   Multiplication property of equality
> 4. If $a = b$, then $\dfrac{a}{c} = \dfrac{b}{c}$ (for $c \neq 0$)   Division property of equality

The addition and subtraction properties of equality indicate that adding or subtracting the same quantity on each side of an equation results in an equivalent equation. This means that if two equal quantities are increased or decreased by the same amount, then the resulting quantities will also be equal.

── **Skill Practice** ──

Solve the equations.
1. $v - 7 = 2$
2. $x + 4 = 4$

Example 1 Applying the Addition and Subtraction Properties of Equality

Solve the equations.

  a. $p - 4 = 11$ **b.** $w + 5 = -2$

Answers

1. 9   2. 0

Solution:

In each equation, the goal is to isolate the variable on one side of the equation. To accomplish this, we use the fact that the sum of a number and its opposite is zero and the difference of a number and itself is zero.

a. $p - 4 = 11$

$p - 4 + 4 = 11 + 4$ To isolate p, add 4 to both sides $(-4 + 4 = 0)$.

$p + 0 = 15$ Simplify.

$p = 15$ Check by substituting $p = 15$ into the original equation.

        Check: $p - 4 = 11$

               $15 - 4 \stackrel{?}{=} 11$

The solution is 15. $11 \stackrel{?}{=} 11$ ✔   True

b. $w + 5 = -2$

$w + 5 - 5 = -2 - 5$ To isolate w, subtract 5 from both sides. $(5 - 5 = 0)$.

$w + 0 = -7$ Simplify.

$w = -7$ Check by substituting $w = -7$ into the original equation.

        Check: $w + 5 = -2$

               $-7 + 5 \stackrel{?}{=} -2$

The solution is -7. $-2 \stackrel{?}{=} -2$ ✔   True

Multiplying or dividing both sides of an equation by the same nonzero quantity also results in an equivalent equation.

Example 2   **Applying the Multiplication and Division Properties of Equality**

Solve the equations using the multiplication or division property of equality.

a. $12x = 60$ **b.** $-\dfrac{2}{9}q = \dfrac{1}{3}$

Solution:

a. $12x = 60$

$\dfrac{12x}{12} = \dfrac{60}{12}$ To obtain a coefficient of 1 for the x-term, divide both sides by 12.

$1x = 5$ Simplify.

$x = 5$ Check: $12x = 60$

             $12(5) \stackrel{?}{=} 60$

The solution is 5. $60 \stackrel{?}{=} 60$ ✔   True

Skill Practice

Solve the equations.

3. $4x = -20$

4. $-\dfrac{2}{3}a = \dfrac{1}{4}$

Answers

3. -5 **4.** $-\dfrac{3}{8}$

b.
$$-\frac{2}{9}q = \frac{1}{3}$$

$$\left(-\frac{9}{2}\right)\left(-\frac{2}{9}q\right) = \frac{1}{3}\left(-\frac{9}{2}\right)$$

To obtain a coefficient of 1 for the q-term, multiply by the reciprocal of $-\frac{2}{9}$, which is $-\frac{9}{2}$.

$$1q = -\frac{3}{2}$$

Simplify. The product of a number and its reciprocal is 1.

$$q = -\frac{3}{2}$$ Check: $-\frac{2}{9}q = \frac{1}{3}$

$$-\frac{2}{9}\left(-\frac{3}{2}\right) \overset{?}{=} \frac{1}{3}$$

The solution is $-\frac{3}{2}$. $\frac{1}{3} \overset{?}{=} \frac{1}{3}$ ✔ True

---

TIP: When applying the multiplication or division property of equality to obtain a coefficient of 1 for the variable term, we will generally use the following convention:

- If the coefficient of the variable term is an integer or decimal, we will divide both sides by the coefficient itself, as in Example 2(a).
- If the coefficient of the variable term is expressed as a fraction, we will usually multiply both sides by its reciprocal, as in Example 2(b).

2. Solving Linear Equations Involving Multiple Steps

In Examples 1 and 2, we used a one-step process to solve linear equations by using the addition, subtraction, multiplication, and division properties of equality. In Example 3, we solve the equation $-2w - 7 = 11$. Solving this equation will require multiple steps. To understand the proper steps, always remember the ultimate goal—to isolate the variable. Therefore, we will first isolate the *term* containing the variable before dividing both sides by -2.

Skill Practice

Solve the equation.
5. $-5y - 5 = 10$

Example 3   **Solving a Linear Equation**

Solve the equation. $-2w - 7 = 11$

Solution:

$$-2w - 7 = 11$$

$$-2w - 7 + 7 = 11 + 7$$ Add 7 to both sides of the equation. This isolates the w-term.

$$-2w = 18$$

$$\frac{-2w}{-2} = \frac{18}{-2}$$ Next, apply the division property of equality to obtain a coefficient of 1 for w. Divide by -2 on both sides.

$$w = -9$$

Check:
$$-2w - 7 = 11$$

$$-2(-9) - 7 \overset{?}{=} 11$$ Substitute $w = -9$ in the original equation.

$$18 - 7 \overset{?}{=} 11$$

The solution is -9. $11 \overset{?}{=} 11$ ✔ True.

Answer

5. -3

In Example 4, the variable x appears on both sides of the equation. In this case, apply the addition or subtraction property of equality to collect the variable terms on one side of the equation and the constant terms on the other side. Then use the multiplication or division property of equality to get a coefficient equal to 1.

Example 4 **Solving a Linear Equation**

Solve the equation. $6x - 4 = 2x - 8$

Solution:

$$6x - 4 = 2x - 8$$

$$6x - 2x - 4 = 2x - 2x - 8 \qquad \text{Subtract } 2x \text{ from both sides leaving } 0x \text{ on the right-hand side.}$$

$$4x - 4 = 0x - 8 \qquad \text{Simplify.}$$

$$4x - 4 = -8 \qquad \text{The } x\text{-terms have now been combined on one side of the equation.}$$

$$4x - 4 + 4 = -8 + 4 \qquad \text{Add } 4 \text{ to both sides of the equation. This combines the constant terms on the } other$$

$$4x = -4 \qquad \text{side of the equation.}$$

$$\frac{4x}{4} = \frac{-4}{4} \qquad \text{To obtain a coefficient of 1 for } x, \text{ divide both sides of the equation by } 4.$$

$$x = -1 \qquad \underline{\text{Check}}:$$

$$6x - 4 = 2x - 8$$

$$6(-1) - 4 \overset{?}{=} 2(-1) - 8$$

$$-6 - 4 \overset{?}{=} -2 - 8$$

The solution is -1. $\qquad -10 \overset{?}{=} -10 \checkmark \;\; \text{True}$

Skill Practice

Solve the equation.
6. $10x - 3 = 4x - 2$

TIP: It is important to note that the variable may be isolated on either side of the equation. We will solve the equation from Example 4 again, this time isolating the variable on the right-hand side.

$$6x - 4 = 2x - 8$$

$$6x - 6x - 4 = 2x - 6x - 8 \qquad \text{Subtract } 6x \text{ on both sides.}$$

$$0x - 4 = -4x - 8$$

$$-4 = -4x - 8$$

$$-4 + 8 = -4x - 8 + 8 \qquad \text{Add } 8 \text{ to both sides.}$$

$$4 = -4x$$

$$\frac{4}{-4} = \frac{-4x}{-4} \qquad \text{Divide both sides by } -4.$$

$$-1 = x \quad \text{or equivalently } x = -1$$

In some cases, it is necessary to simplify both sides of a linear equation before applying the properties of equality. Therefore, we offer the following steps to solve a linear equation in one variable.

Answer

6. $\dfrac{1}{6}$

PROCEDURE Solving a Linear Equation in One Variable

Step 1 Simplify both sides of the equation.
- Clear parentheses
- Combine *like* terms

Step 2 Use the addition or subtraction property of equality to collect the variable terms on one side of the equation.

Step 3 Use the addition or subtraction property of equality to collect the constant terms on the other side of the equation.

Step 4 Use the multiplication or division property of equality to make the coefficient of the variable term equal to 1.

Step 5 Check your answer.

Skill Practice

Solve the equation.

7. $12 + 2 = 7(3 - y)$

Example 5 Solving a Linear Equation

Solve the equation. $7 + 3 = 2(p - 3)$

Solution:

$$7 + 3 = 2(p - 3)$$

$$10 = 2p - 6 \qquad \textbf{Step 1:} \quad \text{Simplify both sides of the equation by clearing parentheses and combining } like \text{ terms.}$$

$$\textbf{Step 2:} \quad \text{The variable terms are already on one side.}$$

$$10 + 6 = 2p - 6 + 6 \qquad \textbf{Step 3:} \quad \text{Add 6 to both sides to collect the constant terms on the other side.}$$

$$16 = 2p$$

$$\frac{16}{2} = \frac{2p}{2} \qquad \textbf{Step 4:} \quad \text{Divide both sides by 2 to obtain a coefficient of 1 for } p.$$

$$8 = p \qquad \textbf{Step 5:} \quad \underline{\text{Check:}}$$

The solution is 8.

$$7 + 3 = 2(p - 3)$$
$$10 \overset{?}{=} 2(8 - 3)$$
$$10 \overset{?}{=} 2(5)$$
$$10 \overset{?}{=} 10 \checkmark \quad \text{True}$$

Answer

7. 1

Example 6 **Solving a Linear Equation**

Solve the equation. $2 + 7x - 5 = 6(x + 3) + 2x$

Solution:

$$2 + 7x - 5 = 6(x + 3) + 2x$$

$-3 + 7x = 6x + 18 + 2x$ **Step 1:** Add *like* terms on the left. Clear parentheses on the right.

$-3 + 7x = 8x + 18$ Combine *like* terms.

$-3 + 7x - 7x = 8x - 7x + 18$ **Step 2:** Subtract $7x$ from both sides.

$-3 = x + 18$ Simplify.

$-3 - 18 = x + 18 - 18$ **Step 3:** Subtract 18 from both sides.

$-21 = x$

$x = -21$ **Step 4:** Because the coefficient of the x term is already 1, there is no need to apply the multiplication or division property of equality.

The solution is -21. **Step 5:** The check is left to the reader.

Skill Practice
Solve the equation.
8. $4(2y - 1) + y = 6y + 3 - y$

Example 7 **Solving a Linear Equation**

Solve the equation. $9 - (z - 3) + 4z = 4z - 5(z + 2) - 6$

Solution:

$$9 - (z - 3) + 4z = 4z - 5(z + 2) - 6$$

$9 - z + 3 + 4z = 4z - 5z - 10 - 6$ **Step 1:** Clear parentheses.

$12 + 3z = -z - 16$ Combine *like* terms.

$12 + 3z + z = -z + z - 16$ **Step 2:** Add z to both sides.

$12 + 4z = -16$

$12 - 12 + 4z = -16 - 12$ **Step 3:** Subtract 12 from both sides.

$4z = -28$

$\dfrac{4z}{4} = \dfrac{-28}{4}$ **Step 4:** Divide both sides by 4.

$z = -7$ **Step 5:** The check is left for the reader.

The solution is -7.

Skill Practice
Solve the equation.
9. $10 - (x + 5) + 3x = 6x - 5(x - 1) - 3$

Answers
8. $\dfrac{7}{4}$ **9.** -3

3. Conditional Equations, Identities, and Contradictions

The solutions to a linear equation are the values of x that make the equation a true statement. A linear equation in one variable has one unique solution. Some types of equations, however, have no solution while others have infinitely many solutions.

I. Conditional Equations

An equation that is true for some values of the variable but false for other values is called a **conditional equation**. The equation $x + 4 = 6$, for example, is true on the condition that $x = 2$. For other values of x, the statement $x + 4 = 6$ is false.

II. Contradictions

Some equations have no solution, such as $x + 1 = x + 2$. There is no value of x, that when increased by 1 will equal the same value increased by 2. If we tried to solve the equation by subtracting x from both sides, we get the contradiction $1 = 2$. This indicates that the equation has no solution. An equation that has no solution is called a **contradiction**.

$$x + 1 = x + 2$$
$$x - x + 1 = x - x + 2$$
$$1 = 2 \quad \text{(contradiction)} \qquad \text{No solution.}$$

III. Identities

An equation that has all real numbers as its solution set is called an **identity**. For example, consider the equation, $x + 4 = x + 4$. Because the left- and right-hand sides are equivalent, any real number substituted for x will result in equal quantities on both sides. If we subtract x from both sides of the equation, we get the identity $4 = 4$. In such a case, the solution is the set of all real numbers.

$$x + 4 = x + 4$$
$$x - x + 4 = x - x + 4$$
$$4 = 4 \quad \text{(identity)} \qquad \text{The solution is all real numbers.}$$

Example 8 Identifying Conditional Equations, Contradictions, and Identities

Solve the equation. Identify each equation as a conditional equation, a contradiction, or an identity.

a. $4k - 5 = 2(2k - 3) + 1$ **b.** $2(b - 4) = 2b - 7$ **c.** $3x + 7 = 2x - 5$

Solution:

a.
$$4k - 5 = 2(2k - 3) + 1$$

$$4k - 5 = 4k - 6 + 1 \qquad \text{Clear parentheses.}$$

$$4k - 5 = 4k - 5 \qquad \text{Combine } like \text{ terms.}$$

$$4k - 4k - 5 = 4k - 4k - 5 \qquad \text{Subtract } 4k \text{ from both sides.}$$

$$-5 = -5 \quad \text{(Identity)}$$

This is an identity. The solution is all real numbers.

b. $2(b - 4) = 2b - 7$

$\quad 2b - 8 = 2b - 7$ $\qquad$ Clear parentheses.

$2b - 2b - 8 = 2b - 2b - 7$ $\qquad$ Subtract $2b$ from both sides.

$\quad -8 = -7$ (Contradiction)

This is a contradiction. There is no solution.

c. $3x + 7 = 2x - 5$

$3x - 2x + 7 = 2x - 2x - 5$ $\qquad$ Subtract $2x$ from both sides.

$\quad x + 7 = -5$ $\qquad$ Simplify.

$x + 7 - 7 = -5 - 7$ $\qquad$ Subtract 7 from both sides.

$\quad x = -12$ (Conditional equation)

This is a conditional equation. The solution is -12. (The equation is true only on the condition that $x = -12$.)

Section 9.2 Practice Exercises

Study Skills Exercises

1. Some instructors are available to answer questions during evening hours via e-mail. Find out if you can contact your instructor by e-mail during evening hours or weekends, and write down the e-mail address.

2. Define the key terms:

   a. Solution to an equation   **b.** Linear equation in one variable

   c. Conditional equation   **d.** Contradiction   **e.** Identity

Objective 1: Solving Linear Equations

For Exercises 3–24, solve the equations using the addition, subtraction, multiplication, or division property of equality.
(See Examples 1–2.)

3. $5w = -30$ **4.** $-7y = 21$ **5.** $x + 8 = -15$ **6.** $z - 23 = -28$

7. $-\dfrac{9}{8} = -\dfrac{3}{4}k$ **8.** $-\dfrac{2}{5}m = 10$ **9.** $a - 9 = 1$ **10.** $b - 2 = -4$

11. $-9x = 1$ **12.** $-2k = -4$ **13.** $-\dfrac{2}{3}h = 8$ **14.** $\dfrac{3}{4}p = 15$

15. $\dfrac{2}{3} + t = 8$ **16.** $\dfrac{3}{4} + y = 15$ **17.** $\dfrac{r}{3} = -12$ **18.** $\dfrac{d}{-4} = 5$

19. $k + 16 = 32$ **20.** $-18 = -9 + t$ **21.** $16k = 32$ **22.** $-18 = -9t$

23. $7 = -4q$ **24.** $-3s = 10$

Objective 2: Solving Linear Equations Involving Multiple Steps

For Exercises 25–58, solve the equations using the steps outlined in the text. **(See Examples 3–7.)**

25. $6z + 1 = 13$ **26.** $5x + 2 = -13$ **27.** $3y - 4 = 14$

28. $-7w - 5 = -19$ **29.** $-2p + 8 = 3$ **30.** $2b - \dfrac{1}{4} = 5$

31. $7w - 6w + 1 = 10 - 4$ **32.** $5v - 3 - 4v = 13$ **33.** $11h - 8 - 9h = -16$

34. $6u - 5 - 8u = -7$ **35.** $3a + 7 = 2a - 19$ **36.** $6b - 20 = 14 + 5b$

37. $-4r - 28 = -58 - r$ **38.** $-6x - 7 = -3 - 8x$ **39.** $-2z - 8 = -z$

40. $-7t + 4 = -6t$ **41.** $3y - 2 = 5y - 2$ **42.** $4 + 10t = -8t + 4$

43. $4q + 14 = 2$ **44.** $6 = 7m - 1$ **45.** $-9 = 4n - 1$

46. $-\dfrac{1}{2} - 4x = 8$ **47.** $6(3x + 2) - 10 = -4$ **48.** $4(2k + 1) - 1 = 5$

49. $17(s + 3) = 4(s - 10) + 13$ **50.** $5(4 + p) = 3(3p - 1) - 9$

51. $6(3t - 4) + 10 = 5(t - 2) - (3t + 4)$ **52.** $-5y + 2(2y + 1) = 2(5y - 1) - 7$

53. $5 - 3(x + 2) = 5$ **54.** $1 - 6(2 - h) = 7$

55. $3(2z - 6) - 4(3z + 1) = 5 - 2(z + 1)$ **56.** $-2(4a + 3) - 5(2 - a) = 3(2a + 3) - 7$

57. $-2[(4p + 1) - (3p - 1)] = 5(3 - p) - 9$ **58.** $5 - (6k + 1) = 2[(5k - 3) - (k - 2)]$

Objective 3: Conditional Equations, Identities, and Contradictions

For Exercises 59–64, identify the equation as a conditional equation, a contradiction, or an identity. Then describe the solution. **(See Example 8.)**

59. $2(k - 7) = 2k - 13$ **60.** $5h + 4 = 5(h + 1) - 1$ **61.** $7x + 3 = 6(x - 2)$

62. $3y - 1 = 1 + 3y$ **63.** $3 - 5.2p = -5.2p + 3$ **64.** $2(q + 3) = 4q + q - 9$

65. A conditional linear equation has (choose one): One solution, no solution, or infinitely many solutions.

66. An equation that is a contradiction has (choose one): One solution, no solution, or infinitely many solutions.

67. An equation that is an identity has (choose one): One solution, no solution, or infinitely many solutions.

68. If the only solution to a linear equation is 5, then is the equation a conditional equation, an identity, or a contradiction?

Mixed Exercises

For Exercises 69–92, find the solution, if possible.

69. $4p - 6 = 8 + 2p$ **70.** $\dfrac{1}{2}t - 2 = 3$ **71.** $2k - 9 = -8$

72. $3(y - 2) + 5 = 5$ **73.** $7(w - 2) = -14 - 3w$ **74.** $0.24 = 0.4m$

75. $2(x + 2) - 3 = 2x + 1$

76. $n + \dfrac{1}{4} = -\dfrac{1}{2}$

77. $0.5b = -23$

78. $3(2r + 1) = 6(r + 2) - 6$

79. $8 - 2q = 4$

80. $\dfrac{x}{7} - 3 = 1$

81. $2 - 4(y - 5) = -4$

82. $4 - 3(4p - 1) = -8$

83. $0.4(a + 20) = 6$

84. $2.2r - 12 = 3.4$

85. $10(2n + 1) - 6 = 20(n - 1) + 12$

86. $\dfrac{2}{5}y + 5 = -3$

87. $c + 0.123 = 2.328$

88. $4(2z + 3) = 8(z - 3) + 36$

89. $\dfrac{4}{5}t - 1 = \dfrac{1}{5}t + 5$

90. $6g - 8 = 4 - 3g$

91. $8 - (3q + 4) = 6 - q$

92. $6w - (8 + 2w) = 2(w - 4)$

Expanding Your Skills

93. Suppose -5 is a solution to the equation $x + a = 10$. Find the value of a.

94. Suppose 6 is a solution to the equation $x + a = -12$. Find the value of a.

95. Suppose 3 is a solution to the equation $ax = 12$. Find the value of a.

96. Suppose 11 is a solution to the equation $ax = 49.5$. Find the value of a.

97. Write an equation that is an identity. Answers may vary.

98. Write an equation that is a contradiction. Answers may vary.

Linear Equations: Clearing Fractions and Decimals

Section 9.3

1. Solving Linear Equations with Fractions

Linear equations that contain fractions can be solved in different ways. The first procedure, illustrated here, uses the method outlined in Section 9.2.

Objectives

1. Solving Linear Equations with Fractions
2. Solving Linear Equations with Decimals

$$\frac{5}{6}x - \frac{3}{4} = \frac{1}{3}$$

$$\frac{5}{6}x - \frac{3}{4} + \frac{3}{4} = \frac{1}{3} + \frac{3}{4} \qquad \text{To isolate the variable term, add } \frac{3}{4} \text{ to both sides.}$$

$$\frac{5}{6}x = \frac{4}{12} + \frac{9}{12} \qquad \text{Find the common denominator on the right-hand side.}$$

$$\frac{5}{6}x = \frac{13}{12} \qquad \text{Simplify.}$$

$$\frac{6}{5}\left(\frac{5}{6}x\right) = \frac{\overset{1}{\cancel{6}}}{5}\left(\frac{13}{\underset{2}{\cancel{12}}}\right) \qquad \text{Multiply by the reciprocal of } \frac{5}{6}, \text{ which is } \frac{6}{5}.$$

$$x = \frac{13}{10} \qquad \text{The solution is } \frac{13}{10}.$$

Sometimes it is simpler to solve an equation with fractions by eliminating the fractions first using a process called **clearing fractions**. To clear fractions in the equation $\frac{5}{6}x - \frac{3}{4} = \frac{1}{3}$, we can multiply both sides of the equation by the least common denominator (LCD) of all terms in the equation. In this case, the LCD of $\frac{5}{6}x$, $-\frac{3}{4}$, and $\frac{1}{3}$ is 12. Because each denominator in the equation is a factor of 12, we can simplify common factors to leave integer coefficients for each term.

TIP: Recall that the multiplication property of equality indicates that multiplying both sides of an equation by a nonzero constant results in an equivalent equation.

Example 1 **Solving a Linear Equation by Clearing Fractions**

Solve the equation by clearing fractions first. $\dfrac{5}{6}x - \dfrac{3}{4} = \dfrac{1}{3}$

Solution:

$$\frac{5}{6}x - \frac{3}{4} = \frac{1}{3}$$

$$12\left(\frac{5}{6}x - \frac{3}{4}\right) = 12\left(\frac{1}{3}\right) \quad \text{Multiply both sides of the equation by the LCD, 12.}$$

$$\frac{\overset{2}{\cancel{12}}}{1}\left(\frac{5}{\cancel{6}}x\right) - \frac{\overset{3}{\cancel{12}}}{1}\left(\frac{3}{\cancel{4}}\right) = \frac{\overset{4}{\cancel{12}}}{1}\left(\frac{1}{\cancel{3}}\right) \quad \text{Apply the distributive property (recall that } 12 = \frac{12}{1}\text{).}$$

$$2(5x) - 3(3) = 4(1) \quad \text{Simplify common factors to clear the fractions.}$$

$$10x - 9 = 4$$

$$10x - 9 + 9 = 4 + 9 \quad \text{Add 9 to both sides.}$$

$$10x = 13$$

$$\frac{10x}{10} = \frac{13}{10} \quad \text{Divide both sides by 10.}$$

$$x = \frac{13}{10} \quad \text{The solution is } \frac{13}{10}.$$

TIP: The fractions in this equation can be eliminated by multiplying both sides of the equation by *any* common multiple of the denominators. For example, try multiplying both sides of the equation by 24:

$$24\left(\frac{5}{6}x - \frac{3}{4}\right) = 24\left(\frac{1}{3}\right)$$

$$\frac{\overset{4}{\cancel{24}}}{1}\left(\frac{5}{6}x\right) - \frac{\overset{6}{\cancel{24}}}{1}\left(\frac{3}{4}\right) = \frac{\overset{8}{\cancel{24}}}{1}\left(\frac{1}{3}\right)$$

$$20x - 18 = 8$$

$$20x = 26$$

$$\frac{20x}{20} = \frac{26}{20}$$

$$x = \frac{13}{10}$$

Answer

1. -3

In this section, we combine the process for clearing fractions and decimals with the general strategies for solving linear equations. To solve a linear equation, it is important to follow the steps listed below.

PROCEDURE Solving a Linear Equation in One Variable

Step 1 Simplify both sides of the equation.
- Clear parentheses
- Consider clearing fractions and decimals (if any are present) by multiplying both sides of the equation by a common denominator of all terms.
- Combine *like* terms

Step 2 Use the addition or subtraction property of equality to collect the variable terms on one side of the equation.

Step 3 Use the addition or subtraction property of equality to collect the constant terms on the other side of the equation.

Step 4 Use the multiplication or division property of equality to make the coefficient of the variable term equal to 1.

Step 5 Check your answer.

Example 2 **Solving a Linear Equation with Fractions**

Solve the equation. $\dfrac{1}{6}x - \dfrac{2}{3} = \dfrac{1}{5}x - 1$

Solution:

$$\frac{1}{6}x - \frac{2}{3} = \frac{1}{5}x - 1 \qquad \text{The LCD of } \tfrac{1}{6}x, -\tfrac{2}{3}, \text{ and } \tfrac{1}{5}x \text{ is 30.}$$

$$30\left(\frac{1}{6}x - \frac{2}{3}\right) = 30\left(\frac{1}{5}x - 1\right) \qquad \text{Multiply by the LCD, } 30.$$

$$\frac{\overset{5}{\cancel{30}}}{1}\cdot\frac{1}{\cancel{6}}x - \frac{\overset{10}{\cancel{30}}}{1}\cdot\frac{2}{\cancel{3}} = \frac{\overset{6}{\cancel{30}}}{1}\cdot\frac{1}{\cancel{5}}x - 30(1) \qquad \text{Apply the distributive property (recall } 30 = \tfrac{30}{1}).$$

$$5x - 20 = 6x - 30 \qquad \text{Clear fractions.}$$

$$5x - 6x - 20 = 6x - 6x - 30 \qquad \text{Subtract } 6x \text{ from both sides.}$$

$$-x - 20 = -30$$

$$-x - 20 + 20 = -30 + 20 \qquad \text{Add } 20 \text{ to both sides.}$$

$$-x = -10$$

$$\frac{-x}{-1} = \frac{-10}{-1} \qquad \text{Divide both sides by } -1.$$

$$x = 10 \qquad \text{The solution is 10.}$$

Skill Practice

Solve the equation.

2. $\dfrac{2}{5}x - \dfrac{1}{2} = \dfrac{7}{4} + \dfrac{3}{10}x$

Answer

2. $\dfrac{45}{2}$

Skill Practice

Solve the equation.

3. $\frac{1}{5}(z + 1) + \frac{1}{4}(z + 3) = 2$

Example 3 Solving a Linear Equation with Fractions

Solve the equation. $\frac{1}{3}(x + 7) - \frac{1}{2}(x + 1) = 4$

Solution:

$$\frac{1}{3}(x + 7) - \frac{1}{2}(x + 1) = 4$$

$$\frac{1}{3}x + \frac{7}{3} - \frac{1}{2}x - \frac{1}{2} = 4 \qquad \text{Clear parentheses.}$$

$$6\left(\frac{1}{3}x + \frac{7}{3} - \frac{1}{2}x - \frac{1}{2}\right) = 6(4) \qquad \begin{array}{l}\text{The LCD of}\\ \frac{1}{3}x, \frac{7}{3}, -\frac{1}{2}x, \text{ and } -\frac{1}{2} \text{ is } 6.\end{array}$$

TIP: In Example 3 both parentheses and fractions are present within the equation. In such a case, we recommend that you clear parentheses first. Then clear the fractions.

$$\frac{\overset{2}{\cancel{6}}}{1} \cdot \frac{1}{3}x + \frac{\overset{2}{\cancel{6}}}{1} \cdot \frac{7}{3} + \frac{\overset{3}{\cancel{6}}}{1}\left(-\frac{1}{2}x\right) + \frac{\overset{3}{\cancel{6}}}{1}\left(-\frac{1}{2}\right) = 6(4) \qquad \begin{array}{l}\text{Apply the distributive}\\ \text{property.}\end{array}$$

$$2x + 14 - 3x - 3 = 24$$

$$-x + 11 = 24 \qquad \text{Combine } like \text{ terms.}$$

$$-x + 11 - 11 = 24 - 11 \qquad \text{Subtract } 11.$$

$$-x = 13$$

$$\frac{-x}{-1} = \frac{13}{-1} \qquad \text{Divide by } -1.$$

$$x = -13 \qquad \begin{array}{l}\text{The check is left to the}\\ \text{reader.}\end{array}$$

Skill Practice

Solve the equation.

4. $\frac{x + 1}{4} + \frac{x + 2}{6} = 1$

Example 4 Solving a Linear Equation with Fractions

Solve. $\frac{x - 2}{5} - \frac{x - 4}{2} = 2$

Solution:

$$\frac{x - 2}{5} - \frac{x - 4}{2} = \frac{2}{1} \qquad \text{The LCD of } \frac{x-2}{5}, \frac{x-4}{2}, \text{ and } \frac{2}{1} \text{ is } 10.$$

$$10\left(\frac{x - 2}{5} - \frac{x - 4}{2}\right) = 10\left(\frac{2}{1}\right) \qquad \text{Multiply both sides by } 10.$$

Avoiding Mistakes

In Example 4, several of the fractions in the equation have two terms in the numerator. It is important to enclose these fractions in parentheses when clearing fractions. In this way, we will remember to use the distributive property to multiply the factors shown in blue with both terms from the numerator of the fractions.

$$\frac{\overset{2}{\cancel{10}}}{1} \cdot \left(\frac{x - 2}{\cancel{5}}\right) - \frac{\overset{5}{\cancel{10}}}{1} \cdot \left(\frac{x - 4}{\cancel{2}}\right) = \frac{10}{1} \cdot \left(\frac{2}{1}\right) \qquad \text{Apply the distributive property.}$$

$$2(x - 2) - 5(x - 4) = 20 \qquad \text{Clear fractions.}$$

$$2x - 4 - 5x + 20 = 20 \qquad \text{Apply the distributive property.}$$

$$-3x + 16 = 20 \qquad \text{Simplify both sides of the equation.}$$

$$-3x + 16 - 16 = 20 - 16 \qquad \text{Subtract } 16 \text{ from both sides.}$$

$$-3x = 4$$

$$\frac{-3x}{-3} = \frac{4}{-3} \qquad \text{Divide both sides by } -3.$$

$$x = -\frac{4}{3} \qquad \text{The check is left to the reader.}$$

Answers

3. $\frac{7}{3}$ **4.** 1

2. Solving Linear Equations with Decimals

The same procedure used to clear fractions in an equation can be used to **clear decimals**. For example, consider the equation

$$2.5x + 3 = 1.7x - 6.6$$

Recall that any terminating decimal can be written as a fraction. Therefore, the equation can be interpreted as

$$\frac{25}{10}x + 3 = \frac{17}{10}x - \frac{66}{10}$$

A convenient common denominator of all terms is 10. Therefore, we can multiply the original equation by 10 to clear decimals. The result is

$$25x + 30 = 17x - 66$$

Multiplying by the appropriate power of 10 moves the decimal points so that all coefficients become integers.

Example 5 **Solving a Linear Equation Containing Decimals**

Solve the equation by clearing decimals. $2.5x + 3 = 1.7x - 6.6$

Solution:

$$2.5x + 3 = 1.7x - 6.6$$

$10(2.5x + 3) = 10(1.7x - 6.6)$	Multiply both sides of the equation by 10.
$25x + 30 = 17x - 66$	Apply the distributive property.
$25x - 17x + 30 = 17x - 17x - 66$	Subtract $17x$ from both sides.
$8x + 30 = -66$	
$8x + 30 - 30 = -66 - 30$	Subtract 30 from both sides.
$8x = -96$	
$\dfrac{8x}{8} = \dfrac{-96}{8}$	Divide both sides by 8.
$x = -12$	

Skill Practice

Solve.
5. $1.2w + 3.5 = 2.1 + w$

TIP: Notice that multiplying a decimal number by 10 has the effect of moving the decimal point one place to the right. Similarly, multiplying by 100 moves the decimal point two places to the right, and so on.

Answer
5. -7

Skill Practice

Solve.

6. $0.25(x + 2) - 0.15(x + 3) = 4$

Example 6 **Solving a Linear Equation Containing Decimals**

Solve the equation by clearing decimals. $0.2(x + 4) - 0.45(x + 9) = 12$

Solution:

$$0.2(x + 4) - 0.45(x + 9) = 12$$

$$0.2x + 0.8 - 0.45x - 4.05 = 12 \qquad \text{Clear parentheses first.}$$

$$100(0.2x + 0.8 - 0.45x - 4.05) = 100(12) \qquad \text{Multiply both sides by } 100.$$

$$20x + 80 - 45x - 405 = 1200 \qquad \text{Apply the distributive property.}$$

$$-25x - 325 = 1200 \qquad \text{Simplify both sides.}$$

$$-25x - 325 + 325 = 1200 + 325 \qquad \text{Add } 325 \text{ to both sides.}$$

$$-25x = 1525$$

$$\frac{-25x}{-25} = \frac{1525}{-25} \qquad \text{Divide both sides by } -25.$$

$$x = -61 \qquad \text{The check is left to the reader.}$$

TIP: The terms with the most digits following the decimal point are $-0.45x$ and -4.05. Each of these is written to the hundredths place. Therefore, we multiply both sides by 100.

Answer

6. 39.5

Section 9.3 Practice Exercises

Study Skills Exercises

1. Most people cannot concentrate on studying for more than 1 hr without taking a break. To make the most of your time, write down a schedule for your next study session. Include breaks where you can eat a meal, walk the dog, or perform other simple tasks that need to be completed.

2. Define the key terms:

    a. Clearing fractions   **b. Clearing decimals**

Review Exercises

For Exercises 3–8, solve the equation.

3. $5(x + 2) - 3 = 4x + 5$

4. $-2(2x - 4x) = 6 + 18$

5. $3(2y + 3) - 4(-y + 1) = 7y - 10$

6. $-(3w + 4) + 5(w - 2) - 3(6w - 8) = 10$

7. $7x + 2 = 7(x - 12)$

8. $2(3x - 6) = 3(2x - 4)$

Objective 1: Solving Linear Equations with Fractions

For Exercises 9–14, determine which of the values could be used to clear fractions or decimals in the given equation.

9. $\dfrac{2}{3}x - \dfrac{1}{6} = \dfrac{x}{9}$

    Values: 6, 9, 12, 18, 24, 36

10. $\dfrac{1}{4}x - \dfrac{2}{7} = \dfrac{1}{2}x + 2$

    Values: 4, 7, 14, 21, 28, 42

11. $0.02x + 0.5 = 0.35x + 1.2$

    Values: 10; 100; 1000; 10,000

12. $0.003 - 0.002x = 0.1x$

Values: 10; 100; 1000; 10,000

13. $\frac{1}{6}x + \frac{7}{10} = x$

Values: 3, 6, 10, 30, 60

14. $2x - \frac{5}{2} = \frac{x}{3} - \frac{1}{4}$

Values: 2, 3, 4, 6, 12, 24

For Exercises 15–36, solve the equation. **(See Examples 1–4.)**

15. $\frac{1}{2}x + 3 = 5$

16. $\frac{1}{3}y - 4 = 9$

17. $\frac{1}{6}y + 2 = \frac{5}{12}$

18. $\frac{2}{15}z + 3 = \frac{7}{5}$

19. $\frac{1}{3}q + \frac{3}{5} = \frac{1}{15}q - \frac{2}{5}$

20. $\frac{3}{7}x - 5 = \frac{24}{7}x + 7$

21. $\frac{12}{5}w + 7 = 31 - \frac{3}{5}w$

22. $-\frac{1}{9}p - \frac{5}{18} = -\frac{1}{6}p + \frac{1}{3}$

23. $\frac{1}{4}(3m - 4) - \frac{1}{5} = \frac{1}{4}m + \frac{3}{10}$

24. $\frac{1}{25}(20 - t) = \frac{4}{25}t - \frac{3}{5}$

25. $\frac{1}{6}(5s + 3) = \frac{1}{2}(s + 11)$

26. $\frac{1}{12}(4n - 3) = \frac{1}{4}(2n + 1)$

27. $\frac{2}{3}x + 4 = \frac{2}{3}x - 6$

28. $-\frac{1}{9}a + \frac{2}{9} = \frac{1}{3} - \frac{1}{9}a$

29. $\frac{1}{6}(2c - 1) = \frac{1}{3}c - \frac{1}{6}$

30. $\frac{3}{2}b - 1 = \frac{1}{8}(12b - 8)$

31. $\frac{2x + 1}{3} + \frac{x - 1}{3} = 5$

32. $\frac{4y - 2}{5} - \frac{y + 4}{5} = -3$

33. $\frac{3w - 2}{6} = 1 - \frac{w - 1}{3}$

34. $\frac{z - 7}{4} = \frac{6z - 1}{8} - 2$

35. $\frac{x + 3}{3} - \frac{x - 1}{2} = 4$

36. $\frac{5y - 1}{2} - \frac{y + 4}{5} = 1$

Objective 2: Solving Linear Equations with Decimals

For Exercises 37–54, solve the equation. **(See Examples 5–6.)**

37. $9.2y - 4.3 = 50.9$

38. $-6.3x + 1.5 = -4.8$

39. $21.1w + 4.6 = 10.9w + 35.2$

40. $0.05z + 0.2 = 0.15z - 10.5$

41. $0.2p - 1.4 = 0.2(p - 7)$

42. $0.5(3q + 87) = 1.5q + 43.5$

43. $0.20x + 53.60 = x$

44. $z + 0.06z = 3816$

45. $0.15(90) + 0.05p = 0.10(90 + p)$

46. $0.25(60) + 0.10x = 0.15(60 + x)$

47. $0.40(y + 10) - 0.60(y + 2) = 2$

48. $0.75(x - 2) + 0.25(x + 4) = 0.5$

49. $0.4x + 0.2 = -3.6 - 0.6x$

50. $0.12x + 3 - 0.8x = 0.22x - 0.6$

51. $0.06(x - 0.5) = 0.06x + 0.01$

52. $0.125x = 0.025(5x + 1)$

53. $-3.5x + 1.3 = -0.3(9x - 5)$

54. $x + 4 = 2(0.4x + 1.3)$

Mixed Exercises

For Exercises 55–64, solve the equation.

55. $0.2x - 1.8 = -3$

56. $9.8h + 2 = 3.8h + 20$

57. $\frac{1}{4}(x + 4) = \frac{1}{5}(2x + 3)$

58. $\frac{2}{3}(y - 1) = \frac{3}{4}(3y - 2)$

59. $0.3(x + 6) - 0.7(x + 2) = 4$

60. $0.05(2t - 1) - 0.03(4t - 1) = 0.2$

61. $\dfrac{2k+5}{4} = 2 - \dfrac{k+2}{3}$

62. $\dfrac{3d-4}{6} + 1 = \dfrac{d+1}{8}$

63. $\dfrac{1}{8}v + \dfrac{2}{3} = \dfrac{1}{6}v + \dfrac{3}{4}$

64. $\dfrac{2}{5}z - \dfrac{1}{4} = \dfrac{3}{10}z + \dfrac{1}{2}$

Expanding Your Skills

For Exercises 65–68, solve the equation.

65. $\dfrac{1}{2}a + 0.4 = -0.7 - \dfrac{3}{5}a$

66. $\dfrac{3}{4}c - 0.11 = 0.23(c - 5)$

67. $0.8 + \dfrac{7}{10}b = \dfrac{3}{2}b - 0.8$

68. $0.78 - \dfrac{1}{25}h = \dfrac{3}{5}h - 0.5$

Problem Recognition Exercises

Equations vs. Expressions

For Exercises 1–30, identify each exercise as an expression or an equation. Then simplify the expression or solve the equation.

1. $2b + 23 - 6b - 5$

2. $10p - 9 + 2p - 3 + 8p - 18$

3. $\dfrac{y}{4} = -2$

4. $-\dfrac{x}{2} = 7$

5. $3(4h - 2) - (5h - 8) = 8 - (2h + 3)$

6. $7y - 3(2y + 5) = 7 - (10 - 10y)$ **7.** $3(8z - 1) + 10 - 6(5 + 3z)$

8. $-5(1 - x) - 3(2x + 3) + 5$

9. $6c + 3(c + 1) = 10$

10. $-9 + 5(2y + 3) = -7$

11. $0.5(2a - 3) - 0.1 = 0.4(6 + 2a)$

12. $0.07(2v - 4) = 0.1(v - 4)$

13. $-\dfrac{5}{9}w + \dfrac{11}{12} = \dfrac{23}{36}$

14. $\dfrac{3}{8}t - \dfrac{5}{8} = \dfrac{1}{2}t + \dfrac{1}{8}$

15. $\dfrac{3}{4}x + \dfrac{1}{2} - \dfrac{1}{8}x + \dfrac{5}{4}$

16. $\dfrac{7}{3}(6 - 12t) + \dfrac{1}{2}(4t + 8)$

17. $2z - 7 = 2(z - 13)$

18. $-6x + 2(x + 1) = -2(2x + 3)$ **19.** $\dfrac{2x-1}{4} + \dfrac{3x+2}{6} = 2$

20. $\dfrac{w-4}{6} - \dfrac{3w-1}{2} = -1$

21. $4b - 8 - b = -3b + 2(3b - 4)$ **22.** $-k - 41 - 2 - k = -2(20 + k) - 3$

23. $\dfrac{4}{3}(6y - 3) = 0$

24. $\dfrac{1}{2}(2c - 4) + 3 = \dfrac{1}{3}(6c + 3)$

25. $3(x + 6) - 7(x + 2) - 4(1 - x)$

26. $-10(2k + 1) - 4(4 - 5k) + 25$ **27.** $3 - 2[4a - 5(a + 1)]$

28. $-9 - 4[3 - 2(q + 3)]$

29. $4 + 2[8 - (6 + x)] = -2(x - 1) - 4 + x$

30. $-1 - 5[2 + 3(w - 2)] = 5(w + 4)$

Applications of Linear Equations and Problem Solving

Section 9.4

1. Problem-Solving Strategies

In Section 3.5, we introduced the problem-solving flowchart for word problems. We present the flowchart here again for your use with the applications presented in the next three sections.

Objectives

1. Problem-Solving Strategies
2. Translations Involving Linear Equations
3. Consecutive Integer Problems
4. Applications of Linear Equations

Problem-Solving Flowchart for Word Problems

Step 1 Read the problem carefully. •Familiarize yourself with the problem. Identify the unknown, and if possible, estimate the answer.

Step 2 Assign labels to unknown quantities. •Identify the unknown quantity or quantities. Let a variable represent one of the unknowns. Draw a picture and write down relevant formulas.

Step 3 Write an equation in words. •Verbalize what quantities must be equal.

Step 4 Write a mathematical equation. •Replace the verbal equation with a mathematical equation using x or another variable.

Step 5 Solve the equation. •Solve for the variable using the steps for solving linear equations.

Step 6 Interpret the results and write the final answer in words. •Once you have obtained a numerical value for the variable, recall what it represents in the context of the problem. Can this value be used to determine other unknowns in the problem? Write an answer to the word problem in *words*.

Avoiding Mistakes

Once you have reached a solution to a word problem, verify that it is reasonable in the context of the problem.

2. Translations Involving Linear Equations

We have already practiced translating an English sentence to a mathematical equation. Recall from Section 3.5 that several key words translate to the algebraic operations of addition, subtraction, multiplication, and division.

Example 1   Translating to a Linear Equation

The sum of a number and negative eleven is negative fifteen. Find the number.

Solution:

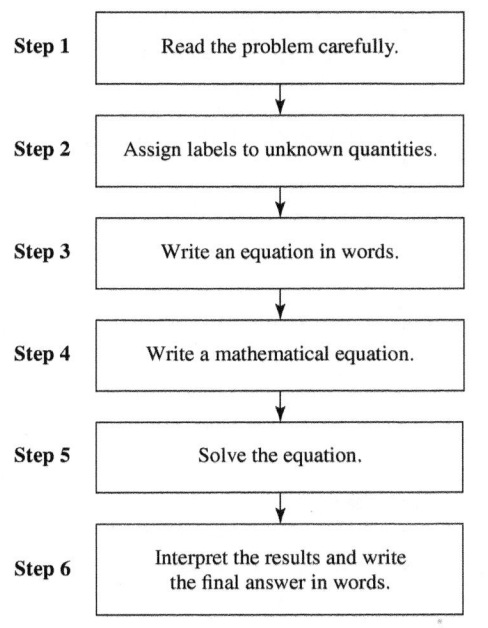

Let x represent the unknown number.

the sum of   is

$$(\text{a number}) + (-11) = (-15)$$

$$x + (-11) = -15$$

$$x + (-11) + 11 = -15 + 11$$

$$x = -4$$

The number is -4.

Step 1: Read the problem.

Step 2: Label the unknown.

Step 3: Write an equation in words.

Step 4: Write a mathematical equation.

Step 5: Solve the equation.

Step 6: Write the final answer in words.

Skill Practice

1. The sum of a number and negative seven is 12. Find the number.

Answer

1. The number is 19.

Skill Practice

2. Thirteen more than twice a number is 5 more than the number. Find the number.

Example 2 Translating to a Linear Equation

Forty less than five times a number is fifty-two less than the number. Find the number.

Solution:

		Step 1: Read the problem.

Let x represent the unknown number. **Step 2:** Label the unknown.

$$\left(\begin{array}{c}5\text{ times}\\ \text{a number}\end{array}\right)\overset{\text{less}}{\underset{-}{\downarrow}}(40)\overset{\text{is}}{\underset{=}{\downarrow}}\left(\begin{array}{c}\text{the}\\ \text{number}\end{array}\right)\overset{\text{less}}{\underset{-}{\downarrow}}(52)$$

Avoiding Mistakes

It is important to remember that subtraction is not a commutative operation. Therefore, the order in which two real numbers are subtracted affects the outcome. The expression "forty less than five times a number" must be translated as: $5x - 40$ (not $40 - 5x$). Similarly, "fifty-two less than the number" must be translated as: $x - 52$ (not $52 - x$).

Step 3: Write an equation in words.

$$5x \qquad - 40 = \qquad x \qquad - 52$$

Step 4: Write a mathematical equation.

$$5x - 40 = x - 52$$

Step 5: Solve the equation.

$$5x - x - 40 = x - x - 52$$

$$4x - 40 = -52$$

$$4x - 40 + 40 = -52 + 40$$

$$4x = -12$$

$$\frac{4x}{4} = \frac{-12}{4}$$

$$x = -3$$

The number is -3.

Step 6: Write the final answer in words.

Skill Practice

3. Three times the sum of a number and eight is 4 more than the number. Find the number.

Example 3 Translating to a Linear Equation

Twice the sum of a number and six is two more than three times the number. Find the number.

Solution:

Step 1: Read the problem.

Let x represent the unknown number. **Step 2:** Label the unknown.

$$\overset{\text{twice}}{\underset{\downarrow}{2}}\ \overset{\text{the sum}}{\underset{\downarrow}{(x + 6)}}\ \overset{\text{is}}{\underset{\downarrow}{=}}\ \overset{\text{2 more than}}{\underset{\downarrow}{3x + 2}}$$

$$\underset{\underset{\text{a number}}{\text{three times}}}{\uparrow}$$

Step 3: Write an equation in words.

Step 4: Write a mathematical equation.

Answers

2. The number is -8.
3. The number is -10.

$$2(x + 6) = 3x + 2$$
$$2x + 12 = 3x + 2$$
$$2x - 2x + 12 = 3x - 2x + 2$$
$$12 = x + 2$$
$$12 - 2 = x + 2 - 2$$
$$10 = x$$

The number is 10.

Step 5: Solve the equation.

Step 6: Write the final answer in words.

> **Avoiding Mistakes**
>
> It is important to enclose "the sum of a number and six" within parentheses so that the entire quantity is multiplied by 2. Forgetting the parentheses would imply that only the x-term is multiplied by 2.
>
> Correct: $2(x + 6)$

3. Consecutive Integer Problems

The word *consecutive* means "following one after the other in order without gaps." The numbers 6, 7, and 8 are examples of three **consecutive integers**. The numbers $-4, -2, 0$, and 2 are examples of **consecutive even integers**. The numbers 23, 25, and 27 are examples of **consecutive odd integers**.

Notice that any two consecutive integers differ by 1. Therefore, if x represents an integer, then $(x + 1)$ represents the next larger consecutive integer (Figure 9-3).

Consecutive integers differ by 1 unit.

Figure 9-3

Any two consecutive even integers differ by 2. Therefore, if x represents an even integer, then $(x + 2)$ represents the next consecutive larger even integer (Figure 9-4).

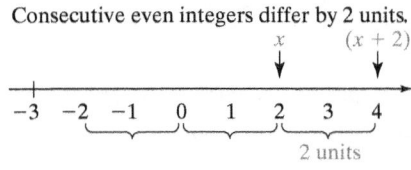

Consecutive even integers differ by 2 units.

Figure 9-4

Likewise, any two consecutive odd integers differ by 2. If x represents an odd integer, then $(x + 2)$ is the next larger odd integer (Figure 9-5).

Consecutive odd integers differ by 2 units.

Figure 9-5

4. The sum of two consecutive even integers is 66. Find the integers.

Example 4 **Solving an Application Involving Consecutive Integers**

The sum of two consecutive odd integers is -188. Find the integers.

Solution:

In this example we have two unknown integers. We can let x represent either of the unknowns.

| | **Step 1:** | Read the problem. |

Suppose x represents the first odd integer.   **Step 2:** Label the variables.

Then $(x + 2)$ represents the second odd integer.

$$\left(\begin{array}{c}\text{First}\\\text{integer}\end{array}\right) + \left(\begin{array}{c}\text{second}\\\text{integer}\end{array}\right) = (\text{total})$$

Step 3: Write an equation in words.

$$x \quad + \quad (x + 2) \quad = -188$$

Step 4: Write a mathematical equation.

$$x + (x + 2) = -188$$

$$2x + 2 = -188$$ **Step 5:** Solve for x.

$$2x + 2 - 2 = -188 - 2$$

$$2x = -190$$

$$\frac{2x}{2} = \frac{-190}{2}$$

$$x = -95$$

TIP: With word problems, it is advisable to check that the answer is reasonable.

The numbers -95 and -93 are consecutive odd integers. Furthermore, their sum is -188 as desired.

The first integer is $x = -95$.   **Step 6:** Interpret the results and write the answer in words.

The second integer is $x + 2 = -95 + 2 = -93$.

The two integers are -95 and -93.

5. Five times the smallest of three consecutive integers is 17 less than twice the sum of the integers. Find the integers.

Example 5 **Solving an Application Involving Consecutive Integers**

Ten times the smallest of three consecutive integers is twenty-two more than three times the sum of the integers. Find the integers.

Solution:

| | **Step 1:** | Read the problem. |

Let x represent the first integer.   **Step 2:** Label the variables.

$x + 1$ represents the second consecutive integer.

$x + 2$ represents the third consecutive integer.

Answers

4. The integers are 32 and 34.
5. The integers are 11, 12, and 13.

$$\begin{pmatrix} 10 \text{ times} \\ \text{the first} \\ \text{integer} \end{pmatrix} = \begin{pmatrix} 3 \text{ times} \\ \text{the sum of} \\ \text{the integers} \end{pmatrix} + 22$$

Step 3: Write an equation in words.

10 times the first integer   is   3 times   22 more than

$$10x = \underbrace{3[(x) + (x+1) + (x+2)]}_{\text{the sum of the integers}} + 22$$

Step 4: Write a mathematical equation.

$$10x = 3(x + x + 1 + x + 2) + 22$$

Step 5: Solve the equation.

$$10x = 3(3x + 3) + 22$$

Clear parentheses.

$$10x = 9x + 9 + 22$$

Combine *like* terms.

$$10x = 9x + 31$$

$$10x - 9x = 9x - 9x + 31$$

$$x = 31$$

Isolate the x-terms on one side.

The first integer is $x = 31$.

The second integer is $x + 1 = 31 + 1 = 32$.

The third integer is $x + 2 = 31 + 2 = 33$.

Step 6: Interpret the results and write the answer in words.

The three integers are 31, 32, and 33.

4. Applications of Linear Equations

Example 6 **Using a Linear Equation in an Application**

A carpenter cuts a 6-ft board in two pieces. One piece must be three times as long as the other. Find the length of each piece.

Solution:

In this problem, one piece must be three times as long as the other. Thus, if x represents the length of one piece, then $3x$ can represent the length of the other.

Step 1: Read the problem completely.

x represents the length of the smaller piece.
$3x$ represents the length of the longer piece.

Step 2: Label the unknowns. Draw a figure.

$3x$ $\qquad$ x

─── **Skill Practice** ───

6. A plumber cuts a 96-in. piece of pipe into two pieces. One piece is five times longer than the other piece. How long is each piece?

Answer

6. One piece is 80 in. and the other is 16 in.

$$\left(\begin{matrix}\text{Length of}\\\text{one piece}\end{matrix}\right) + \left(\begin{matrix}\text{length of}\\\text{other piece}\end{matrix}\right) = \left(\begin{matrix}\text{total length}\\\text{of the board}\end{matrix}\right)$$
Step 3: Set up a verbal equation.

$$x \quad + \quad 3x \quad = \quad 6$$
Step 4: Write an equation.

$$4x = 6$$
Step 5: Solve the equation.

$$\frac{4x}{4} = \frac{6}{4}$$

$$x = 1.5$$

The smaller piece is $x = 1.5$ ft.   **Step 6:** Interpret the results.

The longer piece is $3x$ or $3(1.5 \text{ ft}) = 4.5$ ft.

> **TIP:** The variable can represent either unknown. In Example 6, if we let x represent the length of the longer piece of board, then $\frac{1}{3}x$ would represent the length of the smaller piece. The equation would become $x + \frac{1}{3}x = 6$. Try solving this equation and interpreting the result.

Example 7 **Using a Linear Equation in an Application**

The hit movies *Spider-Man 3* and *Pirates of the Caribbean: At World's End* together brought in $265.8 million during their opening weekends. *Spider-Man 3* earned $78.3 million less than twice what *Pirates of the Caribbean* earned. How much revenue did each movie bring in during its opening weekend?

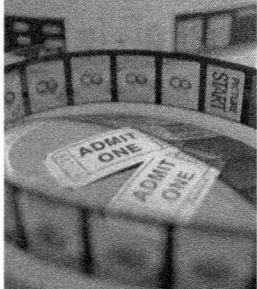

Solution:

In this example, we have two unknowns. The variable, x, can represent *either* quantity. However, the revenue from *Spider-Man 3* is given in terms of the revenue for *Pirates of the Caribbean: At World's End.*   **Step 1:** Read the problem.

Let x represent the revenue for *Pirates of the Caribbean.*   **Step 2:** Label the variables.

Then $2x - 78.3$ represents the revenue for *Spider-Man 3.*

Answer

7. There are 22 women and 18 men.

$$\begin{pmatrix} \text{Revenue from} \\ \textit{Pirates} \end{pmatrix} + \begin{pmatrix} \text{revenue from} \\ \textit{Spider-Man} \end{pmatrix} = \begin{pmatrix} \text{total} \\ \text{revenue} \end{pmatrix}$$

Step 3: Write an equation in words.

$$x \quad + \quad (2x - 78.3) \quad = \quad 265.8$$

Step 4: Write an equation.

$$3x - 78.3 = 265.8$$

Step 5: Solve the equation.

$$3x - 78.3 + 78.3 = 265.8 + 78.3$$

$$3x = 344.1$$

$$\frac{3x}{3} = \frac{344.1}{3}$$

$$x = 114.7$$

- Revenue from *Pirates of the Caribbean:* $x = 114.7$
- Revenue from *Spider-Man 3:* $2x - 78.3 = 2(114.7) - 78.3 = 151.1$

The revenue from *Pirates of the Caribbean: At World's End* was $114.7 million for its opening weekend. The revenue for *Spider-Man 3* was $151.1 million.

Section 9.4 Practice Exercises

Study Skills Exercises

1. The following is a list of steps to help you solve word problems. Check those that you follow on a regular basis when solving a word problem. Place an asterisk next to the steps that you need to improve.

_____ Read through the entire problem before writing anything down.

_____ Write down exactly what you are being asked to find.

_____ Write down what is known and assign variables to what is unknown.

_____ Draw a figure or diagram if it will help you understand the problem.

_____ Highlight key words like total, sum, difference, etc.

_____ Translate the word problem to a mathematical problem.

_____ After solving, check that your answer makes sense.

2. Define the key terms:

   a. Consecutive integers   **b. Consecutive even integers**   **c. Consecutive odd integers**

Objective 2: Translations Involving Linear Equations

For Exercises 3–8, write an expression representing the unknown quantity.

3. In a math class, the number of students who received an "A" in the class was 5 more than the number of students who received a "B." If x represents the number of "B" students, write an expression for the number of "A" students.

4. At a recent motorcycle rally, the number of men exceeded the number of women by 216. If x represents the number of women, write an expression for the number of men.

5. Anna is three times as old as Jake. If x represents Jake's age, write an expression for Anna's age.

6. Rebecca downloaded twice as many songs as Nigel. If x represents the number of songs downloaded by Nigel, write an expression for the number downloaded by Rebecca.

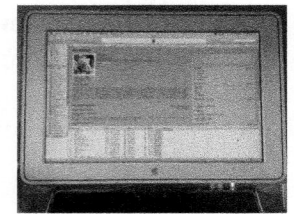

7. Sidney made $20 more than three times Casey's weekly salary. If x represents Casey's weekly salary, write an expression for Sidney's weekly salary.

8. David scored 26 points less than twice the number of points Rich scored in a video game. If x represents the number of points scored by Rich, write an expression representing the number of points scored by David.

For Exercises 9–18, use the problem-solving flowchart on page 619. (**See Examples 1–3.**)

9. Six less than a number is –10. Find the number.

10. Fifteen less than a number is 41. Find the number.

11. Twice the sum of a number and seven is eight. Find the number.

12. Twice the sum of a number and negative two is sixteen. Find the number.

13. A number added to five is the same as twice the number. Find the number.

14. Three times a number is the same as the difference of twice the number and seven. Find the number.

15. The sum of six times a number and ten is equal to the difference of the number and fifteen. Find the number.

16. The difference of fourteen and three times a number is the same as the sum of the number and negative ten. Find the number.

17. If the difference of a number and four is tripled, the result is six more than the number. Find the number.

18. Twice the sum of a number and eleven is twenty-two less than three times the number. Find the number.

Objective 3: Consecutive Integer Problems

19. a. If x represents the smallest of three consecutive integers, write an expression to represent each of the next two consecutive integers.

   b. If x represents the largest of three consecutive integers, write an expression to represent each of the previous two consecutive integers.

20. a. If x represents the smallest of three consecutive odd integers, write an expression to represent each of the next two consecutive odd integers.

   b. If x represents the largest of three consecutive odd integers, write an expression to represent each of the previous two consecutive odd integers.

For Exercises 21–30, use the problem-solving flowchart from page 619. (**See Examples 4–5.**)

21. The sum of two consecutive integers is -67. Find the integers.

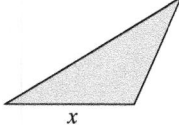 **22.** The sum of two consecutive odd integers is 52. Find the integers.

23. The sum of two consecutive odd integers is 28. Find the integers.

24. The sum of three consecutive even integers is 66. Find the integers.

25. The perimeter of a pentagon (a five-sided polygon) is 80 in. The five sides are represented by consecutive integers. Find the measures of the sides.

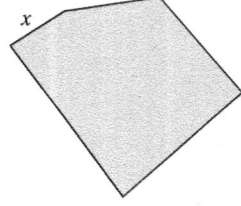

26. The perimeter of a triangle is 96 in. The lengths of the sides are represented by consecutive integers. Find the measures of the sides.

27. The sum of three consecutive even integers is 48 more than twice the smallest of the three integers. Find the integers.

28. The sum of three consecutive odd integers is 89 more than twice the largest integer. Find the integers.

29. Eight times the sum of three consecutive odd integers is 210 more than 10 times the middle integer. Find the integers.

30. Five times the sum of three consecutive even integers is 140 more than ten times the smallest. Find the integers.

Objective 4: Applications of Linear Equations

For Exercises 31–42, use the problem-solving flowchart (page 619) to solve the problems.

31. A board is 86 cm in length and must be cut so that one piece is 20 cm longer than the other piece. Find the length of each piece. (**See Example 6.**)

x $x + 20$

32. A rope is 54 in. in length and must be cut into two pieces. If one piece must be twice as long as the other, find the length of each piece.

33. Karen's age is 12 years more than Clarann's age. The sum of their ages is 58. Find their ages.

34. Maria's age is 15 years less than Orlando's age. The sum of their ages is 29. Find their ages.

35. For a recent year, 31 more Democrats than Republicans were in the U.S. House of Representatives. If the total number of representatives in the House from these two parties was 433, find the number of representatives from each party.

36. For a recent year, the number of men in the U.S. Senate totaled 4 more than 5 times the number of women. Find the number of men and the number of women in the Senate given that the Senate has 100 members.

37. Approximately 5.816 million people watch *The Oprah Winfrey Show*. This is 1.118 million more than watch *The Dr. Phil Show*. How many watch *The Dr. Phil Show*? (*Source: Neilson Media Research*) (**See Example 7.**)

38. Two of the largest Internet retailers are e-Bay and Amazon.com. Recently, the estimated U.S. sales of e-Bay were $0.1 billion less than twice the sales of Amazon.com. Given the total sales of $5.6 billion, determine the sales of e-Bay and Amazon.com.

39. The longest river in Africa is the Nile. It is 2455 km longer than the Congo River, also in Africa. The sum of the lengths of these rivers is 11,195 km. What is the length of each river?

40. The average depth of the Gulf of Mexico is three times the depth of the Red Sea. The difference between the average depths is 1078 m. What is the average depth of the Gulf of Mexico and the average depth of the Red Sea?

41. Asia and Africa are the two largest continents in the world. The land area of Asia is approximately 14,514,000 km² larger than the land area of Africa. Together their total area is 74,644,000 km². Find the land area of Asia and the land area of Africa.

42. Mt. Everest, the highest mountain in the world, is 2654 m higher than Mt. McKinley, the highest mountain in the United States. If the sum of their heights is 15,042 m, find the height of each mountain.

Mixed Exercises

43. A group of hikers walked from Hawk Mt. Shelter to Blood Mt. Shelter along the Appalachian Trail, a total distance of 20.5 mi. It took 2 days for the walk. The second day the hikers walked 4.1 mi less than they did on the first day. How far did they walk each day?

44. $120 is to be divided among three restaurant servers. Angie made $10 more than Marie. Gwen, who went home sick, made $25 less than Marie. How much money should each server get?

45. A 4-ft piece of PVC pipe is cut into three pieces. The longest piece is 12 in. longer than twice the smallest piece. The middle piece is 6 in. less than the longest piece. How long is each piece?

46. A 6-ft piece of copper wire must be cut into three pieces. The middle piece is 16 in. longer than the shortest piece. The longest piece is twice as long as the middle piece. How long is each piece?

47. Three consecutive integers are such that three times the largest exceeds the sum of the two smaller integers by 47. Find the integers.

48. Four times the smallest of three consecutive odd integers is 236 more than the sum of the other two integers. Find the integers.

49. In a recent year, the estimated earnings for Jennifer Lopez was $2.5 million more than half of the earnings for the band U2. If the total earnings were $106 million, what were the earnings for Jennifer Lopez and U2? (*Source: Forbes*)

50. Two of the longest-running TV series are *Gunsmoke* and *The Simpsons. Gunsmoke* ran 97 fewer episodes than twice the number of *The Simpsons.* If the total number of episodes is 998, how many of each show was produced?

51. Five times the difference of a number and three is four less than four times the number. Find the number.

52. Three times the difference of a number and seven is one less than twice the number. Find the number.

53. The sum of the page numbers on two facing pages in a book is 941. What are the page numbers?

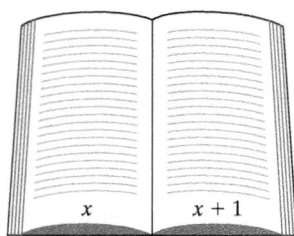

54. Three raffle tickets are represented by three consecutive integers. If the sum of the three integers is 2,666,031, find the numbers.

55. If three is added to five times a number, the result is forty-three more than the number. Find the number.

56. If seven is added to three times a number, the result is thirty-one more than the number.

57. The deepest point in the Pacific Ocean is 676 m more than twice the deepest point in the Arctic Ocean. If the deepest point in the Pacific is 10,920 m, how many meters is the deepest point in the Arctic Ocean?

58. The area of Greenland is 201,900 km^2 less than three times the area of New Guinea. What is the area of New Guinea if the area of Greenland is 2,175,600 km^2?

59. The sum of twice a number and $\frac{3}{4}$ is the same as the difference of four times the number and $\frac{1}{8}$. Find the number.

60. The difference of a number and $-\frac{11}{12}$ is the same as the difference of three times the number and $\frac{1}{6}$. Find the number.

61. The product of a number and 3.86 is equal to 7.15 more than the number. Find the number.

62. The product of a number and 4.6 is 33.12 less than the number. Find the number.

Applications Involving Percents

1. Solving Basic Percent Equations

Recall from Section 6.4 that the word *percent* means "per hundred." For example:

Percent	**Interpretation**
63% of homes have a computer	63 out of 100 homes have a computer.
5% sales tax	5¢ in tax is charged for every 100¢ in merchandise.
15% commission	$15 is earned in commission for every $100 sold.

Percents come up in a variety of applications in day-to-day life. Many such applications follow the basic percent equation:

$$\text{Amount} = (\text{percent})(\text{base}) \qquad \text{Basic percent equation}$$

In Example 1, we apply the basic percent equation to compute **sales tax**.

Objectives

1. Solving Basic Percent Equations
2. Applications Involving Simple Interest
3. Applications Involving Discount and Markup

Example 1 **Computing Sales Tax**

A new digital camera costs $429.95.

a. Compute the sales tax if the tax rate is 4%.

b. Determine the total cost, including tax.

Skill Practice

1. Find the amount of tax on a portable CD player that sells for $89. Assume the tax rate is 6%.
2. Find the total cost including tax.

Solution:

a. Let x represent the amount of tax.

Apply the percent equation to compute sales tax.

$$\text{Amount} = (\text{percent}) \cdot (\text{base})$$
$$\downarrow \qquad\quad \downarrow \qquad\quad \downarrow$$
$$\text{Sales tax} = (\text{tax rate})(\text{price of merchandise})$$

$x = (0.04)(\$429.95)$

$x = \$17.198$

$x = \$17.20$

The tax on the merchandise is $17.20.

Step 1: Read the problem.

Step 2: Label the variable.

Step 3: Write an equation in words.

Step 4: Write a mathematical equation.

Step 5: Solve the equation.

Round to the nearest cent.

Step 6: Interpret the results.

Avoiding Mistakes

Be sure to use the decimal form of a percentage within an equation.

$$4\% = 0.04$$

b. The total cost is found by:

total cost = cost of merchandise + amount of tax

Therefore the total cost is $429.95 + $17.20 = $447.15.

Answers

1. The amount of tax is $5.34.
2. The total cost is $94.34.

In Example 2, we solve a problem in which the percent is unknown.

Example 2 **Finding an Unknown Percent**

A group of 240 college men were asked what intramural sport they most enjoyed playing. The results are in the graph. What percent of the men surveyed preferred tennis?

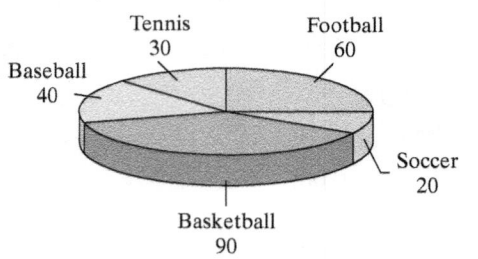

Solution:

	Step 1: Read the problem.
Let x represent the unknown percent.	**Step 2:** Label the variable.

The problem can be rephrased as:

$$30 \text{ is what percent of } 240?$$

$$30 = \quad x \quad \cdot 240 \qquad \textbf{Step 4:} \text{ Write a mathematical equation.}$$

Step 3: Write an equation in words.

$$30 = 240x \qquad \textbf{Step 5:} \text{ Solve the equation.}$$

$$\frac{30}{240} = \frac{240x}{240} \qquad \text{Divide both sides by 240.}$$

$$0.125 = x$$

$$0.125 \times 100\% = 12.5\% \qquad \textbf{Step 6:} \text{ Interpret the results.}$$
Change the value of x to a percent by multiplying by 100%.

In this survey, 12.5% of men prefer tennis.

Example 3 **Solving a Percent Equation with an Unknown Base**

Andrea spends 20% of her monthly paycheck on rent each month. If her rent payment is $750, what is her monthly paycheck?

Solution:

	Step 1: Read the problem.
Let x represent the amount of Andrea's monthly paycheck.	**Step 2:** Label the variables.

The problem can be rephrased as:

$$\$750 \text{ is } 20\% \text{ of what number?}$$

Step 3: Write an equation in words.

$$750 = 0.20 \quad \cdot \quad x \qquad \textbf{Step 4:} \text{ Write a mathematical equation.}$$

$$750 = 0.20x$$

$$\frac{750}{0.20} = \frac{0.20x}{0.20}$$

$$3750 = x$$

Step 5: Solve the equation.

Divide both sides by 0.20.

Andrea's monthly paycheck is $3750.   **Step 6:** Interpret the results.

2. Applications Involving Simple Interest

One important application of percents is in computing simple interest on a loan or on an investment.

Simple interest is interest that is earned on principal (the original amount of money invested in an account). The following formula is used to compute simple interest:

$$\left(\begin{matrix}\text{Simple}\\\text{interest}\end{matrix}\right) = \left(\begin{matrix}\text{principal}\\\text{invested}\end{matrix}\right)\left(\begin{matrix}\text{annual}\\\text{interest rate}\end{matrix}\right)\left(\begin{matrix}\text{time}\\\text{in years}\end{matrix}\right)$$

This formula is often written symbolically as $I = Prt$.

For example, to find the simple interest earned on $2000 invested at 7.5% interest for 3 years, we have

$$I = Prt$$
$$\text{Interest} = (\$2000)(0.075)(3)$$
$$= \$450$$

Example 4 **Applying Simple Interest**

Jorge wants to save money for his daughter's college education. If Jorge needs to have $4340 at the end of 4 years, how much money would he need to invest at a 6% simple interest rate?

Solution:

	Step 1: Read the problem.
Let P represent the original amount invested.	**Step 2:** Label the variables.

$$\left(\begin{matrix}\text{Original}\\\text{principal}\end{matrix}\right) + (\text{interest}) = (\text{total})$$

Step 3: Write an equation in words.

$$(P) \quad + \quad (Prt) \quad = (\text{total})$$
$$P \quad + \quad P(0.06)(4) = 4340$$

Step 4: Write a mathematical equation.

$$P + 0.24P = 4340$$

$$1.24P = 4340$$

Step 5: Solve the equation.

$$\frac{1.24P}{1.24} = \frac{4340}{1.24}$$

$$P = 3500$$

The original investment should be $3500.

Step 6: Interpret the results and write the answer in words.

Skill Practice

5. Cassandra invested some money in her bank account, and after 10 years at 4% simple interest, it has grown to $7700. What was the initial amount invested?

Avoiding Mistakes

The interest is computed on the original principal, P, not on the total amount $4340. That is, the interest is $P(0.06)(4)$, not $(\$4340)(0.06)(4)$.

Answer

5. The initial investment was $5500.

3. Applications Involving Discount and Markup

Applications involving percent increase and percent decrease are abundant in many real-world settings. Sales tax for example is essentially a markup by a state or local government. It is important to understand that percent increase or decrease is always computed on the original amount given.

In Example 5, we illustrate an example of percent decrease in an application where merchandise is discounted.

Example 5   **Applying Percents to a Discount Problem**

After a 38% discount, a used treadmill costs $868 on e-Bay. What was the original cost of the treadmill?

Solution:

	Step 1: Read the problem.
Let x be the original cost of the treadmill.	**Step 2:** Label the variables.

$$\begin{pmatrix} \text{Original} \\ \text{cost} \end{pmatrix} - (\text{discount}) = \begin{pmatrix} \text{sale} \\ \text{price} \end{pmatrix}$$

Step 3: Write an equation in words.

$$x \qquad - 0.38(x) \qquad = 868$$

Step 4: Write a mathematical equation. The discount is a percent of the *original* amount.

$$x - 0.38x = 868$$

Step 5: Solve the equation.

$$0.62x = 868$$

Combine *like* terms.

$$\frac{0.62x}{0.62} = \frac{868}{0.62}$$

Divide by 0.62.

$$x = 1400$$

The original cost of the treadmill was $1400.

Step 6: Interpret the result.

Answer

6. The iPod originally cost $189.

Section 9.5 Practice Exercises

Study Skills Exercises

1. Some instructors allow the use of calculators. What is your instructor's policy regarding calculators in class, on the homework, and on tests?

   Helpful Hint: If you are not permitted to use a calculator on tests, it is a good idea to do your homework in the same way, without a calculator.

2. Define the key terms:

   a. Sales tax   **b. Simple interest**

Review Exercises

For Exercises 3–4, use the steps for problem solving to solve these applications.

3. Find two consecutive integers such that three times the larger is the same as 45 more than the smaller.

4. The height of the Great Pyramid of Giza is 17 m more than twice the height of the pyramid found in Saqqara. If the difference in their heights is 77 m, find the height of each pyramid.

Objective 1: Solving Basic Percent Equations

For Exercises 5–16, find the missing values.

5. 45 is what percent of 360?

6. 338 is what percent of 520?

7. 544 is what percent of 640?

8. 576 is what percent of 800?

9. What is 0.5% of 150?

10. What is 9.5% of 616?

11. What is 142% of 740?

12. What is 156% of 280?

13. 177 is 20% of what number?

14. 126 is 15% of what number?

15. 275 is 12.5% of what number?

16. 594 is 45% of what number?

17. A Craftsman drill is on sale for $99.99. If the sales tax rate is 7%, how much will Molly have to pay for the drill?
    (See Example 1.)

18. Patrick purchased four new tires that were regularly priced at $94.99 each, but are on sale for $20 off per tire. If the sales tax rate is 6%, how much will be charged to Patrick's VISA card?

For Exercises 19–20, use the graph showing the distribution for leading forms of cancer in men. (*Source:* Centers for Disease Control)

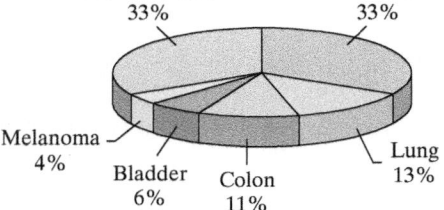

Percent of Cancer Cases by Type (Men)

19. If there are 700,000 cases of cancer in men in the United States, approximately how many are prostate cancer?

20. Approximately how many cases of lung cancer would be expected in 700,000 cancer cases among men in the United States?

21. There were 14,000 cases of cancer of the pancreas diagnosed out of 700,000 cancer cases. What percent is this? **(See Example 2.)**

22. There were 21,000 cases of leukemia diagnosed out of 700,000 cancer cases. What percent is this?

23. Javon is in a 28% tax bracket for his federal income tax. If the amount of money that he paid for federal income tax was $23,520, what was his taxable income? **(See Example 3.)**

24. In a recent survey of college-educated adults, 155 indicated that they regularly work more than 50 hr a week. If this represents 31% of those surveyed, how many people were in the survey?

Objective 2: Applications Involving Simple Interest

For Exercises 25–32, solve these equations involving simple interest.

25. How much interest will Pam earn in 4 years if she invests $3000 in an account that pays 3.5% simple interest?

26. How much interest will Roxanne have to pay if she borrows $2000 for 2 yr at a simple interest rate of 4%?

27. Bob borrowed some money for 1 yr at 5% simple interest. If he had to pay back a total of $1260, how much did he originally borrow? **(See Example 4.)**

28. Mike borrowed some money for 2 yr at 6% simple interest. If he had to pay back a total of $3640, how much did he originally borrow?

29. If $1500 grows to $1950 after 5 yr, find the simple interest rate.

30. If $9000 grows to $10,440 in 2 yr, find the simple interest rate.

31. Perry is planning a vacation to Europe in 2 yr. How much should he invest in a certificate of deposit that pays 3% simple interest to get the $3500 that he needs for the trip? Round to the nearest dollar.

32. Sherica invested in a mutual fund and at the end of 20 yr she has $14,300 in her account. If the mutual fund returned an average yield of 8%, how much did she originally invest?

Objective 3: Applications Involving Discount and Markup

33. A Pioneer car CD/MP3 player costs $170. Circuit City has it on sale for 12% off with free installation.

  a. What is the discount on the CD/MP3 player?

  b. What is the sale price?

34. A laptop computer, originally selling for $899.00, is on sale for 10% off.

  a. What is the discount on the laptop?

  b. What is the sale price?

35. A Sony digital camera is on sale for $400.00. This price is 15% off the original price. What was the original price? Round to the nearest cent. **(See Example 5.)**

36. The *Star Wars: Episode III* DVD is on sale for $18. If this represents an 18% discount rate, what was the original price of the DVD?

37. The original price of an Audio Jukebox was $250. It is on sale for $220. What percent discount does this represent?

38. During the holiday season, the Xbox 360 sold for $425.00 in stores. This product was in such demand that it sold for $800 online. What percent markup does this represent? (Round to the nearest whole percent.)

39. In one area, the cable company marked up the monthly cost by 6%. The new cost is $63.60 per month. What was the cost before the increase?

40. A doctor ordered a dosage of medicine for a patient. After 2 days, she increased the dosage by 20% and the new dosage came to 18 cc. What was the original dosage?

Mixed Exercises

41. Sun Lei bought a laptop computer for $1800. The total cost, including tax, came to $1890. What is the tax rate?

42. Jamie purchased a compact disk and paid $18.26. If the disk price is $16.99, what is the sales tax rate (round to the nearest tenth of a percent)?

43. For a recent year, admission to Walt Disney World cost $74.37, including taxes of 11%. What was the original ticket price before taxes?

44. A hotel room rented for 5 nights costs $706.25 including 13% in taxes. Find the original price of the room (before tax) for the 5 nights. Then find the price per night.

45. Deon purchased a house and sold it for a 24% profit. If he sold the house for $260,400, what was the original purchase price?

46. To meet the rising cost of energy, the yearly membership at a YMCA had to be increased by 12.5% from the past year. The yearly membership fee is currently $450. What was the cost of membership last year?

47. Alina earns $1600 per month plus a 12% commission on pharmaceutical sales. If she sold $25,000 in pharmaceuticals one month, what was her salary that month?

48. Dan sold a beachfront home for $650,000. If his commission rate is 4%, what did he earn in commission?

49. Diane sells women's sportswear at a department store. She earns a regular salary and, as a bonus, she receives a commission of 4% on all sales over $200. If Diane earned an extra $25.80 last week in commission, how much merchandise did she sell over $200?

50. For selling software, Tom received a bonus commission based on sales over $500. If he received $180 in commission for selling a total of $2300 worth of software, what is his commission rate?

Literal Equations and Applications of Geometry   Section 9.6

1. Formulas and Literal Equations

Literal equations are equations that contain several variables. A formula is a literal equation with a specific application. For example, the perimeter of a triangle (distance around the triangle) can be found by the formula $P = a + b + c$, where a, b, and c are the lengths of the sides (Figure 9-6).

Objectives
1. Formulas and Literal Equations
2. Geometry Applications

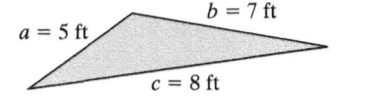

$$P = a + b + c$$
$$= 5 \text{ ft} + 7 \text{ ft} + 8 \text{ ft}$$
$$= 20 \text{ ft}$$

Figure 9-6

   In this section, we will learn how to rewrite formulas to solve for a different variable within the formula. Suppose, for example, that the perimeter of a triangle is known and two of the sides are known (say, sides a and b). Then the third side, c, can be found by subtracting the lengths of the known sides from the perimeter (Figure 9-7).

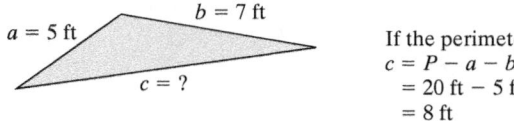

If the perimeter is 20 ft, then
$$c = P - a - b$$
$$= 20 \text{ ft} - 5 \text{ ft} - 7 \text{ ft}$$
$$= 8 \text{ ft}$$

Figure 9-7

To solve a formula for a different variable, we use the same properties of equality outlined in the earlier sections of this chapter. For example, consider the two equations $2x + 3 = 11$ and $wx + y = z$. Suppose we want to solve for x in each case:

$$2x + 3 = 11$$
$$2x + 3 - 3 = 11 - 3 \quad \text{Subtract 3.}$$
$$2x = 8$$
$$\frac{2x}{2} = \frac{8}{2} \quad \text{Divide by 2.}$$
$$x = 4$$

$$wx + y = z$$
$$wx + y - y = z - y \quad \text{Subtract } y.$$
$$wx = z - y$$
$$\frac{wx}{w} = \frac{z - y}{w} \quad \text{Divide by } w.$$
$$x = \frac{z - y}{w}$$

The equation on the left has only one variable and we are able to simplify the equation to find a numerical value for x. The equation on the right has multiple variables. Because we do not know the values of w, y, and z, we are not able to simplify further. The value of x is left as a formula in terms of w, y, and z.

Example 1 Solving for an Indicated Variable

Solve for the indicated variables.

a. $d = rt$ for t **b.** $5x + 2y = 12$ for y

Solution:

a. $d = rt$ for t The goal is to isolate the variable t.

$\dfrac{d}{r} = \dfrac{rt}{r}$ Because the relationship between r and t is multiplication, we reverse the process by dividing both sides by r.

$\dfrac{d}{r} = t$, or equivalently $t = \dfrac{d}{r}$

b. $5x + 2y = 12$ for y The goal is to solve for y.

$5x - 5x + 2y = 12 - 5x$ Subtract $5x$ from both sides to isolate the y-term.

$2y = -5x + 12$ $-5x + 12$ is the same as $12 - 5x$.

$\dfrac{2y}{2} = \dfrac{-5x + 12}{2}$ Divide both sides by 2 to isolate y.

$y = \dfrac{-5x + 12}{2}$

TIP: In the expression $\dfrac{-5x + 12}{2}$ do not try to divide the 2 into the 12. The divisor of 2 is dividing the entire quantity, $-5x + 12$ (not just the 12).

We may, however, apply the divisor to each term individually in the numerator. That is, $\dfrac{-5x + 12}{2}$ can be written in several different forms. Each is correct.

$$y = \frac{-5x + 12}{2} \quad \text{or} \quad y = \frac{-5x}{2} + \frac{12}{2} \Rightarrow y = -\frac{5}{2}x + 6$$

Example 2 Solving Formulas for an Indicated Variable

The formula $C = \frac{5}{9}(F - 32)$ is used to find the temperature, C, in degrees Celsius for a given temperature expressed in degrees Fahrenheit, F. Solve the formula $C = \frac{5}{9}(F - 32)$ for F.

Solution:

$$C = \frac{5}{9}(F - 32)$$

$$C = \frac{5}{9}F - \frac{5}{9} \cdot 32 \qquad \text{Clear parentheses.}$$

$$C = \frac{5}{9}F - \frac{160}{9} \qquad \text{Multiply: } \frac{5}{9} \cdot \frac{32}{1} = \frac{160}{9}.$$

$$9(C) = 9\left(\frac{5}{9}F - \frac{160}{9}\right) \qquad \text{Multiply by the LCD to clear fractions.}$$

$$9C = \frac{9}{1} \cdot \frac{5}{9}F - \frac{9}{1} \cdot \frac{160}{9} \qquad \text{Apply the distributive property.}$$

$$9C = 5F - 160 \qquad \text{Simplify.}$$

$$9C + 160 = 5F - 160 + 160 \qquad \text{Add } 160 \text{ to both sides.}$$

$$9C + 160 = 5F$$

$$\frac{9C + 160}{5} = \frac{5F}{5} \qquad \text{Divide both sides by } 5.$$

$$\frac{9C + 160}{5} = F$$

The answer may be written in several forms:

$$F = \frac{9C + 160}{5} \quad \text{or} \quad F = \frac{9C}{5} + \frac{160}{5} \quad \Rightarrow \quad F = \frac{9}{5}C + 32$$

Skill Practice

3. Solve for the indicated variable.

$$y = \frac{1}{3}(x - 7) \text{ for } x.$$

2. Geometry Applications

In Chapter 7, we presented numerous facts and formulas related to geometry. Sometimes these are needed to solve applications in geometry.

Example 3 Solving a Geometry Application Involving Perimeter

The length of a rectangular lot is 1 m less than twice the width. If the perimeter is 190 m, find the length and width.

Solution:

Step 1: Read the problem.

Let x represent the width of the rectangle. **Step 2:** Label the variables.

Then $2x - 1$ represents the length.

x

$2x - 1$

Skill Practice

4. The length of a rectangle is 10′ less than twice the width. If the perimeter is 178′, find the length and width.

Animation

Answers

3. $x = 3y + 7$
4. The length is 56′, and the width is 33′.

$$P = 2l + 2w$$ **Step 3:** Perimeter formula

$$190 = 2(2x - 1) + 2(x)$$ **Step 4:** Write an equation in terms of x.

$$190 = 4x - 2 + 2x$$ **Step 5:** Solve for x.

$$190 = 6x - 2$$

$$192 = 6x$$

$$\frac{192}{6} = \frac{6x}{6}$$

$$32 = x$$

The width is $x = 32$.

The length is $2x - 1 = 2(32) - 1 = 63$. **Step 6:** Interpret the results and write the answer in words.

The width of the rectangular lot is 32 m and the length is 63 m.

Recall some facts about angles.

- Two angles are complementary if the sum of their measures is 90°.
- Two angles are supplementary if the sum of their measures is 180°.
- The sum of the measures of the angles within a triangle is 180°.
- The measures of vertical angles are equal.

Example 4 **Solving a Geometry Application Involving Complementary Angles**

Two complementary angles are drawn such that one angle is 4° more than seven times the other angle. Find the measure of each angle.

Solution:

Step 1: Read the problem.

Let x represent the measure of one angle. **Step 2:** Label the variables.

Then $7x + 4$ represents the measure of the other angle.

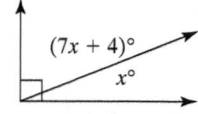

The angles are complementary, so their sum must be 90°.

$$\left(\begin{array}{c}\text{Measure of} \\ \text{first angle}\end{array}\right) + \left(\begin{array}{c}\text{measure of} \\ \text{second angle}\end{array}\right) = 90°$$ **Step 3:** Write an equation in words.

$$x + 7x + 4 = 90$$ **Step 4:** Write a mathematical equation.

$$8x + 4 = 90$$ **Step 5:** Solve for x.

$$8x = 86$$

$$\frac{8x}{8} = \frac{86}{8}$$

$$x = 10.75$$

One angle is $x = 10.75$.

Step 6: Interpret the results and write the answer in words.

The other angle is $7x + 4 = 7(10.75) + 4 = 79.25$.

The angles are $10.75°$ and $79.25°$.

Example 5   **Solving a Geometry Application**

One angle in a triangle is twice as large as the smallest angle. The third angle is $10°$ more than seven times the smallest angle. Find the measure of each angle.

Solution:

Step 1: Read the problem.

Let x represent the measure of the smallest angle.

Step 2: Label the variables.

Then $2x$ and $7x + 10$ represent the measures of the other two angles.

The sum of the angles must be $180°$.

$$\left(\begin{array}{c}\text{Measure of}\\\text{first angle}\end{array}\right) + \left(\begin{array}{c}\text{measure of}\\\text{second angle}\end{array}\right) + \left(\begin{array}{c}\text{measure of}\\\text{third angle}\end{array}\right) = 180°$$

Step 3: Write an equation in words.

$$x \quad + \quad 2x \quad + \quad (7x + 10) = 180$$

Step 4: Write a mathematical equation.

$$x + 2x + 7x + 10 = 180$$

Step 5: Solve for x.

$$10x + 10 = 180$$
$$10x = 170$$
$$x = 17$$

Step 6: Interpret the results and write the answer in words.

The smallest angle is $x = 17$.

The other angles are $2x = 2(17) = 34$

$$7x + 10 = 7(17) + 10 = 129$$

The angles are $17°$, $34°$, and $129°$.

Example 6   **Solving a Geometry Application Involving Circumference**

The distance around a circular garden is 188.4 ft. Find the radius to the nearest tenth of a foot (Figure 9-8). Use 3.14 for π.

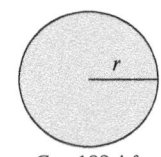

$C = 188.4$ ft

Figure 9-8

Solution:

$$C = 2\pi r$$ Use the formula for the circumference of a circle.

$$188.4 = 2\pi r$$ Substitute 188.4 for C.

$$\frac{188.4}{2\pi} = \frac{2\pi r}{2\pi}$$ Divide both sides by 2π.

$$\frac{188.4}{2\pi} = r$$

$$r \approx \frac{188.4}{2(3.14)}$$

$$= 30.0$$

The radius is approximately 30.0 ft.

Section 9.6 Practice Exercises

Boost *your* GRADE at
ALEKS.com!

- Practice Problems
- Self-Tests
- NetTutor

- e-Professors
- Videos

Study Skills Exercises

1. A good technique for studying for a test is to choose four problems from each section of the chapter and write the problems along with the directions on a 3 × 5 card. On the back of the card, put the page number where you found that problem. Then shuffle the cards and test yourself on the procedure to solve each problem. If you find one that you do not know how to solve, look at the page number and do several of that type. Write four problems you would choose for this section.

2. Define the key term: **Literal equation**

Review Exercises

For Exercises 3–8, solve the equation.

3. $3(2y + 3) - 4(-y + 1) = 7y - 10$

4. $-(3w + 4) + 5(w - 2) - 3(6w - 8) = 10$

5. $\frac{1}{2}(x - 3) + \frac{3}{4} = 3x - \frac{3}{4}$

6. $\frac{5}{6}x + \frac{1}{2} = \frac{1}{4}(x - 4)$

7. $0.5(y + 2) - 0.3 = 0.4y + 0.5$

8. $0.25(500 - x) + 0.15x = 75$

Objective 1: Formulas and Literal Equations

For Exercises 9–40, solve for the indicated variable. (See Examples 1–2.)

9. $P = a + b + c$ for a

10. $P = a + b + c$ for b

11. $x = y - z$ for y

12. $c + d = e$ for d

13. $p = 250 + q$ for q

14. $y = 35 + x$ for x

15. $A = bh$ for b

16. $d = rt$ for r

17. $PV = nrt$ for t

18. $P_1V_1 = P_2V_2$ for V_1

19. $x - y = 5$ for x

20. $x + y = -2$ for y

21. $3x + y = -19$ for y

22. $x - 6y = -10$ for x

23. $2x + 3y = 6$ for y

24. $4x + 3y = 9$ for y

25. $-2x - y = 9$ for x

26. $3x - y = -13$ for x

27. $4x - 3y = 12$ for y

28. $6x - 3y = 4$ for y

29. $ax + by = c$ for y

30. $ax + by = c$ for x

31. $A = P(1 + rt)$ for t

32. $P = 2(L + w)$ for L

33. $a = 2(b + c)$ for c

34. $3(x + y) = z$ for x

35. $Q = \dfrac{x + y}{2}$ for y

36. $Q = \dfrac{a - b}{2}$ for a

37. $M = \dfrac{a}{S}$ for a

38. $A = \dfrac{1}{3}(a + b + c)$ for c

39. $P = I^2 R$ for R

40. $F = \dfrac{GMm}{d^2}$ for m

Objective 2: Geometry Applications

For Exercises 41–62, use the problem-solving flowchart (page 619) from Section 9.4.

41. The perimeter of a rectangular garden is 24 ft. The length is 2 ft more than the width. Find the length and the width of the garden. **(See Example 3.)**

42. In a small rectangular wallet photo, the width is 7 cm less than the length. If the border (perimeter) of the photo is 34 cm, find the length and width.

43. The length of a rectangular parking area is four times the width. The perimeter is 300 yd. Find the length and width of the parking area.

44. The width of Jason's workbench is $\frac{1}{2}$ the length. The perimeter is 240 in. Find the length and the width of the workbench.

45. A builder buys a rectangular lot of land such that the length is 5 m less than two times the width. If the perimeter is 590 m, find the length and the width.

$2w - 5$

w

46. The perimeter of a rectangular pool is 140 yd. If the length is 20 yd less than twice the width, find the length and the width.

$2w - 20$

w

47. A triangular parking lot has two sides that are the same length and the third side is 5 m longer. If the perimeter is 71 m, find the lengths of the sides.

48. The perimeter of a triangle is 16 ft. One side is 3 ft longer than the shortest side. The third side is 1 ft longer than the shortest side. Find the lengths of all the sides.

49. Sometimes memory devices are helpful for remembering mathematical facts. Recall that the sum of two complementary angles is 90°. That is, two complementary angles when added together form a right angle or "corner." The words *Complementary* and *Corner* both start with the letter "*C*." Derive your own memory device for remembering that the sum of two supplementary angles is 180°.

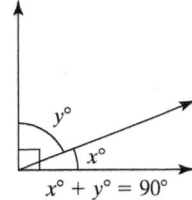

$y°$

$x°$

$x° + y° = 90°$

Complementary angles form a "Corner"

$y°$

$x°$

$x° + y° = 180°$

Supplementary angles . . .

50. What do you know about the measures of two vertical angles?

a

b

51. Two angles are complementary. One angle is 20° less than the other angle. Find the measures of the angles. **(See Example 4.)**

52. Two angles are complementary. One angle is 4° less than three times the other angle. Find the measures of the angles.

53. Two angles are supplementary. One angle is three times as large as the other angle. Find the measures of the angles.

54. Two angles are supplementary. One angle is 6° more than four times the other. Find the measures of the two angles.

55. Find the measures of the vertical angles labeled in the figure by first solving for x.

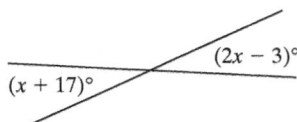

56. Find the measures of the vertical angles labeled in the figure by first solving for y.

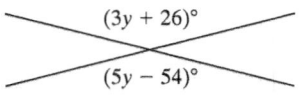

57. The largest angle in a triangle is three times the smallest angle. The middle angle is two times the smallest angle. Given that the sum of the angles in a triangle is 180°, find the measure of each angle. **(See Example 5.)**

58. The smallest angle in a triangle measures 90° less than the largest angle. The middle angle measures 60° less than the largest angle. Find the measure of each angle.

59. The smallest angle in a triangle is half the largest angle. The middle angle measures 30° less than the largest angle. Find the measure of each angle.

60. The largest angle of a triangle is three times the middle angle. The smallest angle measures 10° less than the middle angle. Find the measure of each angle.

61. Find the value of x and the measure of each angle labeled in the figure.

62. Find the value of y and the measure of each angle labeled in the figure.

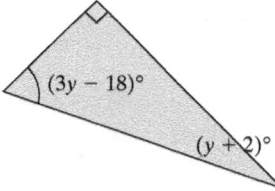

63. **a.** A rectangle has length l and width w. Write a formula for the area.

    b. Solve the formula for the width, w.

    c. The area of a rectangular volleyball court is 1740.5 ft² and the length is 59 ft. Find the width.

64. **a.** A parallelogram has height h and base b. Write a formula for the area.

    b. Solve the formula for the base, b.

    c. Find the base of the parallelogram pictured if the area is 40 m².

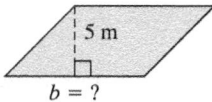

65. a. A rectangle has length l and width w. Write a formula for the perimeter.

b. Solve the formula for the length, l.

c. The perimeter of the soccer field at Giants Stadium is 338 m. If the width is 66 m, find the length.

Perimeter = 338 m

66 m

66. a. A triangle has height h and base b. Write a formula for the area.

b. Solve the formula for the height, h.

c. Find the height of the triangle pictured if the area is 12 km^2.

$h = ?$

$b = 6$ km

67. a. A circle has a radius of r. Write a formula for the circumference. **(See Example 6.)**

b. Solve the formula for the radius, r.

c. The circumference of the circular Buckingham Fountain in Chicago is approximately 880 ft. Find the radius. Round to the nearest foot.

68. a. The length of each side of a square is s. Write a formula for the perimeter of the square.

b. Solve the formula for the length of a side, s.

c. The Pyramid of Khufu (known as the Great Pyramid) at Giza has a square base. If the distance around the bottom is 921.6 m, find the length of the sides at the bottom of the pyramid.

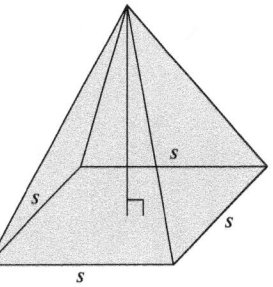

s

s

s

s

Expanding Your Skills

For Exercises 69–70, find the indicated area or volume. Be sure to include the proper units and round each answer to two decimal places if necessary.

69. a. Find the area of a circle with radius 11.5 m.

b. Find the volume of a right circular cylinder with radius 11.5 m and height 25 m.

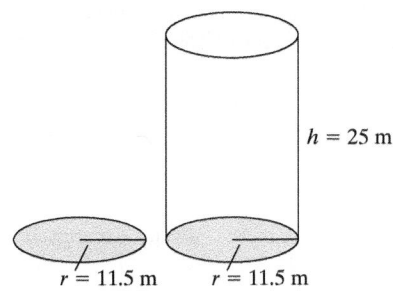

$h = 25$ m

$r = 11.5$ m $r = 11.5$ m

70. a. Find the area of a parallelogram with base 30 in. and height 12 in.

b. Find the area of a triangle with base 30 in. and height 12 in.

c. Compare the areas found in parts (a) and (b).

$h = 12$ in. $h = 12$ in.

$b = 30$ in. $b = 30$ in.

Section 9.7 Linear Inequalities

1. Graphing Linear Inequalities

Consider the following two statements.

$$2x + 7 = 11 \quad \text{and} \quad 2x + 7 < 11$$

The first statement is an equation (it has an = sign). The second statement is an inequality (it has an inequality symbol, $<$). In this section, we will learn how to solve linear *inequalities*, such as $2x + 7 < 11$.

> **DEFINITION A Linear Inequality in One Variable**
>
> A **linear inequality in one variable**, x, is defined as any relationship of the form:
>
> $ax + b < c$, $ax + b \leq c$, $ax + b > c$, or $ax + b \geq c$, where $a \neq 0$.

The following inequalities are linear equalities in one variable.

$$2x - 3 < 6 \qquad -4z - 3 > 0 \qquad a \leq 4 \qquad 5.2y \geq 10.4$$

The number line is a useful tool to visualize the solution set of an equation or inequality. For example, the solution to the equation $x = 2$ can be expressed in a set written as {2} and may be graphed as a single point on the number line.

$$x = 2 \qquad \overset{\text{\small$-6\ -5\ -4\ -3\ -2\ -1\ \ 0\ \ 1\ \ 2\ \ 3\ \ 4\ \ 5\ \ 6$}}{\longrightarrow}$$

The solution set to an inequality is the set of real numbers that make the inequality a true statement. For example, the solution set to the inequality $x \geq 2$ is all real numbers 2 or greater. Because the solution set has an infinite number of values, we cannot list all of the individual solutions. However, we can graph the solution set on the number line.

$$x \geq 2 \qquad \overset{\text{\small$-6\ -5\ -4\ -3\ -2\ -1\ \ 0\ \ 1\ \ 2\ \ 3\ \ 4\ \ 5\ \ 6$}}{\longrightarrow}$$

The square bracket symbol, [, is used on the graph to indicate that the point $x = 2$ is included in the solution set. By convention, square brackets, either [or], are used to *include* a point on a number line. Parentheses, (or), are used to *exclude* a point on a number line.

The solution set of the inequality $x > 2$ includes the real numbers greater than 2 but not including 2. Therefore, a (symbol is used on the graph to indicate that $x = 2$ is not included.

$$x > 2 \qquad \overset{\text{\small$-6\ -5\ -4\ -3\ -2\ -1\ \ 0\ \ 1\ \ 2\ \ 3\ \ 4\ \ 5\ \ 6$}}{\longrightarrow}$$

In Example 1, we demonstrate how to graph linear inequalities. To graph an inequality means that we graph its *solution set*. That is, we graph all of the values on the number line that make the inequality true.

Example 1 **Graphing Linear Inequalities**

Graph the solution sets.

a. $x > -1$ **b.** $c \leq \dfrac{7}{3}$ **c.** $3 > y$

Solution:

a. $x > -1$
-6 -5 -4 -3 -2 -1 0 1 2 3 4 5 6

The solution set is the set of all real numbers strictly greater than -1. Therefore, we graph the region on the number line to the right of -1. Because $x = -1$ is not included in the solution set, we use the (symbol at $x = -1$.

b. $c \leq \frac{7}{3}$ is equivalent to $c \leq 2\frac{1}{3}$.

The solution set is the set of all real numbers less than or equal to $2\frac{1}{3}$. Therefore, graph the region on the number line to the left of and including $2\frac{1}{3}$. Use the symbol] to indicate that $c = 2\frac{1}{3}$ is included in the solution set.

c. $3 > y$ This inequality reads "3 is greater than y." This is equivalent to saying, "y is less than 3." The inequality $3 > y$ can also be written as $y < 3$.

$y < 3$
-6 -5 -4 -3 -2 -1 0 1 2 3 4 5 6

The solution set is the set of real numbers less than 3. Therefore, graph the region on the number line to the left of 3. Use the symbol) to denote that the endpoint, 3, is not included in the solution.

Skill Practice

Graph the solution sets.
1. $y < 0$
2. $x \geq -\dfrac{5}{4}$
3. $5 \geq a$

TIP: Some textbooks use a closed circle or an open circle (● or ○) rather than a bracket or parenthesis to denote inclusion or exclusion of a value on the real number line. For example, the solution sets for the inequalities $x > -1$ and $c \leq \frac{7}{3}$ are graphed here.

$x > -1$
-6 -5 -4 -3 -2 -1 0 1 2 3 4 5 6

$c \leq \frac{7}{3}$

A statement that involves more than one inequality is called a **compound inequality**. One type of compound inequality is used to indicate that one number is between two others. For example, the inequality $-2 < x < 5$ means that $-2 < x$ and $x < 5$. In words, this is easiest to understand if we read the variable first: x is greater than -2 and x is less than 5. The numbers satisfied by these two conditions are those between -2 and 5.

Answers

1.
2.
3.

| Example 2 | **Graphing a Compound Inequality** |

Graph the solution set of the inequality: $-4.1 < y \leq -1.7$

Solution:

$-4.1 < y \leq -1.7$ means that

$-4.1 < y$ and $y \leq -1.7$

Shade the region of the number line greater than -4.1 and less than or equal to -1.7.

2. Set-Builder Notation and Interval Notation

Graphing the solution set to an inequality is one way to define the set. Two other methods are to use **set-builder notation** or **interval notation**.

Set-Builder Notation

The solution to the inequality $x \geq 2$ can be expressed in set-builder notation as follows:

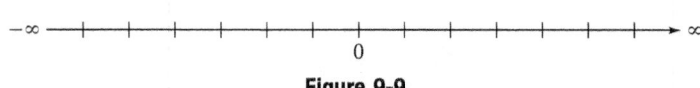

the set of all x such that x is greater than or equal to 2

Interval Notation

To understand interval notation, first think of a number line extending infinitely far to the right and infinitely far to the left. Sometimes we use the infinity symbol, ∞, or negative infinity symbol, $-\infty$, to label the far right and far left ends of the number line (Figure 9-9).

$$-\infty \; \longmapsto\!\!\!\!\!\longmapsto \; \infty$$

Figure 9-9

To express the solution set of an inequality in interval notation, sketch the graph first. Then use the endpoints to define the interval.

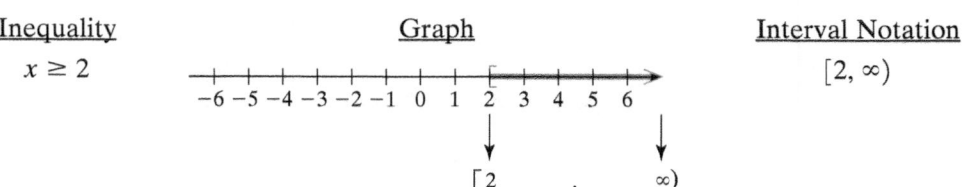

The graph of the solution set $x \geq 2$ begins at 2 and extends infinitely far to the right. The corresponding interval notation begins at 2 and extends to ∞. Notice that a square bracket [is used at 2 for both the graph and the interval notation. A parenthesis is always used at ∞ and for $-\infty$, because there is no endpoint.

Answers

4.

5. $\{b \mid b \geq -20\}$
6. $(-\infty, -30)$

> **PROCEDURE** Using Interval Notation
> - The endpoints used in interval notation are always written from left to right. That is, the smaller number is written first, followed by a comma, followed by the larger number.
> - A parenthesis, (or), indicates that an endpoint is excluded from the set.
> - A square bracket, [or], indicates that an endpoint is included in the set.
> - Parentheses, (and), are always used with $-\infty$ and ∞, respectively.

In Table 9-3, we present examples of eight different scenarios for interval notation and the corresponding graph.

Table 9-3

Interval Notation	Graph	Interval Notation	Graph
(a, ∞)		$[a, \infty)$	
$(-\infty, a)$		$(-\infty, a]$	
(a, b)		$[a, b]$	
$(a, b]$		$[a, b)$	

Example 3 **Using Set-Builder Notation and Interval Notation**

Complete the chart.

Set-Builder Notation	Graph	Interval Notation
	$\xleftarrow{\hspace{1cm}} \begin{array}{cccccccccccccc} & & & & & & & & & & & & & \\ -6 & -5 & -4 & -3 & -2 & -1 & 0 & 1 & 2 & 3 & 4 & 5 & 6 \end{array} \xrightarrow{\hspace{1cm}}$	
		$[-\frac{1}{2}, \infty)$
$\{y \mid -2 \le y < 4\}$		

Solution:

Set-Builder Notation	Graph	Interval Notation
$\{x \mid x < -3\}$	$\begin{array}{cccccccccccccc} -6 & -5 & -4 & -3 & -2 & -1 & 0 & 1 & 2 & 3 & 4 & 5 & 6 \end{array}$	$(-\infty, -3)$
$\{x \mid x \ge -\frac{1}{2}\}$	$\begin{array}{cccccccccccccc} -6 & -5 & -4 & -3 & -2 & -1 & 0 & 1 & 2 & 3 & 4 & 5 & 6 \end{array}$ $-\frac{1}{2}$	$[-\frac{1}{2}, \infty)$
$\{y \mid -2 \le y < 4\}$	$\begin{array}{cccccccccccccc} -6 & -5 & -4 & -3 & -2 & -1 & 0 & 1 & 2 & 3 & 4 & 5 & 6 \end{array}$	$[-2, 4)$

Skill Practice

Express each of the following in set-builder notation and interval notation.

7.

8. $x < \dfrac{3}{2}$

9.

Answers

7. $\{x \mid x \ge -2\}; [-2, \infty)$
8. $\left\{x \mid x < \dfrac{3}{2}\right\}; \left(-\infty, \dfrac{3}{2}\right)$
9. $\{x \mid -3 < x \le 1\}; (-3, 1]$

3. Addition and Subtraction Properties of Inequality

The process to solve a linear inequality is very similar to the method used to solve linear equations. Recall that adding or subtracting the same quantity to both sides of an equation results in an equivalent equation. The addition and subtraction properties of inequality state that the same is true for an inequality.

> **PROPERTY** Addition and Subtraction Properties of Inequality
>
> Let a, b, and c represent real numbers.
>
> 1. *Addition Property of Inequality: If $a < b$,
>   then $a + c < b + c$
>
> 2. *Subtraction Property of Inequality: If $a < b$,
>   then $a - c < b - c$
>
> *These properties may also be stated for $a \leq b$, $a > b$, and $a \geq b$.

To illustrate the addition and subtraction properties of inequality, consider the inequality $5 > 3$. If we add or subtract a real number such as 4 to both sides, the left-hand side will still be greater than the right-hand side. (See Figure 9-10.)

$5 > 3$ $5 + 4 > 3 + 4$

Figure 9-10

Skill Practice

Solve the inequality. Graph the solution set and express in interval notation.

10. $2y - 5 < y - 11$

Example 4 **Solving a Linear Inequality**

Solve the inequality and graph the solution set. Express the solution set in set-builder notation and in interval notation.

$$-2p + 5 < -3p + 6$$

Solution:

$$-2p + 5 < -3p + 6$$

$$-2p + 3p + 5 < -3p + 3p + 6 \qquad \text{Addition property of inequality}$$
$$\text{(add } 3p \text{ to both sides).}$$

$$p + 5 < 6 \qquad \text{Simplify.}$$

$$p + 5 - 5 < 6 - 5 \qquad \text{Subtraction property of inequality.}$$

$$p < 1$$

Graph:

Set-builder notation: $\{p \mid p < 1\}$

Interval notation: $(-\infty, 1)$

Answer

10.

$(-\infty, -6)$

TIP: The solution to an inequality gives a set of values that make the original inequality true. Therefore, you can test your final answer by using *test points*. That is, pick a value in the proposed solution set and verify that it makes the original inequality true. Furthermore, any test point picked outside the solution set should make the original inequality false. For example,

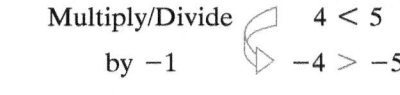

Pick $p = -4$ as an arbitrary test point within the proposed solution set.

$$-2p + 5 < -3p + 6$$
$$-2(-4) + 5 \overset{?}{<} -3(-4) + 6$$
$$8 + 5 \overset{?}{<} 12 + 6$$
$$13 < 18 \; ✔ \quad \text{True}$$

Pick $p = 3$ as an arbitrary test point outside the proposed solution set.

$$-2p + 5 < -3p + 6$$
$$-2(3) + 5 \overset{?}{<} -3(3) + 6$$
$$-6 + 5 \overset{?}{<} -9 + 6$$
$$-1 \overset{?}{<} -3 \quad \text{False}$$

4. Multiplication and Division Properties of Inequality

Multiplying both sides of an equation by the same quantity results in an equivalent equation. However, the same is not always true for an inequality. If you multiply or divide an inequality by a negative quantity, the direction of the inequality symbol must be reversed.

For example, consider multiplying or dividing the inequality, $4 < 5$ by -1.

Figure 9-11

The number 4 lies to the left of 5 on the number line. However, -4 lies to the right of -5 (Figure 9-11). Changing the sign of two numbers changes their relative position on the number line. This is stated formally in the multiplication and division properties of inequality.

PROPERTY Multiplication and Division Properties of Inequality

Let a, b, and c represent real numbers.

*If c is positive and $a < b$, then $ac < bc$ and $\dfrac{a}{c} < \dfrac{b}{c}$

*If c is negative and $a < b$, then $ac > bc$ and $\dfrac{a}{c} > \dfrac{b}{c}$

The second statement indicates that if both sides of an inequality are multiplied or divided by a negative quantity, the inequality sign must be reversed.

*These properties may also be stated for $a \leq b$, $a > b$, and $a \geq b$.

┌─ **Skill Practice** ─────────┐

Solve. Graph the solution set and
express the solution in interval
notation.

11. $-5p + 2 > 22$

└──────────────────────────┘

Example 5	**Solving a Linear Inequality**

Solve the inequality $-5x - 3 \le 12$. Graph the solution set and write the answer in interval notation.

Solution:

$$-5x - 3 \le 12$$

$$-5x - 3 + 3 \le 12 + 3 \qquad \text{Add } 3 \text{ to both sides.}$$

$$-5x \le 15$$

$$\frac{-5x}{-5} \ge \frac{15}{-5} \qquad \text{Divide by } -5.\text{ Reverse the direction of the inequality sign.}$$

$$x \ge -3$$

Interval notation: $[-3, \infty)$

```
  +--+--+--+--[--+--+--+--+--+--+--+-->
 -6 -5 -4 -3 -2 -1  0  1  2  3  4  5  6
```

TIP: The inequality $-5x - 3 \le 12$ could have been solved by isolating x on the right-hand side of the inequality. This would create a positive coefficient on the variable term and eliminate the need to divide by a negative number.

$$-5x - 3 \le 12$$

$$-3 \le 5x + 12$$

$$-15 \le 5x \qquad \text{Notice that the coefficient of } x \text{ is positive.}$$

$$\frac{-15}{5} \le \frac{5x}{5} \qquad \begin{array}{l}\text{Do not reverse the inequality sign because we are}\\ \text{dividing by a positive number.}\end{array}$$

$$-3 \le x, \text{ or equivalently, } x \ge -3$$

┌─ **Skill Practice** ─────────┐

Solve. Graph the solution set and
express the solution in interval
notation.

12. $1.1x - 0.8 > 0.1x + 4.2$

└──────────────────────────┘

Example 6	**Solving a Linear Inequality**

Solve the inequality. Graph the solution set and write the answer in interval notation.

$$1.4x + 4.5 < 0.2x - 0.3$$

Solution:

$$1.4x + 4.5 < 0.2x - 0.3$$

$$1.4x - 0.2x + 4.5 < 0.2x - 0.2x - 0.3 \qquad \text{Subtract } 0.2x \text{ from both sides.}$$

$$1.2x + 4.5 < -0.3 \qquad \text{Simplify.}$$

$$1.2x + 4.5 - 4.5 < -0.3 - 4.5 \qquad \text{Subtract } 4.5 \text{ from both sides.}$$

$$1.2x < -4.8 \qquad \text{Simplify.}$$

$$\frac{1.2x}{1.2} < \frac{-4.8}{1.2} \qquad \begin{array}{l}\text{Divide by } 1.2.\text{ The direction of the}\\ \text{inequality sign is } not \text{ reversed because}\\ \text{we divided by a positive number.}\end{array}$$

$$x < -4$$

Interval notation: $(-\infty, -4)$

```
  <--+--+--+--+--+--+--+--+--+--+--+-->
 -6 -5 -4 -3 -2 -1  0  1  2  3  4  5  6
```

Answers

11.

$(-\infty, -4)$

12.

$(5, \infty)$

Example 7 **Solving Linear Inequalities**

Solve the inequality $-\frac{1}{4}k + \frac{1}{6} \leq 2 + \frac{2}{3}k$. Graph the solution set and write the answer in interval notation.

Solution:

$$-\frac{1}{4}k + \frac{1}{6} \leq 2 + \frac{2}{3}k$$

$$12\left(-\frac{1}{4}k + \frac{1}{6}\right) \leq 12\left(2 + \frac{2}{3}k\right)$$
  Multiply both sides by 12 to clear fractions. (Because we multiplied by a positive number, the inequality sign is not reversed.)

$$\frac{12}{1}\left(-\frac{1}{4}k\right) + \frac{12}{1}\left(\frac{1}{6}\right) \leq 12(2) + \frac{12}{1}\left(\frac{2}{3}k\right)$$
  Apply the distributive property.

$$-3k + 2 \leq 24 + 8k$$
  Simplify.

$$-3k - 8k + 2 \leq 24 + 8k - 8k$$
  Subtract $8k$ from both sides.

$$-11k + 2 \leq 24$$

$$-11k + 2 - 2 \leq 24 - 2$$
  Subtract 2 from both sides.

$$-11k \leq 22$$

$$\frac{-11k}{-11} \geq \frac{22}{-11}$$
  Divide both sides by -11. Reverse the inequality sign.

$$k \geq -2$$

Graph: $\begin{array}{c}\\ \hline \end{array}$ $-4\ -3\ -2\ -1\ 0\ 1\ 2\ 3\ 4$

Interval notation: $[-2, \infty)$

Skill Practice

Solve. Graph the solution set and express the solution in interval notation.

13. $\frac{1}{5}t + 7 \leq \frac{1}{2}t - 2$

5. Solving Inequalities of the Form $a < x < b$

To solve a compound inequality of the form $a < x < b$ we can work with the inequality as a three-part inequality and isolate the variable, x, as demonstrated in Example 8.

Example 8 **Solving a Compound Inequality of the Form $a < x < b$**

Solve the inequality: $-3 \leq 2x + 1 < 7$. Graph the solution and write the answer in interval notation.

Solution:

To solve the compound inequality $-3 \leq 2x + 1 < 7$ isolate the variable x in the middle. The operations performed on the middle portion of the inequality must also be performed on the left-hand side and right-hand side.

Skill Practice

Solve. Graph the solution set and express the solution in interval notation.

14. $-3 \leq -5 + 2y < 11$

Answers

13.

$[30, \infty)$

14.

$[1, 8)$

$$-3 \le 2x + 1 < 7$$

$$-3 - 1 \le 2x + 1 - 1 < 7 - 1 \qquad \text{Subtract } 1 \text{ from all three parts of the inequality.}$$

$$-4 \le 2x < 6 \qquad \text{Simplify.}$$

$$\frac{-4}{2} \le \frac{2x}{2} < \frac{6}{2} \qquad \text{Divide by } 2 \text{ in all three parts of the inequality.}$$

$$-2 \le x < 3$$

Graph:

$$\begin{array}{c} \quad\quad\quad\quad \overset{[\quad\quad\quad\quad)}{} \\ \leftarrow\!+\!+\!+\!+\!+\!+\!+\!+\!+\!+\!+\!+\!+\!\rightarrow \\ -6\ -5\ -4\ -3\ -2\ -1\ \ 0\ \ 1\ \ 2\ \ 3\ \ 4\ \ 5\ \ 6 \end{array}$$

Interval notation: $[-2, 3)$

6. Applications of Linear Inequalities

Table 9-4 provides several commonly used translations to express inequalities.

Table 9-4

English Phrase	Mathematical Inequality
a is less than b	$a < b$
a is greater than b a exceeds b	$a > b$
a is less than or equal to b a is at most b a is no more than b	$a \le b$
a is greater than or equal to b a is at least b a is no less than b	$a \ge b$

Example 9 **Translating Expressions Involving Inequalities**

Translate the English phrases into mathematical inequalities.

a. Claude's annual salary, s, is no more than $40,000.

b. A citizen must be at least 18 years old to vote. (Let a represent a citizen's age.)

c. An amusement park ride has a height requirement between 48 in. and 70 in. (Let h represent height in inches.)

Solution:

a. $s \le 40,000$ Claude's annual salary, s, is no more than $40,000.

b. $a \ge 18$ A citizen must be at least 18 years old to vote.

c. $48 < h < 70$ An amusement park ride has a height requirement between 48 in. and 70 in.

Linear inequalities are found in a variety of applications. Example 10 can help you determine the minimum grade you need on an exam to get an A in your math course.

| Example 10 | **Solving an Application with Linear Inequalities** |

To earn an A in a math class, Alsha must average at least 90 on all of her tests. Suppose Alsha has scored 79, 86, 93, 90, and 95 on her first five math tests. Determine the minimum score she needs on her sixth test to get an A in the class.

Solution:

Let x represent the score on the sixth exam.   Label the variable.

$\left(\begin{array}{c}\text{Average of}\\\text{all tests}\end{array}\right) \geq 90$ Write an equation in words.

$\dfrac{79 + 86 + 93 + 90 + 95 + x}{6} \geq 90$ The average score is found by taking the sum of the test scores and dividing by the number of scores.

$\dfrac{443 + x}{6} \geq 90$ Simplify.

$6\left(\dfrac{443 + x}{6}\right) \geq (90)6$ Multiply both sides by 6 to clear fractions.

$443 + x \geq 540$ Solve the inequality.

$x \geq 540 - 443$ Subtract 443 from both sides.

$x \geq 97$ Interpret the results.

Alsha must score at least 97 on her sixth exam to receive an A in the course.

Section 9.7 Practice Exercises

Study Skills Exercises

1. Find the page numbers for the Chapter Review Exercises, the Chapter Test, and the Cumulative Review Exercises for this chapter.

Chapter Review Exercises _____   Chapter Test _____

Cumulative Review Exercises _____

Compare these features and state the advantages of each.

2. Define the key terms:

    a. Linear inequality in one variable   **b. Compound inequality**

    c. Set-builder notation   **d. Interval notation**

Review Problems

3. Solve the equation. $3(x + 2) - (2x - 7) = -(5x - 1) - 2(x + 6)$

4. Solve the equation. $6 - 8(x + 3) + 5x = 5x - (2x - 5) + 13$

Objectives 1–2: Graphing Linear Inequalities; Set-Builder Notation and Interval Notation

For Exercises 5–10, graph each inequality and write the solution set in interval notation. **(See Examples 1–3.)**

Set-Builder Notation	Graph	Interval Notation
5. $\{x \mid x \geq 6\}$		
6. $\left\{x \mid \frac{1}{2} < x \leq 4\right\}$		
7. $\{x \mid x \leq 2.1\}$		
8. $\left\{x \mid x > \frac{7}{3}\right\}$		
9. $\{x \mid -2 < x \leq 7\}$		
10. $\{x \mid x < -5\}$		

For Exercises 11–16, write each set in set-builder notation and in interval notation. **(See Examples 1–3.)**

Set-Builder Notation	Graph	Interval Notation
11.	$\frac{3}{4}$	
12.	-0.3	
13.	$-1 \quad 8$	
14.	0	
15.	-14	
16.	$0 \quad 9$	

For Exercises 17–22, graph each set and write the set in set-builder notation. **(See Examples 1–3.)**

Set-Builder Notation	Graph	Interval Notation
17.		$[18, \infty)$
18.		$[-10, -2]$
19.		$(-\infty, -0.6)$
20.		$\left(-\infty, \dfrac{5}{3}\right)$
21.		$[-3.5, 7.1)$
22.		$[-10, \infty)$

Objectives 3–4: Properties of Inequality

For Exercises 23–30, solve the equation in part (a). For part (b), solve the inequality and graph the solution set. **(See Examples 4–7.)**

23. a. $x + 3 = 6$
b. $x + 3 > 6$

24. a. $y - 6 = 12$
b. $y - 6 \geq 12$

25. a. $p - 4 = 9$
b. $p - 4 \leq 9$

26. a. $k + 8 = 10$
b. $k + 8 < 10$

27. a. $4c = -12$

b. $4c < -12$

28. a. $5d = -35$

b. $5d > -35$

29. a. $-10z = 15$

b. $-10z \le 15$

30. a. $-2w = 14$

b. $-2w < 14$

Objective 5: Solving Inequalities of the Form $a < x < b$

For Exercises 31–36, graph the solution. **(See Example 8.)**

31. $-1 < y \le 4$

32. $2.5 \le t < 5.7$

33. $0 < x + 3 < 8$

34. $-2 \le x - 4 \le 3$

35. $8 \le 4x \le 24$

36. $-9 < 3x < 12$

Mixed Exercises

For Exercises 37–84, solve the inequality. Graph the solution set and write the set in interval notation.

37. $x + 5 \le 6$

38. $y - 7 < 6$

39. $3q - 7 > 2q + 3$

40. $5r + 4 \ge 4r - 1$

41. $4 < 1 + z$

42. $3 > z - 6$

43. $2 \ge a - 6$

44. $7 \le b + 12$

45. $3c > 6$

46. $4d \le 12$

47. $-3c > 6$

48. $-4d \le 12$

49. $-h \le -14$

50. $-q > -7$

51. $12 \ge -\dfrac{x}{2}$

52. $6 < -\dfrac{m}{3}$

53. $-2 \le p + 1 < 4$

54. $0 < k + 7 < 6$

55. $-3 < 6h - 3 < 12$

56. $-6 \le 4a - 2 \le 12$

57. $5 < \dfrac{1}{2}x < 6$

58. $-6 \le 3x \le 12$

59. $-5 \le 4x - 1 < 15$

60. $-2 < \dfrac{1}{3}x - 2 \le 2$

61. $54 \le 0.6z$

62. $28 < -0.7w$

63. $-\dfrac{2}{3}y < 6$

64. $\dfrac{3}{4}x \le -12$

65. $-2x - 4 \le 11$

66. $-3x + 1 > 0$

67. $-12 > 7x + 9$

68. $8 < 2x - 10$

69. $-7b - 3 \le 2b$

70. $3t \geq 7t - 35$

71. $4n + 2 < 6n + 8$

72. $2w - 1 \leq 5w + 8$

73. $8 - 6(x - 3) > -4x + 12$

74. $3 - 4(h - 2) > -5h + 6$

75. $3(x + 1) - 2 \leq \frac{1}{2}(4x - 8)$

76. $8 - (2x - 5) \geq \frac{1}{3}(9x - 6)$

77. $\frac{7}{6}p + \frac{4}{3} \geq \frac{11}{6}p - \frac{7}{6}$

78. $\frac{1}{3}w - \frac{1}{2} \leq \frac{5}{6}w + \frac{1}{2}$

79. $\frac{y - 6}{3} > y + 4$

80. $\frac{5t + 7}{2} < t - 4$

81. $-1.2a - 0.4 < -0.4a + 2$

82. $-0.4c + 1.2 > -2c - 0.4$

83. $-2x + 5 \geq -x + 5$

84. $4x - 6 < 5x - 6$

For Exercises 85–88, determine whether the given number is a solution to the inequality.

85. $-2x + 5 < 4$; $x = -2$

86. $-3y - 7 > 5$; $y = 6$

87. $4(p + 7) - 1 > 2 + p$; $p = 1$

88. $3 - k < 2(-1 + k)$; $k = 4$

Objective 6: Applications of Linear Inequalities

89. Let x represent a student's average in a math class. The grading scale is given here.

A	$93 \leq x \leq 100$
B+	$89 \leq x < 93$
B	$84 \leq x < 89$
C+	$80 \leq x < 84$
C	$75 \leq x < 80$
F	$0 \leq x < 75$

a. Write the range of scores corresponding to each letter grade in interval notation.

b. If Stephan's average is 84.01, what grade will he receive?

c. If Estella's average is 79.89, what grade will she receive?

90. Let x represent a student's average in a science class. The grading scale is given here.

A	$90 \leq x \leq 100$
B+	$86 \leq x < 90$
B	$80 \leq x < 86$
C+	$76 \leq x < 80$
C	$70 \leq x < 76$
D+	$66 \leq x < 70$
D	$60 \leq x < 66$
F	$0 \leq x < 60$

a. Write the range of scores corresponding to each letter grade in interval notation.

b. If Jacque's average is 89.99, what is her grade?

c. If Marc's average is 66.01, what is his grade?

For Exercises 91–100, translate the English phrase into a mathematical inequality. **(See Example 9.)**

91. The length of a fish, L, was at least 10 in.

92. Tasha's average test score, t, exceeded 90.

93. The wind speed, w, exceeded 75 mph.

94. The height of a cave, h, was no more than 2 ft.

95. The temperature of the water in Blue Spring, t, is no more than 72°F.

96. The temperature on the tennis court, t, was no less than 100°F.

97. The length of the hike, L, was no less than 8 km.

98. The depth, d, of a certain pool was at most 10 ft.

99. The snowfall, h, in Monroe County is between 2 inches and 5 inches.

100. The cost, c, of carpeting a room is between $300 and $400.

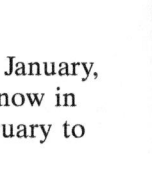 **101.** The average summer rainfall for Miami, Florida, for June, July, and August is 7.4 in. per month. If Miami receives 5.9 in. of rain in June and 6.1 in. in July, how much rain is required in August to exceed the 3-month summer average? **(See Example 10.)**

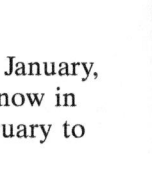 **102.** The average winter snowfall for Burlington, Vermont, for December, January, and February is 18.7 in. per month. If Burlington receives 22 in. of snow in December and 24 in. in January, how much snow is required in February to exceed the 3-month winter average?

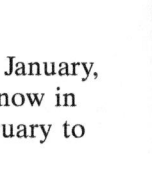 **103.** An artist paints wooden birdhouses. She buys the birdhouses for $9 each. However, for large orders, the price per birdhouse is discounted by a percentage off the original price. Let x represent the number of birdhouses ordered. The corresponding discount is given in the table.

Size of Order	Discount
$x \le 49$	0%
$50 \le x \le 99$	5%
$100 \le x \le 199$	10%
$x \ge 200$	20%

a. If the artist places an order for 190 birdhouses, compute the total cost.

b. Which costs more: 190 birdhouses or 200 birdhouses? Explain your answer.

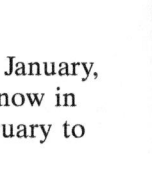 **104.** A wholesaler sells T-shirts to a surf shop at $8 per shirt. However, for large orders, the price per shirt is discounted by a percentage off the original price. Let x represent the number of shirts ordered. The corresponding discount is given in the table.

Number of Shirts Ordered	Discount
$x \le 24$	0%
$25 \le x \le 49$	2%
$50 \le x \le 99$	4%
$100 \le x \le 149$	6%
$x \ge 150$	8%

a. If the surf shop orders 50 shirts, compute the total cost.

b. Which costs more: 148 shirts or 150 shirts? Explain your answer.

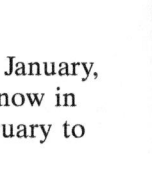 **105.** Maggie sells lemonade at an art show. She has a fixed cost of $75 to cover the registration fee for the art show. In addition, her cost to produce each lemonade is $0.17. If x represents the number of lemonades, then the total cost to produce x lemonades is given by:

$$\text{Cost} = 75 + 0.17x$$

If Maggie sells each lemonade for $2, then her revenue (the amount she brings in) for selling x lemonades is given by:

$$\text{Revenue} = 2.00x$$

a. Write an inequality that expresses the number of lemonades, x, that Maggie must sell to make a profit. Profit is realized when the revenue is greater than the cost (Revenue > Cost).

b. Solve the inequality in part (a).

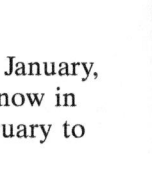 **106.** Two rental car companies rent subcompact cars at a discount. Company A rents for $14.95 per day plus 22 cents per mile. Company B rents for $18.95 a day plus 18 cents per mile. Let x represent the number of miles driven in one day.

The cost to rent a subcompact car for one day from Company A is: $\text{Cost}_A = 14.95 + 0.22x$

The cost to rent a subcompact car for one day from Company B is: $\text{Cost}_B = 18.95 + 0.18x$

a. Write an inequality that expresses the number of miles, x, for which the daily cost to rent from Company A is less than the daily cost to rent from Company B.

b. Solve the inequality in part (a).

Expanding Your Skills

For Exercises 107–112, solve the inequality. Graph the solution set and write the set in interval notation.

107. $3(x + 2) - (2x - 7) \leq (5x - 1) - 2(x + 6)$

108. $6 - 8(y + 3) + 5y > 5y - (2y - 5) + 13$

109. $-2 - \dfrac{w}{4} \leq \dfrac{1 + w}{3}$

110. $\dfrac{z - 3}{4} - 1 > \dfrac{z}{2}$

111. $-0.703 < 0.122p - 2.472$

112. $3.88 - 1.335t \geq 5.66$

Group Activity

Computing Body Mass Index (BMI)

Materials: Calculator

Estimated Time: 10 minutes

Group Size: 2

Body mass index is a statistical measure of an individual's weight in relation to the person's height. It is computed by

$$\text{BMI} = \frac{703W}{h^2}$$

where W is a person's weight in *pounds*.
h is the person's height in *inches*.

The NIH categorizes body mass indices as follows:

Body Mass Index (BMI)	Weight Status
$18.5 \leq \text{BMI} \leq 24.9$	considered ideal
$25.0 \leq \text{BMI} \leq 29.9$	considered overweight
$\text{BMI} \geq 30.0$	considered obese

1. Compute the body mass index for a person 5'4" tall weighing 160 lb. Is this person's weight considered ideal?

2. At the time that basketball legend Michael Jordan played for the Chicago Bulls, he was 210 lb and stood 6'6" tall. What was Michael Jordan's body mass index?

3. For a fixed height, body mass index is a function of a person's weight only. For example, for a person 72 in. tall (6 ft), solve the following inequality to determine the person's ideal weight range.

$$18.5 \leq \frac{703W}{(72)^2} \leq 24.9$$

4. At the time that professional bodybuilder, Jay Cutler, won the Mr. Olympia contest he was 260 lb and stood 5'10" tall.

   a. What was Jay Cutler's body mass index?

   b. As a body builder, Jay Cutler has an extraordinarily small percentage of body fat. Yet, according to the chart, would he be considered overweight or obese? Why do you think that the formula is not an accurate measurement of Mr. Cutler's weight status?

Chapter 9 Summary

Sets of Numbers and the Real Number Line

Key Concepts

Natural numbers: $\{1, 2, 3, \ldots\}$

Whole numbers: $\{0, 1, 2, 3, \ldots\}$

Integers: $\{\ldots -3, -2, -1, 0, 1, 2, 3, \ldots\}$

Rational numbers: The set of numbers that can be expressed in the form $\frac{p}{q}$, where p and q are integers and q does not equal 0. In decimal form, rational numbers are terminating or repeating decimals.

Irrational numbers: A subset of the real numbers whose elements cannot be written as a ratio of two integers. In decimal form, irrational numbers are nonterminating, nonrepeating decimals.

Real numbers: The set of both the rational numbers and the irrational numbers.

Examples

Example 1

$-5, 0$, and 4 are integers.

$-\dfrac{5}{2}, -0.5$, and $0.\overline{3}$ are rational numbers.

$\sqrt{7}, -\sqrt{2}$, and π are irrational numbers.

Example 2

All real numbers can be located on the real number line.

Inequalities:

$a < b$	"a is less than b."
$a > b$	"a is greater than b."
$a \le b$	"a is less than or equal to b."
$a \ge b$	"a is greater than or equal to b."

The **absolute value** of a real number, a, denoted $|a|$, is the distance between a and 0 on the number line.

If $a \ge 0$, $|a| = a$

If $a < 0$, $|a| = -a$

Example 3

$5 < 7$	"5 is less than 7."
$-2 > -10$	"-2 is greater than -10."
$y \le 3.4$	"y is less than or equal to 3.4."
$x \ge \frac{1}{2}$	"x is greater than or equal to $\frac{1}{2}$."

Example 4

$|7| = 7$

$|-7| = 7$

Section 9.2 Solving Linear Equations

Key Concepts

An equation is an algebraic statement that indicates two expressions are equal. **A solution to an equation** is a value of the variable that makes the equation a true statement.

A **linear equation in one variable** can be written in the form $ax + b = c$, where $a \neq 0$.

Steps for Solving a Linear Equation in One Variable:

1. Simplify both sides of the equation.
   - Clear parentheses
   - Combine *like* terms
2. Use the addition or subtraction property of equality to collect the variable terms on one side of the equation.
3. Use the addition or subtraction property of equality to collect the constant terms on the other side of the equation.
4. Use the multiplication or division property of equality to make the coefficient of the variable term equal to 1.
5. Check your answer.

A **conditional equation** is true for some values of the variable but is false for other values.

An equation that has all real numbers as its solution set is an **identity**.

An equation that has no solution is a **contradiction**.

Examples

Example 1

$2x + 1 = 9$ is a linear equation in two variables with solution 4.

Check: $2(4) + 1 \overset{?}{=} 9$

$\qquad\qquad 8 + 1 \overset{?}{=} 9$

$\qquad\qquad\qquad 9 \overset{?}{=} 9$ ✔ True

Example 2

$5y + 7 = 3(y - 1) + 2$

$5y + 7 = 3y - 3 + 2$ Clear parentheses.

$5y + 7 = 3y - 1$ Combine *like* terms.

$2y + 7 = -1$ Isolate the variable term.

$\quad 2y = -8$ Isolate the constant term.

$\quad\; y = -4$ Divide both sides by 2.

Check:

$\quad 5(-4) + 7 \overset{?}{=} 3[(-4) - 1] + 2$

$\qquad\quad -20 + 7 \overset{?}{=} 3(-5) + 2$

$\qquad\qquad\quad -13 \overset{?}{=} -15 + 2$

The solution is -4. $-13 \overset{?}{=} -13$ ✔ True

Example 3

$x + 5 = 7$ is a conditional equation because it is true only on the condition that $x = 2$.

Example 4

$x + 4 = 2(x + 2) - x$

$x + 4 = 2x + 4 - x$

$x + 4 = x + 4$

$\quad 4 = 4$ is an identity

The solution is all real numbers.

Example 5

$y - 5 = 2(y + 3) - y$

$y - 5 = 2y + 6 - y$

$y - 5 = y + 6$

$\quad -5 = 6$ is a contradiction

There is no solution.

Section 9.3   Linear Equations: Clearing Fractions and Decimals

Key Concepts

Steps for Solving a Linear Equation in One Variable:

1. Simplify both sides of the equation.
   - Clear parentheses
   - Consider clearing fractions or decimals (if any are present) by multiplying both sides of the equation by a common denominator of all terms
   - Combine *like* terms
2. Use the addition or subtraction property of equality to collect the variable terms on one side of the equation.
3. Use the addition or subtraction property of equality to collect the constant terms on the other side of the equation.
4. Use the multiplication or division property of equality to make the coefficient of the variable term equal to 1.
5. Check your answer.

Examples

Example 1

$$\frac{1}{2}x - 2 - \frac{3}{4}x = \frac{7}{4}$$

$$\frac{4}{1}\left(\frac{1}{2}x - 2 - \frac{3}{4}x\right) = \frac{4}{1}\left(\frac{7}{4}\right) \qquad \text{Multiply by the LCD.}$$

$$2x - 8 - 3x = 7 \qquad \text{Apply distributive property.}$$

$$-x - 8 = 7 \qquad \text{Combine } like \text{ terms.}$$

$$-x = 15 \qquad \text{Add 8 to both sides.}$$

$$x = -15 \qquad \text{Divide by } -1.$$

The solution -15 checks in the original equation.

Example 2

$$-1.2x - 5.1 = 16.5$$

$$10(-1.2x - 5.1) = 10(16.5) \qquad \text{Multiply both sides by 10.}$$

$$-12x - 51 = 165$$

$$-12x = 216$$

$$\frac{-12x}{-12} = \frac{216}{-12}$$

$$x = -18$$

The solution is -18.

Section 9.4 — Applications of Linear Equations and Problem Solving

Key Concepts

Problem-Solving Steps for Word Problems:

1. Read the problem carefully.
2. Assign labels to unknown quantities.
3. Write an equation in words.
4. Write a mathematical equation.
5. Solve the equation.
6. Interpret the results and write the answer in words.

Examples

Example 1

The perimeter of a triangle is 54 m. The lengths of the sides are represented by three consecutive even integers. Find the lengths of the three sides.

1. Read the problem.

2. Let x represent one side, $x + 2$ represent the second side, and $x + 4$ represent the third side.

3. (First side) + (second side) + (third side) = perimeter

4. $x + (x + 2) + (x + 4) = 54$

5. $3x + 6 = 54$
   $3x = 48$
   $x = 16$

6. $x = 16$ represents the length of the shortest side. The lengths of the other sides are given by $x + 2 = 18$ and $x + 4 = 20$.

   The lengths of the three sides are 16 m, 18 m, and 20 m.

Section 9.5   Applications Involving Percents

Key Concepts

The following formula will help you solve basic percent problems.

$$\text{Amount} = (\text{percent})(\text{base})$$

One common use of percents is in computing **sales tax**.

Another use of percent is in computing **simple interest** using the formula:

$$\begin{pmatrix}\text{Simple} \\ \text{interest}\end{pmatrix} = (\text{principal})\begin{pmatrix}\text{annual} \\ \text{interest} \\ \text{rate}\end{pmatrix}\begin{pmatrix}\text{time in} \\ \text{years}\end{pmatrix}$$

or $I = Prt$.

Examples

Example 1

A dinette set costs $1260.00 after a 5% sales tax is included. What was the price before tax?

$$\begin{pmatrix}\text{Price} \\ \text{before tax}\end{pmatrix} + (\text{tax}) = \begin{pmatrix}\text{total} \\ \text{price}\end{pmatrix}$$

$$x \qquad + 0.05x = 1260$$
$$1.05x = 1260$$
$$x = 1200$$

The dinette set cost $1200 before tax.

Example 2

John Li invests $5400 at 2.5% simple interest. How much interest does he earn after 5 years?

$$I = Prt$$
$$I = (\$5400)(0.025)(5)$$
$$I = \$675$$

Section 9.6   Literal Equations and Applications of Geometry

Key Concepts

A **literal equation** is an equation that has more than one variable. Often such an equation can be manipulated to solve for different variables.

   Formulas from Chapter 7 can be used in applications involving geometry.

Examples

Example 1

$$P = 2a + b, \text{ solve for } a.$$
$$P - b = 2a + b - b$$
$$P - b = 2a$$
$$\frac{P - b}{2} = \frac{2a}{2}$$
$$\frac{P - b}{2} = a \quad \text{or} \quad a = \frac{P - b}{2}$$

Example 2

Find the length of a side of a square whose perimeter is 28 ft.

Use the formula $P = 4s$. Substitute 28 for P and solve:

$$P = 4s$$
$$28 = 4s$$
$$7 = s$$

The length of a side of the square is 7 ft.

Key Concepts

A **linear inequality in one variable**, x, is any relationship in the form: $ax + b < c$, $ax + b > c$, $ax + b \leq c$, or $ax + b \geq c$, where $a \neq 0$.

The solution set to an inequality can be expressed as a graph or in **set-builder notation** or in **interval notation**.

When graphing an inequality or when writing interval notation, a parenthesis, (or), is used to denote that an endpoint is *not included* in a solution set. A square bracket, [or], is used to show that an endpoint *is included* in a solution set. Parenthesis (or) are always used with $-\infty$ and ∞, respectively.

The inequality $a < x < b$ is used to show that x is greater than a and less than b. That is, x is *between a and b*.

Multiplying or dividing an inequality by a negative quantity requires the direction of the inequality sign to be reversed.

Examples

Example 1

$$-2x + 6 \geq 14$$

$-2x + 6 - 6 \geq 14 - 6$	Subtract 6.
$-2x \geq 8$	Simplify.
$\dfrac{-2x}{-2} \leq \dfrac{8}{-2}$	Divide by -2. Reverse the inequality sign.
$x \leq -4$	

Set-builder notation: $\{x \mid x \leq -4\}$

Graph:

$$-4$$

Interval notation: $(-\infty, -4]$

Chapter 9 Review Exercises

Section 9.1

1. Given the set $\{7, \frac{1}{3}, -4, 0, -\sqrt{3}, -0.\overline{2}, \pi, 1\}$,

   a. List the natural numbers.

   b. List the integers.

   c. List the whole numbers.

   d. List the rational numbers.

   e. List the irrational numbers.

   f. List the real numbers.

For Exercises 2–5, determine the absolute value.

2. $\left| \dfrac{1}{2} \right|$ **3.** $|-6|$ **4.** $|-\sqrt{7}|$ **5.** $|0|$

For Exercises 6–14, identify whether the inequality is true or false.

6. $-6 > -1$ **7.** $0 < -5$ **8.** $-10 \leq 0$

9. $5 \neq -5$ **10.** $7 \geq 7$ **11.** $7 \geq -7$

12. $0 \leq -3$ **13.** $-\dfrac{2}{3} \leq -\dfrac{2}{3}$ **14.** $-|-2| > -1$

Section 9.2

For Exercises 15–34, solve the equation.

15. $a + 6 = -2$ **16.** $6 = z - 9$

17. $-\dfrac{3}{4} + k = \dfrac{9}{2}$ **18.** $0.1r = 7$

19. $-5x = 21$ **20.** $\dfrac{t}{3} = -20$

21. $-\dfrac{2}{5}k = \dfrac{4}{7}$ **22.** $-m = -27$

23. $4d + 2 = 6$ **24.** $5c - 6 = -9$

25. $-7c = -3c - 9$ **26.** $-28 = 5w + 2$

27. $\dfrac{b}{3} + 1 = 0$ **28.** $\dfrac{2}{3}h - 5 = 7$

29. $-3p + 7 = 5p + 1$ **30.** $4t - 6 = -12t + 16$

31. $4a - 9 = 3(a - 3)$ **32.** $3(2c + 5) = -2(c - 8)$

33. $7b + 3(b - 1) + 16 = 2(b + 8)$

34. $2 + (17 - x) + 2(x - 1) = 4(x + 2) - 8$

35. Explain the difference between an equation that is a contradiction and an equation that is an identity.

36. Label each equation as a conditional equation, a contradiction, or an identity.

    a. $x + 3 = 3 + x$ **b.** $3x - 19 = 2x + 1$

    c. $5x + 6 = 5x - 28$ **d.** $2x - 8 = 2(x - 4)$

    e. $-8x - 9 = -8(x - 9)$

Section 9.3

For Exercises 37–54, solve the equation.

37. $\dfrac{x}{8} - \dfrac{1}{4} = \dfrac{1}{2}$ **38.** $\dfrac{y}{15} - \dfrac{2}{3} = \dfrac{4}{5}$

39. $\dfrac{x + 5}{2} - \dfrac{2x + 10}{9} = 5$

40. $\dfrac{x - 6}{3} - \dfrac{2x + 8}{2} = 12$

41. $\dfrac{1}{10}p - 3 = \dfrac{2}{5}p$ **42.** $\dfrac{1}{4}y - \dfrac{3}{4} = \dfrac{1}{2}y + 1$

43. $-\dfrac{1}{4}(2 - 3t) = \dfrac{3}{4}$ **44.** $\dfrac{2}{7}(w + 4) = \dfrac{1}{2}$

45. $17.3 - 2.7q = 10.55$

46. $4.9z + 4.6 = 3.2z - 2.2$

47. $5.74a + 9.28 = 2.24a - 5.42$

48. $62.84t - 123.66 = 4(2.36 + 2.4t)$

49. $0.05x + 0.10(24 - x) = 0.75(24)$

50. $0.20(x + 4) + 0.65x = 0.20(854)$

51. $100 - (t - 6) = -(t - 1)$

52. $3 - (x + 4) + 5 = 3x + 10 - 4x$

53. $5t - (2t + 14) = 3t - 14$

54. $9 - 6(2z + 1) = -3(4z - 1)$

Section 9.4

55. Twelve added to the sum of a number and two is forty-four. Find the number.

56. Twenty added to the sum of a number and six is thirty-seven. Find the number.

57. Three times a number is the same as the difference of twice the number and seven. Find the number.

58. Eight less than five times a number is forty-eight less than the number. Find the number.

59. Three times the largest of three consecutive even integers is 76 more than the sum of the other two integers. Find the integers.

60. Ten times the smallest of three consecutive integers is 213 more than the sum of the other two integers. Find the integers.

61. The perimeter of a triangle is 78 in. The lengths of the sides are represented by three consecutive integers. Find the lengths of the sides of the triangle.

62. The perimeter of a pentagon (a five-sided polygon) is 190 cm. The five sides are represented by consecutive integers. Find the lengths of the sides.

63. The minimum salary for a major league baseball player in 1985 was $60,000. This was twice the minimum salary in 1980. What was the minimum salary in 1980?

64. The state of Indiana has approximately 2.1 million more people than Kentucky. Together their population totals 10.3 million. Approximately how many people are in each state?

Section 9.5

For Exercises 65–74, solve the problems involving percents.

65. What is 35% of 68?   **66.** What is 4% of 720?

67. 53.5 is what percent of 428?

68. 68.4 is what percent of 72?

69. 24 is 15% of what number?

70. 8.75 is 0.5% of what number?

71. A novel is discounted 30%. The sale price is $20.65. What was the original price?

72. A couple spent a total of $50.40 for dinner. This included a 20% tip and 6% sales tax on the price of the meal. What was the price of the dinner before tax and tip?

73. Anna Tsao invested $3000 in an account paying 8% simple interest.

   a. How much interest will she earn in $3\frac{1}{2}$ years?

   b. What will her balance be at that time?

74. Eduardo invested money in an account earning 4% simple interest. At the end of 5 years, he had a total of $14,400. How much money did he originally invest?

Section 9.6

For Exercises 75–82, solve for the indicated variable.

75. $C = K - 273$ for K

76. $K = C + 273$ for C

77. $P = 4s$ for s

78. $P = 3s$ for s

79. $y = mx + b$ for x

80. $a + bx = c$ for x

81. $2x + 5y = -2$ for y

82. $4(a + b) = Q$ for b

For Exercises 83–89, use the appropriate geometry formula to solve the problem.

83. The volume of a cone is given by the formula $V = \dfrac{1}{3}\pi r^2 h$.

   a. Solve the formula for h.

   b. Find the height of a right circular cone whose volume is 47.8 in.^{3} and whose radius is 3 in. Round to the nearest tenth of an inch.

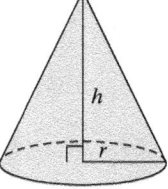

84. Find the height of a parallelogram whose area is 42 m^2 and whose base is 6 m.

85. The smallest angle of a triangle is 2° more than $\frac{1}{4}$ of the largest angle. The middle angle is 2° less than the largest angle. Find the measure of each angle.

86. One angle is 6° less than twice a second angle. If the two angles are complementary, what are their measures?

87. A rectangular window has width 1 ft less than its length. The perimeter is 18 ft. Find the length and the width of the window.

88. Find the measure of the vertical angles by first solving for x.

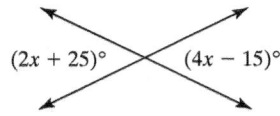
$(2x + 25)°$ $(4x - 15)°$

89. Find the measure of angle y.

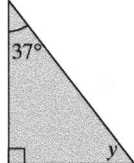
37°
y

Section 9.7

For Exercises 90–92, graph the inequalities and write the set in interval notation.

90. $\{x \mid x > -2\}$ _____

91. $\left\{x \mid x \le \dfrac{1}{2}\right\}$

92. $\{x \mid -1 < x \le 4\}$

93. A landscaper buys potted geraniums from a nursery at a price of $5 per plant. However, for large orders, the price per plant is discounted by a percentage off the original price. Let x represent the number of potted plants ordered. The corresponding discount is given in the following table.

Number of Plants	Discount
$x \le 99$	0%
$100 \le x \le 199$	2%
$200 \le x \le 299$	4%
$x \ge 300$	6%

a. Find the cost to purchase 130 plants.

b. Which costs more, 300 plants or 295 plants? Explain your answer.

For Exercises 94–103, solve the inequality. Graph the solution set and express the answer in interval notation.

94. $c + 6 < 23$

95. $3w - 4 > -5$

96. $-2x - 7 \geq 5$

97. $5(y + 2) \leq -4$

98. $-\dfrac{3}{7}a \leq -21$

99. $1.3 > 0.4t - 12.5$

100. $4k + 23 < 7k - 31$

101. $\dfrac{6}{5}h - \dfrac{1}{5} \leq \dfrac{3}{10} + h$

102. $-6 < 2b \leq 14$

103. $-2 \leq z + 4 \leq 9$

104. The summer average rainfall for Bermuda for June, July, and August is 5.3 in. per month. If Bermuda receives 6.3 in. of rain in June and 7.1 in. in July, how much rain is required in August to exceed the 3-month summer average?

105. Reggie sells hot dogs at a ballpark. He has a fixed cost of \$33 to use the concession stand at the park. In addition, the cost for each hot dog is \$0.40. If x represents the number of hot dogs sold, then the total cost is given by

$$\text{Cost} = 33 + 0.40x$$

If Reggie sells each hot dog for \$1.50, then his revenue (the amount he brings in) for selling x hot dogs is given by

$$\text{Revenue} = 1.50x$$

a. Write an inequality that expresses the number of hot dogs, x, that Reggie must sell to make a profit. Profit is realized when the revenue is greater than the cost (revenue > cost).

b. Solve the inequality in part (a).

Chapter 9   Test

1. Which of the equations have $x = -3$ as a solution?

 a. $4x + 1 = 10$ **b.** $6(x - 1) = x - 21$

 c. $5x - 2 = 2x + 1$ **d.** $\dfrac{1}{3}x + 1 = 0$

2. a. Simplify: $3x - 1 + 2x + 8$

 b. Solve: $3x - 1 = 2x + 8$

For Exercises 3–13, solve the equation.

3. $t + 3 = -13$ **4.** $8 = p - 4$

5. $\dfrac{t}{8} = -\dfrac{2}{9}$ **6.** $-3x + 5 = -2$

7. $2(p - 4) = p + 7$

8. $2 + d = 2 - 3(d - 5) - 2$

9. $\dfrac{3}{7} + \dfrac{2}{5}x = -\dfrac{1}{5}x + 1$ **10.** $3h + 1 = 3(h + 1)$

11. $\dfrac{3x + 1}{2} - \dfrac{4x - 3}{3} = 1$

12. $0.5c - 1.9 = 2.8 + 0.6c$

13. $-5(x + 2) + 8x = -2 + 3x - 8$

14. Solve the equation for y: $3x + y = -4$

15. Solve $C = 2\pi r$ for r.

16. 13% of what is 11.7?

17. One number is four plus one-half of another. The sum of the numbers is 31. Find the numbers.

18. The perimeter of a pentagon (a five-sided polygon) is 315 in. The five sides are represented by consecutive integers. Find the measures of the sides.

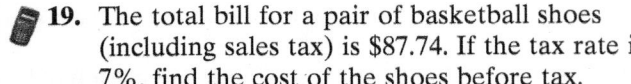 19. The total bill for a pair of basketball shoes (including sales tax) is $87.74. If the tax rate is 7%, find the cost of the shoes before tax.

20. A couple purchased two hockey tickets and two basketball tickets for $153.92. A hockey ticket cost $4.32 more than a basketball ticket. What were the prices of the individual tickets?

21. Clarita borrowed money at a 6% simple interest rate. If she paid back a total of $8000 at the end of 10 yr, how much did she originally borrow?

22. The length of a soccer field for international matches is 40 m less than twice its width. If the perimeter is 370 m, what are the dimensions of the field?

23. Given the triangle, find the measures of each angle by first solving for y.

24. Two angles are complementary. One angle is 26° more than the other angle. What are the measures of the angles?

25. Graph the inequalities and write the sets in interval notation.

   a. $\{x \mid x < 0\}$ ⟶

   b. $\{x \mid -2 \le x < 5\}$ ⟶

For Exercises 26–29, solve the inequality. Graph the solution and write the solution set in interval notation.

26. $5x + 14 > -2x$ ⟶

27. $2(3 - x) \ge 14$ ⟶

28. $3(2y - 4) + 1 > 2(2y - 3) - 8$ ⟶

29. $-13 \le 3p + 2 \le 5$ ⟶

30. The average winter snowfall for Syracuse, New York, for December, January, and February is 27.5 in. per month. If Syracuse receives 24 in. of snow in December and 32 in. in January, how much snow is required in February to exceed the 3-month average?

Chapters 1–9   Cumulative Review Exercises

1. Write the word name for the number.
   300,300.03

For Exercises 2–4, perform the indicated operations.

2. $\left| -\dfrac{1}{5} + \dfrac{7}{10} \right|$

3. $5 - 2[3 - (4 - 7)]$

4. $-3^2 + (-5)^2$

For Exercises 5–6, translate the mathematical expressions and simplify the results.

5. The square root of the difference of five squared and nine

6. The sum of -14 and 12

7. Simplify: $-4[2x - 3(x + 4)] + 5(x - 7)$

For Exercises 8–11, solve the equations.

8. $-2.5x - 5.2 = 12.8$

9. $-5(p - 3) + 2p = 3(5 - p)$

10. $\dfrac{x + 3}{5} - \dfrac{x + 2}{2} = 2$

11. $\dfrac{2}{9}x - \dfrac{1}{3} = x + \dfrac{1}{9}$

12. The sum of two consecutive odd integers is 156. Find the integers.

13. The total bill for a man's three-piece suit (including sales tax) is $374.50. If the tax rate is 7%, find the cost of the suit before tax.

14. If 1,610,000 people travel through Atlanta's Hartsfield Airport in 1 week (7 days), how many people would travel through the airport in a 30-day month?

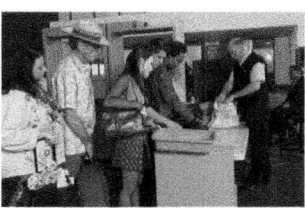

15. The table is a frequency distribution showing the gas mileage for a random sample of vehicles (cars, SUVs, and light trucks).

  a. How many vehicles were in the survey?

  b. What percent of vehicles got less than 15 mpg?

  c. What percent got 25 mph or more?

Gas Mileage (mpg)	Frequency
10–14	6
15–19	12
20–24	11
25–34	8
35–39	2
40–44	1

16. The following data give the ages of 12 students at a college graduation. Find the mean, median, and mode. Round to one decimal place if necessary.

22   24   24   28   29   29
52   32   29   40   29   21

17. Find the diameter, circumference, and area of the circle. Use 3.14 for π.

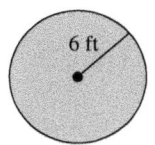

6 ft

18. The area of a triangle is 41 cm². Find the height of the triangle if the base is 12 cm.

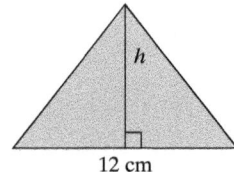

h

12 cm

For Exercises 19–20, solve the inequality. Graph the solution set on a number line and express the solution in interval notation.

19. $-3x - 3(x + 1) < 9$ ───────→

20. $-6 \le 2x - 4 \le 14$ ───────→

Graphing Linear Equations in Two Variables

10

Chapter 10

In this chapter, we study graphing and focus on the graphs of lines.

Are You Prepared?

In Exercises 1–9, we review the skills of locating numbers on a number line and solving equations. Both skills will be used for graphing. For Exercises 1–5, match each number with its position on the number line. Then write the corresponding letter in the space at the bottom of the page.

1. -1 **2.** 5 **3.** -3.7

4. $-\dfrac{23}{4}$ **5.** $\dfrac{19}{3}$

For Exercises 6–9, match the answer with the correct letter on the right. Then record the letter in the space at the bottom of the page.

6. Solve. $2x + 4 = 6$

7. Solve. $5 - 3y = 11$

8. For the equation $3x + 2y = 8$, substitute 0 for x. Then solve for y.

9. For the equation $x + 6y = -3$, substitute 0 for y. Then solve for x.

Answers

A. -2

T. -3

O. 1

N. 4

In a rectangular coordinate system, we use an ___ ___ ___ ___ ___ ___ ___ ___ ___ ___ ___
                                              6   1   5   2   1   2   5   3   7   4   1

to represent the location of a ___ ___ ___ ___ ___ .
                                3   6   4   8   9

671

Section 10.1   Rectangular Coordinate System

1. Interpreting Graphs

Mathematics is a powerful tool used by scientists and has directly contributed to the highly technical world in which we live. Applications of mathematics have led to advances in the sciences, business, computer technology, and medicine.

One fundamental application of mathematics is the graphical representation of numerical information (or **data**). For example, Table 10-1 represents the number of clients admitted to a drug and alcohol rehabilitation program over a 12-month period.

Table 10-1

	Month	Number of Clients
Jan.	1	55
Feb.	2	62
March	3	64
April	4	60
May	5	70
June	6	73
July	7	77
Aug.	8	80
Sept.	9	80
Oct.	10	74
Nov.	11	85
Dec.	12	90

In table form, the information is difficult to picture and interpret. It appears that on a monthly basis, the number of clients fluctuates. However, when the data are represented in a graph, an upward trend is clear (Figure 10-1).

Month ($x = 1$ corresponds to Jan.)

Figure 10-1

From the increase in clients shown in this graph, management for the rehabilitation center might make plans for the future. If the trend continues, management might consider expanding its facilities and increasing its staff to accommodate the expected increase in clients.

Example 1 **Interpreting a Graph**

Refer to Figure 10-1 and Table 10-1.

a. For which month was the number of clients the greatest?

b. How many clients were served in the first month (January)?

c. Which month corresponds to 60 clients served?

d. Between which two consecutive months did the number of clients decrease?

e. Between which two consecutive months did the number of clients remain the same?

Solution:

a. Month 12 (December) corresponds to the highest point on the graph, 90. This represents the greatest number of clients.

b. In month 1 (January), there were 55 clients served.

c. Month 4 (April).

d. The number of clients decreased between months 3 and 4 and between months 9 and 10.

e. The number of clients remained the same between months 8 and 9.

Skill Practice

The graph shows the number of new movie releases each month for a recent year. Month 1 represents January.

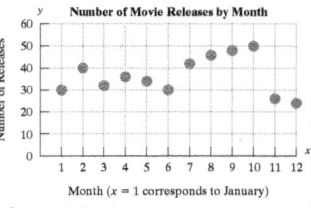

Source: movieweb.com

Refer to the graph to answer the questions.

1. For which month was the number of new releases the greatest?
2. How many movies were released in June (month 6)?
3. Which month corresponds to 40 movies being released?
4. Which two months had the same number of movies released?

2. Plotting Points in a Rectangular Coordinate System

In Example 1, two variables are represented, time and the number of clients. To picture two variables, we use a graph with two number lines drawn at right angles to each other (Figure 10-2). This forms a **rectangular coordinate system**. The horizontal line is called the **x-axis**, and the vertical line is called the **y-axis**. The point where the lines intersect is called the **origin**. On the x-axis, the numbers to the right of the origin are positive, and the numbers to the left are negative. On the y-axis, the numbers above the origin are positive, and the numbers below are negative. The x- and y-axes divide the graphing area into four regions called **quadrants**.

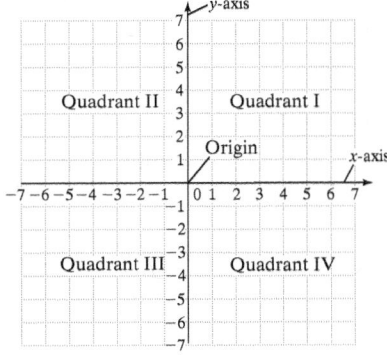

Figure 10-2

Points graphed in a rectangular coordinate system are defined by two numbers as an **ordered pair**, (x, y). The first number (called the **x-coordinate**, or the abscissa) is the horizontal position from the origin. The second number (called the **y-coordinate**, or the ordinate) is the vertical position from the origin. Example 2 shows how points are plotted in a rectangular coordinate system.

Answers

1. Month 10 (October)
2. 30
3. Month 2 (February)
4. Months 1 and 6 (January and June)

5. Plot the points.

$A(3, 4)$ $\quad$ $B(-2, 2)$

$C(4, 0)$ $\quad$ $D\left(\dfrac{5}{2}, -\dfrac{1}{2}\right)$

$E(-5, -2)$

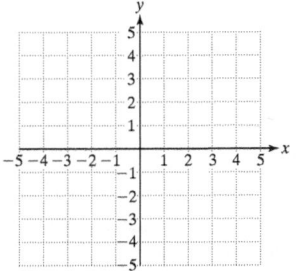

Example 2 **Plotting Points in a Rectangular Coordinate System**

Plot the points.

a. $(4, 5)$ $\qquad$ **b.** $(-4, -5)$ $\qquad$ **c.** $(-1, 3)$ $\qquad$ **d.** $(3, -1)$

e. $\left(\dfrac{1}{2}, -\dfrac{7}{3}\right)$ $\qquad$ **f.** $(-2, 0)$ $\qquad$ **g.** $(0, 0)$ $\qquad$ **h.** $(\pi, 1.1)$

Solution:

See Figure 10-3.

a. The ordered pair $(4, 5)$ indicates that $x = 4$ and $y = 5$. Beginning at the origin, move 4 units in the positive x-direction (4 units to the right) and from there move 5 units in the positive y-direction (5 units up). Then plot the point. The point is in Quadrant I.

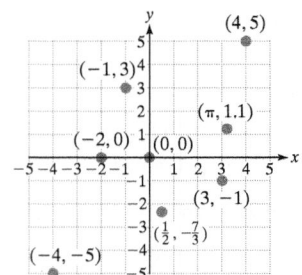

Figure 10-3

b. The ordered pair $(-4, -5)$ indicates that $x = -4$ and $y = -5$. Move 4 units in the negative x-direction (4 units to the left) and from there move 5 units in the negative y-direction (5 units down). Then plot the point. The point is in Quadrant III.

c. The ordered pair $(-1, 3)$ indicates that $x = -1$ and $y = 3$. Move 1 unit to the left and 3 units up. The point is in Quadrant II.

d. The ordered pair $(3, -1)$ indicates that $x = 3$ and $y = -1$. Move 3 units to the right and 1 unit down. The point is in Quadrant IV.

TIP: Notice that changing the order of the x- and y-coordinates changes the location of the point. The point $(-1, 3)$ for example is in Quadrant II, whereas $(3, -1)$ is in Quadrant IV (Figure 10-3). This is why points are represented by *ordered* pairs. The order of the coordinates is important.

e. The improper fraction $-\dfrac{7}{3}$ can be written as the mixed number $-2\dfrac{1}{3}$. Therefore, to plot the point $\left(\dfrac{1}{2}, -\dfrac{7}{3}\right)$ move to the right $\dfrac{1}{2}$ unit and down $2\dfrac{1}{3}$ units. The point is in Quadrant IV.

f. The point $(-2, 0)$ indicates $y = 0$. Therefore, the point is on the x-axis.

g. The point $(0, 0)$ is at the origin.

h. The irrational number, π, can be approximated as 3.14. Thus, the point $(\pi, 1.1)$ is located approximately 3.14 units to the right and 1.1 units up. The point is in Quadrant I.

Answer

5.

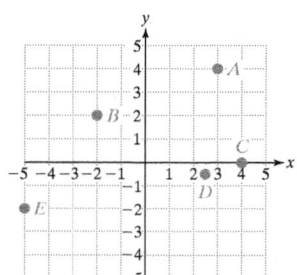

3. Applications of Plotting and Identifying Points

The effective use of graphs for mathematical models requires skill in identifying points and interpreting graphs.

Example 3 Determining Points from a Graph

A map of a national park is drawn so that the origin is placed at the ranger station (Figure 10-4). Four fire observation towers are located at points $A, B, C,$ and D. Estimate the coordinates of the fire towers relative to the ranger station (all distances are in miles).

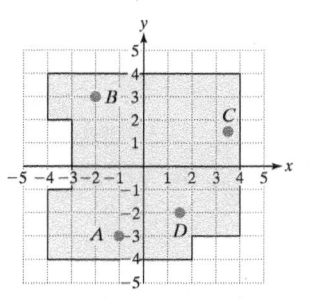

Figure 10-4

Solution:

Point A: $(-1, -3)$

Point B: $(-2, 3)$

Point C: $(3\frac{1}{2}, 1\frac{1}{2})$ or $(\frac{7}{2}, \frac{3}{2})$ or $(3.5, 1.5)$

Point D: $(1\frac{1}{2}, -2)$ or $(\frac{3}{2}, -2)$ or $(1.5, -2)$

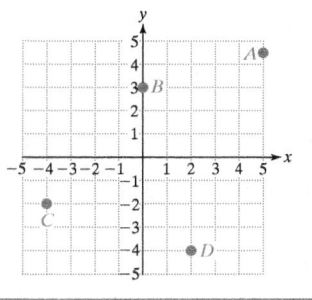

Example 4 Plotting Points in an Application

The daily low temperatures (in degrees Fahrenheit) for one week in January for Sudbury, Ontario, Canada, are given in Table 10-2.

a. Write an ordered pair for each row in the table using the day number as the x-coordinate and the temperature as the y-coordinate.

b. Plot the ordered pairs from part (a) on a rectangular coordinate system.

Table 10-2

Day Number, x	Temperature (°F), y
1	-3
2	-5
3	1
4	6
5	5
6	0
7	-4

Solution:

a. Each ordered pair represents the day number and the corresponding low temperature for that day.

$(1, -3)$ $(2, -5)$ $(3, 1)$ $(4, 6)$ $(5, 5)$ $(6, 0)$ $(7, -4)$

b.

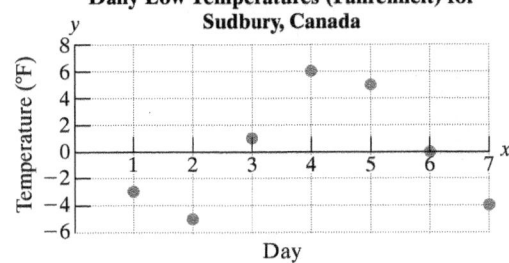

TIP: The graph in Example 4(b) shows only Quadrants I and IV because all x-coordinates are positive.

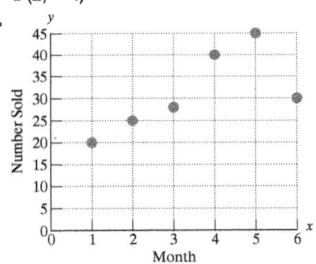

Section 10.1 Practice Exercises

Study Skills Exercises

1. Before you proceed further in Chapter 10, make your test corrections for the Chapter 9 test.

2. Define the key terms:

  a. Data   **b. Ordered pair**   **c. Origin**   **d. Quadrant**   **e. Rectangular coordinate system**

  f. x**-axis**   **g.** y**-axis**   **h.** x**-coordinate**   **i.** y**-coordinate**

Objective 1: Interpreting Graphs

For Exercises 3–6, refer to the graphs to answer the questions.
(See Example 1.)

3. The number of patients served by a certain hospice care center for the first 12 months after it opened is shown in the graph.

  a. For which month was the number of patients greatest?

  b. How many patients did the center serve in the first month?

  c. Between which months did the number of patients decrease?

  d. Between which two months did the number of patients remain the same?

  e. Which month corresponds to 40 patients served?

  f. Approximately how many patients were served during the 10th month?

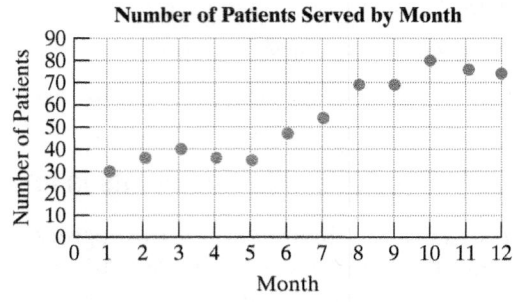

4. The number of housing permits (in thousands) issued by a county in Texas between 2003 and 2009 is shown in the graph.

  a. For which year was the number of permits greatest?

  b. How many permits did the county issue in 2003?

  c. Between which years did the number of permits decrease?

  d. Between which two years did the number of permits remain the same?

  e. Which year corresponds to 7000 permits issued?

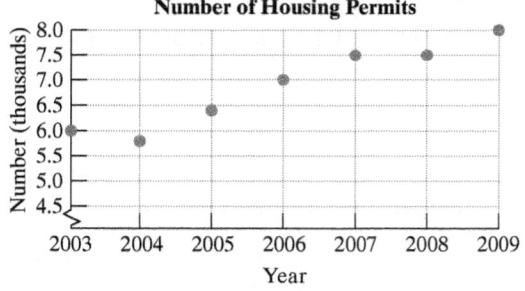

5. The price per share of a stock (in dollars) over a period of 5 days is shown in the graph.

  a. Interpret the meaning of the ordered pair $(1, 89.25)$.

  b. What was the increase in price between day 3 and day 4?

  c. What was the decrease in price between day 4 and day 5?

6. The price per share of a stock (in dollars) over a period of 5 days is shown in the graph.

    a. Interpret the meaning of the ordered pair (1, 10.125).

    b. What was the decrease between day 4 and day 5?

Price per Share ($)

Objective 2: Plotting Points in a Rectangular Coordinate System

7. Plot the points on a rectangular coordinate system. (See Example 2.)

    a. $(2, 6)$ **b.** $(6, 2)$ **c.** $(-7, 3)$

    d. $(-7, -3)$ **e.** $(0, -3)$ **f.** $(-3, 0)$

    g. $(6, -4)$ **h.** $(0, 5)$

8. Plot the points on a rectangular coordinate system.

    a. $(4, 5)$ **b.** $(-4, 5)$ **c.** $(-6, 0)$

    d. $(6, 0)$ **e.** $(4, -5)$ **f.** $(-4, -5)$

    g. $(0, -2)$ **h.** $(0, 0)$

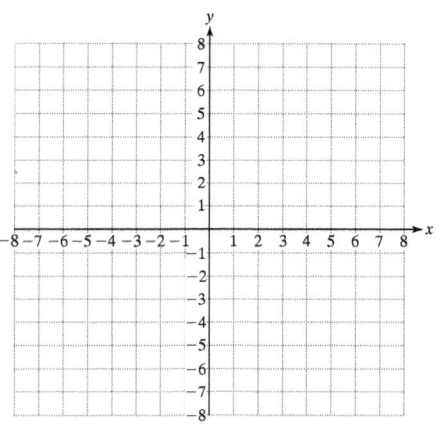

9. Plot the points on a rectangular coordinate system.

    a. $(-1, 5)$ **b.** $(0, 4)$ **c.** $\left(-2, -\dfrac{3}{2}\right)$

    d. $(2, -0.75)$ **e.** $(4, 2)$ **f.** $(-6, 0)$

10. Plot the points on a rectangular coordinate system.

    a. $(7, 0)$ **b.** $(-3, -1)$ **c.** $\left(6\tfrac{3}{5}, 1\right)$

    d. $(0, 1.5)$ **e.** $\left(\dfrac{1}{4}, -4\right)$ **f.** $\left(-\dfrac{1}{4}, 4\right)$

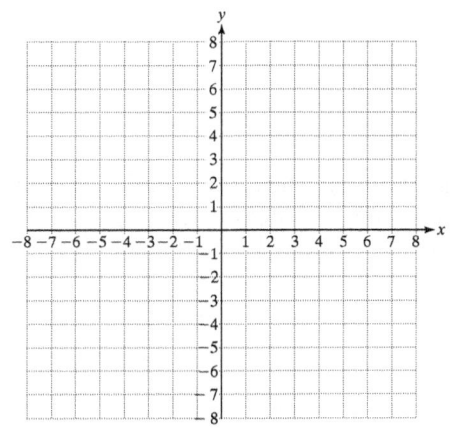

For Exercises 11–18, identify the quadrant in which the given point is found.

11. $(13, -2)$ **12.** $(25, 16)$ **13.** $(-8, 14)$ **14.** $(-82, -71)$

15. $(-5, -19)$ **16.** $(-31, 6)$ **17.** $\left(\dfrac{5}{2}, \dfrac{7}{4}\right)$ **18.** $(9, -40)$

19. Explain why the point $(0, -5)$ is *not* located in Quadrant IV.

20. Explain why the point $(-1, 0)$ is *not* located in Quadrant II.

21. Where is the point $\left(\frac{7}{8}, 0\right)$ located?

22. Where is the point $\left(0, \frac{6}{5}\right)$ located?

Objective 3: Applications of Plotting and Identifying Points

For Exercises 23–24, refer to the graph. **(See Example 3.)**

23. Estimate the coordinates of the points A, B, C, D, E, and F.

24. Estimate the coordinates of the points G, H, I, J, K, and L.

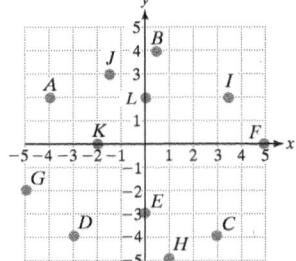

25. A map of a park is laid out with the visitor center located at the origin. Five visitors are in the park located at points A, B, C, D, and E. All distances are in meters.

     a. Estimate the coordinates of each visitor. **(See Example 3.)**

     b. How far apart are visitors C and D?

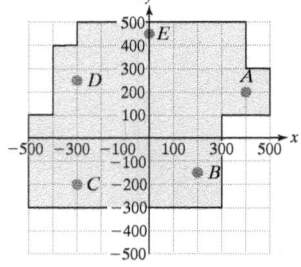

26. A townhouse has a sprinkler system in the backyard. With the water source at the origin, the sprinkler heads are located at points A, B, C, D, and E. All distances are in feet.

     a. Estimate the coordinates of each sprinkler head.

     b. How far is the distance from sprinkler head B to C?

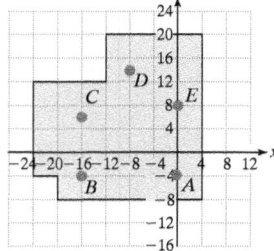

27. A movie theater has kept records of popcorn sales versus movie attendance.

     a. Use the table shown on page 679 to write the corresponding ordered pairs using the movie attendance as the *x*-variable and sales of popcorn as the *y*-variable. Interpret the meaning of the first ordered pair. **(See Example 4.)**

b. Plot the data points on a rectangular coordinate system.

Movie Attendance (Number of People)	Sales of Popcorn ($)
250	225
175	193
315	330
220	209
450	570
400	480
190	185

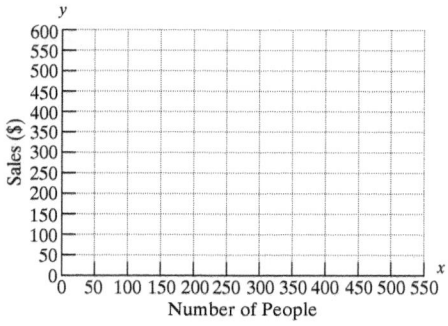

28. The age and systolic blood pressure (in millimeters of mercury, mm Hg) for eight different women are given in the table.

   a. Write the corresponding ordered pairs using the woman's age as the x-variable and the systolic blood pressure as the y-variable. Interpret the meaning of the first ordered pair.

   b. Plot the data points on a rectangular coordinate system.

Age (Years)	Systolic Blood Pressure (mm Hg)
57	149
41	120
71	158
36	115
64	151
25	110
40	118
77	165

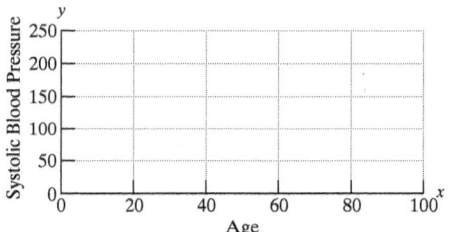

29. The income level defining the poverty line for an individual is given for selected years between 1980 and 2005. Let x represent the number of years since 1980. Let y represent the income defining the poverty level. (*Source: U.S. Department of the Census*)

   (0, 4300)   (5, 5600)   (10, 6800)

   (15, 7900)   (20, 9000)   (25, 10,500)

   a. Interpret the meaning of the ordered pair (10, 6800).

   b. Plot the points on a rectangular coordinate system.

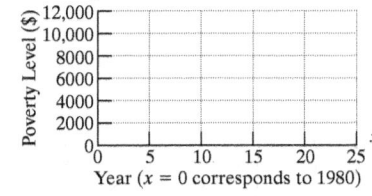

30. The following ordered pairs give the population of the U.S. colonies from 1700 to 1770. Let x represent the year, where $x = 0$ corresponds to 1700, $x = 10$ corresponds to 1710, and so on. Let y represent the population of the colonies. (*Source: Information Please Almanac*)

   (0, 251000)   (10, 332000)   (20, 466000)

   (30, 629000)   (40, 906000)   (50, 1171000)

   (60, 1594000)   (70, 2148000)

   a. Interpret the meaning of the ordered pair (10, 332000).

   b. Plot the points on a rectangular coordinate system.

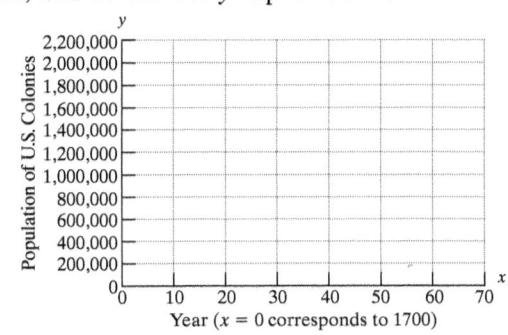

31. The following table shows the average temperature in degrees Celsius for Montreal, Quebec, Canada, by month.

a. Write the corresponding ordered pairs, letting $x = 1$ correspond to the month of January.

b. Plot the ordered pairs on a rectangular coordinate system.

Month, x		Temperature (°C), y
Jan.	1	−10.2
Feb.	2	−9.0
March	3	−2.5
April	4	5.7
May	5	13.0
June	6	18.3
July	7	20.9
Aug.	8	19.6
Sept.	9	14.8
Oct.	10	8.7
Nov.	11	2.0
Dec.	12	−6.9

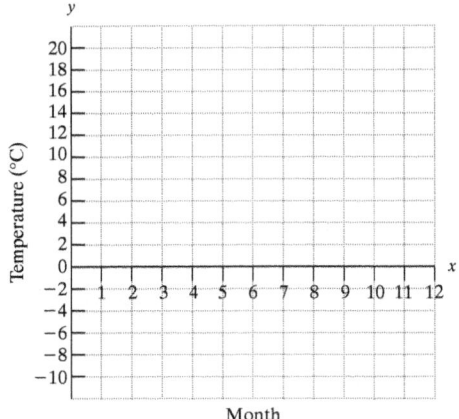

32. The table shows the average temperature in degrees Fahrenheit for Fairbanks, Alaska, by month.

a. Write the corresponding ordered pairs, letting $x = 1$ correspond to the month of January.

b. Plot the ordered pairs on a rectangular coordinate system.

Month, x		Temperature (°F), y
Jan.	1	−12.8
Feb.	2	−4.0
March	3	8.4
April	4	30.2
May	5	48.2
June	6	59.4
July	7	61.5
Aug.	8	56.7
Sept.	9	45.0
Oct.	10	25.0
Nov.	11	6.1
Dec.	12	−10.1

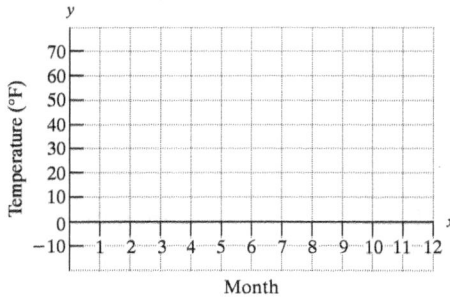

Expanding Your Skills

33. The data in the table give the percent of males and females who have completed 4 or more years of college education for selected years. Let x represent the number of years since 1960. Let y represent the percent of men and the percent of women that completed 4 or more years of college.

Year	x	Percent, y Men	Percent, y Women
1960	0	9.7	5.8
1970	10	13.5	8.1
1980	20	20.1	12.8
1990	30	24.4	18.4
2000	40	27.8	23.6
2005	45	28.9	26.5

a. Plot the data points for men and for women on the same graph.

b. Is the percentage of men with 4 or more years of college increasing or decreasing?

c. Is the percentage of women with 4 or more years of college increasing or decreasing?

34. Use the data and graph from Exercise 33 to answer the questions.

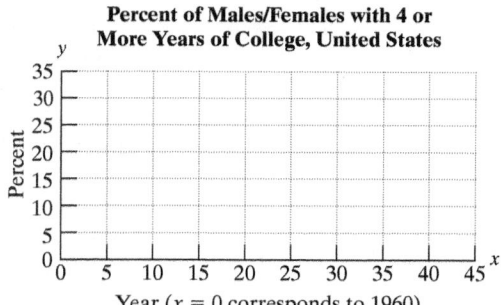

Percent of Males/Females with 4 or More Years of College, United States

a. In which year was the difference in percentages between men and women with 4 or more years of college the greatest?

b. In which year was the difference in percentages between men and women the least?

c. If the trend continues beyond the data in the graph, does it seem possible that in the future, the percentage of women with 4 or more years of college will be greater than or equal to the percentage of men?

Linear Equations in Two Variables

Section 10.2

1. Definition of a Linear Equation in Two Variables

Recall that an equation in the form $ax + b = c$, where $a \neq 0$, is called a linear equation in one variable. A solution to such an equation is a value of x that makes the equation a true statement. For example, $3x + 8 = 2$ has a solution of -2.

In this section, we will look at linear equations in *two* variables.

Objectives

1. **Definition of a Linear Equation in Two Variables**
2. **Graphing Linear Equations in Two Variables by Plotting Points**
3. **x- and y-Intercepts**
4. **Horizontal and Vertical Lines**

> **DEFINITION** Linear Equation in Two Variables
>
> Let A, B, and C be real numbers such that A and B are not both zero. Then, an equation that can be written in the form:
>
> $$Ax + By = C$$
>
> is called a **linear equation in two variables**.

The equation $x + y = 4$ is a linear equation in two variables. A solution to such an equation is an ordered pair (x, y) that makes the equation a true statement. Several solutions to the equation $x + y = 4$ are listed here:

Solution:	Check:
(x, y)	$x + y = 4$
$(2, 2)$	$(2) + (2) = 4$ ✔
$(1, 3)$	$(1) + (3) = 4$ ✔
$(4, 0)$	$(4) + (0) = 4$ ✔
$(-1, 5)$	$(-1) + (5) = 4$ ✔

By graphing these ordered pairs, we see that the solution points line up (Figure 10-5).

Notice that there are infinitely many solutions to the equation $x + y = 4$ so they cannot all be listed. Therefore, to visualize all solutions to the equation $x + y = 4$, we draw the line through the points in the graph. Every point on the line represents an ordered pair solution to the equation $x + y = 4$, and the line represents the set of *all* solutions to the equation.

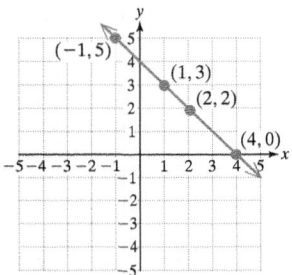

Figure 10-5

Skill Practice

Given the equation
$3x - 2y = -12$
determine whether the given ordered pair is a solution.

1. $(4, 0)$

2. $(-2, 3)$

3. $\left(1, \dfrac{15}{2}\right)$

Example 1   Determining Solutions to a Linear Equation

For the linear equation, $4x - 5y = 8$, determine whether the given ordered pair is a solution.

a. $(2, 0)$ **b.** $(3, 1)$ **c.** $\left(1, -\dfrac{4}{5}\right)$

Solution:

a. $4x - 5y = 8$

   $4(2) - 5(0) \overset{?}{=} 8$ Substitute $x = 2$ and $y = 0$.

   $8 - 0 \overset{?}{=} 8$ ✔ True   The ordered pair $(2, 0)$ is a solution.

b. $4x - 5y = 8$

   $4(3) - 5(1) \overset{?}{=} 8$ Substitute $x = 3$ and $y = 1$.

   $12 - 5 \neq 8$ The ordered pair $(3, 1)$ is *not* a solution.

c. $4x - 5y = 8$

   $4(1) - 5\left(-\dfrac{4}{5}\right) \overset{?}{=} 8$ Substitute $x = 1$ and $y = -\dfrac{4}{5}$.

   $4 + 4 \overset{?}{=} 8$ ✔ True   The ordered pair $\left(1, -\dfrac{4}{5}\right)$ is a solution.

2. Graphing Linear Equations in Two Variables by Plotting Points

In this section, we will graph linear equations in two variables.

> **DEFINITION   The Graph of an Equation in Two Variables**
>
> The graph of an equation in two variables is the graph of all ordered pair solutions to the equation.

The word *linear* means "relating to or resembling a line." It is not surprising then that the solution set for any linear equation in two variables forms a line in a rectangular coordinate system. Because two points determine a line, to graph a linear equation it is sufficient to find two solution points and draw the line between them. We will find three solution points and use the third point as a check point. This process is demonstrated in Example 2.

Answers

1. No   **2.** Yes   **3.** Yes

| Example 2 | **Graphing a Linear Equation** |

Graph the equation $x - 2y = 8$.

Solution:

We will find three ordered pairs that are solutions to $x - 2y = 8$. To find the ordered pairs, choose arbitrary values of x or y, such as those shown in the table. Then complete the table to find the corresponding ordered pairs.

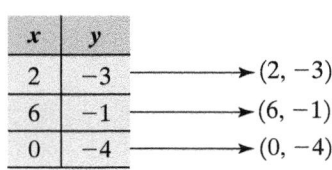

x	y
2	
	−1
0	

→ (2,   )
→ (, −1)
→ (0,   )

TIP: Usually we try to choose arbitrary values that will be convenient to graph.

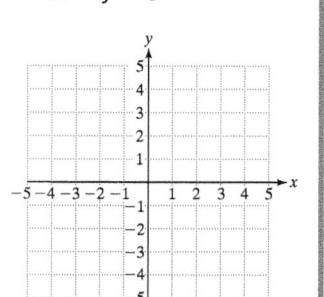
From the first row, substitute $x = 2$:	From the second row, substitute $y = -1$:	From the third row, substitute $x = 0$:
$x - 2y = 8$	$x - 2y = 8$	$x - 2y = 8$
$(2) - 2y = 8$	$x - 2(-1) = 8$	$(0) - 2y = 8$
$-2y = 8 - 2$	$x + 2 = 8$	$-2y = 8$
$-2y = 6$	$x = 8 - 2$	$y = -4$
$y = -3$	$x = 6$	

The completed table is shown below with the corresponding ordered pairs.

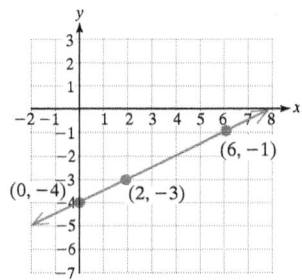

x	y
2	−3
6	−1
0	−4

→ (2, −3)
→ (6, −1)
→ (0, −4)

To graph the equation, plot the three solutions and draw the line through the points (Figure 10-6).

Figure 10-6

TIP: Only two points are needed to graph a line. However, in Example 2, we found a third ordered pair, $(0, -4)$. Notice that this point "lines up" with the other two points. If the three points do not line up, then we know that a mistake was made in solving for at least one of the ordered pairs.

In Example 2, the original values for x and y given in the table were chosen arbitrarily by the authors. It is important to note, however, that once you choose an arbitrary value for x, the corresponding y-value is determined by the equation. Similarly, once you choose an arbitrary value for y, the x-value is determined by the equation.

Answer

4.

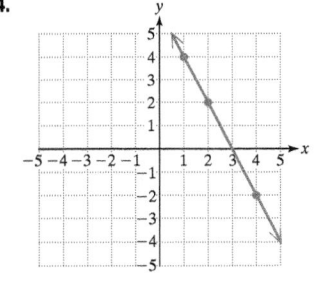

Skill Practice

5. Graph the equation.
$2x + 3y = 12$

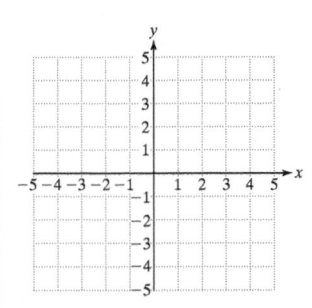

Example 3 **Graphing a Linear Equation**

Graph the equation $4x + 3y = 15$.

Solution:

We will find three ordered pairs that are solutions to the equation $4x + 3y = 15$. In the table, we have selected arbitrary values for x and y and must complete the ordered pairs. Notice that in this case, we are choosing zero for x and zero for y to illustrate that the resulting equation is often easy to solve.

x	y	
0		→ (0,)
	0	→ (, 0)
3		→ (3,)

From the first row, substitute $x = 0$:	From the second row, substitute $y = 0$:	From the third row, substitute $x = 3$:
$4x + 3y = 15$	$4x + 3y = 15$	$4x + 3y = 15$
$4(0) + 3y = 15$	$4x + 3(0) = 15$	$4(3) + 3y = 15$
$3y = 15$	$4x = 15$	$12 + 3y = 15$
$y = 5$	$x = \dfrac{15}{4}$ or $3\dfrac{3}{4}$	$3y = 3$
		$y = 1$

The completed table is shown with the corresponding ordered pairs.

x	y	
0	5	→ (0, 5)
$3\frac{3}{4}$	0	→ $(3\frac{3}{4}, 0)$
3	1	→ (3, 1)

To graph the equation, plot the three solutions and draw the line through the points (Figure 10-7).

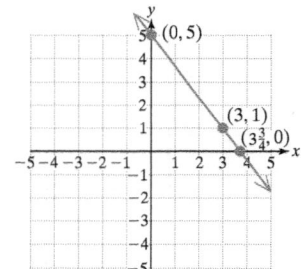

Figure 10-7

Animation

Example 4 **Graphing a Linear Equation in Two Variables**

Graph the equation $y = -\dfrac{1}{3}x + 1$.

Answer

5.

Solution:

Because the y-variable is isolated in the equation, it is easy to substitute a value for x and simplify the right-hand side to find y. Since any number for x can be chosen, select numbers that are multiples of 3. These will simplify easily when multiplied by $-\frac{1}{3}$.

x	y
3	
0	
−3	

$$y = -\frac{1}{3}x + 1$$

<u>Let $x = 3$:</u>

$$y = -\frac{1}{3}(3) + 1$$

$$y = -1 + 1$$

$$y = 0$$

<u>Let $x = 0$:</u>

$$y = -\frac{1}{3}(0) + 1$$

$$y = 0 + 1$$

$$y = 1$$

<u>Let $x = -3$:</u>

$$y = -\frac{1}{3}(-3) + 1$$

$$y = 1 + 1$$

$$y = 2$$

x	y
3	0
0	1
−3	2

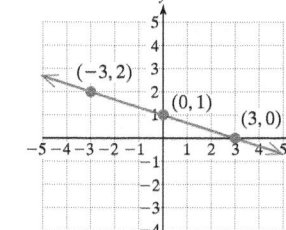

The line through the three ordered pairs $(3, 0)$, $(0, 1)$, and $(-3, 2)$ is shown in Figure 10-8. The line represents the set of all solutions to the equation $y = -\frac{1}{3}x + 1$.

Figure 10-8

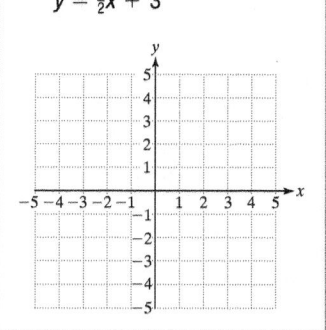
3. *x*- and *y*-Intercepts

The *x*- and *y*-intercepts are the points where the graph intersects the *x*- and *y*-axes, respectively. From Example 4, we see that the *x*-intercept is at the point $(3, 0)$ and the *y*-intercept is at the point $(0, 1)$. See Figure 10-8. Notice that a *y*-intercept is a point on the *y*-axis and must have an *x*-coordinate of 0. Likewise, an *x*-intercept is a point on the *x*-axis and must have a *y*-coordinate of 0.

> **DEFINITION** *x*- and *y*-Intercepts
>
> An **x-intercept** of a graph is a point $(a, 0)$ where the graph intersects the *x*-axis.
>
> A **y-intercept** of a graph is a point $(0, b)$ where the graph intersects the *y*-axis.

In some applications, an *x*-intercept is defined as the *x*-coordinate of a point of intersection that a graph makes with the *x*-axis. For example, if an *x*-intercept is at the point $(3, 0)$, it is sometimes stated simply as 3 (the *y*-coordinate is assumed to be 0). Similarly, a *y*-intercept is sometimes defined as the *y*-coordinate of a point of intersection that a graph makes with the *y*-axis. For example, if a *y*-intercept is at the point $(0, 7)$, it may be stated simply as 7 (the *x*-coordinate is assumed to be 0).

Although any two points may be used to graph a line, in some cases it is convenient to use the *x*- and *y*-intercepts of the line. To find the *x*- and *y*-intercepts of any two-variable equation in *x* and *y*, follow these steps:

> **PROCEDURE** Finding *x*- and *y*-Intercepts
>
> **Step 1** Find the *x*-intercept(s) by substituting $y = 0$ into the equation and solving for *x*.
>
> **Step 2** Find the *y*-intercept(s) by substituting $x = 0$ into the equation and solving for *y*.

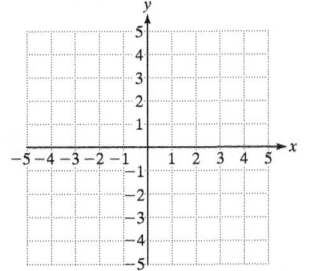
Example 5 Finding the x- and y-Intercepts of a Line ──

Given the equation $-3x + 2y = 8$,

a. Find the x-intercept.

b. Find the y-intercept.

c. Graph the equation.

Solution:

a. To find the x-intercept, substitute $y = 0$.

$$-3x + 2y = 8$$
$$-3x + 2(0) = 8$$
$$-3x = 8$$
$$\frac{-3x}{-3} = \frac{8}{-3}$$
$$x = -\frac{8}{3}$$

The x-intercept is $\left(-\frac{8}{3}, 0\right)$.

b. To find the y-intercept, substitute $x = 0$.

$$-3x + 2y = 8$$
$$-3(0) + 2y = 8$$
$$2y = 8$$
$$y = 4$$

The y-intercept is $(0, 4)$.

c. The line through the ordered pairs $\left(-\frac{8}{3}, 0\right)$ and $(0, 4)$ is shown in Figure 10-9. Note that the point $\left(-\frac{8}{3}, 0\right)$ can be written as $\left(-2\frac{2}{3}, 0\right)$.

The line represents the set of all solutions to the equation $-3x + 2y = 8$.

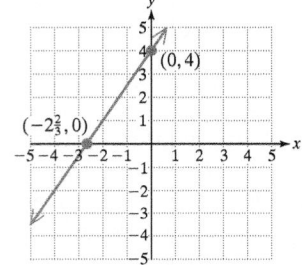

Figure 10-9

Example 6 Finding the x- and y-Intercepts of a Line ──

Given the equation $4x + 5y = 0$,

a. Find the x-intercept.

b. Find the y-intercept.

c. Graph the equation.

Solution:

a. To find the x-intercept, substitute $y = 0$.

$$4x + 5y = 0$$
$$4x + 5(0) = 0$$
$$4x = 0$$
$$x = 0$$

The x-intercept is $(0, 0)$.

b. To find the y-intercept, substitute $x = 0$.

$$4x + 5y = 0$$
$$4(0) + 5y = 0$$
$$5y = 0$$
$$y = 0$$

The y-intercept is $(0, 0)$.

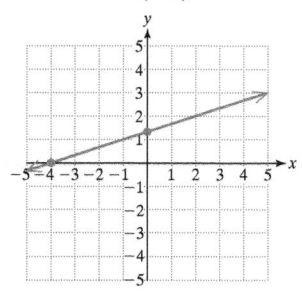

c. Because the *x*-intercept and the *y*-intercept are the same point (the origin), one or more additional points are needed to graph the line. In the table, we have arbitrarily selected additional values for *x* and *y* to find two more points on the line.

x	*y*
−5	
	2

<u>Let x = −5:</u> $4x + 5y = 0$ <u>Let y = 2:</u> $4x + 5y = 0$

$4(-5) + 5y = 0$ $4x + 5(2) = 0$

$-20 + 5y = 0$ $4x + 10 = 0$

$5y = 20$ $4x = -10$

$y = 4$ $x = -\dfrac{10}{4}$

$x = -\dfrac{5}{2}$

The line through the ordered pairs $(0, 0)$, $(-5, 4)$, and $\left(-\frac{5}{2}, 2\right)$ is shown in Figure 10-10. Note that the point $\left(-\frac{5}{2}, 2\right)$ can be written as $\left(-2\frac{1}{2}, 2\right)$.

The line represents the set of all solutions to the equation $4x + 5y = 0$.

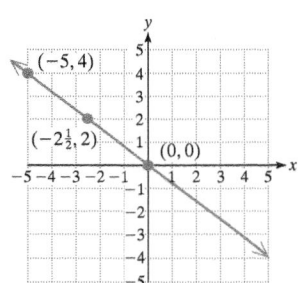

x	*y*
−5	4
$-\frac{5}{2}$	2
0	0

Figure 10-10

4. Horizontal and Vertical Lines

Recall that a linear equation can be written in the form of $Ax + By = C$, where *A* and *B* are not both zero. However, if *A* or *B* is 0, then the line is either parallel to the *x*-axis (horizontal) or parallel to the *y*-axis (vertical), respectively.

> **DEFINITION Equations of Vertical and Horizontal Lines**
>
> **1.** A **vertical line** can be represented by an equation of the form, $x = k$, where *k* is a constant.
>
> **2.** A **horizontal line** can be represented by an equation of the form, $y = k$, where *k* is a constant.

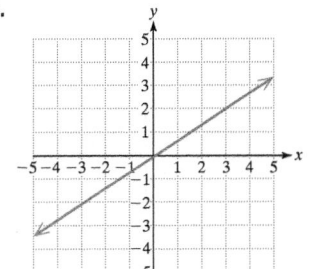

Skill Practice

13. Graph the equation.
$y = -2$

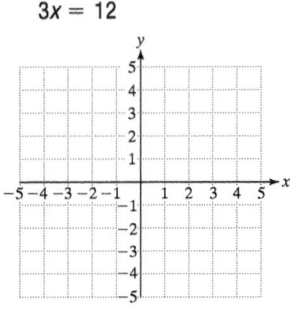

Skill Practice

14. Graph the equation.
$3x = 12$

Answers

13.

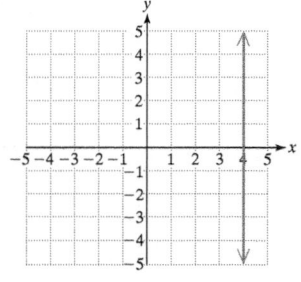

14.

Graphing a Horizontal Line

Graph the equation $y = 3$.

Solution:

Because this equation is in the form $y = k$, the line is horizontal and must cross the y-axis at $y = 3$ (Figure 10-11).

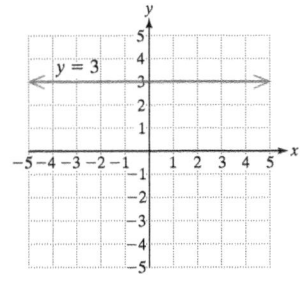

Figure 10-11

Alternative Solution:

Create a table of values for the equation $y = 3$. The choice for the y-coordinate must be 3, but x can be any real number.

x	y
0	3
1	3
2	3

x can be any number. y must be 3.

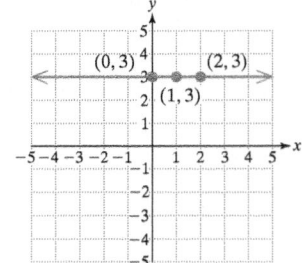

TIP: Notice that a horizontal line has a y-intercept, but does not have an x-intercept (unless the horizontal line is the x-axis itself).

Example 8   **Graphing a Vertical Line**

Graph the equation $4x = -8$.

Solution:

Because the equation does not have a y-variable, we can solve the equation for x.

$4x = -8$ is equivalent to $x = -2$

This equation is in the form $x = k$, indicating that the line is vertical and must cross the x-axis at $x = -2$ (Figure 10-12).

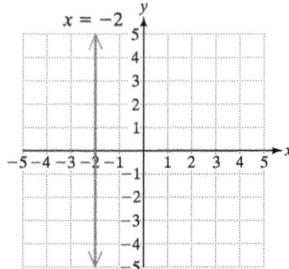

Figure 10-12

Alternative Solution:

Create a table of values for the equation $x = -2$. The choice for the x-coordinate must be -2, but y can be any real number.

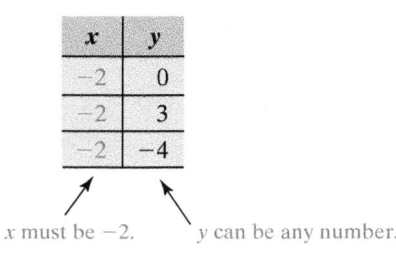

x	y
-2	0
-2	3
-2	-4

x must be -2. y can be any number.

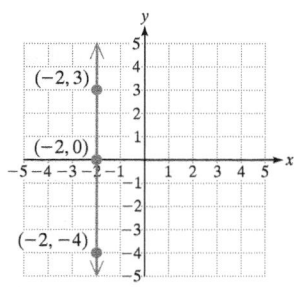

TIP: Notice that a vertical line has an x-intercept but does not have a y-intercept (unless the vertical line is the y-axis itself).

Calculator Connections

Topic: Graphing Linear Equations on an Appropriate Viewing Window

A viewing window of a graphing calculator shows a portion of a rectangular coordinate system. The standard viewing window for many calculators shows the x-axis between -10 and 10 and the y-axis between -10 and 10 (Figure 10-13). Furthermore, the scale defined by the "tick" marks on both the x- and y-axes is usually set to 1.

The "Standard Viewing Window"

Figure 10-13

To graph an equation in x and y on a graphing calculator, the equation must be written with the y-variable isolated. For example, to graph the equation $x + 3y = 3$, we solve for y by applying the steps for solving a literal equation. The result, $y = -\frac{1}{3}x + 1$, can now be entered into a graphing calculator. To enter the equation $y = -\frac{1}{3}x + 1$ use parentheses around the fraction $\frac{1}{3}$. The *Graph* option displays the graph of the line.

Sometimes the standard viewing window does not provide an adequate display for the graph of an equation. For example, the graph of $y = -x + 15$ is visible only in a small portion of the upper right corner of the standard viewing window.

To see where this line crosses the x- and y-axes, we can change the viewing window to accommodate larger values of x and y. Most calculators have a *Range* feature or *Window* feature that allows the user to change the minimum and maximum x- and y-values.

To get a better picture of the equation $y = -x + 15$, change the minimum x-value to -10 and the maximum x-value to 20. Similarly, use a minimum y-value of -10 and a maximum y-value of 20.

Calculator Exercises

For Exercises 1–8, graph the equations on the standard viewing window.

1. $y = -2x + 5$ **2.** $y = 3x - 1$

3. $y = \frac{1}{2}x - \frac{7}{2}$ **4.** $y = -\frac{3}{4}x + \frac{5}{3}$

5. $4x - 7y = 21$ **6.** $2x + 3y = 12$

7. $-3x - 4y = 6$ **8.** $-5x + 4y = 10$

For Exercises 9–12, graph the equations on the given viewing window.

9. $y = 3x + 15$

    Window: $-10 \le x \le 10$
                  $-5 \le y \le 20$

10. $y = -2x - 25$

    Window: $-30 \le x \le 30$
                  $-30 \le y \le 30$

    Xscl = 3 (sets the x-axis tick marks to increments of 3)

    Yscl = 3 (sets the y-axis tick marks to increments of 3)

11. $y = -0.2x + 0.04$

    Window: $-0.1 \le x \le 0.3$
                  $-0.1 \le y \le 0.1$

    Xscl = 0.01 (sets the x-axis tick marks to increments of 0.01)

    Yscl = 0.01 (sets the y-axis tick marks to increments of 0.01)

12. $y = 0.3x - 0.5$

    Window: $-1 \le x \le 3$
                  $-1 \le y \le 1$

    Xscl = 0.1 (sets the x-axis tick marks to increments of 0.1)

    Yscl = 0.1 (sets the y-axis tick marks to increments of 0.1)

Section 10.2 Practice Exercises

Boost *your* GRADE at
ALEKS.com!

• Practice Problems
• Self-Tests
• NetTutor

• e-Professors
• Videos

Study Skills Exercises

1. Sometimes you may run into a problem with homework or you find that you are having trouble keeping up with the pace of the class. A tutor can be a good resource.

    a. Does your college offer tutoring?

    b. Is it free?

    c. Where would you go to sign up for a tutor?

2. Define the key terms:

    a. Horizontal line   **b. Linear equation in two variables**   **c. Vertical line**

    d. x-intercept   **e. y-intercept**

Review Exercises

For Exercises 3–8, refer to the figure to give the coordinates of the labeled points and state the quadrant or axis where the point is located.

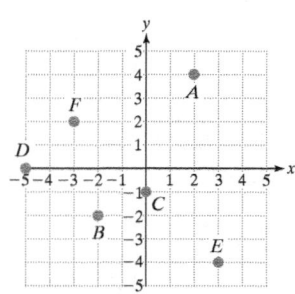

3. A **4.** B

5. C **6.** D

7. E **8.** F

Objective 1: Definition of a Linear Equation in Two Variables

For Exercises 9–17, determine whether the given ordered pair is a solution to the equation. **(See Example 1.)**

9. $x - y = 6$; $(8, 2)$

10. $y = 3x - 2$; $(1, 1)$

11. $y = -\dfrac{1}{3}x + 3$; $(-3, 4)$

12. $y = -\dfrac{5}{2}x + 5$; $(-2, 0)$

13. $4x + 5y = 20$; $(-5, -4)$

14. $y = 7$; $(0, 7)$

15. $y = -2$; $(-2, 6)$

16. $x = 1$; $(0, 1)$

17. $x = -5$; $(-5, 6)$

Objective 2: Graphing Linear Equations in Two Variables by Plotting Points

For Exercises 18–31, complete each table and graph the corresponding ordered pairs. Draw the line defined by the points to represent all solutions to the equation. **(See Examples 2–4.)**

18. $x + y = 3$

x	y
2	
	3
−1	
	0

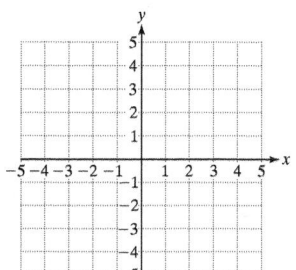

19. $x + y = -2$

x	y
1	
	0
−3	
	2

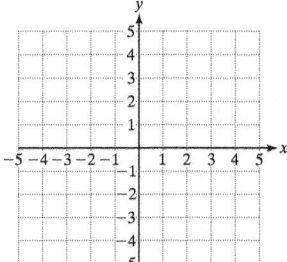

20. $y = 5x + 1$

x	y
1	
	1
−1	

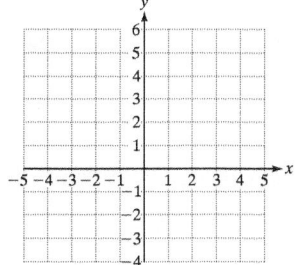

21. $y = -3x - 3$

x	y
−2	
	0
−4	

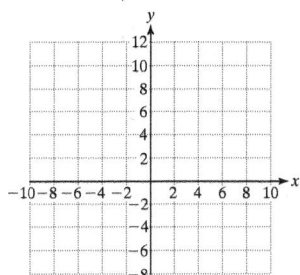

22. $2x - 3y = 6$

x	y
0	
	0
2	

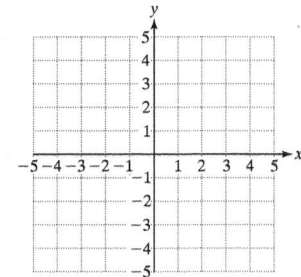

23. $4x + 2y = 8$

x	y
0	
	0
3	

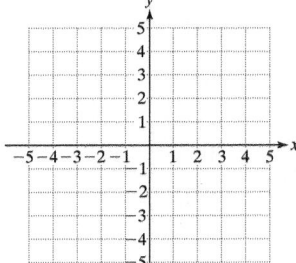

24. $y = \dfrac{2}{7}x - 5$

x	y
7	
−7	
0	

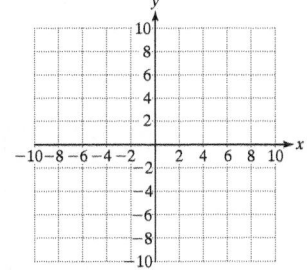

25. $y = -\dfrac{3}{5}x - 2$

x	y
0	
5	
10	

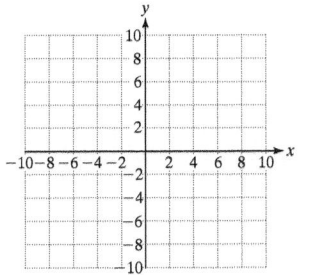

26. $y = 3$

x	y
2	
0	
−1	

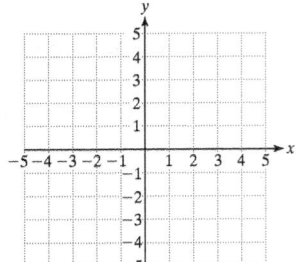

27. $y = -2$

x	y
0	
−3	
5	

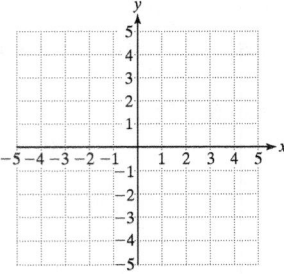

28. $x = -4$

x	y
	1
	−2
	4

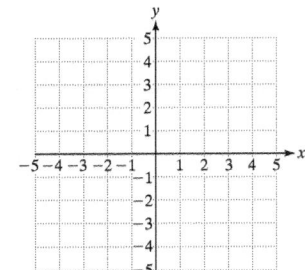

29. $x = \frac{3}{2}$

x	y
	−1
	2
	−3

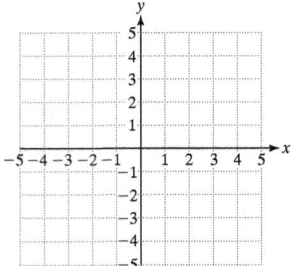

30. $y = -3.4x + 5.8$

x	y
0	
1	
2	

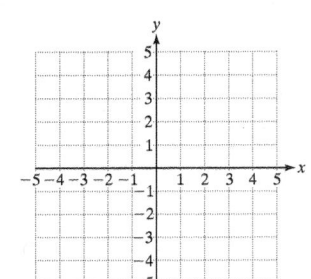

31. $y = -1.2x + 4.6$

x	y
0	
1	
2	

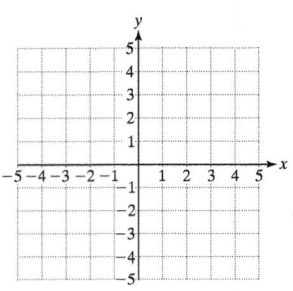

For Exercises 32–43, graph the lines by making a table of at least three ordered pairs and plotting the points.

32. $x = y + 2$

33. $x - y = 4$

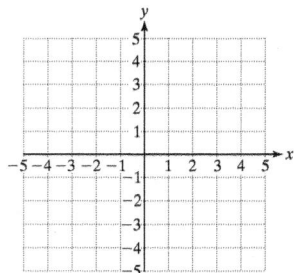

34. $-3x + y = -6$

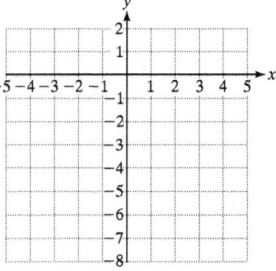

35. $2x - 5y = 10$

36. $y = 4x$

37. $y = -2x$

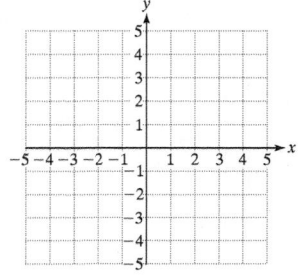

38. $y = -\dfrac{1}{2}x + 3$

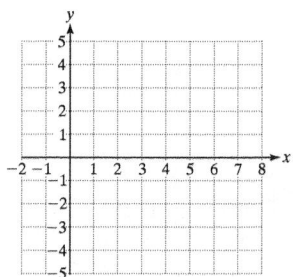

39. $y = \dfrac{1}{4}x - 2$

40. $x + y = 0$

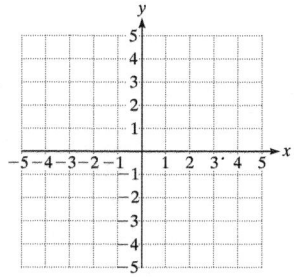

41. $-x + y = 0$

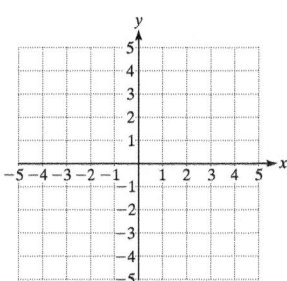

42. $50x - 40y = 200$

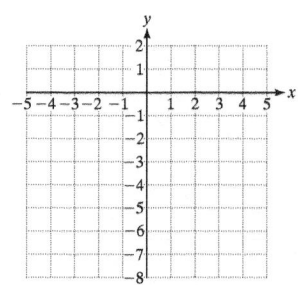

43. $-30x - 20y = 60$

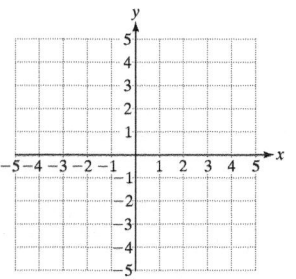

Objective 3: *x*- and *y*-Intercepts

44. The *x*-intercept is on which axis?

45. The *y*-intercept is on which axis?

For Exercises 46–49, estimate the coordinates of the *x*- and *y*-intercepts.

46.

47.

48.

49.

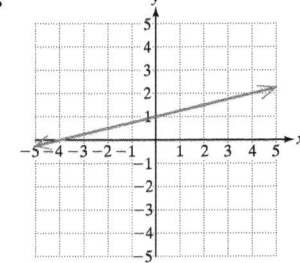

For Exercises 50–61, find the x- and y-intercepts (if they exist), and graph the line. **(See Examples 5–6.)**

50. $5x + 2y = 5$

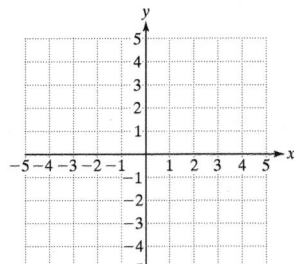

51. $4x - 3y = -9$

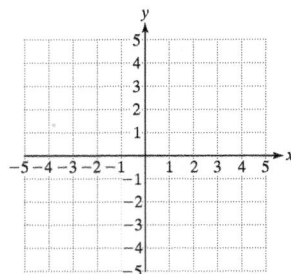

52. $y = \dfrac{2}{3}x - 1$

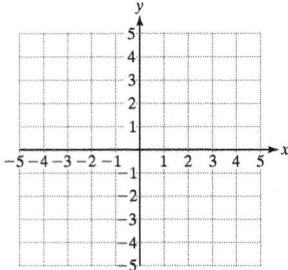

53. $y = -\dfrac{3}{4}x + 2$

54. $x - 3 = y$

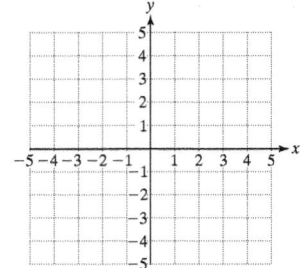

55. $2x + 8 = y$

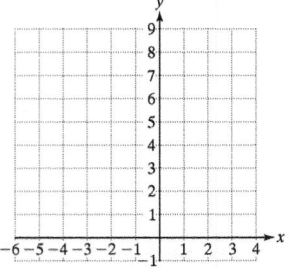

56. $-3x + y = 0$

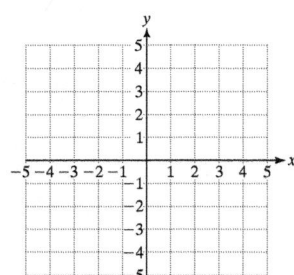

57. $2x - 2y = 0$

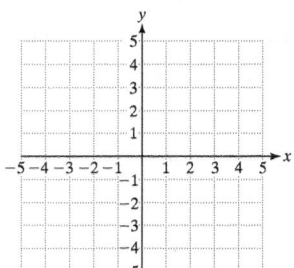

58. $25y = 10x + 100$

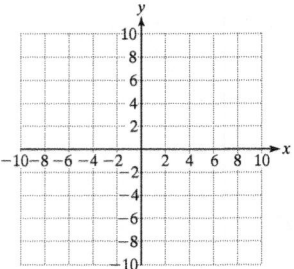

59. $20x = -40y + 200$

60. $x = 2y$

61. $x = -5y$

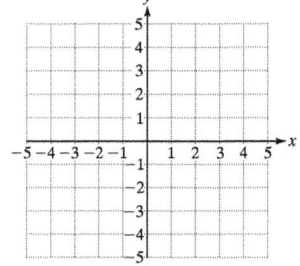

Objective 4: Horizontal and Vertical Lines

For Exercises 62–65, answer true or false. If the statement is false, rewrite it to be true.

62. The line $x = 3$ is horizontal.

63. The line $y = -4$ is horizontal.

64. A line parallel to the y-axis is vertical.

65. A line perpendicular to the x-axis is vertical.

For Exercises 66–74,

a. Identify the equation as representing a horizontal or vertical line.

b. Graph the line.

c. Identify the x- and y-intercepts if they exist. **(See Examples 7–8.)**

66. $x = 3$

67. $y = -1$

68. $-2y = 8$

69. $5x = 20$

70. $x + 3 = 7$

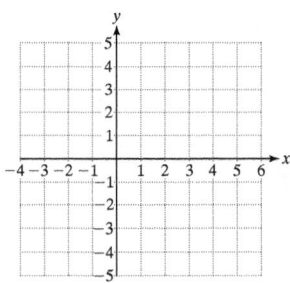

71. $y - 8 = -13$

72. $3y = 0$

73. $5x = 0$

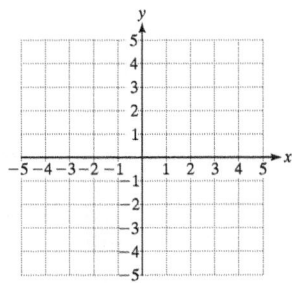

74. $2x + 7 = 10$

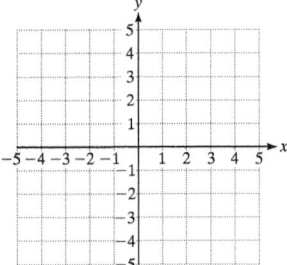

75. Explain why not every line has both an x- and a y-intercept.

76. Which of the lines has an x-intercept?

    a. $2x - 3y = 6$ **b.** $x = 5$ **c.** $2y = 8$ **d.** $-x + y = 0$

77. Which of the lines has a y-intercept?

    a. $y = 2$ **b.** $x + y = 0$ **c.** $2x - 10 = 2$ **d.** $x + 4y = 8$

Expanding Your Skills

78. The store "CDs R US" sells all compact disks for $13.99. The following equation represents the revenue, y, (in dollars) generated by selling x CDs.

$$y = 13.99x \quad (x \geq 0)$$

a. Find y when $x = 13$.

b. Find x when $y = 279.80$.

c. Write the ordered pairs from parts (a) and (b), and interpret their meaning in the context of the problem.

d. Graph the ordered pairs and the line defined by the points.

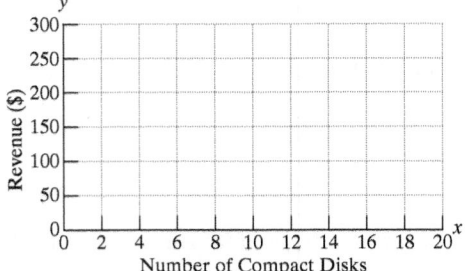

79. The value of a car depreciates once it is driven off of the dealer's lot. For a Hyundai Accent, the value of the car is given by the equation $y = -1531x + 11,599 \, (x \geq 0)$ where y is the value of the car in dollars x years after its purchase. (*Source: Kelly Blue Book*)

a. Find y when $x = 1$.

b. Find x when $y = 7006$.

c. Write the ordered pairs from parts (a) and (b), and interpret their meaning in the context of the problem.

Section 10.3 Slope of a Line and Rate of Change

Objectives

1. **Introduction to Slope**
2. **Slope Formula**
3. **Parallel and Perpendicular Lines**
4. **Applications of Slope: Rate of Change**

1. Introduction to Slope

The x- and y-intercepts represent the points where a line crosses the x- and y-axes. Another important feature of a line is its slope. Geometrically, the slope of a line measures the "steepness" of the line. For example, two ski runs are depicted by the lines in Figure 10-14.

Beginner's Hill   Daredevil Hill

Figure 10-14

By visual inspection, Daredevil Hill is "steeper" than Beginner's Hill. To measure the slope of a line quantitatively, consider two points on the line. The **slope** of the line is the ratio of the vertical change (change in y) between the two points and the horizontal change (change in x). As a memory device, we might think of the slope of a line as "rise over run." See Figure 10-15.

$$\text{Slope} = \frac{\text{change in } y}{\text{change in } x} = \frac{\text{rise}}{\text{run}}$$

Figure 10-15

To move from point A to point B on Beginner's Hill, rise 2 ft and move to the right 6 ft (Figure 10-16).

To move from point A to point B on Daredevil Hill, rise 12 ft and move to the right 6 ft (Figure 10-17).

Daredevil Hill

Figure 10-17

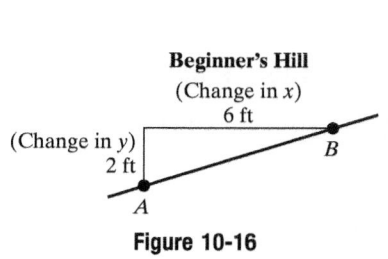

Beginner's Hill

Figure 10-16

$$\text{Slope} = \frac{\text{change in } y}{\text{change in } x} = \frac{2 \text{ ft}}{6 \text{ ft}} = \frac{1}{3}$$

$$\text{Slope} = \frac{\text{change in } y}{\text{change in } x} = \frac{12 \text{ ft}}{6 \text{ ft}} = \frac{2}{1} = 2$$

The slope of Daredevil Hill is greater than the slope of Beginner's Hill, confirming the observation that Daredevil Hill is steeper. On Daredevil Hill there is a 12-ft change in elevation for every 6 ft of horizontal distance (a 2:1 ratio). On Beginner's Hill there is only a 2-ft change in elevation for every 6 ft of horizontal distance (a 1:3 ratio).

Example 1 **Finding Slope in an Application**

Determine the slope of the ramp up the stairs.

Solution:

$$\text{Slope} = \frac{\text{change in } y}{\text{change in } x} = \frac{8 \text{ ft}}{16 \text{ ft}}$$

$$\frac{8}{16} = \frac{1}{2} \qquad \text{Write the ratio for the slope and simplify.}$$

The slope is $\frac{1}{2}$.

Skill Practice

1. Determine the slope of the aircraft's takeoff path.

2. Slope Formula

The slope of a line may be found using any two points on the line—call these points (x_1, y_1) and (x_2, y_2). The change in y between the points can be found by taking the difference of the y-values: $y_2 - y_1$. The change in x can be found by taking the difference of the x-values in the same order: $x_2 - x_1$ (Figure 10-18).

The slope of a line is often symbolized by the letter m and is given by the following formula.

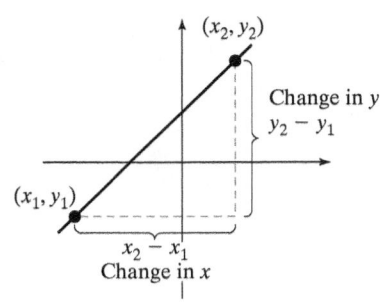

Figure 10-18

Answer

1. $\dfrac{500}{6000} = \dfrac{1}{12}$

The **slope** of a line passing through the distinct points (x_1, y_1) and (x_2, y_2) is

$$m = \frac{y_2 - y_1}{x_2 - x_1} \quad \text{provided } x_2 - x_1 \neq 0$$

Skill Practice

Find the slope of the line through the given points.

2. $(-5, 2)$ and $(1, 3)$

Example 2 **Finding the Slope of a Line Given Two Points**

Find the slope of the line through the points $(-1, 3)$ and $(-4, -2)$.

Solution:

To use the slope formula, first label the coordinates of each point and then substitute the coordinates into the slope formula.

$$\underset{(x_1,\, y_1)}{(-1, 3)} \quad \text{and} \quad \underset{(x_2,\, y_2)}{(-4, -2)} \qquad \text{Label the points.}$$

$$m = \frac{y_2 - y_1}{x_2 - x_1} = \frac{(-2) - (3)}{(-4) - (-1)} \qquad \text{Apply the slope formula.}$$

$$= \frac{-5}{-3}$$

$$= \frac{5}{3} \qquad \text{Simplify to lowest terms.}$$

The slope of the line can be verified from the graph (Figure 10-19).

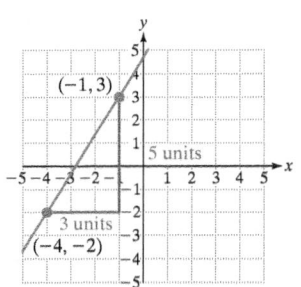

Figure 10-19

TIP: The slope formula is not dependent on which point is labeled (x_1, y_1) and which point is labeled (x_2, y_2). In Example 2, reversing the order in which the points are labeled results in the same slope.

$$\underset{(x_2,\, y_2)}{(-1, 3)} \quad \text{and} \quad \underset{(x_1,\, y_1)}{(-4, -2)} \qquad \text{Label the points.}$$

$$m = \frac{(3) - (-2)}{(-1) - (-4)} = \frac{5}{3} \qquad \text{Apply the slope formula.}$$

Answer

2. $\dfrac{1}{6}$

When you apply the slope formula, you will see that the slope of a line may be positive, negative, zero, or undefined.

- Lines that increase, or rise, from left to right have a positive slope.
- Lines that decrease, or fall, from left to right have a negative slope.
- Horizontal lines have a slope of zero.
- Vertical lines have an undefined slope.

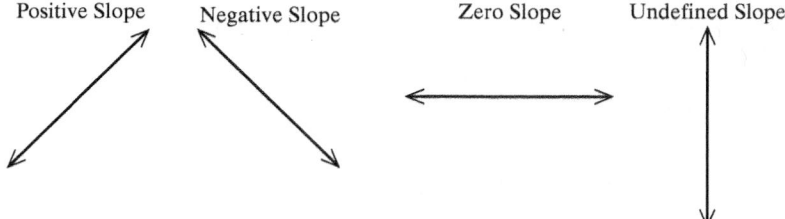

| Example 3 | **Finding the Slope of a Line Given Two Points** |

Find the slope of the line passing through the points $(-5, 0)$ and $(2, -3)$.

Solution:

$$\underset{(x_1, y_1)}{(-5, 0)} \quad \text{and} \quad \underset{(x_2, y_2)}{(2, -3)} \quad \text{Label the points.}$$

$$m = \frac{y_2 - y_1}{x_2 - x_1} = \frac{(-3) - (0)}{(2) - (-5)} \quad \text{Apply the slope formula.}$$

$$= \frac{-3}{7} \quad \text{or} \quad -\frac{3}{7} \quad \text{Simplify.}$$

By graphing the points $(-5, 0)$ and $(2, -3)$, we can verify that the slope is $-\frac{3}{7}$ (Figure 10-20). Notice that the line slopes downward from left to right.

Figure 10-20

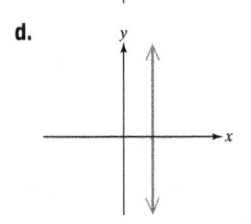

Example 4 Determining the Slope of a Vertical Line

Find the slope of the line passing through the points $(2, -1)$ and $(2, 4)$.

Solution:

$$\underset{(x_1, y_1)}{(2, -1)} \quad \text{and} \quad \underset{(x_2, y_2)}{(2, 4)} \qquad \text{Label the points.}$$

$$m = \frac{y_2 - y_1}{x_2 - x_1} = \frac{(4) - (-1)}{(2) - (2)} \qquad \text{Apply the slope formula.}$$

$$m = \frac{5}{0} \quad \text{Undefined}$$

Because the slope, m, is undefined, we expect the points to form a vertical line as shown in Figure 10-21.

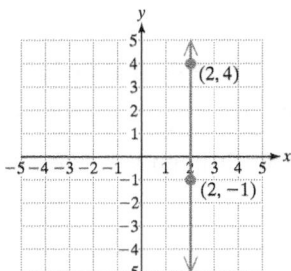

Figure 10-21

Example 5 Determine the Slope of a Horizontal Line

Find the slope of the line passing through the points $(3, -2)$ and $(-4, -2)$.

Solution:

$$\underset{(x_1, y_1)}{(3, -2)} \quad \text{and} \quad \underset{(x_2, y_2)}{(-4, -2)} \qquad \text{Label the points.}$$

$$m = \frac{y_2 - y_1}{x_2 - x_1} = \frac{(-2) - (-2)}{(-4) - (3)} \qquad \text{Apply the slope formula.}$$

$$m = \frac{-2 + 2}{-4 - 3} = \frac{0}{-7} = 0$$

Because the slope is 0, we expect the points to form a horizontal line, as shown in Figure 10-22.

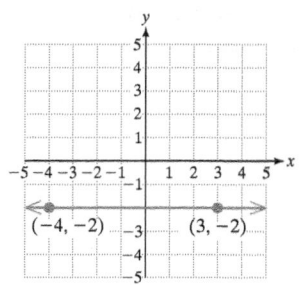

Answers

5. Undefined   **6.** 0

Figure 10-22

3. Parallel and Perpendicular Lines

Lines in the same plane that do not intersect are called **parallel lines**. Parallel lines have the same slope and different y-intercepts (Figure 10-23).

Lines that intersect at a right angle are **perpendicular lines**. If two lines are perpendicular then the slope of one line is the opposite of the reciprocal of the slope of the other line (provided neither line is vertical) (Figure 10-24).

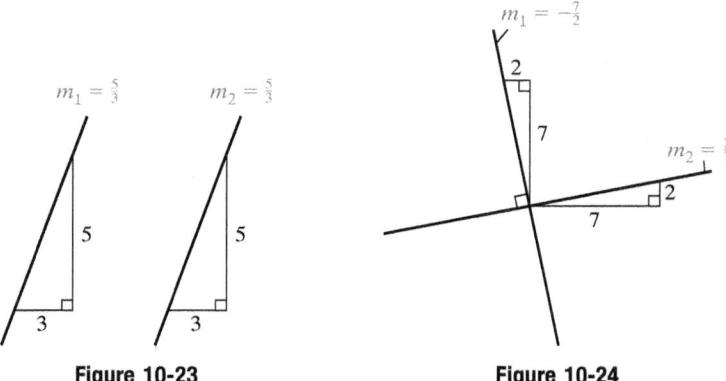

Figure 10-23   Figure 10-24

PROPERTY Slopes of Parallel Lines

If m_1 and m_2 represent the slopes of two parallel (nonvertical) lines, then

$$m_1 = m_2.$$

See Figure 10-23.

PROPERTY Slopes of Perpendicular Lines

If $m_1 \neq 0$ and $m_2 \neq 0$ represent the slopes of two perpendicular lines, then

$$m_1 = -\frac{1}{m_2} \text{ or equivalently, } m_1 m_2 = -1. \text{ See Figure 10-24.}$$

Example 6 **Determining the Slope of Parallel and Perpendicular Lines**

Suppose a given line has a slope of $-\frac{1}{4}$.

  a. Find the slope of a line parallel to the given line.

  b. Find the slope of a line perpendicular to the given line.

Solution:

  a. Parallel lines must have the same slope. The slope of a line parallel to the given line is: $m = -\dfrac{1}{4}$.

  b. Perpendicular lines must have opposite and reciprocal slopes. The slope of a line perpendicular to the given line is: $m = +\dfrac{4}{1}$ or simply, $m = 4$.

Skill Practice

A given line has a slope of $\frac{5}{3}$.

 7. Find the slope of a line parallel to the given line.
 8. Find the slope of a line perpendicular to the given line.

Answers

7. $\dfrac{5}{3}$ **8.** $-\dfrac{3}{5}$

If the slopes of two lines are known, then we can compare the slopes to determine if the lines are parallel, perpendicular, or neither.

Example 7 **Determining If Lines Are Parallel, Perpendicular, or Neither**

Lines l_1 and l_2 pass through the given points. Determine if l_1 and l_2 are parallel, perpendicular, or neither.

$$l_1: \quad (2, -7) \text{ and } (4, 1) \qquad\qquad l_2: \quad (-3, 1) \text{ and } (1, 0)$$

Solution:

Find the slope of each line.

$$l_1: \quad \underset{(x_1, y_1)}{(2, -7)} \text{ and } \underset{(x_2, y_2)}{(4, 1)} \qquad\qquad l_2: \quad \underset{(x_1, y_1)}{(-3, 1)} \text{ and } \underset{(x_2, y_2)}{(1, 0)}$$

$$m_1 = \frac{1 - (-7)}{4 - 2} \qquad\qquad m_2 = \frac{0 - 1}{1 - (-3)}$$

$$m_1 = \frac{8}{2} \qquad\qquad m_2 = \frac{-1}{4}$$

$$m_1 = 4 \qquad\qquad m_2 = -\frac{1}{4}$$

Avoiding Mistakes

You can check that two lines are perpendicular by checking that the product of their slopes is -1.

$$4\left(-\frac{1}{4}\right) = -1$$

One slope is the opposite of the reciprocal of the other slope. Therefore, the lines are perpendicular.

4. Applications of Slope: Rate of Change

In many applications, the interpretation of slope refers to the *rate of change* of the y-variable to the x-variable.

Example 8 **Interpreting Slope in an Application**

The annual median income for males in the United States for selected years is shown in Figure 10-25. The trend is approximately linear. Find the slope of the line and interpret the meaning of the slope in the context of the problem.

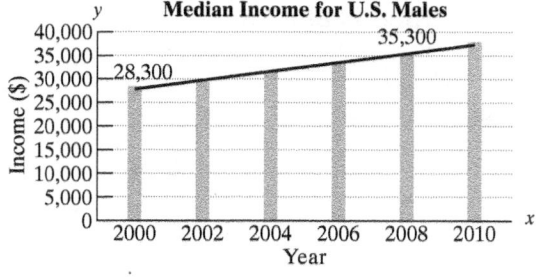

Figure 10-25

Source: U.S. Department of the Census

Solution:

To determine the slope we need to know two points on the line. From the graph, the median income for males in the year 2000 was approximately $28,300. This gives us the ordered pair (2000, 28,300). In the year 2008, the income was $35,300. This gives the ordered pair (2008, 35,300).

$$
\begin{array}{ccc}
(2000, 28{,}300) & \text{and} & (2008, 35{,}300) \\
\underset{(x_1, y_1)}{} & & \underset{(x_2, y_2)}{}
\end{array}
$$
Label the points.

$$m = \frac{y_2 - y_1}{x_2 - x_1} = \frac{35{,}300 - 28{,}300}{2008 - 2000}$$ Apply the slope formula.

$$= \frac{7000}{8}$$

$$= 875$$ Simplify.

The slope is 875. This tells us the rate of change of the y-variable (income) to the x-variable (years). This means that men's median income in the United States increased at a rate of $875 per year during this time period.

Section 10.3 Practice Exercises

Study Skills Exercises

1. Make up a practice test for yourself. Use examples or exercises from the text. Be sure to cover each concept that was presented.

2. Define the key terms: **a. Parallel lines**   **b. Perpendicular lines**   **c. Slope**

Review Exercises

For Exercises 3–8, find the x- and y-intercepts (if they exist). Then graph the line.

3. $x - 3y = 6$

4. $x - 5 = 2$

5. $y = \dfrac{2}{3}x$

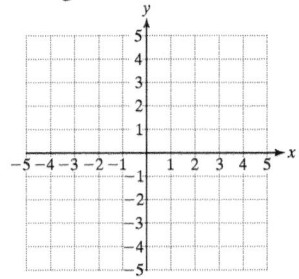

6. $2y - 3 = 0$

7. $4x + y = 8$

8. $2x = 4y$

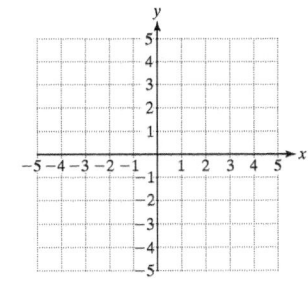

Objective 1: Introduction to Slope

9. Determine the pitch (slope) of the roof.
(See Example 1.)

10. Determine the slope of the stairs.

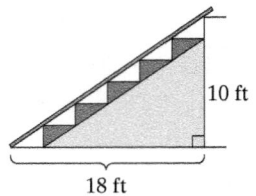

11. Calculate the slope of the handrail.

12. Determine the slope of the treadmill.

Objective 2: Slope Formula

For Exercises 13–16, fill in the blank with the appropriate term: zero, negative, positive, or undefined.

13. The slope of a line parallel to the y-axis is _____.

14. The slope of a horizontal line is ____.

15. The slope of a line that rises from left to right is _____.

16. The slope of a line that falls from left to right is _____.

For Exercises 17–25, determine if the slope is positive, negative, zero, or undefined.

17.

18.

19.

20.

21.

22.

23.

24.

25.
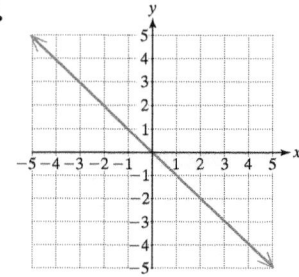

For Exercises 26–34, determine the slope by using the slope formula and any two points on the line. Check your answer by drawing a right triangle and labeling the "rise" and "run."

26.

27.

28.

29.

30.

31.

32.

33.

34.
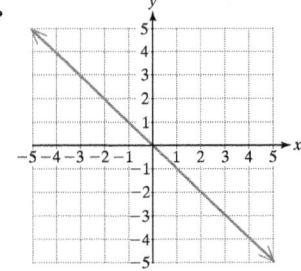

For Exercises 35–52, find the slope of the line that passes through the two points. **(See Examples 2–5.)**

35. $(2, 4)$ and $(-1, 3)$

36. $(0, 4)$ and $(3, 0)$

37. $(-2, 3)$ and $(-1, 0)$

38. $(-3, -4)$ and $(1, -5)$

39. $(1, 5)$ and $(-4, 2)$

40. $(-6, -1)$ and $(-2, -3)$

41. $(5, 3)$ and $(-2, 3)$

42. $(0, -1)$ and $(-4, -1)$

43. $(2, -7)$ and $(2, 5)$

44. $(-4, 3)$ and $(-4, -4)$

45. $\left(\dfrac{1}{2}, \dfrac{3}{5}\right)$ and $\left(\dfrac{1}{4}, -\dfrac{4}{5}\right)$

46. $\left(-\dfrac{2}{7}, \dfrac{1}{3}\right)$ and $\left(\dfrac{8}{7}, -\dfrac{5}{6}\right)$

47. $(3, -1)$ and $(-5, 6)$ **48.** $(-6, 5)$ and $(-10, 4)$ **49.** $(6.8, -3.4)$ and $(-3.2, 1.1)$

50. $(-3.15, 8.25)$ and $(6.85, -4.25)$ **51.** $(1994, 3.5)$ and $(2000, 2.6)$ **52.** $(1988, 4.65)$ and $(1998, 9.25)$

Objective 3: Parallel and Perpendicular Lines

For Exercises 53–60, the slope of a line is given. **(See Example 6.)**

a. Determine the slope of a line parallel to the given line.

b. Determine the slope of a line perpendicular to the given line.

53. $m = -2$ **54.** $m = \dfrac{2}{3}$

55. $m = 0$ **56.** The slope is undefined.

57. $m = \dfrac{4}{5}$ **58.** $m = -4$

59. $m = 1$ **60.** $m = \dfrac{1}{6}$

For Exercises 61–66, let m_1 and m_2 represent the slopes of two lines. Determine if the lines are parallel, perpendicular, or neither. **(See Example 6.)**

61. $m_1 = -2, m_2 = \dfrac{1}{2}$ **62.** $m_1 = \dfrac{2}{3}, m_2 = \dfrac{3}{2}$ **63.** $m_1 = 1, m_2 = \dfrac{4}{4}$

64. $m_1 = \dfrac{3}{4}, m_2 = -\dfrac{8}{6}$ **65.** $m_1 = \dfrac{2}{7}, m_2 = -\dfrac{2}{7}$ **66.** $m_1 = 5, m_2 = 5$

For Exercises 67–72, find the slopes of the lines l_1 and l_2 defined by the two given points. Then determine whether l_1 and l_2 are parallel, perpendicular, or neither. **(See Example 7.)**

67. l_1: $(2, 4)$ and $(-1, -2)$ **68.** l_1: $(0, 0)$ and $(-2, 4)$ **69.** l_1: $(1, 9)$ and $(0, 4)$
      l_2: $(1, 7)$ and $(0, 5)$ l_2: $(1, -5)$ and $(-1, -1)$ l_2: $(5, 2)$ and $(10, 1)$

70. l_1: $(3, -4)$ and $(-1, -8)$ **71.** l_1: $(4, 4)$ and $(0, 3)$ **72.** l_1: $(3, 5)$ and $(-2, -5)$
      l_2: $(5, -5)$ and $(-2, 2)$ l_2: $(1, 7)$ and $(-1, -1)$ l_2: $(2, 0)$ and $(-4, -3)$

Objective 4: Applications of Slope: Rate of Change

73. In 1980, there were 304 thousand male inmates in federal and state prisons. By 2005, the number increased to 1479 thousand. Let x represent the year and let y represent the number of prisoners (in thousands). **(See Example 8.)**

a. Using the ordered pairs $(1980, 304)$ and $(2005, 1479)$, find the slope of the line.

b. Interpret the slope in the context of this problem.

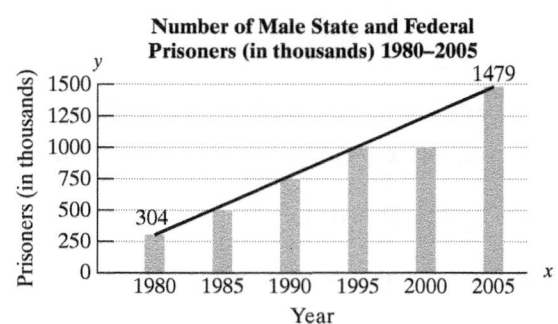

Number of Male State and Federal Prisoners (in thousands) 1980–2005

(Source: U.S. Bureau of Justice Statistics)

74. In the year 1980, there were 12 thousand female inmates in federal and state prisons. By 2005, the number increased to 102 thousand.

Let x represent the year and let y represent the number of prisoners (in thousands).

a. Using the ordered pairs (1980, 12) and (2005, 102), find the slope of the line.

b. Interpret the slope in the context of this problem.

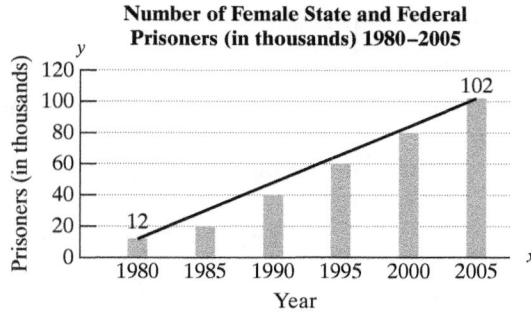

Number of Female State and Federal Prisoners (in thousands) 1980–2005

(*Source:* U.S. Bureau of Justice Statistics)

75. In 1985, the U.S. Postal Service charged $0.22 for first class letters and cards up to 1 oz. By 2007, the price had increased to $0.41. In the graph, x represents the year, and y represents the cost for 1 oz of first class postage.

a. Determine the slope of the line. Round to three decimal places.

b. Interpret the meaning of the slope in the context of this problem.

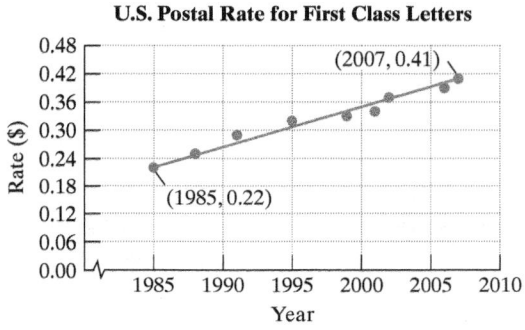

U.S. Postal Rate for First Class Letters

76. The distance, d (in miles), between a lightning strike and an observer is given by the equation $d = 0.2t$, where t is the time (in seconds) between seeing lightning and hearing thunder.

Distance Between Lightning Strike and an Observer

a. If an observer counts 5 sec between seeing lightning and hearing thunder, how far away was the lightning strike?

b. If an observer counts 10 sec between seeing lightning and hearing thunder, how far away was the lightning strike?

c. If an observer counts 15 sec between seeing lightning and hearing thunder, how far away was the lightning strike?

d. What is the slope of the line? Interpret the meaning of the slope in the context of this problem.

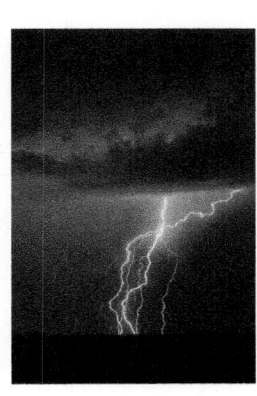

Mixed Exercises

For Exercises 77–80, determine the slope of the line passing through points A and B.

77. Point A is located 3 units up and 4 units to the right of point B.

78. Point A is located 2 units up and 5 units to the left of point B.

79. Point A is located 5 units to the right of point B.

80. Point A is located 3 units down from point B.

81. Graph the line through the point $(1, -2)$ having slope $\frac{2}{3}$. Then give two other points on the line.

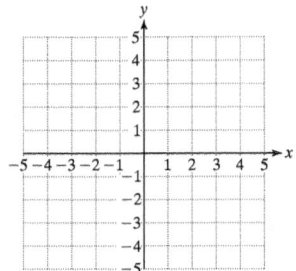

82. Graph the line through the point $(-2, -3)$ having slope $\frac{3}{4}$. Then give two other points on the line.

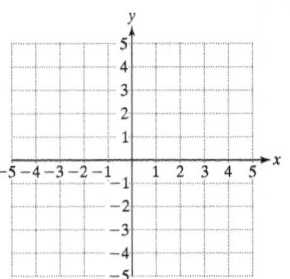

83. Graph the line through the point $(2, 2)$ having slope -3. Then give two other points on the line.

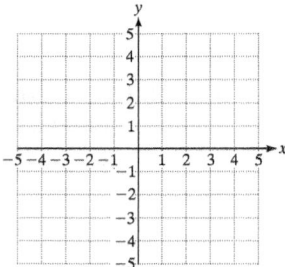

84. Graph the line through the point $(-1, 3)$ having slope -2. Then give two other points on the line.

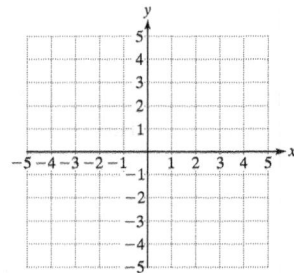

For Exercises 85–90, draw a line as indicated. Answers may vary.

85. Draw a line with a positive slope and a positive y-intercept.

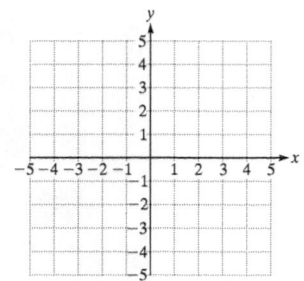

86. Draw a line with a positive slope and a negative y-intercept.

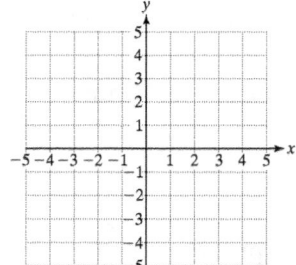

87. Draw a line with a negative slope and a negative y-intercept.

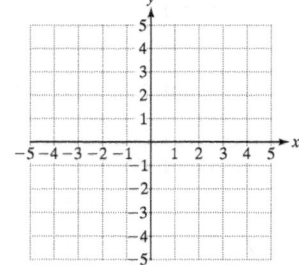

88. Draw a line with a negative slope and positive *y*-intercept.

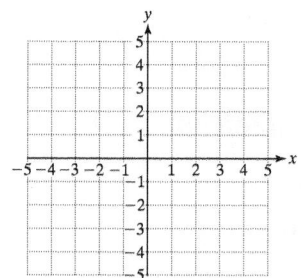

89. Draw a line with a zero slope and a positive *y*-intercept.

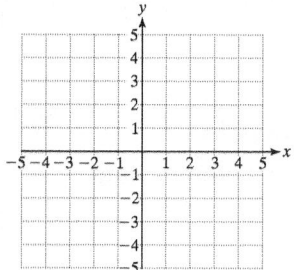

90. Draw a line with undefined slope and a negative *x*-intercept.

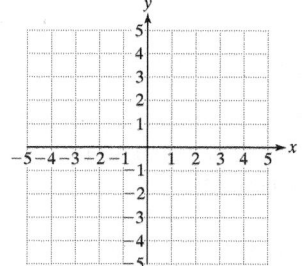

Expanding Your Skills

91. Determine the slope between the points $(a + b, 4m - n)$ and $(a - b, m + 2n)$.

92. Determine the slope between the points $(3c - d, s + t)$ and $(c - 2d, s - t)$.

93. Determine the *x*-intercept of the line $ax + by = c$.

94. Determine the *y*-intercept of the line $ax + by = c$.

95. Find another point on the line that contains the point $(2, -1)$ and has a slope of $\frac{2}{5}$.

96. Find another point on the line that contains the point $(-3, 4)$ and has a slope of $\frac{1}{4}$.

Slope-Intercept Form of a Line

Section 10.4

1. Slope-Intercept Form of a Line

In Section 10.2, we learned that the solutions to an equation of the form $Ax + By = C$ (where A and B are not both zero) represent a line in a rectangular coordinate system. An equation of a line written in this way is said to be in **standard form**. In this section, we will learn a new form, called **slope-intercept form**, which can be used to determine the slope and *y*-intercept of a line.

Let $(0, b)$ represent the *y*-intercept of a line. Let (x, y) represent any other point on the line. Then the slope of the line can be found as follows:

Let $(0, b)$ represent (x_1, y_1), and let (x, y) represent (x_2, y_2). Apply the slope formula.

$$m = \frac{(y_2 - y_1)}{(x_2 - x_1)} \rightarrow m = \frac{y - b}{x - 0}$$ Apply the slope formula.

$$m = \frac{y - b}{x}$$ Simplify.

$$mx = \left(\frac{y - b}{x}\right)x$$ Multiply by *x* to clear fractions.

$$mx = y - b$$

$$mx + b = y - b + b$$ To isolate *y*, add *b* to both sides.

$$mx + b = y \quad \text{or} \quad y = mx + b$$ The equation is in slope-intercept form.

Objectives

1. **Slope-Intercept Form of a Line**
2. **Graphing a Line from Its Slope and *y*-Intercept**
3. **Determining Whether Two Lines Are Parallel, Perpendicular, or Neither**
4. **Writing an Equation of a Line Using Slope-Intercept Form**

> **DEFINITION** Slope-Intercept Form of a Line
>
> $y = mx + b$ is the slope-intercept form of a line.
>
> m is the slope and the point $(0, b)$ is the y-intercept.

Example 1 Identifying the Slope and *y*-Intercept of a Line

For each equation, identify the slope and y-intercept.

   a. $y = 3x - 1$ **b.** $y = -2.7x + 5$ **c.** $y = 4x$

Solution:

Each equation is written in slope-intercept form, $y = mx + b$. The slope is the coefficient of x, and the y-intercept is determined by the constant term.

  a. $y = 3x - 1$ The slope is 3.   The y-intercept is $(0, -1)$.

  b. $y = -2.7x + 5$ The slope is -2.7.   The y-intercept is $(0, 5)$.

  c. $y = 4x$ can be written as $y = 4x + 0$.   The slope is 4.
                                           The y-intercept is $(0, 0)$.

Given the equation of a line, we can write the equation in slope-intercept form by solving the equation for the y-variable. This is demonstrated in the next example.

Example 2 Identifying the Slope and *y*-Intercept of a Line

Given the equation of the line $-5x - 2y = 6$,

  a. Write the equation in slope-intercept form.

  b. Identify the slope and y-intercept.

Solution:

  a. Write the equation in slope-intercept form, $y = mx + b$, by solving for y.

$$-5x - 2y = 6$$

        $-2y = 5x + 6$ Add $5x$ to both sides.

        $\dfrac{-2y}{-2} = \dfrac{5x + 6}{-2}$ Divide both sides by -2.

           $y = \dfrac{5x}{-2} + \dfrac{6}{-2}$ Divide each term by -2 and simplify.

           $y = -\dfrac{5}{2}x - 3$ Slope-intercept form.

  b. The slope is $-\frac{5}{2}$, and the y-intercept is $(0, -3)$.

2. Graphing a Line from Its Slope and *y*-Intercept

Slope-intercept form is a useful tool to graph a line. The y-intercept is a known point on the line. The slope indicates the direction of the line and can be used to find a second point. Using slope-intercept form to graph a line is demonstrated in the next example.

Example 3 Graphing a Line Using the Slope and *y*-Intercept

Graph the equation of the line $y = -\frac{5}{2}x - 3$ by using the slope and *y*-intercept.

Solution:

First plot the *y*-intercept, $(0, -3)$.

The slope, $m = -\frac{5}{2}$, can be written as

$$m = \frac{-5}{2} \quad \longleftarrow \text{The change in } y \text{ is } -5.$$
$$\quad \longleftarrow \text{The change in } x \text{ is } 2.$$

To find a second point on the line, start at the *y*-intercept and move down 5 units and to the right 2 units. Then draw the line through the two points (Figure 10-26).

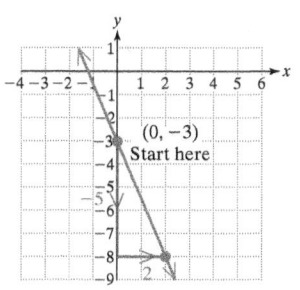

Figure 10-26

Similarly, the slope can be written as

$$m = \frac{5}{-2} \quad \longleftarrow \text{The change in } y \text{ is } 5.$$
$$\quad \longleftarrow \text{The change in } x \text{ is } -2.$$

To find a second point, start at the *y*-intercept and move up 5 units and to the left 2 units. Then draw the line through the two points (Figure 10-27).

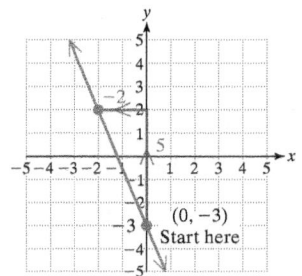

Figure 10-27

Example 4 Graphing a Line from Its Slope and *y*-Intercept

Graph the equation of the line $y = 4x$ by using the slope and *y*-intercept.

Solution:

The line can be written as $y = 4x + 0$. Therefore, we can plot the *y*-intercept at $(0, 0)$. The slope $m = 4$ can be written as

$$m = \frac{4}{1} \quad \begin{array}{l} \longleftarrow \text{The change in } y \text{ is } 4. \\ \longleftarrow \text{The change in } x \text{ is } 1. \end{array}$$

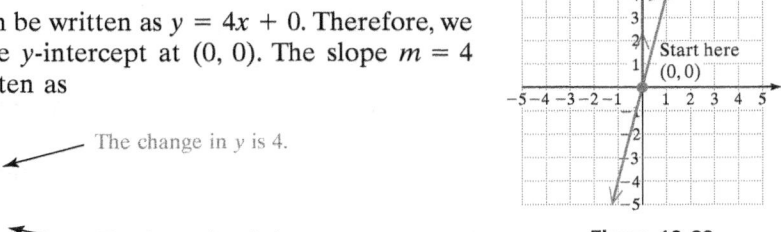

Figure 10-28

To find a second point on the line, start at the *y*-intercept and move up 4 units and to the right 1 unit. Then draw the line through the two points (Figure 10-28).

3. Determining Whether Two Lines Are Parallel, Perpendicular, or Neither

The slope-intercept form provides a means to find the slope of a line by inspection. Recall that if the slopes of two lines are known, then we can compare the slopes to determine if the lines are parallel, perpendicular, or neither parallel nor perpendicular. (Two distinct nonvertical lines are parallel if their slopes are equal. Two lines are perpendicular if the slope of one line is the opposite of the reciprocal of the slope of the other line.)

--- Skill Practice ---

6. Graph the equation by using the slope and the *y*-intercept.
$$y = 2x - 3$$

--- Skill Practice ---

7. Graph the equation by using the slope and the *y*-intercept.
$$y = -\frac{1}{4}x$$

Answers

6.

7.

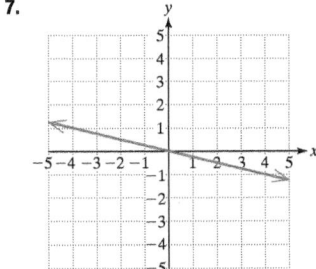

— **Skill Practice** —

For each pair of lines determine if they are parallel, perpendicular, or neither.

8. $y = 3x - 5$
$y = -3x - 15$

9. $x - 5y = 10$
$5x - 1 = -y$

10. $y = \dfrac{5}{6}x - \dfrac{1}{2}$
$y = \dfrac{5}{6}x + \dfrac{1}{2}$

11. $y = -5$
$x = 6$

Example 5 **Determining If Two Lines Are Parallel, Perpendicular, or Neither**

For each pair of lines, determine if they are parallel, perpendicular, or neither.

a. l_1: $y = 3x - 5$ **b.** l_1: $x - 3y = -9$
$\quad\;\; l_2$: $y = 3x + 1$ $\quad\;\; l_2$: $3x = -y + 4$

c. l_1: $y = \frac{3}{2}x + 2$ **d.** l_1: $x = 2$
$\quad\;\; l_2$: $y = \frac{2}{3}x + 1$ $\quad\;\; l_2$: $2y = 8$

Solution:

a. l_1: $y = 3x - 5$ The slope of l_1 is 3.

$\quad\;\; l_2$: $y = 3x + 1$ The slope of l_2 is 3.

Because the slopes are the same, the lines are parallel.

b. First write the equation of each line in slope-intercept form.

l_1: $x - 3y = -9$ l_2: $3x = -y + 4$

$\qquad -3y = -x - 9$ $3x + y = 4$

$\qquad \dfrac{-3y}{-3} = \dfrac{-x}{-3} - \dfrac{9}{-3}$ $y = -3x + 4$

$\qquad\quad y = \dfrac{1}{3}x + 3$

l_1: $y = \frac{1}{3}x + 3$ The slope of l_1 is $\frac{1}{3}$.

l_2: $y = -3x + 4$ The slope of l_2 is -3.

The slope of $\frac{1}{3}$ is the opposite of the reciprocal of -3. Therefore, the lines are perpendicular.

c. l_1: $y = \frac{3}{2}x + 2$ The slope of l_1 is $\frac{3}{2}$.

$\quad\;\; l_2$: $y = \frac{2}{3}x + 1$ The slope of l_2 is $\frac{2}{3}$.

The slopes are not the same. Therefore, the lines are not parallel. The values of the slopes are reciprocals, but they are not opposite in sign. Therefore, the lines are not perpendicular. The lines are neither parallel nor perpendicular.

d. The equation $x = 2$ represents a vertical line because the equation is in the form $x = k$.

The equation $2y = 8$ can be simplified to $y = 4$, which represents a horizontal line.

In this example, we do not need to analyze the slopes because vertical lines and horizontal lines are perpendicular.

4. Writing an Equation of a Line Using Slope-Intercept Form

The slope-intercept form of a line can be used to write an equation of a line when the slope is known and the y-intercept is known.

Answers
8. Neither   **9.** Perpendicular
10. Parallel   **11.** Perpendicular

| Example 6 | Writing an Equation of a Line Using Slope-Intercept Form |

Write an equation of the line whose slope is $\frac{2}{3}$ and whose y-intercept is $(0, 8)$.

Solution:

The slope is given as $m = \frac{2}{3}$, and the y-intercept $(0, b)$ is given as $(0, 8)$. Substitute the values $m = \frac{2}{3}$ and $b = 8$ into the slope-intercept form of a line.

$$y = mx + b$$
$$y = \frac{2}{3}x + 8$$

| Example 7 | Writing an Equation of a Line Using Slope-Intercept Form |

Write an equation of the line that passes through the origin and whose slope is -2.

Solution:

The slope is given as $m = -2$. Furthermore, the line passes through the origin. Therefore, the y-intercept is $(0, 0)$ and the corresponding value of b is 0. The slope-intercept form of the line becomes:

$$y = mx + b$$
$$y = -2x + 0 \text{ or equivalently } y = -2x.$$

Calculator Connections

Topic: Using the *ZSquare* Option in Zoom

In Example 5(b) we found that the equations $y = \frac{1}{3}x + 3$ and $y = -3x + 4$ represent perpendicular lines. We can verify our results by graphing the lines on a graphing calculator.

Notice that the lines do not appear perpendicular in the calculator display. That is, they do not appear to form a right angle at the point of intersection. Because many calculators have a rectangular screen, the standard viewing window is elongated in the horizontal direction. To eliminate this distortion, try using a *ZSquare* option, which is located under the Zoom menu. This feature will set the viewing window so that equal distances on the display denote an equal number of units on the graph.

Calculator Exercises

For each pair of lines, determine if the lines are parallel, perpendicular, or neither. Then use a square viewing window to graph the lines on a graphing calculator to verify your results.

1. $x + y = 1$
  $x - y = -3$

2. $3x + y = -2$
  $6x + 2y = 6$

3. $2x - y = 4$
  $3x + 2y = 4$

4. Graph the lines defined by $y = x + 1$ and $y = 0.99x + 3$. Are these lines parallel? Explain.

5. Graph the lines defined by $y = -2x - 1$ and $y = -2x - 0.99$. Are these lines the same? Explain.

6. Graph the line defined by $y = 0.001x + 3$. Is this line horizontal? Explain.

Section 10.4 Practice Exercises

Study Skills Exercises

1. Write down the page number(s) for the Chapter Summary for this chapter. Describe one way in which you can use the Summary found at the end of each chapter.

2. Define the key terms:

   a. Slope-intercept form of a line   **b. Standard form of a line**

Review Exercises

For Exercises 3–10, determine the x- and y-intercepts, if they exist.

3. $x - 5y = 10$	**4.** $3x + y = -12$	**5.** $3y = -9$	**6.** $2 + y = 5$
7. $-4x = 6y$	**8.** $-x + 3 = 8$	**9.** $5x = 20$	**10.** $y = \dfrac{1}{2}x$

Objective 1: Slope-Intercept Form of a Line

For Exercises 11–30, identify the slope and y-intercept, if they exist. **(See Examples 1–2.)**

11. $y = -2x + 3$	**12.** $y = \dfrac{2}{3}x + 5$	**13.** $y = x - 2$
14. $y = -x + 6$	**15.** $y = -x$	**16.** $y = -5x$
17. $y = \dfrac{3}{4}x - 1$	**18.** $y = x - \dfrac{5}{3}$	**19.** $2x - 5y = 4$
20. $3x + 2y = 9$	**21.** $3x - y = 5$	**22.** $7x - 3y = -6$
23. $x + y = 6$	**24.** $x - y = 1$	**25.** $x + 6 = 8$
26. $-4 + x = 1$	**27.** $-8y = 2$	**28.** $1 - y = 9$
29. $3y - 2x = 0$	**30.** $5x = 6y$	

Objective 2: Graphing a Line from Its Slope and *y*-Intercept

For Exercises 31–34, graph the line using the slope and *y*-intercept. **(See Examples 3–4.)**

31. Graph the line through the point $(0, 2)$, having a slope of -4.

32. Graph the line through the point $(0, -1)$, having a slope of -3.

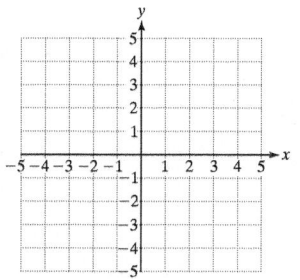

33. Graph the line through the point $(0, -5)$, having a slope of $\frac{3}{2}$.

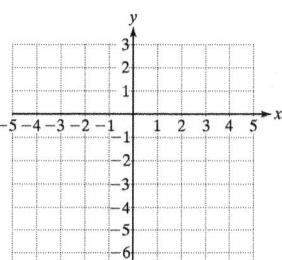

34. Graph the line through the point $(0, 3)$, having a slope of $-\frac{1}{4}$.

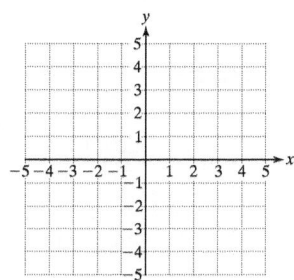

For Exercises 35–40, match the equation with the graph (a–f) by identifying if the slope is positive or negative and if the *y*-intercept is positive, negative, or zero.

35. $y = 2x + 3$

36. $y = -3x - 2$

37. $y = -\frac{1}{3}x + 3$

38. $y = \frac{1}{2}x - 2$

39. $y = x$

40. $y = -2x$

a.

b.

c.

d.

e.

f.

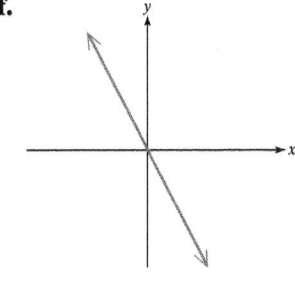

For Exercises 41–52, write each equation in slope-intercept form (if possible) and graph the line. **(See Examples 3–4.)**

41. $x - 2y = 6$

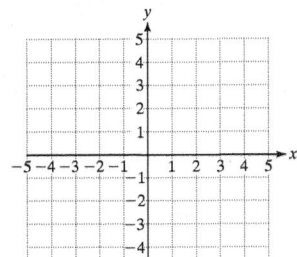

42. $5x - 2y = 2$

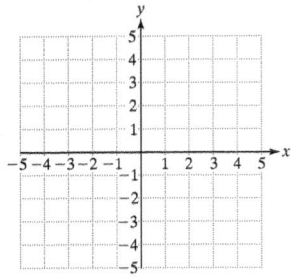

43. $2x + y = 9$

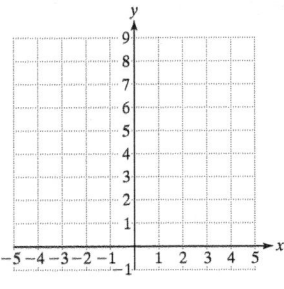

44. $-6x + y = 8$

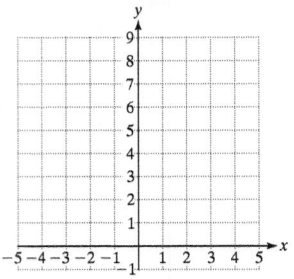

45. $2x = -4y + 6$

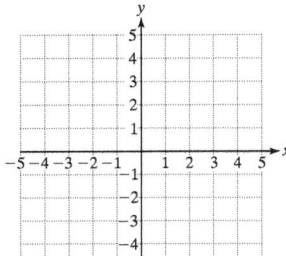

46. $3x = y - 7$

47. $x + y = 0$

48. $x - y = 0$

49. $5y = 4x$

50. $-2x = 5y$

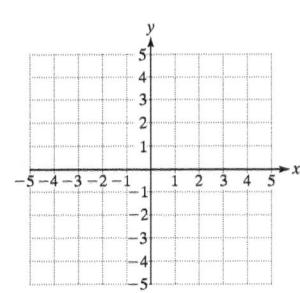

51. $3y + 2 = 0$

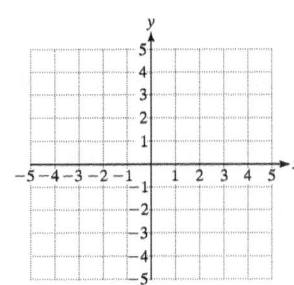

52. $1 + 5y = 6$

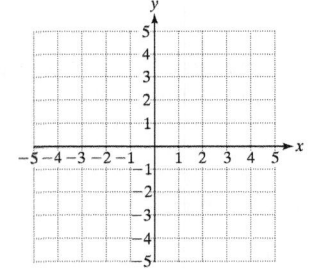

Objective 3: Determining Whether Two Lines Are Parallel, Perpendicular, or Neither

For Exercises 53–68, determine if the equations represent parallel lines, perpendicular lines, or neither. **(See Example 5.)**

53. l_1: $y = -2x - 3$

   l_2: $y = \frac{1}{2}x + 4$

54. l_1: $y = \frac{4}{3}x - 2$

   l_2: $y = -\frac{3}{4}x + 6$

55. l_1: $y = \frac{4}{5}x - \frac{1}{2}$

   l_2: $y = \frac{5}{4}x - \frac{2}{3}$

56. l_1: $y = \frac{1}{5}x + 1$

   l_2: $y = 5x - 3$

57. l_1: $y = -9x + 6$

   l_2: $y = -9x - 1$

58. l_1: $y = 4x - 1$

   l_2: $y = 4x + \frac{1}{2}$

59. l_1: $x = 3$

   l_2: $y = \frac{7}{4}$

60. l_1: $y = \frac{2}{3}$

   l_2: $x = 6$

61. l_1: $2x = 4$

   l_2: $6 = x$

62. l_1: $2y = 7$

   l_2: $y = 4$

63. l_1: $2x + 3y = 6$

   l_2: $3x - 2y = 12$

64. l_1: $4x + 5y = 20$

   l_2: $5x - 4y = 60$

65. l_1: $4x + 2y = 6$ ● **66.** l_1: $3x + y = 5$ **67.** l_1: $y = \dfrac{1}{5}x - 3$ **68.** l_1: $y = \dfrac{1}{3}x + 2$

l_2: $4x + 8y = 16$ l_2: $x + 3y = 18$ l_2: $2x - 10y = 20$ l_2: $-x + 3y = 12$

Objective 4: Writing an Equation of a Line Using Slope-Intercept Form

For Exercises 69–78, write an equation of the line given the following information. Write the answer in slope-intercept form if possible. **(See Examples 6–7.)**

69. The slope is $-\frac{1}{3}$, and the y-intercept is $(0, 2)$.   **70.** The slope is $\frac{2}{3}$, and the y-intercept is $(0, -1)$.

71. The slope is 10, and the y-intercept is $(0, -19)$.   ● **72.** The slope is -14, and the y-intercept is $(0, 2)$.

73. The slope is 0, and the y-intercept is -11.   **74.** The slope is 0, and the y-intercept is $\dfrac{6}{7}$.

75. The slope is 5, and the line passes through the origin.   **76.** The slope is -3, and the line passes through the origin.

77. The slope is 6, and the line passes through the point $(0, -2)$.   **78.** The slope is -4, and the line passes through the point $(0, -3)$.

Expanding Your Skills

79. The cost for a rental car is \$49.95 per day plus a flat fee of \$31.95 for insurance. The equation, $C = 49.95x + 31.95$ represents the total cost, C (in dollars), to rent the car for x days.

  a. Identify the slope. Interpret the meaning of the slope in the context of this problem.

  b. Identify the C-intercept. Interpret the meaning of the C-intercept in the context of this problem.

  c. Use the equation to determine how much it would cost to rent the car for 1 week.

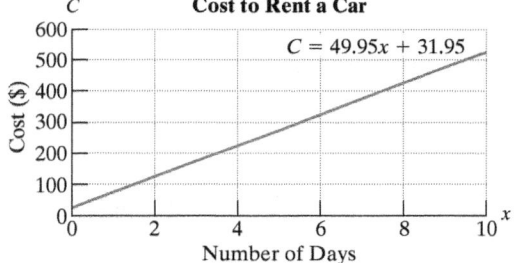

80. A phone bill is determined each month by a \$16.95 flat fee plus \$0.10/min of long distance. The equation $C = 0.10x + 16.95$ represents the total monthly cost, C, for x minutes of long distance.

  a. Identify the slope. Interpret the meaning of the slope in the context of this problem.

  b. Identify the C-intercept. Interpret the meaning of the C-intercept in the context of this problem.

  c. Use the equation to determine the total cost of 234 min of long distance.

81. A linear equation is written in standard form if it can be written as $Ax + By = C$, where A and B are not both zero. Write the equation $Ax + By = C$ in slope-intercept form to show that the slope is given by the ratio, $-\frac{A}{B}$. $(B \neq 0.)$

For Exercises 82–85, use the result of Exercise 81 to find the slope of the line.

82. $2x + 5y = 8$ **83.** $6x + 7y = -9$ **84.** $4x - 3y = -5$ **85.** $11x - 8y = 4$

Problem Recognition Exercises

Linear Equations in Two Variables

For Exercises 1–20, choose the equation(s) from the column on the right whose graph satisfies the condition described. Give all possible answers.

1. Line whose slope is positive.

2. Line whose slope is negative.

3. Line that passes through the origin.

4. Line that contains the point $(3, -2)$.

5. Line whose y-intercept is $(0, 4)$.

6. Line whose y-intercept is $(0, -5)$.

7. Line whose slope is $\dfrac{1}{2}$.

8. Line whose slope is -2.

9. Line whose slope is 0.

10. Line whose slope is undefined.

11. Line that is parallel to the line with equation $y = -\dfrac{2}{3}x + 4$.

12. Line perpendicular to the line with equation $y = 2x + 9$.

13. Line that is vertical.

14. Line that is horizontal.

15. Line whose x-intercept is $(10, 0)$.

16. Line whose x-intercept is $(6, 0)$.

17. Line that is parallel to the x-axis.

18. Line that is perpendicular to the y-axis.

19. Line with a negative slope and positive y-intercept.

20. Line with a positive slope and negative y-intercept.

a. $y = 5x$

b. $2x + 3y = 12$

c. $y = \dfrac{1}{2}x - 5$

d. $3x - 6y = 10$

e. $2y = -8$

f. $y = -2x + 4$

g. $3x = 1$

h. $x + 2y = 6$

Point-Slope Formula

1. Writing an Equation of a Line Using the Point-Slope Formula

In Section 10.4, the slope-intercept form of a line was used as a tool to construct an equation of a line. Another useful tool to determine an equation of a line is the point-slope formula. The point-slope formula can be derived from the slope formula as follows:

Suppose a line passes through a given point (x_1, y_1) and has slope m. If (x, y) is any other point on the line, then:

$$m = \frac{y - y_1}{x - x_1} \qquad \text{Slope formula}$$

$$m(x - x_1) = \frac{y - y_1}{x - x_1}(x - x_1) \qquad \text{Clear fractions.}$$

$$m(x - x_1) = y - y_1$$

$$y - y_1 = m(x - x_1) \qquad \text{Point-slope formula}$$

FORMULA   Point-Slope Formula

The **point-slope formula** is given by

$$y - y_1 = m(x - x_1)$$

where m is the slope of the line and (x_1, y_1) is a known point on the line.

Example 1 demonstrates how to use the point-slope formula to find an equation of a line when a point on the line and slope are given.

Example 1   **Writing an Equation of a Line Using the Point-Slope Formula**

Use the point-slope formula to write an equation of the line having a slope of 3 and passing through the point $(-2, -4)$. Write the answer in slope-intercept form.

Skill Practice

1. Use the point-slope formula to write an equation of the line having a slope of -4 and passing through $(-1, 5)$. Write the answer in slope-intercept form.

Solution:

The slope of the line is given: $m = 3$.

A point on the line is given: $(x_1, y_1) = (-2, -4)$.

Answer

1. $y = -4x + 1$

The point-slope formula:

$$y - y_1 = m(x - x_1)$$

$y - (-4) = 3[x - (-2)]$ Substitute $m = 3$, $x_1 = -2$, and $y_1 = -4$.

$y + 4 = 3(x + 2)$ Simplify. Because the final answer is required in slope-intercept form, simplify the equation and solve for y.

$y + 4 = 3x + 6$ Apply the distributive property.

$y = 3x + 2$ Slope-intercept form

The equation $y = 3x + 2$ from Example 1 is graphed in Figure 10-29. Notice that the line does indeed pass through the point $(-2, -4)$.

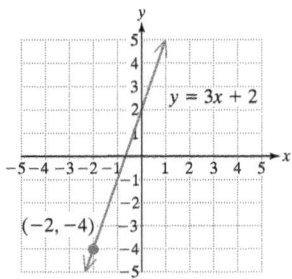

Figure 10-29

2. Writing an Equation of a Line Given Two Points

Example 2 is similar to Example 1; however, the slope must first be found from two given points.

Example 2   **Writing an Equation of a Line Given Two Points**

Use the point-slope formula to find an equation of the line passing through the points $(-2, 5)$ and $(4, -1)$. Write the final answer in slope-intercept form.

Solution:

Given two points on a line, the slope can be found with the slope formula.

$(-2, 5)$ and $(4, -1)$
(x_1, y_1) (x_2, y_2) Label the points.

$$m = \frac{y_2 - y_1}{x_2 - x_1} = \frac{(-1) - (5)}{(4) - (-2)} = \frac{-6}{6} = -1$$

To apply the point-slope formula, use the slope, $m = -1$ and either given point. We will choose the point $(-2, 5)$ as (x_1, y_1).

$$y - y_1 = m(x - x_1)$$

$y - 5 = -1[x - (-2)]$ Substitute $m = -1$, $x_1 = -2$, and $y_1 = 5$.

$y - 5 = -1(x + 2)$ Simplify.

$y - 5 = -x - 2$

$y = -x + 3$

TIP: The point-slope formula can be applied using either given point for (x_1, y_1). In Example 2, using the point $(4, -1)$ for (x_1, y_1) produces the same result.

$$y - y_1 = m(x - x_1)$$

$y - (-1) = -1(x - 4)$

$y + 1 = -x + 4$

$y = -x + 3$

Answer

2. $y = 2x - 3$

The solution to Example 2 can be checked by graphing the line $y = -x + 3$ using the slope and y-intercept. Notice that the line passes through the points $(-2, 5)$ and $(4, -1)$ as expected. See Figure 10-30.

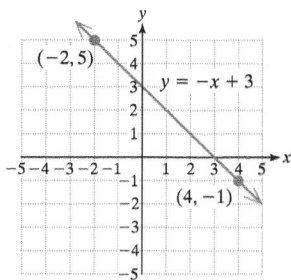

Figure 10-30

3. Writing an Equation of a Line Parallel or Perpendicular to Another Line

> **Example 3**   Writing an Equation of a Line Parallel to Another Line

Use the point-slope formula to find an equation of the line passing through the point $(-1, 0)$ and parallel to the line $y = -4x + 3$. Write the final answer in slope-intercept form.

Solution:

Figure 10-31 shows the line $y = -4x + 3$ (pictured in black) and a line parallel to it (pictured in blue) that passes through the point $(-1, 0)$. The equation of the given line, $y = -4x + 3$, is written in slope-intercept form, and its slope is easily identified as -4. The line parallel to the given line must also have a slope of -4.

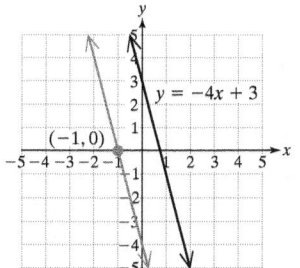

Figure 10-31

Apply the point-slope formula using $m = -4$ and the point $(x_1, y_1) = (-1, 0)$.

$$y - y_1 = m(x - x_1)$$
$$y - 0 = -4[x - (-1)]$$
$$y = -4(x + 1)$$
$$y = -4x - 4$$

> **Example 4**   Writing an Equation of a Line Perpendicular to Another Line

Use the point-slope formula to find an equation of the line passing through the point $(-3, 1)$ and perpendicular to the line $3x + y = -2$. Write the final answer in slope-intercept form.

Solution:

The given line can be written in slope-intercept form as $y = -3x - 2$. The slope of this line is -3. Therefore, the slope of a line perpendicular to the given line is $\frac{1}{3}$.

Apply the point-slope formula with $m = \frac{1}{3}$, and $(x_1, y_1) = (-3, 1)$.

$y - y_1 = m(x - x_1)$ Point-slope formula

$y - (1) = \frac{1}{3}[x - (-3)]$ Substitute $m = \frac{1}{3}$, $x_1 = -3$, and $y_1 = 1$.

$y - 1 = \frac{1}{3}(x + 3)$ To write the final answer in slope-intercept form, simplify the equation and solve for y.

$y - 1 = \frac{1}{3}x + 1$ Apply the distributive property.

$y = \frac{1}{3}x + 2$ Add 1 to both sides.

A sketch of the perpendicular lines $y = \frac{1}{3}x + 2$ and $y = -3x - 2$ is shown in Figure 10-32. Notice that the line $y = \frac{1}{3}x + 2$ passes through the point $(-3, 1)$.

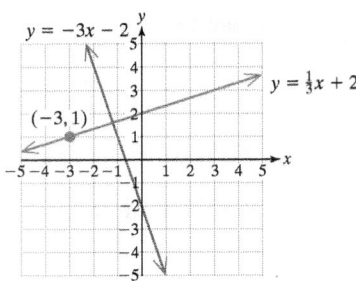

Figure 10-32

4. Different Forms of Linear Equations: A Summary

A linear equation can be written in several different forms, as summarized in Table 10-3.

Table 10-3

Form	Example	Comments
Standard Form $Ax + By = C$	$4x + 2y = 8$	A and B must not both be zero.
Horizontal Line $y = k$ (k is constant)	$y = 4$	The slope is zero, and the y-intercept is $(0, k)$.
Vertical Line $x = k$ (k is constant)	$x = -1$	The slope is undefined, and the x-intercept is $(k, 0)$.
Slope-Intercept Form $y = mx + b$ the slope is m y-intercept is $(0, b)$	$y = -3x + 7$ Slope $= -3$ y-intercept is $(0, 7)$	Solving a linear equation for y results in slope-intercept form. The coefficient of the x-term is the slope, and the constant defines the location of the y-intercept.
Point-Slope Formula $y - y_1 = m(x - x_1)$	$m = -3$ $(x_1, y_1) = (4, 2)$ $y - 2 = -3(x - 4)$	This formula is typically used to build an equation of a line when a point on the line is known and the slope of the line is known.

Concept Connections

5. Explain why the point-slope formula cannot be used to write an equation for a vertical line.
6. Explain how to write an equation for a vertical line.

Answers

5. The point-slope formula requires a value for the slope and a vertical line has an undefined slope.
6. The form $x = k$ must be used. Then the appropriate value is substituted for k.

Although standard form and slope-intercept form can be used to express an equation of a line, often the slope-intercept form is used to give a *unique* representation of the line. For example, the following linear equations are all written in standard form, yet they each define the same line.

$$2x + 5y = 10$$

$$-4x - 10y = -20$$

$$6x + 15y = 30$$

$$\frac{2}{5}x + y = 2$$

The line can be written uniquely in slope-intercept form as: $y = -\frac{2}{5}x + 2$.

Although it is important to understand and apply slope-intercept form and the point-slope formula, they are not necessarily applicable to all problems, particularly when dealing with a horizontal or vertical line.

Example 5 **Writing an Equation of a Line**

Find an equation of the line passing through the point $(2, -4)$ and parallel to the x-axis.

Solution:

Because the line is parallel to the x-axis, the line must be horizontal. Recall that all horizontal lines can be written in the form $y = k$, where k is a constant. A quick sketch can help find the value of the constant. See Figure 10-33.

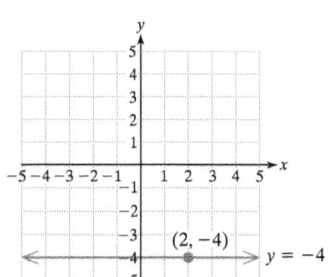

Figure 10-33

Because the line must pass through a point whose y-coordinate is -4, then the equation of the line must be $y = -4$.

── **Skill Practice** ──

7. Write an equation for the vertical line that passes through the point $(-7, 2)$.

Answer
7. $x = -7$

Section 10.5 Practice Exercises

Study Skills Exercises

1. Prepare a one-page summary sheet with the most important information that you need for the test. On the day of the test, look at this sheet several times to refresh your memory instead of trying to memorize new information.

2. Define the key term: **Point-slope formula**

Review Exercises

For Exercises 3–6, graph the equations.

3. $2x - 3y = -3$

4. $y = -2x$

5. $3 - y = 9$

6. $y = \dfrac{4}{5}x$

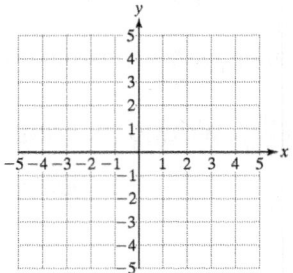

For Exercises 7–10, find the slope of the line that passes through the given points.

7. $(1, -3)$ and $(2, 6)$

8. $(2, -4)$ and $(-2, 4)$

9. $(-2, 5)$ and $(5, 5)$

10. $(6.1, 2.5)$ and $(6.1, -1.5)$

Objective 1: Writing an Equation of a Line Using the Point-Slope Formula

For Exercises 11–22, use the point-slope formula (if possible) to write an equation of the line given the following information. **(See Example 1.)**

11. The slope is 3, and the line passes through the point $(-2, 1)$.

12. The slope is -2, and the line passes through the point $(1, -5)$.

13. The slope is -4, and the line passes through the point $(-3, -2)$.

14. The slope is 5, and the line passes through the point $(-1, -3)$.

15. The slope is $-\frac{1}{2}$, and the line passes through $(-1, 0)$.

16. The slope is $-\frac{3}{4}$, and the line passes through $(2, 0)$.

17. The slope is $\frac{1}{4}$, and the line passes through the point $(-8, 6)$.

18. The slope is $\frac{2}{3}$, and the line passes through the point $(-5, 4)$.

19. The slope is 4.5, and the line passes through the point $(5.2, -2.2)$.

20. The slope is -3.6, and the line passes through the point $(10.0, 8.2)$.

21. The slope is 0, and the line passes through the point $(3, -2)$.

22. The slope is 0, and the line passes through the point $(0, 5)$.

Objective 2: Writing an Equation of a Line Given Two Points

For Exercises 23–28, use the point-slope formula to write an equation of the line given the following information. **(See Example 2.)**

23. The line passes through the points $(-2, -6)$ and $(1, 0)$.

24. The line passes through the points $(-2, 5)$ and $(0, 1)$.

25. The line passes through the points $(0, -4)$ and $(-1, -3)$.

26. The line passes through the points $(1, -3)$ and $(-7, 2)$.

27. The line passes through the points $(2.2, -3.3)$ and $(12.2, -5.3)$.

28. The line passes through the points $(4.7, -2.2)$ and $(-0.3, 6.8)$.

For Exercises 29–34, find an equation of the line through the given points. Write the final answer in slope-intercept form.

29.

30.

31.

32.

33.

34.

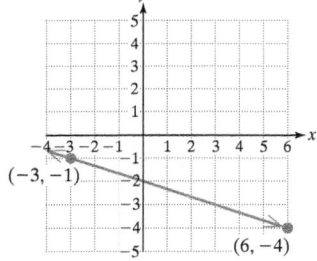

Objective 3: Writing an Equation of a Line Parallel or Perpendicular to Another Line

For Exercises 35–44, use the point-slope formula to write an equation of the line given the following information. **(See Examples 3–4.)**

35. The line passes through the point $(-3, 1)$ and is parallel to the line $y = 4x + 3$.

36. The line passes through the point $(4, -1)$ and is parallel to the line $y = 3x + 1$.

37. The line passes through the point $(4, 0)$ and is parallel to the line $3x + 2y = 8$.

38. The line passes through the point $(2, 0)$ and is parallel to the line $5x + 3y = 6$.

39. The line passes through the point $(-5, 2)$ and is perpendicular to the line $y = \frac{1}{2}x + 3$.

40. The line passes through the point $(-2, -2)$ and is perpendicular to the line $y = \frac{1}{3}x - 5$.

41. The line passes through the point $(0, -6)$ and is perpendicular to the line $-5x + y = 4$.

42. The line passes through the point $(0, -8)$ and is perpendicular to the line $2x - y = 5$.

43. The line passes through the point $(4, 4)$ and is parallel to the line $3x - y = 6$.

44. The line passes through the point $(-1, -7)$ and is parallel to the line $5x + y = -5$.

Objective 4: Different Forms of Linear Equations: A Summary

For Exercises 45–50, match the form or formula on the left with its name on the right.

45. $x = k$ i.   Standard form

46. $y = mx + b$ ii. Point-slope formula

47. $m = \dfrac{y_2 - y_1}{x_2 - x_1}$ iii. Horizontal line

48. $y - y_1 = m(x - x_1)$ iv. Vertical line

49. $y = k$ v.   Slope-intercept form

50. $Ax + By = C$ vi. Slope formula

For Exercises 51–60, find an equation for the line given the following information. **(See Example 5.)**

51. The line passes through the point $(3, 1)$ and is parallel to the line $y = -4$. See the figure.

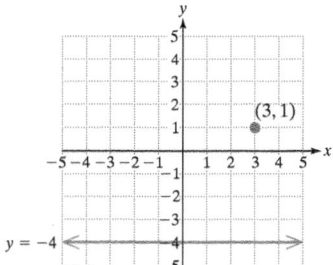

52. The line passes through the point $(-1, 1)$ and is parallel to the line $y = 2$. See the figure.

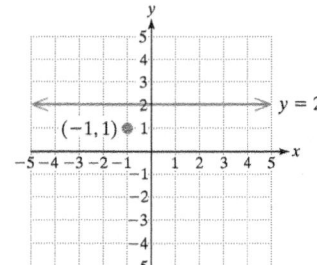

53. The line passes through the point $(2, 6)$ and is perpendicular to the line $y = 1$. (*Hint:* Sketch the line first.)

54. The line passes through the point $(0, 3)$ and is perpendicular to the line $y = -5$. (*Hint:* Sketch the line first.)

55. The line passes through the point $(2, 2)$ and is perpendicular to the line $x = 0$.

56. The line passes through the point $(5, -2)$ and is perpendicular to the line $x = 0$.

57. The slope is undefined, and the line passes through the point $(-6, -3)$.

58. The slope is undefined, and the line passes through the point $(2, -1)$.

59. The line passes through the points $(-4, 0)$ and $(-4, 3)$.

60. The line passes through the points $(1, 3)$ and $(1, -4)$.

Applications of Linear Equations and Modeling | Section 10.6

1. Interpreting a Linear Equation in Two Variables

Linear equations can often be used to describe (or model) the relationship between two variables in a real-world event.

Example 1   Interpreting a Linear Equation

The number of tigers in India decreased from 1900 to 2005. This decrease can be approximated by the equation $y = -350x + 42{,}000$. The variable y represents the number of tigers left in India, and x represents the number of years since 1900.

a. Use the equation to predict the number of tigers in 1960.

b. Use the equation to predict the number of tigers in 2010.

c. Determine the slope of the line. Interpret the meaning of the slope in terms of the number of tigers and the year.

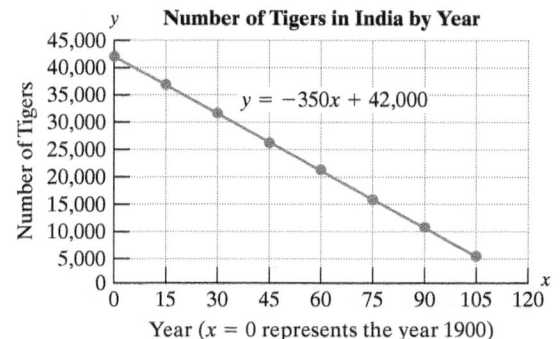

Number of Tigers in India by Year

$y = -350x + 42{,}000$

Year ($x = 0$ represents the year 1900)

d. Determine the x-intercept. Interpret the meaning of the x-intercept in terms of the number of tigers.

Solution:

a. The year 1960 is 60 yr since 1900. Substitute $x = 60$ into the equation.

$y = -350x + 42{,}000$

$y = -350(60) + 42{,}000$

$\quad = 21{,}000$ There were approximately 21,000 tigers in India in 1960.

b. The year 2010 is 110 yr since 1900. Substitute $x = 110$.

$y = -350(110) + 42{,}000$

$\quad = 3500$ There will be approximately 3500 tigers in India in 2010.

c. The slope is -350.   The slope means that the tiger population is decreasing by 350 tigers per year.

d. To find the x-intercept, substitute $y = 0$.

$\quad y = -350x + 42{,}000$

$\quad 0 = -350x + 42{,}000$ Substitute 0 for y.

$-42{,}000 = -350x$

$\quad 120 = x$

The x-intercept is $(120, 0)$. This means that 120 yr after the year 1900, the tiger population would be expected to reach zero. That is, in the year 2020, there will be no tigers left in India if this linear trend continues.

2. Writing a Linear Equation Using Observed Data Points

Example 2 **Writing a Linear Equation from Observed Data Points**

The monthly sales of hybrid cars sold in the United States are given for a recent year. The sales for the first 8 months of the year are shown in Figure 10-34. The value $x = 0$ represents January, $x = 1$ represents February, and so on.

Figure 10-34

a. Use the data points from Figure 10-34 to find a linear equation that represents the monthly sales of hybrid cars in the United States. Let x represent the month number and let y represent the number of vehicles sold.

b. Use the linear equation in part (a) to estimate the number of hybrid vehicles sold in month 7 (August).

Solution:

a. The ordered pairs $(0, 14{,}400)$ and $(5, 23{,}400)$ are given in the graph. Use these points to find the slope.

$$(0, 14{,}400) \quad \text{and} \quad (5, 23{,}400)$$
$$(x_1, y_1) (x_2, y_2)$$ Label the points.

$$m = \frac{y_2 - y_1}{x_2 - x_1} = \frac{23{,}400 - 14{,}400}{5 - 0}$$

$$= \frac{9000}{5}$$

$$= 1800$$ The slope is 1800. This indicates that sales increased by approximately 1800 per month during this time period.

With $m = 1800$, and the y-intercept given as $(0, 14{,}400)$, we have the following linear equation in slope-intercept form.

$$y = 1800x + 14{,}400$$

b. To approximate the sales in month number 7, substitute $x = 7$ into the equation from part (a).

$$y = 1800(7) + 14{,}400 \qquad \text{Substitute } x = 7.$$

$$= 27{,}000$$

The monthly sales for August (month 7) would be 27,000 vehicles.

3. Writing a Linear Equation Given a Fixed Value and a Rate of Change

Another way to look at the equation $y = mx + b$ is to identify the term mx as the variable term and the term b as the constant term. The value of the term mx will change with the value of x (this is why the slope, m, is called a *rate of change*). However, the term b will remain constant regardless of the value of x. With these ideas in mind, we can write a linear equation if the rate of change and the constant are known.

| Example 3 | **Finding a Linear Equation** |

A stack of posters to advertise a school play costs $19.95 plus $1.50 per poster at the printer.

a. Write a linear equation to compute the cost, c, of buying x posters.

b. Use the equation to compute the cost of 125 posters.

Solution:

a. The constant cost is $19.95. The variable cost is $1.50 per poster. If m is replaced with 1.50 and b is replaced with 19.95, the equation is

$c = 1.50x + 19.95$ where c is the cost (in dollars) of buying x posters.

b. Because x represents the number of posters, substitute $x = 125$.

$$c = 1.50(125) + 19.95$$
$$= 187.5 + 19.95$$
$$= 207.45$$

The total cost of buying 125 posters is $207.45.

Calculator Connections

Topic: Using the Evaluate Feature on a Graphing Calculator

In Example 3, the equation $c = 1.50x + 19.95$ was used to represent the cost, c, to buy x posters. To graph this equation on a graphing calculator, first replace the variable c by y.

$$y = 1.50x + 19.95$$

We enter the equation into the calculator and set the viewing window.

To evaluate the equation for a user-defined value of x, use the *Value* feature in the CALC menu.

In this case, we entered $x = 125$, and the calculator returned $y = 207.45$.

Calculator Exercises

Use a graphing calculator to graph the lines on an appropriate viewing window. Evaluate the equation at the given values of x.

1. $y = -4.6x + 27.1$ at $x = 3$

2. $y = -3.6x - 42.3$ at $x = 0$

3. $y = 40x + 105$ at $x = 6$

4. $y = 20x - 65$ at $x = 8$

Section 10.6 Practice Exercises

Study Skills Exercise

1. On test day, take a look at any formulas or important points that you had to memorize before you enter the classroom. Then when you sit down to take your test, write these formulas on the test or on scrap paper. This is called a memory dump. Write down the formulas from Chapter 10.

Review Exercises

2. Determine the slope of the line defined by $2x - 8y = 15$.

For Exercises 3–8, find the x- and y-intercepts of the lines, if possible.

3. $5x + 6y = 30$

4. $3x + 4y = 1$.

5. $y = -2x - 4$

6. $y = 5x$

7. $y = -9$

8. $x = 2$

Objective 1: Interpreting a Linear Equation in Two Variables

9. The minimum hourly wage, y (in dollars per hour), in the United States can be approximated by the equation $y = 0.14x + 1.60$. In this equation, x represents the number of years since 1970 ($x = 0$ represents 1970, $x = 5$ represents 1975, and so on). **(See Example 1.)**

a. Use the equation to approximate the minimum wage in the year 1980.

b. Use the equation to predict the minimum wage in 2010.

c. Determine the y-intercept. Interpret the meaning of the y-intercept in the context of this problem.

d. Determine the slope. Interpret the meaning of the slope in the context of this problem.

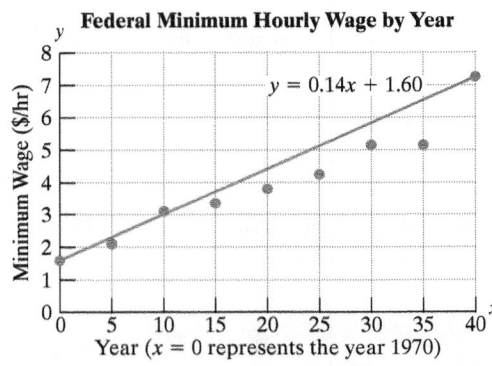

10. The graph depicts the rise in the number of jail inmates in the United States since 1995. Two linear equations are given: one to describe the number of female inmates and one to describe the number of male inmates by year.

Let y represent the number of inmates (in thousands). Let x represent the number of years since 1995.

a. What is the slope of the line representing the number of female inmates? Interpret the meaning of the slope in the context of this problem.

b. What is the slope of the line representing the number of male inmates? Interpret the meaning of the slope in the context of this problem.

c. Which group, males or females, has the larger slope? What does this imply about the rise in the number of male and female prisoners?

d. Assuming this trend continues, use the equation to predict the number of female inmates in 2015.

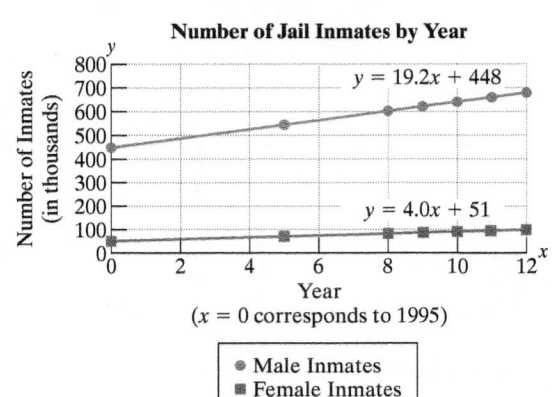

(*Source:* U.S. Bureau of Justice Statistics)

11. The average daily temperature in January for cities along the eastern seaboard of the United States and Canada generally decreases for cities farther north. A city's latitude in the northern hemisphere is a measure of how far north it is on the globe.

The average temperature, y (measured in degrees Fahrenheit), can be described by the equation

$y = -2.333x + 124.0$ where x is the latitude of the city.

City	x Latitude (°N)	y Average Daily Temperature (°F)
Jacksonville, FL	30.3	52.4
Miami, FL	25.8	67.2
Atlanta, GA	33.8	41.0
Baltimore, MD	39.3	31.8
Boston, MA	42.3	28.6
Atlantic City, NJ	39.4	30.9
New York, NY	40.7	31.5
Portland, ME	43.7	20.8
Charlotte, NC	35.2	39.3
Norfolk, VA	36.9	39.1

(*Source:* U.S. National Oceanic and Atmospheric Administration)

a. Use the equation to predict the average daily temperature in January for Philadelphia, Pennsylvania, whose latitude is 40.0°N. Round to one decimal place.

b. Use the equation to predict the average daily temperature in January for Edmundston, New Brunswick, Canada, whose latitude is 47.4°N. Round to one decimal place.

c. What is the slope of the line? Interpret the meaning of the slope in terms of latitude and temperature.

d. From the equation, determine the value of the x-intercept. Round to one decimal place. Interpret the meaning of the x-intercept in terms of latitude and temperature.

12. The graph shows the number of points scored by Shaquille O'Neal and by Allen Iverson according to the number of minutes played for several games. Two linear equations are given: one to describe the number of points scored by O'Neal and one to describe the number of points scored by Iverson. In both equations, y represents the number of points scored and x represents the number of minutes played.

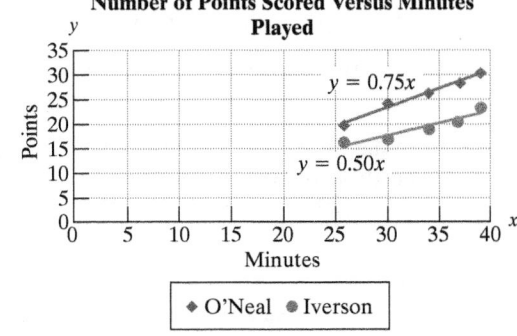

a. What is the slope of the line representing the number of points scored by O'Neal? Interpret the meaning of the slope in the context of this problem.

b. What is the slope of the line representing the number of points scored by Iverson? Interpret the meaning of the slope in the context of this problem.

c. According to these linear equations, approximately how many points would each player expect to score if he played for 36 min? Round to the nearest point.

13. The electric bill charge for a certain utility company is $0.095 per kilowatt-hour. The total cost, y, depends on the number of kilowatt-hours, x, according to the equation $y = 0.095x$, $x \geq 0$.

  a. Determine the cost of using 1000 kilowatt-hours.

  b. Determine the cost of using 2000 kilowatt-hours.

  c. Determine the y-intercept. Interpret the meaning of the y-intercept in the context of this problem.

  d. Determine the slope. Interpret the meaning of the slope in the context of this problem.

14. For a recent year, children's admission to the Minnesota State Fair was $8. Ride tickets were $0.75 each. The equation $y = 0.75x + 8$ represented the cost, y, in dollars to be admitted to the fair and to purchase x ride tickets.

  a. Determine the slope of the line represented by $y = 0.75x + 8$. Interpret the meaning of the slope in the context of this problem.

  b. Determine the y-intercept. Interpret its meaning in the context of this problem.

  c. Use the equation to determine how much money a child needed for admission and to ride 10 rides.

Objective 2: Writing a Linear Equation Using Observed Data Points

15. The average length of stay for community hospitals decreased in the United States from 1980 to 2005. Let x represent the number of years since 1980. Let y represent the average length of a hospital stay in days. **(See Example 2.)**

  a. Find a linear equation that relates the average length of hospital stays versus the year.

  b. Use the linear equation found in part (a) to predict the average length of stay in community hospitals in the year 2010. Round to the nearest day.

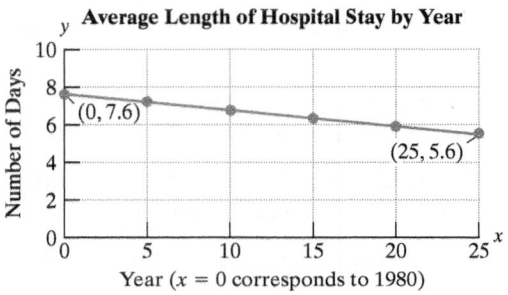

16. The figure depicts a relationship between a person's height, y (in inches), and the length of the person's arm, x (measured in inches from shoulder to wrist).

  a. Use the points $(17, 57.75)$ and $(24, 82.25)$ to find a linear equation relating height to arm length.

  b. What is the slope of the line? Interpret the slope in the context of this problem.

  c. Use the equation from part (a) to estimate the height of a person whose arm length is 21.5 in.

17. The graph shows the average height for boys based on age. Let x represent a boy's age and let y represent his height (in inches).

  a. Find a linear equation that represents the height of a boy versus his age.

  b. Use the linear equation found in part (a) to predict the average height of a 5-year-old boy.

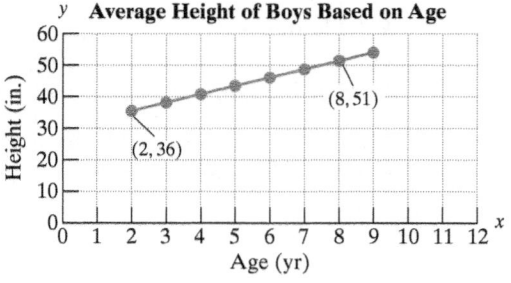

(*Source:* National Parenting Council)

18. Wind energy is one type of renewable energy that does not produce dangerous greenhouse gases as a by-product. The graph shows the consumption of wind energy in the United States for selected years. The variable y represents the amount of wind energy in trillions of Btu, and the variable x represents the number of years since 2000.

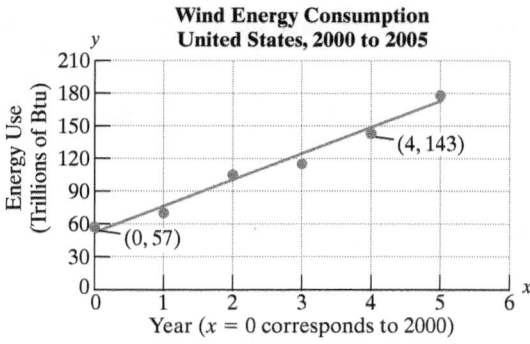

Wind Energy Consumption United States, 2000 to 2005

(4, 143)
(0, 57)
Year ($x = 0$ corresponds to 2000)

(*Source:* United States Department of Energy)

a. Use the points $(0, 57)$ and $(4, 143)$ to determine the slope of the line.

b. Interpret the slope in the context of this problem?

c. Use the points $(0, 57)$ and $(4, 143)$ to find a linear equation relating the consumption of wind energy, y, to the number of years, x, since 2000.

d. If this linear trend continues beyond the observed data values, use the equation in part (c) to predict the consumption of wind energy in the year 2010.

Objective 3: Writing a Linear Equation Given a Fixed Value and a Rate of Change

19. The cost to rent a car, y, for 1 day is $20 plus $0.25 per mile. **(See Example 3.)**

a. Write a linear equation to compute the cost, y, of driving a car x miles for 1 day.

b. Use the equation to compute the cost of driving 258 miles in the rental car for 1 day.

20. A phone bill is determined each month by a $18.95 flat fee plus $0.08 per minute of long distance.

a. Write a linear equation to compute the monthly cost of a phone bill, y, if x minutes of long distance are used.

b. Use the equation to compute the phone bill for a month in which 1 hr and 27 min of long distance was used.

21. The cost to rent a 10 ft by 10 ft storage space is $90 per month plus a nonrefundable deposit of $105.

a. Write a linear equation to compute the cost, y, of renting a 10 ft by 10 ft space for x months.

b. What is the cost of renting such a storage space for 1 year (12 months)?

22. An air-conditioning and heating company has a fixed monthly cost of $5000. Furthermore, each service call costs the company $25.

a. Write a linear equation to compute the total cost, y, for 1 month if x service calls are made.

b. Use the equation to compute the cost for 1 month if 150 service calls are made.

23. A bakery that specializes in bread rents a booth at a flea market. The daily cost to rent the booth is $100. Each loaf of bread costs the bakery $0.80 to produce.

a. Write a linear equation to compute the total cost, y, for 1 day if x loaves of bread are produced.

b. Use the equation to compute the cost for 1 day if 200 loaves of bread are produced.

24. A beverage company rents a booth at an art show to sell lemonade. The daily cost to rent a booth is $35. Each lemonade costs $0.50 to produce.

a. Write a linear equation to compute the total cost, y, for 1 day if x lemonades are produced.

b. Use the equation to compute the cost for 1 day if 350 lemonades are produced.

Group Activity

Modeling a Linear Equation

Materials: Yardstick or other device for making linear measurements

Estimated Time: 15–20 minutes

Group Size: 3

1. The members of each group should measure the length of their arms (in inches) from elbow to wrist. Record this measurement as x and the person's height (in inches) as y. Write these values as ordered pairs for each member of the group. Then write the ordered pairs on the board.

2. Next, copy the ordered pairs collected from all groups in the class and plot the ordered pairs. (This is called a "scatter diagram.")

3. Select two ordered pairs that seem to follow the upward trend of the data. Using these data points, determine the slope of the line.

   Slope: _____

4. Using the data points and slope from question 3, find an equation of the line through the two points. Write the equation in slope-intercept form, $y = mx + b$.

   Equation: _____

5. Using the equation from question 4, estimate the height of a person whose arm length from elbow to wrist is 8.5 in.

6. Suppose a crime scene investigator uncovers a partial skeleton and identifies a bone as a human ulna. (The ulna is one of two bones in the forearm and extends from elbow to wrist.) If the length of the bone is 12 in., estimate the height of the person before death. Would you expect this person to be male or female?

Chapter 10   Summary

Section 10.1   Rectangular Coordinate System

Key Concepts

Graphical representation of numerical **data** is often helpful to study problems in real-world applications.

    A **rectangular coordinate system** is made up of a horizontal line called the **x-axis** and a vertical line called the **y-axis**. The point where the lines meet is the **origin**. The four regions of the plane are called **quadrants**.

    The point (x, y) is an **ordered pair**. The first element in the ordered pair is the point's horizontal position from the origin. The second element in the ordered pair is the point's vertical position from the origin.

Example

Example 1

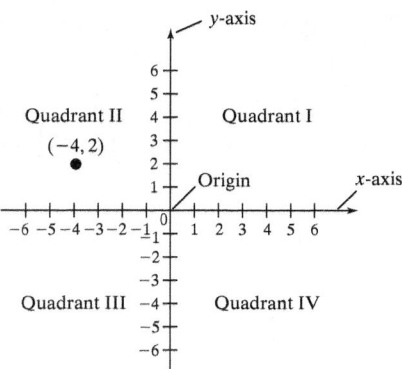

Section 10.2 Linear Equations in Two Variables

Key Concepts

An equation written in the form $Ax + By = C$ (where A and B are not both zero) is a **linear equation in two variables**.

A solution to a linear equation in x and y is an ordered pair (x, y) that makes the equation a true statement. The graph of the set of all solutions of a linear equation in two variables is a line in a rectangular coordinate system.

A linear equation can be graphed by finding at least two solutions and graphing the line through the points.

Examples

Example 1

Graph the equation $2x + y = 2$.

Select arbitrary values of x or y such as those shown in the table. Then complete the table to find the corresponding ordered pairs.

x	y	
0	2	$\longrightarrow (0, 2)$
-1	4	$\longrightarrow (-1, 4)$
1	0	$\longrightarrow (1, 0)$

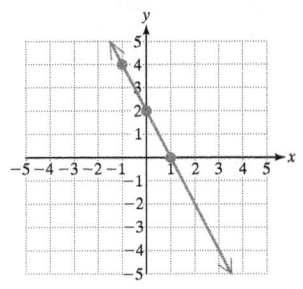

Example 2

For the line $2x + y = 2$, the x-intercept is $(1, 0)$ and the y-intercept is $(0, 2)$.

An **x-intercept** of a graph is a point $(a, 0)$ where the graph intersects the x-axis.
A **y-intercept** of a graph is a point $(0, b)$ where the graph intersects the y-axis.

A **vertical line** can be represented by an equation of the form $x = k$.
A **horizontal line** can be represented by an equation of the form $y = k$.

Example 3

$x = 3$ represents a vertical line

$y = 3$ represents a horizontal line

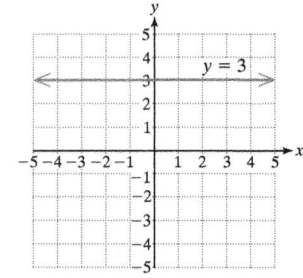

Section 10.3   Slope of a Line and Rate of Change

Key Concepts

The **slope**, m, of a line between two points (x_1, y_1) and (x_2, y_2) is given by

$$m = \frac{y_2 - y_1}{x_2 - x_1} \quad \text{or} \quad \frac{\text{change in } y}{\text{change in } x}$$

The slope of a line may be positive, negative, zero, or undefined.

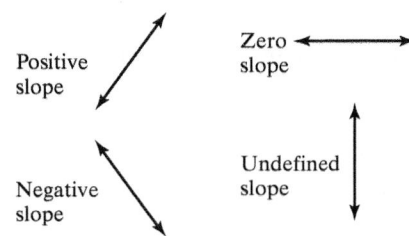

If m_1 and m_2 represent the slopes of two **parallel lines** (nonvertical), then $m_1 = m_2$.

If $m_1 \neq 0$ and $m_2 \neq 0$ represent the slopes of two nonvertical **perpendicular lines**, then

$$m_1 = -\frac{1}{m_2} \quad \text{or equivalently, } m_1 m_2 = -1.$$

Examples

Example 1

Find the slope of the line between $(1, -5)$ and $(-3, 7)$.

$$m = \frac{7 - (-5)}{-3 - 1} = \frac{12}{-4} = -3$$

Example 2

The slope of the line $y = -2$ is 0 because the line is horizontal.

Example 3

The slope of the line $x = 4$ is undefined because the line is vertical.

Example 4

The slopes of two distinct lines are given. Determine whether the lines are parallel, perpendicular, or neither.

a. $m_1 = -7$ and $m_2 = -7$ Parallel

b. $m_1 = -\dfrac{1}{5}$ and $m_2 = 5$ Perpendicular

c. $m_1 = -\dfrac{3}{2}$ and $m_2 = -\dfrac{2}{3}$ Neither

Section 10.4   Slope-Intercept Form of a Line

Key Concepts

The **slope-intercept form** of a line is

$$y = mx + b$$

where m is the slope of the line and $(0, b)$ is the y-intercept.

Slope-intercept form is used to identify the slope and y-intercept of a line when the equation is given.

Slope-intercept form can also be used to graph a line.

Examples

Example 1

Find the slope and y-intercept.

$7x - 2y = 4$

$\quad -2y = -7x + 4 \qquad$ Solve for y.

$$\frac{-2y}{-2} = \frac{-7x}{-2} + \frac{4}{-2}$$

$$y = \frac{7}{2}x - 2$$

The slope is $\frac{7}{2}$. The y-intercept is $(0, -2)$.

Example 2

Graph the line.

$$y = \frac{7}{2}x - 2$$

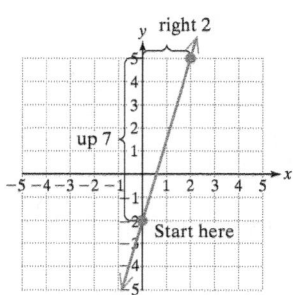

Section 10.5   Point-Slope Formula

Key Concepts

The **point-slope formula** is used primarily to construct an equation of a line given a point and the slope.

Equations of Lines—A Summary:

Standard form: $Ax + By = C$
Horizontal line: $y = k$
Vertical line: $x = k$
Slope-intercept form: $y = mx + b$
Point-slope formula: $y - y_1 = m(x - x_1)$

Examples

Example 1

Find an equation of the line passing through the point $(6, -4)$ and having a slope of $-\frac{1}{2}$.

Label the given information:
$m = -\frac{1}{2}$ and $(x_1, y_1) = (6, -4)$

$$y - y_1 = m(x - x_1)$$

$$y - (-4) = -\frac{1}{2}(x - 6)$$

$$y + 4 = -\frac{1}{2}x + 3$$

$$y = -\frac{1}{2}x - 1$$

Section 10.6   Applications of Linear Equations and Modeling

Key Concepts

Linear equations can often be used to describe or model the relationship between variables in a real-world event. In such applications, the slope may be interpreted as a rate of change.

Examples

Example 1

The number of drug-related arrests for a small city has been growing approximately linearly since 1980.

Let y represent the number of drug arrests, and let x represent the number of years after 1980.

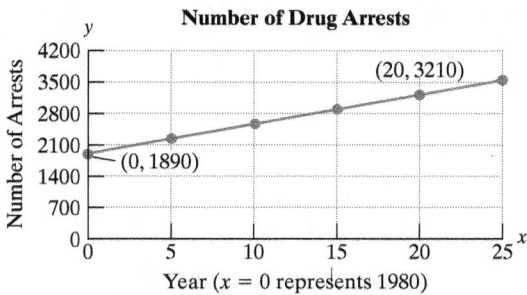

Number of Drug Arrests

Year ($x = 0$ represents 1980)

a. Use the ordered pairs (0, 1890) and (20, 3210) to find an equation of the line shown in the graph.

$$m = \frac{y_2 - y_1}{x_2 - x_1} = \frac{3210 - 1890}{20 - 0}$$

$$= \frac{1320}{20} = 66$$

The slope is 66, indicating that the number of drug arrests is increasing at a rate of 66 per year. $m = 66$, and the y-intercept is (0, 1890). Hence:

$$y = mx + b \implies y = 66x + 1890$$

b. Use the equation in part (a) to predict the number of drug-related arrests in the year 2010. (The year 2010 is 30 years after 1980. Hence, $x = 30$.)

$$y = 66(30) + 1890$$

$$y = 3870$$

The number of drug arrests is predicted to be 3870 by the year 2010.

Chapter 10 Review Exercises

Section 10.1

1. Graph the points on a rectangular coordinate system.

   a. $\left(\frac{1}{2}, 5\right)$ b. $(-1, 4)$ c. $(2, -1)$

   d. $(0, 3)$ e. $(0, 0)$ f. $\left(-\frac{8}{5}, 0\right)$

   g. $(-2, -5)$ h. $(3, 1)$

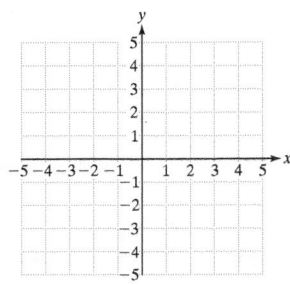

2. Estimate the coordinates of the points A, B, C, D, E, and F.

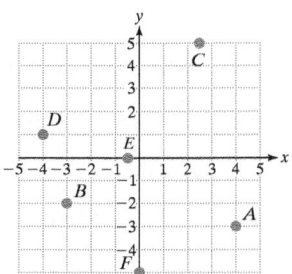

For Exercises 3–8, determine the quadrant in which the given point is found.

3. $(-2, -10)$ 4. $(-4, 6)$

5. $(3, -5)$ 6. $\left(\frac{1}{2}, \frac{7}{5}\right)$

7. $(\pi, -2.7)$ 8. $(-1.2, -6.8)$

9. On which axis is the point $(2, 0)$ found?

10. On which axis is the point $(0, -3)$ found?

11. The price per share of a stock (in dollars) over a period of 5 days is shown in the graph.

   a. Interpret the meaning of the ordered pair $(1, 26.25)$.

   b. On which day was the price the highest?

   c. What was the increase in price between day 1 and day 2?

12. The number of space shuttle launches for selected years is given by the ordered pairs. Let x represent the number of years since 1995. Let y represent the number of launches.

   $(1, 7)$ $(2, 8)$ $(3, 5)$ $(4, 3)$

   $(5, 5)$ $(6, 6)$ $(7, 5)$ $(8, 1)$

   a. Interpret the meaning of the ordered pair $(8, 1)$.

   b. Plot the points on a rectangular coordinate system.

Section 10.2

For Exercises 13–16, determine if the given ordered pair is a solution to the equation.

13. $5x - 3y = 12$; $(0, 4)$

14. $2x - 4y = -6$; $(3, 0)$

15. $y = \dfrac{1}{3}x - 2$; $(9, 1)$

16. $y = -\dfrac{2}{5}x + 1$; $(-10, 5)$

For Exercises 17–20, complete the table and graph the corresponding ordered pairs. Graph the line through the points to represent all solutions to the equation.

17. $3x - y = 5$

x	y
2	
	4
1	

18. $\dfrac{1}{2}x + 3y = 6$

x	y
	2
-2	
	3

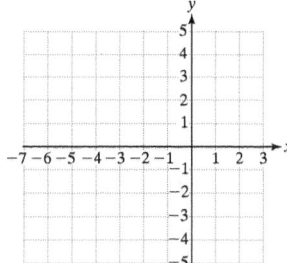

19. $y = \dfrac{2}{3}x - 1$

x	y
0	
3	
-6	

20. $y = -2x - 3$

x	y
0	
-3	
1	

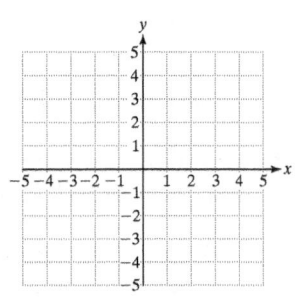

For Exercises 21–24, graph the equation.

21. $x + 2y = 4$

22. $x - y = 5$

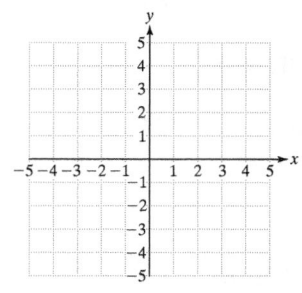

23. $y = 3x$

24. $y = \dfrac{1}{4}x$

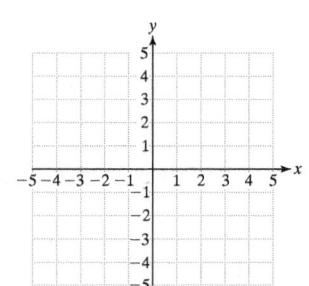

For Exercises 25–28, identify the line as horizontal or vertical. Then graph the equation.

25. $3x - 2 = 10$

26. $2x + 1 = -2$

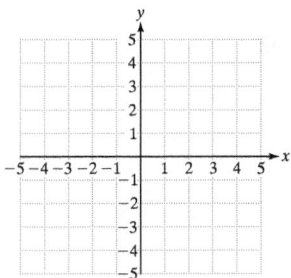

27. $6y + 1 = 13$

28. $5y - 1 = 14$

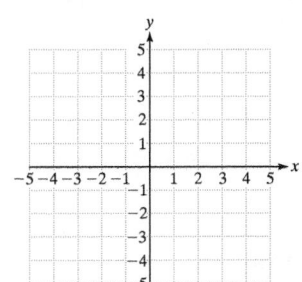

For Exercises 29–36, find the x- and y-intercepts if they exist.

29. $-4x + 8y = 12$ **30.** $2x + y = 6$

31. $y = 8x$ **32.** $5x - y = 0$

33. $6y = -24$ **34.** $2y - 3 = 1$

35. $2x + 5 = 0$ **36.** $-3x + 1 = 0$

Section 10.3

37. What is the slope of the ladder leaning up against the wall?

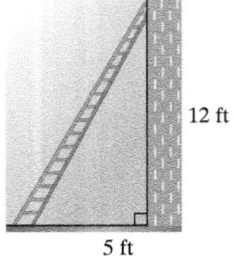

12 ft

5 ft

38. Point A is located 4 units down and 2 units to the right of point B. What is the slope of the line through points A and B?

39. Determine the slope of the line that passes through the points $(7, -9)$ and $(-5, -1)$.

40. Determine the slope of the line that has x- and y-intercepts of $(-1, 0)$ and $(0, 8)$.

41. Determine the slope of the line that passes through the points $(3, 0)$ and $(3, -7)$.

42. Determine the slope of the line given by $y = -1$.

43. A given line has a slope of -5.

   a. What is the slope of a line parallel to the given line?

   b. What is the slope of a line perpendicular to the given line?

44. A given line has a slope of 0.

   a. What is the slope of a line parallel to the given line?

   b. What is the slope of a line perpendicular to the given line?

For Exercises 45–48, find the slopes of the lines l_1 and l_2 from the two given points. Then determine whether l_1 and l_2 are parallel, perpendicular, or neither.

45. l_1: $(3, 7)$ and $(0, 5)$

   l_2: $(6, 3)$ and $(-3, -3)$

46. l_1: $(-2, 1)$ and $(-1, 9)$

   l_2: $(0, -6)$ and $(2, 10)$

47. l_1: $(0, \frac{5}{6})$ and $(2, 0)$

   l_2: $(0, \frac{6}{3})$ and $(-\frac{1}{2}, 0)$

48. l_1: $(1, 1)$ and $(1, -8)$

   l_2: $(4, -5)$ and $(7, -5)$

Section 10.4

For Exercises 49–54, write each equation in slope-intercept form. Identify the slope and the y-intercept.

49. $5x - 2y = 10$ **50.** $3x + 4y = 12$

51. $x - 3y = 0$ **52.** $5y - 8 = 4$

53. $2y = -5$ **54.** $y - x = 0$

For Exercises 55–59, determine whether the equations represent parallel lines, perpendicular lines, or neither.

55. l_1: $y = \dfrac{3}{5}x + 3$ **56.** l_1: $2x - 5y = 10$

   l_2: $y = \dfrac{5}{3}x + 1$ l_2: $5x + 2y = 20$

57. l_1: $3x + 2y = 6$ **58.** l_1: $y = \dfrac{1}{4}x - 3$

   l_2: $-6x - 4y = 4$ l_2: $-x + 4y = 8$

59. l_1: $2x = 4$

   l_2: $y = 6$

60. Write an equation of the line whose slope is $-\frac{4}{3}$ and whose y-intercept is $(0, -1)$.

61. Write an equation of the line that passes through the origin and has a slope of 5.

Section 10.5

62. Write a linear equation in two variables in slope-intercept form. (Answers may vary.)

63. Write a linear equation in two variables in standard form. (Answers may vary.)

64. Write the slope formula to find the slope of the line between the points (x_1, y_1) and (x_2, y_2).

65. Write the point-slope formula.

66. Write an equation of a vertical line (answers may vary).

67. Write an equation of a horizontal line (answers may vary).

For Exercises 68–73, write an equation of a line given the following information.

68. The slope is -6, and the line passes through the point $(-1, 8)$.

69. The slope is $\frac{2}{3}$, and the line passes through the point $(5, 5)$.

70. The line passes through the points $(0, -4)$ and $(8, -2)$.

71. The line passes through the points $(2, -5)$ and $(8, -5)$.

72. The line passes through the point $(5, 12)$ and is perpendicular to the line $y = -\frac{5}{6}x - 3$.

73. The line passes through the point $(-6, 7)$ and is parallel to the line $4x - y = 0$.

Section 10.6

74. The graph shows the average height for girls based on age. (*Source:* National Parenting Council) Let x represent a girl's age, and let y represent her height (in inches).

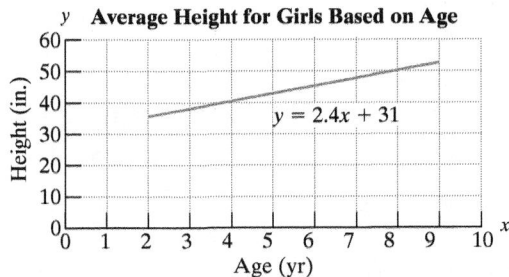

a. Use the equation to estimate the average height of a 7-year-old girl.

b. What is the slope of the line? Interpret the meaning of the slope in the context of the problem.

75. The number of drug prescriptions has increased between 1995 and 2007 (see graph). Let x represent the number of years since 1995. Let y represent the number of prescriptions (in millions).

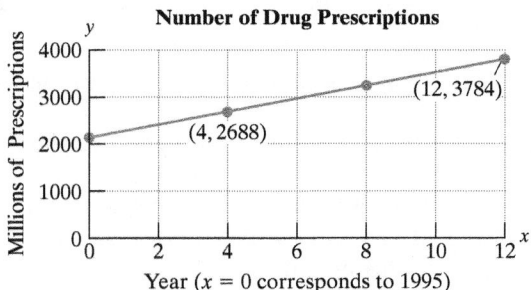

a. Using the ordered pairs $(4, 2688)$ and $(12, 3784)$ find the slope of the line.

b. Interpret the meaning of the slope in the context of this problem.

c. Find a linear equation that represents the number of prescriptions, y, versus the year, x.

d. Predict the number of prescriptions for the year 2010.

76. A water purification company charges $20 per month and a $55 installation fee.

a. Write a linear equation to compute the total cost, y, of renting this system for x months.

b. Use the equation from part (a) to determine the total cost to rent the system for 9 months.

77. A small cleaning company has a fixed monthly cost of $700 and a variable cost of $8 per service call.

a. Write a linear equation to compute the total cost, y, of making x service calls in one month.

b. Use the equation from part (a) to determine the total cost of making 80 service calls.

Chapter 10   Test

1. In which quadrant is the given point found?

    a. $\left(-\dfrac{7}{2}, 4\right)$ **b.** $(4.6, -2)$ **c.** $(-37, -45)$

2. What is the y-coordinate for a point on the x-axis?

3. What is the x-coordinate for a point on the y-axis?

4. The following table depicts a boy's height versus his age. Let x represent the boy's age and y represent his height.

Age (years), x	Height (inches), y
5	46
7	50
9	55
11	60

    a. Write the data as ordered pairs and interpret the meaning of the first ordered pair.

    b. Graph the ordered pairs on a rectangular coordinate system.

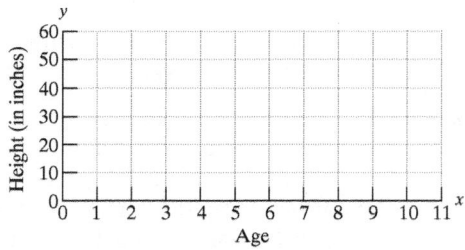

    c. From the graph and table estimate the boy's height at age 10.

    d. The data appear to follow an upward trend up to the boy's teenage years. Do you think this trend will continue? Would it be reasonable to use these data to predict the boy's height at age 25?

5. Determine whether the ordered pair is a solution to the equation $2x - y = 6$.

    a. $(0, 6)$ **b.** $(4, 2)$

    c. $(3, 0)$ **d.** $\left(\dfrac{9}{2}, 3\right)$

6. Given the equation $y = \frac{1}{4}x - 2$, complete the table. Plot the ordered pairs and graph the line through the points to represent the set of all solutions to the equation.

x	y
0	
4	
6	

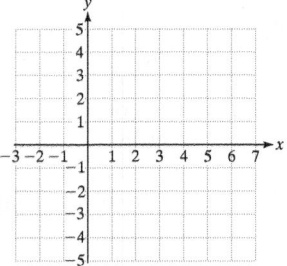

7. If x represents an adult's age, then the person's maximum recommended heart rate, y, during exercise is approximated by the equation

$$y = 220 - x \quad (x \geq 18)$$

    a. Use the equation to find the maximum recommended heart rate for a person who is 18 years old.

    b. Use the equation to complete the following ordered pairs: $(20, \quad)$, $(30, \quad)$, $(40, \quad)$, $(50, \quad)$, $(60, \quad)$.

For Exercises 8–9, determine whether the equation represents a horizontal or vertical line. Then graph the line.

8. $-6y = 18$ **9.** $5x + 1 = 8$

 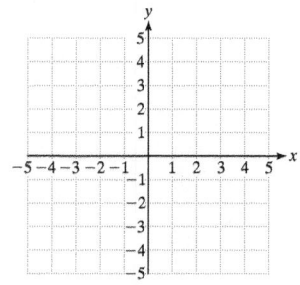

For Exercises 10–13, determine the x- and y-intercepts if they exist.

10. $-4x + 3y = 6$ **11.** $2y = 6x$

12. $x = 4$ **13.** $y - 3 = 0$

14. What is the slope of the hill?

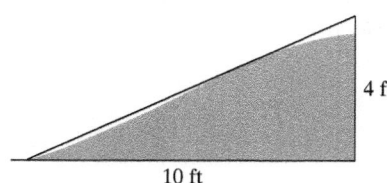

4 ft

10 ft

15. a. Find the slope of the line that passes through the points $(-2, 0)$ and $(-5, -1)$.

   b. Find the slope of the line $4x - 3y = 9$.

16. a. What is the slope of a line parallel to the line $x + 4y = -16$?

   b. What is the slope of a line perpendicular to the line $x + 4y = -16$?

17. a. What is the slope of the line $x = 5$?

   b. What is the slope of the line $y = -3$?

For Exercises 18–19, graph the equations.

18. $y = 8x + 2$

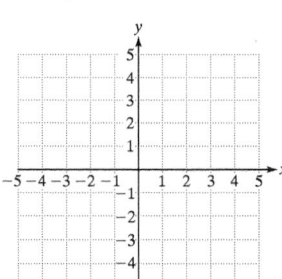

19. $2x + 9y = 0$

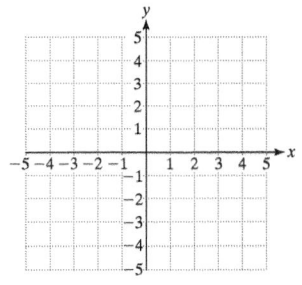

20. Determine whether the equations represent parallel lines, perpendicular lines, or neither.

l_1: $2y = 3x - 3$ l_2: $4x = -6y + 1$

21. Write an equation of the line that has y-intercept $(0, \frac{1}{2})$ and slope $\frac{1}{4}$.

22. Write an equation of the line that passes through the points $(2, 8)$, and $(4, 1)$.

23. Write an equation of the line that passes through the point $(2, -6)$ and is parallel to the x-axis.

24. Write an equation of the line that passes through the point $(3, 0)$ and is parallel to the line $2x + 6y = -5$.

25. Write an equation of the line that passes through the point $(-3, -1)$ and is perpendicular to the line $x + 3y = 9$.

26. Hurricane Floyd dumped rain at an average rate of $\frac{3}{4}$ in./hr on Southport, North Carolina. Further inland, in Lumberton, North Carolina, the storm dropped $\frac{1}{2}$ in. of rain per hour. The following graph depicts the total amount of rainfall (in inches) versus the time (in hours) for both locations in North Carolina.

a. What is the slope of the line representing the rainfall for Southport?

b. What is the slope of the line representing the rainfall for Lumberton?

27. To attend a state fair, the cost is $10 per person to cover exhibits and musical entertainment. There is an additional cost of $1.50 per ride.

a. Write an equation that gives the total cost, y, of visiting the state fair and going on x rides.

b. Use the equation from part (a) to determine the cost of going to the state fair and going on 10 rides.

28. The number of medical doctors for selected years is shown in the graph. Let x represent the number of years since 1980, and let y represent the number of medical doctors (in thousands) in the United States.

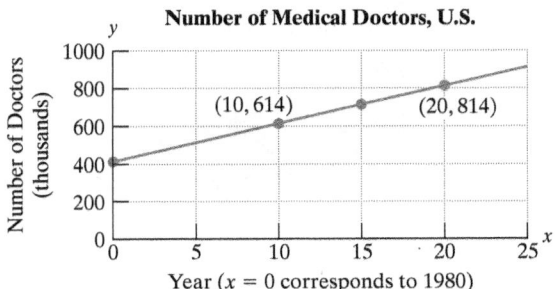

a. Find the slope of the line shown in the graph. Interpret the meaning of the slope in the context of this problem.

b. Find an equation of the line.

c. Use the equation from part (b) to predict the number of medical doctors in the United States for the year 2010.

Chapters 1–10   Cumulative Review Exercises

1. Identify the numbers as rational or irrational.

  a. -3 **b.** $\dfrac{5}{4}$ **c.** $\sqrt{10}$ **d.** 0

2. Write the opposite and the absolute value for each number.

  a. $-\dfrac{2}{3}$ **b.** 5.3

3. Simplify. $32 \div 2 \cdot 4 + 5$

For Exercises 4–5, translate the English phrase into an algebraic expression. Then evaluate the expression.

4. The quotient of $\dfrac{3}{4}$ and $-\dfrac{7}{8}$.

5. The product of -2.1 and -6.

6. Find the length of the missing side.

7. Find the area and perimeter.

8. Julie's favorite dark chocolate comes in 12-oz packages for $3.89. Find the unit cost to the nearest tenth of a cent.

For Exercises 9–12, solve the equation.

9. $6x - 10 = 14$ **10.** $3(m + 2) - 3 = 2m + 8$

11. $\dfrac{2}{3}y - \dfrac{1}{6} = y + \dfrac{4}{3}$ **12.** $1.7z + 2 = -2(0.3z + 1.3)$

13. The area of Texas is $267{,}277$ mi^2. If this is 712 mi^2 less than 29 times the area of Maine, find the area of Maine.

14. For the formula $3a + b = c$, solve for a.

15. Graph the equation $-6x + 2y = 0$.

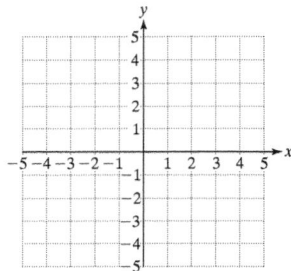

16. Find the x- and y-intercepts of $-2x + 4y = 4$.

17. Write the equation in slope-intercept form. Then identify the slope and the y-intercept.
$3x + 2y = -12$

18. Explain why the line $2x + 3 = 5$ has only one intercept.

19. Find an equation of a line passing through $(2, -5)$ with slope -3.

20. Find an equation of the line passing through $(0, 6)$ and $(-3, 4)$.

Systems of Linear Equations in Two Variables

11

Chapter 11

This chapter is devoted to solving systems of linear equations and inequalities. We will present a graphical method for solving systems and two algebraic methods. Applications of systems of equations in two variables involve two variables that are subject to two conditions.

Are You Prepared?

To prepare yourself, consider this example. At a movie theater, one group of students bought three drinks and two small popcorns for a total of $18.00 (excluding tax). Another group bought five drinks and three popcorns for $28.50. There are two unknown quantities in this scenario: the cost per drink and the cost per popcorn.

Fill in the blanks below using trial and error to determine the cost per drink and the cost per popcorn. You have the correct answer if both equations are true.

In this column, fill in the cost per drink.

In this column, fill in the cost per popcorn.

$$3(\boxed{}) + 2(\boxed{}) \overset{?}{=} \$18.00$$
$$5(\boxed{}) + 3(\boxed{}) \overset{?}{=} \$28.50$$

Are these both true?

If you have trouble with this puzzle, don't fret. Later in the chapter, we'll use the power of algebra to set up and solve a system of equations that will take the guess work away!

Section 11.1 Solving Systems of Equations by the Graphing Method

Objectives

1. Determining Solutions to a System of Linear Equations
2. Solving Systems of Linear Equations by Graphing

1. Determining Solutions to a System of Linear Equations

Recall from Section 10.2 that a linear equation in two variables has an infinite number of solutions. The set of all solutions to a linear equation forms a line in a rectangular coordinate system. Two or more linear equations form a **system of linear equations**. For example, here are three systems of equations:

$$x - 3y = -5 \qquad y = \tfrac{1}{4}x - \tfrac{3}{4} \qquad 5a + b = 4$$
$$2x + 4y = 10 \qquad -2x + 8y = -6 \qquad -10a - 2b = 8$$

A **solution to a system of linear equations** is an ordered pair that is a solution to *both* individual linear equations.

Skill Practice

Determine whether the ordered pair is a solution to the system.

$5x - 2y = 24$
$2x + y = 6$

1. $(6, 3)$

2. $(4, -2)$

Example 1 Determining Solutions to a System of Linear Equations

Determine whether the ordered pairs are solutions to the system.

$$x + y = 4$$
$$-2x + y = -5$$

a. $(3, 1)$ **b.** $(0, 4)$

Solution:

a. Substitute the ordered pair $(3, 1)$ into both equations:

$$x + y = 4 \longrightarrow (3) + (1) \overset{?}{=} 4 \checkmark \qquad \text{True}$$
$$-2x + y = -5 \longrightarrow -2(3) + (1) \overset{?}{=} -5 \checkmark \qquad \text{True}$$

Avoiding Mistakes

It is important to test an ordered pair in *both* equations to determine if the ordered pair is a solution.

Because the ordered pair $(3, 1)$ is a solution to each equation, it is a solution to the *system* of equations.

b. Substitute the ordered pair $(0, 4)$ into both equations.

$$x + y = 4 \longrightarrow (0) + (4) \overset{?}{=} 4 \checkmark \qquad \text{True}$$
$$-2x + y = -5 \longrightarrow -2(0) + (4) \overset{?}{=} -5 \qquad \text{False}$$

Because the ordered pair $(0, 4)$ is not a solution to the second equation, it is *not* a solution to the system of equations.

A solution to a system of two linear equations may be interpreted graphically as a point of intersection of the two lines. Using slope-intercept form to graph the lines from Example 1, we have

$$x + y = 4 \longrightarrow y = -x + 4$$
$$-2x + y = -5 \longrightarrow y = 2x - 5$$

Notice that the lines intersect at $(3, 1)$ (Figure 11-1).

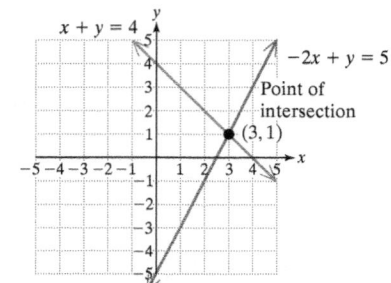

Figure 11-1

Answers

1. No
2. Yes

When two lines are drawn in a rectangular coordinate system, three geometric relationships are possible:

1. Two lines may intersect at *exactly one point.*

2. Two lines may intersect at *no point.* This occurs if the lines are parallel.

3. Two lines may intersect at *infinitely many points* along the line. This occurs if the equations represent the same line (the lines coincide).

┌─ **Concept Connections** ─
3. If the linear equations in a system represent a pair of parallel lines, how many solutions does the system have?
4. If the linear equations in a system represent a pair of perpendicular lines, how many solutions does the system have?

If a system of linear equations has one or more solutions, the system is said to be **consistent.** If a system of linear equations has no solution, it is said to be **inconsistent.**

If two equations represent the same line, the equations are said to be **dependent equations.** In this case, all points on the line are solutions to the system. If two equations represent two different lines, the equations are said to be **independent equations.** In this case, the lines either intersect at one point or are parallel, so the system has either one unique solution or no solution.

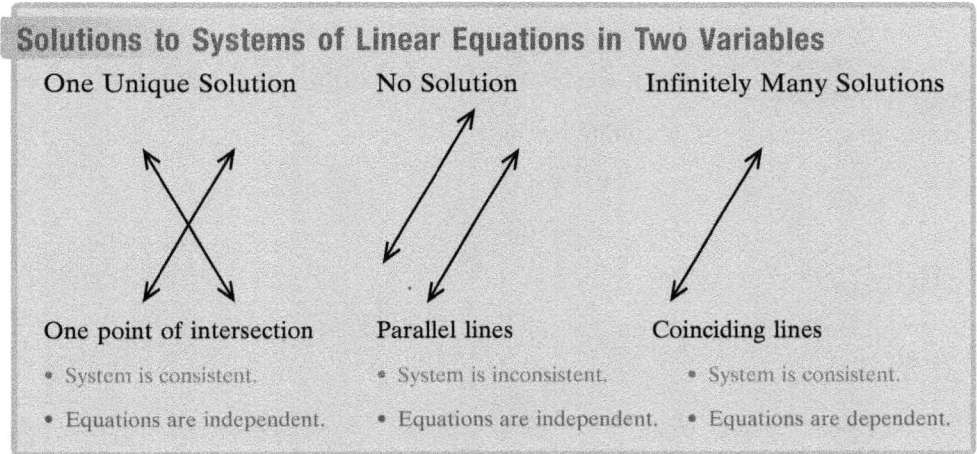

Solutions to Systems of Linear Equations in Two Variables

One Unique Solution

No Solution

Infinitely Many Solutions

One point of intersection

Parallel lines

Coinciding lines

- System is consistent.
- Equations are independent.

- System is inconsistent.
- Equations are independent.

- System is consistent.
- Equations are dependent.

2. Solving Systems of Linear Equations by Graphing

One way to find a solution to a system of equations is to graph the equations and find the point (or points) of intersection. This is called the *graphing method* to solve a system of equations.

Answers

3. Zero **4.** One

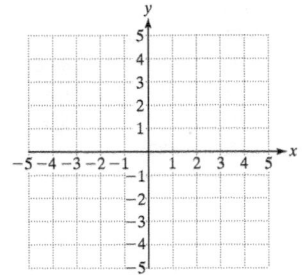
Example 2   Solving a System of Linear Equations by Graphing

Solve the system by the graphing method. $y = 2x$
$$y = 2$$

Solution:

The equation $y = 2x$ is written in slope-intercept form as $y = 2x + 0$. The line passes through the origin, with a slope of 2.

The line $y = 2$ is a horizontal line and has a slope of 0.

Because the lines have different slopes, the lines must be different and nonparallel. From this, we know that the lines must intersect at exactly one point. Graph the lines to find the point of intersection (Figure 11-2).

The point (1, 2) appears to be the point of intersection. This can be confirmed by substituting $x = 1$ and $y = 2$ into both original equations.

$$y = 2x \qquad (2) \overset{?}{=} 2(1) \; ✔ \quad \text{True}$$
$$y = 2 \qquad (2) \overset{?}{=} 2 \; ✔ \quad \text{True}$$

Figure 11-2

The solution is (1, 2).

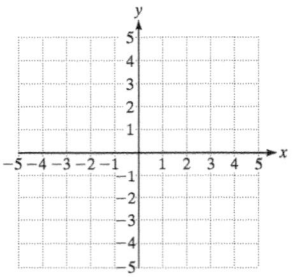
Example 3   Solving a System of Linear Equations by Graphing

Solve the system by the graphing method.

$$x - 2y = -2$$
$$-3x + 2y = 6$$

Solution:

To graph each equation, write the equation in slope-intercept form: $y = mx + b$.

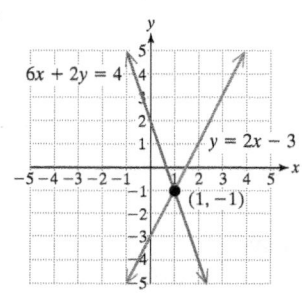
Equation 1

$$x - 2y = -2$$
$$-2y = -x - 2$$
$$\frac{-2y}{-2} = \frac{-x}{-2} - \frac{2}{-2}$$
$$y = \frac{1}{2}x + 1$$

Equation 2

$$-3x + 2y = 6$$
$$2y = 3x + 6$$
$$\frac{2y}{2} = \frac{3x}{2} + \frac{6}{2}$$
$$y = \frac{3}{2}x + 3$$

Figure 11-3

From their slope-intercept forms, we see that the lines have different slopes, indicating that the lines are different and nonparallel. Therefore, the lines must intersect at exactly one point. Graph the lines to find that point (Figure 11-3).

The point $(-2, 0)$ appears to be the point of intersection. This can be confirmed by substituting $x = -2$ and $y = 0$ into both equations.

$$x - 2y = -2 \longrightarrow (-2) - 2(0) \stackrel{?}{=} -2 \; ✔ \quad \text{True}$$

$$-3x + 2y = 6 \longrightarrow -3(-2) + 2(0) \stackrel{?}{=} 6 \; ✔ \quad \text{True}$$

The solution is $(-2, 0)$.

TIP: In Examples 2 and 3, the lines could also have been graphed by using the *x*- and *y*-intercepts or by using a table of points. However, the advantage of writing the equations in slope-intercept form is that we can compare the slopes and *y*-intercepts of the two lines.

1. If the slopes differ, the lines are different and nonparallel and must intersect at exactly one point.

2. If the slopes are the same and the *y*-intercepts are different, the lines are parallel and will not intersect.

3. If the slopes are the same and the *y*-intercepts are the same, the two equations represent the same line.

Example 4 **Graphing an Inconsistent System**

Solve the system by graphing.

$$-x + 3y = -6$$

$$6y = 2x + 6$$

Solution:

To graph the lines, write each equation in slope-intercept form.

Equation 1	**Equation 2**
$-x + 3y = -6$	$6y = 2x + 6$
$3y = x - 6$	
$\dfrac{3y}{3} = \dfrac{x}{3} - \dfrac{6}{3}$	$\dfrac{6y}{6} = \dfrac{2x}{6} + \dfrac{6}{6}$
$y = \dfrac{1}{3}x - 2$	$y = \dfrac{1}{3}x + 1$

Because the lines have the same slope but different *y*-intercepts, they are parallel (Figure 11-4). Two parallel lines do not intersect, which implies that the system has no solution. The system is inconsistent.

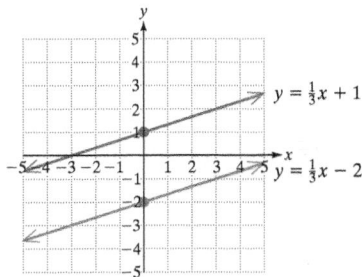

Figure 11-4

Solve the system by graphing.

7. $4x + y = 8$
   $y = -4x + 3$

Answer

7.

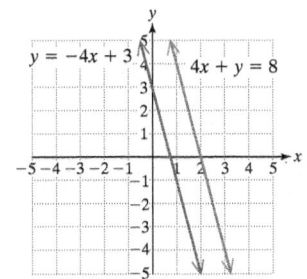

No solution; the lines are parallel. The system is inconsistent.

Skill Practice

Solve the system by graphing.

8. $x - 3y = 4$

$y = \dfrac{1}{3}x - \dfrac{4}{3}$

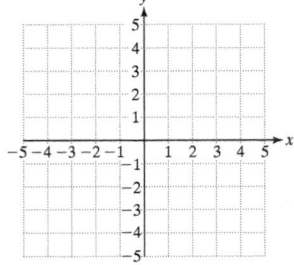

Example 5 **Graphing a System of Dependent Equations**

Solve the system by graphing.

$$x + 4y = 8$$

$$y = -\frac{1}{4}x + 2$$

Solution:

Write the first equation in slope-intercept form. The second equation is already in slope-intercept form.

Equation 1   **Equation 2**

$x + 4y = 8$ $y = -\dfrac{1}{4}x + 2$

$4y = -x + 8$

$\dfrac{4y}{4} = \dfrac{-x}{4} + \dfrac{8}{4}$

$y = -\dfrac{1}{4}x + 2$

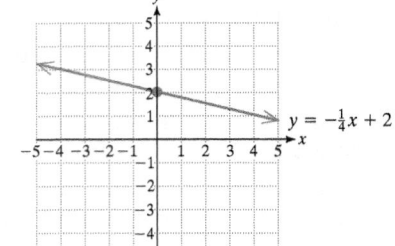

Figure 11-5

Notice that the slope-intercept forms of the two lines are identical. Therefore, the equations represent the same line (Figure 11-5). The equations are dependent, and the solution to the system of equations is the set of all points on the line.

Because the ordered pairs in the solution set cannot all be listed, we can write the solution in set-builder notation: $\{(x, y) \mid y = -\frac{1}{4}x + 2\}$. This can be read as "the set of all ordered pairs (x, y) such that the ordered pairs satisfy the equation $y = -\frac{1}{4}x + 2$."

In summary:

- There are infinitely many solutions to the system of equations.
- The solution set is $\{(x, y) \mid y = -\frac{1}{4}x + 2\}$.
- The equations are dependent.

Answer

8.

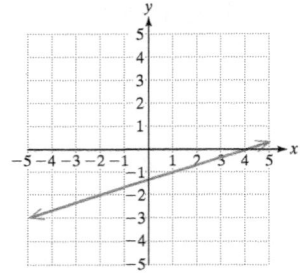

$$\left\{(x, y) \mid y = \frac{1}{3}x - \frac{4}{3}\right\}$$

The equations are dependent.

Calculator Connections

Topic: **Graphing Systems of Linear Equations in Two Variables**

The solution to a system of equations can be found by using either a *Trace* feature or an *Intersect* feature on a graphing calculator to find the point of intersection of two graphs.

For example, consider the system:

$$-2x + y = 6$$

$$5x + y = -1$$

First graph the equations together on the same viewing window. Recall that to enter the equations into the calculator, the equations must be written with the y-variable isolated.

Isolate y.

$-2x + y = 6 \longrightarrow y = 2x + 6$

$5x + y = -1 \longrightarrow y = -5x - 1$

By inspection of the graph, it appears that the solution is $(-1, 4)$. The *Trace* option on the calculator may come close to $(-1, 4)$ but may not show the exact solution (Figure 11-6). However, an *Intersect* feature on a graphing calculator may provide the exact solution (Figure 11-7). See your user's manual for further details.

Using *Trace*

Using *Intersect*

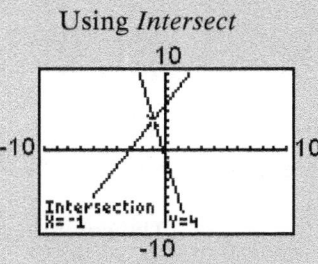

Figure 11-6   **Figure 11-7**

Calculator Exercises

Use a graphing calculator to graph each pair of linear equations on the same viewing window. Use a *Trace* or *Intersect* feature to find the point(s) of intersection, if any.

1. $y = 2x - 3$
$y = -4x + 9$

2. $y = -\frac{1}{2}x + 2$
$y = \frac{1}{3}x - 3$

3. $x + y = 4$ (Example 1)
$-2x + y = -5$

4. $x - 2y = -2$ (Example 3)
$-3x + 2y = 6$

5. $-x + 3y = -6$ (Example 4)
$6y = 2x + 6$

6. $x + 4y = 8$ (Example 5)
$y = -\frac{1}{4}x + 2$

Section 11.1 Practice Exercises

Study Skills Exercise

1. Define the key terms:

    a. System of linear equations
    b. Solution to a system of linear equations
    c. Consistent system

    d. Inconsistent system
    e. Dependent equations
    f. Independent equations

Objective 1: Determining Solutions to a System of Linear Equations

For Exercises 2–10, determine if the given point is a solution to the system. **(See Example 1.)**

2. $4x + y = 10$ $(1, 6)$
$-x + y = 5$

3. $3x - y = 7$ $(2, -1)$
$x - 2y = 4$

4. $x - y = 3$ $(4, 1)$
$x + y = 5$

5. $4y = -3x + 12$ $(0, 4)$
$y = \dfrac{2}{3}x - 4$

6. $y = -\dfrac{1}{3}x + 2$ $(9, -1)$
$x = 2y + 6$

7. $3x - 6y = 9$ $\left(4, \dfrac{1}{2}\right)$
$x - 2y = 3$

8. $x - y = 4$ $(6, 2)$
$3x - 3y = 12$

9. $\dfrac{1}{3}x = \dfrac{2}{5}y - \dfrac{4}{5}$ $(0, 2)$
$\dfrac{3}{4}x + \dfrac{1}{2}y = 2$

10. $\dfrac{1}{4}x + \dfrac{1}{2}y = \dfrac{3}{2}$ $(4, 1)$
$y = \dfrac{3}{2}x - 6$

For Exercises 11–14, match the graph of the system of equations with the appropriate description of the solution.

11.

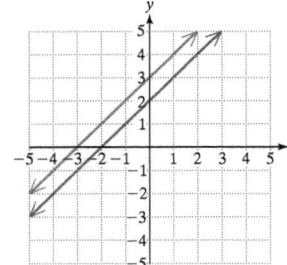

a. The solution is $(1, 3)$.

b. No solution.

c. There are infinitely many solutions.

d. The solution is $(0, 0)$.

12.

13.

14.

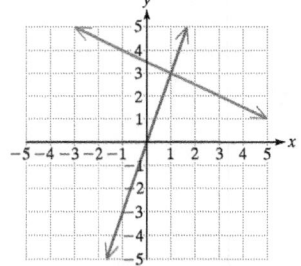

15. Graph each system of equations. **(See Examples 2–5.)**

a. $y = 2x - 3$
$y = 2x + 5$

b. $y = 2x + 1$
$y = 4x - 5$

c. $y = 3x - 5$
$y = 3x - 5$

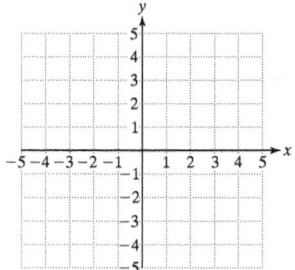

For Exercises 16–26, determine which system of equations (a, b, or c) makes the statement true. (*Hint:* Refer to the graphs from Exercise 15.)

a. $y = 2x - 3$ **b.** $y = 2x + 1$ **c.** $y = 3x - 5$

    $y = 2x + 5$ $y = 4x - 5$ $y = 3x - 5$

16. The lines are parallel.

17. The lines coincide.

18. The lines intersect at exactly one point.

19. The system is inconsistent.

20. The equations are dependent.

21. The lines have the same slope but different y-intercepts.

22. The lines have the same slope and same y-intercept.

23. The lines have different slopes.

24. The system has exactly one solution.

25. The system has infinitely many solutions.

26. The system has no solution.

Objective 2: Solving Systems of Linear Equations by Graphing

For Exercises 27–52, solve the systems by graphing. For systems that do not have one unique solution, state the number of solutions and whether the system is inconsistent or the equations are dependent. **(See Examples 2–5.)**

27. $y = -x + 4$

    $y = x - 2$

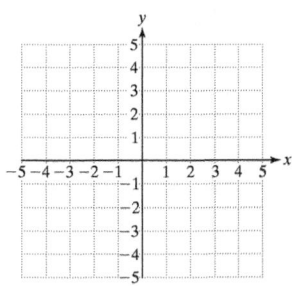

28. $y = 3x + 2$

    $y = 2x$

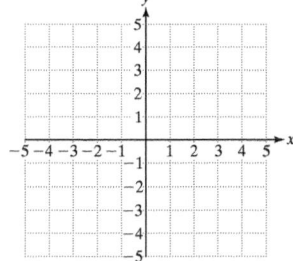

29. $2x + y = 0$

    $3x + y = 1$

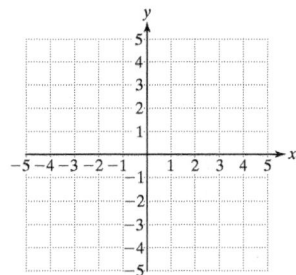

30. $x + y = -1$

    $2x - y = -5$

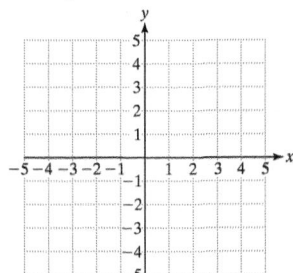

31. $2x + y = 6$

    $x = 1$

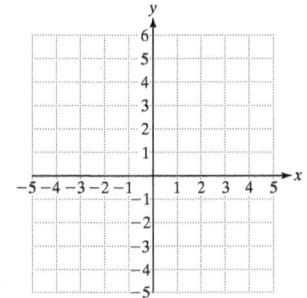

32. $4x + 3y = 9$

    $x = 3$

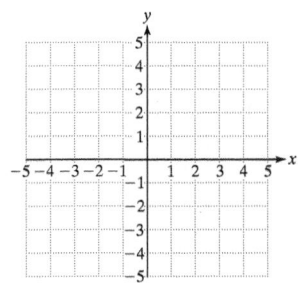

33. $-6x - 3y = 0$
     $4x + 2y = 4$

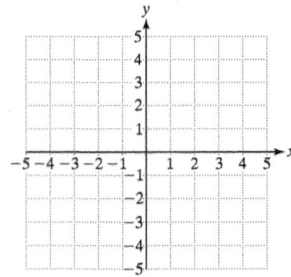

34. $2x - 6y = 12$
     $-3x + 9y = 12$

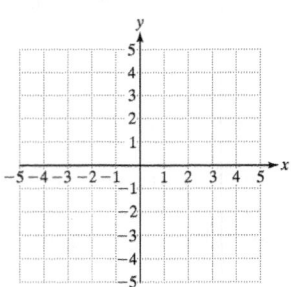

35. $-2x + y = 3$
     $6x - 3y = -9$

36. $x + 3y = 0$
     $-2x - 6y = 0$

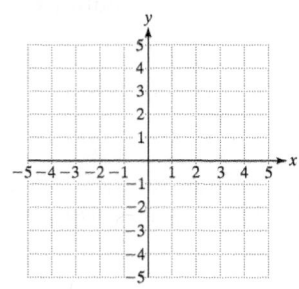

37. $y = 6$
     $2x + 3y = 12$

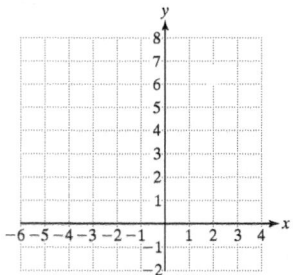

38. $y = -2$
     $x - 2y = 10$

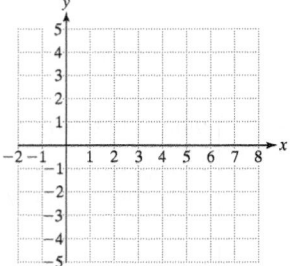

39. $-5x + 3y = -9$
     $y = \dfrac{5}{3}x - 3$

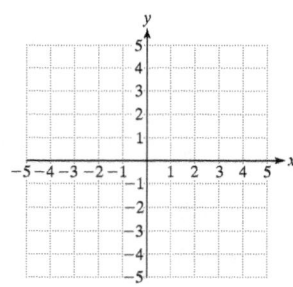

40. $4x + 2y = 6$
     $y = -2x + 3$

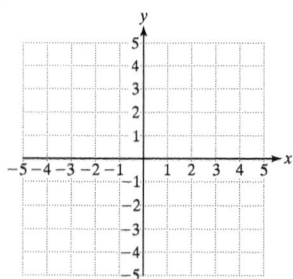

41. $x = 4 + y$
     $3y = -3x$

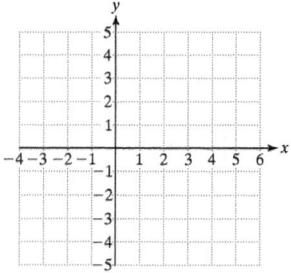

42. $3y = 4x$
     $x - y = -1$

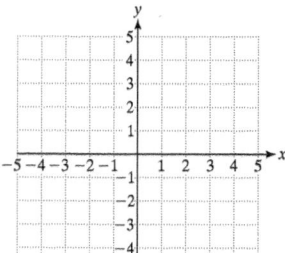

43. $-x + y = 3$
     $4y = 4x + 6$

44. $x - y = 4$
     $3y = 3x + 6$

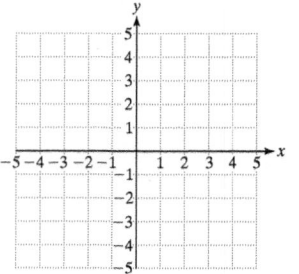

45. $x = 4$
$2y = 4$

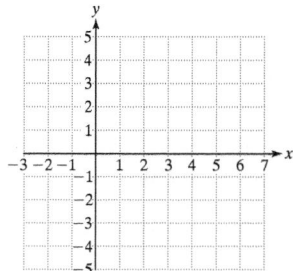

46. $-3x = 6$
$y = 2$

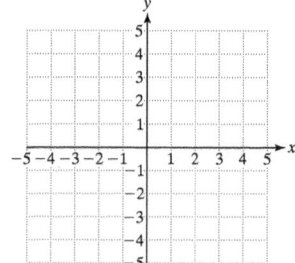

47. $4x + 4y = 8$
$5x + 5y = 5$

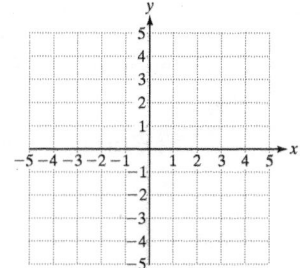

48. $2x + 3y = 8$
$-4x - 6y = 6$

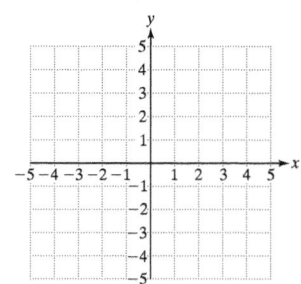

49. $2x + y = 4$
$4x - 2y = -4$

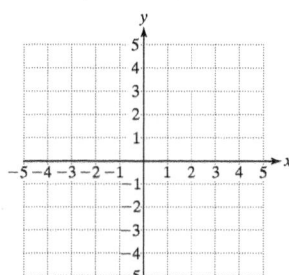

50. $6x + 6y = 3$
$2x - y = 4$

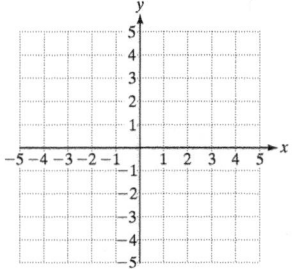

51. $y = 0.5x + 2$
$-x + 2y = 4$

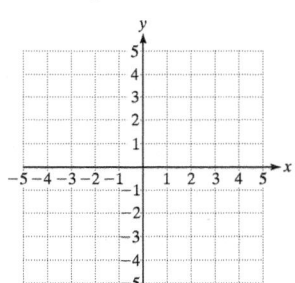

52. $3x - 4y = 6$
$-6x + 8y = -12$

53. Two tennis instructors have two different fee schedules. Owen charges $25 per lesson plus a one-time court fee of $20 at the tennis club. Joan charges $30 per lesson but does not require a court fee. The total cost, y, depends on the number of lessons, x, according to the equations

Owen: $y = 25x + 20$

Joan: $y = 30x$

From the graph, determine the number of lessons for which the total cost is the same for both instructors.

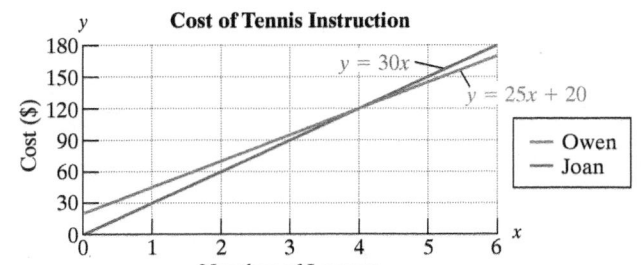

54. The cost to rent a 10 ft by 10 ft storage space is different for two different storage companies. The Storage Bin charges $90 per month plus a nonrefundable deposit of $120. AAA Storage charges $110 per month with no deposit. The total cost, y, to rent a 10 ft by 10 ft space depends on the number of months, x, according to the equations

Total Cost for Storage

The Storage Bin: $y = 90x + 120$

AAA Storage: $y = 110x$

From the graph, determine the number of months required for which the cost to rent space is equal for both companies.

For the systems graphed in Exercises 55–56, explain why the ordered pair cannot be a solution to the system of equations.

55. $(-3, 1)$

56. $(-1, -4)$

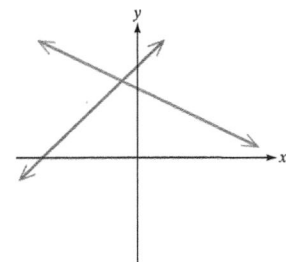

Expanding Your Skills

57. Write a system of linear equations whose solution is $(2, 1)$.

58. Write a system of linear equations whose solution is $(1, 4)$.

59. One equation in a system of linear equations is $x + y = 4$. Write a second equation such that the system will have no solution. (Answers may vary.)

60. One equation in a system of linear equations is $x - y = 3$. Write a second equation such that the system will have infinitely many solutions. (Answers may vary.)

Solving Systems of Equations by the Substitution Method

1. Solving Systems of Linear Equations by Using the Substitution Method

In Section 11.1, we used the graphing method to find the solution set to a system of equations. However, sometimes it is difficult to determine the solution using this method because of limitations in the accuracy of the graph. This is particularly true when the coordinates of a solution are not integer values or when the solution is a point not sufficiently close to the origin. Identifying the coordinates of the point $(\frac{3}{17}, -\frac{23}{9})$ or $(-251, 8349)$, for example, might be difficult from a graph.

In this section and the next, we will cover two algebraic methods to solve a system of equations that do not require graphing. The first method, called the *substitution method*, is demonstrated in Examples 1–5.

Example 1 Solving a System of Linear Equations Using the Substitution Method

Solve by using the substitution method.

$$x = 2y - 3$$
$$-4x + 3y = 2$$

Solution:

The variable x has been isolated in the first equation. The quantity $2y - 3$ is equal to x and therefore can be substituted for x in the second equation. This leaves the second equation in terms of y only.

First equation: $\quad\quad\quad x = \underbrace{2y - 3}$

Second equation: $\quad -4x + 3y = 2$

$$-4(2y - 3) + 3y = 2 \quad\quad \text{This equation now contains only one variable.}$$

$$-8y + 12 + 3y = 2 \quad\quad \text{Solve the resulting equation.}$$

$$-5y + 12 = 2$$

$$-5y = -10$$

$$y = 2$$

To find x, substitute $y = 2$ back into the first equation.

$$x = 2y - 3$$
$$x = 2(2) - 3$$
$$x = 1$$

Check the ordered pair $(1, 2)$ in both original equations.

$$x = 2y - 3 \longrightarrow 1 \overset{?}{=} 2(2) - 3 ✔ \quad\quad \text{True}$$
$$-4x + 3y = 2 \longrightarrow -4(1) + 3(2) \overset{?}{=} 2 ✔ \quad \text{True}$$

The solution is $(1, 2)$ because it checks in both original equations.

Objectives

1. Solving Systems of Linear Equations by Using the Substitution Method
2. Solutions to Systems of Linear Equations: A Summary
3. Applications of the Substitution Method

Skill Practice

Solve the system by using the substitution method.

1. $2x + 3y = -2$
$\quad y = x + 1$

Answer

1. $(-1, 0)$

In Example 1, we eliminated the x-variable from the second equation by substituting an equivalent expression for x. The resulting equation was relatively simple to solve because it had only one variable. This is the premise of the substitution method.

The substitution method can be summarized as follows.

> **PROCEDURE** Solving a System of Equations
> by Using the Substitution Method
> **Step 1** Isolate one of the variables from one equation.
> **Step 2** Substitute the expression found in step 1 into the other equation.
> **Step 3** Solve the resulting equation.
> **Step 4** Substitute the value found in step 3 back into the equation in step 1 to find the value of the remaining variable.
> **Step 5** Check the solution in both original equations and write the answer as an ordered pair.

Skill Practice

Solve the system by using the substitution method.
2. $x + y = 3$
    $-2x + 3y = 9$

Example 2 Solving a System of Linear Equations Using the Substitution Method

Solve the system using the substitution method.

$$x + y = 4$$
$$-5x + 3y = -12$$

Solution:

The x- or y-variable in the first equation is easy to isolate because the coefficients are both 1. While either variable can be isolated, we arbitrarily choose to solve for the x-variable.

$x + y = 4 \longrightarrow x = \underbrace{4 - y}$ **Step 1:** Solve the first equation for x.

$-5(4 - y) + 3y = -12$ **Step 2:** Substitute $4 - y$ for x in the other equation.

$-20 + 5y + 3y = -12$ **Step 3:** Solve for y.

$-20 + 8y = -12$

$8y = 8$

$y = 1$

$x = 4 - y$ **Step 4:** Substitute $y = 1$ into the equation $x = 4 - y$.

$x = 4 - 1$

$x = 3$

Step 5: Check the ordered pair $(3, 1)$ in both original equations.

$$x + y = 4 \qquad (3) + (1) \overset{?}{=} 4 \checkmark \qquad \text{True}$$
$$-5x + 3y = -12 \qquad -5(3) + 3(1) \overset{?}{=} -12 \checkmark \qquad \text{True}$$

The solution is $(3, 1)$ because it checks in both original equations.

Answer

2. $(0, 3)$

TIP: The solution to a system of linear equations can be confirmed by graphing. The system from Example 2 is graphed here.

Example 3 **Solving a System of Linear Equations Using the Substitution Method**

Solve the system by using the substitution method.

$$3x + 5y = 17$$

$$2x - y = -6$$

Solution:

The y-variable in the second equation is the easiest variable to isolate because its coefficient is -1.

$3x + 5y = 17$

$2x - y = -6 \longrightarrow -y = -2x - 6$

$\qquad\qquad\qquad y = \underline{2x + 6}$ **Step 1:** Solve the second equation for y.

$3x + 5(2x + 6) = 17$ **Step 2:** Substitute the quantity $2x + 6$ for y in the other equation.

$3x + 10x + 30 = 17$ **Step 3:** Solve for x.

$\qquad 13x + 30 = 17$

$\qquad\quad\; 13x = 17 - 30$

$\qquad\quad\; 13x = -13$

$\qquad\qquad x = -1$

$y = 2x + 6$ **Step 4:** Substitute $x = -1$ into the equation $y = 2x + 6$.

$y = 2(-1) + 6$

$y = -2 + 6$

$y = 4$

Step 5: The ordered pair $(-1, 4)$ can be checked in the original equations to verify the answer.

$3x + 5y = 17 \longrightarrow 3(-1) + 5(4) \stackrel{?}{=} 17 \longrightarrow -3 + 20 \stackrel{?}{=} 17 \checkmark$ True

$2x - y = -6 \longrightarrow 2(-1) - (4) \stackrel{?}{=} -6 \longrightarrow -2 - 4 \stackrel{?}{=} -6 \checkmark$ True

The solution is $(-1, 4)$.

Skill Practice

Solve the system by using the substitution method.

3. $x + 4y = 11$
$\quad\; 2x - 5y = -4$

Avoiding Mistakes

Do not substitute $y = 2x + 6$ into the same equation from which it came. This mistake will result in an identity:

$$2x - y = -6$$
$$2x - (2x + 6) = -6$$
$$2x - 2x - 6 = -6$$
$$-6 = -6$$

Answer

3. $(3, 2)$

Recall from Section 11.1 that a system of linear equations may represent two parallel lines. In such a case, there is no solution to the system.

Skill Practice

Solve the system by the substitution method.

4. $y = -\dfrac{1}{2}x + 3$

$2x + 4y = 5$

Example 4 Solving an Inconsistent System Using Substitution

Solve the system by using the substitution method.

$$2x + 3y = 6$$
$$y = -\tfrac{2}{3}x + 4$$

Solution:

$$2x + 3y = 6$$

$y = -\tfrac{2}{3}x + 4$ **Step 1:** The variable y is already isolated in the second equation.

$2x + 3(-\tfrac{2}{3}x + 4) = 6$ **Step 2:** Substitute $y = -\tfrac{2}{3}x + 4$ from the second equation into the first equation.

$2x - 2x + 12 = 6$ **Step 3:** Solve the resulting equation.

$12 = 6$ (contradiction)

The equation results in a contradiction. There are no values of x and y that will make 12 equal to 6. Therefore, there is no solution, and the system is inconsistent.

TIP: The answer to Example 4 can be verified by writing each equation in slope-intercept form and graphing the lines.

Equation 1

$$2x + 3y = 6$$

$$3y = -2x + 6$$

$$\frac{3y}{3} = \frac{-2x}{3} + \frac{6}{3}$$

$$y = -\frac{2}{3}x + 2$$

Equation 2

$$y = -\frac{2}{3}x + 4$$

The equations indicate that the lines have the same slope but different y-intercepts. Therefore, the lines must be parallel. There is no point of intersection, indicating that the system has no solution.

Recall that a system of two linear equations may represent the same line. In such a case, the solution is the set of all points on the line.

Answer

4. No solution.

Example 5 **Solving a System of Dependent Equations Using Substitution**

Solve the system by using the substitution method.

$$\frac{1}{2}x - \frac{1}{4}y = 1$$

$$6x - 3y = 12$$

Solution:

$$\frac{1}{2}x - \frac{1}{4}y = 1$$ To make the first equation easier to work with, we have the option of clearing fractions.

$$6x - 3y = 12$$

$$\frac{1}{2}x - \frac{1}{4}y = 1 \xrightarrow{\text{Multiply by 4.}} 4\left(\frac{1}{2}x\right) - 4\left(\frac{1}{4}y\right) = 4(1) \longrightarrow 2x - y = 4$$

Now the system becomes:

$$2x - y = 4$$ The y-variable in the first equation is the easiest to isolate because its coefficient is -1.

$$6x - 3y = 12$$

$$2x - y = 4 \xrightarrow{\text{Solve for } y.} -y = -2x + 4 \longrightarrow y = 2x - 4$$ **Step 1:** Isolate one of the variables.
$$6x - 3y = 12$$

$$6x - 3(2x - 4) = 12$$ **Step 2:** Substitute $y = 2x - 4$ from the first equation into the second equation.

$$6x - 6x + 12 = 12$$ **Step 3:** Solve the resulting equation.
$$12 = 12 \quad \text{(identity)}$$

Because the equation produces an identity, all values of x make this equation true. Thus, x can be any real number. Substituting any real number, x, into the equation $y = 2x - 4$ produces an ordered pair on the line $y = 2x - 4$. Hence, the solution set to the system of equations is the set of all ordered pairs on the line $y = 2x - 4$. This can be written as $\{(x, y)\,|\,y = 2x - 4\}$. The equations are dependent.

Skill Practice

Solve the system by using the substitution method.

5. $2x + \frac{1}{3}y = -\frac{1}{3}$
  $12x + 2y = -2$

TIP: The solution to Example 5 can be verified by writing each equation in slope-intercept form and graphing the lines.

Equation 1	**Equation 2**
$\frac{1}{2}x - \frac{1}{4}y = 1$	$6x - 3y = 12$
Clear fractions $2x - y = 4$	$-3y = -6x + 12$
$-y = -2x + 4$	$\frac{-3y}{-3} = \frac{-6x}{-3} + \frac{12}{-3}$
$y = 2x - 4$	$y = 2x - 4$

Notice that the slope-intercept forms for both equations are identical. The equations represent the same line, indicating that they are dependent. Each point on the line is a solution to the system of equations.

Answer

5. Infinitely many solutions; $\{(x, y)\,|\,12x + 2y = -2\}$; dependent equations

2. Solutions to Systems of Linear Equations: A Summary

The following summary reviews the three different geometric relationships between two lines and the solutions to the corresponding systems of equations.

> **PROCEDURE** Interpreting Solutions to a System of Two Linear Equations
>
> - The lines may intersect at one point (yielding one unique solution).
> - The lines may be parallel and have no point of intersection (yielding no solution). This is detected algebraically when a contradiction (false statement) is obtained (for example, $0 = -3$ and $12 = 6$).
> - The lines may be the same and intersect at all points on the line (yielding an infinite number of solutions). This is detected algebraically when an identity is obtained (for example, $0 = 0$ and $12 = 12$).

3. Applications of the Substitution Method

In Chapter 9, we solved word problems using one linear equation and one variable. In this chapter, we investigate application problems with two unknowns. In such a case, we can use two variables to represent the unknown quantities. However, if two variables are used, we must write a system of *two* distinct equations.

Skill Practice

6. One number is 16 more than another. Their sum is 92. Use a system of equations to find the numbers.

Example 6 Applying the Substitution Method

One number is 3 more than 4 times another. Their sum is 133. Find the numbers.

Solution:

We can use two variables to represent the two unknown numbers.

Let x represent one number.
Let y represent the other number.   Label the variables.

We must now write two equations. Each of the first two sentences gives a relationship between x and y:

One number is 3 more than 4 times another. $\longrightarrow$ $x = 4y + 3$ (first equation)

Their sum is 133. $\longrightarrow$ $x + y = 133$ (second equation)

	Step 1: Notice that x is already isolated in the first equation.
$(4y + 3) + y = 133$	**Step 2:** Substitute $x = 4y + 3$ into the second equation, $x + y = 133$.
$5y + 3 = 133$	**Step 3:** Solve the resulting equation.
$5y = 130$	
$y = 26$	

Answer

6. One number is 38, and the other number is 54.

$x = 4y + 3$

$x = 4(26) + 3$ **Step 4:** To solve for x, substitute $y = 26$ into the equation

$x = 104 + 3$ $x = 4y + 3$.

$x = 107$

One number is 26, and the other is 107.

TIP: Check that the numbers 26 and 107 meet the conditions of Example 6.
- 4 times 26 is 104. Three more than 104 is 107. ✔
- The sum of the numbers should be 133: 26 + 107 = 133. ✔

Example 7 **Using the Substitution Method in a Geometry Application**

Two angles are supplementary. The measure of one angle is 15° more than twice the measure of the other angle. Find the measures of the two angles.

Solution:

Let x represent the measure of one angle.
Let y represent the measure of the other angle.

The sum of the measures of supplementary angles is 180°. ⟶ $x + y = 180$

The measure of one angle is 15° more than
twice the other angle. ⟶ $x = 2y + 15$

$x + y = 180$

$x = 2y + 15$ **Step 1:** The x-variable in the second equation is already isolated.

$(2y + 15) + y = 180$ **Step 2:** Substitute $2y + 15$ into the first equation for x.

$2y + 15 + y = 180$ **Step 3:** Solve the resulting equation.

$3y + 15 = 180$

$3y = 165$

$y = 55$

$x = 2y + 15$ **Step 4:** Substitute $y = 55$ into the equation

$x = 2(55) + 15$ $x = 2y + 15$.

$x = 110 + 15$

$x = 125$

One angle is 55°, and the other is 125°.

Skill Practice

7. The measure of one angle is 2° less than 3 times the measure of another angle. The angles are complementary. Use a system of equations to find the measures of the two angles.

TIP: Check that the angles 55° and 125° meet the conditions of Example 7.
- Because
  55° + 125° = 180°,
  the angles are
  supplementary. ✔
- The angle 125° is 15°
  more than twice 55°:
  125° = 2(55°) + 15°. ✔

Answer
7. The measures of the angles are 23° and 67°.

Section 11.2 Practice Exercises

Review Exercises

For Exercises 1–6, write each pair of lines in slope-intercept form. Then identify whether the lines intersect in exactly one point or if the lines are parallel or coinciding.

1. $2x - y = 4$

$-2y = -4x + 8$

2. $x - 2y = 5$

$3x = 6y + 15$

3. $2x + 3y = 6$

$x - y = 5$

4. $x - y = -1$

$x + 2y = 4$

5. $2x = \dfrac{1}{2}y + 2$

$4x - y = 13$

6. $4y = 3x$

$3x - 4y = 15$

Objective 1: Solving Systems of Linear Equations by Using the Substitution Method

For Exercises 7–10, solve each system using the substitution method. For systems that do not have one unique solution, state the number of solutions and whether the system is inconsistent or the equations are dependent. **(See Example 1.)**

7. $3x + 2y = -3$

$y = 2x - 12$

8. $4x - 3y = -19$

$y = -2x + 13$

9. $x = -4y + 16$

$3x + 5y = 20$

10. $x = -y + 3$

$-2x + y = 6$

11. Given the system: $4x - 2y = -6$

$3x + y = 8$

a. Which variable from which equation is easiest to isolate and why?

b. Solve the system using the substitution method.

12. Given the system: $x - 5y = 2$

$11x + 13y = 22$

a. Which variable from which equation is easiest to isolate and why?

b. Solve the system using the substitution method.

For Exercises 13–48, solve each system using the substitution method. For systems that do not have one unique solution, state the number of solutions and whether the system is inconsistent or the equations are dependent. **(See Examples 1–5.)**

13. $x = 3y - 1$

$2x - 4y = 2$

14. $2y = x + 9$

$y = -3x + 1$

15. $-2x + 5y = 5$

$x = 4y - 10$

16. $y = -2x + 27$

$3x - 7y = -2$

17. $4x - y = -1$

$2x + 4y = 13$

18. $5x - 3y = -2$

$10x - y = 1$

19. $4x - 3y = 11$

$x = 5$

20. $y = -3x - 9$

$y = 12$

21. $4x = 8y + 4$

$5x - 3y = 5$

22. $3y = 6x - 6$

$-3x + y = -4$

23. $x - 3y = -11$

$6x - y = 2$

24. $-2x - y = 9$

$x + 7y = 15$

25. $3x + 2y = -1$

$\dfrac{3}{2}x + y = 4$

26. $5x - 2y = 6$

$-\dfrac{5}{2}x + y = 5$

27. $10x - 30y = -10$

$2x - 6y = -2$

28. $3x + 6y = 6$

$-6x - 12y = -12$

29. $2x + y = 3$

$y = -7$

30. $-3x = 2y + 23$

$x = -1$

31. $x + 2y = -2$

$4x = -2y - 17$

32. $x + y = 1$

$2x - y = -2$

33. $y = -\frac{1}{2}x - 4$

$y = 4x - 13$

34. $y = \frac{2}{3}x - 3$

$y = 6x - 19$

35. $y = 6$

$y - 4 = -2x - 6$

36. $x = 9$

$x - 3 = 6y + 12$

37. $3x + 2y = 4$

$2x - 3y = -6$

38. $4x + 3y = 4$

$-2x + 5y = -2$

39. $y = 0.25x + 1$

$-x + 4y = 4$

40. $y = 0.75x - 3$

$-3x + 4y = -12$

41. $11x + 6y = 17$

$5x - 4y = 1$

42. $3x - 8y = 7$

$10x - 5y = 45$

43. $x + 2y = 4$

$4y = -2x - 8$

44. $-y = x - 6$

$2x + 2y = 4$

45. $2x = 3 - y$

$x + y = 4$

46. $2x = 4 + 2y$

$3x + y = 10$

47. $\frac{x}{3} + \frac{y}{2} = -4$

$x - 3y = 6$

48. $x - 2y = -5$

$\frac{2x}{3} + \frac{y}{3} = 0$

Objective 3: Applications of the Substitution Method

For Exercises 49–58, set up a system of linear equations and solve for the indicated quantities. **(See Examples 6–7.)**

49. Two numbers have a sum of 106. One number is 10 less than the other. Find the numbers.

50. Two positive numbers have a difference of 8. The larger number is 2 less than 3 times the smaller number. Find the numbers.

51. The difference between two positive numbers is 26. The larger number is three times the smaller. Find the numbers.

52. The sum of two numbers is 956. One number is 94 less than 6 times the other. Find the numbers.

53. Two angles are supplementary. One angle is 15° more than 10 times the other angle. Find the measure of each angle.

54. Two angles are complementary. One angle is 1° less than 6 times the other angle. Find the measure of each angle.

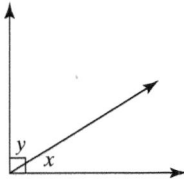

55. Two angles are complementary. One angle is 10° more than 3 times the other angle. Find the measure of each angle.

56. Two angles are supplementary. One angle is 5° less than twice the other angle. Find the measure of each angle.

57. In a right triangle, one of the acute angles is 6° less than the other acute angle. Find the measure of each acute angle.

58. In a right triangle, one of the acute angles is 9° less than twice the other acute angle. Find the measure of each acute angle.

Expanding Your Skills

59. The following system of equations is dependent and has infinitely many solutions. Find three ordered pairs that are solutions to the system of equations.

$$y = 2x + 3$$

$$-4x + 2y = 6$$

60. The following system of equations is dependent and has infinitely many solutions. Find three ordered pairs that are solutions to the system of equations.

$$y = -x + 1$$

$$2x + 2y = 2$$

Section 11.3 Solving Systems of Equations by the Addition Method

1. Solving a System of Linear Equations by Using the Addition Method

Thus far, we have used the graphing method and the substitution method to solve a system of linear equations in two variables. In this section, we present another algebraic method to solve a system of linear equations, called the *addition method* (sometimes called the *elimination method*). The purpose of the addition method is to eliminate one variable.

— **Skill Practice** —

Solve the system using the addition method.

1. $x + y = 13$
   $2x - y = 2$

Example 1 Using the Addition Method

Solve the system using the addition method.

$$x + y = -2$$
$$x - y = -6$$

Solution:

Notice that the coefficients of the y-variables are opposites:

Coefficient is 1.

$$x + 1y = -2$$
$$x - 1y = -6$$

Coefficient is -1.

Because the coefficients of the y-variables are opposites, we can add the two equations to eliminate the y-variable.

$$x + y = -2$$
$$\underline{x - y = -6}$$
$$2x \quad = -8 \quad \longleftarrow \text{ After adding the equations, we have one equation and one variable.}$$

$$2x = -8 \qquad \text{Solve the resulting equation.}$$
$$x = -4$$

To find the value of y, substitute $x = -4$ into *either* of the original equations.

$$x + y = -2 \qquad \text{First equation}$$
$$(-4) + y = -2$$
$$y = -2 + 4$$
$$y = 2$$

The solution is $(-4, 2)$.

Check:

$$x + y = -2 \longrightarrow (-4) + (2) \overset{?}{=} -2 \longrightarrow -2 \overset{?}{=} -2 ✔ \text{ True}$$
$$x - y = -6 \longrightarrow (-4) - (2) \overset{?}{=} -6 \longrightarrow -6 \overset{?}{=} -6 ✔ \text{ True}$$

TIP: Notice that the value $x = -4$ could have been substituted into the second equation to obtain the same value for y.

$$x - y = -6$$
$$(-4) - y = -6$$
$$-y = -6 + 4$$
$$-y = -2$$
$$y = 2$$

Answer

1. $(5, 8)$

Section 11.3 Solving Systems of Equations by the Addition Method **769**

It is important to note that the addition method works on the premise that the two equations have *opposite* values for the coefficients of one of the variables. Sometimes it is necessary to manipulate the original equations to create two coefficients that are opposites. This is accomplished by multiplying one or both equations by an appropriate constant. The process is outlined as follows.

PROCEDURE Solving a System of Equations by Using the Addition Method

Step 1 Write both equations in standard form: $Ax + By = C$.

Step 2 Clear fractions or decimals (optional).

Step 3 Multiply one or both equations by nonzero constants to create opposite coefficients for one of the variables.

Step 4 Add the equations from step 3 to eliminate one variable.

Step 5 Solve for the remaining variable.

Step 6 Substitute the known value from step 5 into one of the original equations to solve for the other variable.

Step 7 Check the solution in both equations.

Example 2 **Solving a System of Linear Equations Using the Addition Method**

Solve the system using the addition method.

$$3x + 5y = 17$$
$$2x - y = -6$$

Solution:

$3x + 5y = 17$ **Step 1:** Both equations are already written in standard form.

$2x - y = -6$ **Step 2:** There are no fractions or decimals.

Notice that neither the coefficients of x nor the coefficients of y are opposites. However, multiplying the second equation by 5 creates the term $-5y$ in the second equation. This is the opposite of the term $+5y$ in the first equation.

$3x + 5y = 17$ $3x + 5y = 17$ **Step 3:** Multiply the second equation by 5.

$2x - y = -6$ $\xrightarrow{\text{Multiply by 5.}}$ $\dfrac{10x - 5y = -30}{13x \qquad = -13}$

                                   Step 4: Add the equations.

                     $13x = -13$ **Step 5:** Solve the equation.

                       $x = -1$

     $3x + 5y = 17$ First equation **Step 6:** Substitute $x = -1$ into one of the original equations.

$3(-1) + 5y = 17$

   $-3 + 5y = 17$

       $5y = 20$

        $y = 4$

The solution is $(-1, 4)$. **Step 7:** Check the solution in both original equations.

Check:

$3x + 5y = 17 \longrightarrow 3(-1) + 5(4) \overset{?}{=} 17 \longrightarrow -3 + 20 \overset{?}{=} 17$ ✔ True

$2x - y = -6 \longrightarrow 2(-1) - (4) \overset{?}{=} -6 \longrightarrow -2 - 4 \overset{?}{=} -6$ ✔ True

---

Skill Practice

Solve the system using the addition method.

2. $4x + 3y = 3$
     $x - 2y = 9$

Answer

2. $(3, -3)$

In Example 3, the system of equations uses the variables a and b instead of x and y. In such a case, we will write the solution as an ordered pair with the variables written in alphabetical order, such as (a, b).

— **Skill Practice** —

Solve the system using the addition method.

3. $8n = 4 - 5m$
$\quad 7m + 6n = -10$

Example 3   **Solve a System of Linear Equations Using the Addition Method**

Solve the system using the addition method.

$$5b = 7a + 8$$
$$-4a - 2b = -10$$

Solution:

Step 1: Write the equations in standard form.

The first equation becomes: $5b = 7a + 8 \longrightarrow -7a + 5b = 8$

The system becomes: $-7a + 5b = 8$
$$-4a - 2b = -10$$

Step 2: There are no fractions or decimals.

Step 3: We need to obtain opposite coefficients on either the a or b term.

Notice that neither the coefficients of a nor the coefficients of b are opposites. However, it is possible to change the coefficients of b to 10 and -10 (this is because the LCM of 5 and 2 is 10). This is accomplished by multiplying the first equation by 2 and the second equation by 5.

$$
\begin{array}{ll}
-7a + 5b = 8 & \xrightarrow{\text{Multiply by 2.}} \quad -14a + 10b = 16 \\
-4a - 2b = -10 & \xrightarrow{\text{Multiply by 5.}} \quad \underline{-20a - 10b = -50} \\
& \phantom{\xrightarrow{\text{Multiply by 5.}}} \quad -34a = -34
\end{array}
$$

Step 4: Add the equations.

$$-34a = -34$$

Step 5: Solve the resulting equation.

$$\frac{-34a}{-34} = \frac{-34}{-34}$$

$$a = 1$$

$5b = 7a + 8$ First equation

Step 6: Substitute $a = 1$ into one of the original equations.

$$5b = 7(1) + 8$$
$$5b = 15$$
$$b = 3$$

The solution is $(1, 3)$.

Step 7: Check the solution in the original equations.

Check:

$5b = 7a + 8 \longrightarrow 5(3) \overset{?}{=} 7(1) + 8 \longrightarrow 15 \overset{?}{=} 7 + 8$ ✔   True

$-4a - 2b = -10 \longrightarrow -4(1) - 2(3) \overset{?}{=} -10 \longrightarrow -4 - 6 \overset{?}{=} -10$ ✔   True

Answer

3. $(-4, 3)$

Example 4   **Solving a System of Linear Equations Using the Addition Method**

Solve the system using the addition method.

$$34x - 22y = 4$$

$$17x - 88y = -19$$

Solution:

The equations are already in standard form. There are no fractions or decimals to clear.

$$34x - 22y = 4 \longrightarrow 34x - 22y = 4$$

$$17x - 88y = -19 \xrightarrow{\text{Multiply by } -2.} \underline{-34x + 176y = 38}$$

$$154y = 42$$

Solve for y. $154y = 42$

$$\frac{154y}{154} = \frac{42}{154}$$

Simplify. $y = \dfrac{3}{11}$

To find the value of x, we normally substitute y into one of the original equations and solve for x. In this example, we will show an alternative method for finding x. By repeating the addition method, this time eliminating y, we can solve for x. This approach allows us to avoid substitution of the fractional value for y.

$$34x - 22y = 4 \xrightarrow{\text{Multiply by } -4.} -136x + 88y = -16$$

$$17x - 88y = -19 \longrightarrow \underline{17x - 88y = -19}$$

$$-119x \qquad = -35$$

Solve for x. $-119x = -35$

$$\frac{-119x}{-119} = \frac{-35}{-119}$$

Simplify. $x = \dfrac{5}{17}$

The solution is $\left(\frac{5}{17}, \frac{3}{11}\right)$. These values can be checked in the original equations:

$$34x - 22y = 4 \qquad\qquad 17x - 88y = -19$$

$$34\left(\frac{5}{17}\right) - 22\left(\frac{3}{11}\right) \overset{?}{=} 4 \qquad\qquad 17\left(\frac{5}{17}\right) - 88\left(\frac{3}{11}\right) \overset{?}{=} -19$$

$$10 - 6 \overset{?}{=} 4 \checkmark \text{ True} \qquad\qquad 5 - 24 \overset{?}{=} -19 \checkmark \text{ True}$$

Skill Practice

Solve the system using the addition method.

4. $15x - 16y = 1$
$\quad\ 45x + \ 4y = 16$

Answer

4. $\left(\dfrac{1}{3}, \dfrac{1}{4}\right)$

Example 5   Solving a System of Linear Equations

Solve the system using the addition method.

$$2x - 5y = 10$$
$$\frac{1}{2}x - \frac{5}{4}y = 1$$

Solution:

$2x - 5y = 10$

$\dfrac{1}{2}x - \dfrac{5}{4}y = 1$ **Step 1:**   The equations are in standard form.

Step 2:   Multiply both sides of the second equation by 4 to clear fractions.

$$\frac{1}{2}x - \frac{5}{4}y = 1 \longrightarrow 4\left(\frac{1}{2}x - \frac{5}{4}y\right) = 4(1) \longrightarrow 2x - 5y = 4$$

Now the system becomes $2x - 5y = 10$
$$2x - 5y = 4$$

To make either the x-coefficients or y-coefficients opposites, multiply either equation by -1.

$$2x - 5y = 10 \xrightarrow{\text{Multiply by } -1.} -2x + 5y = -10 \qquad \textbf{Step 3:} \quad \text{Create opposite}$$
$$2x - 5y = 4 \longrightarrow \underline{\quad 2x - 5y = \quad 4} \qquad\qquad\quad \text{coefficients.}$$
$$0 = -6 \qquad \textbf{Step 4:} \quad \text{Add the equations.}$$

Because the result is a contradiction, there is no solution, and the system of equations is inconsistent. Writing each line in slope-intercept form verifies that the lines are parallel (Figure 11-8).

$$2x - 5y = 10 \xrightarrow{\text{slope-intercept form}} y = \frac{2}{5}x - 2$$

$$\frac{1}{2} - \frac{5}{4}y = 1 \xrightarrow{\text{slope-intercept form}} y = \frac{2}{5}x - \frac{4}{5}$$

There is no solution.

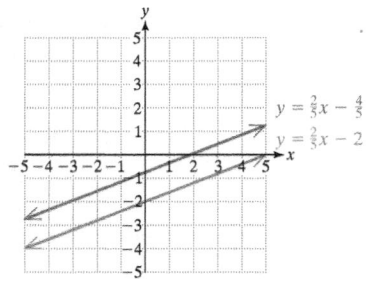

Figure 11-8

Example 6 **Solving a System of Linear Equations**

Solve the system by the addition method.

$$3x - y = 4$$
$$2y = 6x - 8$$

Solution:

$3x - y = 4 \longrightarrow 3x - y = 4$ **Step 1:** Write the equations in standard form.

$2y = 6x - 8 \longrightarrow -6x + 2y = -8$ **Step 2:** There are no fractions or decimals.

Notice that the equations differ exactly by a factor of -2, which indicates that these two equations represent the same line. Multiply the first equation by 2 to create opposite coefficients for the variables.

$$3x - y = 4 \xrightarrow{\text{Multiply by 2.}} 6x - 2y = 8$$

Step 3: Create opposite coefficients.

$$-6x + 2y = -8 \qquad\qquad \underline{-6x + 2y = -8}$$
$$0 = 0$$

Step 4: Add the equations.

Because the resulting equation is an identity, the original equations represent the same line. This can be confirmed by writing each equation in slope-intercept form.

$$3x - y = 4 \longrightarrow -y = -3x + 4 \longrightarrow y = 3x - 4$$
$$-6x + 2y = -8 \longrightarrow 2y = 6x - 8 \longrightarrow y = 3x - 4$$

The solution is the set of all points on the line, or equivalently, $\{(x, y) | y = 3x - 4\}$.

2. Summary of Methods for Solving Systems of Linear Equations in Two Variables

If no method of solving a system of linear equations is specified, you may use the method of your choice. However, we recommend the following guidelines:

1. If one of the equations is written with a variable isolated, the substitution method is a good choice. For example:

$$2x + 5y = 2 \qquad \text{or} \qquad y = \frac{1}{3}x - 2$$
$$x = y - 6 \qquad\qquad\qquad\quad x - 6y = 9$$

2. If both equations are written in standard form, $Ax + By = C$, where none of the variables has coefficients of 1 or -1, then the addition method is a good choice.

$$4x + 5y = 12$$
$$5x + 3y = 15$$

3. If both equations are written in standard form, $Ax + By = C$, and at least one variable has a coefficient of 1 or -1, then either the substitution method or the addition method is a good choice.

Section 11.3 Practice Exercises

Study Skills Exercise

1. Now that you have learned three methods of solving a system of linear equations with two variables, choose a system and solve it all three ways. There are two advantages to this. One is to check your answer. (You should get the same answer using all three methods.) The second advantage is to show you which method is the easiest for you to use.

   Solve the system by using the graphing method, the substitution method, and the addition method.

$$2x + y = -7$$
$$x - 10 = 4y$$

Review Exercises

For Exercises 2–5, check whether the given ordered pair is a solution to the system.

2. $x + y = 8$ $(5, 3)$
   $y = x - 2$

3. $x = y + 1$ $(3, 2)$
   $-x + 2y = 0$

4. $3x + 2y = 14$ $(5, -2)$
   $5x - 2y = 29$

5. $x = 2y - 11$ $(-3, 4)$
   $-x + 5y = 23$

Objective 1: Solving a System of Linear Equations by Using the Addition Method

For Exercises 6–7, answer as true or false.

6. Given the system $5x - 4y = 1$
                      $7x - 2y = 5$

   a. To eliminate the y-variable using the addition method, multiply the second equation by 2.

   b. To eliminate the x-variable, multiply the first equation by 7 and the second equation by -5.

7. Given the system $3x + 5y = -1$
                      $9x - 8y = -26$

   a. To eliminate the x-variable using the addition method, multiply the first equation by -3.

   b. To eliminate the y-variable, multiply the first equation by 8 and the second equation by -5.

8. Given the system $3x - 4y = 2$
                      $17x + y = 35$

   a. Which variable, x or y, is easier to eliminate using the addition method?

   b. Solve the system using the addition method.

9. Given the system $-2x + 5y = -15$
                      $6x - 7y = 21$

   a. Which variable, x or y, is easier to eliminate using the addition method?

   b. Solve the system using the addition method.

For Exercises 10–25, solve the systems using the addition method. **(See Examples 1–4.)**

10. $x + 2y = 8$
     $5x - 2y = 4$

11. $2x - 3y = 11$
     $-4x + 3y = -19$

12. $a + b = 3$
     $3a + b = 13$

13. $-2u + 6v = 10$
     $-2u + v = -5$

14. $-3x + y = 1$
     $-6x - 2y = -2$

15. $5m - 2n = 4$
     $3m + n = 9$

16. $3x - 5y = 13$
$x - 2y = 5$

17. $7a + 2b = -1$
$3a - 4b = 19$

18. $6c - 2d = -2$
$5c = -3d + 17$

19. $2s + 3t = -1$
$5s = 2t + 7$

20. $6y - 4z = -2$
$4y + 6z = 42$

21. $4k - 2r = -4$
$3k - 5r = 18$

22. $2x + 3y = 6$
$x - y = 5$

23. $6x + 6y = 8$
$9x - 18y = -3$

24. $2x - 5y = 4$
$3x - 3y = 4$

25. $6x - 5y = 7$
$4x - 6y = 7$

26. In solving a system of equations, suppose you get the statement $0 = 5$. How many solutions will the system have? What can you say about the graphs of these equations?

27. In solving a system of equations, suppose you get the statement $0 = 0$. How many solutions will the system have? What can you say about the graphs of these equations?

28. In solving a system of equations, suppose you get the statement $3 = 3$. How many solutions will the system have? What can you say about the graphs of these equations?

29. In solving a system of equations, suppose you get the statement $2 = -5$. How many solutions will the system have? What can you say about the graphs of these equations?

30. Suppose in solving a system of linear equations, you get the statement $x = 0$. How many solutions will the system have? What can you say about the graphs of these equations?

31. Suppose in solving a system of linear equations, you get the statement $y = 0$. How many solutions will the system have? What can you say about the graphs of these equations?

For Exercises 32–43, solve the system of equations using the addition method. For systems that do not have one unique solution, state the number of solutions and whether the system is inconsistent or the equations are dependent. **(See Examples 5–6.)**

32. $-2x + y = -5$
$8x - 4y = 12$

33. $x - 3y = 2$
$-5x + 15y = 10$

34. $x + 2y = 2$
$-3x - 6y = -6$

35. $4x - 3y = 6$
$-12x + 9y = -18$

36. $3a + 2b = 11$
$7a - 3b = -5$

37. $4y + 5z = -2$
$5y - 3z = 16$

38. $3x - 5y = 7$
$5x - 2y = -1$

39. $4s + 3t = 9$
$3s + 4t = 12$

40. $2x + 2 = -3y + 9$
$3x - 10 = -4y$

41. $-3x + 6 + 7y = 5$
$5y = 2x$

42. $4x - 5y = 0$
$8(x - 1) = 10y$

43. $y = 2x + 1$
$-3(2x - y) = 0$

Objective 2: Summary of Methods for Solving Systems of Linear Equations in Two Variables

For Exercises 44–63, solve the system of equations by either the addition method or the substitution method. For systems that do not have one unique solution, state the number of solutions and whether the system is inconsistent or the equations are dependent.

44. $5x - 2y = 4$
$y = -3x + 9$

45. $-x = 8y + 5$
$4x - 3y = -20$

46. $0.1x + 0.1y = 0.6$
$0.1x - 0.1y = 0.1$

47. $0.1x + 0.1y = 0.2$
$0.1x - 0.1y = 0.3$

48. $3x = 5y - 9$
$2y = 3x + 3$

49. $10x - 5 = 3y$
$4x + 5y = 2$

50. $y = -5x - 5$
$6x - 3 = -3y$

51. $4x + 5y = -2$
$3x = -2y - 5$

52. $x = -\dfrac{1}{2}$
$6x - 5y = -8$

53. $4x - 2y = 1$
$y = 3$

54. $0.02x + 0.04y = 0.12$
$0.03x - 0.05y = -0.15$

55. $-0.04x + 0.03y = 0.03$
$-0.06x - 0.02y = -0.02$

56. $8x - 16y = 24$
$2x - 4y = 0$

57. $y = -\dfrac{1}{2}x - 5$
$2x + 4y = -8$

58. $\dfrac{m}{2} + \dfrac{n}{5} = \dfrac{13}{10}$
$3m - 3n = m - 10$

59. $\dfrac{a}{4} - \dfrac{3b}{2} = \dfrac{15}{2}$
$a + 2b = -10$

60. $2m - 6n = m + 4$
$3m + 8 = 5m - n$

61. $m - 3n = 10$
$3m + 12n = -12$

62. $9a - 2b = 8$
$18a + 6 = 4b + 22$

63. $a = 5 + 2b$
$3a - 6b = 15$

For Exercises 64–67, set up a system of linear equations, and solve for the indicated quantities.

64. The sum of two positive numbers is 26. Their difference is 14. Find the numbers.

65. The difference of two positive numbers is 2. The sum of the numbers is 36. Find the numbers.

66. Eight times the smaller of two numbers plus 2 times the larger number is 44. Three times the smaller number minus 2 times the larger number is zero. Find the numbers.

67. Six times the smaller of two numbers minus the larger number is −9. Ten times the smaller number plus five times the larger number is 5. Find the numbers.

For Exercises 68–70, solve the system by using each of the three methods: (a) the graphing method, (b) the substitution method, and (c) the addition method.

68. $2x + y = 1$
$-4x - 2y = -2$

69. $3x + y = 6$
$-2x + 2y = 4$

70. $2x - 2y = 6$
$5y = 5x + 5$

Expanding Your Skills

71. Explain why a system of linear equations cannot have exactly two solutions.

72. The solution to the system of linear equations is $(1, 2)$. Find A and B.
$$Ax + 3y = 8$$
$$x + By = -7$$

73. The solution to the system of linear equations is $(-3, 4)$. Find A and B.
$$4x + Ay = -32$$
$$Bx + 6y = 18$$

Problem Recognition Exercises

Systems of Equations

For Exercises 1–6 determine the number of solutions to the system without solving the system. Explain your answers.

1. $y = -4x + 2$
$y = -4x + 2$

2. $y = -4x + 6$
$y = -4x + 1$

3. $y = 4x - 3$
$y = -4x + 5$

4. $y = 7$
$2x + 3y = 1$

5. $2x + 3y = 1$
$2x + 3y = 8$

6. $8x - 2y = 6$
$12x - 3y = 9$

For Exercises 7–26, solve the system using the method of your choice. For systems that do not have one unique solution, state the number of solutions and whether the system is inconsistent or the equations are dependent.

7. $x = -2y + 5$
$2x - 4y = 10$

8. $y = -3x - 4$
$2x - y = 9$

9. $3x - 2y = 22$
$5x + 2y = 10$

10. $-4x + 2y = -2$
$4x - 5y = -7$

11. $\dfrac{1}{3}x + \dfrac{1}{2}y = \dfrac{2}{3}$
$-\dfrac{2}{3}x + y = -\dfrac{4}{3}$

12. $\dfrac{1}{4}x + \dfrac{2}{5}y = 6$
$\dfrac{1}{2}x - \dfrac{1}{10}y = 3$

13. $2c + 7d = -1$
$c = 2$

14. $-3w + 5z = -6$
$z = -4$

15. $y = 0.4x - 0.3$
$-4x + 10y = 20$

16. $x = -0.5y + 0.1$
$-10x - 5y = 2$

17. $3a + 7b = -3$
$-11a + 3b = 11$

18. $2v - 5w = 10$
$9v + 7w = 45$

19. $y = 2x - 14$
$4x - 2y = 28$

20. $x = 5y - 9$
$-2x + 10y = 18$

21. $x + y = 3200$
$0.06x + 0.04y = 172$

22. $x + y = 4500$
$0.07x + 0.05y = 291$

23. $3x + y - 7 = x - 4$
$3x - 4y + 4 = -6y + 5$

24. $7y - 8y - 3 = -3x + 4$
$10x - 5y - 12 = 13$

25. $3x - 6y = -1$
$9x + 4y = 8$

26. $8x - 2y = 5$
$12x + 4y = -3$

Applications of Linear Equations in Two Variables

Objectives

1. **Applications Involving Cost**
2. **Applications Involving Principal and Interest**
3. **Applications Involving Mixtures**
4. **Applications Involving Distance, Rate, and Time**

┌─ **Skill Practice** ─┐

1. Lynn went to a fast-food restaurant and spent $9.00. She purchased 4 hamburgers and 5 orders of fries. The next day, Ricardo went to the same restaurant and purchased 10 hamburgers and 7 orders of fries. He spent $18.10. Use a system of equations to determine the cost of a burger and the cost of an order of fries.

1. Applications Involving Cost

In Sections 9.4–9.6, we solved several applied problems by setting up a linear equation in one variable. When solving an application that involves two unknowns, sometimes it is convenient to use a system of linear equations in two variables.

Example 1 **Using a System of Linear Equations Involving Cost**

At a movie theater a couple buys one large popcorn and two drinks for $5.75. A group of teenagers buys two large popcorns and five drinks for $13.00. Find the cost of one large popcorn and the cost of one drink.

Solution:

In this application we have two unknowns, which we can represent by x and y.

Let x represent the cost of one large popcorn.
Let y represent the cost of one drink.

We must now write two equations. Each of the first two sentences in the problem gives a relationship between x and y:

$$\begin{pmatrix} \text{Cost of 1} \\ \text{large popcorn} \end{pmatrix} + \begin{pmatrix} \text{cost of 2} \\ \text{drinks} \end{pmatrix} = \begin{pmatrix} \text{total} \\ \text{cost} \end{pmatrix} \longrightarrow x + 2y = 5.75$$

$$\begin{pmatrix} \text{Cost of 2} \\ \text{large popcorns} \end{pmatrix} + \begin{pmatrix} \text{cost of 5} \\ \text{drinks} \end{pmatrix} = \begin{pmatrix} \text{total} \\ \text{cost} \end{pmatrix} \longrightarrow 2x + 5y = 13.00$$

To solve this system, we may either use the substitution method or the addition method. We will use the substitution method by solving for x in the first equation.

$$x + 2y = 5.75 \longrightarrow x = -2y + 5.75 \qquad \text{Isolate } x \text{ in the first equation.}$$

$$2x + 5y = 13.00$$

$$2(-2y + 5.75) + 5y = 13.00 \qquad \text{Substitute } x = -2y + 5.75 \text{ into the other equation.}$$

$$-4y + 11.50 + 5y = 13.00$$

$$y + 11.50 = 13.00 \qquad \text{Solve for } y.$$

$$y = 1.50$$

$$x = -2y + 5.75$$

$$x = -2(1.50) + 5.75 \qquad \text{Substitute } y = 1.50 \text{ into the equation } x = -2y + 5.75.$$

$$x = -3.00 + 5.75$$

$$x = 2.75$$

The cost of one large popcorn is $2.75, and the cost of one drink is $1.50.

Check by verifying that the solutions meet the specified conditions.

1 popcorn + 2 drinks = 1($2.75) + 2($1.50) = $5.75 ✔ True
2 popcorns + 5 drinks = 2($2.75) + 5($1.50) = $13.00 ✔ True

Answer

1. The cost of a burger is $1.25, and the cost of an order of fries is $0.80.

2. Applications Involving Principal and Interest

In Section 9.5, we applied the simple interest formula, $I = Prt$, to compute interest earned on money invested or borrowed. If the amount of time is taken to be 1 year, the formula becomes $I = Pr(1)$ or simply $I = Pr$, where I is the simple interest, P is the principal, and r is the annual interest rate.

In Example 2, we apply the concept of simple interest to two accounts to produce a desired amount of interest after 1 yr.

Example 2 **Using a System of Linear Equations Involving Investments**

Joanne has a total of $6000 to deposit in two accounts. One account earns 3.5% simple interest and the other earns 2.5% simple interest. If the total amount of interest at the end of 1 yr is $195, find the amount she deposited in each account.

Solution:

Let x represent the principal deposited in the 2.5% account.
Let y represent the principal deposited in the 3.5% account.

	2.5% Account	3.5% Account	Total
Principal	x	y	6000
Interest $(I = Pr)$	$0.025x$	$0.035y$	195

Each row of the table yields an equation in x and y:

$$\begin{pmatrix} \text{Principal} \\ \text{invested} \\ \text{at } 2.5\% \end{pmatrix} + \begin{pmatrix} \text{principal} \\ \text{invested} \\ \text{at } 3.5\% \end{pmatrix} = \begin{pmatrix} \text{total} \\ \text{principal} \end{pmatrix} \longrightarrow x + y = 6000$$

$$\begin{pmatrix} \text{Interest} \\ \text{earned} \\ \text{at } 2.5\% \end{pmatrix} + \begin{pmatrix} \text{interest} \\ \text{earned} \\ \text{at } 3.5\% \end{pmatrix} = \begin{pmatrix} \text{total} \\ \text{interest} \end{pmatrix} \longrightarrow 0.025x + 0.035y = 195$$

We will choose the addition method to solve the system of equations. First multiply the second equation by 1000 to clear decimals.

$$\begin{array}{ccc} & & \text{Multiply by } -25. \\ x + y = 6000 \longrightarrow & x + y = 6000 & \longrightarrow -25x - 25y = -150{,}000 \\ 0.025x + 0.035y = 195 \longrightarrow & 25x + 35y = 195{,}000 \longrightarrow & \underline{25x + 35y = 195{,}000} \\ & \text{Multiply by 1000.} & 10y = 45{,}000 \end{array}$$

$10y = 45{,}000$ — After eliminating the x-variable, solve for y.

$\dfrac{10y}{10} = \dfrac{45{,}000}{10}$

$y = 4500$ — The amount invested in the 3.5% account is $4500.

$$x + y = 6000 \qquad \text{Substitute } y = 4500 \text{ into the equation } x + y = 6000.$$

$$x + 4500 = 6000$$

$$x = 1500 \qquad \text{The amount invested in the 2.5\% account is \$1500.}$$

Joanne deposited $1500 in the 2.5% account and $4500 in the 3.5% account.

To check, verify that the conditions of the problem have been met.

1. The sum of $1500 and $4500 is $6000 as desired. ✔ True

2. The interest earned on $1500 at 2.5% is: $0.025(\$1500) = \$37.50$
   The interest earned on $4500 at 3.5% is: $\underline{0.035(\$4500) = \$157.50}$

   Total interest: $195.00 ✔ True

3. Applications Involving Mixtures

Example 3 **Using a System of Linear Equations in a Mixture Application**

A 10% alcohol solution is mixed with a 40% alcohol solution to produce 30 L of a 20% alcohol solution. Find the number of liters of 10% solution and the number of liters of 40% solution required for this mixture.

Solution:

Each solution contains a percentage of alcohol plus some other mixing agent such as water. Before we set up a system of equations to model this situation, it is helpful to have background understanding of the problem. In Figure 11-9, the liquid depicted in blue is pure alcohol and the liquid shown in gray is the mixing agent (such as water). Together these liquids form a solution. (Realistically the mixture may not separate as shown, but this image may be helpful for your understanding.)

Let x represent the number of liters of 10% solution.
Let y represent the number of liters of 40% solution.

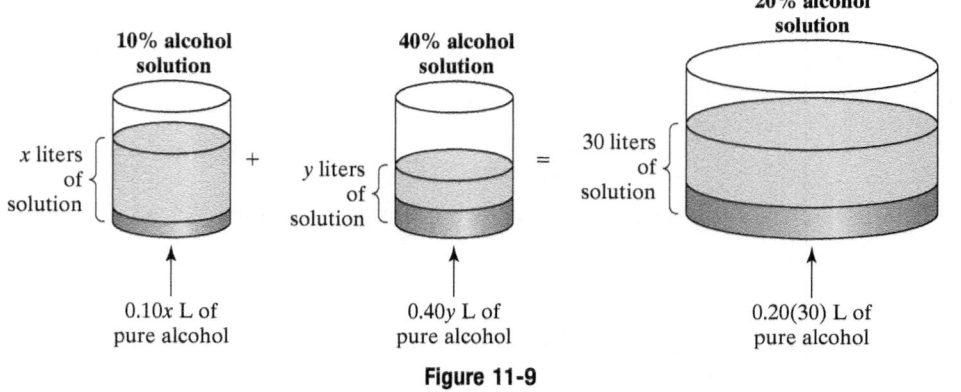

Figure 11-9

The information given in the statement of the problem can be organized in a chart.

	10% Alcohol	40% Alcohol	20% Alcohol
Number of liters of solution	x	y	30
Number of liters of pure alcohol	$0.10x$	$0.40y$	$0.20(30) = 6$

From the first row, we have

$$\begin{pmatrix} \text{Amount of} \\ 10\% \text{ solution} \end{pmatrix} + \begin{pmatrix} \text{amount of} \\ 40\% \text{ solution} \end{pmatrix} = \begin{pmatrix} \text{total amount} \\ \text{of } 20\% \text{ solution} \end{pmatrix} \rightarrow x + y = 30$$

From the second row, we have

$$\begin{pmatrix} \text{Amount of} \\ \text{alcohol in} \\ 10\% \text{ solution} \end{pmatrix} + \begin{pmatrix} \text{amount of} \\ \text{alcohol in} \\ 40\% \text{ solution} \end{pmatrix} = \begin{pmatrix} \text{total amount of} \\ \text{alcohol in} \\ 20\% \text{ solution} \end{pmatrix} \rightarrow 0.10x + 0.40y = 6$$

We will solve the system with the addition method by first clearing decimals.

$$\begin{array}{lll}
x + y = 30 & \xrightarrow{} & x + y = 30 \quad \xrightarrow{\text{Multiply by } -1.} \quad -x - y = -30 \\
0.10x + 0.40y = 6 & \xrightarrow[\text{Multiply by 10.}]{} & x + 4y = 60 \quad \xrightarrow{} \quad \underline{x + 4y = 60} \\
& & 3y = 30
\end{array}$$

$3y = 30$ After eliminating the x-variable, solve for y.

$y = 10$ 10 L of 40% solution is needed.

$x + y = 30$ Substitute $y = 10$ into either of the original equations.

$x + (10) = 30$

$x = 20$ 20 L of 10% solution is needed.

10 L of 40% solution must be mixed with 20 L of 10% solution.

4. Applications Involving Distance, Rate, and Time

The following formula relates the distance traveled to the rate and time of travel.

$$d = rt \qquad \text{distance} = \text{rate} \cdot \text{time}$$

For example, if a car travels at 60 mph for 3 hr, then

$$d = (60 \text{ mph})(3 \text{ hr})$$

$$= 180 \text{ mi}$$

If a car travels at 60 mph for x hr, then

$$d = (60 \text{ mph})(x \text{ hr})$$

$$= 60x \text{ mi}$$

The relationship $d = rt$ is used in Example 4.

Skill Practice

4. Dan and Cheryl paddled their canoe 40 mi in 5 hr with the current and 16 mi in 8 hr against the current. Find the speed of the current and the speed of the canoe in still water.

Example 4 **Using a System of Linear Equations in a Distance, Rate, and Time Application**

A plane travels with a tail wind from Kansas City, Missouri, to Denver, Colorado, a distance of 600 mi in 2 hr. The return trip against a head wind takes 3 hr. Find the speed of the plane in still air and find the speed of the wind.

Solution:

Let p represent the speed of the plane in still air.
Let w represent the speed of the wind.

Notice that when the plane travels with the wind, the net speed is $p + w$.
When the plane travels against the wind, the net speed is $p - w$.

The information given in the problem can be organized in a chart.

	Distance	Rate	Time
With a tail wind	600	$p + w$	2
Against a head wind	600	$p - w$	3

To set up two equations in p and w, recall that $d = rt$.

From the first row, we have

$$\begin{pmatrix}\text{Distance}\\\text{with the wind}\end{pmatrix} = \begin{pmatrix}\text{rate with}\\\text{the wind}\end{pmatrix}\begin{pmatrix}\text{time traveled}\\\text{with the wind}\end{pmatrix} \longrightarrow 600 = (p + w) \cdot 2$$

From the second row, we have

$$\begin{pmatrix}\text{Distance}\\\text{against the wind}\end{pmatrix} = \begin{pmatrix}\text{rate against}\\\text{the wind}\end{pmatrix}\begin{pmatrix}\text{time traveled}\\\text{against the wind}\end{pmatrix} \longrightarrow 600 = (p - w) \cdot 3$$

Using the distributive property to clear parentheses produces the following system:

$$2p + 2w = 600$$
$$3p - 3w = 600$$

The coefficients of the w-variable can be changed to 6 and -6 by multiplying the first equation by 3 and the second equation by 2.

$$2p + 2w = 600 \xrightarrow{\text{Multiply by 3.}} 6p + 6w = 1800$$
$$3p - 3w = 600 \xrightarrow[\text{Multiply by 2.}]{} \underline{6p - 6w = 1200}$$
$$12p \qquad = 3000$$

$$12p = 3000$$

$$\frac{12p}{12} = \frac{3000}{12}$$

$$p = 250 \qquad \text{The speed of the plane in still air is 250 mph.}$$

Answer

4. The speed of the canoe in still water is 5 mph. The speed of the current is 3 mph.

> **TIP:** To create opposite coefficients on the w-variables, we could have divided the first equation by 2 and divided the second equation by 3:
>
> $$2p + 2w = 600 \xrightarrow{\text{Divide by 2.}} p + w = 300$$
> $$3p - 3w = 600 \xrightarrow{\text{Divide by 3.}} \underline{p - w = 200}$$
> $$2p \qquad\quad = 500$$
> $$p = 250$$

$$2p + 2w = 600 \qquad \text{Substitute } p = 250 \text{ into the first equation.}$$
$$2(250) + 2w = 600$$
$$500 + 2w = 600$$
$$2w = 100$$
$$w = 50 \qquad \text{The speed of the wind is 50 mph.}$$

The speed of the plane in still air is 250 mph. The speed of the wind is 50 mph.

Section 11.4 Practice Exercises

Boost _your_ GRADE at ALEKS.com!

- • Practice Problems
- • Self-Tests
- • NetTutor
- • e-Professors
- • Videos

Review Exercises

For Exercises 1–4, solve each system of equations by three different methods:

a. Graphing method   **b.** Substitution method   **c.** Addition method

1. $-2x + y = 6$
  $2x + y = 2$

2. $x - y = 2$
  $x + y = 6$

3. $y = -2x + 6$
  $4x - 2y = 8$

4. $2x = y + 4$
  $4x = 2y + 8$

For Exercises 5–8, set up a system of linear equations in two variables to solve for the unknown quantities.

5. One number is eight more than twice another. Their sum is 20. Find the numbers.

6. The difference of two positive numbers is 264. The larger number is three times the smaller number. Find the numbers.

7. Two angles are complementary. The measure of one angle is 10° less than nine times the measure of the other. Find the measure of each angle.

8. Two angles are supplementary. The measure of one angle is 9° more than twice the measure of the other angle. Find the measure of each angle.

Objective 1: Applications Involving Cost

9. Kent bought three DVDs and two CDs for $62.50. Demond bought one DVD and four CDs for $72.50. Find the cost of one DVD and the cost of one CD. **(See Example 1.)**

10. Tanya bought three adult tickets and one child's ticket to a movie for $23.00. Li bought two adult tickets and five children's tickets for $30.50. Find the cost of one adult ticket and the cost of one children's ticket.

11. Linda bought 100 shares of a technology stock and 200 shares of a mutual fund for $3800. Her sister, Sandy, bought 300 shares of technology stock and 50 shares of a mutual fund for $5350. Find the cost per share of the technology stock and the cost per share of the mutual fund.

12. Two video games and three DVDs can be rented for $19.15. Four video games and one DVD can be rented for $17.35. Find the cost to rent one video game and the cost to rent one DVD.

13. Patricia buys a combination of 44¢ stamps and 29¢ stamps at the Post Office. If she spends exactly $20.50 on 50 stamps, how many of each type did she buy?

14. Bennett purchased some beef and some chicken for a family barbeque. The beef cost $6.00 per pound and the chicken cost $4.50 per pound. He bought a total of 18 lb of meat and spent $96. How much of each type of meat did he purchase?

Objective 2: Applications Involving Principal and Interest

15. Shanelle invested $10,000, and at the end of 1 yr, she received $805 in interest. She invested part of the money in an account earning 10% simple interest and the remaining money in an account earning 7% simple interest. How much did she invest in each account? **(See Example 2.)**

	10% Account	7% Account	Total
Principal invested			
Interest earned			

16. $12,000 was invested in two accounts, one earning 12% simple interest and the other earning 8% simple interest. If the total interest at the end of 1 yr was $1240, how much was invested in each account?

	12% Account	8% Account	Total
Principal invested			
Interest earned			

17. Troy borrowed a total of $12,000 in two different loans to help pay for his new Chevy Silverado. One loan charges 9% simple interest, and the other charges 6% simple interest. If he is charged $810 in interest after 1 yr, find the amount borrowed at each rate.

18. Blake has a total of $4000 to invest in two accounts. One account earns 2% simple interest, and the other earns 5% simple interest. How much should be invested in each account to earn exactly $155 at the end of 1 yr?

19. Suppose a rich uncle dies and leaves you an inheritance of $30,000. You decide to invest part of the money in a relatively safe bond fund that returns 8%. You invest the rest of the money in a riskier stock fund that you hope will return 12% at the end of 1 yr. If you need $3120 at the end of 1 yr to make a down payment on a car, how much should you invest at each rate?

20. As part of his retirement strategy, John plans to invest $200,000 in two different funds. He projects that the moderately high risk investments should return, over time, about 9% per year, while the low risk investments should return about 4% per year. If he wants a supplemental income of $12,000 a year, how should he divide his investments?

Objective 3: Applications Involving Mixtures

21. How much 50% disinfectant solution must be mixed with a 40% disinfectant solution to produce 25 gal of a 46% disinfectant solution? (See Example 3.)

	50% Mixture	40% Mixture	46% Mixture
Amount of solution			
Amount of disinfectant			

22. How many gallons of 20% antifreeze solution and a 10% antifreeze solution must be mixed to obtain 40 gal of a 16% antifreeze solution?

	20% Mixture	10% Mixture	16% Mixture
Amount of solution			
Amount of antifreeze			

23 How much 45% disinfectant solution must be mixed with a 30% disinfectant solution to produce 20 gal of a 39% disinfectant solution?

24. How many gallons of a 25% antifreeze solution and a 15% antifreeze solution must be mixed to obtain 15 gal of a 23% antifreeze solution?

25. A nurse needs 50 mL of a 16% salt solution for a patient. She can only find a 13% salt solution and an 18% salt solution in the supply room. How many milliliters of the 13% solution should be mixed with the 18% solution to produce the desired amount of the 16% solution?

26. Meadowsilver Dairy keeps two kinds of milk on hand, skim milk that has 0.3% butterfat and whole milk that contains 3.3% butterfat. How many gallons of each type of milk does the company need to produce 300 gallons of 1% milk for the P&A grocery store?

Objective 4: Applications Involving Distance, Rate, and Time

27. It takes a boat 2 hr to go 16 mi downstream with the current and 4 hr to return against the current. Find the speed of the boat in still water and the speed of the current. (See Example 4.)

	Distance	Rate	Time
Downstream			
Return			

28. A boat takes 1.5 hr to go 12 mi upstream against the current. It can go 24 mi downstream with the current in the same amount of time. Find the speed of the current and the speed of the boat in still water.

	Distance	Rate	Time
Upstream			
Downstream			

29. A plane can fly 960 mi with the wind in 3 hr. It takes the same amount of time to fly 840 mi against the wind. What is the speed of the plane in still air and the speed of the wind?

30. A plane flies 720 mi with the wind in 3 hr. The return trip takes 4 hr. What is the speed of the wind and the speed of the plane in still air?

31. Tony Markins flew from JFK Airport to London. It took him 6 hr to fly with the wind and 8 hr on the return flight against the wind. If the distance is approximately 3600 mi, determine the speed of the plane in still air and the speed of the wind.

32. A riverboat cruise upstream on the Mississippi River from New Orleans, Louisiana, to Natchez, Mississippi, takes 10 hr and covers 140 mi. The return trip downstream with the current takes only 7 hr. Find the speed of the riverboat in still water and the speed of the current.

Mixed Exercises

33. Debi has $2.80 in a collection of dimes and nickels. The number of nickels is five more than the number of dimes. Find the number of each type of coin.

34. A child is collecting state quarters and new $1 coins. If she has a total of 25 coins, and the number of quarters is nine more than the number of dollar coins, how many of each type of coin does she have?

35. In the 1961–1962 NBA basketball season, Wilt Chamberlain of the Philadelphia Warriors made 2432 baskets. Some of the baskets were free throws (worth 1 point each) and some were field goals (worth 2 points each). The number of field goals was 762 more than the number of free throws.

   a. How many field goals did he make and how many free throws did he make?

   b. What was the total number of points scored?

   c. If Wilt Chamberlain played 80 games during this season, what was the average number of points per game?

36. In the 1971–1972 NBA basketball season, Kareem Abdul-Jabbar of the Milwaukee Bucks made 1663 baskets. Some of the baskets were free throws (worth 1 point each) and some were field goals (worth 2 points each). The number of field goals he scored was 151 more than twice the number of free throws.

   a. How many field goals did he make and how many free throws did he make?

   b. What was the total number of points scored?

   c. If Kareem Abdul-Jabbar played 81 games during this season, what was the average number of points per game?

37. A small plane can fly 350 mi with a tailwind in $1\frac{3}{4}$ hr. In the same amount of time, the same plane can travel only 210 mi with a headwind. What is the speed of the plane in still air and the speed of the wind?

38. A plane takes 2 hr to travel 1000 mi with the wind. It can travel only 880 mi against the wind in the same amount of time. Find the speed of the wind and the speed of the plane in still air.

39. At the holidays, Erica likes to sell a candy/nut mixture to her neighbors. She wants to combine candy that costs $1.80 per pound with nuts that cost $1.20 per pound. If Erica needs 20 lb of mixture that will sell for $1.56 per pound, how many pounds of candy and how many pounds of nuts should she use?

40. Mary Lee's natural food store sells a combination of teas. The most popular is a mixture of a tea that sells for $3.00 per pound with one that sells for $4.00 per pound. If she needs 40 lb of tea that will sell for $3.65 per pound, how many pounds of each tea should she use?

41. A total of $60,000 is invested in two accounts, one that earns 5.5% simple interest, and one that earns 6.5% simple interest. If the total interest at the end of 1 yr is $3750, find the amount invested in each account.

42. Jacques borrows a total of $15,000. Part of the money is borrowed from a bank that charges 12% simple interest per year. Jacques borrows the remaining part of the money from his sister and promises to pay her 7% simple interest per year. If Jacques' total interest for the year is $1475, find the amount he borrowed from each source.

43. In the 1994 Super Bowl, the Dallas Cowboys scored four more points than twice the number of points scored by the Buffalo Bills. If the total number of points scored by both teams was 43, find the number of points scored by each team.

44. In the 1973 Super Bowl, the Miami Dolphins scored twice as many points as the Washington Redskins. If the total number of points scored by both teams was 21, find the number of points scored by each team.

Expanding Your Skills

45. In a survey conducted among 500 college students, 340 said that the campus lacked adequate lighting. If $\frac{4}{5}$ of the women and $\frac{1}{2}$ of the men said that they thought the campus lacked adequate lighting, how many men and how many women were in the survey?

46. During a 1-hr television program, there were 22 commercials. Some commercials were 15 sec and some were 30 sec long. Find the number of 15-sec commercials and the number of 30-sec commercials if the total playing time for commercials was 9.5 min.

Linear Inequalities and Systems of Inequalities in Two Variables

Section 11.5

1. Graphing Linear Inequalities in Two Variables

A **linear inequality in two variables** x and y is an inequality that can be written in one of the following forms: $Ax + By < C$, $Ax + By > C$, $Ax + By \leq C$, or $Ax + By \geq C$.

A solution to a linear inequality in two variables is an ordered pair that makes the inequality true. For example, solutions to the inequality $x + y < 3$ are ordered pairs (x, y) such that the sum of the x- and y-coordinates is less than 3. Several such examples are $(0, 0), (-2, -2), (3, -2)$, and $(-4, 1)$. There are actually infinitely many solutions to this inequality, and therefore it is convenient to express the solution set as a graph. The shaded area in Figure 11-10 represents all solutions (x, y), whose coordinates total less than 3.

Objectives

1. Graphing Linear Inequalities in Two Variables
2. Graphing Systems of Linear Inequalities in Two Variables

Concept Connections

Determine which of the ordered pairs are solutions to the inequality $y < 4x - 2$.
1. $(3, -1)$ **2.** $(0, 0)$

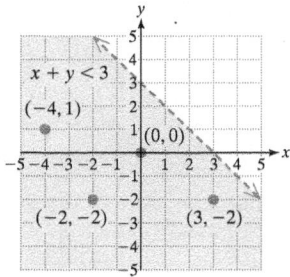

Figure 11-10

To graph a linear inequality in two variables we will use a process called the **test point method**. To use the test point method, first graph the related equation. In this case, the related equation represents a line in the xy-plane. Then choose a test point *not* on the line to determine which side of the line to shade. This process is demonstrated in Example 1.

Answers

1. Solution
2. Not a solution

Skill Practice

Graph the solution set.

3. $3x + 2y \geq -6$

Example 1   **Graphing a Linear Inequality in Two Variables**

Graph the solution set. $2x + y \leq 3$

Solution:

$2x + y \leq 3 \longrightarrow 2x + y = 3$ **Step 1:** Set up the related equation.

Step 2: Graph the related equation.

Graph the line by either setting up a table of points, or by using the slope-intercept form (Figure 11-11).

Figure 11-11

Table:

x	y
1	1
0	3
$\frac{3}{2}$	0

Slope-intercept form:

$$2x + y = 3$$
$$y = -2x + 3$$

Step 3: The solution to $2x + y \leq 3$ includes points for which $2x + y$ is less than *or equal to* 3. Because equality is included, points on the line $2x + y = 3$ are included. A solid line shows that the points on the line are included.

Now we must determine which side of the line to shade. To do so, we choose an arbitrary test point *not* on the line. The point $(0, 0)$ is a convenient choice.

Test point: $(0, 0)$

$$2x + y \leq 3$$
$$2(0) + (0) \overset{?}{\leq} 3$$
$$0 \overset{?}{\leq} 3 \checkmark \quad \text{True}$$

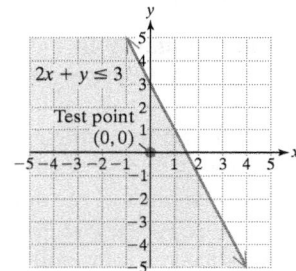

The test point $(0, 0)$ is true in the original inequality. This means that the region from which the test point was taken is part of the solution set. Therefore, shade below the line (Figure 11-12).

Figure 11-12

TIP: If a point above the line is selected as a test point, notice that it will *not* make the original inequality true. For example, test the point $(2, 2)$.

$$2x + y \leq 3$$
$$2(2) + (2) \overset{?}{\leq} 3$$
$$6 \overset{?}{\leq} 3 \quad \text{False}$$

A false result tells us to shade the *other* side of the line.

Answer

3.

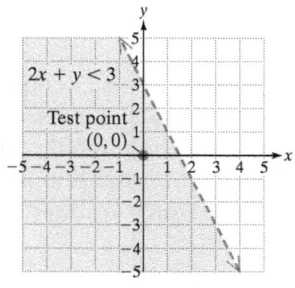

Now suppose the inequality from Example 1 had the strict inequality symbol, $<$. That is, consider the inequality $2x + y < 3$. The boundary line $2x + y = 3$ is *not* included in the solution set, because the expression $2x + y$ must be *strictly less than* 3 (not equal to 3). To show that the boundary line is not included in the solution set, we draw a dashed line (Figure 11-13).

Figure 11-13

The test point method to graph linear inequalities in two variables is summarized as follows:

PROCEDURE   Test Point Method: Summary

Step 1   Set up the related equation.

Step 2   Graph the related equation from step 1. The equation will be a boundary line in the xy-plane.
- If the original inequality is a strict inequality, $<$ or $>$, then the line is *not* part of the solution set. Graph the line as a *dashed line.*
- If the original inequality is not strict, $\leq$ or $\geq$, then the line *is* part of the solution set. Graph the line as a *solid line.*

Step 3   Choose a point not on the line and substitute its coordinates into the original inequality.
- If the test point makes the inequality true, then the region it represents is part of the solution set. Shade that region.
- If the test point makes the inequality false, then the other region is part of the solution set and should be shaded.

| **Example 2** | **Graphing a Linear Inequality in Two Variables** |

Graph the solution set. $4x - 2y > 6$

Solution:

$4x - 2y > 6 \longrightarrow 4x - 2y = 6$ **Step 1:** Set up the related equation.

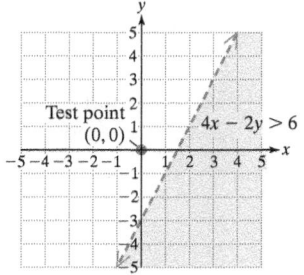

Figure 11-14

Step 2: Graph the equation. Draw a dashed line because the inequality is strict, $>$ (Figure 11-14).

Table:

x	y
0	-3
$\frac{3}{2}$	0
2	1

Slope-intercept form:

$$4x - 2y = 6$$
$$-2y = -4x + 6$$
$$y = 2x - 3$$

Step 3: Choose a test point. Again $(0, 0)$ is a good choice because, when substituted into the original inequality, the arithmetic will be minimal.

$$4x - 2y > 6$$
$$4(0) - 2(0) \overset{?}{>} 6$$
$$0 \overset{?}{>} 6 \quad \text{False}$$

The test point from above the line does not check in the original inequality. Therefore, shade below the line (Figure 11-15).

Figure 11-15

Answer

4.

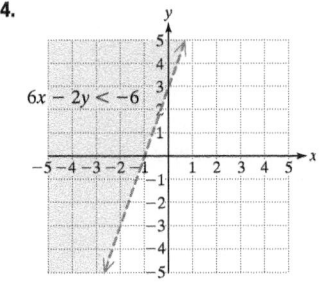

$6x - 2y < -6$

TIP: An inequality can also be graphed by first solving the inequality for *y*. Then,

- Shade *below* the line if the inequality is of the form $y < mx + b$ or $y \leq mx + b$.
- Shade *above* the line if the inequality is of the form $y > mx + b$ or $y \geq mx + b$.

From Example 2, we have

$$4x - 2y > 6$$
$$-2y > -4x + 6$$
$$\frac{-2y}{-2} < \frac{-4x}{-2} + \frac{6}{-2} \quad \text{Reverse the inequality sign.}$$
$$y < 2x - 3 \quad \text{Shade below the line.}$$

Graph the solution set.

5. $-2y < x$

Example 3   **Graphing a Linear Inequality in Two Variables**

Graph the solution set. $2y \geq 5x$

Solution:

$2y \geq 5x \longrightarrow 2y = 5x$ **Step 1:** Set up the related equation.

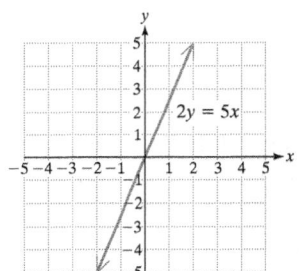

Figure 11-16

Step 2: Graph the equation. Draw a solid line because the symbol $\geq$ is used (Figure 11-16).

Table:

x	y
0	0
1	$\frac{5}{2}$
-1	$-\frac{5}{2}$

Slope-intercept form:

$$2y = 5x$$
$$y = \frac{5}{2}x$$

Step 3: The point $(0, 0)$ cannot be used as a test point because it is on the boundary line. Choose a different point such as $(1, 1)$.

$$2y \geq 5x$$
$$2(1) \overset{?}{\geq} 5(1)$$
$$2 \overset{?}{\geq} 5 \quad \text{False}$$

The test point from below the line does not check in the original inequality. Therefore, shade above the line (Figure 11-17).

Figure 11-17

Answer

5.

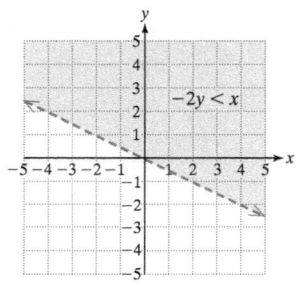

Example 4 **Graphing a Linear Inequality in Two Variables**

Graph the solution set. $2x > -4$

Solution:

$2x > -4 \longrightarrow 2x = -4$

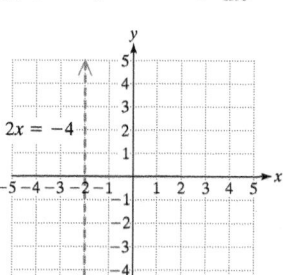

Figure 11-18

Step 1: Set up the related equation.

Step 2: Graph the equation. The equation represents a vertical line.

$$2x = -4$$

$$x = -2$$

Draw a dashed vertical line (Figure 11-18).

Step 3: Choose a test point such as $(0, 0)$.

$$2x > -4$$

$$2(0) \overset{?}{>} -4$$

$$0 \overset{?}{>} -4 \ \checkmark \quad \text{True}$$

The test point from the right of the line checks in the original inequality. Therefore, shade to the right of the line (Figure 11-19).

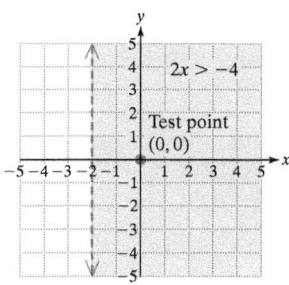

Figure 11-19

Skill Practice
Graph the solution set.
6. $4x \geq 12$

2. Graphing Systems of Linear Inequalities in Two Variables

In Sections 11.1–11.4, we studied systems of linear equations in two variables. Graphically, a solution to such a system is a point of intersection of two lines. In this section, we will study systems of linear *inequalities* in two variables. Graphically, the solution set to such a system is the intersection (or "overlap") of the shaded regions of the two inequalities.

Answer
6.

Skill Practice

Graph the solution set.

7. $x - 3y \geq 3$
   $y > -2x + 4$

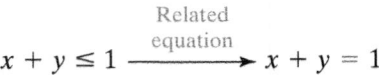

Example 5   **Graphing a System of Linear Inequalities**

Graph the solution set. $y > \dfrac{1}{2}x - 2$

$$x + y \leq 1$$

Solution:

Sketch each inequality.

$$y > \frac{1}{2}x - 2 \xrightarrow[\text{equation}]{\text{Related}} y = \frac{1}{2}x - 2 \qquad\qquad x + y \leq 1 \xrightarrow[\text{equation}]{\text{Related}} x + y = 1$$

The line $y = \dfrac{1}{2}x - 2$ is drawn in red in Figure 11-20. Substituting the test point $(0, 0)$ into the inequality results in a true statement. Therefore, we shade above the line.

The line $x + y = 1$ is drawn in blue in Figure 11-21. Substituting the test point $(0, 0)$ into the inequality results in a true statement. Therefore, we shade below the line.

Figure 11-20

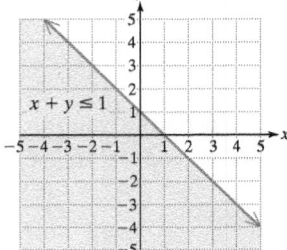

Figure 11-21

Next, we draw these regions on the same graph. The intersection ("overlap") is shown in purple (Figure 11-22).

In Figure 11-23, we show the solution to the system of inequalities. Notice that the portions of the lines not bounding the solution are dashed.

Figure 11-22

Figure 11-23

Answer

7.

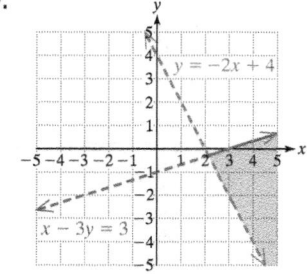

Section 11.5 Practice Exercises

Study Skills Exercise

1. Define the key terms:

   a. Linear inequality in two variables   **b. Test point method**

Review Exercises

For Exercises 2–4, graph the equations.

2. $x = -3$

3. $y = \dfrac{3}{5}x + 2$

4. $y = -\dfrac{4}{3}x$

          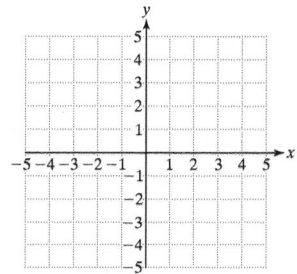

Objective 1: Graphing Linear Inequalities in Two Variables

5. When is a solid line used in the graph of a linear inequality in two variables?

6. When is a dashed line used in the graph of a linear inequality in two variables?

7. What does the shaded region represent in the graph of a linear inequality in two variables?

8. When graphing a linear inequality in two variables, how do you determine which side of the boundary line to shade?

9. Which is the graph of $-2x - y \leq 2$?

   a.   **b.**   **c.**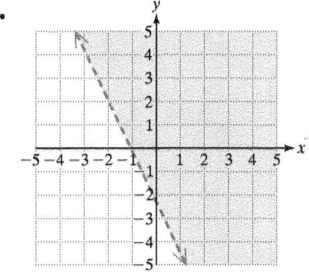

10. Which is the graph of $-3x + y > -1$?

a.

b.

c.

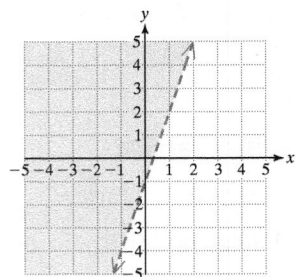

For Exercises 11–16, graph the solution set. Then write three ordered pairs that are solutions to the inequality. **(See Examples 1–4.)**

11. $y \geq -x + 5$

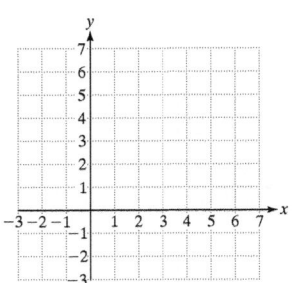

12. $y \leq 2x - 1$

13. $y < 4x$

14. $y > -5x$

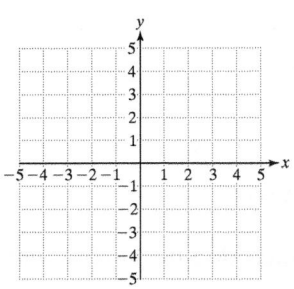

15. $3x + 7y \leq 14$

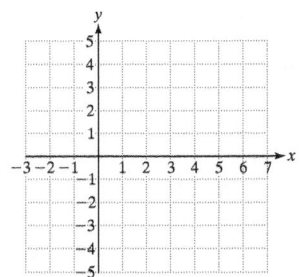

16. $5x - 6y \geq 18$

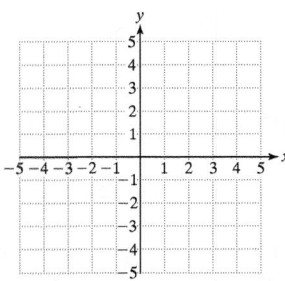

For Exercises 17–34, graph the solution set. **(See Examples 1–4.)**

17. $x - y > 6$

18. $x + y < 5$

19. $x \geq -1$

20. $x \leq 6$

 21. $y < 3$

22. $y > -3$

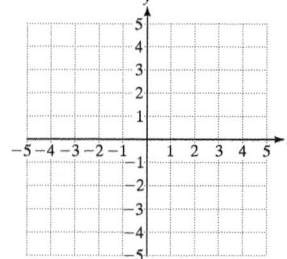

23. $y \leq -\dfrac{3}{4}x + 2$

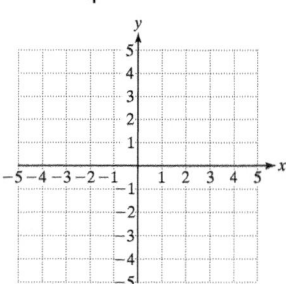

24. $y \geq \dfrac{2}{3}x + 1$

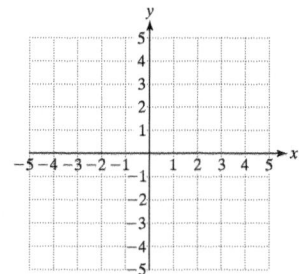

25. $y - 2x > 0$

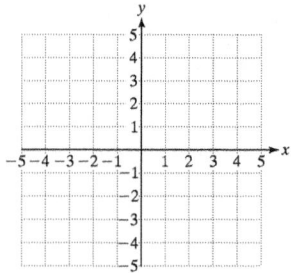

26. $y + 3x < 0$

27. $x \leq 0$

28. $y \leq 0$

 29. $y \geq 0$

30. $x \geq 0$

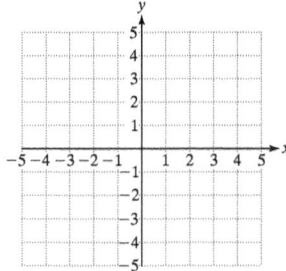

31. $-x \leq \dfrac{1}{2}y - 2$

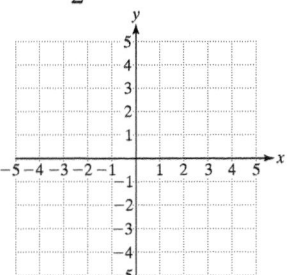

32. $-3 + 2x \leq -y$

33. $2x > 3y$

34. $-4x > 5y$

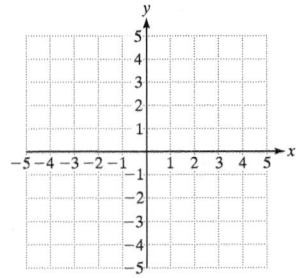

35. a. Describe the graph of the inequality $x + y > 4$. Find three solutions to the inequality. (Answers may vary.)

   b. Describe the graph of the equation $x + y = 4$. Find three solutions to the equation. (Answers may vary.)

   c. Describe the graph of the inequality $x + y < 4$. Find three solutions to the inequality. (Answers may vary.)

36. a. Describe the graph of the inequality $x + y < 3$. Find three solutions to the inequality. (Answers may vary.)

   b. Describe the graph of the equation $x + y = 3$. Find three solutions to the equation. (Answers may vary.)

   c. Describe the graph of the inequality $x + y > 3$. Find three solutions to the inequality. (Answers may vary.)

Objective 2: Graphing Systems of Linear Inequalities in Two Variables

For Exercises 37–54, graph the solution set. **(See Example 5.)**

37. $2x + y < 3$

   $y \geq x + 3$

38. $x + y < 3$

   $y - x \geq 0$

39. $x + \ y \geq -3$

   $x - 2y \geq 6$

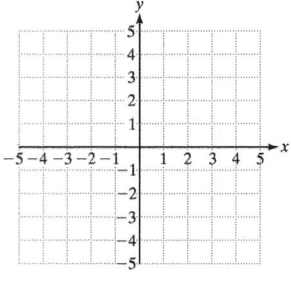

40. $y \geq -3x + 4$

   $x + y \leq 4$

41. $2x + 3y < 6$

   $3x + \ y > -5$

42. $-2x - \ y < 5$

   $x + 2y \geq 2$

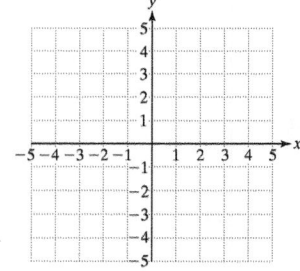

43. $y > 2x$

   $y > -4x$

44. $2y \geq 6x$

   $y \leq x$

45. $y < \dfrac{1}{2}x - 1$

   $5x + y \leq -12$

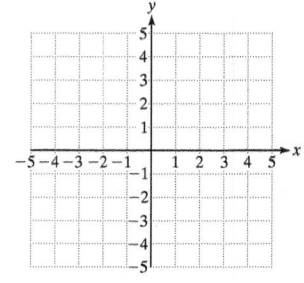

46. $y \geq \frac{1}{3}x + 2$

$4x + y < -2$

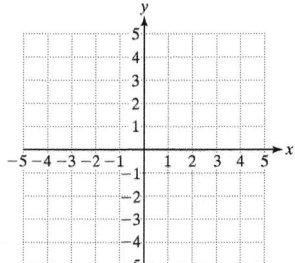

47. $y < 4$

$4x + 3y \geq 12$

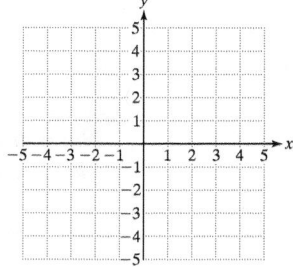

48. $x \geq -3$

$2x + 4y < 4$

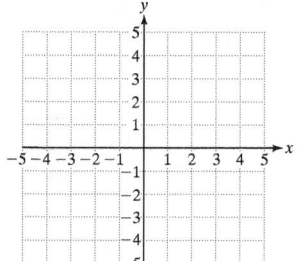

49. $x > -4$

$y \leq 3$

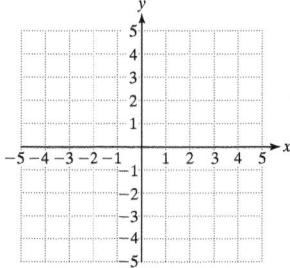

50. $x \leq 3$

$y > 1$

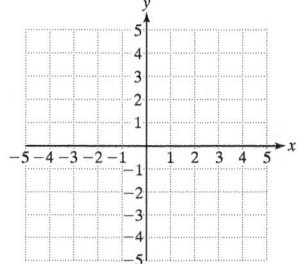

51. $2x \geq 5$

$6 > 3y$

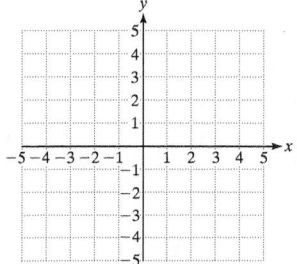

52. $4y \geq 6$

$8 > 2x$

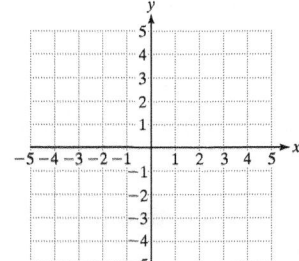

53. $x \geq -4$

$x \leq 1$

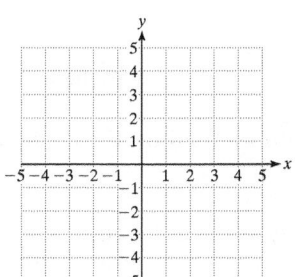

54. $y \geq -2$

$y \leq 3$

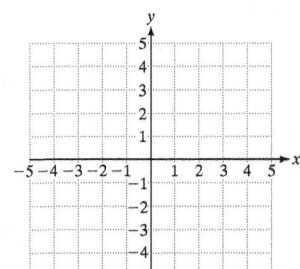

Group Activity

Creating Linear Models from Data

Materials: Two pieces of rope for each group. The ropes should be of different thicknesses. The piece of thicker rope should be between 4 and 5 ft long. The thinner piece of rope should be 8 to 12 in. shorter than the thicker rope. You will also need a yardstick or other device for making linear measurements.

Estimated Time: 30–35 minutes

Group Size: 4 (2 pairs)

1. Each group of 4 should divide into two pairs, and each pair will be given a piece of rope. Each pair will measure the initial length of rope. Then students will tie a series of knots in the rope and measure the new length after each knot is tied. (*Hint:* Try to tie the knots with an equal amount of force each time. Also, as the ropes are straightened for measurement, try to use the same amount of tension in the rope.) The results should be recorded in the table.

Thick Rope		Thin Rope	
Number of Knots, *x*	Length (in.), *y*	Number of Knots, *x*	Length (in.), *y*
0		0	
1		1	
2		2	
3		3	
4		4	

2. Graph each set of data points. Use a different color pen or pencil for each set of points. Does it appear that each set of data follows a linear trend? Draw a line through each set of points.

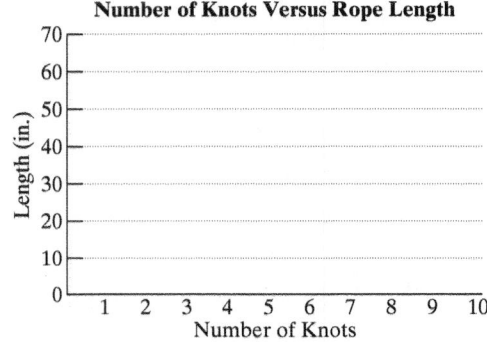

3. Each time a knot is tied, the rope decreases in length. Using the results from question 1, compute the average amount of length lost per knot tied.

For the thick rope, the length decreases by _____ inches per knot tied.

For the thin rope, the length decreases by _____ inches per knot tied.

4. For each set of data points, find an equation of the line through the points. Write the equation in slope-intercept form, $y = mx + b$.

[*Hint:* The slope of the line will be negative and will be represented by the amount of length lost per knot (see question 3). The value of b will be the original length of the rope.]

Equation for the thick rope: _____

Equation for the thin rope: _____

5. Next, you will try to predict the number of knots that you need to tie in each rope so that the ropes will be equal in length. To do this, solve the system of equations in question 4.

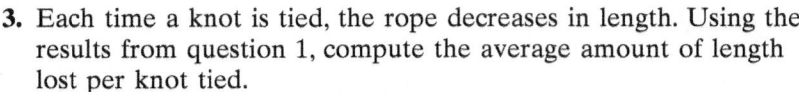

Solution to the system of equations: (_____, _____)

number of knots, *x* length, *y*

Interpret the meaning of the ordered pair in terms of the number of knots tied and the length of the ropes.

6. Check your answer from question 5 by actually tying the required number of knots in each rope. After doing this, are the ropes the same length? What is the length of each rope? Does this match the length predicted from question 5?

Chapter 11   Summary

Solving Systems of Equations by the Graphing Method

Key Concepts

A **system of two linear equations** can be solved by graphing.

A **solution to a system of linear equations** is an ordered pair that satisfies each equation in the system. Graphically, this represents a point of intersection of the lines.

There may be one solution, infinitely many solutions, or no solution.

One solution   Infinitely many solutions   No solution
Consistent   Consistent   Inconsistent
Independent   Dependent   Independent

A system of equations is **consistent** if there is at least one solution. A system is **inconsistent** if there is no solution.

If two equations represent the same line, the equations are said to be **dependent equations**. In this case, all points on the line are solutions to the system. If two equations represent two different lines, the equations are said to be **independent equations**. In this case, the lines either intersect at one point or are parallel, so the system has either one unique solution or no solution.

Examples

Example 1

Solve by graphing.

$x + y = 3$

$2x - y = 0$

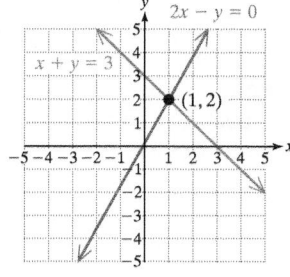

The solution is $(1, 2)$.

Example 2

Solve by graphing.

$3x - 2y = 2$

$-6x + 4y = 4$

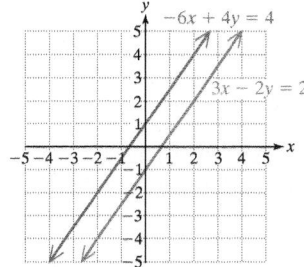

There is no solution. The system is inconsistent.

Example 3

Solve by graphing.

$x + 2y = 2$

$-3x - 6y = -6$

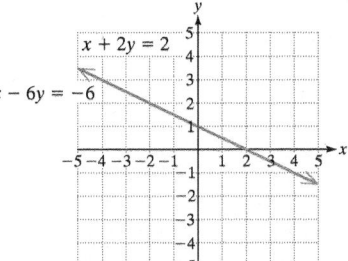

The equations are dependent, and the solution set consists of all points on the line, given by $\{(x, y) \mid x + 2y = 2\}$.

Section 11.2 Solving Systems of Equations by the Substitution Method

Key Concepts

Steps to Solve a System of Equations by Using the Substitution Method:

1. Isolate one of the variables from one equation.
2. Substitute the quantity found in step 1 into the other equation.
3. Solve the resulting equation.
4. Substitute the value found in step 3 back into the equation in step 1 to find the remaining variable.
5. Check the solution in both original equations and write the answer as an ordered pair.

An inconsistent system has no solution and is detected algebraically by a contradiction (such as $0 = 3$).

If two linear equations represent the same line, the equations are dependent. This is detected algebraically by an identity (such as $0 = 0$).

Examples

Example 1

Solve by the substitution method.

$$x + 4y = -11$$
$$3x - 2y = -5$$

Isolate x in the first equation: $x = -4y - 11$
Substitute into the second equation.

$$3(-4y - 11) - 2y = -5 \qquad \text{Solve the equation.}$$
$$-12y - 33 - 2y = -5$$
$$-14y = 28$$
$$y = -2$$

$$\qquad\qquad\qquad\qquad\qquad \text{Substitute}$$
$$x = -4y - 11 \qquad y = -2.$$
$$x = -4(-2) - 11 \qquad \text{Solve for } x.$$
$$x = -3$$

The solution is $(-3, -2)$ and checks in both original equations.

Example 2

Solve by the substitution method.

$$3x + y = 4$$
$$-6x - 2y = 2$$

Isolate y in the first equation: $y = -3x + 4$.
Substitute into the second equation.

$$-6x - 2(-3x + 4) = 2$$
$$-6x + 6x - 8 = 2$$
$$-8 = 2 \qquad \text{Contradiction}$$

The system is inconsistent and has no solution.

Example 3

Solve by the substitution method.

$$y = x + 2 \qquad y \text{ is already isolated.}$$
$$x - y = -2$$

$$x - (x + 2) = -2 \qquad \text{Substitute } y = x + 2 \text{ into the}$$
$$x - x - 2 = -2 \qquad \text{second equation.}$$
$$-2 = -2 \qquad \text{Identity}$$

The equations are dependent. The solution set is all points on the line $y = x + 2$ or $\{(x, y)| y = x + 2\}$.

Section 11.3   Solving Systems of Equations by Using the Addition Method

Key Concepts

Solving a System of Linear Equations

by Using the Addition Method:

1. Write both equations in standard form: $Ax + By = C$.
2. Clear fractions or decimals (optional).
3. Multiply one or both equations by a nonzero constant to create opposite coefficients for one of the variables.
4. Add the equations to eliminate one variable.
5. Solve for the remaining variable.
6. Substitute the known value into one of the original equations to solve for the other variable.
7. Check the solution in both equations.

Examples

Example 1

Solve by using the addition method.

$$5x = -4y - 7 \qquad \text{Write the first equation in}$$
$$6x - 3y = 15 \qquad \text{standard form.}$$

$$5x + 4y = -7 \xrightarrow{\text{Multiply by 3.}} 15x + 12y = -21$$
$$6x - 3y = 15 \xrightarrow{\text{Multiply by 4.}} \underline{24x - 12y = 60}$$
$$39x \qquad = 39$$
$$x = 1$$

$$5x = -4y - 7$$
$$5(1) = -4y - 7$$
$$5 = -4y - 7$$
$$12 = -4y$$
$$-3 = y \qquad \text{The solution is } (1, -3) \text{ and checks in both original equations.}$$

Section 11.4 Applications of Linear Equations in Two Variables

Examples

Example 1

A riverboat travels 36 mi with the current in 2 hr. The return trip takes 3 hr against the current. Find the speed of the current and the speed of the boat in still water.

Let x represent the speed of the boat in still water. Let y represent the speed of the current.

	Distance	Rate	Time
Against current	36	$x - y$	3
With current	36	$x + y$	2

Distance = (rate)(time)

$36 = (x - y) \cdot 3 \longrightarrow 36 = 3x - 3y$

$36 = (x + y) \cdot 2 \longrightarrow 36 = 2x + 2y$

$36 = 3x - 3y \xrightarrow{\text{Multiply by 2.}} 72 = 6x - 6y$

$36 = 2x + 2y \xrightarrow[\text{Multiply by 3.}]{} \dfrac{108 = 6x + 6y}{180 = 12x}$

$$180 = 12x$$

$$15 = x$$

$36 = 2(15) + 2y$

$36 = 30 + 2y$

$6 = 2y$

$3 = y$

The speed of the boat in still water is 15 mph, and the speed of the current is 3 mph.

Example 2

Diane borrows a total of $15,000. Part of the money is borrowed from a lender that charges 8% simple interest. She borrows the rest of the money from her mother and will pay back the money at 5% interest. If the total interest after one year is $900, how much did she borrow from each source?

	8%	5%	Total
Principal	x	y	15,000
Interest	0.08x	0.05y	900

$x + \quad y = 15{,}000$

$0.08x + 0.05y = \quad 900$

Substitute $x = 15{,}000 - y$ into the second equation.

$0.08(15{,}000 - y) + 0.05y = 900$

$1200 - 0.08y + 0.05y = 900$

$1200 - 0.03y = 900$

$-0.03y = -300$

$y = 10{,}000$

$x = 15{,}000 - 10{,}000$

$= 5{,}000$

The amount borrowed at 8% is $5,000.
The amount borrowed from her mother is $10,000.

| Section 11.5 | Linear Inequalities and Systems of Inequalities in Two Variables |

Key Concepts

A **linear inequality in two variables** can be written in one of the forms: $Ax + By < C$, $Ax + By > C$, $Ax + By \leq C$, or $Ax + By \geq C$.

Steps for Using the Test Point Method to Solve a Linear Inequality in Two Variables:

1. Set up the related *equation*.
2. Graph the related equation. This will be a line in the xy-plane.
   - If the original inequality is a strict inequality, $<$ or $>$, then the line is *not* part of the solution set. Therefore, graph the boundary as a dashed line.

   - If the original inequality is not strict, $\leq$ or $\geq$, then the line *is* part of the solution set. Therefore, graph the boundary as a solid line.

3. Choose a point not on the line and substitute its coordinates into the original inequality.
   - If the test point makes the inequality true, then the region it represents is part of the solution set. Shade that region.
   - If the test point makes the inequality false, then the other region is part of the solution set and should be shaded.

Example

Example 1

Graph the inequality. $2x - y < 4$

1. The related equation is $2x - y = 4$.
2. Graph the equation $2x - y = 4$ (dashed line).

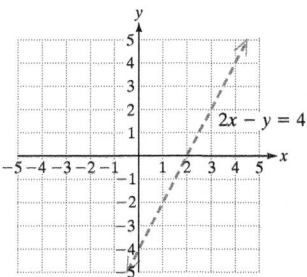

3. Choose an arbitrary test point not on the line such as $(0, 0)$.

$$2x - y < 4$$
$$2(0) - (0) \overset{?}{<} 4$$
$$0 \overset{?}{<} 4 \checkmark \quad \text{True}$$

Shade the region represented by the test point (in this case, above the line).

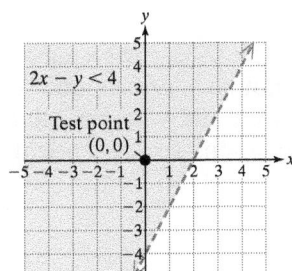

Chapter 11 Review Exercises

Section 11.1

For Exercises 1–4, determine if the ordered pair is a solution to the system.

1. $x - 4y = -4$ $(4, 2)$
$x + 2y = 8$

2. $x - 6y = 6$ $(12, 1)$
$-x + y = 4$

3. $3x + y = 9$ $(1, 3)$
$y = 3$

4. $2x - y = 8$ $(2, -4)$
$x = 2$

For Exercises 5–10, identify whether the system represents intersecting lines, parallel lines, or coinciding lines by comparing slopes and y-intercepts.

5. $y = -\dfrac{1}{2}x + 4$
$y = x - 1$

6. $y = -3x + 4$
$y = 3x + 4$

7. $y = -\dfrac{4}{7}x + 3$
$y = -\dfrac{4}{7}x - 5$

8. $y = 5x - 3$
$y = \dfrac{1}{5}x - 3$

9. $y = 9x - 2$
$9x - y = 2$

10. $x = -5$
$y = 2$

For Exercises 11–18, solve the systems by graphing. For systems that do not have one unique solution, state the number of solutions and whether the system is inconsistent or the equations are dependent.

11. $y = -\dfrac{2}{3}x - 2$
$-x + 3y = -6$

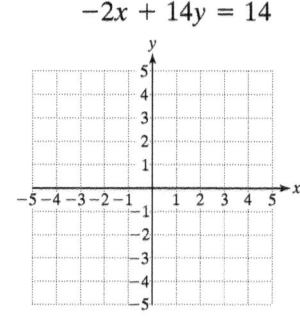

12. $y = -2x - 1$
$2x + 3y = 5$

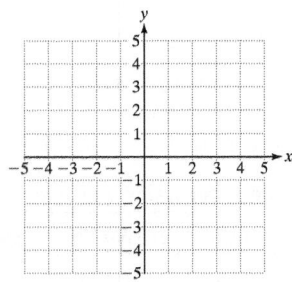

13. $4x = -2y + 10$
$2x + y = 5$

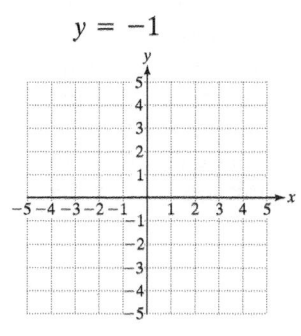

14. $10y = 2x - 10$
$-x + 5y = -5$

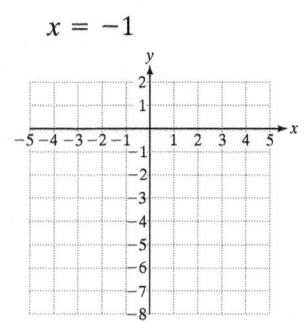

15. $6x - 3y = 9$
$y = -1$

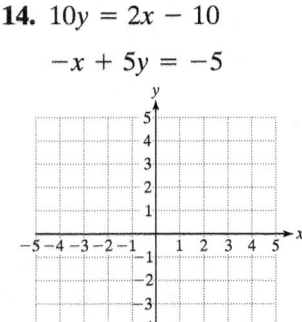

16. $5x + y = -11$
$x = -1$

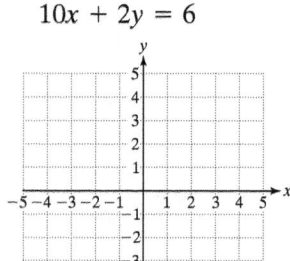

17. $x - 7y = 14$
$-2x + 14y = 14$

18. $y = -5x + 6$
$10x + 2y = 6$

19. A rental car company rents a compact car for $20 a day plus $0.25 per mile. A midsize car rents for $30 a day plus $0.20 per mile.

The cost, y_c, to rent a compact car for one day is given by the equation:

$y_c = 20 + 0.25x$ where x is the number of miles driven

The cost, y_m, to rent a midsize car for one day is given by the equation:

$y_m = 30 + 0.20x$ where x is the number of miles driven

Find the number of miles at which the cost to rent either car for a day would be the same. Confirm your answer with the graph.

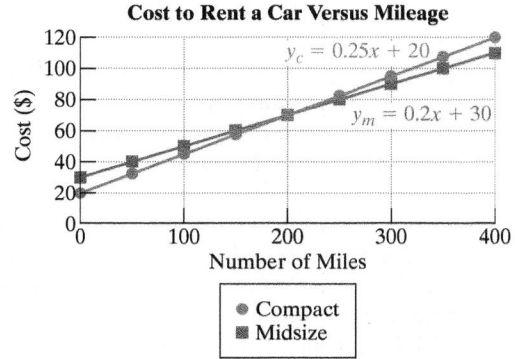

Cost to Rent a Car Versus Mileage

25. Given the system:

$$4x - 3y = 9$$
$$2x + y = 12$$

a. Which variable from which equation is easiest to isolate and why?

b. Solve the system using the substitution method.

For Exercises 26–29, solve the systems using the substitution method.

26. $3x - 2y = 23$
　　$x + 5y = -15$

27. $x + 5y = 20$
　　$3x + 2y = 8$

28. $x - 3y = 9$
　　$5x - 15y = 45$

29. $-3x + y = 15$
　　$6x - 2y = 12$

30. The difference of two positive numbers is 42. The larger number is 2 more than 6 times the smaller number. Find the numbers.

31. In a right triangle, one of the acute angles is 6° less than the other acute angle. Find the measure of each acute angle.

32. Two angles are supplementary. One angle measures 14° less than two times the other angle. Find the measure of each angle.

Section 11.2

For Exercises 20–23, solve the systems using the substitution method.

20. $6x + y = 2$
　　$y = 3x - 4$

21. $2x + 3y = -5$
　　$x = y - 5$

22. $2x + 6y = 10$
　　$x = -3y + 6$

23. $4x + 2y = 4$
　　$y = -2x + 2$

24. Given the system:

$$x + 2y = 11$$
$$5x + 4y = 40$$

a. Which variable from which equation is easiest to isolate and why?

b. Solve the system using the substitution method.

Section 11.3

33. Explain the process for solving a system of two equations using the addition method.

34. Given the system:

$$3x - 5y = 1$$
$$2x - y = -4$$

a. Which variable, x or y, is easier to eliminate using the addition method? (Answers may vary.)

b. Solve the system using the addition method.

35. Given the system:

$$9x - 2y = 14$$
$$4x + 3y = 14$$

a. Which variable, x or y, is easier to eliminate using the addition method? (Answers may vary.)

b. Solve the system using the addition method.

For Exercises 36–43, solve the systems using the addition method.

36. $2x + 3y = 1$

$x - 2y = 4$

37. $x + 3y = 0$

$-3x - 10y = -2$

38. $8x + 8 = -6y + 6$

$10x = 9y - 8$

39. $12x = 5y + 5$

$5y = -1 - 4x$

40. $-4x - 6y = -2$

$6x + 9y = 3$

41. $-8x - 4y = 16$

$10x + 5y = 5$

42. $\dfrac{1}{2}x - \dfrac{3}{4}y = -\dfrac{1}{2}$

$\dfrac{1}{3}x + y = -\dfrac{10}{3}$

43. $0.5x - 0.2y = 0.5$

$0.4x + 0.7y = 0.4$

44. Given the system:

$$4x + 9y = -7$$
$$y = 2x - 13$$

a. Which method would you choose to solve the system, the substitution method or the addition method? Explain your choice. (Answers may vary.)

b. Solve the system.

45. Given the system:

$$5x - 8y = -2$$
$$3x - y = -5$$

a. Which method would you choose to solve the system, the substitution method or the addition method? Explain your choice. (Answers may vary.)

b. Solve the system.

Section 11.4

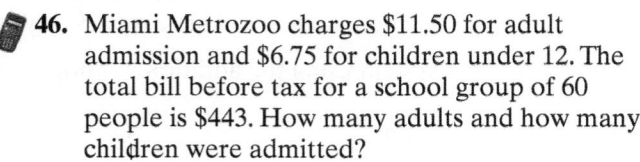
46. Miami Metrozoo charges $11.50 for adult admission and $6.75 for children under 12. The total bill before tax for a school group of 60 people is $443. How many adults and how many children were admitted?

47. As part of his retirement strategy Winston plans to invest $600,000 in two different funds. He projects that the high-risk investments should return, over time, about 12% per year, while the low-risk investments should return about 4% per year. If he wants a supplemental income of $30,000 a year, how should he divide his investments?

48. Suppose that whole milk with 4% fat is mixed with 1% low fat milk to make a 2% reduced fat milk. How much of the whole milk should be mixed with the low fat milk to make 60 gal of 2% reduced fat milk?

49. A boat travels 80 mi downstream with the current in 4 hr and 80 mi upstream against the current in 5 hr. Find the speed of the current and the speed of the boat in still water.

50. A plane travels 870 miles against a headwind in 3 hr. Traveling with a tailwind, the plane travels 700 mi in 2 hr. Find the speed of the plane in still air and the speed of the wind.

51. At Conseco Fieldhouse, home of the Indiana Pacers, the total cost of a soft drink and a hot dog is $8.00. The price of the hot dog is $1.00 more than the cost of the soft drink. Find the cost of a soft drink and the cost of a hot dog.

52. In a recent election 5700 votes were cast and 3675 voters voted for the winning candidate. If $\frac{5}{8}$ of the women and $\frac{2}{3}$ of the men voted for the winning candidate, how many men and how many women voted?

53. Ray played two rounds of golf at Pebble Beach for a total score of 154. If his score in the second round is 10 more than his score in the first round, find the scores for each round.

Section 11.5

For Exercises 54–57, graph the inequalities. Then write three ordered pairs that are in the solution set. (Answers may vary.)

54. $y < 3x - 1$

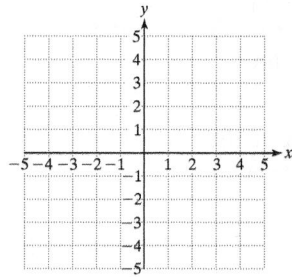

55. $y > -2x + 6$

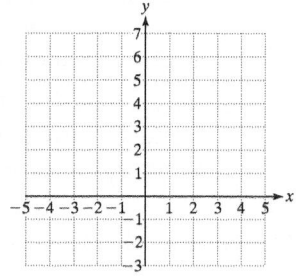

56. $-2x - 3y \geq 8$

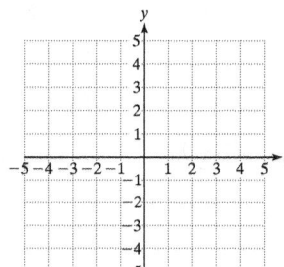

57. $4x - 2y \leq 10$

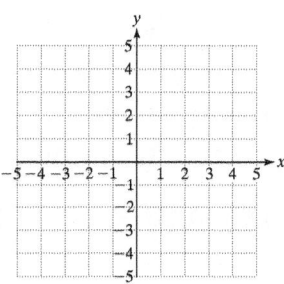

For Exercises 58–63, graph the solution set.

58. $x - 5y \geq 0$

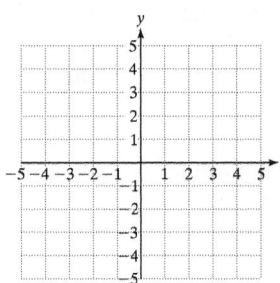

59. $7x - y \leq 0$

60. $x > 5$

61. $y < -4$

62. $y \geq 0$

63. $x \geq 0$

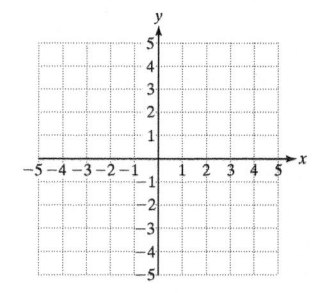

For Exercises 64–67, graph the solution set.

64. $2x - y \geq 8$
     $x + y \leq 3$

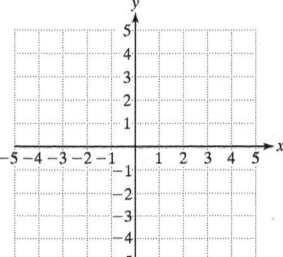

65. $y \leq x - 1$
     $x + 2y \geq 4$

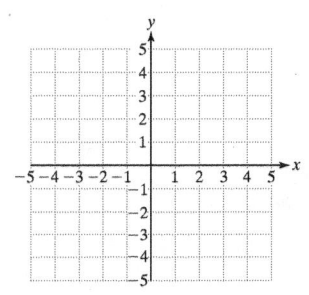

66. $y \leq 2x$
     $-2x - y > -3$

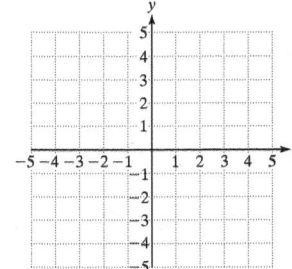

67. $y \leq 4$
     $2x - y < 1$

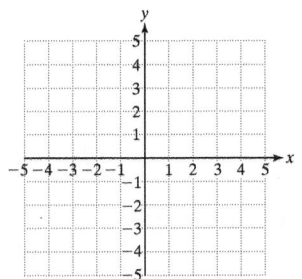

Chapter 11   Test

1. Write each line in slope-intercept form. Then determine if the lines represent intersecting lines, parallel lines, or coinciding lines.

$$5x + 2y = -6$$

$$-\frac{5}{2}x - y = -3$$

For Exercises 2–3 solve the system by graphing.

2. $y = 2x - 4$

   $-2x + 3y = 0$

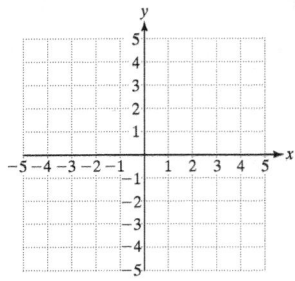

3. $2x + 4y = 6$

   $2y - 3 = -x$

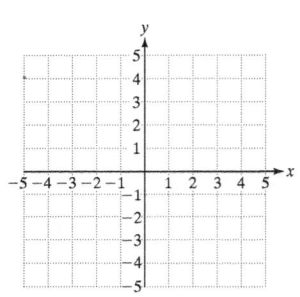

4. Solve the system using the substitution method.

$$x = 5y - 2$$

$$2x + y = -4$$

5. In the 2005 WNBA (basketball) season, the league's leading scorer was Sheryl Swoopes from the Houston Comets. Swoopes scored 17 points more than the second leading scorer, Lauren Jackson from the Seattle Storm. Together they scored a total of 1211 points. How many points did each player score?

6. Solve the system using the addition method.

$$3x - 6y = 8$$

$$2x + 3y = 3$$

7. How many milliliters of a 50% acid solution and how many milliliters of a 20% acid solution must be mixed to produce 36 mL of a 30% acid solution?

8. a. How many solutions does a system of two linear equations have if the equations represent parallel lines?

   b. How many solutions does a system of two linear equations have if the equations represent coinciding lines?

   c. How many solutions does a system of two linear equations have if the equations represent intersecting lines?

For Exercises 9–14, solve the systems using any method.

9. $\frac{1}{3}x + y = \frac{7}{3}$

   $x = \frac{3}{2}y - 11$

10. $2(x - 6) = y$

    $2x - \frac{1}{2}y = x + 5$

11. $3x - 4y = 29$

    $2x + 5y = -19$

12. $2x = 6y - 14$

    $2y = 3 - x$

13. $-0.25x - 0.05y = 0.2$

    $10x + 2y = -8$

14. $3x + 3y = -2y - 7$

    $-3y = 10 - 4x$

15. At Best Buy, Latrell buys four CDs and two DVDs for $54 from the sale rack. Kendra buys two CDs and three DVDs from the same rack for $49. What is the price per CD and the price per DVD?

16. The cost to ride the trolley one-way in San Diego is $2.25. Kelly and Hazel had to buy eight tickets for their group.

    a. What was the total amount of money required?

    b. Kelly and Hazel had only quarters and $1 bills. They also determined that they used twice as many quarters as $1 bills. How many quarters and how many $1 bills did they use?

17. Suppose a total of $5000 is borrowed from two different loans. One loan charges 10% simple interest, and the other charges 8% simple interest. How much was borrowed at each rate if $424 in interest is charged at the end of 1 yr?

18. During the first 13 yr of his football career, Jerry Rice scored a total of 166 touchdowns. One touchdown was scored on a kickoff return, and the remaining 165 were scored rushing or receiving. The number of receiving touchdowns he scored was 5 more than 15 times the number of rushing touchdowns he scored. How many receiving touchdowns and how many rushing touchdowns did he score?

19. A plane travels 910 mi in 2 hr against the wind and 1090 mi in 2 hr with the same wind. Find the speed of the plane in still air and the speed of the wind.

20. The number of calories in a piece of cake is 20 less than 3 times the number of calories in a scoop of ice cream. Together, the cake and ice cream have 460 calories. How many calories are in each?

21. How much 10% acid solution should be mixed with a 25% acid solution to create 100 mL of a 16% acid solution?

22. Graph the solution set. $5x - y \geq -6$.

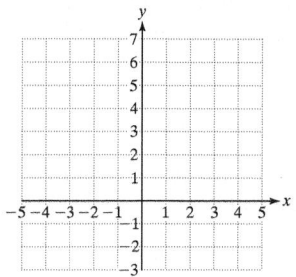

23. Graph the solution set.

$$2x + y > 1$$
$$x + y < 2$$

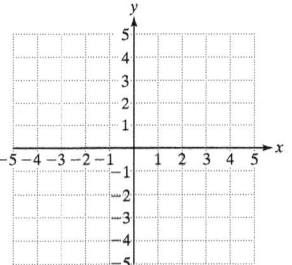

Chapters 1–11   Cumulative Review Exercises

1. Simplify.

$$\frac{|2-5| + 10 \div 2 + 3}{\sqrt{10^2 - 8^2}}$$

2. Find the perimeter and the area of a rectangle with length $5\frac{3}{8}$ in. and width $2\frac{3}{4}$ in.

For Exercises 3–4, fill in the blanks.

3. 42 oz = _____ lb   **4.** 92.5 cm = _____ mm

5. Solve the proportion. $\frac{18}{25} = \frac{x}{40}$

6. Find the mean, median, and mode for the following data values.   93, 83, 71, 84, 93, 80

7. Solve for x. $\frac{1}{3}x - \frac{3}{4} = \frac{1}{2}(x + 2)$

8. Solve for a. $-4(a + 3) + 2 = -5(a + 1) + a$

9. Solve for y. $3x - 2y = 6$

10. Solve for z. Graph the solution set on a number line and write the solution in interval notation:

$$-2(3z + 1) \leq 5(z - 3) + 10$$

11. The largest angle in a triangle is 110°. Of the remaining two angles, one is 4° less than the other angle. Find the measure of the three angles.

12. The YMCA wants to raise $2500 for its summer program for disadvantaged children. If the YMCA has already raised $900, what percent of its goal has been achieved?

13. Two angles are complementary. One angle measures 17° more than the other angle. Find the measure of each angle.

14. The slope of a given line is $-\frac{2}{3}$.

  a. What is the slope of a line parallel to the given line?

  b. What is the slope of a line perpendicular to the given line?

15. Find an equation of the line passing through the point $(2, -3)$ and having a slope of -3. Write the final answer in slope-intercept form.

16. Solve the system of equations.

$$2x + 5y = 10$$
$$2y = 4$$

17. a. Graph the line $2x + y = 3$.

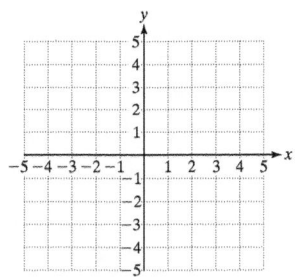

  b. Graph the inequality $2x + y < 3$.

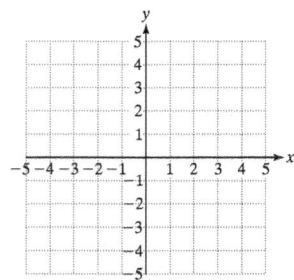

  c. Explain the difference between the graphs in parts (a) and (b).

18. How many gallons of a 15% antifreeze solution should be mixed with a 60% antifreeze solution to produce 60 gal of a 45% antifreeze solution?

19. Use a system of linear equations to solve for x and y.

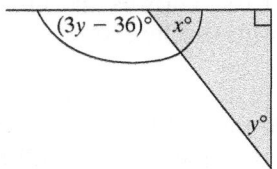

20. In 1920, the average speed for the winner of the Indianapolis 500 car race was 88.6 mph. By 1990, the average speed of the winner was 186.0 mph.

  a. Find the slope of the line shown in the figure. Round to one decimal place.

  b. Interpret the meaning of the slope in the context of this problem.

Polynomials and Properties of Exponents

12

CHAPTER OUTLINE

Chapter 12

In Chapter 12, we begin by covering the properties and applications of expressions involving exponents, including scientific notation. Then we introduce the concept of a polynomial and learn how to add, subtract, multiply, and divide polynomials.

Are You Prepared?

To help you prepare for this chapter, try the problems below to review the related skills that you will need for this chapter. Match the exercise on the left with the answer on the right. Then use the answers from Exercises 1–11 to fill in the blank with the correct key term.

Simplify.

1. 10^2 **2.** 10^5 **3.** -5^2 **4.** $(-5)^2$

Clear parentheses and combine like terms.

5. $3(2x + 4)$

6. $-8(2a - 4b + c)$

7. $-6x + 8x + x$

8. $-3x + 4 - 11x + 5$

9. $3(x + 2) - (x - 5)$

10. $-6(x - 7) - 2(x + 1)$

11. $-(-16a + 32b - 8c)$

F. $6x + 12$

F. 25

N. $-8x + 40$

T. $16a - 32b + 8c$

I. $-14x + 9$

C. $3x$

C. 100

E. $2x + 11$

E. -25

I. $-16a + 32b - 8c$

O. $100,000$

The numerical factor within a term is called the ___ ___ ___ ___ ___ ___ ___ ___ ___ ___ ___.

                                 1 2 3 4 5 6 7 8 9 10 11

Section 12.1 Exponents: Multiplying and Dividing Common Bases

1. Review of Exponential Notation

Recall that an **exponent** is used to show repeated multiplication of the **base**.

DEFINITION Definition of b^n

Let b represent any real number and n represent a positive integer. Then,

$$b^n = \underbrace{b \cdot b \cdot b \cdot b \cdot \ldots b}_{n \text{ factors of } b}$$

Skill Practice

For each expression, identify the base and exponent.

1. 8^3

2. $\left(-\dfrac{1}{4}\right)^2$

3. 0.2^4

Example 1 Evaluating Expressions with Exponents

For each expression, identify the exponent and base. Then evaluate the expression.

a. 6^2 **b.** $\left(-\dfrac{1}{2}\right)^3$ **c.** 0.8^4

Solution:

Expression	Base	Exponent	Result
a. 6^2	6	2	$(6)(6) = 36$
b. $\left(-\dfrac{1}{2}\right)^3$	$-\dfrac{1}{2}$	3	$\left(-\dfrac{1}{2}\right)\left(-\dfrac{1}{2}\right)\left(-\dfrac{1}{2}\right) = -\dfrac{1}{8}$
c. 0.8^4	0.8	4	$(0.8)(0.8)(0.8)(0.8) = 0.4096$

Note that if no exponent is explicitly written for an expression, then the expression has an implied exponent of 1. For example, $x = x^1$.

Consider an expression such as $3y^6$. The factor 3 has an exponent of 1, and the factor y has an exponent of 6. That is, the expression $3y^6$ is interpreted as $3^1 y^6$.

2. Evaluating Expressions with Exponents

Recall from Section 2.4 that particular care must be taken when evaluating exponential expressions involving negative numbers. An exponential expression with a negative base is written with parentheses around the base, such as $(-3)^2$.

To evaluate $(-3)^2$, we have: $(-3)^2 = (-3)(-3) = 9$

If no parentheses are present, the expression -3^2, is the *opposite* of 3^2, or equivalently, $-1 \cdot 3^2$.

$$-3^2 = -1(3^2) = -1(3)(3) = -9$$

Answers

1. Base 8; exponent 3

2. Base $-\dfrac{1}{4}$; exponent 2

3. Base 0.2; exponent 4

Example 2 **Evaluating Expressions with Exponents**

Evaluate each expression.

a. -5^4 **b.** $(-5)^4$ **c.** $(-0.2)^3$ **d.** -0.2^3

Solution:

a. -5^4

$= -1 \cdot 5^4$ 5 is the base with exponent 4.

$= -1 \cdot 5 \cdot 5 \cdot 5 \cdot 5$ Multiply -1 times four factors of 5.

$= -625$

b. $(-5)^4$

$= (-5)(-5)(-5)(-5)$ Parentheses indicate that -5 is the base with exponent 4.

$= 625$ Multiply four factors of -5.

c. $(-0.2)^3$ Parentheses indicate that -0.2 is the base with exponent 3.

$= (-0.2)(-0.2)(-0.2)$ Multiply three factors of -0.2.

$= -0.008$

d. -0.2^3

$= -1 \cdot 0.2^3$ 0.2 is the base with exponent 3.

$= -1 \cdot 0.2 \cdot 0.2 \cdot 0.2$ Multiply -1 times three factors of 0.2.

$= -0.008$

Example 3 **Evaluating Expressions with Exponents**

Evaluate each expression for $a = 2$ and $b = -3$.

a. $5a^2$ **b.** $(5a)^2$ **c.** $5ab^2$ **d.** $(b + a)^2$

Solution:

a. $5a^2$

$= 5(\ )^2$ Use parentheses to substitute a number for a variable.

$= 5(2)^2$ Substitute $a = 2$.

$= 5(4)$ Simplify.

$= 20$

b. $(5a)^2$

$= [5(\ )]^2$ Use parentheses to substitute a number for a variable. The original parentheses are replaced with brackets.

$= [5(2)]^2$ Substitute $a = 2$.

$= (10)^2$ Simplify inside the parentheses first.

$= 100$

c. $5ab^2$

$= 5(2)(-3)^2$ Substitute $a = 2, b = -3$.

$= 5(2)(9)$ Simplify.

$= 90$ Multiply.

d. $(b + a)^2$

$= [(-3) + (2)]^2$ Substitute $b = -3$ and $a = 2$.

$= (-1)^2$ Simplify within the parentheses first.

$= 1$

3. Multiplying and Dividing Common Bases

In this section, we investigate the effect of multiplying or dividing two quantities with the same base. For example, consider the expressions: x^5x^2 and $\frac{x^5}{x^2}$. Simplifying each expression, we have:

$$x^5x^2 = (x \cdot x \cdot x \cdot x \cdot x)(x \cdot x) = \overbrace{x \cdot x \cdot x \cdot x \cdot x \cdot x \cdot x}^{7 \text{ factors of } x} = x^7$$

$$\frac{x^5}{x^2} = \frac{x \cdot x \cdot x \cdot \cancel{x} \cdot \cancel{x}}{\cancel{x} \cdot \cancel{x}} = \frac{x \cdot x \cdot x}{1} = x^3$$

These examples suggest that to multiply two quantities with the same base, we add the exponents. To divide two quantities with the same base, we subtract the exponent in the denominator from the exponent in the numerator. These rules are stated formally in the following two properties.

PROPERTY **Multiplication of Like Bases**

Assume that b is a real number and that m and n represent positive integers. Then,

$$b^m b^n = b^{m+n}$$

PROPERTY **Division of Like Bases**

Assume that $b \neq 0$ is a real number and that m and n represent positive integers such that $m > n$. Then,

$$\frac{b^m}{b^n} = b^{m-n}$$

Example 4 **Simplifying Expressions with Exponents**

Simplify the expressions.

   a. w^3w^4 **b.** $2^3 \cdot 2^4$

Skill Practice

Simplify the expressions.
14. q^4q^8 **15.** $8^4 \cdot 8^8$

Solution:

a. w^3w^4 $(w \cdot w \cdot w)(w \cdot w \cdot w \cdot w)$

    $= w^{3+4}$ To multiply like bases, add the exponents.

    $= w^7$

b. $2^3 \cdot 2^4$ $(2 \cdot 2 \cdot 2)(2 \cdot 2 \cdot 2 \cdot 2)$

    $= 2^{3+4}$ To multiply like bases, add the exponents.
                     (The base is unchanged.)

    $= 2^7$ or 128

Avoiding Mistakes

When we multiply like bases, we add the exponents. The base does not change. In Example 4(b), we have $2^3 \cdot 2^4 = 2^7$.

Example 5 **Simplifying Expressions with Exponents**

Simplify the expressions.

   a. $\dfrac{t^6}{t^4}$ **b.** $\dfrac{5^6}{5^4}$

Skill Practice

Simplify the expressions.
16. $\dfrac{y^{15}}{y^8}$ **17.** $\dfrac{3^{15}}{3^8}$

Solution:

a. $\dfrac{t^6}{t^4}$ $\dfrac{t \cdot t \cdot t \cdot t \cdot t \cdot t}{t \cdot t \cdot t \cdot t}$

    $= t^{6-4}$ To divide like bases subtract the exponents.

    $= t^2$

b. $\dfrac{5^6}{5^4}$ $\dfrac{5 \cdot 5 \cdot 5 \cdot 5 \cdot 5 \cdot 5}{5 \cdot 5 \cdot 5 \cdot 5}$

    $= 5^{6-4}$ To divide like bases subtract the exponents.
                     (The base is unchanged.)

    $= 5^2$ or 25

Answers
14. q^{12} **15.** 8^{12}
16. y^7 **17.** 3^7

Example 6 Simplifying Expressions with Exponents

Simplify the expressions.

a. $\dfrac{z^4 z^5}{z^3}$ **b.** $\dfrac{10^7}{10^2 \cdot 10}$

Solution:

a. $\dfrac{z^4 z^5}{z^3}$

$= \dfrac{z^{4+5}}{z^3}$ Add the exponents in the numerator. (The base is unchanged.)

$= \dfrac{z^9}{z^3}$

$= z^{9-3}$ Subtract the exponents.

$= z^6$

b. $\dfrac{10^7}{10^2 \cdot 10}$

$= \dfrac{10^7}{10^2 \cdot 10^1}$ Note that 10 is equivalent to 10^1.

$= \dfrac{10^7}{10^{2+1}}$ Add the exponents in the denominator. (The base is unchanged.)

$= \dfrac{10^7}{10^3}$

$= 10^{7-3}$ Subtract the exponents.

$= 10^4$ or 10,000 Simplify.

4. Simplifying Expressions with Exponents

Example 7 Simplifying Expressions with Exponents

Use the commutative and associative properties of real numbers and the properties of exponents to simplify the expressions.

a. $(3p^2 q^4)(2pq^5)$ **b.** $\dfrac{16w^9 z^3}{4w^8 z}$

Solution:

a. $(3p^2 q^4)(2pq^5)$

$= (3 \cdot 2)(p^2 p)(q^4 q^5)$ Apply the associative and commutative properties of multiplication to group coefficients and like bases.

$= (3 \cdot 2)p^{2+1} q^{4+5}$ Add the exponents when multiplying like bases.

$= 6p^3 q^9$ Simplify.

b. $\dfrac{16w^9z^3}{4w^8z}$

$\quad = \left(\dfrac{16}{4}\right)\left(\dfrac{w^9}{w^8}\right)\left(\dfrac{z^3}{z}\right)$ Group coefficients and like bases.

$\quad = 4w^{9-8}z^{3-1}$ Subtract the exponents when dividing like bases.

$\quad = 4wz^2$ Simplify.

Section 12.1 Practice Exercises

For this exercise set, assume all variables represent nonzero real numbers.

Study Skills Exercise

1. Define the key terms:

    a. Exponent   **b. Base**

Objective 1: Review of Exponential Notation

For Exercises 2–9, identify the base and the exponent. **(See Example 1.)**

2. c^3 **3.** x^4 **4.** 5^2 **5.** 3^5

6. $(-4)^8$ **7.** $(-1)^4$ **8.** x **9.** q

 10. What base corresponds to the exponent 5 in the expression $x^3y^5z^2$?

11. What base corresponds to the exponent 2 in the expression w^3v^2?

12. What is the exponent for the factor of 2 in the expression $2x^3$?

13. What is the exponent for the factor of p in the expression pq^7?

For Exercises 14–22, write the expression using exponents.

14. $(4n)(4n)(4n)$ **15.** $(-6b)(-6b)$ **16.** $4 \cdot n \cdot n \cdot n$

17. $-6 \cdot b \cdot b$ **18.** $(x-5)(x-5)(x-5)$ **19.** $(y+2)(y+2)(y+2)(y+2)$

20. $\dfrac{4}{x \cdot x \cdot x \cdot x \cdot x}$ **21.** $\dfrac{-2}{t \cdot t \cdot t}$ **22.** $\dfrac{5 \cdot x \cdot x \cdot x}{(y-7)(y-7)}$

Objective 2: Evaluating Expressions with Exponents

For Exercises 23–30, evaluate the two expressions and compare the answers. Do the expressions have the same value? **(See Example 2.)**

23. -5^2 and $(-5)^2$ **24.** -3^4 and $(-3)^4$ **25.** -2^5 and $(-2)^5$ **26.** -5^3 and $(-5)^3$

27. $\left(\frac{1}{2}\right)^3$ and $\frac{1}{2^3}$ **28.** $\left(\frac{1}{5}\right)^2$ and $\frac{1}{5^2}$ **29.** $\left(\frac{3}{10}\right)^2$ and $(0.3)^2$ **30.** $\left(\frac{7}{10}\right)^3$ and $(0.7)^3$

For Exercises 31–38, evaluate the expressions.

31. 16^1 **32.** 20^1 **33.** $(-1)^{21}$ **34.** $(-1)^{30}$

35. $\left(-\frac{1}{3}\right)^2$ **36.** $\left(-\frac{1}{4}\right)^3$ **37.** $-\left(\frac{2}{5}\right)^2$ **38.** $-\left(\frac{3}{5}\right)^2$

For Exercises 39–46, simplify using the order of operations.

39. $3 \cdot 2^4$ **40.** $2 \cdot 0^5$ **41.** $-4(-1)^7$ **42.** $-3(-1)^4$

43. $6^2 - 3^3$ **44.** $4^3 + 2^3$ **45.** $2 \cdot 3^2 + 4 \cdot 2^3$ **46.** $6^2 - 3 \cdot 1^3$

For Exercises 47–58, evaluate each expression for $a = -4$ and $b = 5$. **(See Example 3.)**

47. $-4b^2$ **48.** $3a^2$ **49.** $(-4b)^2$ **50.** $(3a)^2$

51. $(a+b)^2$ **52.** $(a-b)^2$ **53.** $a^2 + 2ab + b^2$ **54.** $a^2 - 2ab + b^2$

55. $-10ab^2$ **56.** $-6a^3b$ **57.** $-10a^2b$ **58.** $-a^2b$

Objective 3: Multiplying and Dividing Common Bases

59. Expand the following expressions first. Then simplify using exponents.

   a. $x^4 \cdot x^3$ **b.** $5^4 \cdot 5^3$

60. Expand the following expressions first. Then simplify using exponents.

   a. $y^2 \cdot y^4$ **b.** $3^2 \cdot 3^4$

For Exercises 61–72, simplify the expressions. Write the answers in exponent form. **(See Example 4.)**

61. z^5z^3 **62.** w^4w^7 **63.** $a \cdot a^8$ **64.** p^4p

65. $4^5 \cdot 4^9$ **66.** $6^7 \cdot 6^5$ **67.** $\left(\frac{2}{3}\right)^3\left(\frac{2}{3}\right)$ **68.** $\left(\frac{1}{x}\right)\left(\frac{1}{x}\right)^2$

69. $c^5c^2c^7$ **70.** $b^7b^2b^8$ **71.** $x \cdot x^4 \cdot x^{10} \cdot x^3$ **72.** $z^7 \cdot z^{11} \cdot z^{60} \cdot z$

73. Expand the expressions. Then simplify.

   a. $\frac{p^8}{p^3}$ **b.** $\frac{8^8}{8^3}$

74. Expand the expressions. Then simplify.

   a. $\frac{w^5}{w^2}$ **b.** $\frac{4^5}{4^2}$

For Exercises 75–90, simplify the expressions. Write the answers in exponent form. **(See Examples 5–6.)**

75. $\dfrac{x^8}{x^6}$

76. $\dfrac{z^5}{z^4}$

77. $\dfrac{a^{10}}{a}$

78. $\dfrac{b^{12}}{b}$

79. $\dfrac{7^{13}}{7^6}$

80. $\dfrac{2^6}{2^4}$

81. $\dfrac{5^8}{5}$

82. $\dfrac{3^5}{3}$

83. $\dfrac{y^{13}}{y^{12}}$

84. $\dfrac{w^7}{w^6}$

85. $\dfrac{h^3 h^8}{h^7}$

86. $\dfrac{n^5 n^4}{n^2}$

87. $\dfrac{7^2 \cdot 7^6}{7}$

88. $\dfrac{5^3 \cdot 5^8}{5}$

89. $\dfrac{10^{20}}{10^3 \cdot 10^8}$

90. $\dfrac{3^{15}}{3^2 \cdot 3^{10}}$

Objective 4: Simplifying Expressions with Exponents (Mixed Exercises)

For Exercises 91–112, use the commutative and associative properties of real numbers and the properties of exponents to simplify the expressions. **(See Example 7.)**

91. $(2x^3)(3x^4)$

92. $(10y)(2y^3)$

93. $(5a^2b)(8a^3b^4)$

94. $(10xy^3)(3x^4y)$

95. $(r^6s^4)(13r^2s)$

96. $(6p^2q^8)(7p^5q^3)$

97. $s^3 \cdot t^5 \cdot t \cdot t^{10} \cdot s^6$

98. $c \cdot c^4 \cdot d^2 \cdot c^3 \cdot d^3$

99. $(-2v^2)(3v)(5v^5)$

100. $(10q^5)(-3q^8)(q)$

101. $\left(\dfrac{2}{3}m^{13}n^8\right)(24m^7n^2)$

102. $\left(\dfrac{1}{4}c^6d^6\right)(28c^2d^7)$

103. $\dfrac{14c^4d^5}{7c^3d}$

104. $\dfrac{36h^5k^2}{9h^3k}$

105. $\dfrac{z^3z^{11}}{z^4z^6}$

106. $\dfrac{w^{12}w^2}{w^4w^5}$

107. $\dfrac{25h^3jk^5}{12h^2k}$

108. $\dfrac{15m^5np^{12}}{4mp^9}$

109. $(-4p^6q^8r^4)(2pqr^2)$

110. $(-5a^4bc)(-10a^2b)$

111. $\dfrac{-12s^2tu^3}{4su^2}$

112. $\dfrac{15w^5x^{10}y^3}{-15w^4x}$

Expanding Your Skills

For Exercises 113–120, simplify the expressions using the addition or subtraction rules of exponents. Assume that a, b, m, and n represent positive integers.

113. $x^n x^{n+1}$

114. $y^a y^{2a}$

115. $p^{3m+5}p^{-m-2}$

116. $q^{4b-3}q^{-4b+4}$

117. $\dfrac{z^{b+1}}{z^b}$

118. $\dfrac{w^{5n+3}}{w^{2n}}$

119. $\dfrac{r^{3a+3}}{r^{3a}}$

120. $\dfrac{t^{3+2m}}{t^{2m}}$

| Section 12.2 | More Properties of Exponents |

Objectives

1. **Power Rule for Exponents**
2. **The Properties**
   $(ab)^m = a^m b^m$ and
   $\left(\dfrac{a}{b}\right)^m = \dfrac{a^m}{b^m}$

1. Power Rule for Exponents

The expression $(x^2)^3$ indicates that the quantity x^2 is cubed.

$$(x^2)^3 = (x^2)(x^2)(x^2) = (x \cdot x)(x \cdot x)(x \cdot x) = x^6$$

From this example, it appears that to raise a base to successive powers, we multiply the exponents and leave the base unchanged. This is stated formally as the power rule for exponents.

> **PROPERTY Power Rule for Exponents**
>
> Assume that b is a real number and that m and n represent positive integers. Then,
>
> $$(b^m)^n = b^{m \cdot n}$$

Skill Practice

Simplify the expressions.

1. $(y^3)^5$
2. $(2^8)^{10}$
3. $(q^5 q^4)^3$

| Example 1 | **Simplifying Expressions with Exponents** |

Simplify the expressions.

a. $(s^4)^2$ **b.** $(3^4)^2$ **c.** $(x^2 x^5)^4$

Solution:

a. $(s^4)^2$

$\quad = s^{4 \cdot 2}$ Multiply exponents. (The base is unchanged.)

$\quad = s^8$

b. $(3^4)^2$

$\quad = 3^{4 \cdot 2}$ Multiply exponents. (The base is unchanged.)

$\quad = 3^8$ or 6561

c. $(x^2 x^5)^4$

$\quad = (x^7)^4$ Simplify inside the parentheses by adding exponents.

$\quad = x^{7 \cdot 4}$ Multiply exponents. (The base is unchanged.)

$\quad = x^{28}$

2. The Properties $(ab)^m = a^m b^m$ and $\left(\frac{a}{b}\right)^m = \frac{a^m}{b^m}$

Consider the following expressions and their simplified forms:

$$(xy)^3 = (xy)(xy)(xy) = (x \cdot x \cdot x)(y \cdot y \cdot y) = x^3 y^3$$

$$\left(\frac{x}{y}\right)^3 = \left(\frac{x}{y}\right)\left(\frac{x}{y}\right)\left(\frac{x}{y}\right) = \left(\frac{x \cdot x \cdot x}{y \cdot y \cdot y}\right) = \frac{x^3}{y^3}$$

The expressions were simplified using the commutative and associative properties of multiplication. The simplified forms for each expression could have been reached in one step by applying the exponent to each factor inside the parentheses.

Answers

1. y^{15} 2. 2^{80} 3. q^{27}

PROPERTY Power of a Product and Power of a Quotient

Assume that a and b are real numbers. Let m represent a positive integer. Then,

$$(ab)^m = a^m b^m$$

$$\left(\frac{a}{b}\right)^m = \frac{a^m}{b^m}, \quad b \neq 0$$

Applying these properties of exponents, we have

$$(xy)^3 = x^3 y^3 \quad \text{and} \quad \left(\frac{x}{y}\right)^3 = \frac{x^3}{y^3}$$

Example 2 **Simplifying Expressions with Exponents**

Simplify the expressions.

a. $(-2xyz)^4$ **b.** $(5x^2y^7)^3$ **c.** $\left(\frac{2}{5}\right)^3$ **d.** $\left(\frac{1}{3xy^4}\right)^2$

Solution:

a. $(-2xyz)^4$

$= (-2)^4 x^4 y^4 z^4$ Raise each factor within parentheses to the fourth power.

$= 16x^4 y^4 z^4$

b. $(5x^2y^7)^3$

$= 5^3 (x^2)^3 (y^7)^3$ Raise each factor within parentheses to the third power.

$= 125x^6 y^{21}$ Multiply exponents and simplify.

c. $\left(\frac{2}{5}\right)^3$

$= \frac{(2)^3}{(5)^3}$ Apply the exponent to each factor in parentheses.

$= \frac{8}{125}$ Simplify.

d. $\left(\frac{1}{3xy^4}\right)^2$

$= \frac{1^2}{3^2 x^2 (y^4)^2}$ Square each factor within parentheses.

$= \frac{1}{9x^2 y^8}$ Multiply exponents and simplify.

Skill Practice

Simplify the expressions.

4. $(3abc)^5$ **5.** $(-2t^2w^4)^3$

6. $\left(\frac{3}{4}\right)^3$ **7.** $\left(\frac{2x^3}{y^5}\right)^2$

Answers

4. $3^5 a^5 b^5 c^5$ or $243 a^5 b^5 c^5$

5. $-8t^6 w^{12}$ **6.** $\frac{27}{64}$ **7.** $\frac{4x^6}{y^{10}}$

The properties of exponents can be used along with the properties of real numbers to simplify complicated expressions.

Skill Practice

Simplify the expression.

8. $\dfrac{(k^5)^2 k^8}{(k^2)^4}$

Example 3 **Simplifying Expressions with Exponents**

Simplify the expression. $\dfrac{(x^2)^6(x^3)}{(x^7)^2}$

Solution:

$\dfrac{(x^2)^6(x^3)}{(x^7)^2}$ Clear parentheses by applying the power rule.

$= \dfrac{x^{2\cdot6}x^3}{x^{7\cdot2}}$ Multiply exponents.

$= \dfrac{x^{12}x^3}{x^{14}}$

$= \dfrac{x^{12+3}}{x^{14}}$ Add exponents in the numerator.

$= \dfrac{x^{15}}{x^{14}}$

$= x^{15-14}$ Subtract exponents.

$= x$ Simplify.

Skill Practice

Simplify the expression.

9. $(4x^4y)(2x^3y^4)^4$

Example 4 **Simplifying Expressions with Exponents**

Simplify the expression. $(3cd^2)(2cd^3)^3$

Solution:

$(3cd^2)(2cd^3)^3$ Clear parentheses by applying the power rule.

$= 3cd^2 \cdot 2^3c^3d^9$ Raise each factor in the second parentheses to the third power.

$= 3 \cdot 2^3cc^3d^2d^9$ Group like factors.

$= 3 \cdot 8c^{1+3}d^{2+9}$ Add exponents on like bases.

$= 24c^4d^{11}$ Simplify.

Answers
8. k^{10} 9. $64x^{16}y^{17}$

Example 5 **Simplifying Expressions with Exponents**

Simplify the expression. $\left(\dfrac{x^7yz^4}{8xz^3}\right)^2$

Solution:

$\left(\dfrac{x^7yz^4}{8xz^3}\right)^2$

$= \left(\dfrac{x^{7-1}yz^{4-3}}{8}\right)^2$ First simplify inside the parentheses by subtracting exponents on like bases.

$= \left(\dfrac{x^6yz}{8}\right)^2$

$= \dfrac{(x^6)^2y^2z^2}{8^2}$ Apply the power rule of exponents.

$= \dfrac{x^{12}y^2z^2}{64}$

Skill Practice

Simplify the expression.

10. $\left(\dfrac{w^2xy^4}{6xy^3}\right)^2$

Answer

10. $\dfrac{w^4y^2}{36}$

Section 12.2   Practice Exercises

For this exercise set assume all variables represent nonzero real numbers.

Review Exercises

For Exercises 1–8, simplify.

1. $4^2 \cdot 4^7$

2. $5^8 \cdot 5^3 \cdot 5$

3. $a^{13} \cdot a \cdot a^6$

4. $y^{14}y^3$

5. $\dfrac{d^{13}d}{d^5}$

6. $\dfrac{3^8 \cdot 3}{3^2}$

7. $\dfrac{7^{11}}{7^5}$

8. $\dfrac{z^4}{z^3}$

9. Explain when to add exponents versus when to subtract exponents.

10. Explain when to add exponents versus when to multiply exponents.

Objective 1: Power Rule for Exponents

For Exercises 11–22, simplify and write answers in exponent form. **(See Example 1.)**

11. $(5^3)^4$

12. $(2^8)^7$

13. $(12^3)^2$

14. $(6^4)^4$

15. $(y^7)^2$

16. $(z^6)^4$

17. $(w^5)^5$

18. $(t^3)^6$

19. $(a^2a^4)^6$

20. $(z \cdot z^3)^2$

21. $(y^3y^4)^2$

22. $(w^5w)^4$

23. Evaluate the two expressions and compare the answers: $(2^2)^3$ and $(2^3)^2$.

24. Evaluate the two expressions and compare the answers: $(4^4)^2$ and $(4^2)^4$.

25. Evaluate the two expressions and compare the answers. Which expression is greater? Why?

$$2^{(2^4)} \quad \text{and} \quad (2^2)^4$$

26. Evaluate the two expressions and compare the answers. Which expression is greater? Why?

$$3^{(2^4)} \quad \text{and} \quad (3^2)^4$$

Objective 2: The Properties $(ab)^m = a^m b^m$ and $\left(\frac{a}{b}\right)^m = \frac{a^m}{b^m}$

For Exercises 27–42, use the appropriate property to clear the parentheses. (See Example 2.)

27. $(5w)^2$

28. $(4y)^3$

29. $(srt)^4$

30. $(wxy)^6$

31. $\left(\dfrac{2}{r}\right)^4$

32. $\left(\dfrac{1}{t}\right)^8$

33. $\left(\dfrac{x}{y}\right)^5$

34. $\left(\dfrac{w}{z}\right)^7$

35. $(-3a)^4$

36. $(2x)^5$

37. $(-3abc)^3$

38. $(-5xyz)^2$

39. $\left(-\dfrac{4}{x}\right)^3$

40. $\left(-\dfrac{1}{w}\right)^4$

41. $\left(-\dfrac{a}{b}\right)^2$

42. $\left(-\dfrac{r}{s}\right)^3$

Mixed Exercises

For Exercises 43–74, simplify the expressions. (See Examples 3–5.)

43. $(6u^2v^4)^3$

44. $(3a^5b^2)^6$

45. $5(x^2y)^4$

46. $18(u^3v^4)^2$

47. $(-h^4)^7$

48. $(-k^6)^3$

49. $(-m^2)^6$

50. $(-n^3)^8$

51. $\left(\dfrac{4}{rs^4}\right)^5$

52. $\left(\dfrac{2}{h^7k}\right)^3$

53. $\left(\dfrac{3p}{q^3}\right)^5$

54. $\left(\dfrac{5x^2}{y^3}\right)^4$

55. $\dfrac{y^8(y^3)^4}{(y^2)^3}$

56. $\dfrac{(w^3)^2(w^4)^5}{(w^4)^2}$

57. $(x^2)^5(x^3)^7$

58. $(y^3)^4(y^2)^5$

59. $(2a^2b)^3(5a^4b^3)^2$

60. $(4c^3d^5)^2(3cd^3)^2$

61. $(-2p^2q^4)^4$

62. $(-7x^4y^5)^2$

63. $(-m^7n^3)^5$

64. $(-a^3b^6)^7$

65. $\dfrac{(5a^3b)^4(a^2b)^4}{(5ab)^2}$

66. $\dfrac{(6s^3)^2(s^4t^5)^2}{(3s^4t^2)^2}$

67. $\left(\dfrac{2c^3d^4}{3c^2d}\right)^2$

68. $\left(\dfrac{x^3y^5z}{5xy^2}\right)^2$

69. $(2c^3d^2)^5\left(\dfrac{c^6d^8}{4c^2d}\right)^3$

70. $\left(\dfrac{s^5t^6}{2s^2t}\right)^2(10s^3t^3)^2$

71. $\left(\dfrac{-3a^3b}{c^2}\right)^3$

72. $\left(\dfrac{-4x^2}{y^4z}\right)^3$

73. $\dfrac{(-8b^6)^2(b^3)^5}{4b}$

74. $\dfrac{(-6a^2)^2(a^3)^4}{9a}$

Expanding Your Skills

For Exercises 75–82, simplify the expressions using the addition or subtraction properties of exponents. Assume that a, b, m, and n represent positive integers.

75. $(x^m)^2$

76. $(y^3)^n$

77. $(5a^{2n})^3$

78. $(3b^4)^m$

79. $\left(\dfrac{m^2}{n^3}\right)^b$

80. $\left(\dfrac{x^5}{y^3}\right)^m$

81. $\left(\dfrac{3a^3}{5b^4}\right)^n$

82. $\left(\dfrac{4m^6}{3n^2}\right)^b$

Definitions of b^0 and b^{-n}

In Sections 12.1 and 12.2, we learned several rules that enable us to manipulate expressions containing *positive* integer exponents. In this section, we present definitions that can be used to simplify expressions with negative exponents or with an exponent of zero.

Objectives

1. Definition of b^0
2. Definition of b^{-n}
3. Properties of Integer Exponents: A Summary

1. Definition of b^0

To begin, consider the following pattern.

$3^3 = 27$ Divide by 3.
$3^2 = 9$ Divide by 3.
$3^1 = 3$ Divide by 3.
$3^0 = 1$

As the exponents decrease by 1, the resulting expressions are divided by 3.

For the pattern to continue, we define $3^0 = 1$.

This pattern suggests that we should define an expression with a zero exponent as follows.

> **DEFINITION**   Definition of b^0
>
> Let b be a nonzero real number. Then, $b^0 = 1$.

Avoiding Mistakes

$b^0 = 1$ provided that b is not zero. Therefore, the expression 0^0 cannot be simplified by this rule.

Example 1   **Simplifying Expressions with a Zero Exponent**

Simplify (assume $z \neq 0$).

a. 4^0 **b.** $(-4)^0$ **c.** -4^0

d. z^0 **e.** $-4z^0$ **f.** $(4z)^0$

Solution:

a. $4^0 = 1$ By definition

b. $(-4)^0 = 1$ By definition

c. $-4^0 = -1 \cdot 4^0 = -1 \cdot 1 = -1$ The exponent 0 applies only to 4.

d. $z^0 = 1$ By definition

e. $-4z^0 = -4 \cdot z^0 = -4 \cdot 1 = -4$ The exponent 0 applies only to z.

f. $(4z)^0 = 1$ The parentheses indicate that the exponent, 0, applies to both factors 4 and z.

Skill Practice

Evaluate the expressions. Assume all variables represent nonzero real numbers.

1. 7^0 **2.** $(-7)^0$
3. -5^0 **4.** y^0
5. $-2x^0$ **6.** $(2x)^0$

The definition of b^0 is consistent with the other properties of exponents learned thus far. For example, we know that $1 = \frac{5^3}{5^3}$. If we subtract exponents, the result is 5^0.

Subtract exponents.

$$1 = \frac{5^3}{5^3} = 5^{3-3} = 5^0.$$ Therefore, 5^0 must be defined as 1.

Answers
1. 1   **2.** 1   **3.** -1
4. 1   **5.** -2 **6.** 1

2. Definition of b^{-n}

To understand the concept of a *negative* exponent, consider the following pattern.

$3^3 = 27$

$\quad\searrow$ Divide by 3.

$3^2 = 9$

$\quad\searrow$ Divide by 3. As the exponents decrease by

$3^1 = 3$ 1, the resulting expressions are

$\quad\searrow$ Divide by 3. divided by 3.

$3^0 = 1$

$\quad\searrow$ Divide by 3.

$3^{-1} = \dfrac{1}{3}$ $\longleftarrow$ For the pattern to continue, we define $3^{-1} = \dfrac{1}{3^1} = \dfrac{1}{3}$.

$3^{-2} = \dfrac{1}{9}$ $\longleftarrow$ For the pattern to continue, we define $3^{-2} = \dfrac{1}{3^2} = \dfrac{1}{9}$.

$3^{-3} = \dfrac{1}{27}$ $\longleftarrow$ For the pattern to continue, we define $3^{-3} = \dfrac{1}{3^3} = \dfrac{1}{27}$.

This pattern suggests that $3^{-n} = \frac{1}{3^n}$ for all integers, n. In general, we have the following definition involving negative exponents.

> **DEFINITION** Definition of b^{-n}
>
> Let n be an integer and b be a nonzero real number. Then,
> $$b^{-n} = \left(\dfrac{1}{b}\right)^n \quad \text{or} \quad \dfrac{1}{b^n}$$

The definition of b^{-n} implies that to evaluate b^{-n}, take the reciprocal of the base and change the sign of the exponent.

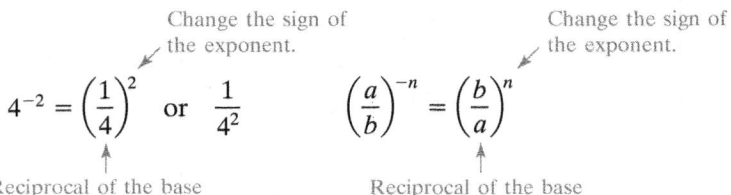

$$4^{-2} = \left(\dfrac{1}{4}\right)^2 \quad \text{or} \quad \dfrac{1}{4^2} \qquad \left(\dfrac{a}{b}\right)^{-n} = \left(\dfrac{b}{a}\right)^n$$

Example 2 Simplifying Expressions with Negative Exponents

Simplify. Assume that $c \neq 0$.   **a.** c^{-3} **b.** 5^{-1} **c.** $(-3)^{-4}$

Solution:

a. $c^{-3} = \dfrac{1}{c^3}$ By definition

b. $5^{-1} = \dfrac{1}{5^1}$ By definition

$\quad\quad = \dfrac{1}{5}$ Simplify.

c. $(-3)^{-4} = \dfrac{1}{(-3)^4}$ The base is -3 and must be enclosed in parentheses.

$\quad\quad\quad = \dfrac{1}{81}$ Simplify. Note that $(-3)^4 = (-3)(-3)(-3)(-3) = 81$.

Example 3   **Simplifying Expressions with Negative Exponents**

Simplify. Assume that $y \neq 0$.   **a.** $\left(\dfrac{1}{4}\right)^{-2}$ **b.** $\left(-\dfrac{3}{5}\right)^{-3}$ **c.** $\dfrac{1}{y^{-5}}$

Skill Practice

Simplify. Assume $w \neq 0$.

10. $\left(\dfrac{1}{3}\right)^{-1}$

11. $\left(-\dfrac{2}{5}\right)^{-2}$

12. $\dfrac{1}{w^{-7}}$

Solution:

a. $\left(\dfrac{1}{4}\right)^{-2} = 4^2$ Take the reciprocal of the base and change the sign of the exponent.

        $= 16$ Simplify.

b. $\left(-\dfrac{3}{5}\right)^{-3} = \left(-\dfrac{5}{3}\right)^{3}$ Take the reciprocal of the base and change the sign of the exponent.

        $= -\dfrac{125}{27}$ Simplify.

c. $\dfrac{1}{y^{-5}} = \left(\dfrac{1}{y}\right)^{-5}$ Apply the power of a quotient rule from Section 5.2.

        $= (y)^5$ Take the reciprocal of the base and change the sign of the exponent.

        $= y^5$

Example 4   **Simplifying Expressions with Negative Exponents**

Simplify. Assume that $x \neq 0$.   **a.** $(5x)^{-3}$ **b.** $5x^{-3}$ **c.** $-5x^{-3}$

Skill Practice

Simplify. Assume $w \neq 0$.

13. $(2w)^{-4}$

14. $2w^{-4}$

15. $-2w^{-4}$

Solution:

a. $(5x)^{-3} = \left(\dfrac{1}{5x}\right)^{3}$ Take the reciprocal of the base and change the sign of the exponent.

        $= \dfrac{(1)^3}{(5x)^3}$ Apply the exponent of 3 to each factor within parentheses.

        $= \dfrac{1}{125x^3}$ Simplify.

b. $5x^{-3} = 5 \cdot x^{-3}$ Note that the exponent, -3, applies only to x.

        $= 5 \cdot \dfrac{1}{x^3}$ Rewrite x^{-3} as $\dfrac{1}{x^3}$.

        $= \dfrac{5}{x^3}$ Multiply.

c. $-5x^{-3} = -5 \cdot x^{-3}$ Note that the exponent, -3, applies only to x, and that -5 is a coefficient.

        $= -5 \cdot \dfrac{1}{x^3}$ Rewrite x^{-3} as $\dfrac{1}{x^3}$.

        $= -\dfrac{5}{x^3}$ Multiply.

Answers

10. 3   **11.** $\dfrac{25}{4}$ **12.** w^7

13. $\dfrac{1}{16w^4}$ **14.** $\dfrac{2}{w^4}$ **15.** $-\dfrac{2}{w^4}$

It is important to note that the definition of b^{-n} is consistent with the other properties of exponents learned thus far. For example, consider the expression

$$\frac{x^4}{x^7} = \frac{\cancel{x} \cdot \cancel{x} \cdot \cancel{x} \cdot \cancel{x}}{\cancel{x} \cdot \cancel{x} \cdot \cancel{x} \cdot \cancel{x} \cdot x \cdot x \cdot x} = \frac{1}{x^3}$$

Subtract exponents.

Hence, $x^{-3} = \dfrac{1}{x^3}$

By subtracting exponents, we have $\dfrac{x^4}{x^7} = x^{4-7} = x^{-3}$

3. Properties of Integer Exponents: A Summary

The definitions of b^0 and b^{-n} allow us to extend the properties of exponents learned in Sections 12.1 and 12.2 to include integer exponents. These are summarized in Table 12-1.

Table 12-1

Properties of Integer Exponents		
Assume that a and b are real numbers ($b \neq 0$) and that m and n represent integers.		
Property	**Example**	**Details/Notes**
Multiplication of Like Bases $b^m b^n = b^{m+n}$	$b^2 b^4 = b^{2+4} = b^6$	$b^2 b^4 = (b \cdot b)(b \cdot b \cdot b \cdot b) = b^6$
Division of Like Bases $\dfrac{b^m}{b^n} = b^{m-n}$	$\dfrac{b^5}{b^2} = b^{5-2} = b^3$	$\dfrac{b^5}{b^2} = \dfrac{\cancel{b} \cdot \cancel{b} \cdot b \cdot b \cdot b}{\cancel{b} \cdot \cancel{b}} = b^3$
The Power Rule $(b^m)^n = b^{m \cdot n}$	$(b^4)^2 = b^{4 \cdot 2} = b^8$	$(b^4)^2 = (b \cdot b \cdot b \cdot b)(b \cdot b \cdot b \cdot b) = b^8$
Power of a Product $(ab)^m = a^m b^m$	$(ab)^3 = a^3 b^3$	$(ab)^3 = (ab)(ab)(ab)$ $= (a \cdot a \cdot a)(b \cdot b \cdot b) = a^3 b^3$
Power of a Quotient $\left(\dfrac{a}{b}\right)^m = \dfrac{a^m}{b^m}$	$\left(\dfrac{a}{b}\right)^3 = \dfrac{a^3}{b^3}$	$\left(\dfrac{a}{b}\right)^3 = \left(\dfrac{a}{b}\right)\left(\dfrac{a}{b}\right)\left(\dfrac{a}{b}\right) = \dfrac{a \cdot a \cdot a}{b \cdot b \cdot b} = \dfrac{a^3}{b^3}$

Definitions		
Assume that b is a real number ($b \neq 0$) and that n represents an integer.		
Definition	**Example**	**Details/Notes**
$b^0 = 1$	$(4)^0 = 1$	Any nonzero quantity raised to the zero power equals 1.
$b^{-n} = \left(\dfrac{1}{b}\right)^n = \dfrac{1}{b^n}$	$b^{-5} = \left(\dfrac{1}{b}\right)^5 = \dfrac{1}{b^5}$	To simplify a negative exponent, take the reciprocal of the base and make the exponent positive.

Example 5 Simplifying Expressions with Exponents

Simplify the expressions. Write the answers with positive exponents only. Assume all variables are nonzero.

a. $\dfrac{a^3 b^{-2}}{c^{-5}}$ **b.** $\dfrac{x^2 x^{-7}}{x^3}$ **c.** $\dfrac{z^2}{w^{-4} w^4 z^{-8}}$

Solution:

a. $\dfrac{a^3 b^{-2}}{c^{-5}}$

$\quad = \dfrac{a^3}{1} \cdot \dfrac{b^{-2}}{1} \cdot \dfrac{1}{c^{-5}}$

$\quad = \dfrac{a^3}{1} \cdot \dfrac{1}{b^2} \cdot \dfrac{c^5}{1}$ Simplify negative exponents.

$\quad = \dfrac{a^3 c^5}{b^2}$ Multiply.

b. $\dfrac{x^2 x^{-7}}{x^3}$

$\quad = \dfrac{x^{2+(-7)}}{x^3}$ Add the exponents in the numerator.

$\quad = \dfrac{x^{-5}}{x^3}$ Simplify.

$\quad = x^{-5-3}$ Subtract the exponents.

$\quad = x^{-8}$

$\quad = \dfrac{1}{x^8}$ Simplify the negative exponent.

c. $\dfrac{z^2}{w^{-4} w^4 z^{-8}}$

$\quad = \dfrac{z^2}{w^{-4+4} z^{-8}}$ Add the exponents in the denominator.

$\quad = \dfrac{z^2}{w^0 z^{-8}}$

$\quad = \dfrac{z^2}{(1) z^{-8}}$ Recall that $w^0 = 1$.

$\quad = z^{2-(-8)}$ Subtract the exponents.

$\quad = z^{10}$ Simplify.

Skill Practice

Simplify the expressions. Assume all variables are nonzero.

16. $\dfrac{x^{-6}}{y^4 z^{-8}}$

17. $\dfrac{x^3 x^{-8}}{x^4}$

18. $\dfrac{p^3}{w^7 w^{-7} z^{-2}}$

Answers

16. $\dfrac{z^8}{y^4 x^6}$ **17.** $\dfrac{1}{x^9}$ **18.** $p^3 z^2$

Skill Practice

Simplify the expressions. Assume all variables are nonzero.

19. $(-5x^{-2}y^3)^{-2}$

20. $\left(\dfrac{3x^{-3}y^{-2}}{4xy^{-3}}\right)^{-2}$

Example 6   **Simplifying Expressions with Exponents**

Simplify the expressions. Write the answers with positive exponents only. Assume that all variables are nonzero.

a. $(-4ab^{-2})^{-3}$ **b.** $\left(\dfrac{2p^{-4}q^3}{5p^2q}\right)^{-2}$

Solution:

a. $(-4ab^{-2})^{-3}$

$= (-4)^{-3}a^{-3}(b^{-2})^{-3}$ Apply the power rule of exponents.

$= (-4)^{-3}a^{-3}b^6$

$= \dfrac{1}{(-4)^3} \cdot \dfrac{1}{a^3} \cdot b^6$ Simplify the negative exponents.

$= \dfrac{1}{-64} \cdot \dfrac{1}{a^3} \cdot b^6$ Simplify.

$= -\dfrac{b^6}{64a^3}$ Multiply fractions.

b. $\left(\dfrac{2p^{-4}q^3}{5p^2q}\right)^{-2}$ First simplify within the parentheses.

$= \left(\dfrac{2p^{-4-2}q^{3-1}}{5}\right)^{-2}$ Divide like bases by subtracting exponents.

$= \left(\dfrac{2p^{-6}q^2}{5}\right)^{-2}$ Simplify.

$= \dfrac{(2p^{-6}q^2)^{-2}}{(5)^{-2}}$ Apply the power rule of a quotient.

$= \dfrac{2^{-2}(p^{-6})^{-2}(q^2)^{-2}}{5^{-2}}$ Apply the power rule of a product.

$= \dfrac{2^{-2}p^{12}q^{-4}}{5^{-2}}$ Simplify.

$= \dfrac{5^2p^{12}}{2^2q^4}$ Simplify the negative exponents.

$= \dfrac{25p^{12}}{4q^4}$ Simplify.

Answers

19. $\dfrac{x^4}{25y^6}$ **20.** $\dfrac{16x^8}{9y^2}$

Example 7   **Simplifying an Expression with Exponents**

Simplify the expression $2^{-1} + 3^{-1} + 5^0$. Write the answer with positive exponents only.

Solution:

$2^{-1} + 3^{-1} + 5^0$

Simplify negative exponents. Simplify $5^0 = 1$.

The least common denominator is 6.

Simplify.

┌─ **Skill Practice** ─┐
Simplify the expressions.
21. $2^{-1} + 4^{-2} + 3^0$
└──────────────────────┘

Answer

21. $\dfrac{25}{16}$

Section 12.3   Practice Exercises

For this set of exercises, assume all variables represent nonzero real numbers.

Study Skills Exercise

1. To help you remember the properties of exponents, write them on 3×5 cards. On each card, write a property on one side and an example using that property on the other side. Keep these cards with you, and when you have a spare moment (such as waiting at the doctor's office), pull out these cards and go over the properties.

Review Exercises

For Exercises 2–9, simplify the expressions.

2. $b^3 b^8$ **3.** $c^7 c^2$ **4.** $\dfrac{x^6}{x^2}$ **5.** $\dfrac{y^9}{y^8}$

6. $\dfrac{9^4 \cdot 9^8}{9}$ **7.** $\dfrac{3^{14}}{3^3 \cdot 3^5}$ **8.** $(6ab^3 c^2)^5$ **9.** $(7w^7 z^2)^4$

Objective 1: Definition of b^0

10. Simplify.

   a. 8^0 **b.** $\dfrac{8^4}{8^4}$

11. Simplify.

   a. d^0 **b.** $\dfrac{d^3}{d^3}$

12. Simplify.

   a. m^0 **b.** $\dfrac{m^5}{m^5}$

For Exercises 13–24, simplify the expression. **(See Example 1.)**

13. p^0 **14.** k^0 **15.** 5^0 **16.** 2^0

17. -4^0 **18.** -1^0 **19.** $(-6)^0$ **20.** $(-2)^0$

21. $(8x)^0$ **22.** $(-3y^3)^0$ **23.** $-7x^0$ **24.** $6y^0$

Objective 2: Definition of b^{-n}

25. Simplify and write the answers with positive exponents.

    a. t^{-5} **b.** $\dfrac{t^3}{t^8}$

26. Simplify and write the answers with positive exponents.

    a. 4^{-3} **b.** $\dfrac{4^2}{4^5}$

For Exercises 27–46, simplify. (See Examples 2–4.)

27. $\left(\dfrac{2}{7}\right)^{-3}$

28. $\left(\dfrac{5}{4}\right)^{-1}$

29. $\left(-\dfrac{1}{5}\right)^{-2}$

30. $\left(-\dfrac{1}{3}\right)^{-3}$

31. a^{-3}

32. c^{-5}

33. 12^{-1}

34. 4^{-2}

35. $(4b)^{-2}$

36. $(3z)^{-1}$

37. $6x^{-2}$

38. $7y^{-1}$

39. $(-8)^{-2}$

40. -8^{-2}

41. $-3y^{-4}$

42. $-6a^{-2}$

43. $(-t)^{-3}$

44. $(-r)^{-5}$

45. $\dfrac{1}{a^{-5}}$

46. $\dfrac{1}{b^{-6}}$

Objective 3: Properties of Integer Exponents: A Summary

47. Explain what is wrong with the following logic. $\dfrac{x^4}{x^{-6}} = x^{4-6} = x^{-2}$

48. Explain what is wrong with the following logic. $\dfrac{y^5}{y^{-3}} = y^{5-3} = y^2$

49. Explain what is wrong with the following logic. $2a^{-3} = \dfrac{1}{2a^3}$

50. Explain what is wrong with the following logic. $5b^{-2} = \dfrac{1}{5b^2}$

Mixed Exercises

For Exercises 51–94, simplify the expression. Write the answer with positive exponents only. (See Examples 5–6.)

51. $x^{-8}x^4$

52. $s^5 s^{-6}$

53. $a^{-8}a^8$

54. $q^3 q^{-3}$

55. $y^{17}y^{-13}$

56. $b^{20}b^{-14}$

57. $(m^{-6}n^9)^3$

58. $(c^4 d^{-5})^{-2}$

59. $(-3j^{-5}k^6)^4$

60. $(6xy^{-11})^{-3}$

61. $\dfrac{p^3}{p^9}$

62. $\dfrac{q^2}{q^{10}}$

63. $\dfrac{r^{-5}}{r^{-2}}$

64. $\dfrac{u^{-2}}{u^{-6}}$

65. $\dfrac{a^2}{a^{-6}}$

66. $\dfrac{p^3}{p^{-5}}$

67. $\dfrac{y^{-2}}{y^6}$

68. $\dfrac{s^{-4}}{s^3}$

69. $\dfrac{7^3}{7^2 \cdot 7^8}$

70. $\dfrac{3^4 \cdot 3}{3^7}$

71. $\dfrac{a^2 a}{a^3}$

72. $\dfrac{t^5}{t^2 t^3}$

73. $\dfrac{a^{-1}b^2}{a^3 b^8}$

74. $\dfrac{k^{-4}h^{-1}}{k^6 h}$

75. $\dfrac{w^{-8}(w^2)^{-5}}{w^3}$

76. $\dfrac{p^2 p^{-7}}{(p^2)^3}$

77. $\dfrac{3^{-2}}{3}$

78. $\dfrac{5^{-1}}{5}$

79. $\left(\dfrac{p^{-1}q^5}{p^{-6}}\right)^0$

80. $\left(\dfrac{ab^{-4}}{a^{-5}}\right)^0$

81. $(8x^3y^0)^{-2}$

82. $(3u^2v^0)^{-3}$

83. $(-8y^{-12})(2y^{16}z^{-2})$

84. $(5p^{-2}q^5)(-2p^{-4}q^{-1})$

85. $\dfrac{-18a^{10}b^6}{108a^{-2}b^6}$

86. $\dfrac{-35x^{-4}y^{-3}}{-21x^2y^{-3}}$

🔘 87. $\dfrac{(-4c^{12}d^7)^2}{(5c^{-3}d^{10})^{-1}}$

88. $\dfrac{(s^3t^{-2})^4}{(3s^{-4}t^6)^{-2}}$

89. $\left(\dfrac{2}{p^6p^3}\right)^{-3}$

90. $\left(\dfrac{5x}{x^7}\right)^{-2}$

91. $\left(\dfrac{5cd^{-3}}{10d^5}\right)^{-2}$

92. $\left(\dfrac{4m^{10}n^4}{2m^{12}n^{-2}}\right)^{-1}$

93. $(2xy^3)\left(\dfrac{9xy}{4x^3y^2}\right)$

94. $(-3a^3)\left(\dfrac{ab}{27a^4b^2}\right)$

For Exercises 95–102, simplify the expression. **(See Example 7.)**

95. $5^{-1} + 2^{-2}$

96. $4^{-2} + 8^{-1}$

97. $10^0 - 10^{-1}$

98. $3^0 - 3^{-2}$

99. $2^{-2} + 1^{-2}$

100. $4^{-1} + 8^{-1}$

101. $4 \cdot 5^0 - 2 \cdot 3^{-1}$

🔘 102. $2 \cdot 4^0 - 3 \cdot 4^{-1}$

Scientific Notation

1. Writing Numbers in Scientific Notation

In many applications in mathematics, it is necessary to work with very large or very small numbers. For example, the number of movie tickets sold in the United States recently is estimated to be 1,500,000,000. The weight of a flea is approximately 0.00066 lb. To avoid writing numerous zeros in very large or small numbers, scientific notation was devised as a shortcut.

The principle behind scientific notation is to use a power of 10 to express the magnitude of the number. For example, the numbers 4000 and 0.07 can be written as:

$$4000 = 4 \times 1000 = 4 \times 10^3$$

$$0.07 = 7.0 \times 0.01 = 7.0 \times 10^{-2} \qquad \text{Note that } 10^{-2} = \frac{1}{100} = 0.01$$

> **DEFINITION** Scientific Notation
>
> A positive number expressed in the form: $a \times 10^n$, where $1 \le a < 10$ and n is an integer is said to be written in **scientific notation**.

To write a positive number in scientific notation, we apply the following guidelines:

1. Move the decimal point so that its new location is to the right of the first nonzero digit. The number should now be greater than or equal to 1 but less than 10. Count the number of places that the decimal point is moved.

2. If the original number is *large* (greater than or equal to 10), use the number of places the decimal point was moved as a *positive* power of 10.

$$450{,}000 \qquad = 4.5 \times 100{,}000 = 4.5 \times 10^5$$

  5 places

3. If the original number is *small* (between 0 and 1), use the number of places the decimal point was moved as a *negative* power of 10.

$$0.0002 \qquad = 2.0 \times 0.0001 = 2.0 \times 10^{-4}$$

  4 places

4. If the original number is greater than or equal to 1 but less than 10, use 0 as the power of 10.

$7.592 = 7.592 \times 10^0$ *Note:* A number between 1 and 10 is seldom written in scientific notation.

5. If the original number is negative, then $-10 < a \le -1$.

$$-450,000 = -4.5 \times 100,000 = -4.5 \times 10^5$$

5 places

Example 1 **Writing Numbers in Scientific Notation**

Write the numbers in scientific notation.

a. 53,000   **b.** 0.00053

Solution:

a. 53,000. = 5.3×10^4 To write 53,000 in scientific notation, the decimal point must be moved four places to the left. Because 53,000 is larger than 10, a *positive* power of 10 is used.

b. 0.00053 = 5.3×10^{-4} To write 0.00053 in scientific notation, the decimal point must be moved four places to the right. Because 0.00053 is less than 1, a *negative* power of 10 is used.

Example 2 **Writing Numbers in Scientific Notation**

Write the numerical values in scientific notation.

a. The number of movie tickets sold in the United States recently is estimated to be 1,500,000,000.

b. The weight of a flea is approximately 0.00066 lb.

c. The temperature on a January day in Fargo dropped to $-43°$F.

d. A bench is 8.2 ft long.

Solution:

a. $1,500,000,000 = 1.5 \times 10^9$ **b.** $0.00066 \text{ lb} = 6.6 \times 10^{-4} \text{ lb}$

c. $-43°\text{F} = -4.3 \times 10^1 \,°\text{F}$ **d.** $8.2 \text{ ft} = 8.2 \times 10^0 \text{ ft}$

---

2. Writing Numbers in Standard Form

Example 3 **Writing Numbers in Standard Form**

Write the numerical values in standard form.

a. The mass of a proton is approximately 1.67×10^{-24} g.

b. The "nearby" star Vega is approximately 1.552×10^{14} miles from Earth.

Solution:

a. 1.67×10^{-24} g $= 0.000\,000\,000\,000\,000\,000\,000\,001\,67$ g

Because the power of 10 is negative, the value of 1.67×10^{-24} is a decimal number between 0 and 1. Move the decimal point 24 places to the *left*.

b. 1.552×10^{14} miles $= 155{,}200{,}000{,}000{,}000$ miles

Because the power of 10 is a positive integer, the value of 1.552×10^{14} is a large number greater than 10. Move the decimal point 14 places to the *right*.

Skill Practice

Write the numerical values in standard form.

5. The probability of winning the California Super Lotto Jackpot is 5.5×10^{-8}.
6. The Sun's mass is 2×10^{30} kilograms.

3. Multiplying and Dividing Numbers in Scientific Notation

To multiply or divide two numbers in scientific notation, use the commutative and associative properties of multiplication to group the powers of 10. For example:

$$400 \times 2000 = (4 \times 10^2)(2 \times 10^3) = (4 \cdot 2) \times (10^2 \cdot 10^3) = 8 \times 10^5$$

$$\frac{0.00054}{150} = \frac{5.4 \times 10^{-4}}{1.5 \times 10^2} = \left(\frac{5.4}{1.5}\right) \times \left(\frac{10^{-4}}{10^2}\right) = 3.6 \times 10^{-6}$$

Example 4 Multiplying and Dividing Numbers in Scientific Notation

Multiply or divide as indicated.

a. $(8.7 \times 10^4)(2.5 \times 10^{-12})$ **b.** $\dfrac{4.25 \times 10^{13}}{8.5 \times 10^{-2}}$

Skill Practice

Multiply or divide as indicated.

7. $(7 \times 10^5)(5 \times 10^3)$
8. $\dfrac{1 \times 10^{-2}}{4 \times 10^{-7}}$

Solution:

a. $(8.7 \times 10^4)(2.5 \times 10^{-12})$

$= (8.7 \cdot 2.5) \times (10^4 \cdot 10^{-12})$ Commutative and associative properties of multiplication

$= 21.75 \times 10^{-8}$ The number 21.75 is not in proper scientific notation because 21.75 is not between 1 and 10.

$= (2.175 \times 10^1) \times 10^{-8}$ Rewrite 21.75 as 2.175×10^1.

$= 2.175 \times (10^1 \times 10^{-8})$ Associative property of multiplication

$= 2.175 \times 10^{-7}$ Simplify.

b. $\dfrac{4.25 \times 10^{13}}{8.5 \times 10^{-2}}$

$= \left(\dfrac{4.25}{8.5}\right) \times \left(\dfrac{10^{13}}{10^{-2}}\right)$ Commutative and associative properties

$= 0.5 \times 10^{15}$ The number 0.5×10^{15} is not in proper scientific notation because 0.5 is not between 1 and 10.

$= (5.0 \times 10^{-1}) \times 10^{15}$ Rewrite 0.5 as 5.0×10^{-1}.

$= 5.0 \times (10^{-1} \times 10^{15})$ Associative property of multiplication

$= 5.0 \times 10^{14}$ Simplify.

Answers

5. 0.000 000 055
6. 2,000,000,000,000,000,000,000,000,000,000
7. 3.5×10^9
8. 2.5×10^4

Calculator Connections

Topic: Using Scientific Notation

Both scientific and graphing calculators can perform calculations involving numbers written in scientific notation. Most calculators use an EE key or an EXP key to enter the power of 10.

Scientific Calculator

Enter: 2.7 EE 5 =   or   2.7 EXP 5 =   **Result:** [270000]

Enter: 7.1 EE 3 +o- =   or   7.1 EXP 3 +o- =   **Result:** [0.0071]

Graphing Calculator

```
2.7E5
         270000
7.1E-3
          .0071
```

We recommend that you use parentheses to enclose each number written in scientific notation when performing calculations. Try using your calculator to perform the calculations from Example 4.

a. $(8.7 \times 10^4)(2.5 \times 10^{-12})$ **b.** $\dfrac{4.25 \times 10^{13}}{8.5 \times 10^{-2}}$

Scientific Calculator

Enter: (8.7 EE 4)   ×   (2.5 EE 12 +o-)   =   **Result:** [0.000000218]

Enter: (4.25 EE 13)   ÷   (8.5 EE 2 +o-)   =   **Result:** [5E14]

Notice that the answer to part (b) is shown on the calculator in scientific notation. The calculator does not have enough room to display 14 zeros. Also notice that the calculator rounds the answer to part (a). The exact answer is 2.175×10^{-7} or 0.0000002175.

Graphing Calculator

```
(8.7E4)*(2.5E-12
)
        2.175E-7
(4.25E13)/(8.5E-
2)
            5E14
```

Avoiding Mistakes

A display of 5E14 on a calculator does not mean 5^{14}. It is scientific notation and means 5×10^{14}.

Calculator Exercises

Use a calculator to perform the indicated operations:

1. $(5.2 \times 10^6)(4.6 \times 10^{-3})$

2. $(2.19 \times 10^{-8})(7.84 \times 10^{-4})$

3. $\dfrac{4.76 \times 10^{-5}}{2.38 \times 10^9}$

4. $\dfrac{8.5 \times 10^4}{4 \times 10^{-1}}$

5. $\dfrac{(9.6 \times 10^7)(4 \times 10^{-3})}{2 \times 10^{-2}}$

6. $\dfrac{(5 \times 10^{-12})(6.4 \times 10^{-5})}{(1.6 \times 10^{-8})(4 \times 10^2)}$

Section 12.4   Practice Exercises

Boost *your* GRADE at ALEKS.com!

- Practice Problems
- Self-Tests
- NetTutor
- e-Professors
- Videos

Study Skills Exercise

1. Define the key term: **Scientific notation**

Review Exercises

For Exercises 2–13, simplify the expression. Assume all variables represent nonzero real numbers.

2. $a^3 a^{-4}$

3. $b^5 b^8$

4. $10^3 \cdot 10^{-4}$

5. $10^5 \cdot 10^8$

6. $\dfrac{x^3}{x^6}$

7. $\dfrac{y^2}{y^7}$

8. $(c^4 d^2)^3$

9. $(x^5 y^{-3})^4$

10. $\dfrac{z^9 z^4}{z^3}$

11. $\dfrac{w^{-2} w^5}{w^{-1}}$

12. $\dfrac{10^9 \cdot 10^4}{10^3}$

13. $\dfrac{10^{-2} \cdot 10^5}{10^{-1}}$

Objective 1: Writing Numbers in Scientific Notation

14. Explain how scientific notation might be valuable in studying astronomy. Answers may vary.

15. Explain how you would write the number 0.000 000 000 23 in scientific notation.

16. Explain how you would write the number 23,000,000,000,000 in scientific notation.

For Exercises 17–28, write the number in scientific notation. **(See Example 1.)**

17. 50,000

18. 900,000

19. 208,000

20. 420,000,000

21. 6,010,000

22. 75,000

23. 0.000008

24. 0.003

25. 0.000125

26. 0.00000025

27. 0.006708

28. 0.02004

For Exercises 29–34, write the numbers in scientific notation. **(See Example 2.)**

29. The mass of a proton is approximately 0.000 000 000 000 000 000 000 0017 g.

30. The total combined salaries of the president, vice president, senators, and representatives of the United States federal government is approximately $85,000,000.

31. The Bill Gates Foundation has over $27,000,000,000 from which it makes contributions to global charities.

32. One gram is equivalent to 0.0035 oz.

33. In the world's largest tanker disaster, *Amoco Cadiz* spilled 68,000,000 gal of oil off Portsall, France, causing widespread environmental damage over 100 miles of Brittany coast.

34. The human heart pumps about 1400 L of blood per day. That means that it pumps approximately 10,000,000 L per year.

Objective 2: Writing Numbers in Standard Form

35. Explain how you would write the number 3.1×10^{-9} in standard form.

36. Explain how you would write the number 3.1×10^9 in standard form.

For Exercises 37–52, write the numbers in standard form. **(See Example 3.)**

37. 5×10^{-5}

38. 2×10^{-7}

39. 2.8×10^3

40. 9.1×10^6

41. 6.03×10^{-4}

42. 7.01×10^{-3}

43. 2.4×10^6

44. 3.1×10^4

45. 1.9×10^{-2}

46. 2.8×10^{-6}

47. 7.032×10^3

48. 8.205×10^2

49. One picogram (pg) is equal to 1×10^{-12} g.

50. A nanometer (nm) is approximately 3.94×10^{-8} in.

51. A normal diet contains between 1.6×10^3 Cal and 2.8×10^3 Cal per day.

52. The total land area of Texas is approximately 2.62×10^5 square miles.

Objective 3: Multiplying and Dividing Numbers in Scientific Notation

For Exercises 53–72, multiply or divide as indicated. Write the answers in scientific notation. **(See Example 4.)**

53. $(2.5 \times 10^6)(2 \times 10^{-2})$

54. $(2 \times 10^{-7})(3 \times 10^{13})$

55. $(1.2 \times 10^4)(3 \times 10^7)$

56. $(3.2 \times 10^{-3})(2.5 \times 10^8)$

57. $\dfrac{7.7 \times 10^6}{3.5 \times 10^2}$

58. $\dfrac{9.5 \times 10^{11}}{1.9 \times 10^3}$

59. $\dfrac{9 \times 10^{-6}}{4 \times 10^7}$

60. $\dfrac{7 \times 10^{-2}}{5 \times 10^9}$

61. $(8 \times 10^{10})(4 \times 10^3)$

62. $(6 \times 10^{-4})(3 \times 10^{-2})$

63. $(3.2 \times 10^{-4})(7.6 \times 10^{-7})$

64. $(5.9 \times 10^{12})(3.6 \times 10^9)$

65. $\dfrac{2.1 \times 10^{11}}{7 \times 10^{-3}}$

66. $\dfrac{1.6 \times 10^{14}}{8 \times 10^{-5}}$

67. $\dfrac{5.7 \times 10^{-2}}{9.5 \times 10^{-8}}$

68. $\dfrac{2.72 \times 10^{-6}}{6.8 \times 10^{-4}}$

69. $6{,}000{,}000{,}000 \times 0.0000000023$

70. $0.000055 \times 40{,}000$

71. $\dfrac{0.0000000003}{6000}$

72. $\dfrac{420{,}000}{0.0000021}$

Mixed Exercises

73. If a piece of paper is 3×10^{-3} in. thick, how thick is a stack of 1.25×10^3 pieces of paper?

74. A box of staples contains 5×10^3 staples and weighs 15 oz. How much does one staple weigh? Write your answer in scientific notation.

75. Bill Gates owned approximately 1,100,000,000 shares of Microsoft stock. If the stock price was $27 per share, how much was Bill Gates' stock worth?

76. A state lottery had a jackpot of 5.2×10^7. This week the winner was a group of office employees that included 13 people. How much would each person receive?

77. Dinosaurs became extinct about 65 million years ago.

    a. Write the number 65 million in scientific notation.

    b. How many days is 65 million years?

    c. How many hours is 65 million years?

    d. How many seconds is 65 million years?

78. The Earth is 111,600,000 km from the Sun.

    a. Write the number 111,600,000 in scientific notation.

    b. If there are 1000 m in a kilometer, how many meters is the Earth from the Sun?

    c. If there are 100 cm in a meter, how many centimeters is the Earth from the Sun?

Problem Recognition Exercises

Properties of Exponents

Simplify completely. Assume that all variables represent nonzero real numbers.

1. $t^3 t^5$

2. $2^3 2^5$

3. $\dfrac{y^7}{y^2}$

4. $\dfrac{p^9}{p^3}$

5. $(r^2 s^4)^2$

6. $(ab^3 c^2)^3$

7. $\dfrac{w^4}{w^{-2}}$

8. $\dfrac{m^{-14}}{m^2}$

9. $\dfrac{y^{-7} x^4}{z^{-3}}$

10. $\dfrac{a^3 b^{-6}}{c^{-8}}$

11. $(2.5 \times 10^{-3})(5 \times 10^5)$

12. $(3.1 \times 10^6)(4 \times 10^{-2})$

13. $\dfrac{4.8 \times 10^7}{6 \times 10^{-2}}$

14. $\dfrac{5.4 \times 10^{-2}}{9 \times 10^6}$

15. $\dfrac{1}{p^{-6} p^{-8} p^{-1}}$

16. $p^6 p^8 p$

17. $\dfrac{v^9}{v^{11}}$

18. $(c^5 d^4)^{10}$

19. $\left(\dfrac{1}{2}\right)^{-1} + \left(\dfrac{1}{3}\right)^0$

20. $\left(\dfrac{1}{4}\right)^0 - \left(\dfrac{1}{5}\right)^{-1}$

21. $(2^5 b^{-3})^{-3}$

22. $(3^{-2} y^3)^{-2}$

23. $\left(\dfrac{3x}{2y}\right)^{-4}$

24. $\left(\dfrac{6c}{5d^3}\right)^{-2}$

25. $(3ab^2)(a^2 b)^3$

26. $(4x^2 y^3)^3 (xy^2)$

27. $\left(\dfrac{xy^2}{x^3 y}\right)^4$

28. $\left(\dfrac{a^3 b}{a^5 b^3}\right)^5$

29. $\dfrac{(t^{-2})^3}{t^{-4}}$

30. $\dfrac{(p^3)^{-4}}{p^{-5}}$

31. $\left(\dfrac{2w^2 x^3}{3y^0}\right)^3$

32. $\left(\dfrac{5a^0 b^4}{4c^3}\right)^2$

33. $\dfrac{q^3 r^{-2}}{s^{-1} t^5}$

34. $\dfrac{n^{-3} m^2}{p^{-3} q^{-1}}$

35. $\dfrac{(y^{-3})^2 (y^5)}{(y^{-3})^{-4}}$

36. $\dfrac{(w^2)^{-4}(w^{-2})}{(w^5)^{-4}}$

37. $\left(\dfrac{-2a^2 b^{-3}}{a^{-4} b^{-5}}\right)^{-3}$

38. $\left(\dfrac{-3x^{-4} y^3}{2x^5 y^{-2}}\right)^{-2}$

39. $(5h^{-2} k^0)^3 (5k^{-2})^{-4}$

40. $(6m^3 n^{-5})^{-4}(6m^0 n^{-2})^5$

Section 12.5   Addition and Subtraction of Polynomials

1. Introduction to Polynomials

One commonly used algebraic expression is called a polynomial. A **polynomial** in one variable, x, is defined as a single term or a sum of terms of the form ax^n, where a is a real number and the exponent, n, is a nonnegative integer. For each term, a is called the **coefficient**, and n is called the **degree of the term**. For example:

Term (Expressed in the Form ax^n)	Coefficient	Degree
$-12z^7$	-12	7
$x^3 \rightarrow$ rewrite as $1x^3$	1	3
$10w \rightarrow$ rewrite as $10w^1$	10	1
$7 \rightarrow$ rewrite as $7x^0$	7	0

If a polynomial has exactly one term, it is categorized as a **monomial**. A two-term polynomial is called a **binomial**, and a three-term polynomial is called a **trinomial**. Usually the terms of a polynomial are written in descending order according to degree. The term with highest degree is called the **leading term**, and its coefficient is called the **leading coefficient**. The **degree of a polynomial** is the greatest degree of all of its terms. Thus, when written in descending order, the leading term determines the degree of the polynomial.

	Expression	Descending Order	Leading Coefficient	Degree of Polynomial
Monomials	$-3x^4$	$-3x^4$	-3	4
	17	17	17	0
Binomials	$4y^3 - 6y^5$	$-6y^5 + 4y^3$	-6	5
	$\dfrac{1}{2} - \dfrac{1}{4}c$	$-\dfrac{1}{4}c + \dfrac{1}{2}$	$-\dfrac{1}{4}$	1
Trinomials	$4p - 3p^3 + 8p^6$	$8p^6 - 3p^3 + 4p$	8	6
	$7a^4 - 1.2a^8 + 3a^3$	$-1.2a^8 + 7a^4 + 3a^3$	-1.2	8

Example 1   Identifying the Parts of a Polynomial

Given: $4.5a - 2.7a^{10} + 1.6 - 3.7a^5$

a. List the terms of the polynomial and state the coefficient and degree of each term.

b. Write the polynomial in descending order.

c. State the degree of the polynomial and the leading coefficient.

Answers

1. a. $8x^4 + 5x^3 + 3x^2 - x$
   b. 4   c. 8

Solution:

a. term: $4.5a$ coefficient: 4.5 degree: 1

    term: $-2.7a^{10}$ coefficient: -2.7 degree: 10

    term: 1.6 coefficient: 1.6 degree: 0

    term: $-3.7a^5$ coefficient: -3.7 degree: 5

b. $-2.7a^{10} - 3.7a^5 + 4.5a + 1.6$

c. The degree of the polynomial is 10 and the leading coefficient is -2.7.

Polynomials may have more than one variable. In such a case, the degree of a term is the sum of the exponents of the variables contained in the term. For example, the term, $32x^2y^5z$, has degree 8 because the exponents applied to x, y, and z are 2, 5, and 1, respectively. The following polynomial has a degree of 11 because the highest degree of its terms is 11.

$$32x^2y^5z \quad - \quad 2x^3y \quad + \quad 2x^2yz^8 \quad + \quad 7$$

$$\underset{\substack{\text{degree} \\ 8}}{\uparrow} \qquad \underset{\substack{\text{degree} \\ 4}}{\uparrow} \qquad \underset{\substack{\text{degree} \\ 11}}{\uparrow} \qquad \underset{\substack{\text{degree} \\ 0}}{\uparrow}$$

2. Addition of Polynomials

Recall that two terms are *like* terms if they each have the same variables, and the corresponding variables are raised to the same powers.

Like Terms: $3x^2, -7x^2$ $-5yz^3, yz^3$

Unlike Terms: $9z^2, 12z^6$ $\dfrac{1}{3}w^6, \dfrac{2}{5}p^6$ $4y, 7$

Recall that the distributive property is used to add or subtract *like* terms. For example,

$3x^2 + 9x^2 - 2x^2$

$= (3 + 9 - 2)x^2$ Apply the distributive property.

$= (10)x^2$ Simplify.

$= 10x^2$

Skill Practice

Add the polynomials.

2. $13a^2b^3 + 2a^2b^3$

3. $(7q^2 - 2q + 4)$
$+ (5q^2 + 6q - 9)$

Example 2 **Adding Polynomials**

Add the polynomials.

a. $3x^2y + 5x^2y$ **b.** $(-3c^3 + 5c^2 - 7c) + (11c^3 + 6c^2 + 3)$

Solution:

a. $3x^2y + 5x^2y$

$\quad\quad = (3 + 5)x^2y$ Apply the distributive property.

$\quad\quad = (8)x^2y$

$\quad\quad = 8x^2y$ Simplify.

b. $(-3c^3 + 5c^2 - 7c) + (11c^3 + 6c^2 + 3)$

$\quad\quad = -3c^3 + 11c^3 + 5c^2 + 6c^2 - 7c + 3$ Clear parentheses and group *like* terms.

$\quad\quad = 8c^3 + 11c^2 - 7c + 3$ Combine *like* terms.

TIP: It is the distributive property that enables us to add *like* terms. We shorten the process by adding the coefficients of *like* terms.

TIP: Polynomials can also be added by combining *like* terms in columns. The sum of the polynomials from Example 2(b) is shown here.

$$\begin{array}{r} -3c^3 + 5c^2 - 7c + 0 \\ + \; 11c^3 + 6c^2 + 0c + 3 \\ \hline 8c^3 + 11c^2 - 7c + 3 \end{array}$$

Place holders such as 0 and 0c may be used to help line up *like* terms.

Skill Practice

Add the polynomials.

4. $(5x^2 - 4xy + y^2)$
$+ (-3x^2 - 5y^2)$

Example 3 **Adding Polynomials**

Add the polynomials. $(4w^2 - 2x) + (3w^2 - 4x^2 + 6x)$

Solution:

$\quad (4w^2 - 2x) + (3w^2 - 4x^2 + 6x)$

$\quad\quad = 4w^2 + 3w^2 - 4x^2 - 2x + 6x$ Clear parentheses and group *like* terms.

$\quad\quad = 7w^2 - 4x^2 + 4x$

TIP: To add these polynomials vertically, align *like* terms in the same column.

$$\begin{array}{r} 4w^2 \quad\quad\; - 2x \\ + \; 3w^2 - 4x^2 + 6x \\ \hline 7w^2 - 4x^2 + 4x \end{array}$$

Answers

2. $15a^2b^3$

3. $12q^2 + 4q - 5$

4. $2x^2 - 4xy - 4y^2$

3. Subtraction of Polynomials

Subtraction of two polynomials requires us to find the opposite of the polynomial being subtracted. To find the opposite of a polynomial, take the opposite of each term. This is equivalent to multiplying the polynomial by -1.

Example 4 Finding the Opposite of a Polynomial

Find the opposite of the polynomials.

a. $5x$ **b.** $3a - 4b - c$ **c.** $5.5y^4 - 2.4y^3 + 1.1y$

Solution:

Expression	Opposite	Simplified Form
a. $5x$	$-(5x)$	$-5x$
b. $3a - 4b - c$	$-(3a - 4b - c)$	$-3a + 4b + c$
c. $5.5y^4 - 2.4y^3 + 1.1y$	$-(5.5y^4 - 2.4y^3 + 1.1y)$	$-5.5y^4 + 2.4y^3 - 1.1y$

Skill Practice

Find the opposite of the polynomials.

5. $x - 3$
6. $3y^2 - 2xy + 6x + 2$
7. $-2.1w^3 + 4.9w^2 - 1.9w$

TIP: Notice that the sign of each term is changed when finding the opposite of a polynomial.

Subtraction of two polynomials is similar to subtracting real numbers. Add the opposite of the second polynomial to the first polynomial.

DEFINITION Subtraction of Polynomials

If A and B are polynomials, then $A - B = A + (-B)$.

Example 5 Subtracting Polynomials

Subtract the polynomials. $(-4p^4 + 5p^2 - 3) - (11p^2 + 4p - 6)$

Solution:

$(-4p^4 + 5p^2 - 3) - (11p^2 + 4p - 6)$

$= (-4p^4 + 5p^2 - 3) + (-11p^2 - 4p + 6)$ Add the opposite of the second polynomial.

$= -4p^4 + 5p^2 - 11p^2 - 4p - 3 + 6$ Group *like* terms.

$= -4p^4 - 6p^2 - 4p + 3$ Combine *like* terms.

Skill Practice

Subtract the polynomials.

8. $(x^2 + 3x - 2)$
    $- (4x^2 + 6x + 1)$

TIP: Two polynomials can also be subtracted in columns by adding the opposite of the second polynomial to the first polynomial. Place holders (shown in red) may be used to help line up *like* terms.

$$-4p^4 + 0p^3 + 5p^2 + 0p - 3$$
$$-(0p^4 + 0p^3 + 11p^2 + 4p - 6) \xrightarrow{\text{Add the opposite}}$$

$$-4p^4 + 0p^3 + 5p^2 + 0p - 3$$
$$+ \;\; -0p^4 - 0p^3 - 11p^2 - 4p + 6$$
$$\overline{-4p^4 \qquad\quad - 6p^2 - 4p + 3}$$

The difference of the polynomials is $-4p^4 - 6p^2 - 4p + 3$.

Answers

5. $-x + 3$
6. $-3y^2 + 2xy - 6x - 2$
7. $2.1w^3 - 4.9w^2 + 1.9w$
8. $-3x^2 - 3x - 3$

Example 6   **Subtracting Polynomials**

Subtract the polynomials. $(a^2 - 2ab + 7b^2) - (-8a^2 - 6ab + 2b^2)$

Solution:

$(a^2 - 2ab + 7b^2) - (-8a^2 - 6ab + 2b^2)$

$= (a^2 - 2ab + 7b^2) + (8a^2 + 6ab - 2b^2)$ Add the opposite of the second polynomial.

$= a^2 + 8a^2 - 2ab + 6ab + 7b^2 - 2b^2$ Group *like* terms.

$= 9a^2 + 4ab + 5b^2$ Combine *like* terms.

TIP: To subtract these polynomials vertically, align *like* terms in the same column. Then add the opposite of the second polynomial to the first.

$$\begin{array}{r} a^2 - 2ab + 7b^2 \\ -(-8a^2 - 6ab + 2b^2) \end{array} \xrightarrow{\text{Add the opposite}} \begin{array}{r} a^2 - 2ab + 7b^2 \\ + 8a^2 + 6ab - 2b^2 \\ \hline 9a^2 + 4ab + 5b^2 \end{array}$$

The difference is $9a^2 + 4ab + 5b^2$.

Subtracting polynomials can also be accomplished by clearing parentheses and combining *like* terms.

$(a^2 - 2ab + 7b^2) - (-8a^2 - 6ab + 2b^2)$

$= a^2 - 2ab + 7b^2 + 8a^2 + 6ab - 2b^2$ Clear parentheses.

$= 9a^2 + 4ab + 5b^2$ Combine *like* terms.

Example 7   **Subtracting Polynomials**

Subtract $\frac{1}{3}t^4 + \frac{1}{2}t^2$ from $t^2 - 4$, and simplify the result.

Solution:

To subtract a from b, we write $b - a$. Thus, to subtract $\overset{a}{\overbrace{\frac{1}{3}t^4 + \frac{1}{2}t^2}}$ from $\overset{b}{\overbrace{t^2 - 4}}$, we have

$\overset{b}{\overbrace{(t^2 - 4)}} - \overset{a}{\overbrace{\left(\frac{1}{3}t^4 + \frac{1}{2}t^2\right)}}$

$= t^2 - 4 - \frac{1}{3}t^4 - \frac{1}{2}t^2$ Apply the distributive property.

$= -\frac{1}{3}t^4 + t^2 - \frac{1}{2}t^2 - 4$ Group *like* terms in descending order.

$= -\frac{1}{3}t^4 + \frac{2}{2}t^2 - \frac{1}{2}t^2 - 4$ The t^2-terms are the only *like* terms.
   Get a common denominator for the t^2-terms.

$= -\frac{1}{3}t^4 + \frac{1}{2}t^2 - 4$ Add *like* terms.

4. Polynomials and Applications to Geometry

Example 8 **Subtracting Polynomials in Geometry**

If the perimeter of the triangle in Figure 12-1 can be represented by the polynomial $2x^2 + 5x + 6$, find a polynomial that represents the length of the missing side.

Figure 12-1

Solution:

The missing side of the triangle can be found by subtracting the sum of the two known sides from the perimeter.

$$\begin{pmatrix} \text{Length} \\ \text{of missing} \\ \text{side} \end{pmatrix} = (\text{perimeter}) - \begin{bmatrix} \text{sum of the} \\ \text{two known sides} \end{bmatrix}$$

$$\begin{pmatrix} \text{Length} \\ \text{of missing} \\ \text{side} \end{pmatrix} = (2x^2 + 5x + 6) - [(2x - 3) + (x^2 + 1)]$$

$$= 2x^2 + 5x + 6 - [2x - 3 + x^2 + 1] \quad \text{Clear inner parentheses.}$$

$$= 2x^2 + 5x + 6 - (x^2 + 2x - 2) \quad \text{Combine } like \text{ terms within [ ].}$$

$$= 2x^2 + 5x + 6 - x^2 - 2x + 2 \quad \text{Apply the distributive property.}$$

$$= 2x^2 - x^2 + 5x - 2x + 6 + 2 \quad \text{Group } like \text{ terms.}$$

$$= x^2 + 3x + 8 \quad \text{Combine } like \text{ terms.}$$

The polynomial $x^2 + 3x + 8$ represents the length of the missing side.

Skill Practice

15. If the perimeter of the triangle is represented by the polynomial $6x - 9$, find the polynomial that represents the missing side.

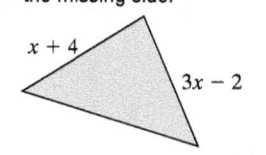

Answer

15. $2x - 11$

Section 12.5   Practice Exercises

Boost *your* GRADE at ALEKS.com!

ALEKS version 3.0

• Practice Problems
• Self-Tests
• NetTutor

• e-Professors
• Videos

Study Skills Exercise

1. Define the key terms:

   a. Polynomial
   b. Coefficient
   c. Degree of term
   d. Monomial
   e. Binomial
   f. Trinomial
   g. Leading term
   h. Leading coefficient
   i. Degree of polynomial

Review Exercises

For Exercises 2–7, simplify the expression.

2. $\dfrac{p^3 \cdot 4p}{p^2}$

3. $(3x)^2(5x^{-4})$

4. $(6y^{-3})(2y^9)$

5. $\dfrac{8t^{-6}}{4t^{-2}}$

6. $\dfrac{8^3 \cdot 8^{-4}}{8^{-2} \cdot 8^6}$

7. $\dfrac{3^4 \cdot 3^{-8}}{3^{12} \cdot 3^{-4}}$

8. Explain the difference between 3.0×10^7 and 3^7.

9. Explain the difference between 4.0×10^{-2} and 4^{-2}.

Objective 1: Introduction to Polynomials

10. Write the polynomial in descending order. $10 - 8a - a^3 + 2a^2 + a^5$

11. Write the polynomial in descending order:

$$6 + 7x^2 - 7x^4 + 9x$$

12. Write the polynomial in descending order:

$$\frac{1}{2}y + y^2 - 12y^4 + y^3 - 6$$

For Exercises 13–24, categorize the expression as a monomial, a binomial, or a trinomial. Then identify the coefficient and degree of the leading term. **(See Example 1.)**

13. $10a^2 + 5a$

14. $7z + 13z^2 - 15$

15. $6x^2$

16. 9

17. $2t - t^4$

18. $7x + 2$

19. $12y^4 - 3y + 1$

20. $5bc^2$

21. 23

22. $4 - 2c$

23. $-32xyz$

24. $w^4 - w^2$

Objective 2: Addition of Polynomials

25. Explain why the terms $3x$ and $3x^2$ are not *like* terms.

26. Explain why the terms $4w^3$ and $4z^3$ are not *like* terms.

For Exercises 27–42, add the polynomials. **(See Examples 2–3.)**

27. $23x^2y + 12x^2y$

28. $-5ab^3 + 17ab^3$

29. $(6y + 3x) + (4y - 3x)$

30. $(2z - 5h) + (-3z + h)$

31. $3b^5d^2 + (5b^5d^2 - 9d)$

32. $4c^2d^3 + (3cd - 10c^2d^3)$

33. $(7y^2 + 2y - 9) + (-3y^2 - y)$

34. $(-3w^2 + 4w - 6) + (5w^2 + 2)$

35. $\quad 6a + 2b - 5c$
$+ \underline{-2a - 2b - 3c}$

36. $\quad -13x + 5y + 10z$
$+ \underline{-3x - 3y + 2z}$

37. $\left(\dfrac{2}{5}a + \dfrac{1}{4}b - \dfrac{5}{6}\right) + \left(\dfrac{3}{5}a - \dfrac{3}{4}b - \dfrac{7}{6}\right)$

38. $\left(\dfrac{5}{9}x + \dfrac{1}{10}y\right) + \left(-\dfrac{4}{9}x + \dfrac{3}{10}y\right)$

39. $\left(z - \dfrac{8}{3}\right) + \left(\dfrac{4}{3}z^2 - z + 1\right)$

40. $\left(-\dfrac{7}{5}r + 1\right) + \left(-\dfrac{3}{5}r^2 + \dfrac{7}{5}r + 1\right)$

41. $\quad 7.9t^3 \qquad\quad + 2.6t - 1.1$
$+ \underline{\qquad - 3.4t^2 + 3.4t - 3.1}$

42. $\quad 0.34y^2 \qquad\quad + 1.23$
$+ \underline{\qquad\quad 3.42y - 7.56}$

Objective 3: Subtraction of Polynomials

For Exercises 43–48, find the opposite of each polynomial. **(See Example 4.)**

43. $4h - 5$

44. $5k - 12$

45. $-2m^2 + 3m - 15$

46. $-n^2 - 6n + 9$

47. $3v^3 + 5v^2 + 10v + 22$

48. $7u^4 + 3v^2 + 17$

For Exercises 49–68, subtract the polynomials. **(See Examples 5–6.)**

49. $4a^3b^2 - 12a^3b^2$

50. $5yz^4 - 14yz^4$

51. $-32x^3 - 21x^3$

52. $-23c^5 - 12c^5$

53. $(7a - 7) - (12a - 4)$

54. $(4x + 3v) - (-3x + v)$

55. $(4k + 3) - (-12k - 6)$

56. $(3h - 15) - (8h + 13)$

57. $25s - (23s + 14)$

58. $3x^2 - (-x^2 - 12)$

59. $(5t^2 - 3t - 2) - (2t^2 + t + 1)$

60. $(k^2 + 2k + 1) - (3k^2 - 6k + 2)$

61. $\quad 10r - 6s + 2t$
$\underline{- (12r - 3s - \ t)}$

62. $\quad a - 14b + 7c$
$\underline{- (-3a - \ 8b + 2c)}$

63. $\left(\dfrac{7}{8}x + \dfrac{2}{3}y - \dfrac{3}{10}\right) - \left(\dfrac{1}{8}x + \dfrac{1}{3}y\right)$

64. $\left(r - \dfrac{1}{12}s\right) - \left(\dfrac{1}{2}r - \dfrac{5}{12}s - \dfrac{4}{11}\right)$

65. $\left(\dfrac{2}{3}h^2 - \dfrac{1}{5}h - \dfrac{3}{4}\right) - \left(\dfrac{4}{3}h^2 - \dfrac{4}{5}h + \dfrac{7}{4}\right)$

66. $\left(\dfrac{3}{8}p^3 - \dfrac{5}{7}p^2 - \dfrac{2}{5}\right) - \left(\dfrac{5}{8}p^3 - \dfrac{2}{7}p^2 + \dfrac{7}{5}\right)$

67. $\quad 4.5x^4 - 3.1x^2 \qquad\quad - 6.7$
$\underline{- (2.1x^4 \qquad\qquad + 4.4x \qquad\quad)}$

68. $\quad 1.3c^3 \qquad\qquad\quad + 4.8$
$\underline{- (\qquad 4.3c^2 - 2c - 2.2)}$

69. Find the difference of $(4b^3 + 6b - 7)$ and $(-12b^2 + 11b + 5)$.

70. Find the difference of $(-5y^2 + 3y - 21)$ and $(-4y^2 - 5y + 23)$.

71. Subtract $(3x^3 - 5x + 10)$ from $(-2x^2 + 6x - 21)$.
(See Example 7.)

72. Subtract $(7a^5 - 2a^3 - 5a)$ from $(3a^5 - 9a^2 + 3a - 8)$.

Objective 4: Polynomials and Applications to Geometry

73. Find a polynomial that represents the perimeter of the figure.

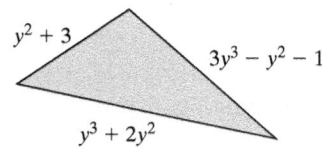

74. Find a polynomial that represents the perimeter of the figure.

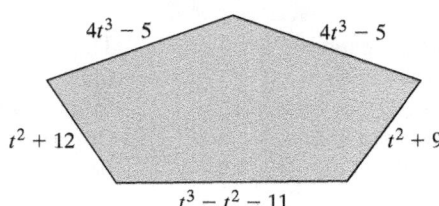

75. If the perimeter of the figure can be represented by the polynomial $5a^2 - 2a + 1$, find a polynomial that represents the length of the missing side. **(See Example 8.)**

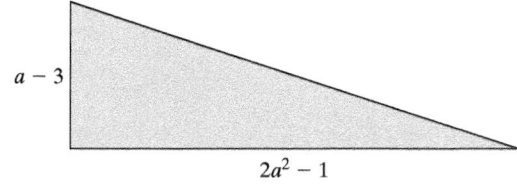

76. If the perimeter of the figure can be represented by the polynomial $6w^3 - 2w - 3$, find a polynomial that represents the length of the missing side.

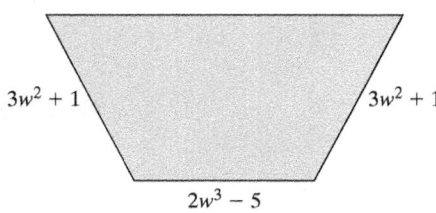

Mixed Exercises

For Exercises 77–92, perform the indicated operation.

77. $(2ab^2 + 9a^2b) + (7ab^2 - 3ab + 7a^2b)$

78. $(8x^2y - 3xy - 6xy^2) + (3x^2y - 12xy)$

79.
$$\begin{array}{r} 4z^5 \quad + \; z^3 - 3z + 13 \\ -(\quad - z^4 - 8z^3 \quad + 15) \end{array}$$

80.
$$\begin{array}{r} -15t^4 \quad\quad - 23t^2 + 16t \\ -(\quad\quad 21t^3 + 18t^2 + \; t) \end{array}$$

81. $(9x^4 + 2x^3 - x + 5) + (9x^3 - 3x^2 + 8x + 3) - (7x^4 - x + 12)$

82. $(-6y^3 - 9y^2 + 23) - (7y^2 + 2y - 11) + (3y^3 - 25)$

83. $(5w^2 - 3w + 2) + (-4w + 6) - (7w^2 - 10)$

84. $(10u^3 - 5u^2 + 4) - (2u^3 + 5u^2 + u) - (u^3 - 3u + 9)$

85. $(7p^2q - 3pq^2) - (8p^2q + pq) + (4pq - pq^2)$

86. $(12c^2d - 2cd + 8cd^2) - (-c^2d + 4cd) - (5cd - 2cd^2)$

87. $(5x - 2x^3) + (2x^3 - 5x)$

88. $(p^2 - 4p + 2) - (2 + p^2 - 4p)$

89.
$$\begin{array}{r} 2a^2b - 4ab + \; ab^2 \\ -(2a^2b + \; ab - 5ab^2) \end{array}$$

90.
$$\begin{array}{r} -3xy + \; 7xy^2 + 5x^2y \\ + \underline{-8xy - 11xy^2 + 3x^2y} \end{array}$$

91. $[(3y^2 - 5y) - (2y^2 + y - 1)] + (10y^2 - 4y - 5)$

92. $(12c^3 - 5c^2 - 2c) + [(7c^3 - 2c^2 + c) - (4c^3 + 4c)]$

Expanding Your Skills

93. Write a binomial of degree 3. (Answers may vary.)

94. Write a trinomial of degree 6. (Answers may vary.)

95. Write a monomial of degree 5. (Answers may vary.)

96. Write a monomial of degree 1. (Answers may vary.)

97. Write a trinomial with the leading coefficient -6. (Answers may vary.)

98. Write a binomial with the leading coefficient 13. (Answers may vary.)

Section 12.6 Multiplication of Polynomials and Special Products

Objectives

1. Multiplication of Polynomials
2. Special Case Products: Difference of Squares and Perfect Square Trinomials
3. Applications to Geometry

1. Multiplication of Polynomials

The properties of exponents covered in Sections 12.1–12.3 can be used to simplify many algebraic expressions including the multiplication of monomials. To multiply monomials, first use the associative and commutative properties of multiplication to group coefficients and like bases. Then simplify the result by using the properties of exponents.

Example 1 **Multiplying Monomials**

Multiply.

a. $(3x^4)(4x^2)$ **b.** $(-4c^5d)(2c^2d^3e)$ **c.** $\left(\frac{1}{3}a^4b^3\right)\left(\frac{3}{4}b^7\right)$

Solution:

a. $(3x^4)(4x^2)$

$= (3 \cdot 4)(x^4x^2)$ Group coefficients and like bases.

$= 12x^6$ Multiply the coefficients and add the exponents on x.

b. $(-4c^5d)(2c^2d^3e)$

$= (-4 \cdot 2)(c^5c^2)(dd^3)(e)$ Group coefficients and like bases.

$= -8c^7d^4e$ Simplify.

c. $\left(\frac{1}{3}a^4b^3\right)\left(\frac{3}{4}b^7\right)$

$= \left(\frac{1}{3}\cdot\frac{3}{4}\right)(a^4)(b^3b^7)$ Group coefficients and like bases.

$= \frac{1}{4}a^4b^{10}$ Simplify.

The distributive property is used to multiply polynomials: $a(b + c) = ab + ac$.

Example 2   Multiplying a Polynomial by a Monomial

Multiply.

a. $2t(4t - 3)$ **b.** $-3a^2\left(-4a^2 + 2a - \frac{1}{3}\right)$

Solution:

a. $2t(4t - 3)$ Multiply each term of the binomial by $2t$.

$= (2t)(4t) + 2t(-3)$ Apply the distributive property.

$= 8t^2 - 6t$ Simplify each term.

b. $-3a^2\left(-4a^2 + 2a - \frac{1}{3}\right)$ Multiply each term of the trinomial by $-3a^2$.

$= (-3a^2)(-4a^2) + (-3a^2)(2a) + (-3a^2)\left(-\frac{1}{3}\right)$ Apply the distributive property.

$= 12a^4 - 6a^3 + a^2$ Simplify each term.

Thus far, we have illustrated polynomial multiplication involving monomials. Next, the distributive property will be used to multiply polynomials with more than one term.

$(x + 3)(x + 5) = x(x + 5) + 3(x + 5)$ Apply the distributive property.

$= x(x + 5) + 3(x + 5)$ Apply the distributive property again.

$= (x)(x) + (x)(5) + (3)(x) + (3)(5)$

$= x^2 + 5x + 3x + 15$

$= x^2 + 8x + 15$ Combine *like* terms.

Note: Using the distributive property results in multiplying each term of the first polynomial by each term of the second polynomial.

$$(x + 3)(x + 5) = (x)(x) + (x)(5) + (3)(x) + (3)(5)$$
$$= x^2 + 5x + 3x + 15$$
$$= x^2 + 8x + 15$$

Skill Practice

Multiply.

6. $(x + 2)(x + 8)$

Example 3 **Multiplying a Polynomial by a Polynomial**

Multiply the polynomials. $(c - 7)(c + 2)$

Solution:

$(c - 7)(c + 2)$ Multiply each term in the first polynomial by each term in the second. That is, apply the distributive property.

$$= (c)(c) + (c)(2) + (-7)(c) + (-7)(2)$$
$$= c^2 + 2c - 7c - 14 \qquad \text{Simplify.}$$
$$= c^2 - 5c - 14 \qquad \text{Combine } like \text{ terms.}$$

TIP: Notice that the product of two *binomials* equals the sum of the products of the **First** terms, the **Outer** terms, the **Inner** terms, and the **Last** terms. The acronym **FOIL** (First Outer Inner Last) can be used as a memory device to multiply two binomials.

Skill Practice

Multiply.

7. $(4a - 3c)(5a - 2c)$

Example 4 **Multiplying a Polynomial by a Polynomial**

Multiply the polynomials. $(10x + 3y)(2x - 4y)$

Solution:

$(10x + 3y)(2x - 4y)$ Multiply each term in the first polynomial by each term in the second. That is, apply the distributive property.

$$= (10x)(2x) + (10x)(-4y) + (3y)(2x) + (3y)(-4y)$$
$$= 20x^2 - 40xy + 6xy - 12y^2 \qquad \text{Simplify each term.}$$
$$= 20x^2 - 34xy - 12y^2 \qquad \text{Combine } like \text{ terms.}$$

Answers

6. $x^2 + 10x + 16$
7. $20a^2 - 23ac + 6c^2$

Example 5 **Multiplying a Polynomial by a Polynomial**

Multiply the polynomials. $(y - 2)(3y^2 + y - 5)$

Solution:

$(y - 2)(3y^2 + y - 5)$ Multiply each term in the first polynomial by each term in the second.

$= (y)(3y^2) + (y)(y) + (y)(-5) + (-2)(3y^2) + (-2)(y) + (-2)(-5)$

$= 3y^3 + y^2 - 5y - 6y^2 - 2y + 10$ Simplify each term.

$= 3y^3 - 5y^2 - 7y + 10$ Combine *like* terms.

> **TIP:** Multiplication of polynomials can be performed vertically by a process similar to column multiplication of real numbers. For example,
>
> | | |
> |---|---|
> | 235 | $3y^2 + y - 5$ |
> | × 21 | × $\quad y - 2$ |
> | 235 | $-6y^2 - 2y + 10$ |
> | 4700 | $3y^3 + y^2 - 5y + 0$ |
> | 4935 | $3y^3 - 5y^2 - 7y + 10$ |
>
> *Note:* When multiplying by the column method, it is important to *align like* terms vertically before adding terms.

Skill Practice

Multiply.

8. $(2y + 4)(3y^2 - 5y + 2)$

Avoiding Mistakes

It is important to note that the acronym FOIL does not apply to Example 5 because the product does not involve two binomials.

2. Special Case Products: Difference of Squares and Perfect Square Trinomials

In some cases the product of two binomials takes on a special pattern.

I. The first special case occurs when multiplying the sum and difference of the same two terms. For example:

$(2x + 3)(2x - 3)$

$= 4x^2 - 6x + 6x - 9$

$= 4x^2 - 9$

Notice that the middle terms are opposites. This leaves only the difference between the square of the first term and the square of the second term. For this reason, the product is called a *difference of squares.*

Note: The binomials $2x + 3$ and $2x - 3$ are called **conjugates**. In one expression, $2x$ and 3 are added, and in the other, $2x$ and 3 are subtracted.

II. The second special case involves the square of a binomial. For example:

$(3x + 7)^2$

$= (3x + 7)(3x + 7)$

$= 9x^2 + 21x + 21x + 49$

$= 9x^2 + 42x + 49$

$= (3x)^2 + 2(3x)(7) + (7)^2$

When squaring a binomial, the product will be a trinomial called a *perfect square trinomial.* The first and third terms are formed by squaring each term of the binomial. The middle term equals twice the product of the terms in the binomial.

Note: The expression $(3x - 7)^2$ also expands to a perfect square trinomial, but the middle term will be negative:

$(3x - 7)(3x - 7) = 9x^2 - 21x - 21x + 49 = 9x^2 - 42x + 49$

Answer

8. $6y^3 + 2y^2 - 16y + 8$

FORMULA Special Case Product Formulas

1. $(a + b)(a - b) = a^2 - b^2$ The product is called a **difference of squares**.

2. $(a + b)^2 = a^2 + 2ab + b^2$
   $(a - b)^2 = a^2 - 2ab + b^2$ } The product is called a **perfect square trinomial**.

You should become familiar with these special case products because they will be used again in the next chapter to factor polynomials.

Example 6 **Finding Special Products**

Multiply the conjugates.

a. $(x - 9)(x + 9)$ **b.** $\left(\dfrac{1}{2}p - 6\right)\left(\dfrac{1}{2}p + 6\right)$

Solution:

a. $(x - 9)(x + 9)$ Apply the formula:
    $(a + b)(a - b) = a^2 - b^2$.

$\overset{a^2 - b^2}{}$

$= (x)^2 - (9)^2$ Substitute $a = x$ and $b = 9$.

$= x^2 - 81$

TIP: The product of two conjugates can be checked by applying the distributive property:

$(x - 9)(x + 9)$

$= x^2 + 9x - 9x - 81$

$= x^2 - 81$

b. $\left(\dfrac{1}{2}p - 6\right)\left(\dfrac{1}{2}p + 6\right)$ Apply the formula: $(a + b)(a - b) = a^2 - b^2$.

$\overset{a^2 - b^2}{}$

$= \left(\dfrac{1}{2}p\right)^2 - (6)^2$ Substitute $a = \dfrac{1}{2}p$ and $b = 6$.

$= \dfrac{1}{4}p^2 - 36$ Simplify each term.

Example 7 **Finding Special Products**

Square the binomials.

a. $(3w - 4)^2$ **b.** $(5x^2 + 2)^2$

Solution:

a. $(3w - 4)^2$ Apply the formula:
    $(a - b)^2 = a^2 - 2ab + b^2$.

$\overset{a^2 - 2ab + b^2}{}$

$= (3w)^2 - 2(3w)(4) + (4)^2$ Substitute $a = 3w, b = 4$.

$= 9w^2 - 24w + 16$ Simplify each term.

TIP: The square of a binomial can be checked by explicitly writing the product of the two binomials and applying the distributive property:

$$(3w - 4)^2 = (3w - 4)(3w - 4) = 9w^2 - 12w - 12w + 16$$
$$= 9w^2 - 24w + 16$$

b. $(5x^2 + 2)^2$

Apply the formula:
$(a + b)^2 = a^2 + 2ab + b^2.$

$a^2 + 2ab + b^2$

$= (5x^2)^2 + 2(5x^2)(2) + (2)^2$ Substitute $a = 5x^2, b = 2.$

$= 25x^4 + 20x^2 + 4$ Simplify each term.

Avoiding Mistakes

The property for squaring two factors is different than the property for squaring two terms:
$(ab)^2 = a^2b^2$ but
$(a + b)^2 = a^2 + 2ab + b^2$

3. Applications to Geometry

Example 8 **Using Special Case Products in an Application of Geometry**

Find a polynomial that represents the volume of the cube (Figure 12-2).

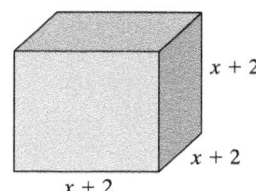

$x + 2$

$x + 2$

$x + 2$

Figure 12-2

Skill Practice

13. Find the polynomial that represents the volume of the cube.

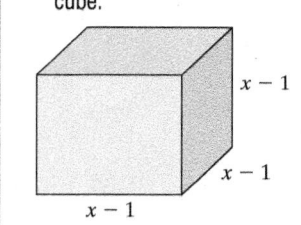

$x - 1$

$x - 1$

$x - 1$

Solution:

Volume = (length)(width)(height)

$V = (x + 2)(x + 2)(x + 2)$ or $V = (x + 2)^3$

To expand $(x + 2)(x + 2)(x + 2)$, multiply the first two factors. Then multiply the result by the last factor.

$V = \underline{(x + 2)(x + 2)}(x + 2)$

$= (x^2 + 4x + 4)(x + 2)$

TIP: $(x + 2)(x + 2) = (x + 2)^2$ and results in a perfect square trinomial.

$(x + 2)^2 = (x)^2 + 2(x)(2) + (2)^2$
$= x^2 + 4x + 4$

$= (x^2)(x) + (x^2)(2) + (4x)(x) + (4x)(2) + (4)(x) + (4)(2)$ Apply the distributive property.

$= x^3 + 2x^2 + 4x^2 + 8x + 4x + 8$ Group *like* terms.

$= x^3 + 6x^2 + 12x + 8$ Combine *like* terms.

The volume of the cube can be represented by

$$V = (x + 2)^3 = x^3 + 6x^2 + 12x + 8.$$

Answer

13. The volume of the cube can be represented by
$x^3 - 3x^2 + 3x - 1.$

Section 12.6 Practice Exercises

Study Skills Exercise

1. Define the key terms:

    a. Conjugates   **b. Difference of squares**   **c. Perfect square trinomial**

Review Exercises

For Exercises 2–9, simplify the expressions (if possible).

2. $4x + 5x$

3. $2y^2 - 4y^2$

4. $(4x)(5x)$

5. $(2y^2)(-4y^2)$

6. $-5a^3b - 2a^3b$

7. $7uvw^2 + uvw^2$

8. $(-5a^3b)(-2a^3b)$

9. $(7uvw^2)(uvw^2)$

Objective 1: Multiplication of Polynomials

For Exercises 10–18, multiply the expressions. **(See Example 1.)**

10. $8(4x)$

11. $-2(6y)$

12. $-10(5z)$

13. $7(3p)$

14. $(x^{10})(4x^3)$

15. $(a^{13}b^4)(12ab^4)$

16. $(4m^3n^7)(-3m^6n)$

17. $(2c^7d)(-c^3d^{11})$

18. $(-5u^2v)(-8u^3v^2)$

For Exercises 19–52, multiply the polynomials. **(See Examples 2–5.)**

19. $8pq(2pq - 3p + 5q)$

20. $5ab(2ab + 6a - 3b)$

21. $(k^2 - 13k - 6)(-4k)$

22. $(h^2 + 5h - 12)(-2h)$

23. $-15pq(3p^2 + p^3q^2 - 2q)$

24. $-4u^2v(2u - 5uv^3 + v)$

25. $(y - 10)(y + 9)$

26. $(x + 5)(x - 6)$

27. $(m - 12)(m - 2)$

28. $(n - 7)(n - 2)$

29. $(3p - 2)(4p + 1)$

30. $(7q + 11)(q - 5)$

31. $(-4w + 8)(-3w + 2)$

32. $(-6z + 10)(-2z + 4)$

33. $(p - 3w)(p - 11w)$

34. $(y - 7x)(y - 10x)$

35. $(6x - 1)(2x + 5)$

36. $(3x + 7)(x - 8)$

37. $(4a - 9)(2a - 1)$

38. $(3b + 5)(b - 5)$

39. $(3t - 7)(3t + 1)$

40. $(5w - 2)(2w - 5)$

41. $(3m + 4n)(m + 8n)$

42. $(7y + z)(3y + 5z)$

43. $(5s + 3)(s^2 + s - 2)$

44. $(t - 4)(2t^2 - t + 6)$

45. $(3w - 2)(9w^2 + 6w + 4)$

46. $(z + 5)(z^2 - 5z + 25)$

47. $(p^2 + p - 5)(p^2 + 4p - 1)$

48. $(-x^2 - 2x + 4)(x^2 + 2x - 6)$

49. $\begin{array}{r} 3a^2 - 4a + 9 \\ \times \underline{ 2a - 5} \end{array}$

50. $\begin{array}{r} 7x^2 - 3x - 4 \\ \times \underline{ 5x + 1} \end{array}$

51. $\begin{array}{r} 4x^2 - 12xy + 9y^2 \\ \times \underline{ 2x - 3y} \end{array}$

52. $\begin{array}{r} 25a^2 + 10ab + b^2 \\ \times \underline{ 5a + b} \end{array}$

Objective 2: Special Case Products: Difference of Squares and Perfect Square Trinomials

For Exercises 53–64, multiply the conjugates. **(See Example 6.)**

53. $(3a - 4b)(3a + 4b)$

54. $(5y + 7x)(5y - 7x)$

55. $(9k + 6)(9k - 6)$

56. $(2h - 5)(2h + 5)$

57. $\left(\frac{1}{2} - t\right)\left(\frac{1}{2} + t\right)$

58. $\left(r + \frac{1}{4}\right)\left(r - \frac{1}{4}\right)$

59. $(u^3 + 5v)(u^3 - 5v)$

60. $(8w^2 - x)(8w^2 + x)$

61. $(2 - 3a)(2 + 3a)$

62. $(1 - 4x^2)(1 + 4x^2)$

63. $\left(\frac{2}{3} - p\right)\left(\frac{2}{3} + p\right)$

64. $\left(\frac{1}{8} - q\right)\left(\frac{1}{8} + q\right)$

For Exercises 65–76, square the binomials. **(See Example 7.)**

65. $(a + 5)^2$

66. $(a - 3)^2$

67. $(x - y)^2$

68. $(x + y)^2$

69. $(2c + 5)^2$

70. $(5d - 9)^2$

71. $(3t^2 - 4s)^2$

72. $(u^2 + 4v)^2$

73. $(7 - t)^2$

74. $(4 + w)^2$

75. $(3 + 4q)^2$

76. $(2 - 3b)^2$

77. **a.** Evaluate $(2 + 4)^2$ by working within the parentheses first.

    b. Evaluate $2^2 + 4^2$.

    c. Compare the answers to parts (a) and (b) and make a conjecture about $(a + b)^2$ and $a^2 + b^2$.

78. **a.** Evaluate $(6 - 5)^2$ by working within the parentheses first.

    b. Evaluate $6^2 - 5^2$.

    c. Compare the answers to parts (a) and (b) and make a conjecture about $(a - b)^2$ and $a^2 - b^2$.

79. **a.** Simplify $(3x + y)^2$.

    b. Simplify $(3xy)^2$.

Objective 3: Applications to Geometry

80. Find a polynomial expression that represents the area of the rectangle shown in the figure.

2x + 5

2x − 5

81. Find a polynomial expression that represents the area of the rectangle shown in the figure.

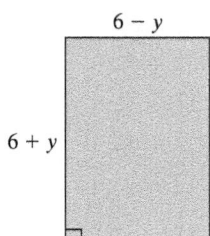

6 − y

6 + y

82. Find a polynomial expression that represents the area of the square shown in the figure.

$4p + 5$

83. Find a polynomial expression that represents the area of the square shown in the figure.

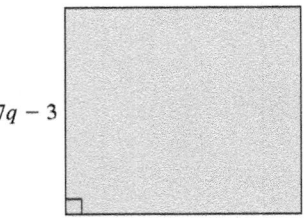

$7q - 3$

84. Find a polynomial that represents the volume of the cube shown in the figure.
(Recall: $V = s^3$)

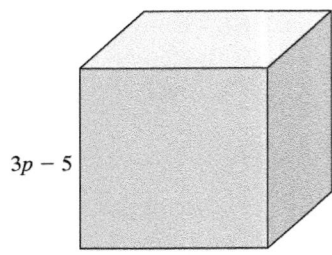

$3p - 5$

85. Find a polynomial that represents the volume of the rectangular solid shown in the figure.
(See Example 8.) (Recall: $V = lwh$)

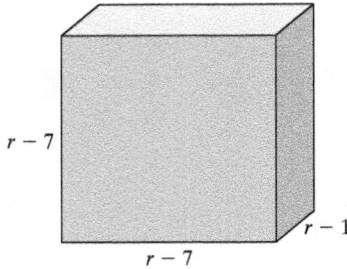

$r - 7$ $r - 1$
    $r - 7$

86. Find a polynomial that represents the area of the triangle shown in the figure.
(Recall: $A = \frac{1}{2}bh$)

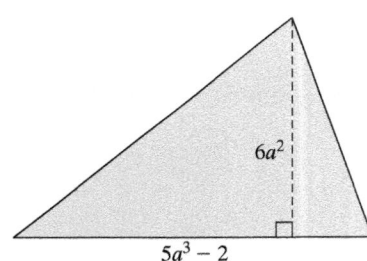

$6a^2$

$5a^3 - 2$

87. Find a polynomial that represents the area of the triangle shown in the figure.

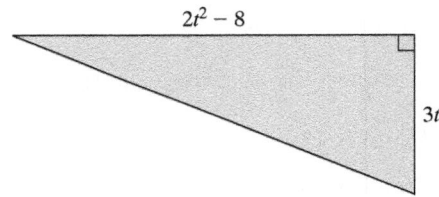

$2t^2 - 8$

$3t$

Mixed Exercises

For Exercises 88–117, multiply the expressions.

88. $(7x + y)(7x - y)$

89. $(9w - 4z)(9w + 4z)$

90. $(5s + 3t)^2$

91. $(5s - 3t)^2$

92. $(7x - 3y)(3x - 8y)$

93. $(5a - 4b)(2a - b)$

94. $\left(\frac{2}{3}t + 2\right)(3t + 4)$

95. $\left(\frac{1}{5}s + 6\right)(5s - 3)$

96. $(5z + 3)(z^2 + 4z - 1)$

97. $(2k - 5)(2k^2 + 3k + 5)$

98. $(3a - 2)(5a + 1 + 2a^2)$

99. $(u + 4)(2 - 3u + u^2)$

100. $(y^2 + 2y + 4)(y - 5)$

101. $(w^2 - w + 6)(w + 2)$

102. $\left(\dfrac{1}{3}m - n\right)^2$

103. $\left(\dfrac{2}{5}p - q\right)^2$

104. $6w^2(7w - 14)$

105. $4v^3(v + 12)$

106. $(4y - 8.1)(4y + 8.1)$

107. $(2h + 2.7)(2h - 2.7)$

108. $(3c^2 + 4)(7c^2 - 8)$

109. $(5k^3 - 9)(k^3 - 2)$

110. $(3.1x + 4.5)^2$

111. $(2.5y + 1.1)^2$

112. $(k - 4)^3$

113. $(h + 3)^3$

114. $(5x + 3)^3$

115. $(2a - 4)^3$

116. $(y^2 + 2y + 1)(2y^2 - y + 3)$

117. $(2w^2 - w - 5)(3w^2 + 2w + 1)$

Expanding Your Skills

For Exercises 118–121, multiply the expressions containing more than two factors.

118. $2a(3a - 4)(a + 5)$

119. $5x(x + 2)(6x - 1)$

120. $(x - 3)(2x + 1)(x - 4)$

121. $(y - 2)(2y - 3)(y + 3)$

122. What binomial when multiplied by $(3x + 5)$ will produce a product of $6x^2 - 11x - 35$? [*Hint:* Let the quantity $(a + b)$ represent the unknown binomial.] Then find a and b such that $(3x + 5)(a + b) = 6x^2 - 11x - 35$.

123. What binomial when multiplied by $(2x - 4)$ will produce a product of $2x^2 + 8x - 24$?

For Exercises 124–126, determine what values of k would create a perfect square trinomial.

124. $x^2 + kx + 25$

125. $w^2 + kw + 9$

126. $a^2 + ka + 16$

Division of Polynomials

Section 12.7

Division of polynomials will be presented in this section as two separate cases: The first case illustrates division by a monomial divisor. The second case illustrates long division by a polynomial with two or more terms.

Objectives

1. Division by a Monomial
2. Long Division

1. Division by a Monomial

To divide a polynomial by a monomial, divide each individual term in the polynomial by the divisor and simplify the result.

> **PROCEDURE Dividing a Polynomial by a Monomial**
> If a, b, and c are polynomials such that $c \neq 0$, then
> $$\frac{a + b}{c} = \frac{a}{c} + \frac{b}{c} \quad \text{Similarly,} \quad \frac{a - b}{c} = \frac{a}{c} - \frac{b}{c}$$

| **Example 1** | **Dividing a Polynomial by a Monomial** |

Divide the polynomials.

a. $\dfrac{5a^3 - 10a^2 + 20a}{5a}$

b. $(12y^2z^3 - 15yz^2 + 6y^2z) \div (-6y^2z)$

Solution:

a. $\dfrac{5a^3 - 10a^2 + 20a}{5a}$

$= \dfrac{5a^3}{5a} - \dfrac{10a^2}{5a} + \dfrac{20a}{5a}$ Divide each term in the numerator by $5a$.

$= a^2 - 2a + 4$ Simplify each term using the properties of exponents.

b. $(12y^2z^3 - 15yz^2 + 6y^2z) \div (-6y^2z)$

$= \dfrac{12y^2z^3 - 15yz^2 + 6y^2z}{-6y^2z}$

$= \dfrac{12y^2z^3}{-6y^2z} - \dfrac{15yz^2}{-6y^2z} + \dfrac{6y^2z}{-6y^2z}$ Divide each term by $-6y^2z$.

$= -2z^2 + \dfrac{5z}{2y} - 1$ Simplify each term.

2. Long Division

If the divisor has two or more terms, a *long division* process similar to the division of real numbers is used. Take a minute to review the long division process for real numbers by dividing 2273 by 5.

$$
\begin{array}{r}
454 \quad \longleftarrow \text{Quotient} \\
5\overline{)2273} \\
\underline{-20}\downarrow \quad \\
27 \quad \\
\underline{-25}\downarrow \\
23 \\
\underline{-20} \\
3 \quad \longleftarrow \text{Remainder}
\end{array}
$$

Therefore, $2273 \div 5 = 454\frac{3}{5}$

A similar procedure is used for long division of polynomials as shown in Example 2.

Example 2 **Using Long Division to Divide Polynomials**

Divide the polynomials using long division: $(2x^2 - x + 3) \div (x - 3)$

Skill Practice

Divide the polynomials using long division.

3. $(3x^2 + 2x - 5) \div (x + 2)$

Solution:

$x - 3)\overline{2x^2 - x + 3}$ Divide the leading term in the dividend by the leading term in the divisor.

$$\frac{2x^2}{x} = 2x$$

This is the first term in the quotient.

$\begin{array}{r} 2x \\ x - 3)\overline{2x^2 - x + 3} \\ -(2x^2 - 6x) \end{array}$ Multiply $2x$ by the divisor $2x(x - 3) = 2x^2 - 6x$ and subtract the result.

$\begin{array}{r} 2x \\ x - 3)\overline{2x^2 - x + 3} \\ \underline{-2x^2 + 6x} \\ 5x \end{array}$ Subtract the quantity $2x^2 - 6x$. To do this, add the opposite.

$\begin{array}{r} 2x + 5 \\ x - 3)\overline{2x^2 - x + 3} \\ \underline{-2x^2 + 6x} \downarrow \\ 5x + 3 \end{array}$ Bring down the next column and repeat the process.
Divide the leading term by x: $(5x)/x = 5$.
Place 5 in the quotient.

$\begin{array}{r} 2x + 5 \\ x - 3)\overline{2x^2 - x + 3} \\ \underline{-2x^2 + 6x} \\ 5x + 3 \\ -(5x - 15) \end{array}$ Multiply the divisor by 5: $5(x - 3) = 5x - 15$ and subtract the result.

$\begin{array}{r} 2x + 5 \\ x - 3)\overline{2x^2 - x + 3} \\ \underline{-2x^2 + 6x} \\ 5x + 3 \\ \underline{-5x + 15} \\ 18 \end{array}$ Subtract the quantity $5x - 15$ by adding the opposite.
The remainder is 18.

Summary:

The quotient is $2x + 5$
The remainder is 18
The divisor is $x - 3$
The dividend is $2x^2 - x + 3$

The solution to a long division problem is usually written in the form:

$$\text{quotient} + \frac{\text{remainder}}{\text{divisor}}$$

Hence,

$$(2x^2 - x + 3) \div (x - 3) = 2x + 5 + \frac{18}{x - 3}$$

The division of polynomials can be checked in the same fashion as the division of real numbers. To check Example 2, we have:

Answer

3. $3x - 4 + \dfrac{3}{x + 2}$

Dividend = (divisor)(quotient) + remainder

$$2x^2 - x + 3 \overset{?}{=} (x - 3)(2x + 5) + (18)$$

$$\overset{?}{=} 2x^2 + 5x - 6x - 15 + (18)$$

$$= 2x^2 - x + 3 \checkmark$$

Skill Practice

Divide the polynomials using long division.

4. $\dfrac{9x^3 + 11x + 10}{3x + 2}$

Example 3 **Using Long Division to Divide Polynomials**

Divide the polynomials using long division: $(2w^3 + 8w^2 - 16) \div (2w + 4)$

Solution:

First note that the dividend has a missing power of w and can be written as $2w^3 + 8w^2 + 0w - 16$. The term $0w$ is a place holder for the missing term. It is helpful to use the place holder to keep the powers of w lined up.

$$\begin{array}{r} w^2 \\ 2w + 4 \overline{)2w^3 + 8w^2 + 0w - 16} \\ -(2w^3 + 4w^2) \end{array}$$

Divide $2w^3 \div 2w = w^2$. This is the first term of the quotient.

Then multiply $w^2(2w + 4) = 2w^3 + 4w^2$.

$$\begin{array}{r} w^2 \\ 2w + 4 \overline{)2w^3 + 8w^2 + 0w - 16} \\ -2w^3 - 4w^2 \\ \hline 4w^2 + 0w \end{array}$$

Subtract by adding the opposite.

Bring down the next column, and repeat the process.

$$\begin{array}{r} w^2 + 2w \\ 2w + 4 \overline{)2w^3 + 8w^2 + 0w - 16} \\ -2w^3 - 4w^2 \\ \hline 4w^2 + 0w \\ -(4w^2 + 8w) \end{array}$$

Divide $4w^2$ by the leading term in the divisor. $4w^2 \div 2w = 2w$. Place $2w$ in the quotient.

Multiply $2w(2w + 4) = 4w^2 + 8w$.

$$\begin{array}{r} w^2 + 2w \\ 2w + 4 \overline{)2w^3 + 8w^2 + 0w - 16} \\ -2w^3 - 4w^2 \\ \hline 4w^2 + 0w \\ -4w^2 - 8w \\ \hline -8w - 16 \end{array}$$

Subtract by adding the opposite.

Bring down the next column and repeat.

$$\begin{array}{r} w^2 + 2w - 4 \\ 2w + 4 \overline{)2w^3 + 8w^2 + 0w - 16} \\ -2w^3 - 4w^2 \\ \hline 4w^2 + 0w \\ -4w^2 - 8w \\ \hline -8w - 16 \\ -(-8w - 16) \end{array}$$

Divide $-8w$ by the leading term in the divisor. $-8w \div 2w = -4$. Place -4 in the quotient.

Multiply $-4(2w + 4) = -8w - 16$.

$$\begin{array}{r} w^2 + 2w - 4 \\ 2w + 4 \overline{)2w^3 + 8w^2 + 0w - 16} \\ -2w^3 - 4w^2 \\ \hline 4w^2 + 0w \\ -4w^2 - 8w \\ \hline -8w - 16 \\ 8w + 16 \\ \hline 0 \end{array}$$

Subtract by adding the opposite.

The remainder is 0.

The quotient is $w^2 + 2w - 4$, and the remainder is 0.

Answer

4. $3x^2 - 2x + 5$

In Example 3, the remainder is zero. Therefore, we say that $2w + 4$ divides *evenly* into $2w^3 + 8w^2 - 16$. For this reason, the divisor and quotient are factors of $2w^3 + 8w^2 - 16$. To check, we have

$$\text{Dividend} = (\text{divisor})(\text{quotient}) + \text{remainder}$$
$$2w^3 + 8w^2 - 16 \stackrel{?}{=} (2w + 4)(w^2 + 2w - 4) + 0$$
$$\stackrel{?}{=} 2w^3 + 4w^2 - 8w + 4w^2 + 8w - 16$$
$$= 2w^3 + 8w^2 - 16 ✔$$

Example 4 **Using Long Division to Divide Polynomials**

Divide the polynomials using long division.

$$\frac{2y + y^4 - 5}{1 + y^2}$$

Solution:

First note that both the dividend and divisor should be written in descending order:

$$\frac{y^4 + 2y - 5}{y^2 + 1}$$

Also note that the dividend and the divisor have missing powers of y. Leave place holders.

$$y^2 + 0y + 1 \overline{)y^4 + 0y^3 + 0y^2 + 2y - 5}$$

Therefore, $\dfrac{y^4 + 2y - 5}{y^2 + 1} = y^2 - 1 + \dfrac{2y - 4}{y^2 + 1}$

Skill Practice

Divide the polynomials using long division.

5. $(4 - x^2 + x^3) \div (2 + x^2)$

Answer

5. $x - 1 + \dfrac{-2x + 6}{x^2 + 2}$

Divide the polynomials using the appropriate method of division.

6. $\dfrac{6x^3 - x^2 + 3x - 5}{2x + 3}$

7. $\dfrac{9w^3 - 18w^2 + 6w + 12}{3w}$

Example 5 **Determining Whether Long Division Is Necessary**

Determine whether long division is necessary for each division of polynomials.

a. $\dfrac{2p^5 - 8p^4 + 4p - 16}{p^2 - 2p + 1}$ **b.** $\dfrac{2p^5 - 8p^4 + 4p - 16}{2p^2}$

c. $(3z^3 - 5z^2 + 10) \div (15z^3)$ **d.** $(3z^3 - 5z^2 + 10) \div (3z + 1)$

Solution:

a. $\dfrac{2p^5 - 8p^4 + 4p - 16}{p^2 - 2p + 1}$ The divisor has three terms. Use long division.

b. $\dfrac{2p^5 - 8p^4 + 4p - 16}{2p^2}$ The divisor has one term. No long division.

c. $(3z^3 - 5z^2 + 10) \div (15z^3)$ The divisor has one term. No long division.

d. $(3z^3 - 5z^2 + 10) \div (3z + 1)$ The divisor has two terms. Use long division.

TIP: Recall that
- Long division is used when the divisor has *two or more terms*.
- If the divisor has *one term*, then divide each term in the dividend by the monomial divisor.

Answers

6. $3x^2 - 5x + 9 + \dfrac{-32}{2x + 3}$

7. $3w^2 - 6w + 2 + \dfrac{4}{w}$

Section 12.7   Practice Exercises

Review Exercises

For Exercises 1–10, perform the indicated operations.

1. $(6z^5 - 2z^3 + z - 6) - (10z^4 + 2z^3 + z^2 + z)$ **2.** $(7a^2 + a - 6) + (2a^2 + 5a + 11)$

3. $(10x + y)(x - 3y)$ **4.** $8b^2(2b^2 - 5b + 12)$

5. $(10x + y) + (x - 3y)$ **6.** $(2w^3 + 5)^2$

7. $\left(\dfrac{4}{3}y^2 - \dfrac{1}{2}y + \dfrac{3}{8}\right) - \left(\dfrac{1}{3}y^2 + \dfrac{1}{4}y - \dfrac{1}{8}\right)$ **8.** $\left(\dfrac{7}{8}w - 1\right)\left(\dfrac{7}{8}w + 1\right)$

9. $(a + 3)(a^2 - 3a + 9)$ **10.** $(2x + 1)(5x - 3)$

Objective 1: Division by a Monomial

11. There are two methods for dividing polynomials. Explain when long division is used.

12. Explain how to check a polynomial division problem.

13. a. Divide $\dfrac{15t^3 + 18t^2}{3t}$

  b. Check by multiplying the quotient by the divisor.

14. a. Divide $(-9y^4 + 6y^2 - y) \div (3y)$

  b. Check by multiplying the quotient by the divisor.

For Exercises 15–30, divide the polynomials. **(See Example 1.)**

15. $(6a^2 + 4a - 14) \div (2)$

16. $\dfrac{4b^2 + 16b - 12}{4}$

17. $\dfrac{-5x^2 - 20x + 5}{-5}$

18. $\dfrac{-3y^3 + 12y - 6}{-3}$

19. $\dfrac{3p^3 - p^2}{p}$

20. $(7q^4 + 5q^2) \div q$

21. $(4m^2 + 8m) \div 4m^2$

22. $\dfrac{n^2 - 8}{n}$

23. $\dfrac{14y^4 - 7y^3 + 21y^2}{-7y^2}$

24. $(25a^5 - 5a^4 + 15a^3 - 5a) \div (-5a)$

25. $(4x^3 - 24x^2 - x + 8) \div (4x)$

26. $\dfrac{20w^3 + 15w^2 - w + 5}{10w}$

27. $\dfrac{-a^3b^2 + a^2b^2 - ab^3}{-a^2b^2}$

28. $(3x^4y^3 - x^2y^2 - xy^3) \div (-x^2y^2)$

29. $(6t^4 - 2t^3 + 3t^2 - t + 4) \div (2t^3)$

30. $\dfrac{2y^3 - 2y^2 + 3y - 9}{2y^2}$

Objective 2: Long Division

31. a. Divide $(z^2 + 7z + 11) \div (z + 5)$

  b. Check by multiplying the quotient by the divisor and adding the remainder.

32. a. Divide $\dfrac{2w^2 - 7w + 3}{w - 4}$

  b. Check by multiplying the quotient by the divisor and adding the remainder.

For Exercises 33–56, divide the polynomials. **(See Examples 2–4.)**

33. $\dfrac{t^2 + 4t + 5}{t + 1}$

34. $(3x^2 + 8x + 5) \div (x + 2)$

35. $(7b^2 - 3b - 4) \div (b - 1)$

36. $\dfrac{w^2 - w - 2}{w - 2}$

37. $\dfrac{5k^2 - 29k - 6}{5k + 1}$

38. $(4y^2 + 25y - 21) \div (4y - 3)$

39. $(4p^3 + 12p^2 + p - 12) \div (2p + 3)$

40. $\dfrac{12a^3 - 2a^2 - 17a - 5}{3a + 1}$

41. $\dfrac{-k - 6 + k^2}{1 + k}$

42. $(1 + h^2 + 3h) \div (2 + h)$

43. $(4x^3 - 8x^2 + 15x - 16) \div (2x - 3)$

44. $\dfrac{3b^3 + b^2 + 17b - 49}{3b - 5}$

45. $\dfrac{3y^3 + 5y^2 + y + 1}{3y - 1}$

46. $\dfrac{4t^3 + 4t^2 - 9t + 3}{2t + 3}$

47. $\dfrac{9 + a^2}{a + 3}$

48. $(3 + m^2) \div (m + 3)$

49. $(4x^3 - 3x - 26) \div (x - 2)$

50. $(4y^3 + y + 1) \div (2y + 1)$

51. $(w^4 + 5w^3 - 5w^2 - 15w + 7) \div (w^2 - 3)$

52. $\dfrac{p^4 - p^3 - 4p^2 - 2p - 15}{p^2 + 2}$

53. $\dfrac{2n^4 + 5n^3 - 11n^2 - 20n + 12}{2n^2 + 3n - 2}$

54. $(6y^4 - 5y^3 - 8y^2 + 16y - 8) \div (2y^2 - 3y + 2)$

55. $(5x^3 - 4x - 9) \div (5x^2 + 5x + 1)$

56. $\dfrac{3a^3 - 5a + 16}{3a^2 - 6a + 7}$

57. Show that $(x^3 - 8) \div (x - 2)$ is *not* $(x^2 + 4)$.

58. Explain why $(y^3 + 27) \div (y + 3)$ is *not* $(y^2 + 9)$.

Mixed Exercises

For Exercises 59–70, determine which method to use to divide the polynomials: monomial division or long division. Then use that method to divide the polynomials. **(See Example 5.)**

59. $\dfrac{9a^3 + 12a^2}{3a}$

60. $\dfrac{3y^2 + 17y - 12}{y + 6}$

61. $(p^3 + p^2 - 4p - 4) \div (p^2 - p - 2)$

62. $(q^3 + 1) \div (q + 1)$

63. $\dfrac{t^4 + t^2 - 16}{t + 2}$

64. $\dfrac{-8m^5 - 4m^3 + 4m^2}{-2m^2}$

65. $(w^4 + w^2 - 5) \div (w^2 - 2)$

66. $(2k^2 + 9k + 7) \div (k + 1)$

67. $\dfrac{n^3 - 64}{n - 4}$

68. $\dfrac{15s^2 + 34s + 28}{5s + 3}$

69. $(9r^3 - 12r^2 + 9) \div (-3r^2)$

70. $(6x^4 - 16x^3 + 15x^2 - 5x + 10) \div (3x + 1)$

Expanding Your Skills

For Exercises 71–78, divide the polynomials and note any patterns.

71. $(x^2 - 1) \div (x - 1)$

72. $(x^3 - 1) \div (x - 1)$

73. $(x^4 - 1) \div (x - 1)$

74. $(x^5 - 1) \div (x - 1)$

75. $x^2 \div (x - 1)$

76. $x^3 \div (x - 1)$

77. $x^4 \div (x - 1)$

78. $x^5 \div (x - 1)$

Problem Recognition Exercises

Operations on Polynomials

Perform the indicated operations and simplify.

1. $(2x - 4)(x^2 - 2x + 3)$ **2.** $(3y^2 + 8)(-y^2 - 4)$ **3.** $(2x - 4) + (x^2 - 2x + 3)$ **4.** $(3y^2 + 8) - (-y^2 - 4)$

5. $(6y - 7)^2$ **6.** $(3z + 2)^2$ **7.** $(6y - 7)(6y + 7)$ **8.** $(3z + 2)(3z - 2)$

9. $(4x + y)^2$ **10.** $(2a + b)^2$ **11.** $(4xy)^2$ **12.** $(2ab)^2$

13. $(-2x^4 - 6x^3 + 8x^2) \div (2x^2)$ **14.** $(-15m^3 + 12m^2 - 3m) \div (-3m)$

15. $(m^3 - 4m^2 - 6) - (3m^2 + 7m) + (-m^3 - 9m + 6)$ **16.** $(n^4 + 2n^2 - 3n) + (4n^2 + 2n - 1) - (4n^5 + 6n - 3)$

17. $(8x^3 + 2x + 6) \div (x - 2)$ **18.** $(-4x^3 + 2x^2 - 5) \div (x - 3)$

19. $(2x - y)(3x^2 + 4xy - y^2)$ **20.** $(3a + b)(2a^2 - ab + 2b^2)$

21. $(x + y^2)(x^2 - xy^2 + y^4)$ **22.** $(m^2 + 1)(m^4 - m^2 + 1)$

23. $(a^2 + 2b) - (a^2 - 2b)$ **24.** $(y^3 - 6z) - (y^3 + 6z)$ **25.** $(a^2 + 2b)(a^2 - 2b)$ **26.** $(y^3 - 6z)(y^3 + 6z)$

27. $(8u + 3v)^2$ **28.** $(2p - t)^2$ **29.** $\dfrac{8p^2 + 4p - 6}{2p - 1}$ **30.** $\dfrac{4v^2 - 8v + 8}{2v + 3}$

31. $\dfrac{12x^3y^7}{3xy^5}$ **32.** $\dfrac{-18p^2q^4}{2pq^3}$ **33.** $(2a - 9)(5a - 6)$ **34.** $(7a + 1)(4a - 3)$

35. $\left(\dfrac{3}{7}x - \dfrac{1}{2}\right)\left(\dfrac{3}{7}x + \dfrac{1}{2}\right)$ **36.** $\left(\dfrac{2}{5}y + \dfrac{4}{3}\right)\left(\dfrac{2}{5}y - \dfrac{4}{3}\right)$ **37.** $\left(\dfrac{1}{9}x^3 + \dfrac{2}{3}x^2 + \dfrac{1}{6}x - 3\right) - \left(\dfrac{4}{3}x^3 + \dfrac{1}{9}x^2 + \dfrac{2}{3}x + 1\right)$

38. $\left(\dfrac{1}{10}y^2 - \dfrac{3}{5}y - \dfrac{1}{15}\right) - \left(\dfrac{7}{5}y^2 + \dfrac{3}{10}y - \dfrac{1}{3}\right)$ **39.** $(0.05x^2 - 0.16x - 0.75) + (1.25x^2 - 0.14x + 0.25)$

40. $(1.6w^3 + 2.8w + 6.1) + (3.4w^3 - 4.1w^2 - 7.3)$

Group Activity

The Pythagorean Theorem and a Geometric "Proof"

Estimated Time: 10–15 minutes

Group Size: 2

Right triangles occur in many applications of mathematics. By definition, a right triangle is a triangle that contains a 90° angle. The two shorter sides in a right triangle are referred to as the "legs," and the longest side is called the "hypotenuse." In the triangle, the legs are labeled as a and b, and the hypotenuse is labeled as c.

Right triangles have an important property that the sum of the squares of the two legs of a right triangle equals the square of the hypotenuse. This fact is referred to as the Pythagorean theorem. In symbols, the Pythagorean theorem is stated as:

$$a^2 + b^2 = c^2$$

1. The following triangles are right triangles. Verify that $a^2 + b^2 = c^2$. (The units may be left off when performing these calculations.)

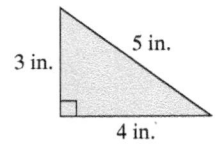

$a = 3$
$b = 4$
$c = 5$

$a^2 + b^2 = c^2$

$(3)^2 + (4)^2 \stackrel{?}{=} (5)^2$

$9 + 16 = 25$ ✔

$a = $ _____
$b = $ _____
$c = $ _____

$a^2 + b^2 = c^2$

$(\_\_)^2 + (\_\_)^2 \stackrel{?}{=} (\_\_)^2$

___ + ___ = ___ ✔

2. The following geometric "proof" of the Pythagorean theorem uses addition, subtraction, and multiplication of polynomials. Consider the square figure. The length of each side of the large outer square is $(a + b)$. Therefore, the area of the large outer square is $(a + b)^2$.

The area of the large outer square can also be found by adding the area of the inner square (pictured in light gray) plus the area of the four right triangles (pictured in dark gray).

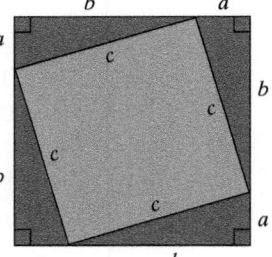

Area of inner square: c^2 Area of the four right triangles: $4 \cdot \left(\frac{1}{2} a b\right)$

½ Base · Height

3. Now equate the two expressions representing the area of the large outer square:

$$\left(\begin{array}{c}\text{Area of outer}\\\text{square}\end{array}\right) = \left(\begin{array}{c}\text{area of inner}\\\text{square}\end{array}\right) + \left(\begin{array}{c}\text{4 times the area}\\\text{of the right triangles}\end{array}\right)$$

_____ = _____ + _____   ← Clear parentheses on both sides of the equation.

_____ = _____ + _____   ← Subtract 2ab from both sides.

_____ = _____

Chapter 12   Summary

Section 12.1   Exponents: Multiplying and Dividing Common Bases

Key Concepts

Definition

$b^n = \underbrace{b \cdot b \cdot b \cdot b \cdot \ldots b}_{n \text{ factors of } b}$ b is the base, n is the exponent

Multiplying Like Bases

$b^m b^n = b^{m+n}$ (m, n positive integers)

Dividing Like Bases

$\dfrac{b^m}{b^n} = b^{m-n}$ ($b \neq 0; m, n$, positive integers)

Examples

Example 1

$3^4 = 3 \cdot 3 \cdot 3 \cdot 3 = 81$ 3 is the base
4 is the exponent

Example 2

Compare: $(-5)^2$ versus -5^2

versus $\begin{cases} (-5)^2 = (-5)(-5) = 25 \\ \\ -5^2 = -1(5^2) = -1(5)(5) = -25 \end{cases}$

Example 3

Simplify: $x^3 \cdot x^4 \cdot x^2 \cdot x = x^{10}$

Example 4

Simplify: $\dfrac{c^4 d^{10}}{c d^5} = c^{4-1} d^{10-5} = c^3 d^5$

Section 12.2   More Properties of Exponents

Key Concepts

Power Rule for Exponents

$(b^m)^n = b^{mn}$ ($b \neq 0; m, n$ positive integers)

Power of a Product and Power of a Quotient

Assume m and n are positive integers and a and b are real numbers where $b \neq 0$.
Then,

$(ab)^m = a^m b^m$ and $\left(\dfrac{a}{b}\right)^m = \dfrac{a^m}{b^m}$

Examples

Example 1

Simplify: $(x^4)^5 = x^{20}$

Example 2

Simplify: $(4uv^2)^3 = 4^3 u^3 (v^2)^3 = 64 u^3 v^6$

Example 3

Simplify: $\left(\dfrac{p^5 q^3}{5 p q^2}\right)^2 = \left(\dfrac{p^{5-1} q^{3-2}}{5}\right)^2 = \left(\dfrac{p^4 q}{5}\right)^2$

$= \dfrac{p^8 q^2}{25}$

Section 12.3 Definitions of b^0 and b^{-n}

Key Concepts

Definitions

If b is a nonzero real number and n is an integer, then:

1. $b^0 = 1$

2. $b^{-n} = \left(\dfrac{1}{b}\right)^n = \dfrac{1}{b^n}$

Examples

Example 1

Simplify: $4^0 = 1$

Example 2

Simplify: $y^{-7} = \dfrac{1}{y^7}$

Example 3

Simplify: $\dfrac{8a^0 b^{-2}}{c^{-5}d}$

$$= \dfrac{8(1)c^5}{b^2 d} = \dfrac{8c^5}{b^2 d}$$

Section 12.4 Scientific Notation

Key Concepts

A positive number written in **scientific notation** is expressed in the form:

$a \times 10^n$ where $1 \le a < 10$ and n is an integer.

Examples

Example 1

Write the numbers in scientific notation:

$35{,}000 = 3.5 \times 10^4$

$0.000\,000\,548 = 5.48 \times 10^{-7}$

Example 2

Multiply: $(3.5 \times 10^4)(2 \times 10^{-6})$

$$= 7 \times 10^{-2}$$

Example 3

Divide: $\dfrac{8.4 \times 10^{-9}}{2.1 \times 10^3} = 4 \times 10^{-9-3} = 4 \times 10^{-12}$

Section 12.5 — Addition and Subtraction of Polynomials

Key Concepts

A **polynomial** in one variable is a finite sum of terms of the form ax^n, where a is a real number and the exponent, n, is a nonnegative integer. For each term, a is called the **coefficient** of the term, and n is the **degree of the term**. The term with highest degree is the **leading term**, and its coefficient is called the **leading coefficient**. The **degree of the polynomial** is the largest degree of all its terms.

To add or subtract polynomials, add or subtract *like* terms.

Examples

Example 1

Given: $4x^5 - 8x^3 + 9x - 5$

Coefficients of each term: $4, -8, 9, -5$

Degree of each term: $\quad 5, 3, 1, 0$

Leading term: $\qquad\qquad 4x^5$

Leading coefficient: $\qquad 4$

Degree of polynomial: $\quad 5$

Example 2

Perform the indicated operations:

$$(2x^4 - 5x^3 + 1) - (x^4 + 3) + (x^3 - 4x - 7)$$
$$= 2x^4 - 5x^3 + 1 - x^4 - 3 + x^3 - 4x - 7$$
$$= 2x^4 - x^4 - 5x^3 + x^3 - 4x + 1 - 3 - 7$$
$$= x^4 - 4x^3 - 4x - 9$$

Section 12.6 — Multiplication of Polynomials and Special Products

Key Concepts

Multiplying Monomials

Use the commutative and associative properties of multiplication to group coefficients and like bases.

Multiplying Polynomials

Multiply each term in the first polynomial by each term in the second polynomial.

Product of Conjugates

Results in a **difference of squares**

$$(a + b)(a - b) = a^2 - b^2$$

Square of a Binomial

Results in a **perfect square trinomial**

$$(a + b)^2 = a^2 + 2ab + b^2$$
$$(a - b)^2 = a^2 - 2ab + b^2$$

Examples

Example 1

Multiply: $(5a^2b)(-2ab^3)$

$$= (5 \cdot -2)(a^2a)(bb^3)$$
$$= -10a^3b^4$$

Example 2

Multiply: $(x - 2)(3x^2 - 4x + 11)$

$$= 3x^3 - 4x^2 + 11x - 6x^2 + 8x - 22$$
$$= 3x^3 - 10x^2 + 19x - 22$$

Example 3

Multiply: $(3w - 4v)(3w + 4v)$

$$= (3w)^2 - (4v)^2$$
$$= 9w^2 - 16v^2$$

Example 4

Multiply: $(5c - 8d)^2$

$$= (5c)^2 - 2(5c)(8d) + (8d)^2$$
$$= 25c^2 - 80cd + 64d^2$$

| **Section 12.7** | **Division of Polynomials** |

Key Concepts

Division of Polynomials

1. Division by a monomial, use the properties:

$$\frac{a+b}{c} = \frac{a}{c} + \frac{b}{c} \quad \text{and} \quad \frac{a-b}{c} = \frac{a}{c} - \frac{b}{c}$$

2. If the divisor has more than one term, use long division.

Examples

Example 1

Divide: $\dfrac{-3x^2 - 6x + 9}{-3x}$

$$= \frac{-3x^2}{-3x} - \frac{6x}{-3x} + \frac{9}{-3x}$$

$$= x + 2 - \frac{3}{x}$$

Example 2

Divide: $(3x^2 - 5x + 1) \div (x + 2)$

$$\begin{array}{r} 3x - 11 \\ x + 2 \overline{)3x^2 - 5x + 1} \\ -(3x^2 + 6x) \\ \hline -11x + 1 \\ -(-11x - 22) \\ \hline 23 \end{array}$$

$$3x - 11 + \frac{23}{x + 2}$$

Chapter 12   Review Exercises

Section 12.1

For Exercises 1–4, identify the base and the exponent.

1. 5^3 2. x^4 3. $(-2)^0$ 4. y

5. Evaluate the expressions.

   a. 6^2 b. $(-6)^2$ c. -6^2

6. Evaluate the expressions.

   a. 4^3 b. $(-4)^3$ c. -4^3

For Exercises 7–20, simplify and write the answers in exponent form. Assume that all variables represent nonzero real numbers.

7. $5^3 \cdot 5^{10}$ 8. $a^7 a^4$

9. $x \cdot x^6 \cdot x^2$ 10. $6^3 \cdot 6 \cdot 6^5$

11. $\dfrac{10^7}{10^4}$ 12. $\dfrac{y^{14}}{y^8}$

13. $\dfrac{b^9}{b}$ 14. $\dfrac{7^8}{7}$

15. $\dfrac{k^2 k^3}{k^4}$ 16. $\dfrac{8^4 \cdot 8^7}{8^{11}}$

17. $\dfrac{2^8 \cdot 2^{10}}{2^3 \cdot 2^7}$ 18. $\dfrac{q^3 q^{12}}{q q^8}$

19. $(3x^2 y)(-4xy^4)$ 20. $(-5ab^3)(-6a^5b)$

21. Explain why $2^2 \cdot 4^4$ does *not* equal 8^6.

22. Explain why $\frac{10^5}{5^2}$ does *not* equal 2^3.

Section 12.2

For Exercises 23–40, simplify the expressions. Write the answers in exponent form. Assume all variables represent nonzero real numbers.

23. $(7^3)^4$

24. $(c^2)^6$

25. $(p^4p^2)^3$

26. $(9^5 \cdot 9^2)^4$

27. $\left(\dfrac{a}{b}\right)^2$

28. $\left(\dfrac{1}{3}\right)^4$

29. $\left(\dfrac{5}{c^2d^5}\right)^2$

30. $\left(-\dfrac{m^2}{4n^6}\right)^5$

31. $(2ab^2)^4$

32. $(-x^7y)^2$

33. $\left(\dfrac{-3x^3}{5y^2z}\right)^3$

34. $\left(\dfrac{r^3}{s^2t^6}\right)^5$

35. $\dfrac{a^4(a^2)^8}{(a^3)^3}$

36. $\dfrac{(8^3)^4 \cdot 8^{10}}{(8^4)^5}$

37. $\dfrac{(4h^2k)^2(h^3k)^4}{(2hk^3)^2}$

38. $\dfrac{(p^3q)^3(2p^2q^4)^4}{(8p)(pq^3)^2}$

39. $\left(\dfrac{2x^4y^3}{4xy^2}\right)^2$

40. $\left(\dfrac{a^4b^6}{ab^4}\right)^3$

Section 12.3

For Exercises 41–62, simplify the expressions. Assume all variables represent nonzero real numbers.

41. 8^0

42. $(-b)^0$

43. $-x^0$

44. 1^0

45. $2y^0$

46. $(2y)^0$

47. z^{-5}

48. 10^{-4}

49. $(6a)^{-2}$

50. $6a^{-2}$

51. $4^0 + 4^{-2}$

52. $9^{-1} + 9^0$

53. $t^{-6}t^{-2}$

54. r^8r^{-9}

55. $\dfrac{12x^{-2}y^3}{6x^4y^{-4}}$

56. $\dfrac{8ab^{-3}c^0}{10a^{-5}b^{-4}c^{-1}}$

57. $(-2m^2n^{-4})^{-4}$

58. $(3u^{-5}v^2)^{-3}$

59. $\dfrac{(k^{-6})^{-2}(k^3)}{5k^{-6}k^0}$

60. $\dfrac{(3h)^{-2}(h^{-5})^{-3}}{h^{-4}h^8}$

61. $2 \cdot 3^{-1} - 6^{-1}$

62. $2^{-1} - 2^{-2} + 2^0$

Section 12.4

63. Write the numbers in scientific notation.

   a. In a recent year there were 97,400,000 packages of M&Ms sold in the United States.

   b. The thickness of a piece of paper is 0.0042 in.

64. Write the numbers in standard form.

   a. A pH of 10 means the hydrogen ion concentration is 1×10^{-10} units.

   b. A fund-raising event for neurospinal research raised $\$2.56 \times 10^5$.

For Exercises 65–68, perform the indicated operations. Write the answers in scientific notation.

65. $(4.1 \times 10^{-6})(2.3 \times 10^{11})$

66. $\dfrac{9.3 \times 10^3}{6 \times 10^{-7}}$

67. $\dfrac{2000}{0.000008}$

68. $(0.000078)(21,000,000)$

69. Use your calculator to evaluate 5^{20}. Why is scientific notation necessary on your calculator to express the answer?

70. Use your calculator to evaluate $(0.4)^{30}$. Why is scientific notation necessary on your calculator to express the answer?

71. The average distance between the Earth and Sun is 9.3×10^7 mi.

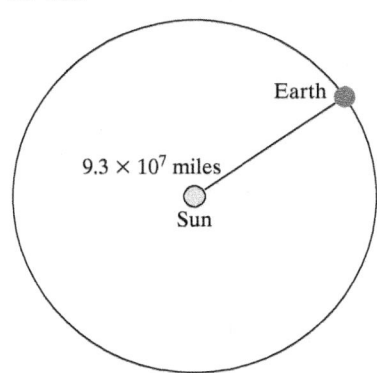

a. If the Earth's orbit is approximated by a circle, find the total distance the Earth travels around the Sun in one orbit. (*Hint:* The circumference of a circle is given by $C = 2\pi r$.) Express the answer in scientific notation.

b. If the Earth makes one complete trip around the Sun in 1 yr (365 days $= 8.76 \times 10^3$ hr), find the average speed that the Earth travels around the Sun in miles per hour. Express the answer in scientific notation.

72. The average distance between the planet Mercury and the Sun is 3.6×10^7 mi.

a. If Mercury's orbit is approximated by a circle, find the total distance Mercury travels around the Sun in one orbit. (*Hint:* The circumference of a circle is given by $C = 2\pi r$.) Express the answer in scientific notation.

b. If Mercury makes one complete trip around the Sun in 88 days (2.112×10^3 hr), find the average speed that Mercury travels around the Sun in miles per hour. Express the answer in scientific notation.

Section 12.5

73. For the polynomial $7x^4 - x + 6$

a. Classify as a monomial, a binomial, or a trinomial.

b. Identify the degree of the polynomial.

c. Identify the leading coefficient.

74. For the polynomial $2y^3 - 5y^7$

a. Classify as a monomial, a binomial, or a trinomial.

b. Identify the degree of the polynomial.

c. Identify the leading coefficient.

For Exercises 75–80, add or subtract as indicated.

75. $(4x + 2) + (3x - 5)$

76. $(7y^2 - 11y - 6) - (8y^2 + 3y - 4)$

77. $(9a^2 - 6) - (-5a^2 + 2a)$

78. $\left(5x^3 - \dfrac{1}{4}x^2 + \dfrac{5}{8}x + 2 \right) + \left(\dfrac{5}{2}x^3 + \dfrac{1}{2}x^2 - \dfrac{1}{8}x \right)$

79. $\quad 8w^4 \qquad\quad - 6w + 3$
$+ \underline{\ 2w^4 + 2w^3 - \ w + 1\ }$

80. $\quad -0.02b^5 + b^4 \qquad\qquad - 0.7b + 0.3$
$+ \underline{\ 0.03b^5 \qquad - 0.1b^3 + \quad b + 0.03\ }$

81. Subtract $(9x^2 + 4x + 6)$ from $(7x^2 - 5x)$.

82. Find the difference of $(x^2 - 5x - 3)$ and $(6x^2 + 4x + 9)$.

83. Write a trinomial of degree 2 with a leading coefficient of -5. (Answers may vary.)

84. Write a binomial of degree 5 with leading coefficient 6. (Answers may vary.)

85. Find a polynomial that represents the perimeter of the given rectangle.

Section 12.6

For Exercises 86–103, multiply the expressions.

86. $(25x^4y^3)(-3x^2y)$ **87.** $(9a^6)(2a^2b^4)$

88. $5c(3c^3 - 7c + 5)$ **89.** $(x^2 + 5x - 3)(-2x)$

90. $(5k - 4)(k + 1)$ **91.** $(4t - 1)(5t + 2)$

92. $(q + 8)(6q - 1)$ **93.** $(2a - 6)(a + 5)$

94. $\left(7a + \dfrac{1}{2} \right)^2$ **95.** $(b - 4)^2$

96. $(4p^2 + 6p + 9)(2p - 3)$

97. $(2w - 1)(-w^2 - 3w - 4)$

98. $\quad 2x^2 - 3x + 4$
$\times \underline{\qquad\quad 2x - 1}$

99. $\quad 4a^2 + \ a - 5$
$\times \underline{\qquad\quad 3a + 2}$

100. $(b - 4)(b + 4)$ **101.** $\left(\dfrac{1}{3}r^4 - s^2 \right)\left(\dfrac{1}{3}r^4 + s^2 \right)$

102. $(-7z^2 + 6)^2$

103. $(2h + 3)(h^4 - h^3 + h^2 - h + 1)$

104. Find a polynomial that represents the area of the given rectangle

$2x - 5$

$x + 4$

Section 12.7

For Exercises 105–117, divide the polynomials.

105. $\dfrac{20y^3 - 10y^2}{5y}$

106. $(18a^3b^2 - 9a^2b - 27ab^2) \div 9ab$

107. $(12x^4 - 8x^3 + 4x^2) \div (-4x^2)$

108. $\dfrac{10z^7w^4 - 15z^3w^2 - 20zw}{-20z^2w}$

109. $\dfrac{x^2 + 7x + 10}{x + 5}$

110. $(2t^2 + t - 10) \div (t - 2)$

111. $(2p^2 + p - 16) \div (2p + 7)$

112. $\dfrac{5a^2 + 27a - 22}{5a - 3}$

113. $\dfrac{b^3 - 125}{b - 5}$

114. $(z^3 + 4z^2 + 5z + 20) \div (5 + z^2)$

115. $(y^4 - 4y^3 + 5y^2 - 3y + 2) \div (y^2 + 3)$

116. $(3t^4 - 8t^3 + t^2 - 4t - 5) \div (3t^2 + t + 1)$

117. $\dfrac{2w^4 + w^3 + 4w - 3}{2w^2 - w + 3}$

Chapter 12   Test

Assume all variables represent nonzero real numbers.

1. Expand the expression using the definition of exponents, then simplify: $\dfrac{3^4 \cdot 3^3}{3^6}$

For Exercises 2–11, simplify the expression. Write the answer with positive exponents only.

2. $9^5 \cdot 9$

3. $\dfrac{q^{10}}{q^2}$

4. $(3a^2b)^3$

5. $\left(\dfrac{2x}{y^3}\right)^4$

6. $(-7)^0$

7. c^{-3}

8. $\dfrac{14^3 \cdot 14^9}{14^{10} \cdot 14}$

9. $\dfrac{(s^2t)^3(7s^4t)^4}{(7s^2t^3)^2}$

10. $(2a^0b^{-6})^2$

11. $\left(\dfrac{6a^{-5}b}{8ab^{-2}}\right)^{-2}$

12. a. Write the number in scientific notation: 43,000,000,000

    b. Write the number in standard form: 5.6×10^{-6}

13. The average amount of water flowing over Niagara Falls is 1.68×10^5 m³/min.

    a. How many cubic meters of water flow over the falls in one day?

    b. How many cubic meters of water flow over the falls in one year?

14. Write the polynomial in descending order:
$4x + 5x^3 - 7x^2 + 11$

    a. Identify the degree of the polynomial.

    b. Identify the leading coefficient of the polynomial.

15. Perform the indicated operations.

$(7w^2 - 11w - 6) + (8w^2 + 3w + 4) - (-9w^2 - 5w + 2)$

16. Subtract $(3x^2 - 5x^3 + 2x)$ from $(10x^3 - 4x^2 + 1)$.

For Exercises 17–23, multiply the polynomials.

17. $-2x^3(5x^2 + x - 15)$ 18. $(4a - 3)(2a - 1)$

19. $(4y - 5)(y^2 - 5y + 3)$ 20. $(2 + 3b)(2 - 3b)$

21. $(5z - 6)^2$ 22. $(5x + 3)(3x - 2)$

23. $(y^2 - 5y + 2)(y - 6)$

24. Find the perimeter and the area of the rectangle shown in the figure.

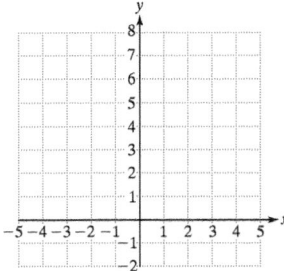

25. $(-12x^8 + x^6 - 8x^3) \div (4x^2)$

26. $\dfrac{2y^2 - 13y + 21}{y - 3}$

27. $(-5w^2 + 2w^3 - 2w + 5) \div (2w + 3)$

28. $\dfrac{3x^4 + x^3 + 4x - 33}{x^2 + 4}$

Chapters 1–12   Cumulative Review Exercises

1. Simplify. $\dfrac{12 - 6 \cdot 3}{-2^2 + \sqrt{16}}$

2. Write the prime factorization of 330.

3. Translate the phrase into a mathematical expression and simplify:

    The difference of the square of five and the square root of four.

4. Solve for x: $\dfrac{1}{2}(x - 6) + \dfrac{2}{3} = \dfrac{1}{4}x$

5. Solve for y: $-2y + 5 = -5(y - 1) + 3y$

6. Determine the circumference of a circle with diameter 12 m. Use 3.14 for π.

7. Determine the area of a circle with diameter 12 m. Use 3.14 for π.

8. For a point in a rectangular coordinate system, in which quadrant are both the x- and y-coordinates negative?

9. For a point in a rectangular coordinate system, on which axis is the x-coordinate zero and the y-coordinate nonzero?

10. Graph. $2x + y = 8$

11. In a triangle, one angle measures 23° more than the smallest angle. The third angle measures 10° more than the sum of the other two angles. Find the measure of each angle.

12. Determine the slope of a line parallel to the line defined by $y = -\dfrac{1}{3}x + 9$.

13. A snow storm lasts for 9 hr and dumps snow at a rate of $1\frac{1}{2}$ in./hr. If there was already 6 in. of snow on the ground before the storm, the snow depth is given by the equation:

$y = \dfrac{3}{2}x + 6$ where y is the snow depth in inches and $x \geq 0$ is the time in hours.

a. Find the snow depth after 4 hr.

b. Find the snow depth at the end of the storm.

c. How long had it snowed when the total depth of snow was $14\frac{1}{4}$ in.?

14. Solve the system of equations.

$$5x + 3y = -3$$
$$3x + 2y = -1$$

15. Solve the inequality. Graph the solution set on the real number line and express the solution in interval notation. $2 - 3(2x + 4) \leq -2x - (x - 5)$

For Exercises 16–17, perform the indicated operations.

16. $(2y + 3z)(-y - 5z)$

17. $(4t - 3)^2$

For Exercises 18–19, divide the polynomials.

18. $(12a^4b^3 - 6a^2b^2 + 3ab) \div (-3ab)$

19. $\dfrac{4m^3 - 5m + 2}{m - 2}$

20. Simplify. Assume all variables represent nonzero real numbers. $\left(\dfrac{2c^2d^4}{8cd^6}\right)^2$

Factoring Polynomials

13

CHAPTER OUTLINE

Chapter 13

Chapter 13 is devoted to a mathematical operation called factoring. The applications of factoring are far-reaching, and in this chapter, we use factoring as a tool to solve a type of equation called a quadratic equation.

Are You Prepared?

Along the way, we will need the skill of recognizing perfect squares and perfect cubes. A perfect square is a number that is a square of a rational number. For example, 49 is a perfect square because $49 = 7^2$. We also will need to recognize perfect cubes. A perfect cube is a number that is a cube of a rational number. For example, 125 is a perfect cube because $125 = 5^3$.

To complete the puzzle, first answer the questions and fill in the appropriate box. Then fill the grid so that every row, every column, and every 2 × 3 box contains the digits 1 through 6.

A. What number squared is 1?
B. What number squared is 16?
C. What number cubed is 1?
D. What number squared is 36?
E. What number squared is 25?
F. What number cubed is 64?
G. What number cubed is 8?
H. What number cubed is 27?

		A		B
	C		D	E
F		1	G	H
2		5		
1	4			2
	5		3	

Objectives

1. Identifying the Greatest Common Factor
2. Factoring out the Greatest Common Factor
3. Factoring out a Negative Factor
4. Factoring out a Binomial Factor
5. Factoring by Grouping

1. Identifying the Greatest Common Factor

This chapter is devoted to a mathematical operation called **factoring**. To factor an integer means to write the integer as a product of two or more integers. To factor a polynomial means to express the polynomial as a product of two or more polynomials.

In the product $2 \cdot 5 = 10$, for example, 2 and 5 are factors of 10.

In the product $(3x + 4)(2x - 1) = 6x^2 + 5x - 4$, the quantities $(3x + 4)$ and $(2x - 1)$ are factors of $6x^2 + 5x - 4$.

We begin our study of factoring by factoring integers. The number 20, for example, can be factored as $1 \cdot 20$ or $2 \cdot 10$ or $4 \cdot 5$ or $2 \cdot 2 \cdot 5$. The product $2 \cdot 2 \cdot 5$ (or equivalently $2^2 \cdot 5$) consists only of prime numbers and is called the **prime factorization.**

The **greatest common factor** (denoted **GCF**) of two or more integers is the greatest factor common to each integer. To find the greatest common factor of two or more integers, it is often helpful to express the numbers as a product of prime factors as shown in the next example.

Skill Practice

Find the GCF.
1. 12 and 20
2. 45, 75, and 30

Example 1   Identifying the GCF

Find the greatest common factor.

a. 24 and 36   **b.** 105, 40, and 60

Solution:

First find the prime factorization of each number. Then find the product of common factors.

a.
```
2|24    2|36
 2|12    2|18
  2|6     3|9
   3       3
```

Factors of 24 = $2 \cdot 2 \cdot 2 \cdot 3$ ← Common factors are circled.
Factors of 36 = $2 \cdot 2 \cdot 3 \cdot 3$ ←

The numbers 24 and 36 share two factors of 2 and one factor of 3. Therefore, the greatest common factor is $2 \cdot 2 \cdot 3 = 12$.

b.
```
5|105    5|40    5|60
 3|21     2|8     3|12
    7      2|4      2|4
            2        2
```

Factors of 105 = $3 \cdot 7 \cdot 5$

Factors of 40 = $2 \cdot 2 \cdot 2 \cdot 5$

Factors of 60 = $2 \cdot 2 \cdot 3 \cdot 5$

The greatest common factor is 5.

Answers
1. 4   **2.** 15

In Example 2, we find the greatest common factor of two or more variable terms.

Example 2 Identifying the Greatest Common Factor

Find the GCF among each group of terms.

a. $7x^3, 14x^2, 21x^4$ **b.** $15a^4b, 25a^3b^2$ **c.** $8c^2d^7e, 6c^3d^4$

Solution:

List the factors of each term.

a. $7x^3 = 7 \cdot x \cdot x \cdot x$

    $14x^2 = 2 \cdot 7 \cdot x \cdot x$ The GCF is $7x^2$.

    $21x^4 = 3 \cdot 7 \cdot x \cdot x \cdot x \cdot x$

b. $15a^4b = 3 \cdot 5 \cdot a \cdot a \cdot a \cdot a \cdot b$

    $25a^3b^2 = 5 \cdot 5 \cdot a \cdot a \cdot a \cdot b \cdot b$ The GCF is $5a^3b$.

TIP: Notice that the expressions $15a^4b$ and $25a^3b^2$ share factors of 5, a, and b. The GCF is the product of the common factors, where each factor is raised to the lowest power to which it occurs in all the original expressions.

$$\left. \begin{array}{l} 15a^4b = 3 \cdot 5a^4b \\ 25a^3b^2 = 5^2a^3b^2 \end{array} \right\} \quad \left. \begin{array}{l} \text{Lowest power of 5 is 1:} \quad 5^1 \\ \text{Lowest power of } a \text{ is 3:} \quad a^3 \\ \text{Lowest power of } b \text{ is 1:} \quad b^1 \end{array} \right\} \quad \text{The GCF is } 5a^3b.$$

c. $\left. \begin{array}{l} 8c^2d^7e = 2^3c^2d^7e \\ 6c^3d^4 = 2 \cdot 3c^3d^4 \end{array} \right\}$ The common factors are 2, c, and d.

$\left. \begin{array}{l} \text{The lowest power of 2 is 1:} \quad 2^1 \\ \text{The lowest power of } c \text{ is 2:} \quad c^2 \\ \text{The lowest power of } d \text{ is 4:} \quad d^4 \end{array} \right\}$ The GCF is $2c^2d^4$.

Sometimes polynomials share a common binomial factor, as shown in Example 3.

Example 3 Finding the Greatest Common Binomial Factor

Find the greatest common factor between the terms: $3x(a + b)$ and $2y(a + b)$

Solution:

$\left. \begin{array}{l} 3x(a + b) \\ 2y(a + b) \end{array} \right\}$ The only common factor is the binomial $(a + b)$.

              The GCF is $(a + b)$.

2. Factoring out the Greatest Common Factor

The process of factoring a polynomial is the reverse process of multiplying polynomials. Both operations use the distributive property: $ab + ac = a(b + c)$.

<u>Multiply</u>

$$5y(y^2 + 3y + 1) = 5y(y^2) + 5y(3y) + 5y(1)$$
$$= 5y^3 + 15y^2 + 5y$$

<u>Factor</u>

$$5y^3 + 15y^2 + 5y = 5y(y^2) + 5y(3y) + 5y(1)$$
$$= 5y(y^2 + 3y + 1)$$

PROCEDURE **Factoring out the Greatest Common Factor**

Step 1 Identify the GCF of all terms of the polynomial.
Step 2 Write each term as the product of the GCF and another factor.
Step 3 Use the distributive property to remove the GCF.

Note: To check the factorization, multiply the polynomials to remove parentheses.

Skill Practice

Factor out the GCF.
7. $6w + 18$
8. $21m^3 - 7m$

Example 4 **Factoring out the Greatest Common Factor**

Factor out the GCF.

a. $4x - 20$ **b.** $6w^2 + 3w$

Solution:

a. $4x - 20$ The GCF is 4.

$= 4(x) - 4(5)$ Write each term as the product of the GCF and another factor.

$= 4(x - 5)$ Use the distributive property to factor out the GCF.

TIP: Any factoring problem can be checked by multiplying the factors:

<u>Check</u>: $4(x - 5) = 4x - 20$ ✔

Avoiding Mistakes

In Example 4(b), the GCF, $3w$, is equal to one of the terms of the polynomial. In such a case, you must leave a 1 in place of that term after the GCF is factored out.

b. $6w^2 + 3w$ The GCF is $3w$.

$= 3w(2w) + 3w(1)$ Write each term as the product of $3w$ and another factor.

$= 3w(2w + 1)$ Use the distributive property to factor out the GCF.

<u>Check</u>: $3w(2w + 1) = 6w^2 + 3w$ ✔

Answers
7. $6(w + 3)$ **8.** $7m(3m^2 - 1)$

Example 5 **Factoring out the Greatest Common Factor**

Factor out the GCF.

a. $15y^3 + 12y^4$ **b.** $9a^4b - 18a^5b + 27a^6b$

Solution:

a. $15y^3 + 12y^4$ The GCF is $3y^3$.

$= 3y^3(5) + 3y^3(4y)$ Write each term as the product of $3y^3$ and another factor.

$= 3y^3(5 + 4y)$ Use the distributive property to factor out the GCF.

Check: $3y^3(5 + 4y) = 15y^3 + 12y^4$ ✔

b. $9a^4b - 18a^5b + 27a^6b$ The GCF is $9a^4b$.

$= 9a^4b(1) - 9a^4b(2a) + 9a^4b(3a^2)$ Write each term as the product of $9a^4b$ and another factor.

$= 9a^4b(1 - 2a + 3a^2)$ Use the distributive property to factor out the GCF.

Check: $9a^4b(1 - 2a + 3a^2)$
$= 9a^4b - 18a^5b + 27a^6b$ ✔

The greatest common factor of the polynomial $2x + 5y$ is 1. If we factor out the GCF, we have $1(2x + 5y)$. A polynomial whose only factors are itself and 1 is called a **prime polynomial**. A prime polynomial cannot be factored further.

3. Factoring out a Negative Factor

Usually it is advantageous to factor out the *opposite* of the GCF when the leading coefficient of the polynomial is negative. This is demonstrated in the next example. Notice that this *changes the signs* of the remaining terms inside the parentheses.

Example 6 **Factoring out a Negative Factor**

Factor out -3 from the polynomial $-3x^2 + 6x - 33$.

Solution:

$-3x^2 + 6x - 33$ The GCF is 3. However, in this case, we will factor out the *opposite* of the GCF, -3.

$= -3(x^2) + (-3)(-2x) + (-3)(11)$ Write each term as the product of -3 and another factor.

$= -3[x^2 + (-2x) + 11]$ Factor out -3.

$= -3(x^2 - 2x + 11)$ Simplify. Notice that each sign within the trinomial has changed.

Check: $-3(x^2 - 2x + 11) = -3x^2 + 6x - 33$ ✔

Example 7   **Factoring out a Negative Factor**

Factor out the quantity $-4pq$ from the polynomial $-12p^3q - 8p^2q^2 + 4pq^3$.

Solution:

$-12p^3q - 8p^2q^2 + 4pq^3$ The GCF is $4pq$. However, in this case, we will factor out the *opposite* of the GCF, $-4pq$.

$= -4pq(3p^2) + (-4pq)(2pq) + (-4pq)(-q^2)$ Write each term as the product of $-4pq$ and another factor.

$= -4pq[3p^2 + 2pq + (-q^2)]$ Factor out $-4pq$. Notice that each sign within the trinomial has changed.

$= -4pq(3p^2 + 2pq - q^2)$ To verify that this is the correct factorization and that the signs are correct, multiply the factors.

Check: $-4pq(3p^2 + 2pq - q^2) = -12p^3q - 8p^2q^2 + 4pq^3$ ✔

4. Factoring out a Binomial Factor

The distributive property can also be used to factor out a common factor that consists of more than one term as shown in Example 8.

Example 8   **Factoring out a Binomial Factor**

Factor out the GCF: $2w(x + 3) - 5(x + 3)$

Solution:

$2w(x + 3) - 5(x + 3)$ The greatest common factor is the quantity $(x + 3)$.

$= (x + 3)(2w) - (x + 3)(5)$ Write each term as the product of $(x + 3)$ and another factor.

$= (x + 3)(2w - 5)$ Use the distributive property to factor out the GCF.

5. Factoring by Grouping

When two binomials are multiplied, the product before simplifying contains four terms. For example:

$$(x + 4)(3a + 2b) = (x + 4)(3a) + (x + 4)(2b)$$

$$= (x + 4)(3a) + (x + 4)(2b)$$

$$= 3ax + 12a + 2bx + 8b$$

In Example 9, we learn how to reverse this process. That is, given a four-term polynomial, we will factor it as a product of two binomials. The process is called *factoring by grouping*.

PROCEDURE   **Factoring by Grouping**

To factor a four-term polynomial by grouping:

Step 1   Identify and factor out the GCF from all four terms.

Step 2   Factor out the GCF from the first pair of terms. Factor out the GCF from the second pair of terms. (Sometimes it is necessary to factor out the opposite of the GCF.)

Step 3   If the two terms share a common binomial factor, factor out the binomial factor.

Example 9   **Factoring by Grouping**

Factor by grouping: $3ax + 12a + 2bx + 8b$

Solution:

$3ax + 12a + 2bx + 8b$ **Step 1:**   Identify and factor out the GCF from all four terms. In this case, the GCF is 1.

$= 3ax + 12a \mid + 2bx + 8b$ Group the first pair of terms and the second pair of terms.

$= 3a(x + 4) + 2b(x + 4)$ **Step 2:**   Factor out the GCF from each pair of terms. *Note:* The two terms now share a common binomial factor of $(x + 4)$.

$= (x + 4)(3a + 2b)$ **Step 3:**   Factor out the common binomial factor.

Check: $(x + 4)(3a + 2b) = 3ax + 2bx + 12a + 8b$ ✔

Note: Step 2 results in two terms with a common binomial factor. If the two binomials are different, step 3 cannot be performed. In such a case, the original polynomial may not be factorable by grouping, or different pairs of terms may need to be grouped and inspected.

Skill Practice

Factor by grouping.
14. $5x + 10y + ax + 2ay$

TIP: One frequently asked question when factoring is whether the order can be switched between the factors. The answer is yes. Because multiplication is commutative, the order in which the factors are written does not matter.

$$(x + 4)(3a + 2b) = (3a + 2b)(x + 4)$$

Answer
14. $(x + 2y)(5 + a)$

Example 10 **Factoring by Grouping**

Factor by grouping: $ax + ay - bx - by$

Solution:

$ax + ay - bx - by$ **Step 1:** Identify and factor out the GCF from all four terms. In this case, the GCF is 1.

$= ax + ay \mid - bx - by$ Group the first pair of terms and the second pair of terms.

$= a(x + y) - b(x + y)$ **Step 2:** Factor out a from the first pair of terms.

    Factor out $-b$ from the second pair of terms. (This causes sign changes within the second parentheses.) The terms in parentheses now match.

$= (x + y)(a - b)$ **Step 3:** Factor out the common binomial factor.

<u>Check:</u> $(x + y)(a - b) = x(a) + x(-b) + y(a) + y(-b)$

$= ax - bx + ay - by$ ✔

Avoiding Mistakes

In step 2, the expression $a(x + y) - b(x + y)$ is not yet factored completely because it is a *difference*, not a product. To factor the expression, you must carry it one step further.

$a(x + y) - b(x + y)$

$= (x + y)(a - b)$

The factored form must be represented as a product.

Example 11 **Factoring by Grouping**

Factor by grouping: $16w^4 - 40w^3 - 12w^2 + 30w$

Solution:

$16w^4 - 40w^3 - 12w^2 + 30w$ **Step 1:** Identify and factor out the GCF from all four terms. In this case, the GCF is $2w$.

$= 2w[8w^3 - 20w^2 - 6w + 15]$

$= 2w[8w^3 - 20w^2 \mid - 6w + 15]$ Group the first pair of terms and the second pair of terms.

$= 2w[4w^2(2w - 5) - 3(2w - 5)]$ **Step 2:** Factor out $4w^2$ from the first pair of terms.

    Factor out -3 from the second pair of terms. (This causes sign changes within the second parentheses. The terms in parentheses now match.)

$= 2w[(2w - 5)(4w^2 - 3)]$ **Step 3:** Factor out the common binomial factor.

$= 2w(2w - 5)(4w^2 - 3)$

Answers

15. $(u - v)(t - 2)$
16. $3b(a + 2)(b - 4)$

Section 13.1 Practice Exercises

Study Skills Exercises

1. The final exam is just around the corner. Your old tests and quizzes provide good material to study for the final exam. Use your old tests to make a list of the chapters on which you need to concentrate. Ask your professor for help if there are still concepts that you do not understand.

2. Define the key terms:

   a. **Factoring** b. **Greatest common factor (GCF)**

   c. **Prime factorization** d. **Prime polynomial**

Objective 1: Identifying the Greatest Common Factor

For Exercises 3–14, identify the greatest common factor. **(See Examples 1–3.)**

3. $28, 63$

4. $24, 40$

5. $42, 30, 60$

6. $20, 52, 32$

7. $3xy, 7y$

8. $10mn, 11n$

9. $12w^3z, 16w^2z$

10. $20cd, 15c^3d$

11. $8x^3y^4z^2, 12xy^5z^4, 6x^2y^8z^3$

12. $15r^2s^2t^5, 5r^3s^4t^3, 30r^4s^3t^2$

13. $7(x - y), 9(x - y)$

14. $(2a - b), 3(2a - b)$

Objective 2: Factoring out the Greatest Common Factor

15. **a.** Use the distributive property to multiply $3(x - 2y)$.

    b. Use the distributive property to factor $3x - 6y$.

16. **a.** Use the distributive property to multiply $a^2(5a + b)$.

    b. Use the distributive property to factor $5a^3 + a^2b$.

For Exercises 17–36, factor out the GCF. **(See Examples 4–5.)**

17. $4p + 12$

18. $3q - 15$

19. $5c^2 - 10c + 15$

20. $16d^3 + 24d^2 + 32d$

21. $x^5 + x^3$

22. $y^2 - y^3$

23. $t^4 - 4t + 8t^2$

24. $7r^3 - r^5 + r^4$

25. $2ab + 4a^3b$

26. $5u^3v^2 - 5uv$

27. $38x^2y - 19x^2y^4$

28. $100a^5b^3 + 16a^2b$

29. $6x^3y^5 - 18xy^9z$

30. $15mp^7q^4 + 12m^4q^3$

31. $5 + 7y^3$

32. $w^3 - 5u^3v^2$

33. $42p^3q^2 + 14pq^2 - 7p^4q^4$

34. $8m^2n^3 - 24m^2n^2 + 4m^3n$

35. $t^5 + 2rt^3 - 3t^4 + 4r^2t^2$

36. $u^2v + 5u^3v^2 - 2u^2 + 8uv$

Objective 3: Factoring out a Negative Factor

37. For the polynomial $-2x^3 - 4x^2 + 8x$

    a. Factor out $-2x$.   **b.** Factor out $2x$.

38. For the polynomial $-9y^5 + 3y^3 - 12y$

    a. Factor out $-3y$.   **b.** Factor out $3y$.

39. Factor out -1 from the polynomial $-8t^2 - 9t - 2$.

40. Factor out -1 from the polynomial $-6x^3 - 2x - 5$.

For Exercises 41–46, factor out the opposite of the greatest common factor. **(See Examples 6–7.)**

41. $-15p^3 - 30p^2$

42. $-24m^3 - 12m^4$

43. $-q^4 + 2q^2 - 9q$

44. $-r^3 + 9r^2 - 5r$

45. $-7x - 6y - 2z$

46. $-4a + 5b - c$

Objective 4: Factoring out a Binomial Factor

For Exercises 47–52, factor out the GCF. **(See Example 8.)**

47. $13(a + 6) - 4b(a + 6)$

48. $7(x^2 + 1) - y(x^2 + 1)$

49. $8v(w^2 - 2) + (w^2 - 2)$

50. $t(r + 2) + (r + 2)$

51. $21x(x + 3) + 7x^2(x + 3)$

52. $5y^3(y - 2) - 15y(y - 2)$

Objective 5: Factoring by Grouping

For Exercises 53–72, factor by grouping. **(See Examples 9–10.)**

53. $8a^2 - 4ab + 6ac - 3bc$

54. $4x^3 + 3x^2y + 4xy^2 + 3y^3$

55. $3q + 3p + qr + pr$

56. $xy - xz + 7y - 7z$

57. $6x^2 + 3x + 4x + 2$

58. $4y^2 + 8y + 7y + 14$

59. $2t^2 + 6t - 5t - 15$

60. $2p^2 - p - 6p + 3$

61. $6y^2 - 2y - 9y + 3$

62. $5a^2 + 30a - 2a - 12$

63. $b^4 + b^3 - 4b - 4$

64. $8w^5 + 12w^2 - 10w^3 - 15$

65. $3j^2k + 15k + j^2 + 5$

66. $2ab^2 - 6ac + b^2 - 3c$

67. $14w^6x^6 + 7w^6 - 2x^6 - 1$

68. $18p^4q - 9p^5 - 2q + p$

69. $ay + bx + by + ax$
    (*Hint:* Rearrange the terms.)

70. $2c + 3ay + ac + 6y$

71. $vw^2 - 3 + w - 3wv$

72. $2x^2 + 6m + 12 + x^2m$

Mixed Exercises

For Exercises 73–78, factor out the GCF first. Then factor by grouping. **(See Example 11.)**

73. $15x^4 + 15x^2y^2 + 10x^3y + 10xy^3$

74. $2a^3b - 4a^2b + 32ab - 64b$

75. $4abx - 4b^2x - 4ab + 4b^2$

76. $p^2q - pq^2 - rp^2q + rpq^2$

77. $6st^2 - 18st - 6t^4 + 18t^3$

78. $15j^3 - 10j^2k - 15j^2k^2 + 10jk^3$

79. The formula $P = 2l + 2w$ represents the perimeter, P, of a rectangle given the length, l, and the width, w. Factor out the GCF and write an equivalent formula in factored form.

80. The formula $P = 2a + 2b$ represents the perimeter, P, of a parallelogram given the base, b, and an adjacent side, a. Factor out the GCF and write an equivalent formula in factored form.

81. The formula $S = 2\pi r^2 + 2\pi rh$ represents the surface area, S, of a cylinder with radius, r, and height, h. Factor out the GCF and write an equivalent formula in factored form.

82. The formula $A = P + Prt$ represents the total amount of money, A, in an account that earns simple interest at a rate, r, for t years. Factor out the GCF and write an equivalent formula in factored form.

Expanding Your Skills

83. Factor out $\dfrac{1}{7}$ from $\dfrac{1}{7}x^2 + \dfrac{3}{7}x - \dfrac{5}{7}$.

84. Factor out $\dfrac{1}{5}$ from $\dfrac{6}{5}y^2 - \dfrac{4}{5}y + \dfrac{1}{5}$.

85. Factor out $\dfrac{1}{4}$ from $\dfrac{5}{4}w^2 + \dfrac{3}{4}w + \dfrac{9}{4}$.

86. Factor out $\dfrac{1}{6}$ from $\dfrac{1}{6}p^2 - \dfrac{3}{6}p + \dfrac{5}{6}$.

87. Write a polynomial that has a GCF of $3x$. (Answers may vary.)

88. Write a polynomial that has a GCF of $7y$. (Answers may vary.)

89. Write a polynomial that has a GCF of $4p^2q$. (Answers may vary.)

90. Write a polynomial that has a GCF of $2ab^2$. (Answers may vary.)

Factoring Trinomials of the Form $x^2 + bx + c$ Section 13.2

1. Factoring Trinomials with a Leading Coefficient of 1

Objective

1. Factoring Trinomials with a Leading Coefficient of 1

In Section 12.6, we learned how to multiply two binomials. We also saw that such a product often results in a trinomial. For example,

$$\underset{\substack{\text{Sum of products of inner} \\ \text{terms and outer terms}}}{(x + 3)(x + 7) = \overset{\substack{\text{Product of} \\ \text{first terms}}}{x^2} + \underbrace{7x + 3x}_{} + \overset{\substack{\text{Product of} \\ \text{last terms}}}{21} = x^2 + 10x + 21}$$

In this section, we want to reverse the process. That is, given a trinomial, we want to *factor* it as a product of two binomials. In particular, we begin our study with the case in which a trinomial has a leading coefficient of 1.

Consider the quadratic trinomial $x^2 + bx + c$. To produce a leading term of x^2, we can construct binomials of the form $(x + \quad)(x + \quad)$. The remaining terms can be obtained from two integers, p and q, whose product is c and whose sum is b.

$$x^2 + bx + c = (x + \overset{\substack{\text{Factors of } c}}{p)(x + q}) = x^2 + qx + px + pq$$
$$= x^2 + \underbrace{(q + p)}_{\text{Sum} = b}x + \underbrace{pq}_{\text{Product} = c}$$

This process is demonstrated in Example 1.

Example 1 **Factoring a Trinomial of the Form $x^2 + bx + c$**

Factor: $x^2 + 4x - 45$

Solution:

$x^2 + 4x - 45 = (x + \square)(x + \square)$ The product of the first terms in the binomials must equal the leading term of the trinomial $x \cdot x = x^2$.

We must fill in the blanks with two integers whose product is -45 and whose sum is 4. The factors must have opposite signs to produce a negative product. The possible factorizations of -45 are:

Product = -45	Sum
$-1 \cdot 45$	44
$-3 \cdot 15$	12
$-5 \cdot 9$	4
$-9 \cdot 5$	-4
$-15 \cdot 3$	-12
$-45 \cdot 1$	-44

$x^2 + 4x - 45 = (x + \square)(x + \square)$

$\qquad = (x + (-5))(x + 9)$ Fill in the blanks with -5 and 9,

$\qquad = (x - 5)(x + 9)$ Factored form

$\qquad$ <u>Check:</u>
$\qquad (x - 5)(x + 9) = x^2 + 9x - 5x - 45$
$\qquad\qquad\qquad\qquad = x^2 + 4x - 45 ✔$

One frequently asked question is whether the order of factors can be reversed. The answer is yes because multiplication of polynomials is a commutative operation. Therefore, in Example 1, we can express the factorization as $(x - 5)(x + 9)$ or as $(x + 9)(x - 5)$.

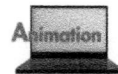

Example 2 **Factoring a Trinomial of the Form $x^2 + bx + c$**

Factor: $w^2 - 15w + 50$

Solution:

$w^2 - 15w + 50 = (w + \square)(w + \square)$ The product $w \cdot w = w^2$.

Find two integers whose product is 50 and whose sum is -15. To form a positive product, the factors must be either both positive or both negative. The sum must be negative, so we will choose negative factors of 50.

$$
\begin{array}{c c}
\underline{\text{Product} = 50} & \underline{\text{Sum}} \\
(-1)(-50) & -51 \\
(-2)(-25) & -27 \\
(-5)(-10) & -15
\end{array}
$$

$$
\begin{aligned}
w^2 - 15w + 50 &= (w + \square)(w + \square) \\
&= (w + (-5))(w + (-10)) \\
&= (w - 5)(w - 10) \qquad \text{Factored form}
\end{aligned}
$$

Check:

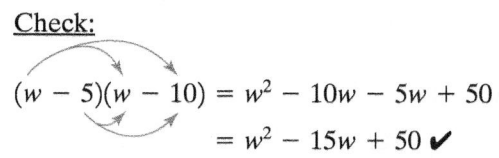

$$
\begin{aligned}
(w - 5)(w - 10) &= w^2 - 10w - 5w + 50 \\
&= w^2 - 15w + 50 \checkmark
\end{aligned}
$$

Practice will help you become proficient in factoring polynomials. As you do your homework, keep these important guidelines in mind:

- To factor a trinomial, write the trinomial in descending order such as $x^2 + bx + c$.
- For all factoring problems, always factor out the GCF from all terms first.

Furthermore, we offer the following rules for determining the signs within the binomial factors.

PROCEDURE   Sign Rules for Factoring Trinomials

Given the trinomial $x^2 + bx + c$, the signs within the binomial factors are determined as follows:

Case 1 If c is *positive*, then the signs in the binomials must be the same (either both positive or both negative). The correct choice is determined by the middle term. If the middle term is positive, then both signs must be positive. If the middle term is negative, then both signs must be negative.

c is positive.

$$
\begin{array}{c c}
x^2 + 6x + 8 & \qquad x^2 - 6x + 8 \\
(x + 2)(x + 4) & \qquad (x - 2)(x - 4) \\
\text{Same signs} & \qquad \text{Same signs}
\end{array}
$$

Case 2 If c is *negative*, then the signs in the binomials must be different.

c is negative.

$$
\begin{array}{c c}
x^2 + 2x - 35 & \qquad x^2 - 2x - 35 \\
(x + 7)(x - 5) & \qquad (x - 7)(x + 5) \\
\text{Different signs} & \qquad \text{Different signs}
\end{array}
$$

Example 3   **Factoring Trinomials**

Factor.   **a.** $-8p - 48 + p^2$ **b.** $-40t - 30t^2 + 10t^3$

Solution:

a. $-8p - 48 + p^2$

$= p^2 - 8p - 48$ Write in descending order.

$= (p \quad \square)(p \quad \square)$ Find two integers whose product is -48 and whose sum is -8. The numbers are -12 and 4.

$= (p - 12)(p + 4)$ Factored form

b. $-40t - 30t^2 + 10t^3$

$= 10t^3 - 30t^2 - 40t$ Write in descending order.

$= 10t(t^2 - 3t - 4)$ Factor out the GCF.

$= 10t(t \quad \square)(t \quad \square)$ Find two integers whose product is -4 and whose sum is -3. The numbers are -4 and 1.

$= 10t(t - 4)(t + 1)$ Factored form

Example 4   **Factoring Trinomials**

Factor.   **a.** $-a^2 + 6a - 8$ **b.** $-2c^2 - 22cd - 60d^2$

Solution:

a. $-a^2 + 6a - 8$ It is generally easier to factor a trinomial with a *positive* leading coefficient. Therefore, we will factor out -1 from all terms.

$= -1(a^2 - 6a + 8)$

$= -1(a \quad \square)(a \quad \square)$ Find two integers whose product is 8 and whose sum is -6. The numbers are -4 and -2.

$= -1(a - 4)(a - 2)$

Avoiding Mistakes

Recall that factoring out -1 from a polynomial changes the signs of all terms within parentheses.

b. $-2c^2 - 22cd - 60d^2$

$= -2(c^2 + 11cd + 30d^2)$ Factor out -2.

$= -2(c \quad \square d)(c \quad \square d)$ Notice that the second pair of terms has a factor of d. This will produce a product of d^2.

$= -2(c + 5d)(c + 6d)$ Find two integers whose product is 30 and whose sum is 11. The numbers are 5 and 6.

To factor a trinomial of the form $x^2 + bx + c$, we must find two integers whose product is c and whose sum is b. If no such integers exist, then the trinomial is not factorable and is called a **prime polynomial**.

Example 5 Factoring Trinomials

Factor: $x^2 - 13x + 8$

Solution:

$x^2 - 13x + 8$ The trinomial is in descending order. The GCF is 1.

$= (x \quad \square)(x \quad \square)$ Find two integers whose product is 8 and whose sum is -13. No such integers exist.

The trinomial $x^2 - 13x + 8$ is prime.

Section 13.2 Practice Exercises

Study Skills Exercises

1. Sometimes the problems on a test do not appear in the same order as the concepts appear in the text. In order to better prepare for a test, try to practice with problems taken from the book but placed in random order. Choose 30 problems from various chapters, randomize the order, and use the problems to review for the test. Repeat the process several times for additional practice.

2. Define the key term **prime polynomial**.

Review Exercises

For Exercises 3–6, factor completely.

3. $4x^3y^7 - 12x^4y^5 + 8xy^8$

4. $9a^6b^3 - 27a^3b^6 - 3a^2b^2$

5. $ax + 2bx - 5a - 10b$

6. $m^2 - mx - 3pm + 3px$

Objective 1: Factoring Trinomials with a Leading Coefficient of 1

For Exercises 7–20, factor completely. **(See Examples 1, 2, and 5.)**

7. $x^2 + 10x + 16$

8. $y^2 + 18y + 80$

9. $z^2 - 11z + 18$

10. $w^2 - 7w + 12$

11. $z^2 - 3z - 18$

12. $w^2 + 4w - 12$

13. $p^2 - 3p - 40$

14. $a^2 - 10a + 9$

 15. $t^2 + 6t - 40$

16. $m^2 - 12m + 11$

17. $x^2 - 3x + 20$

18. $y^2 + 6y + 18$

19. $n^2 + 8n + 16$

20. $v^2 + 10v + 25$

For Exercises 21–24, assume that b and c represent positive integers.

21. When factoring a polynomial of the form $x^2 + bx + c$, pick an appropriate combination of signs.

a. ($+$)($+$)   **b.** ($-$)($-$)   **c.** ($+$)($-$)

22. When factoring a polynomial of the form $x^2 + bx - c$, pick an appropriate combination of signs.

a. ($+$)($+$)   **b.** ($-$)($-$)   **c.** ($+$)($-$)

23. When factoring a polynomial of the form $x^2 - bx - c$, pick an appropriate combination of signs.

a. ($+$)($+$)   **b.** ($-$)($-$)   **c.** ($+$)($-$)

24. When factoring a polynomial of the form $x^2 - bx + c$, pick an appropriate combination of signs.

a. ($+$)($+$)   **b.** ($-$)($-$)   **c.** ($+$)($-$)

25. Which is the correct factorization of $y^2 - y - 12$? Explain. $(y - 4)(y + 3)$ or $(y + 3)(y - 4)$

26. Which is the correct factorization of $x^2 + 14x + 13$? Explain. $(x + 13)(x + 1)$ or $(x + 1)(x + 13)$

27. Which is the correct factorization of $w^2 + 2w + 1$? Explain. $(w + 1)(w + 1)$ or $(w + 1)^2$

28. Which is the correct factorization of $z^2 - 4z + 4$? Explain. $(z - 2)(z - 2)$ or $(z - 2)^2$

29. In what order should a trinomial be written before attempting to factor it?

30. Referring to page 889, write two important guidelines to follow when factoring trinomials.

For Exercises 31–48, factor completely. Be sure to factor out the GCF when necessary. **(See Examples 3–4.)**

31. $-13x + x^2 - 30$

32. $12y - 160 + y^2$

33. $-18w + 65 + w^2$

34. $17t + t^2 + 72$

35. $22t + t^2 + 72$

36. $10q - 1200 + q^2$

37. $3x^2 - 30x - 72$

38. $2z^2 + 4z - 198$

39. $8p^3 - 40p^2 + 32p$

40. $5w^4 - 35w^3 + 50w^2$

41. $y^4z^2 - 12y^3z^2 + 36y^2z^2$

42. $t^4u^2 + 6t^3u^2 + 9t^2u^2$

43. $-x^2 + 10x - 24$

44. $-y^2 - 12y - 35$

45. $-m^2 + m + 6$

46. $-n^2 + 5n + 6$

47. $-4 - 2c^2 - 6c$

48. $-40d - 30 - 10d^2$

Mixed Exercises

For Exercises 49–66, factor completely.

49. $x^3y^3 - 19x^2y^3 + 60xy^3$

50. $y^2z^5 + 17yz^5 + 60z^5$

51. $12p^2 - 96p + 84$

52. $5w^2 - 40w - 45$

53. $-2m^2 + 22m - 20$

54. $-3x^2 - 36x - 81$

55. $c^2 + 6cd + 5d^2$

56. $x^2 + 8xy + 12y^2$

57. $a^2 - 9ab + 14b^2$

58. $m^2 - 15mn + 44n^2$

59. $a^2 + 4a + 18$

60. $b^2 - 6a + 15$

61. $2q + q^2 - 63$

62. $-32 - 4t + t^2$

63. $x^2 + 20x + 100$

64. $z^2 - 24z + 144$

65. $t^2 + 18t - 40$

66. $d^2 + 2d - 99$

67. A student factored a trinomial as $(2x - 4)(x - 3)$. The instructor did not give full credit. Why?

68. A student factored a trinomial as $(y + 2)(5y - 15)$. The instructor did not give full credit. Why?

69. What polynomial factors as $(x - 4)(x + 13)$?

70. What polynomial factors as $(q - 7)(q + 10)$?

Expanding Your Skills

For Exercises 71–74, factor completely.

71. $x^4 + 10x^2 + 9$ **72.** $y^4 + 4y^2 - 21$ **73.** $w^4 + 2w^2 - 15$ **74.** $p^4 - 13p^2 + 40$

75. Find all integers, b, that make the trinomial $x^2 + bx + 6$ factorable.

76. Find all integers, b, that make the trinomial $x^2 + bx + 10$ factorable.

77. Find a value of c that makes the trinomial $x^2 + 6x + c$ factorable.

78. Find a value of c that makes the trinomial $x^2 + 8x + c$ factorable.

Factoring Trinomials: Trial-and-Error Method

Section 13.3

In Section 13.2, we learned how to factor trinomials of the form $x^2 + bx + c$. These trinomials have a leading coefficient of 1. In this section and the next, we will consider the more general case in which the leading coefficient may be *any* integer. That is, we will factor quadratic trinomials of the form $ax^2 + bx + c$ (where $a \neq 0$). The method presented in this section is called the trial-and-error method.

Objective

1. Factoring Trinomials by the Trial-and-Error Method

1. Factoring Trinomials by the Trial-and-Error Method

To understand the basis of factoring trinomials of the form $ax^2 + bx + c$, first consider the multiplication of two binomials:

$$\overset{\text{Product of } 2 \cdot 1}{\downarrow} \qquad \overset{\text{Product of } 3 \cdot 2}{\downarrow}$$
$$(2x + 3)(1x + 2) = 2x^2 + \underbrace{\mathbf{4x + 3x}}_{\substack{\text{Sum of products of inner} \\ \text{terms and outer terms}}} + 6 = 2x^2 + 7x + 6$$

To factor the trinomial, $2x^2 + 7x + 6$, this operation is reversed.

$$\overset{\text{Factors of 2}}{2x^2 + 7x + 6 = (\square x \quad \square)(\square x \quad \square)}$$
$$\underset{\text{Factors of 6}}{}$$

We need to fill in the blanks so that the product of the first terms in the binomials is $2x^2$ and the product of the last terms in the binomials is 6. Furthermore, the factors of $2x^2$ and 6 must be chosen so that the sum of the products of the inner terms and outer terms equals $7x$.

To produce the product $2x^2$, we might try the factors $2x$ and x within the binomials:

$$(2x \quad \square)(x \quad \square)$$

To produce a product of 6, the remaining terms in the binomials must either both be positive or both be negative. To produce a positive middle term, we will try positive factors of 6 in the remaining blanks until the correct product is found. The possibilities are $1 \cdot 6, 2 \cdot 3, 3 \cdot 2,$ and $6 \cdot 1$.

$(2x + 1)(x + 6) = 2x^2 + 12x + 1x + 6 = 2x^2 + 13x + 6$ Wrong middle term

$(2x + 2)(x + 3) = 2x^2 + 6x + 2x + 6 = 2x^2 + 8x + 6$ Wrong middle term

$(2x + 3)(x + 2) = 2x^2 + 4x + 3x + 6 = 2x^2 + 7x + 6$ Correct!

$(2x + 6)(x + 1) = 2x^2 + 2x + 6x + 6 = 2x^2 + 8x + 6$ Wrong middle term

The correct factorization of $2x^2 + 7x + 6$ is $(2x + 3)(x + 2)$. ✔

As this example shows, we factor a trinomial of the form $ax^2 + bx + c$ by shuffling the factors of a and c within the binomials until the correct product is obtained. However, sometimes it is not necessary to test all the possible combinations of factors. In the previous example, the GCF of the original trinomial is 1. Therefore, any binomial factor whose terms share a common factor *greater than 1* does not need to be considered. In this case, the possibilities $(2x + 2)(x + 3)$ and $(2x + 6)(x + 1)$ cannot work.

$(2x + 2)(x + 3)$ $(2x + 6)(x + 1)$

Common   Common
factor of 2   factor of 2

The steps to factor a trinomial by the trial-and-error method are outlined in the following box.

PROCEDURE Trial-and-Error Method to Factor $ax^2 + bx + c$

Step 1 Factor out the GCF.

Step 2 List all pairs of positive factors of a and pairs of positive factors of c. Consider the reverse order for one of the lists of factors.

Step 3 Construct two binomials of the form:

Factors of a

$(\square x \quad \square)(\square x \quad \square)$

Factors of c

Step 4 Test each combination of factors and signs until the correct product is found.

Step 5 If no combination of factors produces the correct product, the trinomial cannot be factored further and is a **prime polynomial**.

Before we begin Example 1, keep these two important guidelines in mind:

- For any factoring problem you encounter, always factor out the GCF from all terms first.
- To factor a trinomial, write the trinomial in the form $ax^2 + bx + c$.

Example 1   **Factoring a Trinomial by the Trial-and-Error Method**

Factor the trinomial by the trial-and-error method: $10x^2 - 9x - 1$

Solution:

$10x^2 - 9x - 1$ **Step 1:** Factor out the GCF from all terms. In this case, the GCF is 1.

The trinomial is written in the form $ax^2 + bx + c$.

To factor $10x^2 - 9x - 1$, two binomials must be constructed in the form:

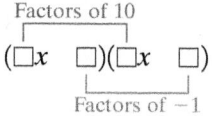

$(\Box x \quad \Box)(\Box x \quad \Box)$ **Step 2:** To produce the product $10x^2$, we might try $5x$ and $2x$, or $10x$ and $1x$. To produce a product of -1, we will try the factors $(1)(-1)$ and $(-1)(1)$.

Step 3: Construct all possible binomial factors using different combinations of the factors of $10x^2$ and -1.

$(5x + 1)(2x - 1) = 10x^2 - 5x + 2x - 1 = 10x^2 - 3x - 1$ Wrong middle term

$(5x - 1)(2x + 1) = 10x^2 + 5x - 2x - 1 = 10x^2 + 3x - 1$ Wrong middle term

Because the numbers 1 and -1 did not produce the correct trinomial when coupled with $5x$ and $2x$, try using $10x$ and $1x$.

$(10x - 1)(1x + 1) = 10x^2 + 10x - 1x - 1 = 10x^2 + 9x - 1$ Wrong middle term

$(10x + 1)(1x - 1) = 10x^2 - 10x + 1x - 1 = 10x^2 - 9x - 1$ Correct!

Therefore, $10x^2 - 9x - 1 = (10x + 1)(x - 1)$.

Skill Practice

Factor using the trial-and-error method.
1. $3b^2 + 8b + 4$

In Example 1, the factors of -1 must have opposite signs to produce a negative product. Therefore, one binomial factor is a sum and one is a difference. Determining the correct signs is an important aspect of factoring trinomials. We suggest the following guidelines:

Chapter 13 Factoring Polynomials

PROCEDURE Sign Rules for the Trial-and-Error Method

Given the trinomial $ax^2 + bx + c, (a > 0)$, the signs can be determined as follows:

- If c *is positive*, then the signs in the binomials must be the same (either both positive or both negative). The correct choice is determined by the middle term. If the middle term is positive, then both signs must be positive. If the middle term is negative, then both signs must be negative.

$$c \text{ is positive} \qquad\qquad c \text{ is positive}$$
$$20x^2 + 43x + 21 \qquad\qquad 20x^2 - 43x + 21$$
$$(4x + 3)(5x + 7) \qquad\qquad (4x - 3)(5x - 7)$$
$$\underbrace{}_{\text{Same signs}} \qquad\qquad \underbrace{}_{\text{Same signs}}$$

- If c *is negative*, then the signs in the binomial must be different. The middle term in the trinomial determines which factor gets the positive sign and which gets the negative sign.

$$c \text{ is negative} \qquad\qquad c \text{ is negative}$$
$$x^2 + 3x - 28 \qquad\qquad x^2 - 3x - 28$$
$$(x + 7)(x - 4) \qquad\qquad (x - 7)(x + 4)$$
$$\underbrace{}_{\text{Different signs}} \qquad\qquad \underbrace{}_{\text{Different signs}}$$

Factor.

2. $-25w + 6w^2 + 4$

Example 2 **Factoring a Trinomial**

Factor the trinomial: $13y - 6 + 8y^2$

Solution:

$13y - 6 + 8y^2$

$= 8y^2 + 13y - 6$ Write the polynomial in descending order.

$(\square y \ \square)(\square y \ \square)$ **Step 1:** The GCF is 1.

Factors of 8	Factors of 6
$1 \cdot 8$	$1 \cdot 6$
$2 \cdot 4$	$2 \cdot 3$
	$3 \cdot 2$
	$6 \cdot 1$

Step 2: List the positive factors of 8 and positive factors of 6. Consider the reverse order in one list of factors.

$3 \cdot 2$ and $6 \cdot 1$ (reverse order)

Step 3: Construct all possible binomial factors using different combinations of the factors of 8 and 6.

$(2y \ 1)(4y \ 6)$
$(2y \ 2)(4y \ 3)$
$(2y \ 3)(4y \ 2)$
$(2y \ 6)(4y \ 1)$
$(1y \ 1)(8y \ 6)$
$(1y \ 3)(8y \ 2)$

Without regard to signs, these factorizations cannot work because the terms in the binomials share a common factor greater than 1.

Test the remaining factorizations. Keep in mind that to produce a product of -6, the signs within the parentheses must be opposite (one positive and one negative). Also, the sum of the products of the inner terms and outer terms must be combined to form $13y$.

Answer

2. $(6w - 1)(w - 4)$

$(1y \quad 6)(8y \quad 1)$ *Incorrect.*   Wrong middle term.
Regardless of the signs, the product of inner terms, 48y, and the product of outer terms, 1y, cannot be combined to form the middle term 13y.

$(1y \quad 2)(8y \quad 3)$ *Correct.*   The terms 16y and 3y can be combined to form the middle term 13y, provided the signs are applied correctly. We require $+16y$ and $-3y$.

The correct factorization of $8y^2 + 13y - 6$ is $(y + 2)(8y - 3)$.

Remember that the first step in any factoring problem is to remove the GCF. By removing the GCF, the remaining terms of the trinomial will be simpler and may have smaller coefficients.

Example 3   **Factoring a Trinomial by the Trial-and-Error Method**

Factor the trinomial by the trial-and-error method: $40x^3 - 104x^2 + 10x$

Skill Practice
Factor.
3. $8t^3 + 38t^2 + 24t$

Solution:

$40x^3 - 104x^2 + 10x$

$= 2x(20x^2 - 52x + 5)$ **Step 1:** The GCF is 2x.

$= 2x(\square x \quad \square)(\square x \quad \square)$ **Step 2:** List the factors of 20 and factors of 5. Consider the reverse order in one list of factors.

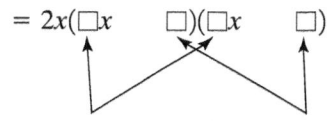

Factors of 20	Factors of 5
$1 \cdot 20$	$1 \cdot 5$
$2 \cdot 10$	$5 \cdot 1$
$4 \cdot 5$	

Step 3: Construct all possible binomial factors using different combinations of the factors of 20 and factors of 5. The signs in the parentheses must both be negative.

TIP: Notice that when the GCF, 2x, is removed from the original trinomial, the new trinomial has smaller coefficients. This makes the factoring process simpler. It is easier to list the factors of 20 and 5 than the factors of 40 and 10.

$= 2x(1x - 1)(20x - 5)$
$= 2x(2x - 1)(10x - 5)$ *Incorrect.*   Once the GCF has been removed from the original polynomial, the binomial factors cannot contain a GCF greater than 1.
$= 2x(4x - 1)(5x - 5)$

$= 2x(1x - 5)(20x - 1)$ *Incorrect.*   Wrong middle term.
$2x(x - 5)(20x - 1)$
$= 2x(20x^2 - 1x - 100x + 5)$
$= 2x(20x^2 - 101x + 5)$

$= 2x(4x - 5)(5x - 1)$ *Incorrect.*   Wrong middle term.
$2x(4x - 5)(5x - 1)$
$= 2x(20x^2 - 4x - 25x + 5)$
$= 2x(20x^2 - 29x + 5)$

$= 2x(2x - 5)(10x - 1)$ *Correct.* $2x(2x - 5)(10x - 1)$
$= 2x(20x^2 - 2x - 50x + 5)$
$= 2x(20x^2 - 52x + 5)$
$= 40x^3 - 104x^2 + 10x$

The correct factorization is $2x(2x - 5)(10x - 1)$.

Answer
3. $2t(4t + 3)(t + 4)$

Often it is easier to factor a trinomial when the leading coefficient is positive. If the leading coefficient is negative, consider factoring out the opposite of the GCF.

Example 4 **Factoring a Trinomial by the Trial-and-Error Method**

Factor: $-45x^2 - 3xy + 18y^2$

Solution:

$-45x^2 - 3xy + 18y^2$

$= -3(15x^2 + xy - 6y^2)$ **Step 1:** Factor out -3 to make the leading coefficient positive.

$= -3(\Box x \;\; \Box y)(\Box x \;\; \Box y)$ **Step 2:** List the factors of 15 and 6.

Factors of 15   Factors of 6

$1 \cdot 15$ $1 \cdot 6$

$3 \cdot 5$ $2 \cdot 3$

             $3 \cdot 2$

             $6 \cdot 1$ **Step 3:** We will construct all binomial combinations, without regard to signs first.

$-3(x \;\; y)(15x \;\; 6y)$

$-3(x \;\; 2y)(15x \;\; 3y)$

$-3(3x \;\; 3y)(5x \;\; 2y)$ *Incorrect.* The binomials contain a common factor.

$-3(3x \;\; 6y)(5x \;\; y)$

Test the remaining factorizations. The signs within parentheses must be opposite to produce a product of $-6y^2$. Also, the sum of the products of the inner terms and outer terms must be combined to form $1xy$.

$-3(x \;\; 3y)(15x \;\; 2y)$ *Incorrect.* Regardless of signs, $45xy$ and $2xy$ cannot be combined to equal xy.

$-3(x \;\; 6y)(15x \;\; y)$ *Incorrect.* Regardless of signs, $90xy$ and xy cannot be combined to equal xy.

$-3(3x \;\; y)(5x \;\; 6y)$ *Incorrect.* Regardless of signs, $5xy$ and $18xy$ cannot be combined to equal xy.

$-3(3x \;\; 2y)(5x \;\; 3y)$ *Correct.* The terms $10xy$ and $9xy$ can be combined to form xy provided that the signs are applied correctly. We require $10xy$ and $-9xy$.

$-3(3x + 2y)(5x - 3y)$ Factored form

Recall that a prime polynomial is a polynomial whose only factors are itself and 1. Not every trinomial is factorable by the methods presented in this text.

Example 5 **Factoring a Trinomial by the Trial-and-Error Method**

Factor the trinomial by the trial-and-error method: $2p^2 - 8p + 3$

Solution:

$2p^2 - 8p + 3$ | **Step 1:** The GCF is 1.

$= (1p \ \square)(2p \ \square)$ | **Step 2:** List the factors of 2 and the factors of 3.

Factors of 2   Factors of 3

$1 \cdot 2$ $1 \cdot 3$

                    $3 \cdot 1$

Step 3: Construct all possible binomial factors using different combinations of the factors of 2 and 3. Because the third term in the trinomial is positive, both signs in the binomial must be the same. Because the middle term coefficient is negative, both signs will be negative.

$(p - 1)(2p - 3) = 2p^2 - 3p - 2p + 3$

$\qquad\qquad\quad = 2p^2 - 5p + 3$ *Incorrect.*   Wrong middle term.

$(p - 3)(2p - 1) = 2p^2 - p - 6p + 3$

$\qquad\qquad\quad = 2p^2 - 7p + 3$ *Incorrect.*   Wrong middle term.

None of the combinations of factors results in the correct product. Therefore, the polynomial $2p^2 - 8p + 3$ is prime and cannot be factored further.

In Example 6, we use the trial-and-error method to factor a higher degree trinomial into two binomial factors.

Example 6 **Factoring a Higher Degree Trinomial**

Factor the trinomial: $3x^4 + 8x^2 + 5$

Solution:

$3x^4 + 8x^2 + 5$ | **Step 1:** The GCF is 1.

$= (\square x^2 + \square)(\square x^2 + \square)$ | **Step 2:** To produce the product $3x^4$, we must use $3x^2$, and $1x^2$. To produce a product of 5, we will try the factors $(1)(5)$ and $(5)(1)$.

Step 3: Construct all possible binomial factors using the combinations of factors of $3x^4$ and 5.

$(3x^2 + 1)(x^2 + 5) = 3x^4 + 15x^2 + 1x^2 + 5 = 3x^4 + 16x^2 + 5$ Wrong middle term

$(3x^2 + 5)(x^2 + 1) = 3x^4 + 3x^2 + 5x^2 + 5 = 3x^4 + 8x^2 + 5$ Correct!

Therefore, $3x^4 + 8x^2 + 5 = (3x^2 + 5)(x^2 + 1)$

Skill Practice

Factor.

5. $3a^2 + a + 4$

Skill Practice

Factor.

6. $2y^4 - y^2 - 15$

Answers

5. Prime   **6.** $(y^2 - 3)(2y^2 + 5)$

Section 13.3 Practice Exercises

Study Skills Exercises

1. In addition to studying the material for a test, here are some other activities that people use when preparing for a test. Circle the importance of each statement.

	not important	somewhat important	very important
a. Get a good night's sleep the night before the test.	1	2	3
b. Eat a good meal before the test.	1	2	3
c. Wear comfortable clothes on the day of the test.	1	2	3
d. Arrive early to class on the day of the test.	1	2	3

2. Define the key term **prime polynomial**.

Review Exercises

For Exercises 3–8, factor completely.

3. $21a^2b^2 + 12ab^2 - 15a^2b$

4. $5uv^2 - 10u^2v + 25u^2v^2$

5. $mn - m - 2n + 2$

6. $5x - 10 - xy + 2y$

7. $6a^2 - 30a - 84$

8. $10b^2 + 20b - 240$

Objective 1: Factoring Trinomials by the Trial-and-Error Method

For Exercises 9–12, assume a, b, and c represent positive integers.

9. When factoring a polynomial of the form $ax^2 + bx + c$, pick an appropriate combination of signs.

 a. (+)(+)
 b. (−)(−)
 c. (+)(−)

10. When factoring a polynomial of the form $ax^2 - bx - c$, pick an appropriate combination of signs.

 a. (+)(+)
 b. (−)(−)
 c. (+)(−)

11. When factoring a polynomial of the form $ax^2 - bx + c$, pick an appropriate combination of signs.

 a. (+)(+)
 b. (−)(−)
 c. (+)(−)

12. When factoring a polynomial of the form $ax^2 + bx - c$, pick an appropriate combination of signs.

 a. (+)(+)
 b. (−)(−)
 c. (+)(−)

For Exercises 13–30, factor completely by using the trial-and-error method. **(See Examples 1, 2, and 5.)**

13. $2y^2 - 3y - 2$

14. $2w^2 + 5w - 3$

15. $3n^2 + 13n + 4$

16. $2a^2 + 7a + 6$

17. $5x^2 - 14x - 3$

18. $7y^2 + 9y - 10$

19. $12c^2 - 5c - 2$　　　　**20.** $6z^2 + z - 12$　　　　**21.** $-12 + 10w^2 + 37w$

22. $-10 + 10p^2 + 21p$　　**23.** $-5q - 6 + 6q^2$　　　**24.** $17a - 2 + 3a^2$

25. $6b - 23 + 4b^2$　　　　**26.** $8 + 7x^2 - 18x$　　　**27.** $-8 + 25m^2 - 10m$

28. $8q^2 + 31q - 4$　　　　**29.** $6y^2 + 19xy - 20x^2$　**30.** $12y^2 - 73yz + 6z^2$

For Exercises 31–38, factor completely. Be sure to factor out the GCF first. **(See Examples 3–4.)**

31. $2m^2 - 12m - 80$　　**32.** $3c^2 - 33c + 72$　　　**33.** $2y^5 + 13y^4 + 6y^3$

34. $3u^8 - 13u^7 + 4u^6$　　**35.** $-a^2 - 15a + 34$　　　**36.** $-x^2 - 7x - 10$

37. $80m^2 - 100mp - 30p^2$　**38.** $60w^2 + 550wz - 500z^2$

For Exercises 39–44, factor the higher degree polynomial. **(See Example 6.)**

39. $x^4 + 10x^2 + 9$　　　**40.** $y^4 + 4y^2 - 21$　　　**41.** $w^4 + 2w^2 - 15$

42. $p^4 - 13p^2 + 40$　　　**43.** $2x^4 - 7x^2 - 15$　　　**44.** $5y^4 + 11y^2 + 2$

Mixed Exercises

For Exercises 45–92, factor the trinomial completely.

45. $20z - 18 - 2z^2$　　**46.** $25t - 5t^2 - 30$　　**47.** $42 - 13q + q^2$　　**48.** $-5w - 24 + w^2$

49. $6t^2 + 7t - 3$　　　**50.** $4p^2 - 9p + 2$　　　**51.** $4m^2 - 20m + 25$　　**52.** $16r^2 + 24r + 9$

53. $5c^2 - c + 2$　　　**54.** $7s^2 + 2s + 9$　　　**55.** $6x^2 - 19xy + 10y^2$　**56.** $15p^2 + pq - 2q^2$

57. $12m^2 + 11mn - 5n^2$　**58.** $4a^2 + 5ab - 6b^2$　**59.** $30r^2 + 5r - 10$　　**60.** $36x^2 - 18x - 4$

61. $4s^2 - 8st + t^2$　　**62.** $6u^2 - 10uv + 5v^2$　**63.** $10t^2 - 23t - 5$　　**64.** $16n^2 + 14n + 3$

65. $14w^2 + 13w - 12$　**66.** $12x^2 - 16x + 5$　　**67.** $x^2 + 7x - 18$　　**68.** $y^2 - 6y - 40$

69. $a^2 - 10a - 24$　　**70.** $b^2 + 6b - 7$　　　**71.** $r^2 + 5r - 24$　　**72.** $t^2 + 20t + 100$

73. $x^2 + 9xy + 20y^2$　**74.** $p^2 - 13pq + 36q^2$　**75.** $v^2 + 2v + 15$　　**76.** $x^2 - x - 1$

77. $a^2 + 21ab + 20b^2$　**78.** $x^2 - 17xy - 18y^2$　**79.** $t^2 - 10t + 21$　　**80.** $z^2 - 15z + 36$

81. $5d^3 + 3d^2 - 10d$　**82.** $3y^3 - y^2 + 12y$　　**83.** $4b^3 - 4b^2 - 80b$　**84.** $2w^2 + 20w + 42$

85. $x^2y^2 - 13xy^2 + 30y^2$　**86.** $p^2q^2 - 14pq^2 + 33q^2$　**87.** $-12u^3 - 22u^2 + 20u$　**88.** $-18z^4 + 15z^3 + 12z^2$

89. $8x^4 + 14x^2 + 3$　**90.** $6y^4 - 5y^2 - 4$　　**91.** $10z^4 + 9z^2 - 9$　　**92.** $6p^4 + 17p^2 + 10$

Expanding Your Skills

For Exercises 93–96, each pair of trinomials looks similar but differs by one sign. Factor each trinomial and see how their factored forms differ.

93. a. $x^2 - 10x - 24$

    b. $x^2 - 10x + 24$

95. a. $x^2 - 5x - 6$

    b. $x^2 - 5x + 6$

94. a. $x^2 - 13x - 30$

    b. $x^2 - 13x + 30$

96. a. $x^2 - 10x + 9$

    b. $x^2 + 10x + 9$

Section 13.4   Factoring Trinomials: AC-Method

Objective

1. Factoring Trinomials by the AC-Method

In Section 13.2, we factored trinomials with a leading coefficient of 1. In Section 13.3, we learned the trial-and-error method to factor the more general case in which the leading coefficient is any integer. In this section, we provide an alternative method to factor trinomials, called the ac-method.

1. Factoring Trinomials by the AC-Method

The product of two binomials results in a four-term expression that can sometimes be simplified to a trinomial. To factor the trinomial, we want to reverse the process.

Multiply:

Multiply the binomials.   Add the middle terms.

$$(2x + 3)(x + 2) = \longrightarrow 2x^2 + 4x + 3x + 6 = \longrightarrow 2x^2 + 7x + 6$$

Factor:

$$2x^2 + 7x + 6 = \longrightarrow 2x^2 + 4x + 3x + 6 = \longrightarrow (2x + 3)(x + 2)$$

Rewrite the middle term as   Factor by grouping.
a sum or difference of terms.

To factor a quadratic trinomial, $ax^2 + bx + c$, by the ac-method, we rewrite the middle term, bx, as a sum or difference of terms. The goal is to produce a four-term polynomial that can be factored by grouping. The process is outlined as follows.

PROCEDURE   AC-Method: Factoring $ax^2 + bx + c$ $(a \neq 0)$

Step 1   Factor out the GCF from all terms.

Step 2   Multiply the coefficients of the first and last terms (ac).

Step 3   Find two integers whose product is ac and whose sum is b. (If no pair of integers can be found, then the trinomial cannot be factored further and is a **prime polynomial**.)

Step 4   Rewrite the middle term, bx, as the sum of two terms whose coefficients are the integers found in step 3.

Step 5   Factor the polynomial by grouping.

The ac-method for factoring trinomials is illustrated in Example 1. However, before we begin, keep these two important guidelines in mind:

- For any factoring problem you encounter, always factor out the GCF from all terms first.
- To factor a trinomial, write the trinomial in the form $ax^2 + bx + c$.

Example 1 **Factoring a Trinomial by the AC-Method**

Factor the trinomial by the ac-method: $2x^2 + 7x + 6$

Solution:

$2x^2 + 7x + 6$ **Step 1:** Factor out the GCF from all terms. In this case, the GCF is 1.

$2x^2 + 7x + 6$ **Step 2:** The trinomial is written in the form $ax^2 + bx + c$.

$a = 2, b = 7, c = 6$ Find the product $ac = (2)(6) = 12$.

12	12
$1 \cdot 12$	$(-1)(-12)$
$2 \cdot 6$	$(-2)(-6)$
$3 \cdot 4$	$(-3)(-4)$

Step 3: List all factors of ac and search for the pair whose sum equals the value of b. That is, list the factors of 12 and find the pair whose sum equals 7.

The numbers 3 and 4 satisfy both conditions: $3 \cdot 4 = 12$ and $3 + 4 = 7$.

$2x^2 + 7x + 6$

$= 2x^2 + 3x + 4x + 6$ **Step 4:** Write the middle term of the trinomial as the sum of two terms whose coefficients are the selected pair of numbers: 3 and 4.

$= 2x^2 + 3x \mid + 4x + 6$ **Step 5:** Factor by grouping.

$= x(2x + 3) + 2(2x + 3)$

$= (2x + 3)(x + 2)$

Check: $(2x + 3)(x + 2) = 2x^2 + 4x + 3x + 6$

$= 2x^2 + 7x + 6$ ✔

Skill Practice

Factor by the ac-method.
1. $2x^2 + 5x + 3$

TIP: One frequently asked question is whether the order matters when we rewrite the middle term of the trinomial as two terms (step 3). The answer is no. From the previous example, the two middle terms in step 3 could have been reversed to obtain the same result:

$$2x^2 + 7x + 6$$
$$= 2x^2 + 4x + 3x + 6$$
$$= 2x(x + 2) + 3(x + 2)$$
$$= (x + 2)(2x + 3)$$

This example also points out that the order in which two factors are written does not matter. The expression $(x + 2)(2x + 3)$ is equivalent to $(2x + 3)(x + 2)$ because multiplication is a commutative operation.

Answer
1. $(x + 1)(2x + 3)$

Skill Practice

Factor by the ac-method.

2. $13w + 6w^2 + 6$

Avoiding Mistakes

Before factoring a trinomial, be sure to write the trinomial in descending order. That is, write it in the form $ax^2 + bx + c$.

Example 2 — Factoring Trinomials by the AC-Method

Factor the trinomial by the ac-method: $-2x + 8x^2 - 3$

Solution:

$-2x + 8x^2 - 3$ First rewrite the polynomial in the form $ax^2 + bx + c$.

$= 8x^2 - 2x - 3$ **Step 1:** The GCF is 1.

$a = 8, b = -2, c = -3$ **Step 2:** Find the product $ac = (8)(-3) = -24$.

Step 3: List all the factors of -24 and find the pair of factors whose sum equals -2.

-24	-24
$-1 \cdot 24$	$-24 \cdot 1$
$-2 \cdot 12$	$-12 \cdot 2$
$-3 \cdot 8$	$-8 \cdot 3$
$-4 \cdot 6$	$-6 \cdot 4$

The numbers -6 and 4 satisfy both conditions: $(-6)(4) = -24$ and $-6 + 4 = -2$.

$= 8x^2 - 2x - 3$ **Step 4:** Write the middle term of the trinomial as two terms whose coefficients are the selected pair of numbers, -6 and 4.

$= 8x^2 - 6x + 4x - 3$

$= 8x^2 - 6x + 4x - 3$ **Step 5:** Factor by grouping.

$= 2x(4x - 3) + 1(4x - 3)$

$= (4x - 3)(2x + 1)$

Check: $(4x - 3)(2x + 1) = 8x^2 + 4x - 6x - 3$

$= 8x^2 - 2x - 3$ ✔

Skill Practice

Factor by the ac-method.

3. $9y^3 - 30y^2 + 24y$

Example 3 — Factoring a Trinomial by the AC-Method

Factor the trinomial by the ac-method: $10x^3 - 85x^2 + 105x$

Solution:

$10x^3 - 85x^2 + 105x$ **Step 1:** Factor out the GCF of $5x$.

$= 5x(2x^2 - 17x + 21)$ The trinomial is in the form $ax^2 + bx + c$.

$a = 2, b = -17, c = 21$ **Step 2:** Find the product $ac = (2)(21) = 42$.

Step 3: List all the factors of 42 and find the pair whose sum equals -17.

42	42
$1 \cdot 42$	$(-1)(-42)$
$2 \cdot 21$	$(-2)(-21)$
$3 \cdot 14$	$(-3)(-14)$
$6 \cdot 7$	$(-6)(-7)$

The numbers -3 and -14 satisfy both conditions: $(-3)(-14) = 42$ and $-3 + (-14) = -17$.

Answers

2. $(2w + 3)(3w + 2)$

3. $3y(3y - 4)(y - 2)$

$= 5x(2x^2 - 17x + 21)$

Step 4: Write the middle term of the trinomial as two terms whose coefficients are the selected pair of numbers, -3 and -14.

$= 5x(2x^2 - 3x - 14x + 21)$

$= 5x(2x^2 - 3x \mid - 14x + 21)$

Step 5: Factor by grouping.

$= 5x[x(2x - 3) - 7(2x - 3)]$

$= 5x(2x - 3)(x - 7)$

TIP: Notice when the GCF is removed from the original trinomial, the new trinomial has smaller coefficients. This makes the factoring process simpler because the product ac is smaller. It is much easier to list the factors of 42 than the factors of 1050.

Original trinomial	With the GCF factored out
$10x^3 - 85x^2 + 105x$	$5x(2x^2 - 17x + 21)$
$ac = (10)(105) = 1050$	$ac = (2)(21) = 42$

In most cases, it is easier to factor a trinomial with a positive leading coefficient.

Example 4 **Factoring a Trinomial by the AC-Method**

Factor: $-18x^2 + 21xy + 15y^2$

Solution:

$-18x^2 + 21xy + 15y^2$

Step 1: Factor out the GCF.

$= -3(6x^2 - 7xy - 5y^2)$

Factor out -3 to make the leading term positive.

Step 2: The product $ac = (6)(-5) = -30$.

Step 3: The numbers -10 and 3 have a product of -30 and a sum of -7.

$= -3[6x^2 - 10xy + 3xy - 5y^2]$

Step 4: Rewrite the middle term, $-7xy$ as $-10xy + 3xy$.

$= -3[6x^2 - 10xy \mid + 3xy - 5y^2]$

Step 5: Factor by grouping.

$= -3[2x(3x - 5y) + y(3x - 5y)]$

$= -3(3x - 5y)(2x + y)$

Factored form.

Recall that a prime polynomial is a polynomial whose only factors are itself and 1. It also should be noted that not every trinomial is factorable by the methods presented in this text.

Skill Practice

Factor.

5. $4x^2 + 5x + 2$

Example 5   **Factoring a Trinomial by the AC-Method**

Factor the trinomial by the ac-method: $2p^2 - 8p + 3$

Solution:

$2p^2 - 8p + 3$ **Step 1:** The GCF is 1.

                        Step 2: The product $ac = 6$.

6	6
$1 \cdot 6$	$(-1)(-6)$
$2 \cdot 3$	$(-2)(-3)$

Step 3: List the factors of 6. Notice that no pair of factors has a sum of -8. Therefore, the trinomial cannot be factored.

The trinomial $2p^2 - 8p + 3$ is a prime polynomial.

In Example 6, we use the ac-method to factor a higher degree trinomial.

Skill Practice

Factor.

6. $3y^4 + 2y^2 - 8$

Example 6   **Factoring a Higher Degree Trinomial**

Factor the trinomial: $2x^4 + 5x^2 + 2$

Solution:

$2x^4 + 5x^2 + 2$ **Step 1:** The GCF is 1.

$a = 2, b = 5, c = 2$ **Step 2:** Find the product $ac = (2)(2) = 4$.

                        Step 3: The numbers 1 and 4 have a product of 4 and a sum of 5.

$2x^4 + x^2 + 4x^2 + 2$ **Step 4:** Rewrite the middle term, $5x^2$, as $x^2 + 4x^2$.

$2x^4 + x^2 + 4x^2 + 2$ **Step 5:** Factor by grouping.

$x^2(2x^2 + 1) + 2(2x^2 + 1)$

$(2x^2 + 1)(x^2 + 2)$ Factored form.

Answers

5. Prime
6. $(3y^2 - 4)(y^2 + 2)$

Section 13.4   Practice Exercises

Boost *your* GRADE at ALEKS.com!

ALEKS
version 3.0

- Practice Problems
- Self-Tests
- NetTutor
- e-Professors
- Videos

Study Skills Exercise

1. Define the key term **prime polynomial**.

Review Exercises

For Exercises 2–4, factor completely.

2. $5x(x - 2) - 2(x - 2)$ 3. $8(y + 5) + 9y(y + 5)$ 4. $6ab + 24b - 12a - 48$

Objective 1: Factoring Trinomials by the AC-Method

For Exercises 5–12, find the pair of integers whose product and sum are given.

5. Product: 12   Sum: 13   6. Product: 12   Sum: 7

7. Product: 8 Sum: -9 **8.** Product: -4 Sum: -3

9. Product: -20 Sum: 1 **10.** Product: -6 Sum: -1

11. Product: -18 Sum: 7 **12.** Product: -72 Sum: -6

For Exercises 13–42, factor the trinomials using the ac-method. **(See Examples 1–6.)**

13. $3x^2 + 13x + 4$ **14.** $2y^2 + 7y + 6$ **15.** $4w^2 - 9w + 2$

16. $2p^2 - 3p - 2$ **17.** $2m^2 + 5m - 3$ **18.** $6n^2 + 7n - 3$

19. $8k^2 - 6k - 9$ **20.** $9h^2 - 12h + 4$ **21.** $4k^2 - 20k + 25$

22. $16h^2 + 24h + 9$ **23.** $5x^2 + x + 7$ **24.** $4y^2 - y + 2$

25. $10 + 9z^2 - 21z$ **26.** $13x + 4x^2 - 12$ **27.** $50y + 24 + 14y^2$

28. $-24 + 10w + 4w^2$ **29.** $12y^2 + 8yz - 15z^2$ **30.** $20a^2 + 3ab - 9b^2$

31. $-15w^2 + 22w + 5$ **32.** $-16z^2 + 34z + 15$ **33.** $-12x^2 + 20xy - 8y^2$

34. $-6p^2 - 21pq - 9q^2$ **35.** $18y^3 + 60y^2 + 42y$ **36.** $8t^3 - 4t^2 - 40t$

37. $a^4 + 5a^2 + 6$ **38.** $y^4 - 2y^2 - 35$ **39.** $6x^4 - x^2 - 15$

40. $8t^4 + 2t^2 - 3$ **41.** $8p^4 + 37p^2 - 15$ **42.** $2a^4 + 11a^2 + 14$

Mixed Exercises

For Exercises 43–75, factor completely.

43. $20p^2 - 19p + 3$ **44.** $4p^2 + 5pq - 6q^2$ **45.** $6u^2 - 19uv + 10v^2$

46. $15m^2 + mn - 2n^2$ **47.** $12a^2 + 11ab - 5b^2$ **48.** $3r^2 - rs - 14s^2$

49. $3h^2 + 19hk - 14k^2$ **50.** $2x^2 - 13xy + y^2$ **51.** $3p^2 + 20pq - q^2$

52. $3 - 14z + 16z^2$ **53.** $10w + 1 + 16w^2$ **54.** $b^2 + 16 - 8b$

55. $1 + q^2 - 2q$ **56.** $25x - 5x^2 - 30$ **57.** $20a - 18 - 2a^2$

58. $-6 - t + t^2$ **59.** $-6 + m + m^2$ **60.** $72x^2 + 18x - 2$

61. $20y^2 - 78y - 8$ **62.** $p^3 - 6p^2 - 27p$ **63.** $w^5 - 11w^4 + 28w^3$

64. $3x^3 + 10x^2 + 7x$ **65.** $4r^3 + 3r^2 - 10r$ **66.** $2p^3 - 38p^2 + 120p$

67. $4q^3 - 4q^2 - 80q$ **68.** $x^2y^2 + 14x^2y + 33x^2$ **69.** $a^2b^2 + 13ab^2 + 30b^2$

70. $-k^2 - 7k - 10$ **71.** $-m^2 - 15m + 34$ **72.** $-3n^2 - 3n + 90$

73. $-2h^2 + 28h - 90$ **74.** $x^4 - 7x^2 + 10$ **75.** $m^4 + 10m^2 + 21$

76. Is the expression $(2x + 4)(x - 7)$ factored completely? Explain why or why not.

77. Is the expression $(3x + 1)(5x - 10)$ factored completely? Explain why or why not.

Section 13.5	Difference of Squares and Perfect Square Trinomials

Objectives

1. **Factoring a Difference of Squares**
2. **Factoring Perfect Square Trinomials**

1. Factoring a Difference of Squares

Up to this point, we have learned several methods of factoring, including:

- Factoring out the greatest common factor from a polynomial
- Factoring a four-term polynomial by grouping
- Factoring trinomials by the ac-method or by the trial-and-error method

In this section, we begin by factoring a special binomial called a difference of squares. Recall from Section 12.6 that the product of two conjugates results in a **difference of squares**:

$$(a + b)(a - b) = a^2 - b^2$$

Therefore, to factor a difference of squares, the process is reversed. Identify a and b and construct the conjugate factors.

> **FORMULA   Factored Form of a Difference of Squares**
>
> $$a^2 - b^2 = (a + b)(a - b)$$

We know that the numbers, 1, 4, 9, 16, 25, and so on are perfect squares. It is also important to recognize that a variable expression is a perfect square if its exponent is a multiple of 2. For example:

Perfect Squares

$$x^2 = (x)^2$$
$$x^4 = (x^2)^2$$
$$x^6 = (x^3)^2$$
$$x^8 = (x^4)^2$$
$$x^{10} = (x^5)^2$$

Skill Practice

Factor completely.
1. $a^2 - 64$
2. $25q^2 - 49w^2$
3. $98m^3n - 50mn$

Answers
1. $(a + 8)(a - 8)$
2. $(5q + 7w)(5q - 7w)$
3. $2mn(7m + 5)(7m - 5)$

Example 1   Factoring Differences of Squares

Factor the binomials.

   a. $y^2 - 25$ **b.** $49s^2 - 4t^4$ **c.** $18w^2z - 2z$

Solution:

a. $y^2 - 25$ The binomial is a difference of squares.

   $= (y)^2 - (5)^2$ Write in the form: $a^2 - b^2$, where $a = y, b = 5$.

   $= (y + 5)(y - 5)$ Factor as $(a + b)(a - b)$.

b. $49s^2 - 4t^4$ The binomial is a difference of squares.

   $= (7s)^2 - (2t^2)^2$ Write in the form $a^2 - b^2$, where $a = 7s$ and $b = 2t^2$.

   $= (7s + 2t^2)(7s - 2t^2)$ Factor as $(a + b)(a - b)$.

c. $18w^2z - 2z$ The GCF is $2z$.

$= 2z(9w^2 - 1)$ $(9w^2 - 1)$ is a difference of squares.

$= 2z[(3w)^2 - (1)^2]$ Write in the form: $a^2 - b^2$, where $a = 3w, b = 1$.

$= 2z(3w + 1)(3w - 1)$ Factor as $(a + b)(a - b)$.

The difference of squares $a^2 - b^2$ factors as $(a - b)(a + b)$. However, the *sum* of squares is not factorable.

PROPERTY   **Sum of Squares**

Suppose a and b have no common factors. Then the **sum of squares** $a^2 + b^2$ is *not* factorable over the real numbers.

That is, $a^2 + b^2$ is prime over the real numbers.

To see why $a^2 + b^2$ is not factorable, consider the product of binomials:

$(a + b)(a - b) = a^2 - b^2$ Wrong sign

$(a + b)(a + b) = a^2 + 2ab + b^2$ Wrong middle term

$(a - b)(a - b) = a^2 - 2ab + b^2$ Wrong middle term

After exhausting all possibilities, we see that if a and b share no common factors, then the sum of squares $a^2 + b^2$ is a prime polynomial.

Example 2   **Factoring Binomials**

Factor the binomials, if possible.   **a.** $p^2 - 9$ **b.** $p^2 + 9$

Solution:

a. $p^2 - 9$ Difference of squares

$= (p - 3)(p + 3)$ Factor as $a^2 - b^2 = (a - b)(a + b)$.

b. $p^2 + 9$ Sum of squares

    Prime (cannot be factored)

Skill Practice

Factor the binomials, if possible.
4. $t^2 - 144$
5. $t^2 + 144$

Some factoring problems require several steps. Always be sure to factor completely.

Example 3   **Factoring the Difference of Squares**

Factor completely: $w^4 - 81$

Solution:

$w^4 - 81$ The GCF is 1. $w^4 - 81$ is a difference of squares.

$= (w^2)^2 - (9)^2$ Write in the form: $a^2 - b^2$, where $a = w^2, b = 9$.

$= (w^2 + 9)(w^2 - 9)$ Factor as $(a + b)(a - b)$.

$= (w^2 + 9)(w + 3)(w - 3)$ Note that $w^2 - 9$ can be factored further as a difference of squares. (The binomial $w^2 + 9$ is a sum of squares and cannot be factored further.)

Skill Practice

Factor completely.
6. $y^4 - 1$

Answers
4. $(t - 12)(t + 12)$
5. Prime
6. $(y + 1)(y - 1)(y^2 + 1)$

Factor completely.

7. $p^3 + 7p^2 - 9p - 63$

Example 4   **Factoring a Polynomial**

Factor completely: $y^3 - 5y^2 - 4y + 20$

Solution:

$y^3 - 5y^2 - 4y + 20$ The GCF is 1. The polynomial has four terms. Factor by grouping.

$= y^3 - 5y^2 \mid - 4y + 20$

$= y^2(y - 5) - 4(y - 5)$

$= (y - 5)(y^2 - 4)$ The expression $y^2 - 4$ is a difference of squares and can be factored further as $(y - 2)(y + 2)$.

$= (y - 5)(y - 2)(y + 2)$

Check: $(y - 5)(y - 2)(y + 2) = (y - 5)(y^2 - 2y + 2y - 4)$

$= (y - 5)(y^2 - 4)$

$= (y^3 - 4y - 5y^2 + 20)$

$= y^3 - 5y^2 - 4y + 20 \checkmark$

2. Factoring Perfect Square Trinomials

Recall from Section 12.6 that the square of a binomial always results in a **perfect square trinomial**.

$$(a + b)^2 = (a + b)(a + b) \xrightarrow{\text{Multiply.}} = a^2 + 2ab + b^2$$

$$(a - b)^2 = (a - b)(a - b) \xrightarrow{\text{Multiply.}} = a^2 - 2ab + b^2$$

For example, $(3x + 5)^2 = (3x)^2 + 2(3x)(5) + (5)^2$

$$= 9x^2 + 30x + 25 \text{ (perfect square trinomial)}$$

We now want to reverse this process by factoring a perfect square trinomial. The trial-and-error method or the ac-method can always be used; however, if we recognize the pattern for a perfect square trinomial, we can use one of the following formulas to reach a quick solution.

> **FORMULA**   **Factored Form of a Perfect Square Trinomial**
>
> $$a^2 + 2ab + b^2 = (a + b)^2$$
> $$a^2 - 2ab + b^2 = (a - b)^2$$

For example, $9x^2 + 30x + 25$ is a perfect square trinomial with $a = 3x$ and $b = 5$. Therefore, it factors as

$$9x^2 + 30x + 25 = (3x)^2 + 2(3x)(5) + (5)^2 = (3x + 5)^2$$
$$a^2 \quad + 2 \ (a) \ (b) + (b)^2 = (a + b)^2$$

Answer

7. $(p - 3)(p + 3)(p + 7)$

To apply the formula to factor a perfect square trinomial, we must first be sure that the trinomial is indeed a perfect square trinomial.

PROCEDURE Checking for a Perfect Square Trinomial

Step 1 Determine whether the first and third terms are both perfect squares and have positive coefficients.

Step 2 If this is the case, identify a and b, and determine if the middle term equals $2ab$ or $-2ab$.

Example 5 Factoring Perfect Square Trinomials

Factor the trinomials completely.

a. $x^2 + 14x + 49$ **b.** $25y^2 - 20y + 4$

Solution:

a. $x^2 + 14x + 49$ The GCF is 1.

- The first and third terms are positive.

- The first term is a perfect square: $x^2 = (x)^2$.

Perfect squares

$x^2 + 14x + 49$

- The third term is a perfect square: $49 = (7)^2$.

- The middle term is twice the product of x and 7: $14x = 2(x)(7)$

$= (x)^2 + 2(x)(7) + (7)^2$ The trinomial is in the form $a^2 + 2ab + b^2$, where $a = x$ and $b = 7$.

$= (x + 7)^2$ Factor as $(a + b)^2$.

b. $25y^2 - 20y + 4$ The GCF is 1.

Perfect squares

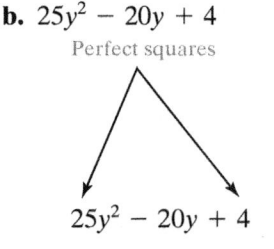

$25y^2 - 20y + 4$

- The first and third terms are positive.

- The first term is a perfect square: $25y^2 = (5y)^2$.

- The third term is a perfect square: $4 = (2)^2$.

$= (5y)^2 - 2(5y)(2) + (2)^2$ • In the middle: $20y = 2(5y)(2)$

$= (5y - 2)^2$ Factor as $(a - b)^2$.

Skill Practice

Factor completely.

8. $x^2 - 6x + 9$

9. $81w^2 + 72w + 16$

TIP: The sign of the middle term in a perfect square trinomial determines the sign within the binomial of the factored form.

$a^2 + 2ab + b^2 = (a + b)^2$

$a^2 - 2ab + b^2 = (a - b)^2$

Answers

8. $(x - 3)^2$

9. $(9w + 4)^2$

Example 6 **Factoring Perfect Square Trinomials**

Factor the trinomials completely.

a. $18c^3 - 48c^2d + 32cd^2$ **b.** $5w^2 + 50w + 45$

Solution:

a. $18c^3 - 48c^2d + 32cd^2$

$= 2c(9c^2 - 24cd + 16d^2)$ The GCF is $2c$.

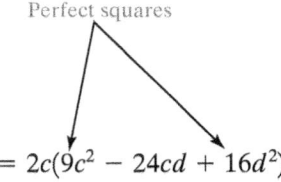

Perfect squares

$= 2c(9c^2 - 24cd + 16d^2)$

- The first and third terms are positive.
- The first term is a perfect square: $9c^2 = (3c)^2$.
- The third term is a perfect square: $16d^2 = (4d)^2$.

$= 2c[(3c)^2 - 2(3c)(4d) + (4d)^2]$ • In the middle: $24cd = 2(3c)(4d)$

$= 2c(3c - 4d)^2$ Factor as $(a - b)^2$.

b. $5w^2 + 50w + 45$

$= 5(w^2 + 10w + 9)$ The GCF is 5.

Perfect squares

The first and third terms are perfect squares.

$$w^2 = (w)^2 \quad \text{and} \quad 9 = (3)^2$$

$= 5(w^2 + 10w + 9)$

However, the middle term is not 2 times the product of w and 3. Therefore, this is not a perfect square trinomial.

$$10w \neq 2(w)(3)$$

$= 5(w + 9)(w + 1)$ To factor, use the trial-and-error method.

TIP: To help you identify a perfect square trinomial, we recommend that you familiarize yourself with the first several perfect squares.

$(1)^2 = 1$	$(6)^2 = 36$	$(11)^2 = 121$
$(2)^2 = 4$	$(7)^2 = 49$	$(12)^2 = 144$
$(3)^2 = 9$	$(8)^2 = 64$	$(13)^2 = 169$
$(4)^2 = 16$	$(9)^2 = 81$	$(14)^2 = 196$
$(5)^2 = 25$	$(10)^2 = 100$	$(15)^2 = 225$

If you do not recognize that a trinomial is a perfect square trinomial, you may still use the trial-and-error method or ac-method to factor it.

Section 13.5 Practice Exercises

Study Skills Exercise

1. Define the key terms:

    a. Difference of squares   **b. Sum of squares**   **c. Perfect square trinomial**

Review Exercises

For Exercises 2–10, factor completely.

2. $3x^2 + x - 10$ **3.** $6x^2 - 17x + 5$ **4.** $6a^2b + 3a^3b$

5. $15x^2y^5 - 10xy^6$ **6.** $5p^2q + 20p^2 - 3pq - 12p$ **7.** $ax + ab - 6x - 6b$

8. $-6x + 5 + x^2$ **9.** $6y - 40 + y^2$ **10.** $a^2 + 7a + 1$

Objective 1: Factoring a Difference of Squares

11. What binomial factors as $(x - 5)(x + 5)$?   **12.** What binomial factors as $(n - 3)(n + 3)$?

13. What binomial factors as $(2p - 3q)(2p + 3q)$?   **14.** What binomial factors as $(7x - 4y)(7x + 4y)$?

For Exercises 15–38, factor the binomials completely. **(See Examples 1–3.)**

15. $x^2 - 36$ **16.** $r^2 - 81$ **17.** $3w^2 - 300$ **18.** $t^3 - 49t$

19. $4a^2 - 121b^2$ **20.** $9x^2 - y^2$ **21.** $49m^2 - 16n^2$ **22.** $100a^2 - 49b^2$

23. $9q^2 + 16$ **24.** $36 + s^2$ **25.** $y^2 - 4z^2$ **26.** $b^2 - 144c^2$

27. $a^2 - b^4$ **28.** $y^4 - x^2$ **29.** $25p^2q^2 - 1$ **30.** $81s^2t^2 - 1$

31. $c^6 - 25$ **32.** $z^6 - 4$ **33.** $50 - 32t^2$ **34.** $63 - 7h^2$

35. $z^4 - 16$ **36.** $y^4 - 625$ **37.** $a^4 - \dfrac{1}{81}$ **38.** $\dfrac{1}{16} - z^4$

For Exercises 39–46, factor the polynomials completely. **(See Example 4.)**

39. $x^3 + 5x^2 - 9x - 45$ **40.** $b^3 + 6b^2 - 4b - 24$ **41.** $c^3 - c^2 - 25c + 25$ **42.** $t^3 + 2t^2 - 16t - 32$

43. $2x^2 - 18 + x^2y - 9y$ **44.** $5a^2 - 5 + a^2b - b$ **45.** $x^2y^2 - 9x^2 - 4y^2 + 36$ **46.** $w^2z^2 - w^2 - 25z^2 + 25$

Objective 2: Factoring Perfect Square Trinomials

47. Multiply. $(3x + 5)^2$ **48.** Multiply. $(2y - 7)^2$

49. a. Which trinomial is a perfect square
    trinomial? $x^2 + 4x + 4$ or $x^2 + 5x + 4$

    b. Factor the trinomials from part (a).

50. a. Which trinomial is a perfect square trinomial?
    $x^2 + 13x + 36$ or $x^2 + 12x + 36$

    b. Factor the trinomials from part (a).

For Exercises 51–68, factor completely. (*Hint:* Look for the pattern of a perfect square trinomial.) **(See Examples 5–6.)**

51. $x^2 + 18x + 81$

52. $y^2 - 8y + 16$

53. $25z^2 - 20z + 4$

54. $36p^2 + 60p + 25$

55. $49a^2 + 42ab + 9b^2$

56. $25m^2 - 30mn + 9n^2$

57. $-2y + y^2 + 1$

58. $4 + w^2 - 4w$

59. $80z^2 + 120zw + 45w^2$

60. $36p^2 - 24pq + 4q^2$

61. $9y^2 + 78y + 25$

62. $4y^2 + 20y + 9$

63. $2a^2 - 20a + 50$

64. $3t^2 + 18t + 27$

65. $4x^2 + x + 9$

66. $c^2 - 4c + 16$

67. $4x^2 + 4xy + y^2$

68. $100y^2 + 20yz + z^2$

Expanding Your Skills

For Exercises 69–76, factor the difference of squares.

69. $(y - 3)^2 - 9$

70. $(x - 2)^2 - 4$

71. $(2p + 1)^2 - 36$

72. $(4q + 3)^2 - 25$

73. $16 - (t + 2)^2$

74. $81 - (a + 5)^2$

75. $100 - (2b - 5)^2$

76. $49 - (3k - 7)^2$

77. a. Write a polynomial that represents the area of the shaded region in the figure.

    b. Factor the expression from part (a).

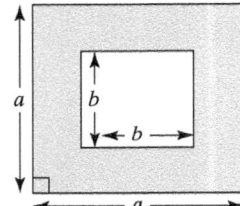

78. a. Write a polynomial that represents the area of the shaded region in the figure.

    b. Factor the expression from part (a).

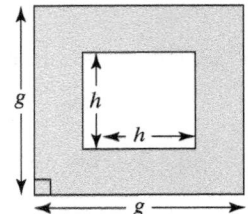

Problem Recognition Exercises

Factoring Strategy

PROCEDURE Factoring Strategy

Step 1 Factor out the GCF (Section 13.1).

Step 2 Identify whether the polynomial has two terms, three terms, or more than three terms.

Step 3 If the polynomial has more than three terms, try factoring by grouping (Section 13.1).

Step 4 If the polynomial has three terms, check first for a perfect square trinomial. Otherwise, factor the trinomial with the trial-and-error method or the ac-method (Sections 13.3 or 13.4).

Step 5 If the polynomial has two terms, determine if it fits the pattern for
   • A difference of squares: $a^2 - b^2 = (a - b)(a + b)$ (Section 13.5)
   • A sum of squares: $a^2 + b^2$ prime

Step 6 Be sure to factor the polynomial completely.

Step 7 Check by multiplying.

1. What is meant by a prime factor?

2. What is the first step in factoring any polynomial?

3. When factoring a binomial, what patterns can you look for?

4. What technique should be considered when factoring a four-term polynomial?

For Exercises 5–66,

a. Factor out the GCF from each polynomial. Then identify the category in which the polynomial best fits. Choose from
- difference of squares
- sum of squares
- trinomial (perfect square trinomial)
- trinomial (nonperfect square trinomial)
- four terms-grouping
- none of these

b. Factor the polynomial completely.

5. $2a^2 - 162$

6. $y^2 + 4y + 3$

7. $6w^2 - 6w$

8. $16z^4 - 81$

9. $3t^2 + 13t + 4$

10. $3ac + ad - 3bc - bd$

11. $7p^2 - 29p + 4$

12. $3q^2 - 9q - 12$

13. $-2x^2 + 8x - 8$

14. $18a^2 + 12a$

15. $4t^2 - 100$

16. $4t^2 - 31t - 8$

17. $10c^2 + 10c + 10$

18. $2xw - 10x + 3yw - 15y$

19. $4q^2 - 9$

20. $64 + 16k + k^2$

21. $s^2t + 5t + 6s^2 + 30$

22. $2x^2 + 2x - xy - y$

23. $3y^2 + y + 1$

24. $c^2 + 8c + 9$

25. $a^2 + 2a + 1$

26. $b^2 + 10b + 25$

27. $-t^2 - 4t + 32$

28. $-p^3 - 5p^2 - 4p$

29. $x^2y^2 - 49$

30. $6x^2 - 21x - 45$

31. $20y^2 - 14y + 2$

32. $5a^2bc^3 - 7abc^2$

33. $8a^2 - 50$

34. $t^2 + 2t - 63$

35. $b^2 + 2b - 80$

36. $ab + ay - b^2 - by$

37. $6x^3y^4 + 3x^2y^5$

38. $14u^2 - 11uv + 2v^2$

39. $9p^2 - 36pq + 4q^2$

40. $4q^2 - 8q - 6$

41. $9w^2 + 3w - 15$

42. $9m^2 + 16n^2$

43. $5b^2 - 30b + 45$

44. $6r^2 + 11r + 3$

45. $4s^2 + 4s - 15$

46. $16a^4 - 1$

47. $p^3 + p^2c - 9p - 9c$

48. $81u^2 - 90uv + 25v^2$

49. $4x^2 + 16$

50. $x^2 - 5x - 6$

51. $q^2 + q - 7$

52. $2ax - 6ay + 4bx - 12by$

53. $8m^3 - 10m^2 - 3m$

54. $21x^4y + 41x^3y + 10x^2y$

55. $2m^4 - 128$

56. $8uv - 6u + 12v - 9$

57. $4t^2 - 20t + st - 5s$

58. $12x^2 - 12x + 3$

59. $p^2 + 2pq + q^2$

60. $6n^3 + 5n^2 - 4n$

61. $4k^3 + 4k^2 - 3k$

62. $64 - y^2$

63. $36b - b^3$

64. $b^2 - 4b + 10$

65. $y^2 + 6y + 8$

66. $c^4 - 12c^2 + 20$

Section 13.6 Solving Equations Using the Zero Product Rule

Objectives

1. Definition of a Quadratic Equation
2. Zero Product Rule
3. Solving Equations by Factoring

1. Definition of a Quadratic Equation

In Section 9.2, we solved linear equations in one variable. These are equations of the form $ax + b = c \, (a \neq 0)$. A linear equation in one variable is sometimes called a first-degree polynomial equation because the highest degree of all its terms is 1. A second-degree polynomial equation in one variable is called a quadratic equation.

> **DEFINITION   A Quadratic Equation in One Variable**
> If a, b, and c are real numbers such that $a \neq 0$, then a **quadratic equation** is an equation that can be written in the form
> $$ax^2 + bx + c = 0$$

The following equations are quadratic because they can each be written in the form $ax^2 + bx + c = 0, (a \neq 0)$.

$$-4x^2 + 4x = 1 \qquad x(x - 2) = 3 \qquad (x - 4)(x + 4) = 9$$
$$-4x^2 + 4x - 1 = 0 \qquad x^2 - 2x = 3 \qquad x^2 - 16 = 9$$
$$x^2 - 2x - 3 = 0 \qquad x^2 - 25 = 0$$
$$x^2 + 0x - 25 = 0$$

2. Zero Product Rule

One method for solving a quadratic equation is to factor and apply the zero product rule. The **zero product rule** states that if the product of two factors is zero, then one or both of its factors is zero.

> **PROPERTY   Zero Product Rule**
> If $ab = 0$, then $a = 0$ or $b = 0$.

Example 1 **Using the Zero Product Rule**

Solve the equation by using the zero product rule. $(x - 4)(x + 3) = 0$

Solution:

$(x - 4)(x + 3) = 0$ Apply the zero product rule.

$x - 4 = 0$ or $x + 3 = 0$ Set each factor equal to zero.

$x = 4$ or $x = -3$ Solve each equation for x.

Check: $x = 4$ Check: $x = -3$

$(4 - 4)(4 + 3) \overset{?}{=} 0$ $(-3 - 4)(-3 + 3) \overset{?}{=} 0$

$(0)(7) \overset{?}{=} 0$ ✔ $(-7)(0) \overset{?}{=} 0$ ✔

The solutions are 4 and -3.

Skill Practice

1. Solve.
 $(x + 1)(x - 8) = 0$

Example 2 **Using the Zero Product Rule**

Solve the equation by using the zero product rule. $(2x + 1)(x - 5) = 0$

Solution:

$(2x + 1)(x - 5) = 0$ Apply the zero product rule.

$2x + 1 = 0$ or $x - 5 = 0$ Set each factor equal to zero.

$2x = -1$ or $x = 5$ Solve each equation for x.

$x = -\dfrac{1}{2}$ or $x = 5$

The solutions $-\dfrac{1}{2}$ and 5 check in the original equation.

Skill Practice

2. Solve.
 $(4x - 5)(x + 6) = 0$

Example 3 **Using the Zero Product Rule**

Solve the equation using the zero product rule. $x(3x - 7) = 0$

Solution:

$x(3x - 7) = 0$ Apply the zero product rule.

$x = 0$ or $3x - 7 = 0$ Set each factor equal to zero.

$x = 0$ or $3x = 7$ Solve each equation for x.

$x = 0$ or $x = \dfrac{7}{3}$

The solutions 0 and $\dfrac{7}{3}$ check in the original equation.

Skill Practice

3. Solve.
 $x(4x + 9) = 0$

Answers

1. $-1, 8$ **2.** $\dfrac{5}{4}, -6$ **3.** $0, -\dfrac{9}{4}$

3. Solving Equations by Factoring

Quadratic equations, like linear equations, arise in many applications in mathematics, science, and business. The following steps summarize the factoring method for solving a quadratic equation.

PROCEDURE Solving a Quadratic Equation by Factoring

Step 1 Write the equation in the form: $ax^2 + bx + c = 0$.

Step 2 Factor the quadratic expression completely.

Step 3 Apply the zero product rule. That is, set each factor equal to zero, and solve the resulting equations.

Note: The solution(s) found in step 3 may be checked by substitution in the original equation.

Skill Practice

Solve the equation.

4. $2y^2 + 19y = -24$

Example 4   **Solving a Quadratic Equation**

Solve the quadratic equation. $2x^2 - 9x = 5$

Solution:

$$2x^2 - 9x = 5$$

$$2x^2 - 9x - 5 = 0 \qquad \text{Write the equation in the form } ax^2 + bx + c = 0.$$

$$(2x + 1)(x - 5) = 0 \qquad \text{Factor the polynomial completely.}$$

$$2x + 1 = 0 \quad \text{or} \quad x - 5 = 0 \qquad \text{Set each factor equal to zero.}$$

$$2x = -1 \quad \text{or} \quad x = 5 \qquad \text{Solve each equation.}$$

$$x = -\frac{1}{2} \quad \text{or} \quad x = 5$$

$$\underline{\text{Check: } x = -\frac{1}{2}} \qquad\qquad \underline{\text{Check: } x = 5}$$

$$2x^2 - 9x = 5 \qquad\qquad 2x^2 - 9x = 5$$

$$2\left(-\frac{1}{2}\right)^2 - 9\left(-\frac{1}{2}\right) \overset{?}{=} 5 \qquad 2(5)^2 - 9(5) \overset{?}{=} 5$$

$$2\left(\frac{1}{4}\right) + \frac{9}{2} \overset{?}{=} 5 \qquad\qquad 2(25) - 45 \overset{?}{=} 5$$

$$\frac{1}{2} + \frac{9}{2} \overset{?}{=} 5 \qquad\qquad 50 - 45 \overset{?}{=} 5 \checkmark$$

$$\frac{10}{2} \overset{?}{=} 5 \checkmark$$

The solutions are $-\frac{1}{2}$ and 5.

Answer

4. $-8, -\frac{3}{2}$

Example 5 Solving a Quadratic Equation

Solve the quadratic equation. $4x^2 + 24x = 0$

Solution:

$4x^2 + 24x = 0$ The equation is already in the form $ax^2 + bx + c = 0$. (Note that $c = 0$.)

$4x(x + 6) = 0$ Factor completely.

$4x = 0$ or $x + 6 = 0$ Set each factor equal to zero.

$x = 0$ or $x = -6$

The solutions are 0 and -6. They both check in the original equation.

Example 6 Solving a Quadratic Equation

Solve the quadratic equation. $5x(5x + 2) = 10x + 9$

Solution:

$5x(5x + 2) = 10x + 9$

$25x^2 + 10x = 10x + 9$ Clear parentheses.

$25x^2 + 10x - 10x - 9 = 0$ Set the equation equal to zero.

$25x^2 - 9 = 0$ The equation is in the form $ax^2 + bx + c = 0$. (Note that $b = 0$.)

$(5x - 3)(5x + 3) = 0$ Factor completely.

$5x - 3 = 0$ or $5x + 3 = 0$ Set each factor equal to zero.

$5x = 3$ or $5x = -3$ Solve each equation.

$\dfrac{5x}{5} = \dfrac{3}{5}$ or $\dfrac{5x}{5} = \dfrac{-3}{5}$

$x = \dfrac{3}{5}$ or $x = -\dfrac{3}{5}$

The solutions are $\dfrac{3}{5}$ and $-\dfrac{3}{5}$. They both check in the original equation.

The zero product rule can be used to solve higher degree polynomial equations provided the equations can be set to zero and written in factored form.

Skill Practice

Solve the equation.

7. $5(p - 4)(p + 7)$
$(2p - 9) = 0$

Example 7 Solving Higher Degree Polynomial Equations

Solve the equation. $-6(y + 3)(y - 5)(2y + 7) = 0$

Solution:

$-6(y + 3)(y - 5)(2y + 7) = 0$ The equation is already in factored form and equal to zero.

Set each factor equal to zero.

Solve each equation for y.

$-6 = 0$ or $y + 3 = 0$ or $y - 5 = 0$ or $2y + 7 = 0$

No solution, $y = -3$ or $y = 5$ or $y = -\dfrac{7}{2}$

Notice that when the constant factor is set equal to zero, the result is a contradiction, $-6 = 0$. The constant factor does not produce a solution to the equation. Therefore, the only solutions are $-3, 5$, and $-\frac{7}{2}$. Each solution can be checked in the original equation.

Skill Practice

Solve the equation.

8. $x^3 + 3x^2 - 4x$
$- 12 = 0$

Example 8 Solving a Higher Degree Polynomial Equation

Solve the equation. $w^3 + 5w^2 - 9w - 45 = 0$

Solution:

$w^3 + 5w^2 - 9w - 45 = 0$ This is a higher degree polynomial equation.

$w^3 + 5w^2 - 9w - 45 = 0$ The equation is already set equal to zero. Now factor.

$w^2(w + 5) - 9(w + 5) = 0$ Because there are four terms, try factoring
$(w + 5)(w^2 - 9) = 0$ by grouping.

$(w + 5)(w - 3)(w + 3) = 0$ $w^2 - 9$ is a difference of squares and can be factored further.

$w + 5 = 0$ or $w - 3 = 0$ or $w + 3 = 0$ Set each factor equal to zero.

$w = -5$ or $w = 3$ or $w = -3$ Solve each equation.

Answers

7. $4, -7, \dfrac{9}{2}$ **8.** $-2, -3, 2$

The solutions are $-5, -3$ and 3. Each solution checks in the original equation.

Section 13.6   Practice Exercises

Study Skills Exercise

1. Define the key terms:

a. Quadratic equation   **b. Zero product rule**

Review Exercises

For Exercises 2–7, factor completely.

2. $6a - 8 - 3ab + 4b$

3. $4b^2 - 44b + 120$

4. $8u^2v^2 - 4uv$

5. $3x^2 + 10x - 8$

6. $3h^2 - 75$

7. $4x^2 + 16y^2$

Objective 1: Definition of a Quadratic Equation

For Exercises 8–13, identify the equations as linear, quadratic, or neither.

8. $4 - 5x = 0$

9. $5x^3 + 2 = 0$

10. $3x - 6x^2 = 0$

11. $1 - x + 2x^2 = 0$

12. $7x^4 + 8 = 0$

13. $3x + 2 = 0$

Objective 2: Zero Product Rule

For Exercises 14–22, solve the equations using the zero product rule. **(See Examples 1–3.)**

14. $(x - 5)(x + 1) = 0$

15. $(x + 3)(x - 1) = 0$

16. $(3x - 2)(3x + 2) = 0$

17. $(2x - 7)(2x + 7) = 0$

18. $2(x - 7)(x - 7) = 0$

19. $3(x + 5)(x + 5) = 0$

20. $(3x - 2)(2x - 3) = 0$

21. $x(5x - 1) = 0$

22. $x(3x + 8) = 0$

23. For a quadratic equation of the form $ax^2 + bx + c = 0$, what must be done before applying the zero product rule?

24. What are the requirements needed to use the zero product rule to solve a quadratic equation or higher degree polynomial equation?

Objective 3: Solving Equations by Factoring

For Exercises 25–72, solve the equations. **(See Examples 4–8.)**

25. $p^2 - 2p - 15 = 0$

26. $y^2 - 7y - 8 = 0$

27. $z^2 + 10z - 24 = 0$

28. $w^2 - 10w + 16 = 0$

29. $2q^2 - 7q = 4$

30. $4x^2 - 11x = 3$

31. $0 = 9x^2 - 4$

32. $4a^2 - 49 = 0$

33. $2k^2 - 28k + 96 = 0$

34. $0 = 2t^2 + 20t + 50$

35. $0 = 2m^3 - 5m^2 - 12m$

36. $3n^3 + 4n^2 + n = 0$

37. $5(3p + 1)(p - 3)(p + 6) = 0$

38. $4(2x - 1)(x - 10)(x + 7) = 0$

39. $x(x - 4)(2x + 3) = 0$

40. $x(3x + 1)(x + 1) = 0$

41. $-5x(2x + 9)(x - 11) = 0$

42. $-3x(x + 7)(3x - 5) = 0$

43. $x^3 - 16x = 0$

44. $t^3 - 36t = 0$

45. $3x^2 + 18x = 0$

46. $2y^2 - 20y = 0$

47. $16m^2 = 9$

48. $9n^2 = 1$

49. $2y^3 + 14y^2 = -20y$

50. $3d^3 - 6d^2 = 24d$

51. $5t - 2(t - 7) = 0$

52. $8h = 5(h - 9) + 6$

53. $2c(c - 8) = -30$

54. $3q(q - 3) = 12$

55. $b^3 = -4b^2 - 4b$

56. $x^3 + 36x = 12x^2$

57. $3(a^2 + 2a) = 2a^2 - 9$

58. $9(k - 1) = -4k^2$

59. $2n(n + 2) = 6$

60. $3p(p - 1) = 18$

61. $x(2x + 5) - 1 = 2x^2 + 3x + 2$

62. $3z(z - 2) - z = 3z^2 + 4$

63. $27q^2 = 9q$

64. $21w^2 = 14w$

65. $3(c^2 - 2c) = 0$

66. $2(4d^2 + d) = 0$

67. $y^3 - 3y^2 - 4y + 12 = 0$

68. $t^3 + 2t^2 - 16t - 32 = 0$

69. $(x - 1)(x + 2) = 18$

70. $(w + 5)(w - 3) = 20$

71. $(p + 2)(p + 3) = 1 - p$

72. $(k - 6)(k - 1) = -k - 2$

Problem Recognition Exercises

Polynomial Expressions and Polynomial Equations

For Exercises 1–30, factor each expression and solve each equation.

1. a. $x^2 + 6x - 7$
  b. $x^2 + 6x - 7 = 0$

2. a. $c^2 + 8c + 12$
  b. $c^2 + 8c + 12 = 0$

3. a. $2y^2 + 7y + 3$
  b. $2y^2 + 7y + 3 = 0$

4. a. $3x^2 - 8x + 5$
  b. $3x^2 - 8x + 5 = 0$

5. a. $5q^2 + q - 4 = 0$
  b. $5q^2 + q - 4$

6. a. $6a^2 - 7a - 3 = 0$
  b. $6a^2 - 7a - 3$

7. a. $4b^2 - 81$
  b. $4b^2 - 81 = 0$

8. a. $36t^2 - 49$
  b. $36t^2 - 49 = 0$

9. a. $8x^2 + 16x + 6 = 0$
  b. $8x^2 + 16x + 6$

10. a. $12y^2 + 40y + 32 = 0$
  b. $12y^2 + 40y + 32$

11. a. $x^3 - 8x^2 - 20x$
  b. $x^3 - 8x^2 - 20x = 0$

12. a. $k^3 + 5k^2 - 14k$
  b. $k^3 + 5k^2 - 14k = 0$

13. a. $b^3 + b^2 - 9b - 9 = 0$
  b. $b^3 + b^2 - 9b - 9$

14. a. $x^3 - 8x^2 - 4x + 32 = 0$
  b. $x^3 - 8x^2 - 4x + 32$

15. $2s^2 - 6s + rs - 3r$

16. $6t^2 + 3t + 10tu + 5u$

17. $8x^3 - 2x = 0$

18. $2b^3 - 50b = 0$

19. $2x^3 - 4x^2 + 2x = 0$

20. $3t^3 + 18t^2 + 27t = 0$

21. $7c^2 - 2c + 3 = 7(c^2 + c)$

22. $3z(2z + 4) = -7 + 6z^2$

23. $5z^2 + 2z = 7$

24. $4h^2 + 25h = -6$

25. $3b(b + 6) = b - 10$

26. $3y^2 + 1 = y(y - 3)$

27. $5(2x - 3) - 2(3x + 1) = 4 - 3x$

28. $11 - 6a = -4(2a - 3) - 1$

29. $(x - 3)(x - 4) = 6$

30. $(x + 5)(x + 9) = 21$

Applications of Quadratic Equations

1. Applications of Quadratic Equations

Example 1 Translating to a Quadratic Equation

The product of two consecutive integers is 48 more than the larger integer. Find the integers.

Solution:

Let x represent the first (smaller) integer.

Then $x + 1$ represents the second (larger) integer.   Label the variables.

(First integer)(second integer) = (second integer) + 48   Verbal model

$$x(x + 1) = (x + 1) + 48 \qquad \text{Algebraic equation}$$

$$x^2 + x = x + 49 \qquad \text{Simplify.}$$

$$x^2 + x - x - 49 = 0 \qquad \text{Set one side of the equation equal to zero.}$$

$$x^2 - 49 = 0$$

$$(x - 7)(x + 7) = 0 \qquad \text{Factor.}$$

$x - 7 = 0 \quad$ or $\quad x + 7 = 0 \qquad$ Set each factor equal to zero.

$x = 7 \quad$ or $\quad x = -7 \qquad$ Solve for x.

Recall that x represents the smaller integer. Therefore, there are two possibilities for the pairs of consecutive integers.

If $x = 7$, then the larger integer is $x + 1$ or $7 + 1 = 8$.

If $x = -7$, then the larger integer is $x + 1$ or $-7 + 1 = -6$.

The integers are 7 and 8, or -7 and -6.

Skill Practice

1. The product of two consecutive odd integers is 9 more than 10 times the smaller integer. Find the pair of integers.

Example 2 Using a Quadratic Equation in a Geometry Application

A rectangular sign has an area of 40 ft². If the width is 3 feet shorter than the length, what are the dimensions of the sign?

Solution:

Let x represent the length of the sign.   Label the variables.
Then $x - 3$ represents the width (Figure 13-1).

The problem gives information about the length of the sides and about the area. Therefore, we can form a relationship by using the formula for the area of a rectangle.

$x - 3$

x

Figure 13-1

Skill Practice

2. The length of a rectangle is 5 ft more than the width. The area is 36 ft². Find the length and width.

$A = l \cdot w$	Area equals length times width.
$40 = x(x - 3)$	Set up an algebraic equation.
$40 = x^2 - 3x$	Clear parentheses.
$0 = x^2 - 3x - 40$	Write the equation in the form, $ax^2 + bx + c = 0$.
$0 = (x - 8)(x + 5)$	Factor.
$0 = x - 8$ or $0 = x + 5$	Set each factor equal to zero.
$8 = x$ or $-5 \cancel{=} x$	Because x represents the length of a rectangle, reject the negative solution.

The variable x represents the length of the sign. The length is 8 ft.

The expression $x - 3$ represents the width. The width is 8 ft − 3 ft, or 5 ft.

Skill Practice

3. An object is launched into the air from the ground and its height is given by $h = -16t^2 + 144t$, where h is the height in feet after t seconds. Find the time required for the object to hit the ground.

Example 3 **Using a Quadratic Equation in an Application**

A stone is dropped off a 64-ft cliff and falls into the ocean below. The height of the stone above sea level is given by the equation

$h = -16t^2 + 64$ where h is the stone's height in feet, and t is the time in seconds.

Find the time required for the stone to hit the water.

Solution:

When the stone hits the water, its height is zero. Therefore, substitute $h = 0$ into the equation.

$h = -16t^2 + 64$	The equation is quadratic.
$0 = -16t^2 + 64$	Substitute $h = 0$.
$0 = -16(t^2 - 4)$	Factor out the GCF.
$0 = -16(t - 2)(t + 2)$	Factor as a difference of squares.
$-16 \cancel{=} 0$ or $t - 2 = 0$ or $t + 2 = 0$	Set each factor to zero.
No solution, $\quad t = 2$ or $t \cancel{=} -2$	Solve for t.

The negative value of t is rejected because the stone cannot fall for a negative time. Therefore, the stone hits the water after 2 seconds.

Answer

3. 9 seconds

In Example 3, we can analyze the path of the stone as it falls from the cliff. Use the equation $h = -16t^2 + 64$ to compute the height values at various times between 0 and 2 seconds (Table 13-1). The ordered pairs can be graphed where t is used in place of x and h is used in place of y. The graph of the height of the stone versus time is shown in Figure 13-2.

Table 13-1

Time, t (sec)	Height, h (ft)
0.0	64
0.5	60
1.0	48
1.5	28
2.0	0

Figure 13-2

2. Pythagorean Theorem

Recall that a right triangle is a triangle that contains a 90° angle. Furthermore, the Pythagorean theorem tells us that for a right triangle, the sum of the squares of the two legs equals the square of the hypotenuse (see Section 7.6). For the right triangle shown in Figure 13-3, the Pythagorean theorem is stated as:

$$a^2 + b^2 = c^2$$

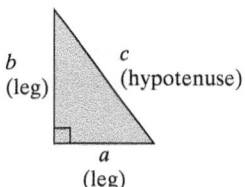

Figure 13-3

The Pythagorean theorem is used to write quadratic equations for the applications in Examples 4 and 5.

Example 4 **Applying the Pythagorean Theorem**

Find the length of the missing side of the right triangle.

Solution:

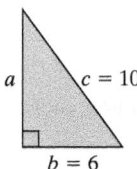

Label the triangle.

$a^2 + b^2 = c^2$ Apply the Pythagorean theorem.

$a^2 + 6^2 = 10^2$ Substitute $b = 6$ and $c = 10$.

$a^2 + 36 = 100$ Simplify.

The equation is quadratic. Set one side of the equation equal to zero.

Skill Practice

4. Find the length of the missing side.

Answer

4. The length of the third side is 12 m.

$$a^2 + 36 - 100 = 100 - 100 \quad \text{Subtract 100 from both sides.}$$

$$a^2 - 64 = 0$$

$$(a + 8)(a - 8) = 0 \quad \text{Factor.}$$

$$a + 8 = 0 \text{ or } a - 8 = 0 \quad \text{Set each factor equal to zero.}$$

$$a \cancel{=} -8 \text{ or } a = 8 \quad \text{Because } x \text{ represents the length of a side of a triangle, reject the negative solution.}$$

The third side is 8 ft.

Skill Practice

5. A 5-yd ladder leans against a wall. The distance from the bottom of the wall to the top of the ladder is 1 yd more than the distance from the bottom of the wall to the bottom of the ladder. Find both distances.

5 yd, $x + 1$, x

Example 5 **Using a Quadratic Equation in an Application**

A 13-ft board is used as a ramp to unload furniture off a loading platform. If the distance between the top of the board and the ground is 7 ft less than the distance between the bottom of the board and the base of the platform, find both distances.

Solution:

Let x represent the distance between the bottom of the board and the base of the platform. Then $x - 7$ represents the distance between the top of the board and the ground (Figure 13-4).

13 ft, $x - 7$, x

Figure 13-4

$$a^2 + b^2 = c^2 \quad \text{Pythagorean theorem}$$

$$x^2 + (x - 7)^2 = (13)^2$$

$$x^2 + (x)^2 - 2(x)(7) + (7)^2 = 169$$

$$x^2 + x^2 - 14x + 49 = 169$$

$$2x^2 - 14x + 49 = 169 \quad \text{Combine } like \text{ terms.}$$

$$2x^2 - 14x + 49 - 169 = 169 - 169 \quad \text{Set the equation equal to zero.}$$

$$2x^2 - 14x - 120 = 0 \quad \text{Write the equation in the form } ax^2 + bx + c = 0.$$

$$2(x^2 - 7x - 60) = 0 \quad \text{Factor.}$$

$$2(x - 12)(x + 5) = 0$$

$$2 \cancel{=} 0 \quad \text{or} \quad x - 12 = 0 \quad \text{or} \quad x + 5 = 0 \quad \text{Set each factor equal to zero.}$$

$$x = 12 \quad \text{or} \quad x \cancel{=} -5 \quad \text{Solve both equations for } x.$$

Avoiding Mistakes

Recall that the square of a binomial results in a perfect square trinomial.

$$(a - b)^2 = a^2 - 2ab + b^2$$

Don't forget the middle term.

Recall that x represents the distance between the bottom of the board and the base of the platform. We reject the negative value of x because a distance cannot be negative. Therefore, the distance between the bottom of the board and the base of the platform is 12 ft. The distance between the top of the board and the ground is $x - 7 = 5$ ft.

Answer

5. The distance along the wall to the top of the ladder is 4 yd. The distance on the ground from the ladder to the wall is 3 yd.

Section 13.7 Practice Exercises

Review Exercises

For Exercises 1–8, solve the quadratic equations.

1. $(6x + 1)(x + 4) = 0$

2. $9x(3x + 2) = 0$

3. $49x^2 - 25 = 0$

4. $4x^2 - 1 = 0$

5. $x^2 - 5x = 6$

6. $6x^2 - 7x = 10$

7. $x(x - 18) = -81$

8. $x(x - 20) = -100$

Objective 1: Applications of Quadratic Equations

9. If eleven is added to the square of a number, the result is sixty. Find all such numbers.

10. If a number is added to two times its square, the result is thirty-six. Find all such numbers.

11. If twelve is added to six times a number, the result is twenty-eight less than the square of the number. Find all such numbers.

12. The square of a number is equal to twenty more than the number. Find all such numbers.

13. The product of two consecutive odd integers is sixty-three. Find all such integers. **(See Example 1.)**

14. The product of two consecutive even integers is forty-eight. Find all such integers.

15. The sum of the squares of two consecutive integers is one more than ten times the larger number. Find all such integers.

16. The sum of the squares of two consecutive integers is nine less than ten times the sum of the integers. Find all such integers.

17. The length of a rectangular room is 5 yd more than the width. If 300 yd^2 of carpeting cover the room, what are the dimensions of the room? **(See Example 2.)**

18. The width of a rectangular painting is 2 in. less than the length. The area is 120 in.^{2} Find the length and width.

19. The width of a rectangular slab of concrete is 3 m less than the length. The area is 28 m^2.

  a. What are the dimensions of the rectangle?

  b. What is the perimeter of the rectangle?

20. The width of a rectangular picture is 7 in. less than the length. The area of the picture is 78 in.^{2}

  a. What are the dimensions of the picture?

  b. What is the perimeter of the picture?

21. The base of a triangle is 3 ft more than the height. If the area is 14 ft^2, find the base and the height.

22. The height of a triangle is 15 cm more than the base. If the area is 125 cm^2, find the base and the height.

23. In a physics experiment, a ball is dropped off a 144-ft platform. The height of the ball above the ground is given by the equation

$h = -16t^2 + 144$ where h is the ball's height in feet, and t is the time in seconds after the ball is dropped ($t \geq 0$).

Find the time required for the ball to hit the ground. (*Hint:* Let $h = 0$.) **(See Example 3.)**

24. A stone is dropped off a 256-ft cliff. The height of the stone above the ground is given by the equation

$h = -16t^2 + 256$ where h is the stone's height in feet, and t is the time in seconds after the stone is dropped ($t \geq 0$).

Find the time required for the stone to hit the ground.

25. An object is shot straight up into the air from ground level with an initial speed of 24 ft/sec. The height of the object (in feet) is given by the equation

$h = -16t^2 + 24t$ where t is the time in seconds after launch ($t \geq 0$).

Find the time(s) when the object is at ground level.

26. A rocket is launched straight up into the air from the ground with initial speed of 64 ft/sec. The height of the rocket (in feet) is given by the equation

$h = -16t^2 + 64t$ where t is the time in seconds after launch ($t \geq 0$).

Find the time(s) when the rocket is at ground level.

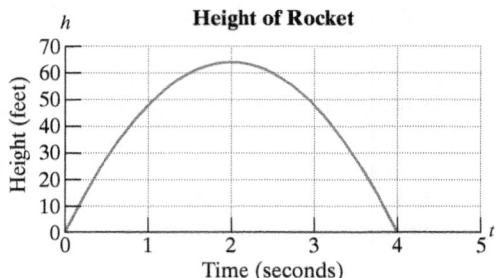

Objective 2: Pythagorean Theorem

27. Sketch a right triangle and label the sides with the words *leg* and *hypotenuse*.

28. State the Pythagorean theorem.

For Exercises 29–32, find the length of the missing side of the right triangle. **(See Example 4.)**

29.

30.

31.

32.

33. Find the length of the supporting brace.

34. Find the height of the airplane above the ground.

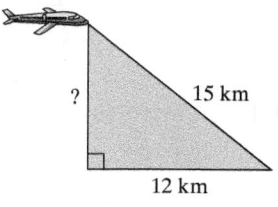

35. Darcy holds the end of a kite string 3 ft (1 yd) off the ground and wants to estimate the height of the kite. Her friend Jenna is 24 yd away from her, standing directly under the kite as shown in the figure. If Darcy has 30 yd of string out, find the height of the kite (ignore the sag in the string).

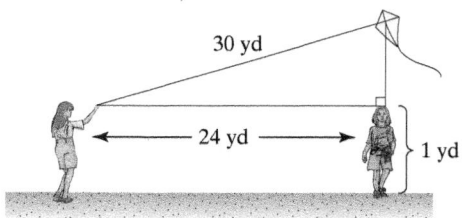

36. Two cars leave the same point at the same time, one traveling north and the other traveling east. After an hour, one car has traveled 48 mi and the other has traveled 64 mi. How many miles apart were they at that time?

37. A 17-ft ladder rests against the side of a house. The distance between the top of the ladder and the ground is 7 ft more than the distance between the base of the ladder and the bottom of the house. Find both distances. **(See Example 5.)**

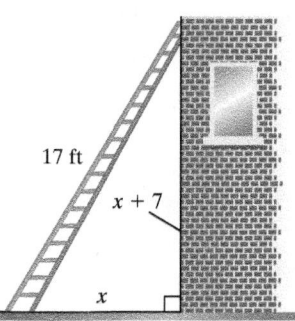

38. Two boats leave a marina. One travels east, and the other travels south. After 30 min, the second boat has traveled 1 mi farther than the first boat and the distance between the boats is 5 mi. Find the distance each boat traveled.

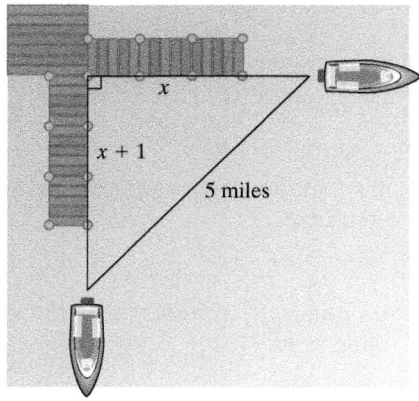

39. One leg of a right triangle is 4 m less than the hypotenuse. The other leg is 2 m less than the hypotenuse. Find the length of the hypotenuse.

40. The longer leg of a right triangle is 1 cm less than twice the shorter leg. The hypotenuse is 1 cm greater than twice the shorter leg. Find the length of the shorter leg.

Group Activity

Building a Factoring Test

Estimated Time: 15–20 minutes

Group Size: 3

In this activity, each group will make a test for this chapter. Then the groups will trade papers and take the test.

For questions 1–8, write a polynomial that has the given conditions.

1. A trinomial with a GCF not equal to 1. The GCF should include a constant and at least one variable.

    1. _____

2. A four-term polynomial that is factorable by grouping.

    2. _____

3. A factorable trinomial with a leading coefficient of 1. (The trinomial should factor as a product of two binomials.)

    3. _____

4. A factorable trinomial with a leading coefficient not equal to 1. (The trinomial should factor as a product of two binomials.)

    4. _____

5. A trinomial that requires the GCF to be removed. The resulting trinomial should factor as a product of two binomials.

    5. _____

6. A difference of squares.

    6. _____

7. A perfect square trinomial.

    7. _____

8. A sum of squares that requires the GCF to be removed.

    8. _____

9. Write a quadratic *equation* that has solutions $x = 4$ and $x = -7$.

    9. _____

10. Write a quadratic *equation* that has solutions $x = 0$ and $x = -\dfrac{2}{3}$.

    10. _____

Chapter 13 Summary

Section 13.1 — Greatest Common Factor and Factoring by Grouping

Key Concepts

The **greatest common factor** (GCF) is the greatest factor common to all terms of a polynomial. To factor out the GCF from a polynomial, use the distributive property.

    A four-term polynomial may be factorable by grouping.

Steps to Factoring by Grouping

1. Identify and factor out the GCF from all four terms.
2. Factor out the GCF from the first pair of terms. Factor out the GCF or its opposite from the second pair of terms.
3. If the two terms share a common binomial factor, factor out the binomial factor.

Examples

Example 1

$3x(a + b) - 5(a + b)$ Greatest common factor is $(a + b)$.

$= (a + b)(3x - 5)$

Example 2

$60xa - 30xb - 80ya + 40yb$

$= 10[6xa - 3xb - 8ya + 4yb]$ Factor out GCF.

$= 10[3x(2a - b) - 4y(2a - b)]$ Factor by grouping.

$= 10(2a - b)(3x - 4y)$

Section 13.2 — Factoring Trinomials of the Form $x^2 + bx + c$

Key Concepts

Factoring a Trinomial with a Leading Coefficient of 1

A trinomial of the form $x^2 + bx + c$ factors as

$$x^2 + bx + c = (x \ \Box)(x \ \Box)$$

where the remaining terms are given by two integers whose product is c and whose sum is b.

Examples

Example 1

Factor: $x^2 - 14x + 45$

$x^2 - 14x + 45$ The integers -5 and -9 have a product of 45 and a sum of -14.

$= (x \ \Box)(x \ \Box)$

$= (x - 5)(x - 9)$

Section 13.3 Factoring Trinomials: Trial-and-Error Method

Key Concepts

Trial-and-Error Method for Factoring Trinomials in the Form $ax^2 + bx + c$ **(where $a \neq 0$)**

1. Factor out the GCF from all terms.
2. List the pairs of factors of a and the pairs of factors of c. Consider the reverse order in one of the lists.
3. Construct two binomials of the form

4. Test each combination of factors and signs until the product forms the correct trinomial.
5. If no combination of factors produces the correct product, then the trinomial is prime.

Examples

Example 1

$10y^2 + 35y - 20$

$= 5(2y^2 + 7y - 4)$

The pairs of factors of 2 are: $2 \cdot 1$
The pairs of factors of -4 are:

$$-1(4) \qquad 1(-4)$$
$$-2(2) \qquad 2(-2)$$
$$-4(1) \qquad 4(-1)$$

$(2y - 2)(y + 2) = 2y^2 + 2y - 4$ No

$(2y - 4)(y + 1) = 2y^2 - 2y - 4$ No

$(2y + 1)(y - 4) = 2y^2 - 7y - 4$ No

$(2y + 2)(y - 2) = 2y^2 - 2y - 4$ No

$(2y + 4)(y - 1) = 2y^2 + 2y - 4$ No

$(2y - 1)(y + 4) = 2y^2 + 7y - 4$ Yes

$10y^2 + 35y - 20 = 5(2y - 1)(y + 4)$

Section 13.4 Factoring Trinomials: AC-Method

Key Concepts

AC-Method for Factoring Trinomials of the Form $ax^2 + bx + c$ **(where $a \neq 0$)**

1. Factor out the GCF from all terms.
2. Find the product ac.
3. Find two integers whose product is ac and whose sum is b. (If no pair of integers can be found, then the trinomial is prime.)
4. Rewrite the middle term (bx) as the sum of two terms whose coefficients are the numbers found in step 3.
5. Factor the polynomial by grouping.

Examples

Example 1

$10y^2 + 35y - 20$

$= 5(2y^2 + 7y - 4)$ First factor out the GCF.

Identify the product $ac = (2)(-4) = -8$.

Find two integers whose product is -8 and whose sum is 7. The numbers are 8 and -1.

$5[2y^2 + 8y - 1y - 4]$

$= 5[2y(y + 4) - 1(y + 4)]$

$= 5(y + 4)(2y - 1)$

Section 13.5 — Difference of Squares and Perfect Square Trinomials

Key Concepts

Factoring a Difference of Squares

$$a^2 - b^2 = (a - b)(a + b)$$

Factoring a Perfect Square Trinomial

The factored form of a **perfect square trinomial** is the square of a binomial:

$$a^2 + 2ab + b^2 = (a + b)^2$$

$$a^2 - 2ab + b^2 = (a - b)^2$$

Examples

Example 1

$$25z^2 - 4y^2$$
$$= (5z - 2y)(5z + 2y)$$

Example 2

Factor: $25y^2 + 10y + 1$
$$= (5y)^2 + 2(5y)(1) + (1)^2$$
$$= (5y + 1)^2$$

Section 13.6 — Solving Equations Using the Zero Product Rule

Key Concepts

An equation of the form $ax^2 + bx + c = 0$, where $a \neq 0$, is a **quadratic equation**.

The zero product rule states that if $ab = 0$, then $a = 0$ or $b = 0$. The zero product rule can be used to solve a quadratic equation or a higher degree polynomial equation that is factored and set to zero.

Examples

Example 1

The equation $2x^2 - 17x + 30 = 0$ is a quadratic equation.

Example 2

$$3w(w - 4)(2w + 1) = 0$$
$$3w = 0 \ \text{ or } \ w - 4 = 0 \ \text{ or } \ 2w + 1 = 0$$
$$w = 0 \ \text{ or } \ w = 4 \ \text{ or } \ w = -\frac{1}{2}$$

Example 3

$$4x^2 = 34x - 60$$
$$4x^2 - 34x + 60 = 0$$
$$2(2x^2 - 17x + 30) = 0$$
$$2(2x - 5)(x - 6) = 0$$
$$2 \neq 0 \ \text{ or } \ 2x - 5 = 0 \ \text{ or } \ x - 6 = 0$$
$$x = \frac{5}{2} \ \text{ or } \ x = 6$$

Section 13.7	Applications of Quadratic Equations

Key Concepts

Use the zero product rule to solve applications.

Examples

Example 1

Find two consecutive integers such that the sum of their squares is 61.

Let x represent one integer.
Let $x + 1$ represent the next consecutive integer.

$$x^2 + (x + 1)^2 = 61$$
$$x^2 + x^2 + 2x + 1 = 61$$
$$2x^2 + 2x - 60 = 0$$
$$2(x^2 + x - 30) = 0$$
$$2(x - 5)(x + 6) = 0$$
$$x = 5 \quad \text{or} \quad x = -6$$

If $x = 5$, then the next consecutive integer is 6.
If $x = -6$, then the next consecutive integer is -5.
The integers are 5 and 6, or -6 and -5.

Some applications involve the Pythagorean theorem.

$$a^2 + b^2 = c^2$$

Example 2

Find the length of the missing side.

x 25 ft

7 ft

$$x^2 + (7)^2 = (25)^2$$
$$x^2 + 49 = 625$$
$$x^2 - 576 = 0$$
$$(x - 24)(x + 24) = 0$$
$$x = 24 \quad \text{or} \quad x = -24$$

The length of the side is 24 ft.

Chapter 13 Review Exercises

Section 13.1

For Exercises 1–4, identify the greatest common factor for each group of terms.

1. $15a^2b^4, 30a^3b, 9a^5b^3$ **2.** $3(x + 5), x(x + 5)$

3. $2c^3(3c - 5), 4c(3c - 5)$ **4.** $-2wyz, -4xyz$

For Exercises 5–10, factor out the greatest common factor.

5. $6x^2 + 2x^4 - 8x$ **6.** $11w^3y^3 - 44w^2y^5$

7. $-t^2 + 5t$ **8.** $-6u^2 - u$

9. $3b(b + 2) - 7(b + 2)$

10. $2(5x + 9) + 8x(5x + 9)$

For Exercises 11–14, factor by grouping.

11. $7w^2 + 14w + wb + 2b$

12. $b^2 - 2b + yb - 2y$

13. $60y^2 - 45y - 12y + 9$

14. $6a - 3a^2 - 2ab + a^2b$

Section 13.2

For Exercises 15–24, factor completely.

15. $x^2 - 10x + 21$ **16.** $y^2 - 19y + 88$

17. $-6z + z^2 - 72$ **18.** $-39 + q^2 - 10q$

19. $3p^2w + 36pw + 60w$ **20.** $2m^4 + 26m^3 + 80m^2$

21. $-t^2 + 10t - 16$ **22.** $-w^2 - w + 20$

23. $a^2 + 12ab + 11b^2$ **24.** $c^2 - 3cd - 18d^2$

Section 13.3

For Exercises 25–28, let a, b, and c represent positive integers.

25. When factoring a polynomial of the form $ax^2 - bx - c$, should the signs of the binomials be both positive, both negative, or different?

26. When factoring a polynomial of the form should the signs of the binomials be both positive, both negative, or different?

27. When factoring a polynomial of the form $ax^2 + bx + c$, should the signs of the binomials be both positive, both negative, or different?

28. When factoring a polynomial of the form $ax^2 + bx - c$, should the signs of the binomials be both positive, both negative, or different?

For Exercises 29–40, factor the trinomial using the trial-and-error method.

29. $2y^2 - 5y - 12$ **30.** $4w^2 - 5w - 6$

31. $10z^2 + 29z + 10$ **32.** $8z^2 + 6z - 9$

33. $2p^2 - 5p + 1$ **34.** $5r^2 - 3r + 7$

35. $10w^2 - 60w - 270$ **36.** $3y^2 - 18y - 48$

37. $9c^2 - 30cd + 25d^2$ **38.** $x^2 + 12x + 36$

39. $v^4 - 2v^2 - 3$ **40.** $x^4 + 7x^2 + 10$

41. In Exercises 29–40, which trinomials are perfect square trinomials?

Section 13.4

For Exercises 42–43, find a pair of integers whose product and sum are given.

42. Product: -5 sum: 4

43. Product: 15 sum: -8

For Exercises 44–57, factor the trinomial using the ac-method.

44. $3c^2 - 5c - 2$ **45.** $4y^2 + 13y + 3$

46. $t^2 + 13t + 12$ **47.** $4x^3 + 17x^2 - 15x$

48. $w^3 + 4w^2 - 5w$ **49.** $p^2 - 8pq + 15q^2$

50. $40v^2 + 22v - 6$ **51.** $40s^2 + 30s - 100$

52. $a^3b - 10a^2b^2 + 24ab^3$ **53.** $2z^6 + 8z^5 - 42z^4$

54. $3m + 9m^2 - 2$ **55.** $10 + 6p^2 + 19p$

56. $49x^2 + 140x + 100$ **57.** $9w^2 - 6wz + z^2$

58. In Exercises 42–57, which trinomials are perfect square trinomials?

Section 13.5

For Exercises 59–60, write the formula to factor each binomial, if possible.

59. $a^2 - b^2$ **60.** $a^2 + b^2$

For Exercises 61–76, factor completely.

61. $a^2 - 49$ **62.** $d^2 - 64$

63. $100 - 81t^2$ **64.** $4 - 25k^2$

65. $x^2 + 16$ **66.** $y^2 + 121$

67. $y^2 + 12y + 36$ **68.** $t^2 + 16t + 64$

69. $9a^2 - 12a + 4$ **70.** $25x^2 - 40x + 16$

71. $-3v^2 - 12v - 12$ **72.** $-2x^2 + 20x - 50$

73. $2c^4 - 18$ **74.** $72x^2 - 2y^2$

75. $p^3 + 3p^2 - 16p - 48$ **76.** $4k - 8 - k^3 + 2k^2$

Section 13.6

77. For which of the following equations can the zero product rule be applied directly? Explain.

$(x - 3)(2x + 1) = 0$ or $(x - 3)(2x + 1) = 6$

For Exercises 78–93, solve the equation using the zero product rule.

78. $(4x - 1)(3x + 2) = 0$

79. $(a - 9)(2a - 1) = 0$

80. $3w(w + 3)(5w + 2) = 0$

81. $6u(u - 7)(4u - 9) = 0$

82. $7k^2 - 9k - 10 = 0$

83. $4h^2 - 23h - 6 = 0$

84. $q^2 - 144 = 0$ **85.** $r^2 = 25$

86. $5v^2 - v = 0$ **87.** $x(x - 6) = -8$

88. $36t^2 + 60t = -25$ **89.** $9s^2 + 12s = -4$

90. $3(y^2 + 4) = 20y$ **91.** $2(p^2 - 66) = -13p$

92. $2y^3 - 18y^2 = -28y$ **93.** $x^3 - 4x = 0$

Section 13.7

94. The base of a parallelogram is 1 ft longer than twice the height. If the area is 78 ft², what are the base and height of the parallelogram?

95. A ball is tossed into the air from ground level with initial speed of 16 ft/sec. The height of the ball is given by the equation

$$h = -16t^2 + 16t \quad (t \geq 0)$$

where h is the ball's height in feet, and t is the time in seconds.

Find the time(s) when the ball is at ground level.

96. Find the length of the ramp.

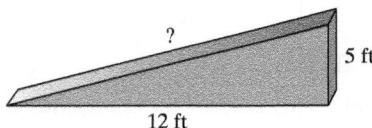

? / 5 ft / 12 ft

97. A right triangle has one leg that is 2 ft longer than the other leg. The hypotenuse is 2 ft less than twice the shorter leg. Find the lengths of all sides of the triangle.

98. If the square of a number is subtracted from 60, the result is −4. Find all such numbers.

99. The product of two consecutive integers is 44 more than 14 times their sum.

100. The base of a triangle is 1 m longer than twice the height. If the area of the triangle is 18 m², find the base and height.

Chapter 13   Test

1. Factor out the GCF: $15x^4 - 3x + 6x^3$

2. Factor by grouping: $7a - 35 - a^2 + 5a$

3. Factor the trinomial: $6w^2 - 43w + 7$

4. Factor the difference of squares: $169 - p^2$

5. Factor the perfect square trinomial:
   $q^2 - 16q + 64$

For Exercises 6–23, factor completely.

6. $a^2 + 12a + 32$

7. $x^2 + x - 42$

8. $2y^2 - 17y + 8$

9. $6z^2 + 19z + 8$

10. $9t^2 - 100$

11. $v^2 - 81$

12. $3a^2 + 27ab + 54b^2$

13. $c^4 - 1$

14. $xy - 7x + 3y - 21$

15. $49 + p^2$

16. $-10u^2 + 30u - 20$

17. $12t^2 - 75$

18. $5y^2 - 50y + 125$

19. $21q^2 + 14q$

20. $2x^3 + x^2 - 8x - 4$

21. $m^2n^2 - 81$

22. $16a^2 - 64b^2$

23. $3x^2y - 6xy - 24y$

For Exercises 24–28, solve the equation.

24. $(2x - 3)(x + 5) = 0$

25. $x^2 - 7x = 0$

26. $x^2 - 6x = 16$

27. $x(5x + 4) = 1$

28. $y^3 + 10y^2 - 9y - 90 = 0$

29. A tennis court has an area of 312 yd². If the length is 2 yd more than twice the width, find the dimensions of the court.

30. The product of two consecutive odd integers is 35. Find the integers.

31. The height of a triangle is 5 in. less than the length of the base. The area is 42 in². Find the length of the base and the height of the triangle.

32. The hypotenuse of a right triangle is 2 ft less than three times the shorter leg. The longer leg is 3 ft less than three times the shorter leg. Find the length of the shorter leg.

Chapters 1–13   Cumulative Review Exercises

1. Simplify. $\dfrac{|4 - 25 \div (-5) \cdot 2|}{\sqrt{8^2 + 6^2}}$

2. Solve. $5 - 2(t + 4) = 3t + 12$

3. Solve for y. $3x - 2y = 8$

4. In a sample of college students, 384 reported that they watch less than 4 hr of television a week. If this represents 32% of the sample, how many students were surveyed?

5. Solve the inequality. Graph the solution on a number line and write the solution set in interval notation.

$$-\dfrac{5}{12}x \le \dfrac{5}{3}$$ _____→

6. Given the equation $y = x + 4$

   a. Is the equation linear?

   b. Identify the slope.

   c. Identify the y-intercept.

   d. Identify the x-intercept.

   e. Graph the line.

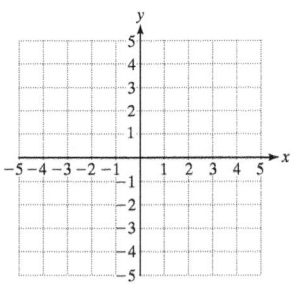

7. Consider the equation, $x = 5$.

   a. Does the equation present a horizontal or vertical line?

   b. Determine the slope of the line, if it exists.

   c. Identify the x-intercept, if it exists.

   d. Identify the y-intercept, if it exists.

8. Find an equation of the line passing through the point $(-3, 5)$ and having a slope of 3. Write the final answer in slope-intercept form.

9. Solve the system. $2x - 3y = 4$
$5x - 6y = 13$

For Exercises 10–12, perform the indicated operations.

10. $2\left(\dfrac{1}{3}y^3 - \dfrac{3}{2}y^2 - 7\right) - \left(\dfrac{2}{3}y^3 + \dfrac{1}{2}y^2 + 5y\right)$

11. $(4p^2 - 5p - 1)(2p - 3)$

12. $(2w - 7)^2$

13. Divide using long division:
$(r^4 + 2r^3 - 5r + 1) \div (r - 3)$

14. Simplify. $\dfrac{c^{12}c^{-5}}{c^3}$

15. Divide. Write the final answer in scientific notation: $\dfrac{8 \times 10^{-3}}{5 \times 10^{-6}}$

For Exercises 16–19, factor completely.

16. $w^4 - 16$

17. $2ax + 10bx - 3ya - 15yb$

18. $4x^2 - 8x - 5$

19. $5y^2 + 20$

20. Solve. $4x(2x - 1)(x + 5) = 0$

Rational Expressions

14

CHAPTER OUTLINE

Chapter 14

In this chapter, we define a rational expression as a ratio of two polynomials. Then we perform operations on rational expressions and solve rational equations.

Are You Prepared?

You may find it helpful to review operations with fractions before you begin this chapter. Try the matching puzzle, then record the letter in the spaces below to complete the sentence

1. Add. $\dfrac{7}{4} + \dfrac{5}{3} + \dfrac{1}{2}$

2. Multiply. $\dfrac{5}{3} \cdot \dfrac{11}{4}$

3. Fraction that is not in lowest terms.

4. In this problem, a common denominator is not required.

5. Fractions can be eliminated from this problem by multiplying by the LCD.

a. $\dfrac{7}{8}x + \dfrac{2}{3} = \dfrac{1}{2}$ t. $\dfrac{45}{12}$

r. $\dfrac{47}{12}$ p. $\dfrac{34}{3} \cdot \dfrac{1}{4}$

n. $\dfrac{7}{8} + \dfrac{1}{3} - \dfrac{1}{2}$ o. $\dfrac{55}{12}$

The enemy of a good student is $\underline{}\ \underline{}\ \underset{4}{\underline{}}\ \underset{1}{\underline{}}\ \underset{2}{\underline{c}}\ \quad \underset{1}{\underline{}}\ \underset{5}{\underline{s}}\ \underset{3}{\underline{}}\ \underset{}{\underline{i}}\ \underset{5}{\underline{n}}\ \underset{3}{\underline{}}\ \underset{2}{\underline{i}}\ \underline{n}$.

Section 14.1   **Introduction to Rational Expressions**

Objectives

1. Definition of a Rational Expression
2. Evaluating Rational Expressions
3. Restricted Values of a Rational Expression
4. Simplifying Rational Expressions to Lowest Terms
5. Simplifying a Ratio of −1

Section 14.1   Introduction to Rational Expressions

1. Definition of a Rational Expression

In Section 9.1, we defined a rational number as the ratio of two integers, $\frac{p}{q}$, where $q \neq 0$.

$$\text{Examples of rational numbers:} \quad \frac{2}{3}, -\frac{1}{5}, 9$$

In a similar way, we define a **rational expression** as the ratio of two polynomials, $\frac{p}{q}$, where $q \neq 0$.

$$\text{Examples of rational expressions:} \quad \frac{3x - 6}{x^2 - 4}, \quad \frac{3}{4}, \quad \frac{6r^5 + 2r}{7r^2}$$

2. Evaluating Rational Expressions

— **Skill Practice** —

Evaluate the expression for the given values of x.
$$\frac{x - 3}{x + 5}$$

1. $x = 2$
2. $x = 0$
3. $x = 3$
4. $x = -5$

Example 1   **Evaluating Rational Expressions**

Evaluate the rational expression (if possible) for the given values of x: $\dfrac{12}{x - 3}$

   a. $x = 0$ **b.** $x = 1$ **c.** $x = -3$ **d.** $x = 3$

Solution:

Substitute the given value for the variable. Then use the order of operations to simplify.

a. $\dfrac{12}{x - 3}$

$\dfrac{12}{(0) - 3}$ Substitute $x = 0$.

$= \dfrac{12}{-3}$

$= -4$

b. $\dfrac{12}{x - 3}$

$\dfrac{12}{(1) - 3}$ Substitute $x = 1$.

$= \dfrac{12}{-2}$

$= -6$

c. $\dfrac{12}{x - 3}$

$\dfrac{12}{(-3) - 3}$ Substitute $x = -3$.

$= \dfrac{12}{-6}$

$= -2$

d. $\dfrac{12}{x - 3}$

$\dfrac{12}{(3) - 3}$ Substitute $x = 3$.

$= \dfrac{12}{0}$ Undefined.

Recall that division by zero is undefined.

Answers

1. $-\dfrac{1}{7}$ 2. $-\dfrac{3}{5}$

3. 0 4. Undefined

3. Restricted Values of a Rational Expression

In Example 1 we saw that not all values of x can be substituted into a rational expression. The values that make the denominator zero must be restricted.

The expression $\dfrac{12}{x-3}$ is undefined for $x = 3$, so we call $x = 3$ a restricted value.

Restricted values of a rational expression are all values that make the expression undefined, that is, make the denominator equal to zero.

Example 2 Finding the Restricted Values of Rational Expressions

Identify the restricted values for each expression.

a. $\dfrac{y-3}{2y+7}$ **b.** $\dfrac{-5}{x}$

Solution:

a. $\dfrac{y-3}{2y+7}$

$2y + 7 = 0$ — Set the denominator equal to zero.

$2y = -7$ — Solve the equation.

$\dfrac{2y}{2} = \dfrac{-7}{2}$

$y = -\dfrac{7}{2}$ — The restricted value is $y = -\frac{7}{2}$.

b. $\dfrac{-5}{x}$

$x = 0$ — Set the denominator equal to zero. The restricted value is $x = 0$.

Example 3 Finding the Restricted Values of Rational Expressions

Identify the restricted values for each expression.

a. $\dfrac{a+10}{a^2-25}$ **b.** $\dfrac{2x^3+5}{x^2+9}$

Solution:

a. $\dfrac{a + 10}{a^2 - 25}$

$a^2 - 25 = 0$ Set the denominator equal to zero. The equation is quadratic.

$(a - 5)(a + 5) = 0$ Factor.

$a - 5 = 0$ or $a + 5 = 0$ Set each factor equal to zero.

$a = 5$ or $a = -5$

The restricted values are $a = 5$ and $a = -5$.

b. $\dfrac{2x^3 + 5}{x^2 + 9}$

The quantity x^2 cannot be negative for any real number, x, so the denominator $x^2 + 9$ cannot equal zero. Therefore, there are no restricted values.

4. Simplifying Rational Expressions to Lowest Terms

In many cases, it is advantageous to simplify or reduce a fraction to lowest terms. The same is true for rational expressions.

The method for simplifying rational expressions mirrors the process for simplifying fractions. In each case, factor the numerator and denominator. Common factors in the numerator and denominator form a ratio of 1 and can be reduced.

Simplifying a fraction: $\dfrac{21}{35} \xrightarrow{\text{Factor}} \dfrac{3 \cdot \overset{1}{\cancel{7}}}{5 \cdot \cancel{7}} = \dfrac{3}{5} \cdot (1) = \dfrac{3}{5}$

Simplifying a rational expression: $\dfrac{2x - 6}{x^2 - 9} \xrightarrow{\text{Factor}} \dfrac{2(\overset{1}{\cancel{x - 3}})}{(x + 3)(\cancel{x - 3})} = \dfrac{2}{(x + 3)}(1) = \dfrac{2}{x + 3}$

Informally, to simplify a rational expression to lowest terms, we simplify the ratio of common factors to 1. Formally, this is accomplished by applying the fundamental principle of rational expressions.

PROPERTY **Fundamental Principle of Rational Expressions**

Let p, q, and r represent polynomials where $q \neq 0$ and $r \neq 0$. Then

$$\frac{pr}{qr} = \frac{p}{q} \cdot \frac{r}{r} = \frac{p}{q} \cdot 1 = \frac{p}{q}$$

Example 4 **Simplifying a Rational Expression to Lowest Terms**

Given the expression $\dfrac{2p - 14}{p^2 - 49}$

a. Factor the numerator and denominator.

b. Identify the restricted values.

c. Simplify the expression to lowest terms.

Solution:

a. $\dfrac{2p - 14}{p^2 - 49}$

Factor out the GCF in the numerator.

$= \dfrac{2(p - 7)}{(p + 7)(p - 7)}$

Factor the denominator as a difference of squares.

b. $(p + 7)(p - 7) = 0$

To find the restricted values, set the denominator equal to zero. The equation is quadratic.

$p + 7 = 0$ or $p - 7 = 0$ Set each factor equal to 0.

$p = -7$ or $p = 7$

The restricted values are $p = -7$ and $p = 7$.

c. $\dfrac{2(\overset{1}{\cancel{p - 7}})}{(p + 7)(\cancel{p - 7})}$

Simplify the ratio of common factors to 1.

$= \dfrac{2}{p + 7}$ (provided $p \neq 7$ and $p \neq -7$)

In Example 4, it is important to note that the expressions

$$\dfrac{2p - 14}{p^2 - 49} \quad \text{and} \quad \dfrac{2}{p + 7}$$

are equal for all values of p that make each expression a real number. Therefore,

$$\dfrac{2p - 14}{p^2 - 49} = \dfrac{2}{p + 7}$$

for all values of p except $p = 7$ and $p = -7$. (At $p = 7$ and $p = -7$, the original denominator is zero.) This is why the restricted values are always determined before the expression is simplified.

From this point forward, we will write statements of equality between two rational expressions with the assumption that they are equal for all values of the variable for which each expression is defined.

Skill Practice

Given: $\dfrac{5z + 25}{z^2 + 3z - 10}$

10. Factor the numerator and the denominator.

11. Identify the restricted values.

12. Simplify the rational expression to lowest terms.

Answers

10. $\dfrac{5(z + 5)}{(z + 5)(z - 2)}$

11. $z = -5, z = 2$

12. $\dfrac{5}{z - 2}$ $(z \neq 2, z \neq -5)$

Example 5 **Simplifying a Rational Expression to Lowest Terms**

Simplify to lowest terms. $\dfrac{18a^4}{9a^5}$

Solution:

$$\dfrac{18a^4}{9a^5}$$

$$=\dfrac{2\cdot 3\cdot 3\cdot a\cdot a\cdot a\cdot a}{3\cdot 3\cdot a\cdot a\cdot a\cdot a\cdot a}$$ Factor the numerator and denominator.

$$=\dfrac{2\cdot(3\cdot 3\cdot a\cdot a\cdot a\cdot a)}{(3\cdot 3\cdot a\cdot a\cdot a\cdot a)\cdot a}$$ Simplify common factors to lowest terms.

$$=\dfrac{2}{a}$$

TIP: The expression $\dfrac{18a^4}{9a^5}$ can also be simplified using the properties of exponents.

$$\dfrac{18a^4}{9a^5}=2a^{4-5}=2a^{-1}=\dfrac{2}{a}$$

Example 6 **Simplifying a Rational Expression to Lowest Terms**

Simplify to lowest terms. $\dfrac{2c-8}{10c^2-80c+160}$

Solution:

$$\dfrac{2c-8}{10c^2-80c+160}$$

$$=\dfrac{2(c-4)}{10(c^2-8c+16)}$$ Factor out the GCF.

$$=\dfrac{2(c-4)}{10(c-4)^2}$$ Factor the denominator.

$$=\dfrac{2(c-4)}{2\cdot 5(c-4)(c-4)}$$ Simplify the ratio of common factors to 1.

$$=\dfrac{1}{5(c-4)}$$

The process to simplify a rational expression to lowest terms is based on the identity property of multiplication. Therefore, this process applies only to factors. (Remember that factors are multiplied.)

Answers

13. $\dfrac{5q}{3}$ **14.** $\dfrac{x-1}{2x-3}$

For example,

$$\frac{3x}{3y} = \frac{\overset{1}{3} \cdot x}{3 \cdot y} = 1 \cdot \frac{x}{y} = \frac{x}{y}$$

↑
Simplify

Terms that are added or subtracted cannot be reduced to lowest terms. For example,

$$\frac{x + 3}{y + 3}$$

↑
Cannot be simplified

The objective of simplifying a rational expression to lowest terms is to create an equivalent expression that is simpler to use. Consider the rational expression from Example 6 in its original form and in its reduced form. If we choose an arbitrary value of c from the domain and substitute that value into each expression, we see that the reduced form is easier to evaluate. For example, substitute $c = 3$:

Original Expression	**Simplified Expression**
$\dfrac{2c - 8}{10c^2 - 80c + 160}$	$\dfrac{1}{5(c - 4)}$

Substitute $c = 3$

$$= \frac{2(3) - 8}{10(3)^2 - 80(3) + 160} \qquad\qquad = \frac{1}{5(3 - 4)}$$

$$= \frac{6 - 8}{10(9) - 240 + 160} \qquad\qquad = \frac{1}{5(-1)}$$

$$= \frac{-2}{90 - 240 + 160} \qquad\qquad = -\frac{1}{5}$$

$$= \frac{-2}{10} \quad \text{or} \quad -\frac{1}{5}$$

5. Simplifying a Ratio of −1

When two factors are identical in the numerator and denominator, they form a ratio of 1 and can be reduced. Sometimes we encounter two factors that are opposites and form a ratio of −1. For example,

Simplified Form	**Details/Notes**
$\dfrac{-5}{5} = -1$	The ratio of a number and its opposite is −1.
$\dfrac{100}{-100} = -1$	The ratio of a number and its opposite is −1.

$$\frac{x + 7}{-x - 7} = -1 \qquad \frac{x + 7}{-x - 7} = \frac{x + 7}{-1(x + 7)} = \frac{\overset{1}{x + 7}}{-1(x + 7)} = \frac{1}{-1} = -1$$

factor out −1

$$\frac{2 - x}{x - 2} = -1 \qquad \frac{2 - x}{x - 2} = \frac{-1(-2 + x)}{x - 2} = \frac{-1(\overset{1}{x - 2})}{x - 2} = \frac{-1}{1} = -1$$

> **Avoiding Mistakes**
>
> While the expression $2 - x$ and $x - 2$ are opposites, the expressions $2 - x$ and $2 + x$ are *not*.
>
> Therefore, $\dfrac{2 - x}{2 + x}$ does not simplify to −1.

Recognizing factors that are opposites is useful when simplifying rational expressions.

Example 7 **Simplifying a Rational Expression to Lowest Terms**

Simplify to lowest terms. $\qquad \dfrac{3c - 3d}{d - c}$

Solution:

$$\dfrac{3c - 3d}{d - c}$$

$$= \dfrac{3(c - d)}{d - c} \qquad \text{Factor the numerator and denominator.}$$

Notice that $(c - d)$ and $(d - c)$ are opposites and form a ratio of -1.

$$= \dfrac{3(\overset{-1}{\cancel{c - d}})}{\cancel{d - c}} \qquad \underline{\text{Details:}} \quad \dfrac{3(c - d)}{d - c} = \dfrac{3(c - d)}{-1(-d + c)} = \dfrac{3(c - d)}{-1(c - d)}$$

$$= 3(-1) \qquad\qquad\qquad\qquad\qquad\qquad\qquad\qquad = \dfrac{3}{-1} = -3$$

$$= -3$$

TIP: It is important to recognize that a rational expression can be written in several equivalent forms. In particular, two numbers with opposite signs form a negative quotient. Therefore, a number such as $-\frac{3}{4}$ can be written as:

$$-\dfrac{3}{4} \quad \text{or} \quad \dfrac{-3}{4} \quad \text{or} \quad \dfrac{3}{-4}$$

The negative sign can be written in the numerator, in the denominator, or out in front of the fraction. We demonstrate this concept in Example 8.

Example 8 **Simplifying a Rational Expression to Lowest Terms**

Simplify to lowest terms. $\qquad \dfrac{5 - y}{y^2 - 25}$

Solution:

$$\dfrac{5 - y}{y^2 - 25}$$

$$= \dfrac{5 - y}{(y - 5)(y + 5)} \qquad \text{Factor the numerator and denominator.}$$

Notice that $5 - y$ and $y - 5$ are opposites and form a ratio of -1.

$$= \dfrac{\overset{-1}{\cancel{5 - y}}}{(\cancel{y - 5})(y + 5)} \qquad \underline{\text{Details:}} \quad \dfrac{5 - y}{(y - 5)(y + 5)} = \dfrac{-1(-5 + y)}{(y - 5)(y + 5)}$$

$$\qquad\qquad\qquad\qquad\qquad\qquad\qquad = \dfrac{-1(y - 5)}{(y - 5)(y + 5)} = \dfrac{-1}{y + 5}$$

$$= \dfrac{-1}{y + 5} \quad \text{or} \quad \dfrac{1}{-(y + 5)} \quad \text{or} \quad -\dfrac{1}{y + 5}$$

Study Skills Exercises

1. Review Section 4.2 in this text. Write an example of how to simplify (reduce) a fraction, multiply two fractions, divide two fractions, add two fractions, and subtract two fractions. Then as you learn about rational expressions, compare the operations on rational expressions with those on fractions. This is a great place to use 3 × 5 cards again. Write an example of an operation with fractions on one side and the same operation with rational expressions on the other side.

2. Define the key terms:

   a. Rational expression   **b. Restricted values of a rational expression**

Objective 1: Definition of a Rational Expression

3. **a.** What is a rational number?

   b. What is a rational expression?

4. **a.** Write an example of a rational number. (Answers will vary.)

   b. Write an example of a rational expression. (Answers will vary.)

Objective 2: Evaluating Rational Expressions

For Exercises 5–10, substitute the given number into the expression and simplify (if possible). **(See Example 1.)**

5. $\dfrac{1}{x - 6}$; $x = -2$

6. $\dfrac{w - 10}{w + 6}$; $w = 0$

7. $\dfrac{w - 4}{2w + 8}$; $w = 0$

8. $\dfrac{y - 8}{2y^2 + y - 1}$; $y = 8$

9. $\dfrac{(a - 7)(a + 1)}{(a - 2)(a + 5)}$; $a = 2$

10. $\dfrac{(a + 4)(a + 1)}{(a - 4)(a - 1)}$; $a = 1$

11. A bicyclist rides 24 mi against a wind and returns 24 mi with the same wind. His average speed for the return trip traveling with the wind is 8 mph faster than his speed going out against the wind. If x represents the bicyclist's speed going out against the wind, then the total time, t, required for the round trip is given by

$$t = \frac{24}{x} + \frac{24}{x + 8} \qquad \text{where } t \text{ is measured in hours.}$$

   a. Find the time required for the round trip if the cyclist rides 12 mph against the wind.

   b. Find the time required for the round trip if the cyclist rides 24 mph against the wind.

12. The manufacturer of mountain bikes has a fixed cost of $56,000, plus a variable cost of $140 per bike. The average cost per bike, y (in dollars), is given by the equation:

$$y = \frac{56{,}000 + 140x}{x} \qquad \text{where } x \text{ represents the number of bikes produced.}$$

   a. Find the average cost per bike if the manufacturer produces 1000 bikes.

   b. Find the average cost per bike if the manufacturer produces 2000 bikes.

   c. Find the average cost per bike if the manufacturer produces 10,000 bikes.

Objective 3: Restricted Values of a Rational Expression

For Exercises 13–24, identify the restricted values. **(See Examples 2–3.)**

13. $\dfrac{5}{k + 2}$

14. $\dfrac{-3}{h - 4}$

15. $\dfrac{x + 5}{(2x - 5)(x + 8)}$

16. $\dfrac{4y + 1}{(3y + 7)(y + 3)}$

17. $\dfrac{b + 12}{b^2 + 5b + 6}$

18. $\dfrac{c - 11}{c^2 - 5c - 6}$

19. $\dfrac{x - 4}{x^2 + 9}$

20. $\dfrac{x + 1}{x^2 + 4}$

21. $\dfrac{y^2 - y - 12}{12}$

22. $\dfrac{z^2 + 10z + 9}{9}$

23. $\dfrac{t - 5}{t}$

24. $\dfrac{2w + 7}{w}$

25. Construct a rational expression that is undefined for $x = 2$. (Answers will vary.)

26. Construct a rational expression that is undefined for $x = 5$. (Answers will vary.)

27. Construct a rational expression that is undefined for $x = -3$ and $x = 7$. (Answers will vary.)

28. Construct a rational expression that is undefined for $x = -1$ and $x = 4$. (Answers will vary.)

29. Evaluate the expressions for $x = -1$.

   a. $\dfrac{3x^2 - 2x - 1}{6x^2 - 7x - 3}$ **b.** $\dfrac{x - 1}{2x - 3}$

30. Evaluate the expressions for $x = 4$.

   a. $\dfrac{(x + 5)^2}{x^2 + 6x + 5}$ **b.** $\dfrac{x + 5}{x + 1}$

31. Evaluate the expressions for $x = 1$.

   a. $\dfrac{5x + 5}{x^2 - 1}$ **b.** $\dfrac{5}{x - 1}$

32. Evaluate the expressions for $x = -3$.

   a. $\dfrac{2x^2 - 4x - 6}{2x^2 - 18}$ **b.** $\dfrac{x + 1}{x + 3}$

Objective 4: Simplifying Rational Expressions to Lowest Terms

For Exercises 33–42,

   a. Identify the restricted values.

   b. Simplify the expression to lowest terms. **(See Example 4.)**

33. $\dfrac{3y + 6}{6y + 12}$

34. $\dfrac{8x - 8}{4x - 4}$

35. $\dfrac{t^2 - 1}{t + 1}$

36. $\dfrac{r^2 - 4}{r - 2}$

37. $\dfrac{7w}{21w^2 - 35w}$

38. $\dfrac{12a^2}{24a^2 - 18a}$

39. $\dfrac{9x^2 - 4}{6x + 4}$

40. $\dfrac{8b - 20}{4b^2 - 25}$

41. $\dfrac{a^2 + 3a - 10}{a^2 + a - 6}$

42. $\dfrac{t^2 + 3t - 10}{t^2 + t - 20}$

For Exercises 43–84, simplify the expression to lowest terms. **(See Examples 5–6.)**

43. $\dfrac{7b^2}{21b}$

44. $\dfrac{15c^3}{3c^5}$

45. $\dfrac{18st^5}{12st^3}$

46. $\dfrac{20a^4b^2}{25ab^2}$

47. $\dfrac{-24x^2y^5z}{8xy^4z^3}$

48. $\dfrac{60rs^4t^2}{-12r^4s^2t^3}$

49. $\dfrac{3(y+2)}{6(y+2)}$

50. $\dfrac{8(x-1)}{4(x-1)}$

51. $\dfrac{(p-3)(p+5)}{(p+5)(p+4)}$

52. $\dfrac{(c+4)(c-1)}{(c+4)(c+2)}$

53. $\dfrac{(m+11)}{4(m+11)(m-11)}$

54. $\dfrac{(n-7)}{9(n+2)(n-7)}$

55. $\dfrac{x(2x+1)^2}{4x^3(2x+1)}$

56. $\dfrac{(p+2)(p-3)^4}{(p+2)^2(p-3)^2}$

57. $\dfrac{5}{20a-25}$

58. $\dfrac{7}{14c-21}$

59. $\dfrac{4w-8}{w^2-4}$

60. $\dfrac{3x+15}{x^2-25}$

61. $\dfrac{3x^2-6x}{9xy+18x}$

62. $\dfrac{6p^2+12p}{2pq-4p}$

63. $\dfrac{2x+4}{x^2-3x-10}$

64. $\dfrac{5z+15}{z^2-4z-21}$

65. $\dfrac{a^2-49}{a-7}$

66. $\dfrac{b^2-64}{b-8}$

67. $\dfrac{q^2+25}{q+5}$

68. $\dfrac{r^2+36}{r+6}$

69. $\dfrac{y^2+6y+9}{2y^2+y-15}$

70. $\dfrac{h^2+h-6}{h^2+2h-8}$

71. $\dfrac{3x^2+7x-6}{x^2+7x+12}$

72. $\dfrac{x^2-5x-14}{2x^2-x-10}$

73. $\dfrac{5q^2+5}{q^4-1}$

74. $\dfrac{4t^2+16}{t^4-16}$

75. $\dfrac{ac-ad+2bc-2bd}{2ac+ad+4bc+2bd}$ (*Hint:* Factor by grouping.)

76. $\dfrac{3pr-ps-3qr+qs}{3pr-ps+3qr-qs}$ (*Hint:* Factor by grouping.)

77. $\dfrac{2t^2-3t}{2t^4-13t^3+15t^2}$

78. $\dfrac{4m^3+3m^2}{4m^3+7m^2+3m}$

79. $\dfrac{49p^2-28pq+4q^2}{14p-4q}$

80. $\dfrac{3x-3y}{2x^2-4xy+2y^2}$

81. $\dfrac{5x^3+4x^2-45x-36}{x^2-9}$

82. $\dfrac{x^2-1}{ax^3-bx^2-ax+b}$

83. $\dfrac{2x^2-xy-3y^2}{2x^2-11xy+12y^2}$

84. $\dfrac{2c^2+cd-d^2}{5c^2+3cd-2d^2}$

Objective 5: Simplifying a Ratio of −1

85. What is the relationship between $x-2$ and $2-x$?

86. What is the relationship between $w+p$ and $-w-p$?

For Exercises 87–98, simplify to lowest terms. (See Examples 7–8.)

87. $\dfrac{x-5}{5-x}$

88. $\dfrac{8-p}{p-8}$

89. $\dfrac{-4-y}{4+y}$

90. $\dfrac{z+10}{-z-10}$

91. $\dfrac{3y-6}{12-6y}$

92. $\dfrac{4q-4}{12-12q}$

93. $\dfrac{k+5}{5-k}$

94. $\dfrac{2+n}{2-n}$

95. $\dfrac{10x-12}{10x+12}$

96. $\dfrac{4t-16}{16+4t}$

97. $\dfrac{x^2-x-12}{16-x^2}$

98. $\dfrac{49-b^2}{b^2-10b+21}$

Section 14.2 Multiplication and Division of Rational Expressions

Objectives

1. Multiplication of Rational Expressions
2. Division of Rational Expressions

1. Multiplication of Rational Expressions

Recall from Section 4.3 that to multiply fractions, we multiply the numerators and multiply the denominators. The same is true for multiplying rational expressions.

> **PROPERTY** Multiplication of Rational Expressions
>
> Let p, q, r, and s represent polynomials, such that $q \neq 0$, $s \neq 0$. Then,
>
> $$\frac{p}{q} \cdot \frac{r}{s} = \frac{pr}{qs}$$

For example:

Multiply the Fractions

$$\frac{2}{3} \cdot \frac{5}{7} = \frac{10}{21}$$

Multiply the Rational Expressions

$$\frac{2x}{3y} \cdot \frac{5z}{7} = \frac{10xz}{21y}$$

Sometimes it is possible to simplify a ratio of common factors to 1 *before* multiplying. To do so, we must first factor the numerators and denominators of each fraction.

$$\frac{15}{14} \cdot \frac{21}{10} = \frac{3 \cdot \overset{1}{\cancel{5}}}{2 \cdot \cancel{7}} \cdot \frac{3 \cdot \overset{1}{\cancel{7}}}{2 \cdot \cancel{5}} = \frac{9}{4}$$

The same process is also used to multiply rational expressions.

> **PROCEDURE** Multiplying Rational Expressions
>
> **Step 1** Factor the numerators and denominators of all rational expressions.
> **Step 2** Simplify the ratios of common factors to 1.
> **Step 3** Multiply the remaining factors in the numerator, and multiply the remaining factors in the denominator.

Skill Practice

Multiply.

1. $\dfrac{7a}{3b} \cdot \dfrac{15b}{14a^2}$

Answer

1. $\dfrac{5}{2a}$

Example 1 Multiplying Rational Expressions

Multiply. $\dfrac{5a^2b}{2} \cdot \dfrac{6a}{10b}$

Solution:

$$\frac{5a^2b}{2} \cdot \frac{6a}{10b}$$

$$= \frac{5 \cdot a \cdot a \cdot b}{2} \cdot \frac{2 \cdot 3 \cdot a}{2 \cdot 5 \cdot b} \qquad \text{Factor into prime factors.}$$

$$= \frac{\overset{1}{\cancel{5}} \cdot a \cdot a \cdot \overset{1}{\cancel{b}}}{2} \cdot \frac{\overset{1}{\cancel{2}} \cdot 3 \cdot a}{\cancel{2} \cdot \cancel{5} \cdot \cancel{b}} \qquad \text{Simplify.}$$

$$= \frac{3a^3}{2} \qquad \text{Multiply remaining factors.}$$

Example 2 **Multiplying Rational Expressions**

Multiply. $\dfrac{3c - 3d}{6c} \cdot \dfrac{2}{c^2 - d^2}$

Solution:

$\dfrac{3c - 3d}{6c} \cdot \dfrac{2}{c^2 - d^2}$

$= \dfrac{3(c - d)}{2 \cdot 3 \cdot c} \cdot \dfrac{2}{(c - d)(c + d)}$ Factor.

$= \dfrac{\overset{1}{\cancel{3}}(\overset{1}{c - \cancel{d}})}{\cancel{2} \cdot \cancel{3} \cdot c} \cdot \dfrac{\cancel{2}}{(\cancel{c - d})(c + d)}$ Simplify.

$= \dfrac{1}{c(c + d)}$ Multiply remaining factors.

Skill Practice

Multiply.

2. $\dfrac{4x - 8}{x + 6} \cdot \dfrac{x^2 + 6x}{2x}$

Avoiding Mistakes

If all the factors in the numerator reduce to a ratio of 1, a factor of 1 is left in the numerator.

Example 3 **Multiplying Rational Expressions**

Multiply. $\dfrac{35 - 5x}{5x + 5} \cdot \dfrac{x^2 + 5x + 4}{x^2 - 49}$

Solution:

$\dfrac{35 - 5x}{5x + 5} \cdot \dfrac{x^2 + 5x + 4}{x^2 - 49}$

$= \dfrac{5(7 - x)}{5(x + 1)} \cdot \dfrac{(x + 4)(x + 1)}{(x - 7)(x + 7)}$ Factor the numerators and denominators completely.

$= \dfrac{\overset{1}{\cancel{5}}(\overset{-1}{\cancel{7 - x}})}{\cancel{5}(\cancel{x + 1})} \cdot \dfrac{(x + 4)(\overset{1}{\cancel{x + 1}})}{(\cancel{x - 7})(x + 7)}$ Simplify the ratios of common factors to 1 or −1.

$= \dfrac{-1(x + 4)}{x + 7}$ Multiply remaining factors.

$= \dfrac{-(x + 4)}{x + 7}$ or $\dfrac{x + 4}{-(x + 7)}$ or $-\dfrac{x + 4}{x + 7}$

Skill Practice

Multiply.

3. $\dfrac{p^2 + 4p + 3}{5p + 10} \cdot \dfrac{p^2 - p - 6}{9 - p^2}$

TIP: The ratio $\dfrac{7 - x}{x - 7} = -1$ because $7 - x$ and $x - 7$ are opposites.

---

2. Division of Rational Expressions

Recall that to divide fractions, multiply the first fraction by the reciprocal of the second.

$$\dfrac{21}{10} \div \dfrac{49}{15} \xrightarrow[\text{of the second fraction}]{\text{multiply by the reciprocal}} \dfrac{21}{10} \cdot \dfrac{15}{49} \xrightarrow{\text{factor}} \dfrac{3 \cdot \overset{1}{\cancel{7}}}{2 \cdot \cancel{5}} \cdot \dfrac{3 \cdot \overset{1}{\cancel{5}}}{\cancel{7} \cdot 7} = \dfrac{9}{14}$$

The same process is used to divide rational expressions.

PROPERTY **Division of Rational Expressions**

Let p, q, r, and s represent polynomials, such that $q \neq 0$, $r \neq 0$, $s \neq 0$. Then,

$$\dfrac{p}{q} \div \dfrac{r}{s} = \dfrac{p}{q} \cdot \dfrac{s}{r} = \dfrac{ps}{qr}$$

Answers

2. $2(x - 2)$

3. $\dfrac{-(p + 1)}{5}$ or $\dfrac{p + 1}{-5}$ or $-\dfrac{p + 1}{5}$

952   **Chapter 14** Rational Expressions

Skill Practice

Divide.

4. $\dfrac{7y - 14}{y + 1} \div \dfrac{y^2 + 2y - 8}{2y + 2}$

Avoiding Mistakes

When dividing rational expressions, take the reciprocal of the second fraction and change to multiplication *before* reducing like factors.

Example 4 **Dividing Rational Expressions**

Divide. $\dfrac{5t - 15}{2} \div \dfrac{t^2 - 9}{10}$

Solution:

$\dfrac{5t - 15}{2} \div \dfrac{t^2 - 9}{10}$

$= \dfrac{5t - 15}{2} \cdot \dfrac{10}{t^2 - 9}$ Multiply the first fraction by the reciprocal of the second.

$= \dfrac{5(t - 3)}{2} \cdot \dfrac{2 \cdot 5}{(t - 3)(t + 3)}$ Factor each polynomial.

$= \dfrac{5\overset{1}{(t - 3)}}{\overset{}{2}} \cdot \dfrac{\overset{}{2} \cdot 5}{\overset{1}{(t - 3)}(t + 3)}$ Simplify the ratio of common factors to 1.

$= \dfrac{25}{t + 3}$

Skill Practice

Divide.

5. $\dfrac{4x^2 - 9}{2x^2 - x - 3} \div \dfrac{20x + 30}{x^2 + 7x + 6}$

Example 5 **Dividing Rational Expressions**

Divide. $\dfrac{p^2 - 11p + 30}{10p^2 - 250} \div \dfrac{30p - 5p^2}{2p + 4}$

Solution:

$\dfrac{p^2 - 11p + 30}{10p^2 - 250} \div \dfrac{30p - 5p^2}{2p + 4}$

$= \dfrac{p^2 - 11p + 30}{10p^2 - 250} \cdot \dfrac{2p + 4}{30p - 5p^2}$ Multiply the first fraction by the reciprocal of the second.

Factor the trinomial.
$p^2 - 11p + 30 = (p - 5)(p - 6)$

$= \dfrac{(p - 5)(p - 6)}{2 \cdot 5(p - 5)(p + 5)} \cdot \dfrac{2(p + 2)}{5p(6 - p)}$ Factor out the GCF.
$2p + 4 = 2(p + 2)$

Factor out the GCF. Then factor the difference of squares.
$10p^2 - 250 = 10(p^2 - 25)$
$\qquad\qquad = 2 \cdot 5(p - 5)(p + 5)$

Factor out the GCF.
$30p - 5p^2 = 5p(6 - p)$

$= \dfrac{\overset{1}{(p - 5)}\overset{-1}{(p - 6)}}{\overset{}{2} \cdot 5\overset{}{(p - 5)}(p + 5)} \cdot \dfrac{\overset{1}{2}(p + 2)}{5p\overset{}{(6 - p)}}$ Simplify the ratio of common factors to 1 or −1.

$= -\dfrac{(p + 2)}{25p(p + 5)}$

Answers

4. $\dfrac{14}{y + 4}$ **5.** $\dfrac{x + 6}{10}$

Example 6 **Dividing Rational Expressions**

Divide. $\dfrac{\frac{3x}{4y}}{\frac{5x}{6y}}$

Solution:

 This fraction bar denotes division ($\div$). This expression is called a complex fraction because it has one or more rational expressions in its numerator or denominator.

$= \dfrac{3x}{4y} \div \dfrac{5x}{6y}$

$= \dfrac{3x}{4y} \cdot \dfrac{6y}{5x}$ Multiply by the reciprocal of the second fraction.

$= \dfrac{3 \cdot \overset{1}{\cancel{x}}}{\cancel{2} \cdot 2 \cdot \cancel{y}} \cdot \dfrac{\overset{1}{\cancel{2}} \cdot 3 \cdot \overset{1}{\cancel{y}}}{5 \cdot \cancel{x}}$ Simplify the ratio of common factors to 1.

$= \dfrac{9}{10}$

Sometimes multiplication and division of rational expressions appear in the same problem. In such a case, apply the order of operations by multiplying or dividing in order from left to right.

Example 7 **Multiplying and Dividing Rational Expressions**

Perform the indicated operations. $\dfrac{4}{c^2 - 9} \div \dfrac{6}{c - 3} \cdot \dfrac{3c}{8}$

Solution:

In this example, division occurs first, before multiplication. Parentheses may be inserted to reinforce the proper order.

$\left(\dfrac{4}{c^2 - 9} \div \dfrac{6}{c - 3} \right) \cdot \dfrac{3c}{8}$

$= \left(\dfrac{4}{c^2 - 9} \cdot \dfrac{c - 3}{6} \right) \cdot \dfrac{3c}{8}$ Multiply the first fraction by the reciprocal of the second.

$= \left(\dfrac{2 \cdot 2}{(c - 3)(c + 3)} \cdot \dfrac{c - 3}{2 \cdot 3} \right) \cdot \dfrac{3 \cdot c}{2 \cdot 2 \cdot 2}$ Now that each operation is written as multiplication, factor the polynomials and reduce the common factors.

$= \dfrac{\overset{1}{\cancel{2}} \cdot \overset{1}{\cancel{2}}}{\cancel{(c - 3)}(c + 3)} \cdot \dfrac{\overset{1}{\cancel{(c - 3)}}}{2 \cdot \cancel{3}} \cdot \dfrac{\overset{1}{\cancel{3}} \cdot c}{2 \cdot 2 \cdot 2}$

$= \dfrac{c}{4(c + 3)}$ Simplify.

Section 14.2 Practice Exercises

Review Exercises

For Exercises 1–8, multiply or divide the fractions.

1. $\dfrac{3}{5} \cdot \dfrac{1}{2}$

2. $\dfrac{6}{7} \cdot \dfrac{5}{12}$

3. $\dfrac{3}{4} \div \dfrac{3}{8}$

4. $\dfrac{18}{5} \div \dfrac{2}{5}$

5. $6 \cdot \dfrac{5}{12}$

6. $\dfrac{7}{25} \cdot 5$

7. $\dfrac{\frac{21}{4}}{\frac{7}{5}}$

8. $\dfrac{\frac{9}{2}}{\frac{3}{4}}$

Objective 1: Multiplication of Rational Expressions

For Exercises 9–24, multiply. **(See Examples 1–3.)**

9. $\dfrac{2xy}{5x^2} \cdot \dfrac{15}{4y}$

10. $\dfrac{7s}{t^2} \cdot \dfrac{t^2}{14s^2}$

11. $\dfrac{6x^3}{9x^6y^2} \cdot \dfrac{18x^4y^7}{4y}$

12. $\dfrac{10a^2b}{15b^2} \cdot \dfrac{30b}{2a^3}$

13. $\dfrac{4x - 24}{20x} \cdot \dfrac{5x}{8}$

14. $\dfrac{5a + 20}{a} \cdot \dfrac{3a}{10}$

15. $\dfrac{3y + 18}{y^2} \cdot \dfrac{4y}{6y + 36}$

16. $\dfrac{2p - 4}{6p} \cdot \dfrac{4p^2}{8p - 16}$

17. $\dfrac{10}{2 - a} \cdot \dfrac{a - 2}{16}$

18. $\dfrac{b - 3}{6} \cdot \dfrac{20}{3 - b}$

19. $\dfrac{b^2 - a^2}{a - b} \cdot \dfrac{a}{a^2 - ab}$

20. $\dfrac{(x - y)^2}{x^2 + xy} \cdot \dfrac{x}{y - x}$

21. $\dfrac{y^2 + 2y + 1}{5y - 10} \cdot \dfrac{y^2 - 3y + 2}{y^2 - 1}$

22. $\dfrac{6a^2 - 6}{a^2 + 6a + 5} \cdot \dfrac{a^2 + 5a}{12a}$

23. $\dfrac{10x}{2x^2 + 3x + 1} \cdot \dfrac{x^2 + 7x + 6}{5x}$

24. $\dfrac{b - 3}{b^2 + b - 12} \cdot \dfrac{4b + 16}{b + 1}$

Objective 2: Division of Rational Expressions

For Exercises 25–38, divide. **(See Examples 4–6.)**

25. $\dfrac{4x}{7y} \div \dfrac{2x^2}{21xy}$

26. $\dfrac{6cd}{5d^2} \div \dfrac{8c^3}{10d}$

27. $\dfrac{\frac{8m^4n^5}{5n^6}}{\frac{24mn}{15m^3}}$

28. $\dfrac{\frac{10a^3b}{3a}}{\frac{5b}{9ab}}$

29. $\dfrac{4a + 12}{6a - 18} \div \dfrac{3a + 9}{5a - 15}$

30. $\dfrac{8b - 16}{3b + 3} \div \dfrac{5b - 10}{2b + 2}$

31. $\dfrac{3x - 21}{6x^2 - 42x} \div \dfrac{7}{12x}$

32. $\dfrac{4a^2 - 4a}{9a - 9} \div \dfrac{5}{12a}$

33. $\dfrac{m^2 - n^2}{9} \div \dfrac{3n - 3m}{27m}$

34. $\dfrac{9 - b^2}{15b + 15} \div \dfrac{b - 3}{5b}$

35. $\dfrac{3p + 4q}{p^2 + 4pq + 4q^2} \div \dfrac{4}{p + 2q}$

36. $\dfrac{x^2 + 2xy + y^2}{2x - y} \div \dfrac{x + y}{5}$

37. $\dfrac{p^2 - 2p - 3}{p^2 - p - 6} \div \dfrac{p^2 - 1}{p^2 + 2p}$

38. $\dfrac{4t^2 - 1}{t^2 - 5t} \div \dfrac{2t^2 + 5t + 2}{t^2 - 3t - 10}$

Mixed Exercises

For Exercises 39–64, multiply or divide as indicated.

39. $(w + 3) \cdot \dfrac{w}{2w^2 + 5w - 3}$

40. $\dfrac{5t + 1}{5t^2 - 31t + 6} \cdot (t - 6)$

41. $\dfrac{\dfrac{5t - 10}{12}}{\dfrac{4t - 8}{8}}$

42. $\dfrac{\dfrac{6m + 6}{5}}{\dfrac{3m + 3}{10}}$

43. $\dfrac{q + 1}{5q^2 - 28q - 12} \cdot (5q + 2)$

44. $(r - 5) \cdot \dfrac{4r}{2r^2 - 7r - 15}$

45. $\dfrac{2a^2 + 13a - 24}{8a - 12} \div (a + 8)$

46. $\dfrac{3y^2 + 20y - 7}{5y + 35} \div (3y - 1)$

47. $\dfrac{y^2 + 5y - 36}{y^2 - 2y - 8} \cdot \dfrac{y + 2}{y - 6}$

48. $\dfrac{z^2 - 11z + 28}{z - 1} \cdot \dfrac{z + 1}{z^2 - 6z - 7}$

49. $\dfrac{2t^2 + t - 1}{t^2 + 3t + 2} \cdot \dfrac{t + 4}{2t - 1}$

50. $\dfrac{3p^2 - 2p - 8}{3p^2 - 5p - 12} \cdot \dfrac{p + 1}{p - 2}$

51. $(5t - 1) \div \dfrac{5t^2 + 9t - 2}{3t + 8}$

52. $(2q - 3) \div \dfrac{2q^2 + 5q - 12}{q - 7}$

53. $\dfrac{x^2 + 2x - 3}{x^2 - 3x + 2} \cdot \dfrac{x^2 + 2x - 8}{x^2 + 4x + 3}$

54. $\dfrac{y^2 + y - 12}{y^2 - y - 20} \cdot \dfrac{y^2 + y - 30}{y^2 - 2y - 3}$

55. $\dfrac{\dfrac{w^2 - 6w + 9}{8}}{\dfrac{9 - w^2}{4w + 12}}$

56. $\dfrac{\dfrac{p^2 - 6p + 8}{24}}{\dfrac{16 - p^2}{6p + 6}}$

57. $\dfrac{5k^2 + 7k + 2}{k^2 + 5k + 4} \div \dfrac{5k^2 + 17k + 6}{k^2 + 10k + 24}$

58. $\dfrac{4h^2 - 5h + 1}{h^2 + h - 2} \div \dfrac{6h^2 - 7h + 2}{2h^2 + 3h - 2}$

59. $\dfrac{ax + a + bx + b}{2x^2 + 4x + 2} \cdot \dfrac{4x + 4}{a^2 + ab}$

60. $\dfrac{3my + 9m + ny + 3n}{9m^2 + 6mn + n^2} \cdot \dfrac{30m + 10n}{5y^2 + 15y}$

61. $\dfrac{y^4 - 1}{2y^2 - 3y + 1} \div \dfrac{2y^2 + 2}{8y^2 - 4y}$

62. $\dfrac{x^4 - 16}{6x^2 + 24} \div \dfrac{x^2 - 2x}{3x}$

63. $\dfrac{x^2 - xy - 2y^2}{x + 2y} \div \dfrac{x^2 - 4xy + 4y^2}{x^2 - 4y^2}$

64. $\dfrac{4m^2 - 4mn - 3n^2}{8m^2 - 18n^2} \div \dfrac{3m + 3n}{6m^2 + 15mn + 9n^2}$

For Exercises 65–68, multiply or divide as indicated. **(See Example 7.)**

65. $\dfrac{b^3 - 3b^2 + 4b - 12}{b^4 - 16} \cdot \dfrac{3b^2 + 5b - 2}{3b^2 - 10b + 3} \div \dfrac{3}{6b - 12}$

66. $\dfrac{x^2 - 25}{3x^2 + 3xy} \cdot \dfrac{x^2 + 4x + xy + 4y}{x^2 + 9x + 20} \div \dfrac{x - 5}{x}$

67. $\dfrac{a^2 - 5a}{a^2 + 7a + 12} \div \dfrac{a^3 - 7a^2 + 10a}{a^2 + 9a + 18} \div \dfrac{a + 6}{a + 4}$

68. $\dfrac{t^2 + t - 2}{t^2 + 5t + 6} \div \dfrac{t - 1}{t} \div \dfrac{5t - 5}{t + 3}$

Section 14.3 | Least Common Denominator

1. Least Common Denominator

In Sections 14.1 and 14.2, we learned how to simplify, multiply, and divide rational expressions. Our next goal is to add and subtract rational expressions. As with fractions, rational expressions may be added or subtracted only if they have the same denominator.

Recall from Section 4.4 that the **least common denominator (LCD)** of two or more rational expressions is defined as the least common multiple of the denominators. For example, consider the fractions $\frac{1}{20}$ and $\frac{1}{8}$. By inspection, you can probably see that the least common denominator is 40. To understand why, find the prime factorization of both denominators:

$$20 = 2^2 \cdot 5 \quad \text{and} \quad 8 = 2^3$$

A common multiple of 20 and 8 must be a multiple of 5, a multiple of 2^2, and a multiple of 2^3. However, any number that is a multiple of $2^3 = 8$ is automatically a multiple of $2^2 = 4$. Therefore, it is sufficient to construct the least common denominator as the product of unique prime factors, in which each factor is raised to its highest power.

$$\text{The LCD of } \frac{1}{20} \text{ and } \frac{1}{8} \text{ is } 2^3 \cdot 5 = 40.$$

> **PROCEDURE** Finding the Least Common Denominator of Two or More Rational Expressions
>
> **Step 1** Factor all denominators completely.
> **Step 2** The LCD is the product of unique prime factors from the denominators, in which each factor is raised to the highest power to which it appears in any denominator.

Example 1 Finding the Least Common Denominator of Rational Expressions

Find the LCD of the rational expressions.

a. $\dfrac{5}{14}; \dfrac{3}{49}; \dfrac{1}{8}$ b. $\dfrac{5}{3x^2z}; \dfrac{7}{x^5y^3}$

Solution:

a. Factor the denominators, 14, 49, and 8.

	2's	7's
14 =	2	7
49 =		$\boxed{7^2}$
8 =	$\boxed{2^3}$	

We circle the factor of 2 raised to its greatest power. We circle the factor of 7 raised to its greatest power. The LCD is their product.

The least common denominator (LCD) is $2^3 \cdot 7^2 = 392$.

b. The denominators are already factored.

	3's	**x's**	**y's**	**z's**
$3x^2z =$	③	x^2		ⓩ
$x^5y^3 =$		ⓧ⁵	ⓨ³	

We circle the factors of $3, x, y$, and z, each raised to its corresponding highest power.

The least common denominator (LCD) is $3^1x^5y^3z^1$ or simply $3x^5y^3z$.

Example 2 **Finding the Least Common Denominator of Rational Expressions**

Find the LCD for each pair of rational expressions.

a. $\dfrac{a + b}{a^2 - 25}; \dfrac{1}{2a - 10}$ **b.** $\dfrac{x - 5}{x^2 - 2x}; \dfrac{1}{x^2 - 4x + 4}$

Solution:

a. $\dfrac{a + b}{a^2 - 25}; \dfrac{1}{2a - 10}$

$= \dfrac{a + b}{(a - 5)(a + 5)}; \dfrac{1}{2(a - 5)}$ Factor the denominators.

The LCD is $2(a - 5)(a + 5)$.   The LCD is the product of unique factors, each raised to its highest power.

b. $\dfrac{x - 5}{x^2 - 2x}; \dfrac{1}{x^2 - 4x + 4}$

$= \dfrac{x - 5}{x(x - 2)}; \dfrac{1}{(x - 2)^2}$ Factor the denominators.

The LCD is $x(x - 2)^2$.   The LCD is the product of unique factors, each raised to its highest power.

Skill Practice
Find the LCD.

3. $\dfrac{x}{x^2 - 16}; \dfrac{2}{3x + 12}$

4. $\dfrac{6}{t^2 + 5t - 14};$
$\dfrac{8}{t^2 - 3t + 2}$

Concept Connections

5. Nadia thought that the LCD for the rational expressions $\frac{5}{x}$ and $\frac{1}{x+3}$ should be $x + 3$. Explain why this is not the LCD. What is the correct LCD?

2. Writing Rational Expressions with the Least Common Denominator

To add or subtract two rational expressions, the expressions must have the same denominator. Therefore, we must first practice the skill of converting each rational expression into an equivalent expression with the LCD as its denominator. The process is as follows: Identify the LCD for the two expressions. Then, multiply the numerator and denominator of each fraction by the factors from the LCD that are missing from the original denominators.

Answers

3. $3(x - 4)(x + 4)$
4. $(t + 7)(t - 2)(t - 1)$
5. The unique factors that appear in the denominators are x and $x + 3$, both of which are needed in the LCD. The correct LCD is $x(x + 3)$.

Example 3 **Converting to the Least Common Denominator**

Find the LCD of each pair of rational expressions. Then convert each expression to an equivalent fraction with the denominator equal to the LCD.

a. $\dfrac{3}{2ab}; \dfrac{6}{5a^2}$ **b.** $\dfrac{4}{x+1}; \dfrac{7}{x-4}$

Solution:

a. $\dfrac{3}{2ab}; \dfrac{6}{5a^2}$ The LCD is $10a^2b$.

$\dfrac{3}{2ab} = \dfrac{3 \cdot 5a}{2ab \cdot 5a} = \dfrac{15a}{10a^2b}$

The first expression is missing the factor $5a$ from the denominator.

$\dfrac{6}{5a^2} = \dfrac{6 \cdot 2b}{5a^2 \cdot 2b} = \dfrac{12b}{10a^2b}$

The second expression is missing the factor $2b$ from the denominator.

b. $\dfrac{4}{x+1}; \dfrac{7}{x-4}$ The LCD is $(x+1)(x-4)$.

$\dfrac{4}{x+1} = \dfrac{4(x-4)}{(x+1)(x-4)} = \dfrac{4x-16}{(x+1)(x-4)}$

The first expression is missing the factor $(x-4)$ from the denominator.

$\dfrac{7}{x-4} = \dfrac{7(x+1)}{(x-4)(x+1)} = \dfrac{7x+7}{(x-4)(x+1)}$

The second expression is missing the factor $(x+1)$ from the denominator.

Example 4 **Converting to the Least Common Denominator**

Find the LCD of each pair of rational expressions. Then convert each expression to an equivalent fraction with the denominator equal to the LCD.

$$\dfrac{w+2}{w^2-w-12}; \dfrac{1}{w^2-9}$$

Solution:

$\dfrac{w+2}{w^2-w-12}; \dfrac{1}{w^2-9}$

To find the LCD, factor each denominator.

$\dfrac{w+2}{(w-4)(w+3)}; \dfrac{1}{(w-3)(w+3)}$

The LCD is $(w-4)(w+3)(w-3)$.

$\dfrac{w+2}{(w-4)(w+3)} = \dfrac{(w+2)(w-3)}{(w-4)(w+3)(w-3)}$

The first expression is missing the factor $(w-3)$ from the denominator.

$= \dfrac{w^2-w-6}{(w-4)(w+3)(w-3)}$

$\dfrac{1}{(w-3)(w+3)} = \dfrac{1(w-4)}{(w-3)(w+3)(w-4)}$

The second expression is missing the factor $(w-4)$ from the denominator.

$= \dfrac{w-4}{(w-3)(w+3)(w-4)}$

Example 5 Converting to the Least Common Denominator

Find the LCD of the expressions $\dfrac{3}{x-7}$ and $\dfrac{1}{7-x}$.

Solution:

Notice that the expressions $x-7$ and $7-x$ are opposites and differ by a factor of -1. Therefore, we may use either $x-7$ or $7-x$ as a common denominator. Each case is shown below.

Converting to the Denominator $x-7$

$\dfrac{3}{x-7}; \dfrac{1}{7-x}$

Leave the first fraction unchanged because it has the desired LCD.

$\dfrac{1}{7-x} = \dfrac{(-1)1}{(-1)(7-x)}$

Multiply the *second* rational expression by the ratio $\frac{-1}{-1}$ to change its denominator to $x-7$.

$= \dfrac{-1}{-7+x}$

Apply the distributive property.

$= \dfrac{-1}{x-7}$

Converting to the Denominator $7-x$

$\dfrac{3}{x-7}; \dfrac{1}{7-x}$

Leave the second fraction unchanged because it has the desired LCD.

$\dfrac{3}{x-7} = \dfrac{(-1)3}{(-1)(x-7)};$

Multiply the *first* rational expression by the ratio $\frac{-1}{-1}$ to change its denominator to $7-x$.

$= \dfrac{-3}{-x+7}$

Apply the distributive property.

$= \dfrac{-3}{7-x}$

TIP: In Example 5, the expressions

$\dfrac{3}{x-7}$ and $\dfrac{1}{7-x}$

have opposite factors in the denominators. In such a case, you do not need to include *both* factors in the LCD.

Answers

9. a. The LCD is $(w-2)$ or $(2-w)$.

b. $\dfrac{9}{w-2} = \dfrac{9}{w-2};$

$\dfrac{11}{2-w} = \dfrac{-11}{w-2}$

or

$\dfrac{9}{w-2} = \dfrac{-9}{2-w};$

$\dfrac{11}{2-w} = \dfrac{11}{2-w}$

Section 14.3 Practice Exercises

Boost *your* GRADE at ALEKS.com!

ALEKS version 3.0

- Practice Problems
- Self-Tests
- NetTutor
- e-Professors
- Videos

Study Skills Exercise

1. Define the key term **least common denominator**.

Review Exercises

2. Evaluate the expression for the given values of x. $\dfrac{2x}{x+5}$

 a. $x = 1$ **b.** $x = 5$ **c.** $x = -5$

For Exercises 3–4, identify the restricted values. Then simplify the expression to lowest terms.

3. $\dfrac{3x + 3}{5x^2 - 5}$

4. $\dfrac{x + 2}{x^2 - 3x - 10}$

For Exercises 5–8, multiply or divide as indicated.

5. $\dfrac{a + 3}{a + 7} \cdot \dfrac{a^2 + 3a - 10}{a^2 + a - 6}$

6. $\dfrac{6(a + 2b)}{2(a - 3b)} \cdot \dfrac{4(a + 3b)(a - 3b)}{9(a + 2b)(a - 2b)}$

7. $\dfrac{16y^2}{9y + 36} \div \dfrac{8y^3}{3y + 12}$

8. $\dfrac{5b^2 + 6b + 1}{b^2 + 5b + 6} \div (5b + 1)$

9. Which of the expressions are equivalent to $-\dfrac{5}{x - 3}$? Circle all that apply.

   a. $\dfrac{-5}{x - 3}$ **b.** $\dfrac{5}{-x + 3}$ **c.** $\dfrac{5}{3 - x}$ **d.** $\dfrac{5}{-(x - 3)}$

10. Which of the expressions are equivalent to $\dfrac{4 - a}{6}$? Circle all that apply.

   a. $\dfrac{a - 4}{-6}$ **b.** $\dfrac{a - 4}{6}$ **c.** $\dfrac{-(4 - a)}{-6}$ **d.** $-\dfrac{a - 4}{6}$

Objective 1: Least Common Denominator

11. Explain why the least common denominator of $\frac{1}{x^3}, \frac{1}{x^5}$, and $\frac{1}{x^4}$ is x^5.

12. Explain why the least common denominator of $\frac{2}{y^3}, \frac{9}{y^6}$, and $\frac{4}{y^5}$ is y^6.

For Exercises 13–30, identify the LCD. **(See Examples 1–2.)**

13. $\dfrac{4}{15}; \dfrac{5}{9}$

14. $\dfrac{7}{12}; \dfrac{1}{18}$

15. $\dfrac{1}{16}; \dfrac{1}{4}; \dfrac{1}{6}$

16. $\dfrac{1}{2}; \dfrac{11}{12}; \dfrac{3}{8}$

17. $\dfrac{1}{7}; \dfrac{2}{9}$

18. $\dfrac{2}{3}; \dfrac{5}{8}$

19. $\dfrac{1}{3x^2y}; \dfrac{8}{9xy^3}$

20. $\dfrac{5}{2a^4b^2}; \dfrac{1}{8ab^3}$

21. $\dfrac{6}{w^2}; \dfrac{7}{y}$

22. $\dfrac{2}{r}; \dfrac{3}{s^2}$

23. $\dfrac{p}{(p + 3)(p - 1)}; \dfrac{2}{(p + 3)(p + 2)}$

24. $\dfrac{6}{(q + 4)(q - 4)}; \dfrac{q^2}{(q + 1)(q + 4)}$

25. $\dfrac{7}{3t(t + 1)}; \dfrac{10t}{9(t + 1)^2}$

26. $\dfrac{13x}{15(x - 1)^2}; \dfrac{5}{3x(x - 1)}$

27. $\dfrac{y}{y^2 - 4}; \dfrac{3y}{y^2 + 5y + 6}$

28. $\dfrac{4}{w^2 - 3w + 2}; \dfrac{w}{w^2 - 4}$

29. $\dfrac{5}{3 - x}; \dfrac{7}{x - 3}$

30. $\dfrac{4}{x - 6}; \dfrac{9}{6 - x}$

31. Explain why a common denominator of

$$\frac{b+1}{b-1} \quad \text{and} \quad \frac{b}{1-b}$$

could be either $(b-1)$ or $(1-b)$.

32. Explain why a common denominator of

$$\frac{1}{6-t} \quad \text{and} \quad \frac{t}{t-6}$$

could be either $(6-t)$ or $(t-6)$.

Objective 2: Writing Rational Expressions with the Least Common Denominator

For Exercises 33–56, find the LCD. Then convert each expression to an equivalent expression with the denominator equal to the LCD. **(See Examples 3–5.)**

33. $\dfrac{6}{5x^2}; \dfrac{1}{x}$

34. $\dfrac{3}{y}; \dfrac{7}{9y^2}$

35. $\dfrac{4}{5x^2}; \dfrac{y}{6x^3}$

36. $\dfrac{3}{15b^2}; \dfrac{c}{3b^2}$

37. $\dfrac{5}{6a^2b}; \dfrac{a}{12b}$

38. $\dfrac{x}{15y^2}; \dfrac{y}{5xy}$

39. $\dfrac{6}{m+4}; \dfrac{3}{m-1}$

40. $\dfrac{3}{n-5}; \dfrac{7}{n+2}$

41. $\dfrac{6}{2x-5}; \dfrac{1}{x+3}$

42. $\dfrac{4}{m+3}; \dfrac{-3}{5m+1}$

43. $\dfrac{6}{(w+3)(w-8)}; \dfrac{w}{(w-8)(w+1)}$

44. $\dfrac{t}{(t+2)(t+12)}; \dfrac{18}{(t-2)(t+2)}$

45. $\dfrac{6p}{p^2-4}; \dfrac{3}{p^2+4p+4}$

46. $\dfrac{5}{q^2-6q+9}; \dfrac{q}{q^2-9}$

47. $\dfrac{1}{a-4}; \dfrac{a}{4-a}$

48. $\dfrac{3b}{2b-5}; \dfrac{2b}{5-2b}$

49. $\dfrac{4}{x-7}; \dfrac{y}{14-2x}$

50. $\dfrac{4}{3x-15}; \dfrac{z}{5-x}$

51. $\dfrac{1}{a+b}; \dfrac{6}{-a-b}$

52. $\dfrac{p}{-q-8}; \dfrac{1}{q+8}$

53. $\dfrac{-3}{24y+8}; \dfrac{5}{18y+6}$

54. $\dfrac{r}{10r+5}; \dfrac{2}{16r+8}$

55. $\dfrac{3}{5z}; \dfrac{1}{z+4}$

56. $\dfrac{-1}{4a-8}; \dfrac{5}{4a}$

Expanding Your Skills

For Exercises 57–58, find the LCD. Then convert each expression to an equivalent expression with the denominator equal to the LCD.

57. $\dfrac{z}{z^2+9z+14}; \dfrac{-3z}{z^2+10z+21}; \dfrac{5}{z^2+5z+6}$

58. $\dfrac{6}{w^2-3w-4}; \dfrac{1}{w^2+6w+5}; \dfrac{-9w}{w^2+w-20}$

Addition and Subtraction of Rational Expressions

Objectives

1. Addition and Subtraction of Rational Expressions with the Same Denominator
2. Addition and Subtraction of Rational Expressions with Different Denominators
3. Using Rational Expressions in Translations

1. Addition and Subtraction of Rational Expressions with the Same Denominator

To add or subtract rational expressions, the expressions must have the same denominator. As with fractions, we add or subtract rational expressions with the same denominator by combining the terms in the numerator and then writing the result over the common denominator. Then, if possible, we simplify the expression to lowest terms.

> **PROPERTY Addition and Subtraction of Rational Expressions**
>
> Let p, q, and r represent polynomials where $q \neq 0$. Then,
>
> **1.** $\dfrac{p}{q} + \dfrac{r}{q} = \dfrac{p+r}{q}$ **2.** $\dfrac{p}{q} - \dfrac{r}{q} = \dfrac{p-r}{q}$

Skill Practice

Add or subtract as indicated.

1. $\dfrac{3}{14} + \dfrac{4}{14}$

2. $\dfrac{2}{7d} - \dfrac{9}{7d}$

Example 1 **Adding and Subtracting Rational Expressions with a Common Denominator**

Add or subtract as indicated.

a. $\dfrac{1}{12} + \dfrac{7}{12}$ **b.** $\dfrac{2}{5p} - \dfrac{7}{5p}$

Solution:

a. $\dfrac{1}{12} + \dfrac{7}{12}$ The fractions have the same denominator.

$= \dfrac{1+7}{12}$ Add the terms in the numerators, and write the result over the common denominator.

$= \dfrac{8}{12}$

$= \dfrac{2}{3}$ Simplify to lowest terms.

b. $\dfrac{2}{5p} - \dfrac{7}{5p}$ The rational expressions have the same denominator.

$= \dfrac{2-7}{5p}$ Subtract the terms in the numerators, and write the result over the common denominator.

$= \dfrac{-5}{5p}$

$= \dfrac{(-\overset{-1}{5})}{\overset{}{5}p}$ Simplify to lowest terms.

$= -\dfrac{1}{p}$

Answers

1. $\dfrac{1}{2}$ **2.** $-\dfrac{1}{d}$

Example 2 Adding and Subtracting Rational Expressions with a Common Denominator

Add or subtract as indicated.

a. $\dfrac{2}{3d+5} + \dfrac{7d}{3d+5}$ **b.** $\dfrac{x^2}{x-3} - \dfrac{-5x+24}{x-3}$

Skill Practice

Add or subtract as indicated.

3. $\dfrac{x^2+2}{x+3} + \dfrac{4x+1}{x+3}$

4. $\dfrac{4t-9}{2t+1} - \dfrac{t-5}{2t+1}$

Solution:

a. $\dfrac{2}{3d+5} + \dfrac{7d}{3d+5}$ The rational expressions have the same denominator.

$= \dfrac{2+7d}{3d+5}$ Add the terms in the numerators, and write the result over the common denominator.

$= \dfrac{7d+2}{3d+5}$ Because the numerator and denominator share no common factors, the expression is in lowest terms.

b. $\dfrac{x^2}{x-3} - \dfrac{-5x+24}{x-3}$ The rational expressions have the same denominator.

$= \dfrac{x^2-(-5x+24)}{x-3}$ Subtract the terms in the numerators, and write the result over the common denominator.

$= \dfrac{x^2+5x-24}{x-3}$ Simplify the numerator.

$= \dfrac{(x+8)(x-3)}{(x-3)}$ Factor the numerator and denominator to determine if the rational expression can be simplified.

$= \dfrac{(x+8)\cancel{(x-3)}^1}{\cancel{(x-3)}}$ Simplify to lowest terms.

$= x+8$

Avoiding Mistakes

When subtracting rational expressions, use parentheses to group the terms in the numerator that follow the subtraction sign. This will help you remember to apply the distributive property.

2. Addition and Subtraction of Rational Expressions with Different Denominators

To add or subtract two rational expressions with unlike denominators, we must convert the expressions to equivalent expressions with the same denominator. For example, consider adding

$$\frac{1}{10} + \frac{12}{5y}$$

The LCD is $10y$. For each expression, identify the factors from the LCD that are missing from the denominator. Then multiply the numerator and denominator of the expression by the missing factor(s).

$$\underset{\underset{y}{\text{Missing}}}{\frac{1}{10}} + \underset{\underset{2}{\text{Missing}}}{\frac{12}{5y}}$$

Answers

3. $x+1$ **4.** $\dfrac{3t-4}{2t+1}$

$$= \frac{1 \cdot y}{10 \cdot y} + \frac{12 \cdot 2}{5y \cdot 2}$$

$$= \frac{y}{10y} + \frac{24}{10y}$$ The rational expressions now have the same denominators.

$$= \frac{y + 24}{10y}$$ Add the numerators.

After successfully adding or subtracting two rational expressions, always check to see if the final answer is simplified. If necessary, factor the numerator and denominator, and reduce common factors. The expression

$$\frac{y + 24}{10y}$$

is in lowest terms because the numerator and denominator do not share any common factors.

PROCEDURE **Adding or Subtracting Rational Expressions**

Step 1 Factor the denominators of each rational expression.
Step 2 Identify the LCD.
Step 3 Rewrite each rational expression as an equivalent expression with the LCD as its denominator.
Step 4 Add or subtract the numerators, and write the result over the common denominator.
Step 5 Simplify to lowest terms.

Skill Practice

Add.

5. $\dfrac{4}{3x} + \dfrac{1}{2x^2}$

Avoiding Mistakes

Do not reduce after rewriting the fractions with the LCD. You will revert back to the original expression.

Example 3 **Subtracting Rational Expressions with Different Denominators**

Subtract. $\dfrac{4}{7k} - \dfrac{3}{k^2}$

Solution:

$$\frac{4}{7k} - \frac{3}{k^2}$$

Step 1: The denominators are already factored.

Step 2: The LCD is $7k^2$.

$$= \frac{4 \cdot k}{7k \cdot k} - \frac{3 \cdot 7}{k^2 \cdot 7}$$ **Step 3:** Write each expression with the LCD.

$$= \frac{4k}{7k^2} - \frac{21}{7k^2}$$

$$= \frac{4k - 21}{7k^2}$$ **Step 4:** Subtract the numerators, and write the result over the LCD.

Step 5: The expression is in lowest terms because the numerator and denominator share no common factors.

Answer

5. $\dfrac{8x + 3}{6x^2}$

Example 4 **Subtracting Rational Expressions with Different Denominators**

Subtract. $\dfrac{2q - 4}{3} - \dfrac{q + 1}{2}$

Skill Practice
Subtract.
6. $\dfrac{q}{12} - \dfrac{q - 2}{4}$

Solution:

$\dfrac{2q - 4}{3} - \dfrac{q + 1}{2}$

Step 1: The denominators are already factored.

Step 2: The LCD is 6.

$= \dfrac{2(2q - 4)}{2 \cdot 3} - \dfrac{3(q + 1)}{3 \cdot 2}$

Step 3: Write each expression with the LCD.

$= \dfrac{2(2q - 4) - 3(q + 1)}{6}$

Step 4: Subtract the numerators, and write the result over the LCD.

$= \dfrac{4q - 8 - 3q - 3}{6}$

$= \dfrac{q - 11}{6}$

Step 5: The expression is in lowest terms because the numerator and denominator share no common factors.

Example 5 **Adding Rational Expressions with Different Denominators**

Add. $\dfrac{1}{x - 5} + \dfrac{-10}{x^2 - 25}$

Skill Practice
Add.
7. $\dfrac{1}{x - 4} + \dfrac{-8}{x^2 - 16}$

Solution:

$\dfrac{1}{x - 5} + \dfrac{-10}{x^2 - 25}$

$= \dfrac{1}{x - 5} + \dfrac{-10}{(x - 5)(x + 5)}$

Step 1: Factor the denominators.

Step 2: The LCD is $(x - 5)(x + 5)$.

$= \dfrac{1(x + 5)}{(x - 5)(x + 5)} + \dfrac{-10}{(x - 5)(x + 5)}$

Step 3: Write each expression with the LCD.

$= \dfrac{1(x + 5) + (-10)}{(x - 5)(x + 5)}$

Step 4: Add the numerators, and write the result over the LCD.

$= \dfrac{x + 5 - 10}{(x - 5)(x + 5)}$

$= \dfrac{\overset{1}{x - 5}}{(x - 5)(x + 5)}$

Step 5: Simplify.

$= \dfrac{1}{x + 5}$

Skill Practice

Subtract.

8. $\dfrac{2y}{y-1} - \dfrac{1}{y} - \dfrac{2y+1}{y^2-y}$

Example 6 **Adding and Subtracting Rational Expressions with Different Denominators**

Add or subtract as indicated. $\dfrac{p+2}{p-1} - \dfrac{2}{p+6} - \dfrac{14}{p^2+5p-6}$

Solution:

$\dfrac{p+2}{p-1} - \dfrac{2}{p+6} - \dfrac{14}{p^2+5p-6}$

$= \dfrac{p+2}{p-1} - \dfrac{2}{p+6} - \dfrac{14}{(p-1)(p+6)}$ **Step 1:** Factor the denominators.

                                      Step 2: The LCD is $(p-1)(p+6)$.

                                        Step 3: Write each expression with the LCD.

$= \dfrac{(p+2)(p+6)}{(p-1)(p+6)} - \dfrac{2(p-1)}{(p+6)(p-1)} - \dfrac{14}{(p-1)(p+6)}$

$= \dfrac{(p+2)(p+6) - 2(p-1) - 14}{(p-1)(p+6)}$ **Step 4:** Combine the numerators, and write the result over the LCD.

$= \dfrac{p^2 + 6p + 2p + 12 - 2p + 2 - 14}{(p-1)(p+6)}$ **Step 5:** Clear parentheses in the numerator.

$= \dfrac{p^2 + 6p}{(p-1)(p+6)}$ Combine *like* terms.

$= \dfrac{p(p+6)}{(p-1)(p+6)}$ Factor the numerator to determine if the expression is in lowest terms.

$= \dfrac{p(\overset{1}{\cancel{p+6}})}{(p-1)(\cancel{p+6})}$ Simplify to lowest terms.

$= \dfrac{p}{p-1}$

When the denominators of two rational expressions are opposites, we can produce identical denominators by multiplying one of the expressions by the ratio $\dfrac{-1}{-1}$. This is demonstrated in the next example.

Answer

8. $\dfrac{2y-3}{y-1}$

Example 7 **Adding Rational Expressions with Different Denominators**

Add the rational expressions. $\dfrac{1}{d-7} + \dfrac{5}{7-d}$

Solution:

$\dfrac{1}{d-7} + \dfrac{5}{7-d}$

The expressions $d - 7$ and $7 - d$ are opposites and differ by a factor of -1. Therefore, multiply the numerator and denominator of *either* expression by -1 to obtain a common denominator.

$= \dfrac{1}{d-7} + \dfrac{(-1)5}{(-1)(7-d)}$

Note that $-1(7 - d) = -7 + d$ or $d - 7$.

$= \dfrac{1}{d-7} + \dfrac{-5}{d-7}$

Simplify.

$= \dfrac{1 + (-5)}{d-7}$

Add the terms in the numerators, and write the result over the common denominator.

$= \dfrac{-4}{d-7}$

Skill Practice

Add or subtract as indicated.

9. $\dfrac{3}{p-8} + \dfrac{1}{8-p}$

3. Using Rational Expressions in Translations

Example 8 **Using Rational Expressions in Translations**

Translate the English phrase into a mathematical expression. Then simplify by combining the rational expressions.

The difference of the reciprocal of n and the quotient of n and 3

Solution:

The difference of the reciprocal of n and the quotient of n and 3

$$\underset{\substack{\text{The reciprocal} \\ \text{of } n}}{\left(\dfrac{1}{n}\right)} \overset{\substack{\text{The difference of}}}{-} \underset{\substack{\text{The quotient} \\ \text{of } n \text{ and } 3}}{\left(\dfrac{n}{3}\right)}$$

$\dfrac{1}{n} - \dfrac{n}{3}$

The LCD is $3n$.

$= \dfrac{3 \cdot 1}{3 \cdot n} - \dfrac{n \cdot n}{3 \cdot n}$

Write each expression with the LCD.

$= \dfrac{3 - n^2}{3n}$

Subtract the numerators.

Skill Practice

Translate the English phrase into a mathematical expression. Then simplify by combining the rational expressions.

10. The sum of 1 and the quotient of 2 and a

Answers

9. $\dfrac{2}{p-8}$ or $\dfrac{-2}{8-p}$

10. $1 + \dfrac{2}{a}$; $\dfrac{a+2}{a}$

Section 14.4 Practice Exercises

Review Exercises

1. For the rational expression $\dfrac{x^2 - 4x - 5}{x^2 - 7x + 10}$

   a. Find the value of the expression (if possible) when $x = 0, 1, -1, 2,$ and 5.

   b. Factor the denominator and identify the restricted values.

   c. Simplify the expression to lowest terms.

2. For the rational expression $\dfrac{a^2 + a - 2}{a^2 - 4a - 12}$

   a. Find the value of the expression (if possible) when $a = 0, 1, -2, 2,$ and 6.

   b. Factor the denominator, and identify the restricted values.

   c. Simplify the expression to lowest terms.

For Exercises 3–4, multiply or divide as indicated.

3. $\dfrac{2b^2 - b - 3}{2b^2 - 3b - 9} \div \dfrac{b^2 - 1}{4b + 6}$

4. $\dfrac{6t - 1}{5t - 30} \cdot \dfrac{10t - 25}{2t^2 - 3t - 5}$

Objective 1: Addition and Subtraction of Rational Expressions with the Same Denominator

For Exercises 5–26, add or subtract the expressions with like denominators as indicated. **(See Examples 1–2.)**

5. $\dfrac{7}{8} + \dfrac{3}{8}$

6. $\dfrac{1}{3} + \dfrac{7}{3}$

7. $\dfrac{9}{16} - \dfrac{3}{16}$

8. $\dfrac{14}{15} - \dfrac{4}{15}$

9. $\dfrac{5a}{a + 2} - \dfrac{3a - 4}{a + 2}$

10. $\dfrac{2b}{b - 3} - \dfrac{b - 9}{b - 3}$

11. $\dfrac{5c}{c + 6} + \dfrac{30}{c + 6}$

12. $\dfrac{12}{2 + d} + \dfrac{6d}{2 + d}$

13. $\dfrac{5}{t - 8} - \dfrac{2t + 1}{t - 8}$

14. $\dfrac{7p + 1}{2p + 1} - \dfrac{p - 4}{2p + 1}$

15. $\dfrac{9x^2}{3x - 7} - \dfrac{49}{3x - 7}$

16. $\dfrac{4w^2}{2w - 1} - \dfrac{1}{2w - 1}$

17. $\dfrac{m^2}{m + 5} + \dfrac{10m + 25}{m + 5}$

18. $\dfrac{k^2}{k - 3} - \dfrac{6k - 9}{k - 3}$

19. $\dfrac{2a}{a + 2} + \dfrac{4}{a + 2}$

20. $\dfrac{5b}{b + 4} + \dfrac{20}{b + 4}$

21. $\dfrac{x^2}{x + 5} - \dfrac{25}{x + 5}$

22. $\dfrac{y^2}{y - 7} - \dfrac{49}{y - 7}$

23. $\dfrac{r}{r^2 + 3r + 2} + \dfrac{2}{r^2 + 3r + 2}$

24. $\dfrac{x}{x^2 - x - 12} - \dfrac{4}{x^2 - x - 12}$

25. $\dfrac{1}{3y^2 + 22y + 7} - \dfrac{-3y}{3y^2 + 22y + 7}$

26. $\dfrac{5}{2x^2 + 13x + 20} + \dfrac{2x}{2x^2 + 13x + 20}$

For Exercises 27–28, find an expression that represents the perimeter of the figure (assume that $x > 0, y > 0$, and $t > 0$).

27.

28.

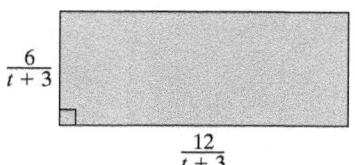

Objective 2: Addition and Subtraction of Rational Expressions with Different Denominators

For Exercises 29–70, add or subtract the expressions with unlike denominators as indicated. **(See Examples 3–7.)**

29. $\dfrac{5}{4} + \dfrac{3}{2a}$

30. $\dfrac{11}{6p} + \dfrac{-7}{4p}$

31. $\dfrac{4}{5xy^3} + \dfrac{2x}{15y^2}$

32. $\dfrac{5}{3a^2b} + \dfrac{-7}{6b^2}$

33. $\dfrac{2}{s^3t^3} - \dfrac{3}{s^4t}$

34. $\dfrac{1}{p^2q} - \dfrac{2}{pq^3}$

35. $\dfrac{z}{3z - 9} - \dfrac{z - 2}{z - 3}$

36. $\dfrac{3w - 8}{2w - 4} - \dfrac{w - 3}{w - 2}$

37. $\dfrac{5}{a + 1} + \dfrac{4}{3a + 3}$

38. $\dfrac{2}{c - 4} + \dfrac{1}{5c - 20}$

39. $\dfrac{k}{k^2 - 9} - \dfrac{4}{k - 3}$

40. $\dfrac{7}{h + 2} - \dfrac{2h - 3}{h^2 - 4}$

41. $\dfrac{3a - 7}{6a + 10} - \dfrac{10}{3a^2 + 5a}$

42. $\dfrac{k + 2}{8k} - \dfrac{3 - k}{12k}$

43. $\dfrac{x}{x - 4} + \dfrac{3}{x + 1}$

44. $\dfrac{4}{y - 3} + \dfrac{y}{y - 5}$

45. $\dfrac{6a}{a^2 - b^2} + \dfrac{2a}{a^2 + ab}$

46. $\dfrac{7x}{x^2 + 2xy + y^2} + \dfrac{3x}{x^2 + xy}$

47. $\dfrac{p}{3} - \dfrac{4p - 1}{-3}$

48. $\dfrac{r}{7} - \dfrac{r - 5}{-7}$

49. $\dfrac{4n}{n - 8} - \dfrac{2n - 1}{8 - n}$

50. $\dfrac{m}{m - 2} - \dfrac{3m + 1}{2 - m}$

51. $\dfrac{5}{x} + \dfrac{3}{x + 2}$

52. $\dfrac{6}{y - 1} + \dfrac{9}{y}$

53. $\dfrac{5}{p - 3} - \dfrac{2}{p - 1}$

54. $\dfrac{1}{7x} + \dfrac{5}{2y^2}$

55. $\dfrac{y}{4y + 2} + \dfrac{3y}{6y + 3}$

56. $\dfrac{4}{q^2 - 2q} - \dfrac{5}{3q - 6}$

57. $\dfrac{4w}{w^2 + 2w - 3} + \dfrac{2}{1 - w}$

58. $\dfrac{z - 23}{z^2 - z - 20} - \dfrac{2}{5 - z}$

59. $\dfrac{3a - 8}{a^2 - 5a + 6} + \dfrac{a + 2}{a^2 - 6a + 8}$

60. $\dfrac{3b + 5}{b^2 + 4b + 3} + \dfrac{-b + 5}{b^2 + 2b - 3}$

61. $\dfrac{3x}{x^2 + x - 6} + \dfrac{x}{x^2 + 5x + 6}$

62. $\dfrac{x}{x^2 + 5x + 4} - \dfrac{2x}{x^2 - 2x - 3}$

63. $\dfrac{3y}{2y^2 - y - 1} - \dfrac{4y}{2y^2 - 7y - 4}$

64. $\dfrac{5}{6y^2 - 7y - 3} + \dfrac{4y}{3y^2 + 4y + 1}$

65. $\dfrac{3}{2p - 1} - \dfrac{4p + 4}{4p^2 - 1}$

66. $\dfrac{1}{3q - 2} - \dfrac{6q + 4}{9q^2 - 4}$

67. $\dfrac{m}{m + n} - \dfrac{m}{m - n} + \dfrac{1}{m^2 - n^2}$

68. $\dfrac{x}{x + y} - \dfrac{2xy}{x^2 - y^2} + \dfrac{y}{x - y}$

69. $\dfrac{2}{a + b} + \dfrac{2}{a - b} - \dfrac{4a}{a^2 - b^2}$

70. $\dfrac{-2x}{x^2 - y^2} + \dfrac{1}{x + y} - \dfrac{1}{x - y}$

For Exercises 71–72, find an expression that represents the perimeter of the figure (assume that $x > 0$ and $t > 0$).

71.

72.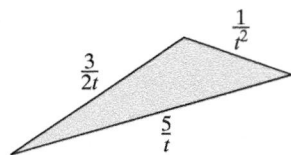

Objective 3: Using Rational Expressions in Translations

73. Let a number be represented by n. Write the reciprocal of n.

74. Write the reciprocal of the sum of a number and 6.

75. Write the quotient of 5 and the sum of a number and 2.

76. Let a number be represented by p. Write the quotient of 12 and p.

For Exercises 77–80, translate the English phrases into algebraic expressions. Then simplify by combining the rational expressions. **(See Example 8.)**

77. The sum of a number and the quantity seven times the reciprocal of the number.

78. The sum of a number and the quantity five times the reciprocal of the number.

79. The difference of the reciprocal of n and the quotient of 2 and n.

80. The difference of the reciprocal of m and the quotient of $3m$ and 7.

Expanding Your Skills

For Exercises 81–84, perform the indicated operations.

81. $\dfrac{2p}{p^2 + 5p + 6} - \dfrac{p + 1}{p^2 + 2p - 3} + \dfrac{3}{p^2 + p - 2}$

82. $\dfrac{3t}{8t^2 + 2t - 1} - \dfrac{5t}{2t^2 - 9t - 5} + \dfrac{2}{4t^2 - 21t + 5}$

83. $\dfrac{3m}{m^2 + 3m - 10} + \dfrac{5}{4 - 2m} - \dfrac{1}{m + 5}$

84. $\dfrac{2n}{3n^2 - 8n - 3} + \dfrac{1}{6 - 2n} - \dfrac{3}{3n + 1}$

For Exercises 85–88, simplify by applying the order of operations.

85. $\left(\dfrac{2}{k + 1} + 3\right)\left(\dfrac{k + 1}{4k + 7}\right)$

86. $\left(\dfrac{p + 1}{3p + 4}\right)\left(\dfrac{1}{p + 1} + 2\right)$

87. $\left(\dfrac{1}{10a} - \dfrac{b}{10a^2}\right) \div \left(\dfrac{1}{10} - \dfrac{b}{10a}\right)$

88. $\left(\dfrac{1}{2m} + \dfrac{n}{2m^2}\right) \div \left(\dfrac{1}{4} + \dfrac{n}{4m}\right)$

Problem Recognition Exercises

Operations on Rational Expressions

In Sections 14.1–14.4, we learned how to simplify, add, subtract, multiply, and divide rational expressions. The procedure for each operation is different, and it takes considerable practice to determine the correct method to apply for a given problem. The following review exercises give you the opportunity to practice the specific techniques for simplifying rational expressions.

For Exercises 1–20, perform any indicated operations and simplify the expression.

1. $\dfrac{5}{3x+1} - \dfrac{2x-4}{3x+1}$

2. $\dfrac{\dfrac{w+1}{w^2-16}}{\dfrac{w+1}{w+4}}$

3. $\dfrac{3}{y} \cdot \dfrac{y^2-5y}{6y-9}$

4. $\dfrac{-1}{x+3} + \dfrac{2}{2x-1}$

5. $\dfrac{x-9}{9x-x^2}$

6. $\dfrac{1}{p} - \dfrac{3}{p^2+3p} + \dfrac{p}{3p+9}$

7. $\dfrac{c^2+5c+6}{c^2+c-2} \div \dfrac{c}{c-1}$

8. $\dfrac{2x^2-5x-3}{x^2-9} \cdot \dfrac{x^2+6x+9}{10x+5}$

9. $\dfrac{6a^2b^3}{72ab^7c}$

10. $\dfrac{2a}{a+b} - \dfrac{b}{a-b} - \dfrac{-4ab}{a^2-b^2}$

11. $\dfrac{p^2+10pq+25q^2}{p^2+6pq+5q^2} \div \dfrac{10p+50q}{2p^2-2q^2}$

12. $\dfrac{3k-8}{k-5} + \dfrac{k-12}{k-5}$

13. $\dfrac{20x^2+10x}{4x^3+4x^2+x}$

14. $\dfrac{w^2-81}{w^2+10w+9} \cdot \dfrac{w^2+w+2zw+2z}{w^2-9w+zw-9z}$

15. $\dfrac{8x^2-18x-5}{4x^2-25} \div \dfrac{4x^2-11x-3}{3x-9}$

16. $\dfrac{xy+7x+5y+35}{x^2+ax+5x+5a}$

17. $\dfrac{a}{a^2-9} - \dfrac{3}{6a-18}$

18. $\dfrac{4}{y^2-36} + \dfrac{2}{y^2-4y-12}$

19. $(t^2+5t-24)\left(\dfrac{t+8}{t-3}\right)$

20. $\dfrac{6b^2-7b-10}{b-2}$

Section 14.5   Complex Fractions

1. Simplifying Complex Fractions (Method I)

A **complex fraction** is a rational expression containing one or more fractions in the numerator, denominator, or both. For example,

$$\frac{\dfrac{1}{ab}}{\dfrac{2}{b}} \quad \text{and} \quad \frac{1 + \dfrac{3}{4} - \dfrac{1}{6}}{\dfrac{1}{2} + \dfrac{1}{3}}$$

are complex fractions.

Two methods will be presented to simplify complex fractions. The first method (Method I) follows the order of operations to simplify the numerator and denominator separately before dividing. The process is summarized as follows.

> **TIP:** The process to simplify a complex fraction by using the order of operations was first introduced in Section 4.7, Examples 5 and 6.

> **PROCEDURE** Simplifying a Complex Fraction (Method I)
> **Step 1** Add or subtract expressions in the numerator to form a single fraction. Add or subtract expressions in the denominator to form a single fraction.
> **Step 2** Divide the rational expressions from Step 1 by multiplying the numerator of the complex fraction by the reciprocal of the denominator of the complex fraction.
> **Step 3** Simplify to lowest terms if possible.

Skill Practice

Simplify the expression.

1. $\dfrac{\dfrac{6x}{y}}{\dfrac{9}{2y}}$

Example 1   Simplifying Complex Fractions (Method I)

Simplify the expression. $\dfrac{\dfrac{1}{ab}}{\dfrac{2}{b}}$

Solution:

Step 1: The numerator and denominator of the complex fraction are already single fractions.

$$\frac{\dfrac{1}{ab}}{\dfrac{2}{b}} \longleftarrow \text{This fraction bar denotes division } (\div).$$

$$= \frac{1}{ab} \div \frac{2}{b}$$

$$= \frac{1}{ab} \cdot \frac{b}{2} \qquad \textbf{Step 2:} \text{ Multiply the numerator of the complex fraction by the reciprocal of } \tfrac{2}{b}, \text{ which is } \tfrac{b}{2}.$$

$$= \frac{1}{a\cancel{b}} \cdot \frac{\cancel{b}^{\,1}}{2} \qquad \textbf{Step 3:} \text{ Reduce common factors and simplify.}$$

$$= \frac{1}{2a}$$

Answer

1. $\dfrac{4x}{3}$

Sometimes it is necessary to simplify the numerator and denominator of a complex fraction before the division can be performed. This is illustrated in Example 2.

Example 2 **Simplifying Complex Fractions (Method I)**

Simplify the expression. $\dfrac{1+\dfrac{3}{4}-\dfrac{1}{6}}{\dfrac{1}{2}+\dfrac{1}{3}}$

Skill Practice
Simplify the expression.

2. $\dfrac{\dfrac{3}{4}-\dfrac{1}{6}+2}{\dfrac{1}{3}+\dfrac{1}{2}}$

Solution:

$\dfrac{1+\dfrac{3}{4}-\dfrac{1}{6}}{\dfrac{1}{2}+\dfrac{1}{3}}$

Step 1: Combine fractions in the numerator and denominator separately.

$=\dfrac{1\cdot\dfrac{12}{12}+\dfrac{3}{4}\cdot\dfrac{3}{3}-\dfrac{1}{6}\cdot\dfrac{2}{2}}{\dfrac{1}{2}\cdot\dfrac{3}{3}+\dfrac{1}{3}\cdot\dfrac{2}{2}}$

The LCD in the numerator is 12. The LCD in the denominator is 6.

$=\dfrac{\dfrac{12}{12}+\dfrac{9}{12}-\dfrac{2}{12}}{\dfrac{3}{6}+\dfrac{2}{6}}$

$=\dfrac{\dfrac{19}{12}}{\dfrac{5}{6}}$

Form a single fraction in the numerator and in the denominator.

$=\dfrac{19}{\overset{}{12}_2}\cdot\dfrac{\overset{1}{6}}{5}$

Step 2: Multiply by the reciprocal of $\frac{5}{6}$, which is $\frac{6}{5}$.

$=\dfrac{19}{10}$

Step 3: Simplify.

Answer
2. $\frac{31}{10}$

Example 3 **Simplifying Complex Fractions (Method I)**

Simplify the expression. $\dfrac{\dfrac{1}{x} + \dfrac{1}{y}}{x - \dfrac{y^2}{x}}$

Solution:

$\dfrac{\dfrac{1}{x} + \dfrac{1}{y}}{x - \dfrac{y^2}{x}}$

The LCD in the numerator is xy. The LCD in the denominator is x.

$= \dfrac{\dfrac{1 \cdot y}{x \cdot y} + \dfrac{1 \cdot x}{y \cdot x}}{\dfrac{x \cdot x}{1 \cdot x} - \dfrac{y^2}{x}}$

Rewrite the expressions using common denominators.

$= \dfrac{\dfrac{y}{xy} + \dfrac{x}{xy}}{\dfrac{x^2}{x} - \dfrac{y^2}{x}}$

$= \dfrac{\dfrac{y + x}{xy}}{\dfrac{x^2 - y^2}{x}}$

Form single fractions in the numerator and denominator.

$= \dfrac{y + x}{xy} \cdot \dfrac{x}{x^2 - y^2}$

Multiply by the reciprocal of the denominator.

$= \dfrac{\overset{1}{\cancel{y + x}}}{xy} \cdot \dfrac{\overset{1}{\cancel{x}}}{\cancel{(x + y)}(x - y)}$

Factor and reduce. Note that $(y + x) = (x + y)$.

$= \dfrac{1}{y(x - y)}$

Simplify.

2. Simplifying Complex Fractions (Method II)

We will now simplify the expressions from Examples 2 and 3 again using a second method to simplify complex fractions (Method II). Recall that multiplying the numerator and denominator of a rational expression by the same quantity does not change the value of the expression because we are multiplying by a number equivalent to 1. This is the basis for Method II.

PROCEDURE Simplifying a Complex Fraction (Method II)

Step 1 Multiply the numerator and denominator of the complex fraction by the LCD of *all* individual fractions within the expression.

Step 2 Apply the distributive property, and simplify the numerator and denominator.

Step 3 Simplify to lowest terms if possible.

Example 4 **Simplifying Complex Fractions (Method II)**

Simplify the expression.
$$\frac{1 + \frac{3}{4} - \frac{1}{6}}{\frac{1}{2} + \frac{1}{3}}$$

Solution:

$$\frac{1 + \frac{3}{4} - \frac{1}{6}}{\frac{1}{2} + \frac{1}{3}}$$

The LCD of the expressions $1, \frac{3}{4}, \frac{1}{6}, \frac{1}{2},$ and $\frac{1}{3}$ is 12.

$$= \frac{12\left(1 + \frac{3}{4} - \frac{1}{6}\right)}{12\left(\frac{1}{2} + \frac{1}{3}\right)}$$

Step 1: Multiply the numerator and denominator of the complex fraction by 12.

$$= \frac{12 \cdot 1 + 12 \cdot \frac{3}{4} - 12 \cdot \frac{1}{6}}{12 \cdot \frac{1}{2} + 12 \cdot \frac{1}{3}}$$

Step 2: Apply the distributive property.

$$= \frac{12 \cdot 1 + \overset{3}{12} \cdot \frac{3}{4} - \overset{2}{12} \cdot \frac{1}{6}}{\overset{6}{12} \cdot \frac{1}{2} + \overset{4}{12} \cdot \frac{1}{3}}$$

Simplify each term.

$$= \frac{12 + 9 - 2}{6 + 4}$$

$$= \frac{19}{10}$$

Step 3: Simplify.

Example 5 **Simplifying a Complex Fraction (Method II)**

Simplify the expression.
$$\frac{\frac{1}{x} + \frac{1}{y}}{x - \frac{y^2}{x}}$$

Solution:

$$\frac{\frac{1}{x} + \frac{1}{y}}{x - \frac{y^2}{x}}$$

The LCD of the expressions $\frac{1}{x}, \frac{1}{y}, x,$ and $\frac{y^2}{x}$ is xy.

$$= \frac{xy\left(\frac{1}{x} + \frac{1}{y}\right)}{xy\left(x - \frac{y^2}{x}\right)}$$

Step 1: Multiply numerator and denominator of the complex fraction by xy.

$$= \frac{xy \cdot \frac{1}{x} + xy \cdot \frac{1}{y}}{xy \cdot x - xy \cdot \frac{y^2}{x}}$$

Step 2: Apply the distributive property, and simplify each term.

$$= \frac{y + x}{x^2 y - y^3}$$

$$= \frac{y + x}{y(x^2 - y^2)}$$

Step 3: Factor completely, and reduce common factors.

$$= \frac{\overset{1}{\cancel{y + x}}}{y\cancel{(x + y)}(x - y)}$$

Note that $(y + x) = (x + y)$.

$$= \frac{1}{y(x - y)}$$

Example 6 Simplifying a Complex Fraction (Method II)

Simplify the expression. $\dfrac{\frac{1}{k+1} - 1}{\frac{1}{k+1} + 1}$

Solution:

$$\frac{\frac{1}{k+1} - 1}{\frac{1}{k+1} + 1}$$

The LCD of $\frac{1}{k+1}$ and 1 is $(k+1)$.

$$= \frac{(k+1)\left(\frac{1}{k+1} - 1\right)}{(k+1)\left(\frac{1}{k+1} + 1\right)}$$

Step 1: Multiply numerator and denominator of the complex fraction by $(k+1)$.

$$= \frac{(k+1)\cdot \frac{1}{(k+1)} - (k+1)\cdot 1}{(k+1)\cdot \frac{1}{(k+1)} + (k+1)\cdot 1}$$

Step 2: Apply the distributive property.

$$= \frac{1 - (k+1)}{1 + (k+1)}$$

Simplify.

$$= \frac{1 - k - 1}{1 + k + 1}$$

$$= \frac{-k}{k+2}$$

Step 3: The expression is already in lowest terms.

Section 14.5 Practice Exercises

Boost *your* GRADE at ALEKS.com!

ALEKS
version 3.0

- Practice Problems
- Self-Tests
- NetTutor
- e-Professors
- Videos

Study Skills Exercise

1. Define the key term **complex fraction**.

Review Exercises

For Exercises 2–3, identify the restricted values, and simplify the expression.

2. $\dfrac{y(2y + 9)}{y^2(2y + 9)}$

3. $\dfrac{a + 5}{2a^2 + 7a - 15}$

For Exercises 4–6, perform the indicated operations.

4. $\dfrac{2}{w - 2} + \dfrac{3}{w}$

5. $\dfrac{6}{5} - \dfrac{3}{5k - 10}$

6. $\dfrac{x^2 - 2xy + y^2}{x^4 - y^4} \div \dfrac{3x^2y - 3xy^2}{x^2 + y^2}$

Objectives 1–2: Simplifying Complex Fractions (Methods I and II)

For Exercises 7–34, simplify the complex fractions. **(See Examples 1–6.)**

7. $\dfrac{\dfrac{7}{18y}}{\dfrac{2}{9}}$

8. $\dfrac{\dfrac{a^2}{2a - 3}}{\dfrac{5a}{8a - 12}}$

9. $\dfrac{\dfrac{3x + 2y}{2y}}{\dfrac{6x + 4y}{2}}$

10. $\dfrac{\dfrac{2x - 10}{4}}{\dfrac{x^2 - 5x}{3x}}$

11. $\dfrac{\dfrac{8a^4b^3}{3c}}{\dfrac{a^7b^2}{9c}}$

12. $\dfrac{\dfrac{12x^2}{5y}}{\dfrac{8x^6}{9y^2}}$

13. $\dfrac{\dfrac{4r^3s}{t^5}}{\dfrac{2s^7}{r^2t^9}}$

14. $\dfrac{\dfrac{5p^4q}{w^4}}{\dfrac{10p^2}{qw^2}}$

15. $\dfrac{\dfrac{1}{8} + \dfrac{4}{3}}{\dfrac{1}{2} - \dfrac{5}{12}}$

16. $\dfrac{\dfrac{8}{9} - \dfrac{1}{3}}{\dfrac{7}{6} + \dfrac{1}{9}}$

17. $\dfrac{\dfrac{1}{h} + \dfrac{1}{k}}{\dfrac{1}{hk}}$

18. $\dfrac{\dfrac{1}{b} + 1}{\dfrac{1}{b}}$

19. $\dfrac{\dfrac{n + 1}{n^2 - 9}}{\dfrac{2}{n + 3}}$

20. $\dfrac{\dfrac{5}{k - 5}}{\dfrac{k + 1}{k^2 - 25}}$

21. $\dfrac{2 + \dfrac{1}{x}}{4 + \dfrac{1}{x}}$

22. $\dfrac{6 + \dfrac{6}{k}}{1 + \dfrac{1}{k}}$

23. $\dfrac{\dfrac{m}{7} - \dfrac{7}{m}}{\dfrac{1}{7} + \dfrac{1}{m}}$

24. $\dfrac{\dfrac{2}{p} + \dfrac{p}{2}}{\dfrac{p}{3} - \dfrac{3}{p}}$

25. $\dfrac{\dfrac{1}{5} - \dfrac{1}{y}}{\dfrac{7}{10} + \dfrac{1}{y^2}}$

26. $\dfrac{\dfrac{1}{m^2} + \dfrac{2}{3}}{\dfrac{1}{m} - \dfrac{5}{6}}$

27. $\dfrac{\dfrac{8}{a + 4} + 2}{\dfrac{12}{a + 4} - 2}$

28. $\dfrac{\dfrac{2}{w + 1} + 3}{\dfrac{3}{w + 1} + 4}$

29. $\dfrac{1 - \dfrac{4}{t^2}}{1 - \dfrac{2}{t} - \dfrac{8}{t^2}}$

30. $\dfrac{1 - \dfrac{9}{p^2}}{1 - \dfrac{1}{p} - \dfrac{6}{p^2}}$

31. $\dfrac{t + 4 + \dfrac{3}{t}}{t - 4 - \dfrac{5}{t}}$

32. $\dfrac{\dfrac{9}{4m} + \dfrac{9}{2m^2}}{\dfrac{3}{2} + \dfrac{3}{m}}$

33. $\dfrac{\dfrac{1}{k - 6} - 1}{\dfrac{2}{k - 6} - 2}$

34. $\dfrac{\dfrac{3}{y - 3} + 4}{8 + \dfrac{6}{y - 3}}$

For Exercises 35–38, translate the English phrases into algebraic expressions. Then simplify the expressions.

35. The sum of one-half and two-thirds, divided by five.

36. The quotient of ten and the difference of two-fifths and one-fourth.

37. The quotient of three and the sum of two-thirds and three-fourths.

38. The difference of three-fifths and one-half, divided by four.

39. In electronics, resistors oppose the flow of current. For two resistors in parallel, the total resistance is given by

$$R = \dfrac{1}{\dfrac{1}{R_1} + \dfrac{1}{R_2}}$$

  a. Find the total resistance if $R_1 = 2\,\Omega$ (ohms) and $R_2 = 3\,\Omega$.

  b. Find the total resistance if $R_1 = 10\,\Omega$ and $R_2 = 15\,\Omega$.

40. Suppose that Joëlle makes a round trip to a location that is d miles away. If the average rate going to the location is r_1 and the average rate on the return trip is given by r_2, the average rate of the entire trip, R, is given by

$$R = \dfrac{2d}{\dfrac{d}{r_1} + \dfrac{d}{r_2}}$$

  a. Find the average rate of a trip to a destination 30 mi away when the average rate going there was 60 mph and the average rate returning home was 45 mph. (Round to the nearest tenth of a mile per hour.)

  b. Find the average rate of a trip to a destination that is 50 mi away if the driver travels at the same rates as in part (a). (Round to the nearest tenth of a mile per hour.)

  c. Compare your answers from parts (a) and (b) and explain the results in the context of the problem.

Expanding Your Skills

For Exercises 41–48, simplify the complex fractions using either method.

41. $\dfrac{2x^{-1} + 8y^{-1}}{4x^{-1}}$

$\left(Hint: 2x^{-1} = \dfrac{2}{x} \right)$

42. $\dfrac{6a^{-1} + 4b^{-1}}{8b^{-1}}$

43. $\dfrac{(mn)^{-2}}{m^{-2} + n^{-2}}$

44. $\dfrac{(xy)^{-1}}{2x^{-1} + 3y^{-1}}$

45. $\dfrac{\dfrac{1}{z^2 - 9} + \dfrac{2}{z + 3}}{\dfrac{3}{z - 3}}$

46. $\dfrac{\dfrac{5}{w^2 - 25} - \dfrac{3}{w + 5}}{\dfrac{4}{w - 5}}$

47. $\dfrac{\dfrac{2}{x - 1} + 2}{\dfrac{2}{x + 1} - 2}$

48. $\dfrac{\dfrac{1}{y - 3} + 1}{\dfrac{2}{y + 3} - 1}$

For Exercises 49–50, simplify the complex fractions. (*Hint:* Use the order of operations and begin with the fraction on the lower right.)

49. $1 + \dfrac{1}{1 + 1}$

50. $1 + \dfrac{1}{1 + \dfrac{1}{1 + 1}}$

Rational Equations

1. Introduction to Rational Equations

Thus far we have studied two specific types of equations in one variable: linear equations and quadratic equations. Recall,

$$ax + b = c, \text{ where } a \neq 0, \text{ is a \textbf{linear equation}}$$

$$ax^2 + bx + c = 0, \text{ where } a \neq 0, \text{ is a \textbf{quadratic equation}}.$$

We will now study another type of equation called a rational equation.

Objectives

1. **Introduction to Rational Equations**
2. **Solving Rational Equations**
3. **Solving Formulas Involving Rational Expressions**

> **DEFINITION** Rational Equation
>
> An equation with one or more rational expressions is called a **rational equation**.

The following equations are rational equations:

$$\frac{1}{x} + \frac{1}{3} = \frac{5}{6} \qquad \frac{6}{t^2 - 7t + 12} + \frac{2t}{t - 3} = \frac{3t}{t - 4}$$

To understand the process of solving a rational equation, first review the process of clearing fractions from Section 9.3. We can clear the fractions in an equation by multiplying both sides of the equation by the LCD of all terms.

Example 1 Solving an Equation Containing Fractions

Solve. $\dfrac{y}{2} + \dfrac{y}{4} = 6$

Solution:

$$\frac{y}{2} + \frac{y}{4} = 6 \qquad \text{The LCD of all terms in the equation is } 4.$$

$$4\left(\frac{y}{2} + \frac{y}{4}\right) = 4(6) \qquad \begin{array}{l}\text{Multiply both sides of the equation by 4 to clear}\\ \text{fractions.}\end{array}$$

$$\overset{2}{\cancel{4}} \cdot \frac{y}{2} + \overset{1}{\cancel{4}} \cdot \frac{y}{4} = 4(6) \qquad \text{Apply the distributive property.}$$

$$2y + y = 24 \qquad \text{Clear fractions.}$$

$$3y = 24 \qquad \text{Solve the resulting equation (linear).}$$

$$y = 8$$

$$\underline{\text{Check:}} \quad \frac{y}{2} + \frac{y}{4} = 6$$

$$\frac{(8)}{2} + \frac{(8)}{4} \overset{?}{=} 6$$

$$4 + 2 \overset{?}{=} 6$$

The solution is 8. $6 \overset{?}{=} 6 \; ✔ \; \text{(True)}$

Skill Practice

Solve the equation.

1. $\dfrac{t}{5} - \dfrac{t}{4} = 2$

Answer

1. -40

2. Solving Rational Equations

The same process of clearing fractions is used to solve rational equations when variables are present in the denominator. Variables in the denominator make it necessary to take note of the restricted values.

Example 2   **Solving a Rational Equation**

Solve the equation. $\dfrac{x+1}{x} + \dfrac{1}{3} = \dfrac{5}{6}$

Solution:

$$\frac{x+1}{x} + \frac{1}{3} = \frac{5}{6}$$

The LCD of all the expressions is $6x$. The restricted value is $x = 0$.

$$6x \cdot \left(\frac{x+1}{x} + \frac{1}{3}\right) = 6x \cdot \left(\frac{5}{6}\right)$$

Multiply by the LCD.

$$\overset{1}{6x} \cdot \left(\frac{x+1}{x}\right) + \overset{2}{6x} \cdot \left(\frac{1}{3}\right) = \overset{1}{6x} \cdot \left(\frac{5}{6}\right)$$

Apply the distributive property.

$$6(x+1) + 2x = 5x$$

Clear fractions.

$$6x + 6 + 2x = 5x$$

Solve the resulting equation.

$$8x + 6 = 5x$$

$$3x = -6$$

$$x = -2$$

-2 is not a restricted value.

Check: $\dfrac{x+1}{x} + \dfrac{1}{3} = \dfrac{5}{6}$

$$\frac{(-2)+1}{(-2)} + \frac{1}{3} \overset{?}{=} \frac{5}{6}$$

$$\frac{-1}{-2} + \frac{1}{3} \overset{?}{=} \frac{5}{6}$$

$$\frac{1}{2} + \frac{1}{3} \overset{?}{=} \frac{5}{6}$$

$$\frac{3}{6} + \frac{2}{6} \overset{?}{=} \frac{5}{6}$$

The solution is -2.

$$\frac{5}{6} \overset{?}{=} \frac{5}{6} \quad \checkmark \text{ (True)}$$

Example 3 Solving a Rational Equation

Solve the equation. $1 + \dfrac{3a}{a-2} = \dfrac{6}{a-2}$

Solution:

$$1 + \frac{3a}{a-2} = \frac{6}{a-2}$$

The LCD of all the expressions is $a - 2$. The restricted value is $a = 2$.

$$(a-2)\left(1 + \frac{3a}{a-2}\right) = (a-2)\left(\frac{6}{a-2}\right)$$

Multiply by the LCD.

$$(a-2)1 + (a-2)\left(\frac{3a}{a-2}\right) = (a-2)\left(\frac{6}{a-2}\right)$$

Apply the distributive property.

$$a - 2 + 3a = 6$$

Solve the resulting equation (linear).

$$4a - 2 = 6$$

$$4a = 8$$

$$a = 2$$ 2 is a restricted value.

Check: $1 + \dfrac{3a}{a-2} = \dfrac{6}{a-2}$

$$1 + \frac{3(2)}{(2)-2} \stackrel{?}{=} \frac{6}{(2)-2}$$

$$1 + \frac{6}{0} \stackrel{?}{=} \frac{6}{0}$$

The denominator is 0 when $a = 2$.

Because the value $a = 2$ makes the denominator zero in one (or more) of the rational expressions within the equation, the equation is undefined for $a = 2$. No other potential solutions exist for the equation.

The equation $1 + \dfrac{3a}{a-2} = \dfrac{6}{a-2}$ has no solution.

Examples 1–3 show that the steps to solve a rational equation mirror the process of clearing fractions from Section 9.3. However, there is one significant difference. The solutions of a rational equation must not make the denominator equal to zero for any expression within the equation. When $a = 2$ is substituted into the expression

$$\frac{3a}{a-2} \quad \text{or} \quad \frac{6}{a-2}$$

the denominator is zero and the expression is undefined. Therefore, 2 cannot be a solution to the equation

$$1 + \frac{3a}{a-2} = \frac{6}{a-2}$$

The steps to solve a rational equation are summarized as follows.

> **PROCEDURE** Solving a Rational Equation
> **Step 1** Factor the denominators of all rational expressions. Identify the restricted values.
> **Step 2** Identify the LCD of all expressions in the equation.
> **Step 3** Multiply both sides of the equation by the LCD.
> **Step 4** Solve the resulting equation.
> **Step 5** Check potential solutions in the original equation.

After multiplying by the LCD and then simplifying, the rational equation will be either a linear equation or higher degree equation.

Skill Practice

Solve the equation.

4. $\dfrac{z}{2} - \dfrac{1}{2z} = \dfrac{12}{z}$

Example 4 **Solving a Rational Equation**

Solve the equation. $\qquad 1 - \dfrac{4}{p} = -\dfrac{3}{p^2}$

Solution:

$$1 - \dfrac{4}{p} = -\dfrac{3}{p^2}$$

Step 1: The denominators are already factored. The restricted value is $p = 0$.

Step 2: The LCD of all expressions is p^2.

$$p^2\left(1 - \dfrac{4}{p}\right) = p^2\left(-\dfrac{3}{p^2}\right)$$

Step 3: Multiply by the LCD.

$$p^2(1) - \overset{p}{\cancel{p^2}}\left(\dfrac{4}{\cancel{p}}\right) = \overset{1}{\cancel{p^2}}\left(-\dfrac{3}{\cancel{p^2}}\right)$$

Apply the distributive property.

$$p^2 - 4p = -3$$

Step 4: Solve the resulting quadratic equation.

$$p^2 - 4p + 3 = 0$$

Set the equation equal to zero and factor.

$$(p - 3)(p - 1) = 0$$

$$p - 3 = 0 \quad \text{or} \quad p - 1 = 0$$

Set each factor equal to zero.

$$p = 3 \quad \text{or} \quad p = 1$$

3 and 1 are not restricted values.

Step 5: Check: $p = 3$ Check: $p = 1$

$$1 - \dfrac{4}{p} = -\dfrac{3}{p^2} \qquad 1 - \dfrac{4}{p} = -\dfrac{3}{p^2}$$

$$1 - \dfrac{4}{(3)} \overset{?}{=} -\dfrac{3}{(3)^2} \qquad 1 - \dfrac{4}{(1)} \overset{?}{=} -\dfrac{3}{(1)^2}$$

$$\dfrac{3}{3} - \dfrac{4}{3} \overset{?}{=} -\dfrac{3}{9} \qquad 1 - 4 \overset{?}{=} -3$$

Both solutions 3 and 1 check.

$$-\dfrac{1}{3} \overset{?}{=} -\dfrac{1}{3} \checkmark \qquad -3 \overset{?}{=} -3 \checkmark$$

Answer

4. $5, -5$

Example 5 **Solving a Rational Equation**

Solve the equation. $\dfrac{6}{t^2 - 7t + 12} + \dfrac{2t}{t - 3} = \dfrac{3t}{t - 4}$

Skill Practice

Solve the equation.

5. $\dfrac{-8}{x^2 + 6x + 8} + \dfrac{x}{x + 4}$

$= \dfrac{2}{x + 2}$

Solution:

$\dfrac{6}{t^2 - 7t + 12} + \dfrac{2t}{t - 3} = \dfrac{3t}{t - 4}$

$\dfrac{6}{(t - 3)(t - 4)} + \dfrac{2t}{t - 3} = \dfrac{3t}{t - 4}$

Step 1: Factor the denominators. The restricted values are $t = 3$ and $t = 4$.

Step 2: The LCD is $(t - 3)(t - 4)$.

Step 3: Multiply by the LCD on both sides.

$(t - 3)(t - 4)\left(\dfrac{6}{(t - 3)(t - 4)} + \dfrac{2t}{t - 3}\right) = (t - 3)(t - 4)\left(\dfrac{3t}{t - 4}\right)$

$(t-3)(t-4)\left(\dfrac{6}{(t-3)(t-4)}\right) + (t-3)(t - 4)\left(\dfrac{2t}{t-3}\right) = (t - 3)(t-4)\left(\dfrac{3t}{t-4}\right)$

$6 + 2t(t - 4) = 3t(t - 3)$

$6 + 2t^2 - 8t = 3t^2 - 9t$

$0 = 3t^2 - 2t^2 - 9t + 8t - 6$

$0 = t^2 - t - 6$

$0 = (t - 3)(t + 2)$

$t - 3 = 0$ or $t + 2 = 0$

$t = 3$ or $t = -2$

Step 4: Solve the resulting equation.

Because the resulting equation is quadratic, set the equation equal to zero and factor.

Set each factor equal to zero.

3 is a restricted value, but -2 is not restricted.

Step 5: Check the potential solutions in the original equation.

Concept Connections

6. Explain why it is important to check the solution(s) to a rational equation.

Check: $t = 3$

3 cannot be a solution to the equation because it will make a denominator zero in the original equation.

$\dfrac{6}{t^2 - 7t + 12} + \dfrac{2t}{t - 3} = \dfrac{3t}{t - 4}$

$\dfrac{6}{(3)^2 - 7(3) + 12} + \dfrac{2(3)}{(3) - 3} \overset{?}{=} \dfrac{3(3)}{(3) - 4}$

$\underbrace{\dfrac{6}{0} + \dfrac{6}{0}}_{\text{Zero in the denominator}} \overset{?}{=} \dfrac{9}{-1}$

Check: $t = -2$

$\dfrac{6}{t^2 - 7t + 12} + \dfrac{2t}{t - 3} = \dfrac{3t}{t - 4}$

$\dfrac{6}{(-2)^2 - 7(-2) + 12} + \dfrac{2(-2)}{(-2) - 3} \overset{?}{=} \dfrac{3(-2)}{(-2) - 4}$

$\dfrac{6}{4 + 14 + 12} + \dfrac{-4}{-5} \overset{?}{=} \dfrac{-6}{-6}$

$\dfrac{6}{30} + \dfrac{4}{5} \overset{?}{=} 1$

$\dfrac{1}{5} + \dfrac{4}{5} = 1$ ✔ (True)

$t = -2$ is a solution.

The only solution is -2.

Answers

5. 4; (The value -4 does not check.)

6. It is important to check that the solutions are not restricted values of any expression in the equation.

Example 6 **Translating to a Rational Equation**

Ten times the reciprocal of a number is added to four. The result is equal to the quotient of twenty-two and the number. Find the number.

Solution:

Let x represent the number.

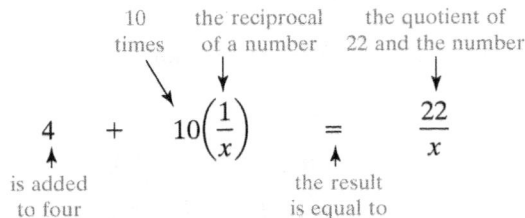

$$4 + \frac{10}{x} = \frac{22}{x}$$

Step 1: The denominators are already factored. The restricted value is $x = 0$.

Step 2: The LCD is x.

$$x\left(4 + \frac{10}{x}\right) = x\left(\frac{22}{x}\right)$$

Step 3: Multiply both sides by the LCD.

$$4x + 10 = 22$$

Apply the distributive property.

$$4x = 12$$

Step 4: Solve the resulting linear equation.

$x = 3$ is a potential solution.

Step 5: 3 is not a restricted value. Substituting $x = 3$ into the original equation verifies that it is a solution.

The number is 3.

3. Solving Formulas Involving Rational Expressions

A rational equation may have more than one variable. To solve for a specific variable within a rational equation, we can still apply principle of clearing fractions.

Example 7 **Solving Formulas Involving Rational Equations**

Solve for k. $\quad F = \dfrac{ma}{k}$

Solution:

To solve for k, we must clear fractions so that k appears in the numerator.

$$F = \dfrac{ma}{k} \qquad \text{The LCD is } k.$$

$$k \cdot (F) = k \cdot \left(\dfrac{ma}{k}\right) \qquad \text{Multiply both sides of the equation by the LCD.}$$

$$kF = ma \qquad \text{Clear fractions.}$$

$$\dfrac{kF}{F} = \dfrac{ma}{F} \qquad \text{Divide both sides by } F.$$

$$k = \dfrac{ma}{F}$$

Example 8 **Solving Formulas Involving Rational Equations**

Solve for b. $\quad h = \dfrac{2A}{B + b}$

Solution:

To solve for b, we must clear fractions so that b appears in the numerator.

$$h = \dfrac{2A}{B + b} \qquad \text{The LCD is } (B + b).$$

$$h(B + b) = \left(\dfrac{2A}{B + b}\right) \cdot (B + b) \qquad \text{Multiply both sides of the equation by the LCD.}$$

$$hB + hb = 2A \qquad \text{Apply the distributive property.}$$

$$hb = 2A - hB \qquad \text{Subtract } hB \text{ from both sides to isolate the } b \text{ term.}$$

$$\dfrac{hb}{h} = \dfrac{2A - hB}{h} \qquad \text{Divide by } h.$$

$$b = \dfrac{2A - hB}{h}$$

TIP: The solution to Example 8 can be written in several forms. The quantity

$$\frac{2A - hB}{h}$$

can be left as a single rational expression or can be split into two fractions and simplified.

$$b = \frac{2A - hB}{h} = \frac{2A}{h} - \frac{hB}{h} = \frac{2A}{h} - B$$

Skill Practice

10. Solve for h.

$$\frac{b}{x} = \frac{a}{h} + 1$$

Example 9   **Solving Formulas Involving Rational Expressions**

Solve for z. $y = \dfrac{x - z}{x + z}$

Solution:

To solve for z, we must clear fractions so that z appears in the numerator.

$$y = \frac{x - z}{x + z} \qquad \text{LCD is } (x + z).$$

$$y(x + z) = \left(\frac{x - z}{x + z}\right)(x + z) \qquad \text{Multiply both sides of the equation by the LCD.}$$

$$yx + yz = x - z \qquad \text{Apply the distributive property.}$$

$$yz + z = x - yx \qquad \text{Collect } z \text{ terms on one side of the equation and collect terms not containing } z \text{ on the other side.}$$

$$z(y + 1) = x - yx \qquad \text{Factor out } z.$$

$$z = \frac{x - yx}{y + 1} \qquad \text{Divide by } y + 1 \text{ to solve for } z.$$

Answer

10. $h = \dfrac{ax}{b - x}$ or $\dfrac{-ax}{x - b}$

Section 14.6   Practice Exercises

Study Skills Exercise

1. Define the key terms:

   a. Linear equation   **b. Quadratic equation**   **c. Rational equation**

Review Exercises

For Exercises 2–7, perform the indicated operations.

2. $\dfrac{2}{x - 3} - \dfrac{3}{x^2 - x - 6}$

3. $\dfrac{2x - 6}{4x^2 + 7x - 2} \div \dfrac{x^2 - 5x + 6}{x^2 - 4}$

4. $\dfrac{2y}{y - 3} + \dfrac{4}{y^2 - 9}$

5. $\dfrac{h - \dfrac{1}{h}}{\dfrac{1}{5} - \dfrac{1}{5h}}$

6. $\dfrac{w - 4}{w^2 - 9} \cdot \dfrac{w - 3}{w^2 - 8w + 16}$

7. $1 + \dfrac{1}{x} - \dfrac{12}{x^2}$

Objective 1: Introduction to Rational Equations

For Exercises 8–13, solve the equations by first clearing the fractions. **(See Example 1.)**

8. $\frac{1}{3}z + \frac{2}{3} = -2z + 10$

9. $\frac{5}{2} + \frac{1}{2}b = 5 - \frac{1}{3}b$

10. $\frac{3}{2}p + \frac{1}{3} = \frac{2p-3}{4}$

11. $\frac{5}{3} - \frac{1}{6}k = \frac{3k+5}{4}$

12. $\frac{2x-3}{4} + \frac{9}{10} = \frac{x}{5}$

13. $\frac{4y+2}{3} - \frac{7}{6} = -\frac{y}{6}$

Objective 2: Solving Rational Equations

14. For the equation

$$\frac{1}{w} - \frac{1}{2} = -\frac{1}{4}$$

    a. Identify the restricted values.

    b. Identify the LCD of the fractions in the equation.

    c. Solve the equation.

15. For the equation

$$\frac{3}{z} - \frac{4}{5} = -\frac{1}{5}$$

    a. Identify the restricted values.

    b. Identify the LCD of the fractions in the equation.

    c. Solve the equation.

16. Identify the LCD of all the denominators in the equation.

$$\frac{x+1}{x^2 + 2x - 3} = \frac{1}{x+3} - \frac{1}{x-1}$$

For Exercises 17–46, solve the equations. **(See Examples 2–5.)**

17. $\frac{1}{8} = \frac{3}{5} + \frac{5}{y}$

18. $\frac{2}{7} - \frac{1}{x} = \frac{2}{3}$

19. $\frac{4}{t} = \frac{3}{t} + \frac{1}{8}$

20. $\frac{9}{b} - \frac{8}{b} = \frac{1}{4}$

21. $\frac{5}{6x} + \frac{7}{x} = 1$

22. $\frac{14}{3x} - \frac{5}{x} = 2$

23. $1 - \frac{2}{y} = \frac{3}{y^2}$

24. $1 - \frac{2}{m} = \frac{8}{m^2}$

25. $\frac{a+1}{a} = 1 + \frac{a-2}{2a}$

26. $\frac{7b-4}{5b} = \frac{9}{5} - \frac{4}{b}$

27. $\frac{w}{5} - \frac{w+3}{w} = -\frac{3}{w}$

28. $\frac{t}{12} + \frac{t+3}{3t} = \frac{1}{t}$

29. $\frac{2}{m+3} = \frac{5}{4m+12} - \frac{3}{8}$

30. $\frac{2}{4n-4} - \frac{7}{4} = \frac{-3}{n-1}$

31. $\frac{p}{p-4} - 5 = \frac{4}{p-4}$

32. $\frac{-5}{q+5} = \frac{q}{q+5} + 2$

33. $\frac{2t}{t+2} - 2 = \frac{t-8}{t+2}$

34. $\frac{4w}{w-3} - 3 = \frac{3w-1}{w-3}$

35. $\frac{x^2-x}{x-2} = \frac{12}{x-2}$

36. $\frac{x^2+9}{x+4} = \frac{-10x}{x+4}$

37. $\frac{x^2+3x}{x-1} = \frac{4}{x-1}$

38. $\frac{2x^2-21}{2x-3} = \frac{-11x}{2x-3}$

39. $\frac{2x}{x+4} - \frac{8}{x-4} = \frac{2x^2+32}{x^2-16}$

40. $\frac{4x}{x+3} - \frac{12}{x-3} = \frac{4x^2+36}{x^2-9}$

41. $\dfrac{x}{x+6} = \dfrac{72}{x^2-36} + 4$

42. $\dfrac{y}{y+4} = \dfrac{32}{y^2-16} + 3$

43. $\dfrac{5}{3x-3} - \dfrac{2}{x-2} = \dfrac{7}{x^2-3x+2}$

44. $\dfrac{6}{5a+10} - \dfrac{1}{a-5} = \dfrac{4}{a^2-3a-10}$

45. $\dfrac{y-2}{y-3} = \dfrac{11}{y^2-7y+12} + \dfrac{y}{y-4}$

46. $\dfrac{6}{w+1} - \dfrac{3}{w+5} = \dfrac{18}{w^2+6w+5}$

For Exercises 47–50, translate to a rational equation and solve. **(See Example 6.)**

47. The reciprocal of a number is added to three. The result is the quotient of 25 and the number. Find the number.

48. The difference of three and the reciprocal of a number is equal to the quotient of 20 and the number. Find the number.

49. If a number added to five is divided by the difference of the number and two, the result is three-fourths. Find the number.

50. If twice a number added to three is divided by the number plus one, the result is three-halves. Find the number.

Objective 3: Solving Formulas Involving Rational Expressions

For Exercises 51–68, solve for the indicated variable. **(See Examples 7–9.)**

51. $K = \dfrac{ma}{F}$ for m

52. $K = \dfrac{ma}{F}$ for a

53. $K = \dfrac{IR}{E}$ for E

54. $K = \dfrac{IR}{E}$ for R

55. $I = \dfrac{E}{R+r}$ for R

56. $I = \dfrac{E}{R+r}$ for r

57. $h = \dfrac{2A}{B+b}$ for B

58. $\dfrac{C}{\pi r} = 2$ for r

59. $\dfrac{V}{\pi h} = r^2$ for h

60. $\dfrac{V}{lw} = h$ for w

61. $x = \dfrac{at+b}{t}$ for t

62. $\dfrac{T+mf}{m} = g$ for m

63. $\dfrac{x-y}{xy} = z$ for x

64. $\dfrac{w-n}{wn} = P$ for w

65. $a + b = \dfrac{2A}{h}$ for h

66. $1 + rt = \dfrac{A}{P}$ for P

67. $\dfrac{1}{R} = \dfrac{1}{R_1} + \dfrac{1}{R_2}$ for R

68. $\dfrac{b+a}{ab} = \dfrac{1}{f}$ for b

Problem Recognition Exercises

Comparing Rational Equations and Rational Expressions

Often adding or subtracting rational expressions is confused with solving rational equations. When adding rational expressions, we combine the terms to simplify the expression. When solving an equation, we clear the fractions and find numerical solutions, if possible. Both processes begin with finding the LCD, but the LCD is used differently in each process. Compare these two examples.

Example 1:

Add. $\dfrac{4}{x} + \dfrac{x}{3}$ (The LCD is $3x$.)

$= \dfrac{3}{3} \cdot \left(\dfrac{4}{x}\right) + \left(\dfrac{x}{3}\right) \cdot \dfrac{x}{x}$

$= \dfrac{12}{3x} + \dfrac{x^2}{3x}$

$= \dfrac{12 + x^2}{3x}$ The final answer is a rational expression.

Example 2:

Solve. $\dfrac{4}{x} + \dfrac{x}{3} = -\dfrac{8}{3}$ (The LCD is $3x$.)

$\dfrac{3x}{1}\left(\dfrac{4}{x} + \dfrac{x}{3}\right) = \dfrac{3x}{1}\left(-\dfrac{8}{3}\right)$

$12 + x^2 = -8x$

$x^2 + 8x + 12 = 0$

$(x + 2)(x + 6) = 0$

$x + 2 = 0 \text{ or } x + 6 = 0$

$x = -2 \text{ or } x = -6$ The final answers are numbers. The solutions -2 and -6 both check in the original equation.

For Exercises 1–12, solve the equation or simplify the expression by combining the terms.

1. $\dfrac{y}{2y + 4} - \dfrac{2}{y^2 + 2y}$

2. $\dfrac{1}{x + 2} + 2 = \dfrac{x + 11}{x + 2}$

3. $\dfrac{5t}{2} - \dfrac{t - 2}{3} = 5$

4. $3 - \dfrac{2}{a - 5}$

5. $\dfrac{7}{6p^2} + \dfrac{2}{9p} + \dfrac{1}{3p^2}$

6. $\dfrac{3b}{b + 1} - \dfrac{2b}{b - 1}$

7. $4 + \dfrac{2}{h - 3} = 5$

8. $\dfrac{2}{w + 1} + \dfrac{3}{(w + 1)^2}$

9. $\dfrac{1}{x - 6} - \dfrac{3}{x^2 - 6x} = \dfrac{4}{x}$

10. $\dfrac{3}{m} - \dfrac{6}{5} = -\dfrac{3}{m}$

11. $\dfrac{7}{2x + 2} + \dfrac{3x}{4x + 4}$

12. $\dfrac{10}{2t - 1} - 1 = \dfrac{t}{2t - 1}$

Applications of Rational Equations and Proportions

Objectives

1. Solving Proportions
2. Applications of Proportions and Similar Polygons
3. Distance, Rate, and Time Applications
4. Work Applications

Skill Practice

Solve the proportion.

1. $\dfrac{10}{b} = \dfrac{2}{33}$

---

1. Solving Proportions

In this section, we look at how rational equations can be used to solve a variety of applications. The first four applications involve proportions.

A proportion can be solved by multiplying both sides of the equation by the LCD and clearing fractions.

Example 1 Solving a Proportion

Solve the proportion. $\dfrac{3}{11} = \dfrac{123}{w}$

Solution:

$$\frac{3}{11} = \frac{123}{w} \qquad \text{The LCD is } 11w.$$

$$11w\left(\frac{3}{11}\right) = 11w\left(\frac{123}{w}\right) \qquad \text{Multiply by the LCD and clear fractions.}$$

$$3w = 11 \cdot 123 \qquad \text{Solve the resulting equation (linear).}$$

$$3w = 1353$$

$$\frac{3w}{3} = \frac{1353}{3}$$

$$w = 451$$

$$\underline{\text{Check: }} w = 451$$

$$\frac{3}{11} = \frac{123}{w}$$

$$\frac{3}{11} \overset{?}{=} \frac{123}{(451)}$$

The solution is 451.

$$\frac{3}{11} \overset{?}{=} \frac{3}{11} \quad \checkmark \text{ (True)} \qquad \text{Simplify to lowest terms.}$$

Answer

1. 165

TIP: Recall from Chapter 6 that a proportion can also be solved by equating cross products. That is, for $b \neq 0$ and $d \neq 0$, the proportion $\frac{a}{b} = \frac{c}{d}$ is equivalent to $ad = bc$. Consider the proportion from Example 1:

$$\frac{3}{11} \diagup\!\!\!\diagdown \frac{123}{w}$$

$3 \cdot w = 11 \cdot 123$ Equate the cross products.

$3w = 1353$ Solve the resulting equation.

$$\frac{3w}{3} = \frac{1353}{3}$$

$w = 451$ The solution is 451.

2. Applications of Proportions and Similar Polygons

Example 2   **Using a Proportion in an Application**

For a recent year, the population of Alabama was approximately 4.2 million. At that time, Alabama had seven representatives in the U.S. House of Representatives. In the same year, North Carolina had a population of approximately 7.2 million. If representation in the House is based on population in equal proportions for each state, how many representatives did North Carolina have?

Solution:

Let x represent the number of representatives for North Carolina.

Set up a proportion by writing two equivalent ratios.

population of Alabama $\longrightarrow$ $\dfrac{4.2}{7} = \dfrac{7.2}{x}$ $\longleftarrow$ population of North Carolina
number of representatives $\longrightarrow$ $\phantom{\dfrac{4.2}{7}}$ $\longleftarrow$ number of representatives

$$\frac{4.2}{7} = \frac{7.2}{x}$$

$7x \cdot \dfrac{4.2}{7} = 7x \cdot \dfrac{7.2}{x}$ Multiply by the LCD, $7x$.

$4.2x = (7.2)(7)$ Solve the resulting linear equation.

$4.2x = 50.4$

$$\frac{4.2x}{4.2} = \frac{50.4}{4.2}$$

$x = 12$ North Carolina had 12 representatives.

In Chapter 7, we found that corresponding sides of similar triangles are proportional.

Skill Practice

2. A university has a ratio of students to faculty of 105 to 2. If the student population at the university is 15,750, how many faculty members are needed?

Answer

2. 300

Skill Practice

3. Donna has drawn a pattern from which to make a scarf. Assuming that the triangles are similar (the pattern and scarf have the same shape), find the length of side x (in yards).

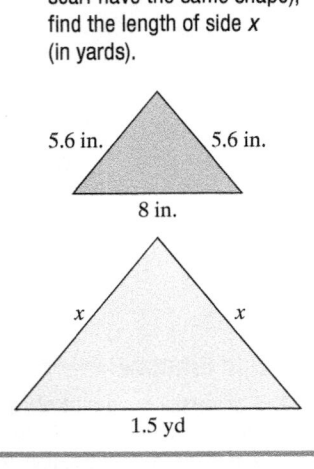

Example 3 — Using Similar Triangles in an Application

On a sunny day, a 6-ft man casts a 3.2-ft shadow on the ground. At the same time, a building casts an 80-ft shadow. How tall is the building?

Solution:

We illustrate the scenario in Figure 14-1. Note, however, that the distances are not drawn to scale.

Let h represent the height of the building in feet.

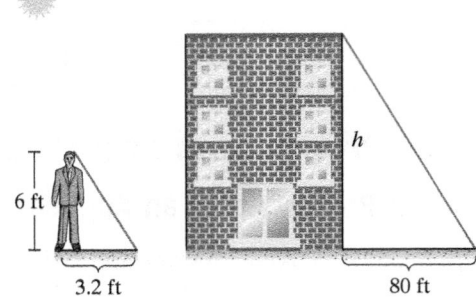

Figure 14-1

We will assume that the triangles are similar because the readings were taken at the same time of day.

$$\frac{6}{h} = \frac{3.2}{80}$$ Translate to a proportion.

$$80h \cdot \frac{6}{h} = \frac{3.2}{80} \cdot 80h$$ Multiply by the LCD, $80h$.

$$480 = 3.2h$$

$$\frac{480}{3.2} = \frac{\overset{1}{3.2}h}{\underset{1}{3.2}}$$ Divide both sides by 3.2.

$$150 = h$$ Divide. $480 \div 3.2 = 150$

The height of the building is 150 ft.

In addition to studying similar triangles, we present similar polygons. Recall from Section 1.3 that a polygon is a flat figure formed by line segments connected at their ends. If the corresponding sides of two polygons are proportional, then we have **similar polygons**.

Answer

3. Side x is 1.05 yd long.

Example 4 **Using Similar Polygons in an Application**

A negative for a photograph is 3.5 cm by 2.5 cm. If the width of the resulting picture is 4 in., what is the length of the picture? See Figure 14-2.

2.5 cm

3.5 cm

4 in.

x

Figure 14-2

Skill Practice

4. The first- and second-place plaques for a softball tournament have the same shape but are different sizes. Find the length of side x.

10 in.

x

8 in.

5 in.

Solution:

Let x represent the length of the photo.

The photo and its negative are similar polygons.

$$\frac{3.5}{x} = \frac{2.5}{4}$$ Translate to a proportion.

$$4x \cdot \frac{3.5}{x} = \frac{2.5}{4} \cdot 4x$$ Multiply by the LCD, $4x$.

$$14 = 2.5x$$

$$\frac{14}{2.5} = \frac{2.5x}{2.5}$$ Divide both sides by 2.5.

$$5.6 = x$$ Divide. $14 \div 2.5 = 5.6$

The picture is 5.6 in. long.

3. Distance, Rate, and Time Applications

In Section 11.4 we presented applications involving the relationship among the variables distance, rate, and time. Recall that $d = rt$.

Answer

4. Side x is 6.25 in.

5. Alison paddles her kayak in a river where the current of the water is 2 mph. She can paddle 20 mi with the current in the same time that she can paddle 10 mi against the current. Find the speed of the kayak in still water.

Example 5 **Using a Rational Equation in a Distance, Rate, and Time Application**

A small plane flies 440 mi with the wind from Memphis, TN, to Oklahoma City, OK. In the same amount of time, the plane flies 340 miles against the wind from Oklahoma City to Little Rock, AR (see Figure 14-3). If the wind speed is 30 mph, find the speed of the plane in still air.

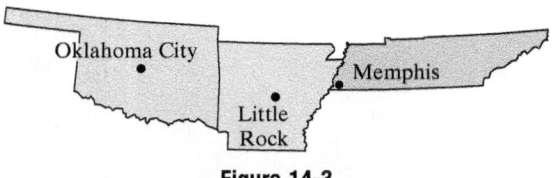

Figure 14-3

Solution:

Let x represent the speed of the plane in still air.

Then $x + 30$ is the speed of the plane with the wind.

$x - 30$ is the speed of the plane against the wind.

Organize the given information in a chart.

	Distance	**Rate**	**Time**
With the wind	440	$x + 30$	$\dfrac{440}{x + 30}$
Against the wind	340	$x - 30$	$\dfrac{340}{x - 30}$

Because $d = rt$, then $t = \dfrac{d}{r}$

The plane travels with the wind for the same amount of time as it travels against the wind, so we can equate the two expressions for time.

$$\left(\begin{array}{c}\text{Time with}\\ \text{the wind}\end{array}\right) = \left(\begin{array}{c}\text{time against}\\ \text{the wind}\end{array}\right)$$

$$\frac{440}{x + 30} = \frac{340}{x - 30}$$ The LCD is $(x + 30)(x - 30)$.

$$(x + 30)(x - 30) \cdot \frac{440}{x + 30} = (x + 30)(x - 30) \cdot \frac{340}{x - 30}$$

$$440(x - 30) = 340(x + 30)$$

$$440x - 13{,}200 = 340x + 10{,}200$$ Solve the resulting linear equation.

$$100x = 23{,}400$$

$$x = 234$$

The plane's speed in still air is 234 mph.

Answer

5. 6 mph

Example 6 **Using a Rational Equation in a Distance, Rate, and Time Application**

A motorist drives 100 mi between two cities in a bad rainstorm. For the return trip in sunny weather, she averages 10 mph faster and takes $\frac{1}{2}$ hr less time. Find the average speed of the motorist in the rainstorm and in sunny weather.

Solution:

Let x represent the motorist's speed during the rain.

Then $x + 10$ represents the speed in sunny weather.

	Distance	Rate	Time
Trip during rainstorm	100	x	$\dfrac{100}{x}$
Trip during sunny weather	100	$x + 10$	$\dfrac{100}{x + 10}$

Because $d = rt$, then $t = \dfrac{d}{r}$

Because the same distance is traveled in $\frac{1}{2}$ hr less time, the difference between the time of the trip during the rainstorm and the time during sunny weather is $\frac{1}{2}$ hr.

$\left(\begin{matrix}\text{Time during}\\\text{the rainstorm}\end{matrix}\right) - \left(\begin{matrix}\text{time during}\\\text{sunny weather}\end{matrix}\right) = \left(\frac{1}{2}\text{ hr}\right)$ Verbal model

$\dfrac{100}{x} - \dfrac{100}{x + 10} = \dfrac{1}{2}$ Mathematical equation

$2x(x + 10)\left(\dfrac{100}{x} - \dfrac{100}{x + 10}\right) = 2x(x + 10)\left(\dfrac{1}{2}\right)$ Multiply by the LCD.

$2x(x + 10)\left(\dfrac{100}{x}\right) - 2x(x + 10)\left(\dfrac{100}{x + 10}\right) = 2x(x + 10)\left(\dfrac{1}{2}\right)$ Apply the distributive property.

$200(x + 10) - 200x = x(x + 10)$ Clear fractions.

$200x + 2000 - 200x = x^2 + 10x$ Solve the resulting equation (quadratic).

$2000 = x^2 + 10x$

$0 = x^2 + 10x - 2000$ Set the equation equal to zero.

$0 = (x - 40)(x + 50)$ Factor.

$x = 40$ or $x = -50$

Because a rate of speed cannot be negative, reject $x = -50$. Therefore, the speed of the motorist in the rainstorm is 40 mph. Because $x + 10 = 40 + 10 = 50$, the average speed for the return trip in sunny weather is 50 mph.

Skill Practice

6. Harley rode his mountain bike 12 mi to the top of the mountain and the same distance back down. His speed going up was 8 mph slower than coming down. The ride up took 2 hr longer than the ride coming down. Find his speeds.

Avoiding Mistakes

The equation

$$\dfrac{100}{x} - \dfrac{100}{x + 10} = \dfrac{1}{2}$$

is not a proportion because the left-hand side has more than one fraction. Do not try to multiply the cross products. Instead, multiply by the LCD to clear fractions.

Answer

6. Uphill speed was 4 mph; downhill speed was 12 mph.

4. Work Applications

Example 7 demonstrates how work rates are related to a portion of a job that can be completed in one unit of time.

Example 7   **Using a Rational Equation in a Work Problem**

A new printing press can print the morning edition in 2 hr, whereas the old printer required 4 hr. How long would it take to print the morning edition if both printers were working together?

Solution:

Let x represent the time required for both printers working together to complete the job.

One method to approach this problem is to determine the portion of the job that each printer can complete in 1 hr and extend that rate to the portion of the job completed in x hr.

- The old printer can perform the job in 4 hr. Therefore, it completes $\frac{1}{4}$ of the job in 1 hr and $\frac{1}{4}x$ jobs in x hr.
- The new printer can perform the job in 2 hr. Therefore, it completes $\frac{1}{2}$ of the job in 1 hr and $\frac{1}{2}x$ jobs in x hr.

	Work Rate	**Time**	**Portion of Job Completed**
Old printer	$\dfrac{1 \text{ job}}{4 \text{ hr}}$	x hours	$\dfrac{1}{4}x$
New printer	$\dfrac{1 \text{ job}}{2 \text{ hr}}$	x hours	$\dfrac{1}{2}x$

The sum of the portions of the job completed by each printer must equal one whole job.

$$\begin{pmatrix} \text{Portion of job} \\ \text{completed by} \\ \text{old printer} \end{pmatrix} + \begin{pmatrix} \text{portion of job} \\ \text{completed by} \\ \text{new printer} \end{pmatrix} = \begin{pmatrix} 1 \\ \text{whole} \\ \text{job} \end{pmatrix}$$

$\frac{1}{4}x + \frac{1}{2}x = 1$ The LCD is 4.

$4\left(\frac{1}{4}x + \frac{1}{2}x\right) = 4(1)$ Multiply by the LCD.

$\overset{1}{4} \cdot \frac{1}{4}x + \overset{2}{4} \cdot \frac{1}{2}x = 4 \cdot 1$ Apply the distributive property.

$x + 2x = 4$ Solve the resulting linear equation.

$3x = 4$

$x = \dfrac{4}{3}$ or $x = 1\dfrac{1}{3}$ The time required to print the morning edition using both printers is $1\frac{1}{3}$ hr.

TIP: An alternative approach to solving a "work" problem is to add rates of speed. In Example 7, we could have set up an equation as follows.

$$\left(\begin{array}{c}\text{Rate of speed} \\ \text{of old printer}\end{array}\right) + \left(\begin{array}{c}\text{rate of speed} \\ \text{of new printer}\end{array}\right) = \left(\begin{array}{c}\text{rate of speed of} \\ \text{both working together}\end{array}\right)$$

$$\frac{1 \text{ job}}{4 \text{ hr}} + \frac{1 \text{ job}}{2 \text{ hr}} = \frac{1 \text{ job}}{x \text{ hr}}$$

$$\frac{1}{4} + \frac{1}{2} = \frac{1}{x}$$

$$4x\left(\frac{1}{4} + \frac{1}{2}\right) = 4x\left(\frac{1}{x}\right) \qquad \text{Multiply by the LCD, } 4x.$$

$$x + 2x = 4$$

$$3x = 4$$

$$x = \frac{4}{3} \qquad \text{The time required for both printers working together is } 1\frac{1}{3} \text{ hr.}$$

Section 14.7   Practice Exercises

Study Skills Exercise

1. Define the key terms:

    a. Proportion   **b. Similar polygons**

Review Exercises

For Exercises 2–7, determine whether each of the following is an equation or an expression. If it is an equation, solve it. If it is an expression, perform the indicated operation.

2. $\dfrac{b}{5} + 3 = 9$

3. $\dfrac{m}{m-1} - \dfrac{2}{m+3}$

4. $\dfrac{2}{a+5} + \dfrac{5}{a^2-25}$

5. $\dfrac{3y+6}{20} \div \dfrac{4y+8}{8}$

6. $\dfrac{z^2+z}{24} \cdot \dfrac{8}{z+1}$

7. $\dfrac{3}{p+3} = \dfrac{12p+19}{p^2+7p+12} - \dfrac{5}{p+4}$

8. Determine whether 1 is a solution to the equation. $\dfrac{1}{x-1} + \dfrac{1}{2} = \dfrac{2}{x^2-1}$

Objective 1: Solving Proportions

For Exercises 9–22, solve the proportions. **(See Example 1.)**

9. $\dfrac{8}{5} = \dfrac{152}{p}$

10. $\dfrac{6}{7} = \dfrac{96}{y}$

11. $\dfrac{19}{76} = \dfrac{z}{4}$

12. $\dfrac{15}{135} = \dfrac{w}{9}$

13. $\dfrac{5}{3} = \dfrac{a}{8}$

14. $\dfrac{b}{14} = \dfrac{3}{8}$

15. $\dfrac{2}{1.9} = \dfrac{x}{38}$

16. $\dfrac{16}{1.3} = \dfrac{30}{p}$

17. $\dfrac{y+1}{2y} = \dfrac{2}{3}$

18. $\dfrac{w-2}{4w} = \dfrac{1}{6}$

19. $\dfrac{9}{2z-1} = \dfrac{3}{z}$

20. $\dfrac{1}{t} = \dfrac{1}{4-t}$

21. $\dfrac{8}{9a-1} = \dfrac{5}{3a+2}$

22. $\dfrac{4p+1}{3} = \dfrac{2p-5}{6}$

23. Charles' law describes the relationship between the initial and final temperature and volume of a gas held at a constant pressure.

$$\dfrac{V_i}{V_f} = \dfrac{T_i}{T_f}$$

    a. Solve the equation for V_f.

    b. Solve the equation for T_f.

24. The relationship between the area, height, and base of a triangle is given by the proportion

$$\dfrac{A}{b} = \dfrac{h}{2}$$

    a. Solve the equation for A.

    b. Solve the equation for b.

Objective 2: Applications of Proportions and Similar Polygons

For Exercises 25–36, solve using proportions.

25. Toni drives her Honda Civic 132 mi on the highway on 4 gal of gas. At this rate how many miles can she drive on 9 gal of gas? **(See Example 2.)**

26. Tim takes his pulse for 10 sec and counts 12 beats. How many beats per minute is this?

27. Suppose a household of 4 people produces 128 lb of garbage in one week. At this rate, how many pounds will 48 people produce in 1 week?

28. Property tax on a $180,000 house is $4000. At this rate, how much tax would be paid on a $216,000 home?

29. Andrew is on a low-carbohydrate diet. If his diet book tells him that an 8-oz serving of pineapple contains 19.2 g of carbohydrate, how many grams of carbohydrate does a 5-oz serving contain?

30. Cooking oatmeal requires 1 cup of water for every $\frac{1}{2}$ cup of oats. How many cups of water will be required for $\frac{3}{4}$ cup of oats?

31. A map has a scale of 75 mi/in. If two cities measure 3.5 in. apart, how many miles does this represent?

32. A map has a scale of 50 mi/in. If two cities measure 6.5 in. apart, how many miles does this represent?

33. The height of a flagpole can be determined by comparing the shadow of the flagpole and the shadow of a yardstick. From the figure, determine the height of the flagpole. **(See Example 3.)**

34. A 15-ft flagpole casts a 4-ft shadow. How long will the shadow be for a 90-ft building?

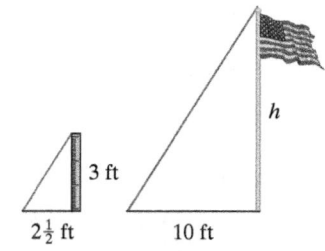

Figure for Exercise 33

35. A person 1.6 m tall stands next to a lifeguard observation platform. If the person casts a shadow of 1 m and the lifeguard platform casts a shadow of 1.5 m, how high is the platform?

36. A 32-ft tree casts a shadow of 18 ft. How long will the shadow be for a 22-ft tree?

For Exercises 37–38, the pairs of polygons are similar. Solve for the indicated variables. **(See Example 4.)**

37.

38.

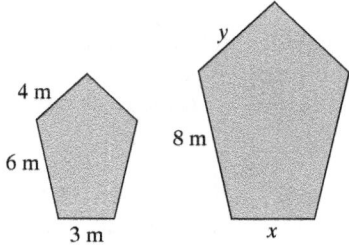

39. A carpenter makes a schematic drawing of a porch he plans to build. On the drawing, 2 in. represents 7 ft. Find the lengths denoted by x, y, and z.

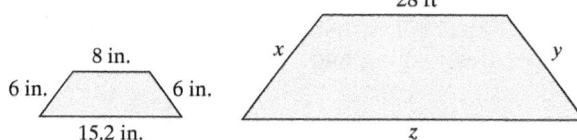

40. The Great Cookie Company has a sign on the front of its store as shown in the figure. The company would like to put a sign of the same shape in the back, but with dimensions $\frac{1}{3}$ as large. Find the lengths denoted by x and y.

Objective 3: Distance, Rate, and Time Applications

41. A boat travels 54 mi upstream against the current in the same amount of time it takes to travel 66 mi downstream with the current. If the current is 2 mph, what is the speed of the boat in still water? (Use $t = \frac{d}{r}$ to complete the table.) **(See Example 5.)**

	Distance	Rate	Time
With the current (downstream)			
Against the current (upstream)			

42. A plane flies 630 mi with the wind in the same time that it takes to fly 455 mi against the wind. If this plane flies at the rate of 217 mph in still air, what is the speed of the wind? (Use $t = \frac{d}{r}$ to complete the table.)

	Distance	Rate	Time
With the wind			
Against the wind			

43. The jet stream is a fast flowing air current found in the atmosphere at around 36,000 ft above the surface of the Earth. During one summer day, the speed of the jet stream is 35 mph. A plane flying with the jet stream can fly 700 mi in the same amount of time that it would take to fly 500 mi against the jet stream. What is the speed of the plane in still air?

44. A fisherman travels 9 mi downstream with the current in the same time that he travels 3 mi upstream against the current. If the speed of the current is 6 mph, what is the speed at which the fisherman travels in still water?

45. An athlete in training rides his bike 20 mi and then immediately follows with a 10-mi run. The total workout takes him 2.5 hr. He also knows that he bikes about twice as fast as he runs. Determine his biking speed and his running speed.

46. Devon can cross-country ski 5 km/hr faster than his sister Shanelle. Devon skis 45 km in the same time Shanelle skis 30 km. Find their speeds.

47. Floyd can walk 2 mph faster then his wife, Rachel. It takes Rachel 3 hr longer than Floyd to hike a 12-mi trail through the park. Find their speeds. **(See Example 6.)**

48. Janine bikes 3 mph faster than her sister, Jessica. Janine can ride 36 mi in 1 hr less time than Jessica can ride the same distance. Find each of their speeds.

49. Sergio rode his bike 4 mi. Then he got a flat tire and had to walk back 4 mi. It took him 1 hr longer to walk than it did to ride. If his rate walking was 9 mph less than his rate riding, find the two rates.

50. Amber jogs 10 km in $\frac{3}{4}$ hr less than she can walk the same distance. If her walking rate is 3 km/hr less than her jogging rate, find her rates jogging and walking (in km/hr).

Objective 4: Work Applications

51. If it takes a person 2 hr to paint a room, what fraction of the room would be painted in 1 hr?

52. If it takes a copier 3 hr to complete a job, what fraction of the job would be completed in 1 hr?

53. If the cold-water faucet is left on, the sink will fill in 10 min. If the hot-water faucet is left on, the sink will fill in 12 min. How long would it take the sink to fill if both faucets are left on? **(See Example 7.)**

54. The CUT-IT-OUT lawn mowing company consists of two people: Tina and Bill. If Tina cuts a lawn by herself, she can do it in 4 hr. If Bill cuts the same lawn himself, it takes him an hour longer than Tina. How long would it take them if they worked together?

55. A manuscript needs to be printed. One printer can do the job in 50 min, and another printer can do the job in 40 min. How long would it take if both printers were used?

56. A pump can empty a small pond in 4 hr. Another more efficient pump can do the job in 3 hr. How long would it take to empty the pond if both pumps were used?

57. A pipe can fill a reservoir in 16 hr. A drainage pipe can drain the reservoir in 24 hr. How long would it take to fill the reservoir if the drainage pipe were left open by mistake? (*Hint:* The rate at which water drains should be negative.)

58. A hole in the bottom of a child's plastic swimming pool can drain the pool in 60 min. If the pool had no hole, a hose could fill the pool in 40 min. How long would it take the hose to fill the pool with the hole?

59. Tim and Al are bricklayers. Tim can construct an outdoor grill in 5 days. If Al helps Tim, they can build it in only 2 days. How long would it take Al to build the grill alone?

60. Norma is a new and inexperienced secretary. It takes her 3 hr to prepare a mailing. If her boss helps her, the mailing can be completed in 1 hr. How long would it take the boss to do the job by herself?

Expanding Your Skills

For Exercises 61–64, solve using proportions.

61. The ratio of smokers to nonsmokers in a restaurant is 2 to 7. There are 100 more nonsmokers than smokers. How many smokers and nonsmokers are in the restaurant?

62. The ratio of fiction to nonfiction books sold in a bookstore is 5 to 3. One week there were 180 more fiction books sold than nonfiction. Find the number of fiction and nonfiction books sold during that week.

63. There are 440 students attending a biology lecture. The ratio of male to female students at the lecture is 6 to 5. How many men and women are attending the lecture?

64. The ratio of dogs to cats at the humane society is 5 to 8. The total number of dogs and cats is 650. How many dogs and how many cats are at the humane society?

Group Activity

Computing Monthly Mortgage Payments

Materials: A calculator

Estimated Time: 15–20 minutes

Group Size: 3

When a person borrows money to buy a house, the bank usually requires a down payment of between 0% and 20% of the cost of the house. The bank then issues a loan for the remaining balance on the house. The loan to buy a house is called a *mortgage*. Monthly payments are made to pay off the mortgage over a period of years.

A formula to calculate the monthly payment, P, for a loan is given by the complex fraction:

$$P = \frac{\frac{Ar}{12}}{1 - \frac{1}{\left(1 + \frac{r}{12}\right)^{12t}}}$$

where
P is the monthly payment
A is the original amount of the mortgage
r is the annual interest rate
t is the term of the loan in years

Suppose a person wants to buy a $200,000 house. The bank requires a down payment of 20%, and the loan is issued for 30 yr at 7.5% interest for 30 yr.

1. Find the amount of the down payment. _____

2. Find the amount of the mortgage. _____

3. Find the monthly payment (to the nearest cent). _____

4. Multiply the monthly payment found in question 3 by the total number of months in a 30-yr period. Interpret what this value means in the context of the problem.

5. How much total interest was paid on the loan for the house? _____

6. What was the total amount paid to the bank (include the down payment). _____

Chapter 14 Summary

Section 14.1 Introduction to Rational Expressions

Key Concepts

A **rational expression** is a ratio of the form $\frac{p}{q}$ where p and q are polynomials and $q \neq 0$.

The **restricted values** of an algebraic expression are all real numbers that when substituted for the variable make the expression undefined. For a rational expression, the restricted values are all real numbers that make the denominator zero.

Simplifying a Rational Expression to Lowest Terms

Factor the numerator and denominator completely, and reduce factors whose ratio is equal to 1 or to -1. A rational expression written in lowest terms will still have the same restricted values as the original expression.

Examples

Example 1

$\dfrac{x + 2}{x^2 - 5x - 14}$ is a rational expression.

Example 2

To identify restricted values of $\dfrac{x + 2}{x^2 - 5x - 14}$ factor the

denominator: $\dfrac{x + 2}{(x + 2)(x - 7)}$

The restricted values are $x = -2$ and $x = 7$.

Example 3

Simplify to lowest terms. $\dfrac{x + 2}{x^2 - 5x - 14}$

$\dfrac{\overset{1}{\cancel{x + 2}}}{\cancel{(x + 2)}(x - 7)}$ Simplify.

$= \dfrac{1}{x - 7}$ (provided $x \neq 7, x \neq -2$).

| **Section 14.2** | **Multiplication and Division of Rational Expressions** |

Key Concepts

Multiplying Rational Expressions

Multiply the numerators and multiply the denominators. That is, if $q \neq 0$ and $s \neq 0$, then

$$\frac{p}{q} \cdot \frac{r}{s} = \frac{pr}{qs}$$

Factor the numerator and denominator completely. Then reduce factors whose ratio is 1 or −1.

Dividing Rational Expressions

Multiply the first expression by the reciprocal of the second expression. That is, for $q \neq 0$, $r \neq 0$, and $s \neq 0$,

$$\frac{p}{q} \div \frac{r}{s} = \frac{p}{q} \cdot \frac{s}{r} = \frac{ps}{qr}$$

Examples

Example 1

Multiply. $\dfrac{b^2 - a^2}{a^2 - 2ab + b^2} \cdot \dfrac{a^2 - 3ab + 2b^2}{2a + 2b}$

$$= \frac{\overset{-1}{(b - a)}\overset{1}{(b + a)}}{(a - b)(a - b)} \cdot \frac{(a - 2b)\overset{1}{(a - b)}}{2(a + b)}$$

$$= -\frac{a - 2b}{2} \quad \text{or} \quad \frac{2b - a}{2}$$

Example 2

Divide. $\dfrac{x - 2}{15} \div \dfrac{x^2 + 2x - 8}{20x}$

$$= \frac{x - 2}{15} \cdot \frac{20x}{x^2 + 2x - 8}$$

$$= \frac{\overset{1}{(x - 2)}}{\underset{3}{15}} \cdot \frac{\overset{4}{20x}}{\underset{1}{(x - 2)}(x + 4)}$$

$$= \frac{4x}{3(x + 4)}$$

Section 14.3 Least Common Denominator

Key Concepts

Converting a Rational Expression to an Equivalent Expression with a Different Denominator

Multiply numerator and denominator of the rational expression by the missing factors necessary to create the desired denominator.

Finding the Least Common Denominator (LCD) of Two or More Rational Expressions

1. Factor all denominators completely.
2. The LCD is the product of unique factors from the denominators, where each factor is raised to its highest power.

Examples

Example 1

Convert $\dfrac{-3}{x-2}$ to an equivalent expression with the indicated denominator:

$$\frac{-3}{x-2} = \frac{}{5(x-2)(x+2)}$$

Multiply numerator and denominator by the missing factors from the denominator.

$$\frac{-3 \cdot 5(x+2)}{(x-2) \cdot 5(x+2)} = \frac{-15x-30}{5(x-2)(x+2)}$$

Example 2

Identify the LCD. $\dfrac{1}{8x^3y^2z}; \dfrac{5}{6xy^4}$

1. Write the denominators as a product of prime factors:

$$\frac{1}{2^3x^3y^2z}; \frac{5}{2 \cdot 3xy^4}$$

2. The LCD is $2^3 3x^3y^4z$ or $24x^3y^4z$

Section 14.4 Addition and Subtraction of Rational Expressions

Key Concepts

To add or subtract rational expressions, the expressions must have the same denominator.

Steps to Add or Subtract Rational Expressions

1. Factor the denominators of each rational expression.
2. Identify the LCD.
3. Rewrite each rational expression as an equivalent expression with the LCD as its denominator.
4. Add or subtract the numerators, and write the result over the common denominator.
5. Simplify.

Examples

Example 1

Subtract. $\dfrac{c}{c^2-c-12} - \dfrac{1}{2c-8}$

$$= \frac{c}{(c-4)(c+3)} - \frac{1}{2(c-4)}$$

The LCD is $2(c-4)(c+3)$.

$$= \frac{2c}{2(c-4)(c+3)} - \frac{1(c+3)}{2(c-4)(c+3)}$$

$$= \frac{2c-(c+3)}{2(c-4)(c+3)}$$

$$= \frac{2c-c-3}{2(c-4)(c+3)} = \frac{c-3}{2(c-4)(c+3)}$$

Section 14.5   Complex Fractions

Key Concepts

Complex fractions can be simplified by using Method I or Method II.

Method I

1. Add or subtract expressions in the numerator to form a single fraction. Add or subtract expressions in the denominator to form a single fraction.
2. Divide the rational expressions from step 1 by multiplying the numerator of the complex fraction by the reciprocal of the denominator of the complex fraction.
3. Simplify to lowest terms, if possible.

Method II

1. Multiply the numerator and denominator of the complex fraction by the LCD of all individual fractions within the expression.
2. Apply the distributive property, and simplify the result.
3. Simplify to lowest terms, if possible.

Examples

Example 1

Simplify.
$$\dfrac{1 - \dfrac{4}{w^2}}{1 - \dfrac{1}{w} - \dfrac{6}{w^2}} = \dfrac{\dfrac{w^2}{w^2} - \dfrac{4}{w^2}}{\dfrac{w^2}{w^2} - \dfrac{w}{w^2} - \dfrac{6}{w^2}}$$

$$= \dfrac{\dfrac{w^2 - 4}{w^2}}{\dfrac{w^2 - w - 6}{w^2}} = \dfrac{w^2 - 4}{w^2} \cdot \dfrac{w^2}{w^2 - w - 6}$$

$$= \dfrac{(w - 2)\overset{1}{\cancel{(w + 2)}}}{w^2} \cdot \dfrac{w^2}{(w - 3)\underset{1}{\cancel{(w + 2)}}}$$

$$= \dfrac{w - 2}{w - 3}$$

Example 2

Simplify.
$$\dfrac{1 - \dfrac{4}{w^2}}{1 - \dfrac{1}{w} - \dfrac{6}{w^2}} = \dfrac{w^2\left(1 - \dfrac{4}{w^2}\right)}{w^2\left(1 - \dfrac{1}{w} - \dfrac{6}{w^2}\right)}$$

$$= \dfrac{w^2 - 4}{w^2 - w - 6} = \dfrac{(w - 2)\overset{1}{\cancel{(w + 2)}}}{(w - 3)\cancel{(w + 2)}}$$

$$= \dfrac{w - 2}{w - 3}$$

| Section 14.6 | **Rational Equations** |

Key Concepts

An equation with one or more rational expressions is called a **rational equation**.

Steps to Solve a Rational Equation

1. Factor the denominators of all rational expressions. Identify the restricted values.
2. Identify the LCD of all expressions in the equation.
3. Multiply both sides of the equation by the LCD.
4. Solve the resulting equation.
5. Check each potential solution in the original equation.

Examples

Example 1

Solve. $\dfrac{1}{w} - \dfrac{1}{2w - 1} = \dfrac{-2w}{2w - 1}$

The restricted values are $w = 0$ and $w = \dfrac{1}{2}$.

The LCD is $w(2w - 1)$.

$$\cancel{w}(2w - 1)\frac{1}{\cancel{w}} - w\cancel{(2w - 1)}\frac{1}{\cancel{2w - 1}}$$

$$= w\cancel{(2w - 1)}\frac{-2w}{\cancel{2w - 1}}$$

$(2w - 1)(1) - w(1) = w(-2w)$

$2w - 1 - w = -2w^2$ Quadratic equation

$2w^2 + w - 1 = 0$

$(2w - 1)(w + 1) = 0$

       $w \cancel{=} \frac{1}{2}$ or $w = -1$

      Does not check.   Checks.

Example 2

Solve for I. $q = \dfrac{VQ}{I}$

$$I \cdot q = \dfrac{VQ}{\cancel{I}} \cdot \cancel{I}$$

$$Iq = VQ$$

$$I = \dfrac{VQ}{q}$$

| Section 14.7 | Applications of Rational Equations and Proportions |

Key Concepts and Examples

Solving Proportions

An equation that equates two rates or ratios is called a **proportion**:

$$\frac{a}{b} = \frac{c}{d} \quad (b \neq 0, d \neq 0)$$

To solve a proportion, multiply both sides of the equation by the LCD.

Examples 2 and 3 give applications of rational equations.

Example 2

Two cars travel from Los Angeles to Las Vegas. One car travels an average of 8 mph faster than the other car. If the faster car travels 189 mi in the same time as the slower car travels 165 mi, what is the average speed of each car?

Let r represent the speed of the slower car.
Let $r + 8$ represent the speed of the faster car.

	Distance	Rate	Time
Slower car	165	r	$\dfrac{165}{r}$
Faster car	189	$r + 8$	$\dfrac{189}{r + 8}$

$$\frac{165}{r} = \frac{189}{r + 8}$$

$$165(r + 8) = 189r$$

$$165r + 1320 = 189r$$

$$1320 = 24r$$

$$55 = r$$

The slower car travels 55 mph, and the faster car travels $55 + 8 = 63$ mph.

Examples

Example 1

A 90-g serving of a particular ice cream contains 10 g of fat. How much fat does 400 g of the same ice cream contain?

$$\frac{10 \text{ g fat}}{90 \text{ g ice cream}} = \frac{x \text{ grams fat}}{400 \text{ g ice cream}}$$

$$\frac{10}{90} = \frac{x}{400}$$

$$\overset{40}{\cancel{3600}} \cdot \left(\frac{10}{\cancel{90}}\right) = \left(\frac{x}{\cancel{400}}\right) \cdot \overset{9}{\cancel{3600}}$$

$$400 = 9x$$

$$x = \frac{400}{9} \approx 44.4 \text{ g}$$

Example 3

Beth and Cecelia have a house cleaning business. Beth can clean a particular house in 5 hr by herself. Cecelia can clean the same house in 4 hr. How long would it take if they cleaned the house together?

Let x be the number of hours it takes for both Beth and Cecelia to clean the house.

Beth can clean $\frac{1}{5}$ of the house in an hour and $\frac{1}{5}x$ of the house in x hr.
Cecelia can clean $\frac{1}{4}$ of the house in an hour and $\frac{1}{4}x$ of the house in x hr.

$$\frac{1}{5}x + \frac{1}{4}x = 1 \qquad \text{Together they clean one whole house.}$$

$$20\left(\frac{1}{5}x + \frac{1}{4}x\right) = (1)20$$

$$4x + 5x = 20$$

$$9x = 20$$

$$x = \frac{20}{9}, \text{ or } 2\frac{2}{9} \text{ hr working together.}$$

Section 14.1

1. For the rational expression $\dfrac{t-2}{t+9}$

   a. Evaluate the expression (if possible) for $t = 0, 1, 2, -3, -9$

   b. Identify the restricted values.

2. For the rational expression $\dfrac{k+1}{k-5}$

   a. Evaluate the expression for $k = 0, 1, 5, -1, -2$

   b. Identify the restricted values.

3. Which of the rational expressions are equal to -1?

   a. $\dfrac{2-x}{x-2}$ **b.** $\dfrac{x-5}{x+5}$

   c. $\dfrac{-x-7}{x+7}$ **d.** $\dfrac{x^2-4}{4-x^2}$

For Exercises 4–13, identify the restricted values. Then simplify the expressions to lowest terms.

4. $\dfrac{x-3}{(2x-5)(x-3)}$ **5.** $\dfrac{h+7}{(3h+1)(h+7)}$

6. $\dfrac{4a^2+7a-2}{a^2-4}$ **7.** $\dfrac{2w^2+11w+12}{w^2-16}$

8. $\dfrac{z^2-4z}{8-2z}$ **9.** $\dfrac{15-3k}{2k^2-10k}$

10. $\dfrac{2b^2+4b-6}{4b+12}$ **11.** $\dfrac{3m^2-12m-15}{9m+9}$

12. $\dfrac{n+3}{n^2+6n+9}$ **13.** $\dfrac{p+7}{p^2+14p+49}$

Section 14.2

For Exercises 14–27, multiply or divide as indicated.

14. $\dfrac{3y^3}{3y-6} \cdot \dfrac{y-2}{y}$ **15.** $\dfrac{2u+10}{u} \cdot \dfrac{u^3}{4u+20}$

16. $\dfrac{11}{v-2} \cdot \dfrac{2v^2-8}{22}$ **17.** $\dfrac{8}{x^2-25} \cdot \dfrac{3x+15}{16}$

18. $\dfrac{4c^2+4c}{c^2-25} \div \dfrac{8c}{c^2-5c}$ **19.** $\dfrac{q^2-5q+6}{2q+4} \div \dfrac{2q-6}{q+2}$

20. $\left(\dfrac{-2t}{t+1}\right)(t^2-4t-5)$ **21.** $(s^2-6s+8)\left(\dfrac{4s}{s-2}\right)$

22. $\dfrac{\dfrac{a^2+5a+1}{7a-7}}{\dfrac{a^2+5a+1}{a-1}}$ **23.** $\dfrac{\dfrac{n^2+n+1}{n^2-4}}{\dfrac{n^2+n+1}{n+2}}$

24. $\dfrac{5h^2-6h+1}{h^2-1} \div \dfrac{16h^2-9}{4h^2+7h+3} \cdot \dfrac{3-4h}{30h-6}$

25. $\dfrac{3m-3}{6m^2+18m+12} \cdot \dfrac{2m^2-8}{m^2-3m+2} \div \dfrac{m+3}{m+1}$

26. $\dfrac{x-2}{x^2-3x-18} \cdot \dfrac{6-x}{x^2-4}$

27. $\dfrac{4y^2-1}{1+2y} \div \dfrac{y^2-4y-5}{5-y}$

Section 14.3

For Exercises 28–33, identify the LCD. Then write each fraction as an equivalent fraction with the LCD as its denominator.

28. $\dfrac{2}{5a}; \dfrac{3}{10b}$ **29.** $\dfrac{7}{4x}; \dfrac{11}{6y}$

30. $\dfrac{1}{x^2y^4}; \dfrac{3}{xy^5}$ **31.** $\dfrac{5}{ab^3}; \dfrac{3}{ac^2}$

32. $\dfrac{5}{p+2}; \dfrac{p}{p-4}$ **33.** $\dfrac{6}{q}; \dfrac{1}{q+8}$

34. Determine the LCD.

$$\dfrac{6}{n^2-9}; \dfrac{5}{n^2-n-6}$$

35. Determine the LCD.

$$\dfrac{8}{m^2-16}; \dfrac{7}{m^2-m-12}$$

36. State two possible LCDs that could be used to add the fractions.

$$\frac{7}{c - 2} + \frac{4}{2 - c}$$

37. State two possible LCDs that could be used to subtract the fractions.

$$\frac{10}{3 - x} - \frac{5}{x - 3}$$

Section 14.4

For Exercises 38–49, add or subtract as indicated.

38. $\dfrac{h + 3}{h + 1} + \dfrac{h - 1}{h + 1}$

39. $\dfrac{b - 6}{b - 2} + \dfrac{b + 2}{b - 2}$

40. $\dfrac{a^2}{a - 5} - \dfrac{25}{a - 5}$

41. $\dfrac{x^2}{x + 7} - \dfrac{49}{x + 7}$

42. $\dfrac{y}{y^2 - 81} + \dfrac{2}{9 - y}$

43. $\dfrac{3}{4 - t^2} + \dfrac{t}{2 - t}$

44. $\dfrac{4}{3m} - \dfrac{1}{m + 2}$

45. $\dfrac{5}{2r + 12} - \dfrac{1}{r}$

46. $\dfrac{4p}{p^2 + 6p + 5} - \dfrac{3p}{p^2 + 5p + 4}$

47. $\dfrac{3q}{q^2 + 7q + 10} - \dfrac{2q}{q^2 + 6q + 8}$

48. $\dfrac{1}{h} + \dfrac{h}{2h + 4} - \dfrac{2}{h^2 + 2h}$

49. $\dfrac{x}{3x + 9} - \dfrac{3}{x^2 + 3x} + \dfrac{1}{x}$

Section 14.5

For Exercises 50–57, simplify the complex fractions.

50. $\dfrac{\dfrac{a - 4}{3}}{\dfrac{a - 2}{3}}$

51. $\dfrac{\dfrac{z + 5}{z}}{\dfrac{z - 5}{3}}$

52. $\dfrac{\dfrac{2 - 3w}{2}}{\dfrac{2}{w} - 3}$

53. $\dfrac{\dfrac{2}{y} + 6}{\dfrac{3y + 1}{4}}$

54. $\dfrac{\dfrac{y}{x} - \dfrac{x}{y}}{\dfrac{1}{x} + \dfrac{1}{y}}$

55. $\dfrac{\dfrac{b}{a} - \dfrac{a}{b}}{\dfrac{1}{b} - \dfrac{1}{a}}$

56. $\dfrac{\dfrac{6}{p + 2} + 4}{\dfrac{8}{p + 2} - 4}$

57. $\dfrac{\dfrac{25}{k + 5} + 5}{\dfrac{5}{k + 5} - 5}$

Section 14.6

For Exercises 58–65, solve the equations.

58. $\dfrac{2}{x} + \dfrac{1}{2} = \dfrac{1}{4}$

59. $\dfrac{1}{y} + \dfrac{3}{4} = \dfrac{1}{4}$

60. $\dfrac{2}{h - 2} + 1 = \dfrac{h}{h + 2}$

61. $\dfrac{w}{w - 1} = \dfrac{3}{w + 1} + 1$

62. $\dfrac{t + 1}{3} - \dfrac{t - 1}{6} = \dfrac{1}{6}$

63. $\dfrac{4p - 4}{p^2 + 5p - 14} + \dfrac{2}{p + 7} = \dfrac{1}{p - 2}$

64. $\dfrac{1}{z + 2} = \dfrac{4}{z^2 - 4} - \dfrac{1}{z - 2}$

65. $\dfrac{y + 1}{y + 3} = \dfrac{y^2 - 11y}{y^2 + y - 6} - \dfrac{y - 3}{y - 2}$

66. Four times a number is added to 5. The sum is then divided by 6. The result is $\frac{7}{2}$. Find the number.

67. Solve the formula $\dfrac{V}{h} = \dfrac{\pi r^2}{3}$ for h.

68. Solve the formula $\dfrac{A}{b} = \dfrac{h}{2}$ for b.

Section 14.7

For Exercises 69–70, solve the proportions.

69. $\dfrac{m + 2}{8} = \dfrac{m}{3}$

70. $\dfrac{12}{a} = \dfrac{5}{8}$

71. A bag of popcorn states that it contains 4 g of fat per serving. If a serving is 2 oz, how many grams of fat are in a 5-oz bag?

72. Bud goes 10 mph faster on his Harley Davidson motorcycle than Ed goes on his Honda motorcycle. If Bud travels 105 mi in the same time that Ed travels 90 mi, what are the rates of the two bikers?

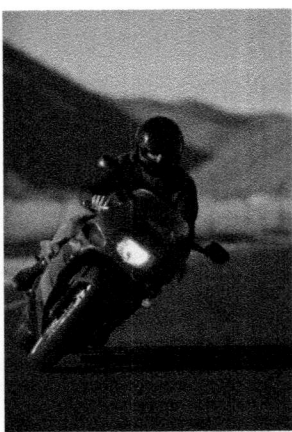

73. There are two pumps set up to fill a small swimming pool. One pump takes 24 min by itself to fill the pool, but the other takes 56 min by itself. How long would it take if both pumps work together?

74. The height of a building can be approximated by comparing the shadows of the building and of a meterstick. From the figure, find the height of the building.

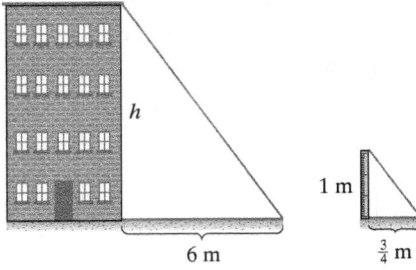

75. The polygons shown in the figure are similar. Solve for x and y.

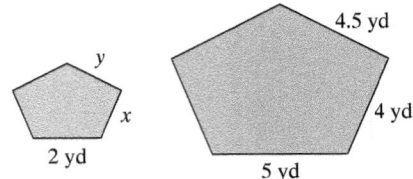

Chapter 14   Test

For Exercises 1–2,

  a. Identify the restricted values.

  b. Simplify the rational expression to lowest terms.

1. $\dfrac{5(x-2)(x+1)}{30(2-x)}$ **2.** $\dfrac{7a^2-42a}{a^3-4a^2-12a}$

3. Identify the rational expressions that are equal to -1.

  a. $\dfrac{x+4}{x-4}$ **b.** $\dfrac{7-2x}{2x-7}$

  c. $\dfrac{9x^2+16}{-9x^2-16}$ **d.** $-\dfrac{x+5}{x+5}$

For Exercises 4–9, perform the indicated operation.

4. $\dfrac{2}{y^2+4y+3}+\dfrac{1}{3y+9}$

5. $\dfrac{9-b^2}{5b+15}\div\dfrac{b-3}{b+3}$

6. $\dfrac{w^2-4w}{w^2-8w+16}\cdot\dfrac{w-4}{w^2+w}$

7. $\dfrac{t}{t-2}-\dfrac{8}{t^2-4}$

8. $\dfrac{1}{x+4}+\dfrac{2}{x^2+2x-8}+\dfrac{x}{x-2}$ **9.** $\dfrac{1-\dfrac{4}{m}}{m-\dfrac{16}{m}}$

For Exercises 10–13, solve the equation.

10. $\dfrac{3}{a}+\dfrac{5}{2}=\dfrac{7}{a}$

11. $\dfrac{p}{p-1}+\dfrac{1}{p}=\dfrac{p^2+1}{p^2-p}$

12. $\dfrac{3}{c-2}-\dfrac{1}{c+1}=\dfrac{7}{c^2-c-2}$

13. $\dfrac{4x}{x-4} = 3 + \dfrac{16}{x-4}$

14. Solve the formula $\dfrac{C}{2} = \dfrac{A}{r}$ for r.

15. If $\frac{3}{2}$ is added to the reciprocal of a number the result is $\frac{2}{5}$ times the reciprocal of that number. Find the number.

16. Solve the proportion.

$$\dfrac{y+7}{-4} = \dfrac{1}{4}$$

17. A recipe for vegetable soup calls for $\frac{1}{2}$ cup of carrots for six servings. How many cups of carrots are needed to prepare 15 servings?

18. A motorboat can travel 28 mi downstream in the same amount of time as it can travel 18 mi upstream. Find the speed of the current if the boat can travel 23 mph in still water.

19. Two printers working together can complete a job in 2 hr. If one printer requires 6 hr to do the job alone, how many hours would the second printer need to complete the job alone?

20. The figure shows two picture frames that are similar. Use this information to solve for x and y.

21. Find the LCD of the following pairs of rational expressions.

a. $\dfrac{x}{3(x+3)}; \dfrac{7}{5(x+3)}$ **b.** $\dfrac{-2}{3x^2y}; \dfrac{4}{xy^2}$

22. The amount of medication prescribed for a patient is proportional to the patient's weight. If a 160-lb person is prescribed 6 mL of a medicine, then how much medicine would be prescribed to a 220-lb person?

Chapters 1–14   Cumulative Review Exercises

For Exercises 1–2, simplify completely.

1. $\left(\dfrac{1}{2}\right)^{-4} + 2^4$

2. $|3-5| + |-2+7|$

3. Solve. $\dfrac{1}{2} - \dfrac{3}{4}(y-1) = \dfrac{5}{12}$

4. Complete the table.

Set-Builder Notation	Graph	Interval Notation
$\{x \mid x \geq -1\}$		
		$(-\infty, 5)$

5. The perimeter of a rectangular swimming pool is 104 m. The length is 1 m more than twice the width. Find the length and width.

6. The height of a triangle is 2 in. less than the base. The area is 40 in.^{2} Find the base and height of the triangle.

7. Simplify. $\left(\dfrac{4x^{-1}y^{-2}}{z^4}\right)^{-2} (2y^{-1}z^3)^3$

8. The length and width of a rectangle are given in terms of x.

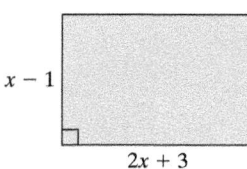

a. Write a polynomial that represents the perimeter of the rectangle.

b. Write a polynomial that represents the area of the rectangle.

9. Factor completely: $25x^2 - 30x + 9$

10. Factor. $10cd + 5d - 6c - 3$

11. Identify the restricted values of the expression.

$$\frac{x + 3}{(x - 5)(2x + 1)}$$

12. Simplify to lowest terms.

$$\frac{x^2 - 9}{x^2 + 8x + 15}$$

13. Divide. $\dfrac{2x - 6}{x^2 - 16} \div \dfrac{10x^2 - 90}{x^2 - x - 12}$

14. Simplify.

$$\frac{\dfrac{3}{4} - \dfrac{1}{x}}{\dfrac{1}{3x} - \dfrac{1}{4}}$$

15. Solve.

$$\frac{7}{y^2 - 4} = \frac{3}{y - 2} + \frac{2}{y + 2}$$

16. Solve the proportion.

$$\frac{2b - 5}{6} = \frac{4b}{7}$$

17. Determine the x- and y-intercepts.

   a. $-2x + 4y = 8$ **b.** $y = 5x$

18. Determine the slope

   a. of the line containing the points $(0, -6)$ and $(-5, 1)$.

   b. of the line $y = -\dfrac{2}{3}x - 6$

   c. of a line parallel to a line having a slope of 4.

   d. of a line perpendicular to a line having a slope of 4.

19. Find an equation of a line passing through the point $(1, 2)$ and having a slope of 5. Write the answer in slope-intercept form.

20. A group of teenagers buys 2 large popcorns and 6 drinks at the movie theater for $16. A couple buys 1 large popcorn and 2 drinks for $6.50. Find the price for 1 large popcorn and the price for 1 drink.

Radicals

15

Chapter 15

Chapter 15 is devoted to the study of radicals and their applications. We first present the techniques to add, subtract, multiply, and divide radical expressions. This is followed by radical equations and their applications.

Are You Prepared?

The skill of multiplying radicals is similar to multiplying polynomials. This puzzle will help you practice multiplying polynomials.

Circle the correct response. Write the corresponding letters in the box below to complete the sentence.

1. $2xy(2x - 4y + xy)$

   ANT $4x^2y - 8xy^2 + 2x^2y^2$

   ENT $4x^2y - 8xy^2 + 2xy$

2. $(2x - y)(3x + 4y)$

   HAG $6x^2 + 5xy - 4y^2$

   HOG $6x^2 - 5xy - 4y^2$

3. $(2x + 3y)^2$

   ING $4x^2 + 9y^2$

   REM $4x^2 + 12xy + 9y^2$

4. $(5x - y)(5x + y)$

   THE $5x^2 - y^2$

   ORE $25x^2 - y^2$

5. $(x^2 - 3y)(x + y)$

   RAD $x^3 - 2xy - 3y^2$

   PYT $x^3 + x^2y - 3xy - 3y^2$

6. $(8x^2y^3)(-3xy^4)$

   HEO $-24x^3y^7$

   HOE $-24x^2y^{12}$

One application in which square roots are used is with the

5	2	4	1	6	3

Section 15.1   Introduction to Roots and Radicals

Objectives

1. Definition of a Square Root
2. Definition of an nth-Root
3. Translations Involving nth-Roots
4. Pythagorean Theorem

1. Definition of a Square Root

Recall that to square a number means to multiply the number by itself: $b^2 = b \cdot b$. To find a square root of a number, we reverse the process of squaring a number. For example, finding a square root of 49 is equivalent to asking: "What number when squared equals 49?"

One obvious answer to this question is 7 because $(7)^2 = 49$. But -7 will also work because $(-7)^2 = 49$.

> **DEFINITION**   **Square Root**
>
> b is a **square root** of a if $b^2 = a$.

Skill Practice

Identify the square roots of the numbers.

1. 64
2. -36
3. 36
4. $\dfrac{25}{16}$

Example 1   **Identifying the Square Roots of a Number**

Identify the square roots of

   a. 9   **b.** 121   **c.** 0   **d.** -4

Solution:

   a. 3 is a square root of 9 because $(3)^2 = 9$.
        -3 is a square root of 9 because $(-3)^2 = 9$.

   b. 11 is a square root of 121 because $(11)^2 = 121$.
        -11 is a square root of 121 because $(-11)^2 = 121$.

   c. 0 is a square root of 0 because $(0)^2 = 0$.

   d. There are no real numbers that when squared will equal a negative number. Therefore, there are no real-valued square roots of -4.

TIP: All positive real numbers have two real-valued square roots: one positive and one negative. Zero has only one square root, which is 0 itself. Finally, for any negative real number, there are no real-valued square roots.

Recall from Section 1.7 that the positive square root of a real number can be denoted with a radical sign, $\sqrt{}$.

> **DEFINITION**   **Notation for Positive and Negative Square Roots**
>
> Let a represent a positive real number. Then,
>
>   **1.** $\sqrt{a}$ is the **positive square root** of a. The positive square root is also called the **principal square root**.
>   **2.** $-\sqrt{a}$ is the **negative square root** of a.
>   **3.** $\sqrt{0} = 0$

Answers

1. $8; -8$
2. There are no real-valued square roots.
3. $6; -6$ 4. $\dfrac{5}{4}; -\dfrac{5}{4}$

Example 2 **Simplifying Square Roots**

Simplify the square roots.

   a. $\sqrt{36}$ **b.** $\sqrt{225}$ **c.** $\sqrt{1}$ **d.** $\sqrt{\dfrac{9}{4}}$ **e.** $\sqrt{0.49}$

Solution:

   a. $\sqrt{36}$ denotes the positive square root of 36. $\sqrt{36} = 6$

   b. $\sqrt{225}$ denotes the positive square root of 225. $\sqrt{225} = 15$

   c. $\sqrt{1}$ denotes the positive square root of 1. $\sqrt{1} = 1$

   d. $\sqrt{\dfrac{9}{4}}$ denotes the positive square root of $\dfrac{9}{4}$. $\sqrt{\dfrac{9}{4}} = \dfrac{3}{2}$

   e. $\sqrt{0.49}$ denotes the positive square root. $\sqrt{0.49} = 0.7$

Skill Practice

Simplify the square roots.

  5. $\sqrt{81}$ **6.** $\sqrt{144}$

  7. $\sqrt{0}$ **8.** $\sqrt{\dfrac{1}{4}}$

  9. $\sqrt{0.09}$

The numbers 36, 225, 1, $\frac{9}{4}$, and 0.49 are **perfect squares** because their square roots are rational numbers. Radicals that cannot be simplified to rational numbers are irrational numbers. Recall that an irrational number cannot be written as a terminating or repeating decimal. For example, the symbol $\sqrt{13}$ is used to represent the exact value of the square root of 13. The symbol $\sqrt{42}$ is used to represent the exact value of the square root of 42. These values are irrational numbers but can be approximated by rational numbers by using a calculator.

$$\sqrt{13} \approx 3.605551275 \qquad \sqrt{42} \approx 6.480740698$$

Note: The only way to denote the *exact* values of the square root of 13 and the square root of 42 is $\sqrt{13}$ and $\sqrt{42}$.

A negative number cannot have a real number as a square root because no real number when squared is negative. For example, $\sqrt{-25}$ is *not a real number* because there is no real number, b, for which $(b)^2 = -25$.

TIP: Before using a calculator to evaluate a square root, try estimating the value first.

$\sqrt{13}$ must be a number between 3 and 4 because $\sqrt{9} < \sqrt{13} < \sqrt{16}$.

$\sqrt{42}$ must be a number between 6 and 7 because $\sqrt{36} < \sqrt{42} < \sqrt{49}$.

Example 3 **Evaluating Square Roots if Possible**

Simplify the square roots if possible.

   a. $\sqrt{-100}$ **b.** $-\sqrt{100}$ **c.** $\sqrt{-64}$

Solution:

   a. $\sqrt{-100}$ Not a real number

   b. $-\sqrt{100}$

       $-1 \cdot \sqrt{100}$ The expression $-\sqrt{100}$ is equivalent to $-1 \cdot \sqrt{100}$.

       $-1 \cdot 10 = -10$

   c. $\sqrt{-64}$ Not a real number

Skill Practice

Simplify the square roots if possible.

  10. $\sqrt{-25}$ **11.** $-\sqrt{25}$

  12. $\sqrt{-4}$

Answers

  5. 9   **6.** 12

  7. 0   **8.** $\dfrac{1}{2}$

  9. 0.3   **10.** Not a real number

  11. -5 **12.** Not a real number

2. Definition of an *n*th-Root

Finding a square root of a number is the reverse process of squaring a number. This concept can be extended to finding a third root (called a cube root), a fourth root, and in general, an *n*th-root.

> **DEFINITION** *n*th-Root
>
> b is an **nth-root** of a if $b^n = a$.

The radical sign, $\sqrt{}$, is used to denote the principal square root of a number. The symbol, $\sqrt[n]{}$, is used to denote the principal *n*th-root of a number.

In the expression $\sqrt[n]{a}$, *n* is called the **index** of the radical, and *a* is called the **radicand**. For a square root, the index is 2, but it is usually not written ($\sqrt[2]{a}$ is denoted simply as $\sqrt{a}$). A radical with an index of 3 is called a **cube root**, $\sqrt[3]{a}$.

> **DEFINITION** $\sqrt[n]{a}$
>
> **1.** If *n* is a positive *even* integer and $a > 0$, then $\sqrt[n]{a}$ is the principal (positive) *n*th-root of *a*.
> **2.** If $n > 1$ is a positive *odd* integer, then $\sqrt[n]{a}$ is the *n*th-root of *a*.
> **3.** If $n > 1$ is a positive integer, then $\sqrt[n]{0} = 0$.

For the purpose of simplifying radicals, it is helpful to know the following patterns:

Perfect cubes	Perfect fourth powers	Perfect fifth powers
$1^3 = 1$	$1^4 = 1$	$1^5 = 1$
$2^3 = 8$	$2^4 = 16$	$2^5 = 32$
$3^3 = 27$	$3^4 = 81$	$3^5 = 243$
$4^3 = 64$	$4^4 = 256$	$4^5 = 1024$
$5^3 = 125$	$5^4 = 625$	$5^5 = 3125$

Example 4 Simplifying *n*th-Roots

Simplify the expressions, if possible.

a. $\sqrt[3]{8}$ **b.** $\sqrt[4]{16}$ **c.** $\sqrt[5]{32}$ **d.** $\sqrt[3]{-64}$

e. $\sqrt[3]{\frac{125}{27}}$ **f.** $\sqrt{0.01}$ **g.** $\sqrt[4]{-81}$

Solution:

a. $\sqrt[3]{8} = 2$ Because $(2)^3 = 8$

b. $\sqrt[4]{16} = 2$ Because $(2)^4 = 16$

c. $\sqrt[5]{32} = 2$ Because $(2)^5 = 32$

d. $\sqrt[3]{-64} = -4$ Because $(-4)^3 = -64$

e. $\sqrt[3]{\frac{125}{27}} = \frac{5}{3}$ Because $\left(\frac{5}{3}\right)^3 = \frac{125}{27}$

f. $\sqrt{0.01} = 0.1$ Because $(0.1)^2 = 0.01$

Note: $\sqrt{0.01}$ is equivalent to $\sqrt{\dfrac{1}{100}} = \dfrac{1}{10}$, or 0.1.

g. $\sqrt[4]{-81}$ is not a real number because no real number raised to the fourth power equals -81.

> **Avoiding Mistakes**
>
> When evaluating $\sqrt[n]{a}$, where n is *even*, always choose the principal (positive) root.
> $$\sqrt[4]{16} = 2 \quad (\text{not } -2)$$
> $$\sqrt{0.01} = 0.1 \quad (\text{not } -0.1)$$

Example 4(g) illustrates that an nth-root of a negative number is not a real number if the index is even because no real number raised to an even power is negative.

Finding an nth-root of a variable expression is similar to finding an nth-root of a numerical expression. However, for roots with an even index, particular care must be taken to obtain a nonnegative solution.

> **DEFINITION** $\sqrt[n]{a^n}$
>
> **1.** If n is a positive odd integer, then $\sqrt[n]{a^n} = a$
>
> **2.** If n is a positive even integer, then $\sqrt[n]{a^n} = |a|$

The absolute value bars are necessary for roots with an even index because the variable, a, may represent a positive quantity or a negative quantity. By using absolute value bars, we ensure that $\sqrt[n]{a^n} = |a|$ is nonnegative and represents the principal nth-root of a.

> **Example 5** **Simplifying Expressions of the Form** $\sqrt[n]{a^n}$

Simplify the expressions.

a. $\sqrt{(-3)^2}$ **b.** $\sqrt{x^2}$ **c.** $\sqrt[3]{x^3}$ **d.** $\sqrt[4]{x^4}$ **e.** $\sqrt[5]{x^5}$

Solution:

a. $\sqrt{(-3)^2} = |-3| = 3$ Because the index is *even*, absolute value bars are necessary to make the answer nonnegative.

b. $\sqrt{x^2} = |x|$ Because the index is *even*, absolute value bars are necessary to make the answer nonnegative.

c. $\sqrt[3]{x^3} = x$ Because the index is *odd*, no absolute value bars are necessary.

d. $\sqrt[4]{x^4} = |x|$ Because the index is *even*, absolute value bars are necessary to make the answer nonnegative.

e. $\sqrt[5]{x^5} = x$ Because the index is *odd*, no absolute value bars are necessary.

> **Skill Practice**
>
> Simplify.
> **21.** $\sqrt{(-6)^2}$ **22.** $\sqrt[4]{a^4}$
> **23.** $\sqrt[3]{w^3}$ **24.** $\sqrt[6]{p^6}$
> **25.** $\sqrt[3]{(-2)^3}$

If n is an even integer, then $\sqrt[n]{a^n} = |a|$. However, if the variable a is assumed to be nonnegative, then the absolute value bars may be omitted, that is, $\sqrt[n]{a^n} = a$ provided $a \geq 0$. In many examples and exercises, we will make the assumption that the variables within a radical expression are positive real numbers. In such a case, the absolute value bars are not needed to evaluate $\sqrt[n]{a^n}$.

It is helpful to become familiar with the patterns associated with perfect squares and perfect cubes involving variable expressions.

Answers
21. 6   **22.** $|a|$ **23.** w
24. $|p|$ **25.** -2

The following powers of x are perfect squares:

Perfect squares

$(x^1)^2 = x^2$
$(x^2)^2 = x^4$
$(x^3)^2 = x^6$
$(x^4)^2 = x^8$
$\ldots$

> **TIP:** Any expression raised to an even power (multiple of 2) is a perfect square.

The following powers of x are perfect cubes:

Perfect cubes

$(x^1)^3 = x^3$
$(x^2)^3 = x^6$
$(x^3)^3 = x^9$
$(x^4)^3 = x^{12}$
$\ldots$

> **TIP:** Any expression raised to a power that is a multiple of 3 is a perfect cube.

Skill Practice

Simplify the expressions. Assume the variables represent positive real numbers.

26. $\sqrt{y^{10}}$ **27.** $\sqrt[3]{x^{12}}$

28. $\sqrt{x^4 y^2}$ **29.** $\sqrt{25c^4}$

Example 6 **Simplifying nth-Roots**

Simplify the expressions. Assume that the variables are positive real numbers.

a. $\sqrt{c^6}$ **b.** $\sqrt[3]{d^{15}}$ **c.** $\sqrt{a^2 b^2}$ **d.** $\sqrt[3]{64z^6}$

Solution:

a. $\sqrt{c^6}$ The expression c^6 is a perfect square.

$\quad \sqrt{c^6} = c^3$ This is because $\sqrt{(c^3)^2} = c^3$.

b. $\sqrt[3]{d^{15}}$ The expression d^{15} is a perfect cube.

$\quad \sqrt[3]{d^{15}} = d^5$ This is because $\sqrt[3]{(d^5)^3} = d^5$.

c. $\sqrt{a^2 b^2} = ab$ This is because $\sqrt{a^2 b^2} = \sqrt{(ab)^2} = ab$.

d. $\sqrt[3]{64z^6} = 4z^2$ This is because $\sqrt[3]{(4z^2)^3} = 4z^2$.

> **TIP:** A perfect nth-root can be simplified by dividing the power of the radicand by the index.
>
> $$\sqrt[3]{d^{15}} = d^{15/3} = d^5$$

3. Translations Involving nth-Roots

It is important to understand the vocabulary and language associated with nth-roots. For instance, you must be able to distinguish between the square of a number and the square *root* of a number. The following example offers practice translating between English form and algebraic form.

Answers
26. y^5 **27.** x^4
28. $x^2 y$ **29.** $5c^2$

Example 7 **Translating from English Form to Algebraic Form**

Translate each English phrase into an algebraic expression.

a. The difference of the square of x and the principal square root of 7

b. The quotient of 1 and the cube root of z

Solution:

a. $x^2 - \sqrt{7}$

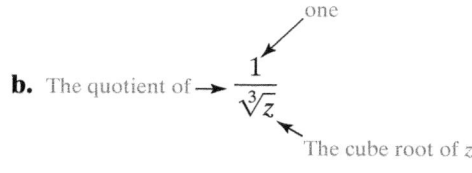

b. The quotient of $\rightarrow \dfrac{1}{\sqrt[3]{z}}$

one

The cube root of z

The difference of

The
square
of x

The
square root
of 7

Skill Practice

Translate the English phrases into algebraic expressions.

30. The product of the square of y and the principal square root of x.

31. The sum of 2 and the cube root of y.

4. Pythagorean Theorem

Recall that the **Pythagorean theorem** relates the lengths of the three sides of a right triangle (Figure 15-1).

$$a^2 + b^2 = c^2$$

The principal square root can be used to solve for an unknown side of a right triangle if the lengths of the other two sides are known.

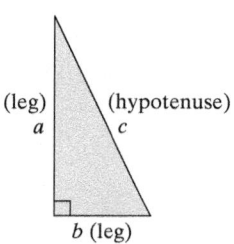

(leg)
a

(hypotenuse)
c

b (leg)

Figure 15-1

Example 8 **Applying the Pythagorean Theorem**

Use the Pythagorean theorem and the definition of the principal square root of a number to find the length of the unknown side.

Solution:

Label the sides of the triangle.

$a^2 + b^2 = c^2$

$a^2 + (8)^2 = (10)^2$ Apply the Pythagorean theorem.

$a^2 + 64 = 100$ Simplify.

$a^2 = 100 - 64$

$a^2 = 36$ This equation is quadratic. One method for solving the equation is to set the equation equal to zero, factor, and apply the zero product rule. However, we can also use the definition of a square root to solve for a.

$a = \sqrt{36}$ or $a = -\sqrt{36}$ By definition, a must be one of the square roots of 36 (either 6 or -6). However, because a represents a distance, choose the *positive* (principal) square root of 36.

$a = 6$

The third side is 6 in. long.

? | 10 in.

8 in.

a | $c = 10$ in.

$b = 8$ in.

Skill Practice

32. Use the Pythagorean theorem to find the length of the unknown side.

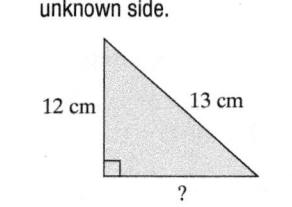

12 cm | 13 cm

?

Answers

30. $y^2\sqrt{x}$ **31.** $2 + \sqrt[3]{y}$

32. 5 cm

Skill Practice

33. A wire is attached to the top of a 20-ft pole. How long is the wire if it reaches a point on the ground 15 ft from the base of the pole?

?   20 ft

15 ft

Answer

33. The wire is 25 ft long.

Example 9   **Applying the Pythagorean Theorem**

A bridge across a river is 600 yd long. A boat ramp at point R is 200 yd due north of point P on the bridge, such that the line segments $\overline{PQ}$ and $\overline{PR}$ form a right angle (Figure 15-2). How far does a kayak travel if it leaves from the boat ramp and paddles to point Q? Use a calculator and round the answer to the nearest yard.

Figure 15-2

Solution:

Label the triangle:

$$a^2 + b^2 = c^2$$

c $a = 200$ yd

$b = 600$ yd

$$(200)^2 + (600)^2 = c^2 \qquad \text{Apply the Pythagorean theorem.}$$

$$40{,}000 + 360{,}000 = c^2 \qquad \text{Simplify.}$$

$$400{,}000 = c^2 \qquad \begin{array}{l}\text{By definition, } c \text{ must be one of the square} \\ \text{roots of 400,000. Because the value of } c \text{ is a}\end{array}$$

$$c = \sqrt{400{,}000} \qquad \begin{array}{l}\text{distance, choose the positive square root of} \\ 400{,}000.\end{array}$$

$$c \approx 632 \qquad \begin{array}{l}\text{Use a calculator to approximate the positive} \\ \text{square root of 400,000.}\end{array}$$

The kayak must travel approximately 632 yd.

Calculator Connections

Topic: Evaluating Square Roots and Higher Order Roots on a Calculator

A calculator can be used to approximate the value of a radical expression. To evaluate a square root, use the $\sqrt{}$ key. For example, evaluate: $\sqrt{25}$, $\sqrt{60}$, $\sqrt{\frac{13}{3}}$

Scientific Calculator

Enter: 25 $\boxed{\sqrt{x}}$ **Result:** $\boxed{ 5}$

Enter: 60 $\boxed{\sqrt{x}}$ **Result:** $\boxed{ 7.745966692}$

Enter: 13 $\boxed{\div}$ 3 $\boxed{=}$ $\boxed{\sqrt{x}}$ **Result:** $\boxed{ 2.081665999}$

Graphing Calculator

On the graphing calculator, the radicand is enclosed in parentheses.

```
√(25)
                    5
√(60)
        7.745966692
√(13/3)
        2.081665999
```

TIP: The values $\sqrt{60}$ and $\sqrt{\frac{13}{3}}$ are approximated on the calculator to 10 digits. However, $\sqrt{60}$ and $\sqrt{\frac{13}{3}}$ are actually irrational numbers. Their decimal forms are nonterminating and nonrepeating. The only way to represent the exact answers is by writing the radical forms, $\sqrt{60}$ and $\sqrt{\frac{13}{2}}$.

To evaluate cube roots, your calculator may have a $\sqrt[3]{}$ key. Otherwise, for cube roots and roots of higher index (fourth roots, fifth roots, and so on), try using the $\sqrt[x]{y}$ key or $\sqrt[x]{}$ key. For example, evaluate $\sqrt[3]{64}$, $\sqrt[4]{81}$, and $\sqrt[3]{162}$:

Scientific Calculator

Enter: 64 2nd $\sqrt[x]{y}$ 3 =   **Result:** | 4 |

Enter: 81 2nd $\sqrt[x]{y}$ 4 =   **Result:** | 3 |

Enter: 162 2nd $\sqrt[x]{y}$ 3 =   **Result:** | 5.451361778 |

Graphing Calculator

On a graphing calculator, the index is usually entered first.

```
3×√(64)
                 4
4×√(81)
                 3
3×√(162)
        5.451361778
```

Calculator Exercises

Estimate the value of each radical. Then use a calculator to approximate the radical to three decimal places. **(See the Tip on page 1015.)**

1. $\sqrt{5}$	**2.** $\sqrt{17}$	**3.** $\sqrt{50}$	**4.** $\sqrt{96}$
5. $\sqrt{33}$	**6.** $\sqrt{145}$	**7.** $\sqrt{80}$	**8.** $\sqrt{170}$
9. $\sqrt[3]{7}$	**10.** $\sqrt[3]{28}$	**11.** $\sqrt[3]{65}$	**12.** $\sqrt[3]{124}$

Section 15.1 Practice Exercises

Study Skill Exercise

1. Define the key terms:

    a. Square root   **b. Positive square root**   **c. Principal square root**   **d. Negative square root**

    e. Perfect square   **f.** *n*th-root   **g. Index**   **h. Radicand**

    i. Cube root   **j. Pythagorean theorem**

Objective 1: Definition of a Square Root

For Exercises 2–9, determine the square roots. **(See Example 1.)**

2. 4	**3.** 144	**4.** -64	**5.** -49
6. 81	**7.** 0	**8.** $\dfrac{16}{9}$	**9.** $\dfrac{1}{25}$

10. a. What is the principal square root of 64?

b. What is the negative square root of 64?

11. a. What is the principal square root of 169?

b. What is the negative square root of 169?

12. Does every number have two square roots? Explain.

13. Which number has only one square root?

14. Which of the following are perfect squares?

{0, 1, 4, 15, 30, 49, 72, 81, 144, 300, 625, 900}

15. Which of the following are perfect squares?

{8, 9, 12, 16, 25, 36, 42, 64, 95, 121, 140, 169}

For Exercises 16–31, evaluate the square roots. **(See Example 2.)**

16. $\sqrt{16}$

17. $\sqrt{4}$

18. $\sqrt{81}$

19. $\sqrt{49}$

20. $\sqrt{0.25}$

21. $\sqrt{0.16}$

22. $\sqrt{0.64}$

23. $\sqrt{0.09}$

24. $\sqrt{\dfrac{1}{9}}$

25. $\sqrt{\dfrac{25}{16}}$

26. $\sqrt{\dfrac{49}{121}}$

27. $\sqrt{\dfrac{1}{144}}$

28. $\sqrt{64 + 36}$

29. $\sqrt{16 + 9}$

30. $\sqrt{169 - 144}$

31. $\sqrt{225 - 144}$

32. Explain the difference between $\sqrt{-16}$ and $-\sqrt{16}$.

33. Using the definition of a square root, explain why $\sqrt{-16}$ does not have a real-valued square root.

34. Evaluate. $-\sqrt{|-25|}$

For Exercises 35–46, evaluate the square roots, if possible. **(See Example 3.)**

35. $-\sqrt{4}$

36. $-\sqrt{1}$

37. $\sqrt{-4}$

38. $\sqrt{-1}$

39. $\sqrt{-\dfrac{4}{49}}$

40. $-\sqrt{-\dfrac{9}{25}}$

41. $-\sqrt{-\dfrac{1}{36}}$

42. $-\sqrt{\dfrac{1}{36}}$

43. $-\sqrt{400}$

44. $-\sqrt{121}$

45. $\sqrt{-900}$

46. $\sqrt{-169}$

Objective 2: Definition of an *n*th-Root

47. Which of the following are perfect cubes?

{0, 1, 3, 9, 27, 36, 42, 90, 125}

48. Which of the following are perfect cubes?

{6, 8, 16, 20, 30, 64, 111, 150, 216}

49. Does $\sqrt[3]{-27}$ have a real-valued cube root?

50. Does $\sqrt[3]{-8}$ have a real-valued cube root?

For Exercises 51–66, evaluate the *n*th roots, if possible. **(See Example 4.)**

51. $\sqrt[3]{27}$

52. $\sqrt[3]{-27}$

53. $\sqrt[3]{64}$

54. $\sqrt[3]{-64}$

55. $-\sqrt[4]{16}$

56. $-\sqrt[4]{81}$

57. $\sqrt[4]{-1}$

58. $\sqrt[4]{0}$

59. $\sqrt[4]{-256}$

60. $\sqrt[4]{-625}$

61. $\sqrt[5]{-32}$

62. $-\sqrt[5]{32}$

63. $-\sqrt[6]{1}$

64. $\sqrt[6]{64}$

65. $\sqrt[6]{0}$

66. $\sqrt[6]{-1}$

For Exercises 67–86, simplify the expressions. **(See Example 5.)**

67. $\sqrt{(4)^2}$

68. $\sqrt{(8)^2}$

69. $\sqrt{(-4)^2}$

70. $\sqrt{(-8)^2}$

71. $\sqrt[3]{(5)^3}$

72. $\sqrt[3]{(7)^3}$

73. $\sqrt[3]{(-5)^3}$

74. $\sqrt[3]{(-7)^3}$

75. $\sqrt[4]{(2)^4}$

76. $\sqrt[4]{(10)^4}$

77. $\sqrt[4]{(-2)^4}$

78. $\sqrt[4]{(-10)^4}$

79. $\sqrt{a^2}$

80. $\sqrt{b^2}$

81. $\sqrt[3]{y^3}$

82. $\sqrt[3]{z^3}$

83. $\sqrt[4]{w^4}$

84. $\sqrt[4]{p^4}$

85. $\sqrt[5]{x^5}$

86. $\sqrt[5]{y^5}$

87. Determine which of the expressions are perfect squares. Then state a rule for determining perfect squares based on the exponent of the expression.

$\{x^2, a^3, y^4, z^5, (ab)^6, (pq)^7, w^8x^8, c^9d^9, m^{10}, n^{11}\}$

88. Determine which of the expressions are perfect cubes. Then state a rule for determining perfect cubes based on the exponent of the expression.

$\{a^2, b^3, c^4, d^5, e^6, (xy)^7, (wz)^8, (pq)^9, t^{10}s^{10}, m^{11}n^{11}, u^{12}v^{12}\}$

89. Determine which of the expressions are perfect fourth powers. Then state a rule for determining perfect fourth powers based on the exponent of the expression.

$\{m^2, n^3, p^4, q^5, r^6, s^7, t^8, u^9, v^{10}, (ab)^{11}, (cd)^{12}\}$

90. Determine which of the expressions are perfect fifth powers. Then state a rule for determining perfect fifth powers based on the exponent of the expression.

$\{a^2, b^3, c^4, d^5, e^6, k^7, w^8, x^9, y^{10}, z^{11}\}$

For Exercises 91–106, simplify the expressions. Assume the variables represent positive real numbers. **(See Example 6.)**

91. $\sqrt{y^{12}}$

92. $\sqrt{z^{20}}$

93. $\sqrt{a^8b^{30}}$

94. $\sqrt{t^{50}s^{60}}$

95. $\sqrt[3]{q^{24}}$

96. $\sqrt[3]{x^{33}}$

97. $\sqrt[3]{8w^6}$

98. $\sqrt[3]{-27x^{27}}$

99. $\sqrt{(5x)^2}$

100. $\sqrt{(6w)^2}$

101. $-\sqrt{25x^2}$

102. $-\sqrt{36w^2}$

103. $\sqrt[3]{(5p^2)^3}$

104. $\sqrt[3]{(2k^4)^3}$

105. $\sqrt[3]{125p^6}$

106. $\sqrt[3]{8k^{12}}$

Objective 3: Translations Involving *n*th-Roots

For Exercises 107–110, translate the English phrase to an algebraic expression. **(See Example 7.)**

107. The sum of the principal square root of q and the square of p

108. The product of the principal square root of 11 and the cube of x

109. The quotient of 6 and the principal fourth root of x

110. The difference of the square of y and 1

Objective 4: Pythagorean Theorem

For Exercises 111–116, find the length of the third side of each triangle using the Pythagorean theorem. Round the answer to the nearest tenth if necessary. **(See Example 8.)**

111.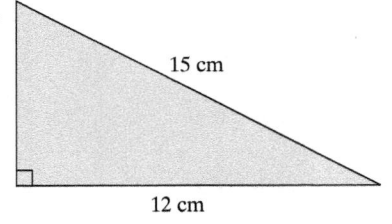
15 cm
12 cm

112.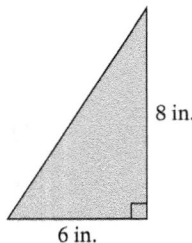
8 in.
6 in.

113.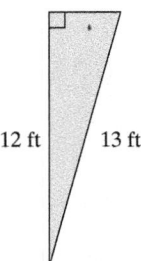
12 ft   13 ft

114.
5 m
4 m

115.
6.5 cm
2.4 cm

116.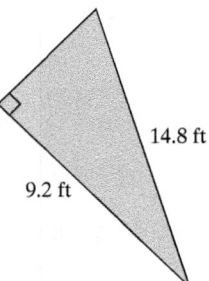
14.8 ft
9.2 ft

117. Find the length of the diagonal of the square tile shown in the figure. Round the answer to the nearest tenth of an inch.

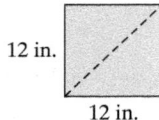
12 in.
12 in.

118. A baseball diamond is 90 ft on a side. Find the distance between home plate and second base. Round the answer to the nearest tenth of a foot.

Second base
90 ft
?
90 ft
Home plate

119. A new plasma television is listed as being 42 in. This distance is the diagonal distance across the screen. If the screen measures 28 inches in height, what is the actual width of the screen? Round to the nearest tenth of an inch.
(See Example 9.)

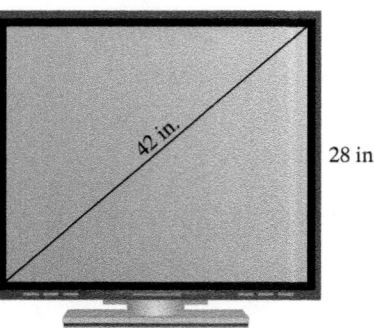
42 in.   28 in.

120. A marine biologist wants to track the migration of a pod of whales. He receives a radio signal from a tagged humpback whale and determines that the whale is 21 mi east and 37 mi north of his laboratory. Find the direct distance between the whale and the laboratory. Round to the nearest tenth of a mile.

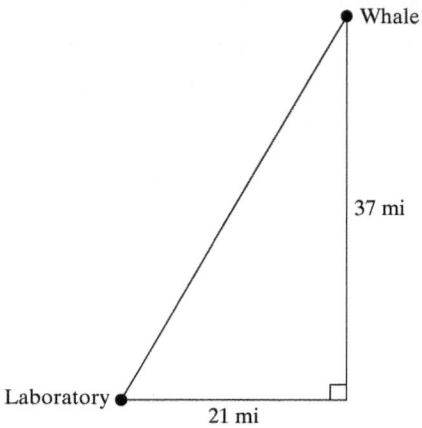
Whale
37 mi
Laboratory
21 mi

121. On a map, the cities Asheville, North Carolina, Roanoke, Virginia, and Greensboro, North Carolina, form a right triangle (see the figure). The distance between Asheville and Roanoke is 300 km. The distance between Roanoke and Greensboro is 134 km. How far is it from Greensboro to Asheville? Round the answer to the nearest kilometer.

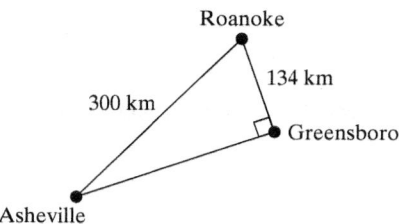

122. Jackson, Mississippi, is west of Meridian, Mississippi, a distance of 141 km. Tupelo, Mississippi, is north of Meridian, a distance of 209 km. How far is it from Jackson to Tupelo? Round the answer to the nearest kilometer.

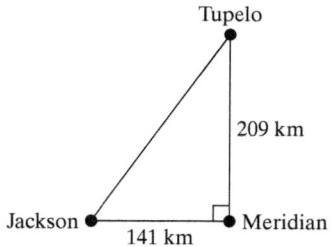

Expanding Your Skills

123. For what values of x will $\sqrt{x}$ be a real number?

124. For what values of x will $\sqrt{-x}$ be a real number?

Simplifying Radicals

Section 15.2

1. Multiplication Property of Radicals

You may have already recognized certain properties of radicals involving a product.

Objectives

1. Multiplication Property of Radicals
2. Simplifying Radicals Using the Multiplication Property of Radicals
3. Simplifying Radicals Using the Order of Operations
4. Simplifying Cube Roots

PROPERTY Multiplication Property of Radicals

Let a and b represent real numbers such that $\sqrt[n]{a}$ and $\sqrt[n]{b}$ are both real. Then,

$$\sqrt[n]{ab} = \sqrt[n]{a} \cdot \sqrt[n]{b} \quad \text{Multiplication property of radicals}$$

The multiplication property of radicals indicates that a product within a radicand can be written as a product of radicals provided the roots are real numbers.

$$\sqrt{100} = \sqrt{25} \cdot \sqrt{4}$$

The reverse process is also true. A product of radicals can be written as a single radical provided the roots are real numbers and they have the same indices.

Same index
$$\sqrt{2} \cdot \sqrt{18} = \sqrt{36}$$

2. Simplifying Radicals Using the Multiplication Property of Radicals

In algebra, it is customary to simplify radical expressions as much as possible.

DEFINITION Simplified Form of a Radical

Consider any radical expression where the radicand is written as a product of prime factors. The expression is in **simplified form** if all of the following conditions are met:

1. The radicand has no factor raised to a power greater than or equal to the index.
2. There are no radicals in the denominator of a fraction.
3. The radicand does not contain a fraction.

The expression $\sqrt{x^2}$ is not simplified because it fails condition 1. Because x^2 is a perfect square, $\sqrt{x^2}$ is easily simplified.

$$\sqrt{x^2} = x \quad (\text{for } x \geq 0)$$

However, how is an expression such as $\sqrt{x^7}$ simplified? This and many other radical expressions are simplified using the multiplication property of radicals. Examples 1–3 illustrate how nth powers can be removed from the radicands of nth-roots.

Example 1 Using the Multiplication Property to Simplify a Radical Expression

Use the multiplication property of radicals to simplify the expression $\sqrt{x^7}$. Assume $x \geq 0$.

Solution:

The expression $\sqrt{x^7}$ is equivalent to $\sqrt{x^6 \cdot x}$. By applying the multiplication property of radicals, we have

$$\sqrt{x^6 \cdot x} = \sqrt{x^6} \cdot \sqrt{x} \qquad x^6 \text{ is a perfect square because } (x^3)^2 = x^6$$
$$= x^3 \cdot \sqrt{x} \qquad \text{Simplify.}$$
$$= x^3\sqrt{x}$$

In Example 1, the expression x^7 is not a perfect square. Therefore, to simplify $\sqrt{x^7}$, it was necessary to write the expression as the product of the largest perfect square and a remaining, or "leftover," factor: $\sqrt{x^7} = \sqrt{x^6 \cdot x}$.

Example 2 Using the Multiplication Property to Simplify Radicals

Use the multiplication property of radicals to simplify the expressions. Assume the variables represent positive real numbers.

a. $\sqrt{a^{15}}$ **b.** $\sqrt{x^2 y^5}$ **c.** $\sqrt{s^9 t^{11}}$

Solution:

The goal is to rewrite each radicand as the product of the largest perfect square and a leftover factor.

a. $\sqrt{a^{15}}$
$$= \sqrt{a^{14} \cdot a} \qquad a^{14} \text{ is the largest perfect square in the radicand.}$$
$$= \sqrt{a^{14}} \cdot \sqrt{a} \qquad \text{Apply the multiplication property of radicals.}$$
$$= a^7\sqrt{a} \qquad \text{Simplify.}$$

b. $\sqrt{x^2y^5}$

$\quad = \sqrt{x^2y^4 \cdot y}$ $\qquad$ x^2y^4 is the largest perfect square in the radicand.

$\quad = \sqrt{x^2y^4} \cdot \sqrt{y}$ $\qquad$ Apply the multiplication property of radicals.

$\quad = xy^2\sqrt{y}$ $\qquad$ Simplify.

c. $\sqrt{s^9t^{11}}$

$\quad = \sqrt{s^8t^{10} \cdot st}$ $\qquad$ s^8t^{10} is the largest perfect square in the radical.

$\quad = \sqrt{s^8t^{10}} \cdot \sqrt{st}$ $\qquad$ Apply the multiplication property of radicals.

$\quad = s^4t^5\sqrt{st}$ $\qquad$ Simplify.

Each expression in Example 2 involves a radicand that is a product of variable factors. If a numerical factor is present, sometimes it is necessary to factor the coefficient before simplifying the radical.

Example 3 **Using the Multiplication Property to Simplify Radicals**

Use the multiplication property of radicals to simplify the expressions. Assume the variables represent positive real numbers.

a. $\sqrt{50}$ $\qquad$ **b.** $5\sqrt{24a^6}$ $\qquad$ **c.** $\sqrt{81x^4y^3}$

Skill Practice

Simplify the expressions. Assume the variables represent positive real numbers.

8. $\sqrt{12}$ $\qquad$ **9.** $\sqrt{60x^2}$

10. $7\sqrt{18t^{10}}$

Solution:

The goal is to rewrite each radicand as the product of the largest perfect square and a leftover factor.

a. Write the radicand as a product of prime factors. From the prime factorization, the largest perfect square is easily identified.

$\sqrt{50} = \sqrt{5^2 \cdot 2}$ $\qquad$ Factor the radicand. $\qquad$ $2\overline{)50}$
$\qquad\qquad\qquad\qquad$ 5^2 is the largest perfect square. $\quad$ $5\overline{)25}$
$\qquad\qquad\qquad\qquad\qquad\qquad\qquad\qquad\qquad\qquad\qquad$ 5

$\quad = \sqrt{5^2} \cdot \sqrt{2}$ $\qquad$ Apply the multiplication property of radicals.

$\quad = 5\sqrt{2}$ $\qquad$ Simplify.

b. $5\sqrt{24a^6} = 5\sqrt{2^3 \cdot 3 \cdot a^6}$ $\qquad$ Write the radicand as a product of prime factors: $24 = 2^3 \cdot 3$.

$\quad = 5\sqrt{2^2a^6 \cdot 2 \cdot 3}$ $\qquad$ 2^2a^6 is the largest perfect square in the radicand.

$\quad = 5\sqrt{2^2a^6} \cdot \sqrt{2 \cdot 3}$ $\qquad$ Apply the multiplication property of radicals.

$\quad = 5 \cdot 2a^3\sqrt{6}$ $\qquad$ Simplify the radical.

$\quad = 10a^3\sqrt{6}$ $\qquad$ Simplify the coefficient of the radical.

TIP: The expression $\sqrt{50}$ can also be written as:
$\sqrt{25 \cdot 2}$
$= \sqrt{25} \cdot \sqrt{2}$
$= 5\sqrt{2}$

Answers

8. $2\sqrt{3}$ $\quad$ **9.** $2x\sqrt{15}$
10. $21t^5\sqrt{2}$

c. $\sqrt{81x^4y^3} = \sqrt{3^4x^4y^3}$ Write the radical as a product of prime factors. *Note:* $81 = 3^4$.

$= \sqrt{3^4x^4y^2 \cdot y}$ $3^4x^4y^2$ is the largest square in the radicand.

$= \sqrt{3^4x^4y^2} \cdot \sqrt{y}$ Apply the multiplication property of radicals.

$= 3^2x^2y \cdot \sqrt{y}$ Simplify the radical.

$= 9x^2y\sqrt{y}$ Simplify the coefficient of the radical.

Avoiding Mistakes

The multiplication property of radicals allows us to simplify a product of factors within a radical. For example,

$$\sqrt{x^2y^2} = \sqrt{x^2} \cdot \sqrt{y^2} = xy \quad \text{(for } x \ge 0 \text{ and } y \ge 0\text{)}$$

However, this rule does not apply to *terms* that are added or subtracted *within* the radical. For example,

$$\sqrt{x^2 + y^2} \quad \text{and} \quad \sqrt{x^2 - y^2}$$

cannot be simplified.

3. Simplifying Radicals Using the Order of Operations

Often a radical can be simplified by applying the order of operations. In Example 4, the first step will be to simplify the expression within the radicand.

Skill Practice

Simplify the expressions. Assume the variables represent positive real numbers.

11. $\sqrt{\dfrac{y^{11}}{y^3}}$

12. $\sqrt{\dfrac{8}{50}}$

13. $\sqrt{\dfrac{32z^3}{2z}}$

Example 4   **Simplifying Radicals Using the Order of Operations**

Simplify the expressions. Assume the variables represent positive real numbers.

a. $\sqrt{\dfrac{a^5}{a^3}}$ **b.** $\sqrt{\dfrac{6}{96}}$ **c.** $\sqrt{\dfrac{27x^5}{3x}}$

Solution:

a. $\sqrt{\dfrac{a^5}{a^3}}$ The radical contains a fraction. However, the fraction can be simplified.

$= \sqrt{a^2}$ Reduce the fraction to lowest terms.

$= a$ Simplify the radical.

b. $\sqrt{\dfrac{6}{96}}$ The radical contains a fraction that can be simplified.

$= \sqrt{\dfrac{1}{16}}$ Reduce the fraction to lowest terms.

$= \dfrac{1}{4}$ Simplify.

c. $\sqrt{\dfrac{27x^5}{3x}}$ The fraction within the radicand can be simplified.

$= \sqrt{9x^4}$ Reduce to lowest terms.

$= 3x^2$ Simplify.

Answers

11. y^4 **12.** $\dfrac{2}{5}$ **13.** $4z$

Example 5 **Simplifying Radical Expressions**

Simplify the expressions.

a. $\dfrac{5\sqrt{20}}{2}$ **b.** $\dfrac{2-\sqrt{36}}{12}$

Solution:

a. $\dfrac{5\sqrt{20}}{2} = \dfrac{5\sqrt{2^2 \cdot 5}}{2}$ Following the order of operations, first simplify the radical. 2^2 is the largest perfect square in the radicand.

$= \dfrac{5\sqrt{2^2} \cdot \sqrt{5}}{2}$ Apply the multiplication property of radicals.

$= \dfrac{5 \cdot 2\sqrt{5}}{2}$ Simplify the radical.

$= \dfrac{5 \cdot 2\sqrt{5}}{2}$ Simplify to lowest terms.

$= 5\sqrt{5}$

b. $\dfrac{2-\sqrt{36}}{12}$

$= \dfrac{2-6}{12}$ Following the order of operations, first simplify the radical.

$= \dfrac{-4}{12}$ Next, simplify the numerator.

$= -\dfrac{1}{3}$ Reduce the fraction to lowest terms.

Skill Practice

Simplify the expression.

14. $\dfrac{7\sqrt{18}}{3}$

15. $\dfrac{5+\sqrt{49}}{6}$

Avoiding Mistakes

$\dfrac{5\sqrt{20}}{2}$ cannot be simplified as written because 20 is under the radical and 2 is not. To reduce to lowest terms, the radical must be simplified first, $\dfrac{5 \cdot 2\sqrt{5}}{2}$. Then factors outside the radical can be simplified.

4. Simplifying Cube Roots

Example 6 **Simplifying Cube Roots**

Use the multiplication property of radicals to simplify the expressions.

a. $\sqrt[3]{z^5}$ **b.** $\sqrt[3]{-80}$

Solution:

a. $\sqrt[3]{z^5}$

$= \sqrt[3]{z^3 \cdot z^2}$ z^3 is the largest perfect cube in the radicand.

$= \sqrt[3]{z^3} \cdot \sqrt[3]{z^2}$ Apply the multiplication property of radicals.

$= z\sqrt[3]{z^2}$ Simplify.

b. $\sqrt[3]{-80}$

$= \sqrt[3]{-1 \cdot 2^4 \cdot 5}$ Factor the radicand.

$= \sqrt[3]{-1 \cdot 2^3 \cdot 2 \cdot 5}$ -1 and 2^3 are perfect cubes.

$= \sqrt[3]{-1} \cdot \sqrt[3]{2^3} \cdot \sqrt[3]{2 \cdot 5}$ Apply the multiplication property of radicals.

$= -1 \cdot 2 \cdot \sqrt[3]{10}$ Simplify.

$= -2\sqrt[3]{10}$

$\begin{array}{r} 2\overline{)80} \\ 2\overline{)40} \\ 2\overline{)20} \\ 2\overline{)10} \\ 5 \end{array}$

Skill Practice

Simplify.

16. $\sqrt[3]{y^4}$ **17.** $\sqrt[3]{-24}$

Answers

14. $7\sqrt{2}$ **15.** 2
16. $y\sqrt[3]{y}$ **17.** $-2\sqrt[3]{3}$

Example 7 **Simplifying Cube Roots**

Simplify the expressions.

a. $\sqrt[3]{\dfrac{a^{16}}{a}}$ **b.** $\sqrt[3]{\dfrac{2}{16}}$

Solution:

a. $\sqrt[3]{\dfrac{a^{16}}{a}}$ The radical contains a fraction that can be simplified.

$= \sqrt[3]{a^{15}}$ Reduce to lowest terms.

$= a^5$ Simplify.

b. $\sqrt[3]{\dfrac{2}{16}}$ The radical contains a fraction that can be simplified.

$= \sqrt[3]{\dfrac{1}{8}}$ Reduce to lowest terms.

$= \dfrac{1}{2}$ Simplify.

Answers

18. x^2 **19.** 3

Calculator Connections

Topic: Verifying Simplified Radicals

A calculator can support the multiplication property of radicals. For example, use a calculator to evaluate $\sqrt{50}$ and its simplified form $5\sqrt{2}$.

Scientific Calculator

Enter: 50 $\boxed{\sqrt{x}}$ **Result:** $\boxed{7.071067812}$

Enter: 2 $\boxed{\sqrt{x}}$ $\boxed{\times}$ 5 $\boxed{=}$ **Result:** $\boxed{7.071067812}$

Graphing Calculator

```
√(50)
        7.071067812
5*√(2)
        7.071067812
```

TIP: The decimal approximation for $\sqrt{50}$ and $5\sqrt{2}$ agree for the first 10 digits. This in itself does not make $\sqrt{50} = 5\sqrt{2}$. It is the multiplication property of radicals that guarantees that the expressions are equal.

Calculator Exercises

Simplify the radical expressions algebraically. Then use a calculator to approximate the original expression and its simplified form.

1. $\sqrt{125}$ **2.** $\sqrt{18}$ **3.** $\sqrt[3]{54}$ **4.** $\sqrt[3]{108}$

Section 15.2 Practice Exercises

Study Skills Exercise

1. Define the key terms:

    a. Simplified form of a radical   **b. Multiplication property of radicals**

Review Exercises

2. Which of the following are perfect squares? $\{2, 4, 6, 16, 20, 25, x^2, x^3, x^{15}, x^{20}, x^{25}\}$

3. Which of the following are perfect cubes? $\{3, 6, 8, 9, 12, 27, y^3, y^8, y^9, y^{12}, y^{27}\}$

4. Which of the following are perfect fourth powers? $\{4, 16, 20, 25, 81, w^4, w^{16}, w^{20}, w^{25}, w^{81}\}$

For Exercises 5–12, simplify the expressions, if possible. Assume the variables represent positive real numbers.

5. $-\sqrt{25}$ **6.** $\sqrt{-25}$ **7.** $-\sqrt[3]{27}$ **8.** $\sqrt[3]{-27}$

9. $\sqrt[4]{a^8}$ **10.** $\sqrt[5]{b^{15}}$ **11.** $\sqrt{4x^2y^4}$ **12.** $\sqrt{9p^{10}}$

13. On a map, Seattle, Washington, is 378 km west of Spokane, Washington. Portland, Oregon, is 236 km south of Seattle. Approximate the distance between Portland and Spokane to the nearest kilometer.

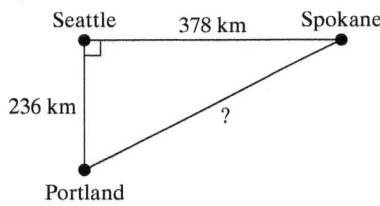

14. A new roof is needed on a shed. How many square feet of tar paper would be needed to cover the top of the roof?

Objective 2: Simplifying Radicals Using the Multiplication Property of Radicals

For Exercises 15–50, use the multiplication property of radicals to simplify the expressions. Assume the variables represent positive real numbers. **(See Examples 1–3.)**

15. $\sqrt{18}$ **16.** $\sqrt{75}$ **17.** $\sqrt{28}$ **18.** $\sqrt{40}$

19. $6\sqrt{20}$ **20.** $10\sqrt{27}$ **21.** $-2\sqrt{50}$ **22.** $-11\sqrt{8}$

23. $\sqrt{a^5}$ **24.** $\sqrt{b^9}$ **25.** $\sqrt{w^{22}}$ **26.** $\sqrt{p^{18}}$

27. $\sqrt{m^4n^5}$ **28.** $\sqrt{c^2d^9}$ **29.** $x\sqrt{x^{13}y^{10}}$ **30.** $v\sqrt{u^{10}v^7}$

31. $3\sqrt{t^{10}}$ **32.** $-4\sqrt{m^8n^4}$ **33.** $\sqrt{8x^3}$ **34.** $\sqrt{27y^5}$

35. $\sqrt{16z^3}$ **36.** $\sqrt{9y^5}$ **37.** $-\sqrt{45w^6}$ **38.** $-\sqrt{56v^8}$

39. $\sqrt{z^{25}}$

40. $\sqrt{25p^{49}}$

41. $-\sqrt{15z^{11}}$

42. $-\sqrt{6k^{15}}$

43. $5\sqrt{104a^2b^7}$

44. $3\sqrt{88m^4n^{11}}$

45. $\sqrt{26pq}$

46. $\sqrt{15a}$

47. $m\sqrt{m^{10}n^{16}}$

48. $c^2\sqrt{c^4d^{12}}$

49. $\sqrt{48a^3b^5c^4}$

50. $\sqrt{18xy^4z^3}$

Objective 3: Simplifying Radicals Using the Order of Operations

For Exercises 51–70, use the order of operations, if necessary, to simplify the expressions. Assume the variables represent positive real numbers. **(See Examples 4–5.)**

51. $\sqrt{\dfrac{a^9}{a}}$

52. $\sqrt{\dfrac{x^5}{x}}$

53. $\sqrt{\dfrac{y^{15}}{y^5}}$

54. $\sqrt{\dfrac{c^{31}}{c^{11}}}$

55. $\sqrt{\dfrac{5}{20}}$

56. $\sqrt{\dfrac{3}{75}}$

57. $\sqrt{\dfrac{40}{10}}$

58. $\sqrt{\dfrac{80}{5}}$

59. $\sqrt{\dfrac{32x^3}{8x}}$

60. $\sqrt{\dfrac{200b^{11}}{2b^5}}$

61. $\sqrt{\dfrac{50p^7}{2p}}$

62. $\sqrt{\dfrac{45t^9}{5t^5}}$

63. $\dfrac{3\sqrt{20}}{2}$

64. $\dfrac{5\sqrt{18}}{3}$

65. $\dfrac{5\sqrt{24}}{10}$

66. $\dfrac{2\sqrt{27}}{6}$

67. $\dfrac{10+\sqrt{4}}{3}$

68. $\dfrac{-1+\sqrt{25}}{4}$

69. $\dfrac{20-\sqrt{36}}{2}$

70. $\dfrac{3-\sqrt{81}}{3}$

For Exercises 71–74, find the exact length of the third side of each triangle using the Pythagorean theorem. Write the answer as a simplified radical.

71.

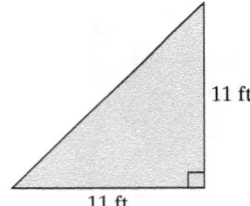

11 ft

11 ft

72.

21 m

20 m

73.

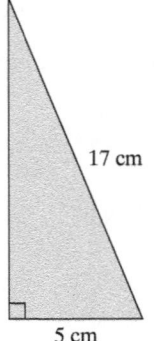

17 cm

5 cm

74.

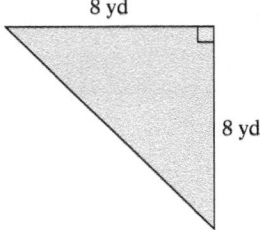

8 yd

8 yd

Objective 4: Simplifying Cube Roots

For Exercises 75–86, simplify the cube roots. **(See Examples 6–7.)**

75. $\sqrt[3]{a^8}$

76. $\sqrt[3]{8v^3}$

77. $7\sqrt[3]{16z^3}$

78. $5\sqrt[3]{54t^6}$

79. $\sqrt[3]{16a^5b^6}$

80. $\sqrt[3]{81p^9q^{11}}$

81. $\sqrt[3]{\dfrac{z^4}{z}}$

82. $\sqrt[3]{\dfrac{w^8}{w^2}}$

83. $\sqrt[3]{-\dfrac{32}{4}}$

84. $\sqrt[3]{-\dfrac{128}{2}}$

85. $\sqrt[3]{40}$

86. $\sqrt[3]{54}$

Mixed Exercises

For Exercises 87–110, simplify the expressions. Assume the variables represent positive real numbers.

87. $\sqrt{\dfrac{3}{27}}$

88. $\sqrt{\dfrac{5}{125}}$

89. $\sqrt{16a^3}$

90. $\sqrt{125x^6}$

91. $\sqrt{\dfrac{4x^3}{x}}$

92. $\sqrt{\dfrac{9z^5}{z}}$

93. $\sqrt{8p^2q}$

94. $\sqrt{6cd^3}$

95. $\sqrt{32}$

96. $\sqrt{64}$

97. $\sqrt{52u^4v^7}$

98. $\sqrt{44p^8q^{10}}$

99. $\sqrt{216}$

100. $\sqrt{250}$

101. $\sqrt[3]{216}$

102. $\sqrt[3]{250}$

103. $\sqrt[3]{16a^3}$

104. $\sqrt[3]{125x^6}$

105. $\sqrt[3]{\dfrac{x^5}{x^2}}$

106. $\sqrt[3]{\dfrac{y^{11}}{y^2}}$

107. $\dfrac{-6\sqrt{20}}{12}$

108. $\dfrac{-5\sqrt{32}}{10}$

109. $\dfrac{-4-\sqrt{25}}{18}$

110. $\dfrac{8-\sqrt{100}}{2}$

Expanding Your Skills

For Exercises 111–114, simplify the expressions. Assume the variables represent positive real numbers.

111. $\sqrt{(-2-5)^2+(-4+3)^2}$

112. $\sqrt{(-1-7)^2+[1-(-1)]^2}$

113. $\sqrt{x^2+10x+25}$

114. $\sqrt{x^2+6x+9}$

Addition and Subtraction of Radicals　　Section 15.3

1. Definition of *Like* Radicals

DEFINITION *Like* Radicals

Two radical terms are said to be *like* **radicals** if they have the same index and the same radicand.

Objectives

1. Definition of *Like* Radicals
2. Addition and Subtraction of Radicals

The following are pairs of *like* radicals:

Indices and radicands are the same.
Both indices are 2. Both radicands are 6.

Indices and radicands are the same.
Both indices are 3. Both radicands are 17y.

These pairs are *not like* radicals:

$9\sqrt{3}$ and $9\sqrt[3]{3}$ Radicals have different indices.

$8ab\sqrt{5}$ and $ab\sqrt{10}$ Radicals have different radicands.

Different radicands

2. Addition and Subtraction of Radicals

To add or subtract *like* radicals, use the distributive property. For example,

$$3\sqrt{7} + 5\sqrt{7} = (3+5)\sqrt{7}$$
$$= 8\sqrt{7}$$

$$9\sqrt{2y} - 4\sqrt{2y} = (9-4)\sqrt{2y}$$
$$= 5\sqrt{2y}$$

Avoiding Mistakes

The process of adding *like* radicals with the distributive property is similar to adding *like* terms. The numerical coefficients are added, and the radical factor is unchanged.

$\sqrt{5} + \sqrt{5}$
$= 1\sqrt{5} + 1\sqrt{5}$
$= 2\sqrt{5}$ Correct

Be careful: $\sqrt{5} + \sqrt{5} \neq \sqrt{10}$
In general,
$\sqrt{x} + \sqrt{y} \neq \sqrt{x+y}$

Example 1 Adding and Subtracting Radicals

Add or subtract the radicals as indicated. Assume all variables represent positive real numbers.

a. $\sqrt{5} + \sqrt{5}$ **b.** $6\sqrt{15} + 3\sqrt{15} + \sqrt{15}$

c. $\sqrt{xy} - 6\sqrt{xy} + 4\sqrt{xy}$

Solution:

a. $\sqrt{5} + \sqrt{5}$

$= 1\sqrt{5} + 1\sqrt{5}$ *Note:* $\sqrt{5} = 1\sqrt{5}$.

$= (1+1)\sqrt{5}$ Apply the distributive property.

$= 2\sqrt{5}$ Simplify.

b. $6\sqrt{15} + 3\sqrt{15} + \sqrt{15}$ The radicals have the same radicand and same index.

$= 6\sqrt{15} + 3\sqrt{15} + 1\sqrt{15}$ *Note:* $\sqrt{15} = 1\sqrt{15}$.

$= (6+3+1)\sqrt{15}$ Apply the distributive property.

$= 10\sqrt{15}$

c. $\sqrt{xy} - 6\sqrt{xy} + 4\sqrt{xy}$ The radicals have the same radicand and same index.

$= 1\sqrt{xy} - 6\sqrt{xy} + 4\sqrt{xy}$ *Note:* $\sqrt{xy} = 1\sqrt{xy}$.

$= (1 - 6 + 4)\sqrt{xy}$ Apply the distributive property.

$= -1\sqrt{xy}$ Simplify.

$= -\sqrt{xy}$

From Example 1, you can see that the process of adding or subtracting *like* radicals is similar to combining *like* terms.

$$x + x \qquad \text{similarly,} \qquad \sqrt{5} + \sqrt{5}$$
$$= 1x + 1x \qquad\qquad\qquad = 1\sqrt{5} + 1\sqrt{5}$$
$$= 2x \qquad\qquad\qquad\qquad = 2\sqrt{5}$$

The end result is that the numerical coefficients are added or subtracted, and the radical factor is unchanged.

    Sometimes it is necessary to simplify radicals before adding or subtracting.

Example 2   **Simplifying Radicals before Adding or Subtracting**

Add or subtract the radicals as indicated.

a. $\sqrt{20} + 7\sqrt{5}$ **b.** $\sqrt{50} - \sqrt{8}$

Solution:

a. $\sqrt{20} + 7\sqrt{5}$ Because the radicands are different, try simplifying the radicals first.

$= \sqrt{2^2 \cdot 5} + 7\sqrt{5}$ Factor the radicand.

$= 2\sqrt{5} + 7\sqrt{5}$ The terms are *like* radicals.

$= (2 + 7)\sqrt{5}$ Apply the distributive property.

$= 9\sqrt{5}$ Simplify.

b. $\sqrt{50} - \sqrt{8}$ Because the radicands are different, try simplifying the radicals first.

$= \sqrt{5^2 \cdot 2} - \sqrt{2^2 \cdot 2}$ Factor the radicands.

$= 5\sqrt{2} - 2\sqrt{2}$ The terms are *like* radicals.

$= (5 - 2)\sqrt{2}$ Apply the distributive property.

$= 3\sqrt{2}$ Simplify.

Add or subtract the radicals as indicated. Assume the variables represent positive real numbers.

6. $4x\sqrt{12} - \sqrt{27x^2}$

7. $\sqrt{28y^3} - y\sqrt{63y} + \sqrt{700}$

Example 3   **Simplifying Radicals before Adding or Subtracting**

Add or subtract the radicals as indicated. Assume the variables represent positive real numbers.

a. $-4\sqrt{3x^2} - x\sqrt{27} + 5x\sqrt{3}$ **b.** $a\sqrt{8a^5} + 6\sqrt{2a^7} + \sqrt{9a}$

Solution:

a. $-4\sqrt{3x^2} - x\sqrt{27} + 5x\sqrt{3}$ — Simplify each radical.

$= -4\sqrt{3x^2} - x\sqrt{3^2 \cdot 3} + 5x\sqrt{3}$ — Factor the radicands.

$= -4x\sqrt{3} - 3x\sqrt{3} + 5x\sqrt{3}$ — The terms are *like* radicals.

$= (-4x - 3x + 5x)\sqrt{3}$ — Apply the distributive property.

$= -2x\sqrt{3}$ — Simplify.

b. $a\sqrt{8a^5} + 6\sqrt{2a^7} + \sqrt{9a}$ — Simplify each radical.

$= a\sqrt{2^3a^5} + 6\sqrt{2a^7} + \sqrt{3^2a}$ — Factor the radicals.

$= a\sqrt{2^2a^4 \cdot 2a} + 6\sqrt{a^6 \cdot 2a} + \sqrt{3^2 \cdot a}$

$= a \cdot 2a^2\sqrt{2a} + 6 \cdot a^3\sqrt{2a} + 3\sqrt{a}$ — Simplify the radicals.

$= 2a^3\sqrt{2a} + 6a^3\sqrt{2a} + 3\sqrt{a}$ — The first two terms are *like* radicals.

$= (2a^3 + 6a^3)\sqrt{2a} + 3\sqrt{a}$ — Apply the distributive property.

$= 8a^3\sqrt{2a} + 3\sqrt{a}$

It is important to realize that only *like* radicals can be added or subtracted. The next example provides extra practice for recognizing *unlike* radicals.

Explain why the radicals cannot be simplified further.

8. $12 - 7\sqrt{5}$

9. $2\sqrt{3} - 3\sqrt{2}$

Example 4   **Recognizing *Unlike* Radicals**

Explain why the radicals cannot be simplified further by adding or subtracting.

a. $2\sqrt{7} - 5\sqrt{3}$ **b.** $7 + 4\sqrt{5}$

Solution:

a. $2\sqrt{7} - 5\sqrt{3}$ Radicands are not the same.

b. $7 + 4\sqrt{5}$ One term has a radical, and one does not.

Answers

6. $5x\sqrt{3}$

7. $-y\sqrt{7y} + 10\sqrt{7}$

8. One term has a radical, and one does not.

9. The radicands are not the same.

Calculator Connections

Title: Verifying Radical Expressions on a Calculator

A calculator can be used to evaluate a radical expression and its simplified form. For example, use a calculator to evaluate the expression on the left and its simplified form on the right: $2\sqrt{5} + 6\sqrt{5} = 8\sqrt{5}$

Scientific Calculator

Enter: 5 $\boxed{\sqrt{x}}$ $\boxed{\times}$ 2 $\boxed{=}$ $\boxed{+}$ 5 $\boxed{\sqrt{x}}$ $\boxed{\times}$ 6 $\boxed{=}$ **Result:** $\boxed{17.88854382}$

Enter: 5 $\boxed{\sqrt{x}}$ $\boxed{\times}$ 8 $\boxed{=}$ **Result:** $\boxed{17.88854382}$

Graphing Calculator

```
2√(5)+6√(5)
        17.88854382
8√(5)
        17.88854382
```

A calculator can help you determine when a rule has been applied *incorrectly*. For example, use a calculator to show that $\sqrt{3} + \sqrt{5} \neq \sqrt{8}$.

Scientific Calculator

Enter: 3 $\boxed{\sqrt{x}}$ $\boxed{+}$ 5 $\boxed{\sqrt{x}}$ $\boxed{=}$ **Result:** $\boxed{3.968118785}$ ⎤ Values are

Enter: 8 $\boxed{\sqrt{x}}$ **Result:** $\boxed{2.828427125}$ ⎦ not equal.

Graphing Calculator

```
√(3)+√(5)
        3.968118785       ← Values are
√(8)                        not equal.
        2.828427125
```

Section 15.3   Practice Exercises

Boost *your* GRADE at
ALEKS.com!

ALEKS version 3.0

• Practice Problems   • e-Professors
• Self-Tests   • Videos
• NetTutor

Study Skills Exercise

1. Define the key term *like* **radicals**.

Review Exercises

For Exercises 2–9, simplify the expressions. Assume the variables represent positive real numbers.

2. $\sqrt{25w^2}$ 3. $\sqrt[3]{8y^3}$ 4. $\sqrt[3]{4z^4}$ 5. $\sqrt{36x^3}$

6. $\sqrt{\dfrac{9a^6}{a^2}}$ 7. $\dfrac{\sqrt{25c^6}}{16}$ 8. $\sqrt{\dfrac{12x^3}{3x}}$ 9. $\sqrt{-25}$

Objective 1: Definition of *Like* Radicals

10. How do you determine whether two radicals are *like* or *unlike*?

11. Write two radicals that are considered *unlike*.

12. From the three pairs of radicals, identify the pair of *like* radicals:

  a. $2\sqrt{x}$ and $8\sqrt[3]{x}$

  b. $\sqrt{5}$ and $-3\sqrt{5}$

  c. $3a\sqrt{3}$ and $3a\sqrt{2}$

13. From the three pairs of radicals, identify the pair of *like* radicals:

  a. $13\sqrt{5b}$ and $13b\sqrt{5}$

  b. $\sqrt[4]{x^2y}$ and $\sqrt[3]{x^2y}$

  c. $-2\sqrt[3]{y^2}$ and $6\sqrt[3]{y^2}$

Objective 2: Addition and Subtraction of Radicals

For Exercises 14–28, add or subtract the expressions, if possible. Assume the variables represent positive real numbers. **(See Example 1.)**

14. $8\sqrt{6} + 2\sqrt{6}$

15. $3\sqrt{2} + 5\sqrt{2}$

16. $4\sqrt{3} - 2\sqrt{3} + 5\sqrt{3}$

17. $5\sqrt{7} - 3\sqrt{7} + 2\sqrt{7}$

18. $\sqrt{11} + \sqrt{11}$

19. $\sqrt{10} + \sqrt{10}$

20. $12\sqrt{x} - 3\sqrt{x}$

21. $15\sqrt{y} - 4\sqrt{y}$

22. $-3\sqrt{a} + 2\sqrt{a} + \sqrt{a}$

23. $5\sqrt{c} - 6\sqrt{c} + \sqrt{c}$

24. $7x\sqrt{11} - 9x\sqrt{11}$

25. $8y\sqrt{15} - 3y\sqrt{15}$

26. $9\sqrt{2} - 9\sqrt{5}$

27. $x\sqrt{y} - y\sqrt{x}$

28. $a\sqrt{b} + b\sqrt{a}$

For Exercises 29–32, translate the English phrase into an algebraic expression. Then simplify the expression.

29. The sum of three times the cube root of six and eight times the cube root of six.

30. The difference of negative two times the cube root of *w* and five times the cube root of *w*.

31. Four times the square root of five, minus six times the square root of five.

32. Eight times the square root of two, plus the square root of two.

Mixed Exercises

For Exercises 33–62, simplify. Then add or subtract the expressions, if possible. Assume the variables represent positive real numbers. **(See Examples 2 and 3.)**

33. $2\sqrt{12} + \sqrt{48}$

34. $5\sqrt{32} + 2\sqrt{50}$

35. $4\sqrt{45} - 6\sqrt{20}$

36. $8\sqrt{54} - 4\sqrt{24}$

37. $\dfrac{1}{2}\sqrt{8} + \dfrac{1}{3}\sqrt{18}$

38. $\dfrac{1}{4}\sqrt{32} - \dfrac{1}{5}\sqrt{50}$

39. $6p\sqrt{20p^2} + p^2\sqrt{80}$

40. $2q\sqrt{48} + \sqrt{27q^2}$

41. $-2\sqrt{2k} + 6\sqrt{8k}$

42. $5\sqrt{27x} - 4\sqrt{12x}$

43. $11\sqrt{a^4b} - a^2\sqrt{b} - 9a\sqrt{a^2b}$

44. $-7\sqrt{x^4y} + 5x^2\sqrt{y} - 6x\sqrt{x^2y}$

45. $4\sqrt{5} - \sqrt{5}$

46. $-3\sqrt{10} - \sqrt{10}$

47. $\dfrac{5}{6}z\sqrt{6} + \dfrac{7}{9}z\sqrt{6}$

48. $\dfrac{3}{4}a\sqrt{b} + \dfrac{1}{6}a\sqrt{b}$

49. $1.1\sqrt{10} - 5.6\sqrt{10} + 2.8\sqrt{10}$

50. $0.25\sqrt{x} + 1.50\sqrt{x} - 0.75\sqrt{x}$

51. $4\sqrt{x^3} - 2x\sqrt{x}$

52. $8\sqrt{y^9} - 2y^2\sqrt{y^5}$

53. $4\sqrt{7} + \sqrt{63} - 2\sqrt{28}$

54. $8\sqrt{3} - 2\sqrt{27} + \sqrt{75}$

55. $\sqrt{16w} + \sqrt{24w} + \sqrt{40w}$

56. $\sqrt{54y} + \sqrt{81y} - \sqrt{12y}$

57. $\sqrt{x^6 y} + 5x^2\sqrt{x^2 y}$

58. $7\sqrt{a^5 b^2} - a^2\sqrt{ab^2}$

59. $4\sqrt{6} + 2\sqrt{3} - 8\sqrt{6}$

60. $-7\sqrt{y} - \sqrt{z} + 2\sqrt{z}$

61. $x\sqrt{8} - 2\sqrt{18x^2} + \sqrt{2x}$

62. $5\sqrt{p^5} - 2p\sqrt{p} + p\sqrt{16p^3}$

For Exercises 63–64, find the exact perimeter of each figure.

63.
$\sqrt{18}$ m $\sqrt{8}$ m
$\sqrt{32}$ m

64.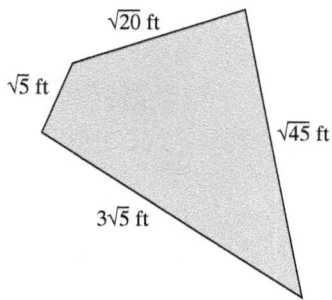
$\sqrt{20}$ ft
$\sqrt{5}$ ft
$\sqrt{45}$ ft
$3\sqrt{5}$ ft

65. Find the exact perimeter of a rectangle whose width is $2\sqrt{3}$ in. and whose length is $3\sqrt{12}$ in.

66. Find the exact perimeter of a square whose side length is $5\sqrt{8}$ cm.

For Exercises 67–72, determine the reason why the following radical expressions cannot be combined by addition or subtraction. **(See Example 4.)**

67. $\sqrt{5} + 5\sqrt{2}$

68. $3\sqrt{10} + 10\sqrt{3}$

69. $3 + 5\sqrt{7}$

70. $-2 + 5\sqrt{11}$

71. $5\sqrt{2} + \sqrt[3]{2}$

72. $\sqrt[4]{6} - 3\sqrt{6}$

Expanding Your Skills

73. Find the slope of the line through the points: $(4, 2\sqrt{3})$ and $(1, \sqrt{3})$.

74. Find the slope of the line through the points: $(7, 4\sqrt{5})$ and $(2, 3\sqrt{5})$.

75. A golfer hits a golf ball at an angle of 30° with an initial velocity of 46.0 meters/second (m/sec). The horizontal position of the ball, x (measured in meters), depends on the number of seconds, t, after the ball is struck according to the equation:

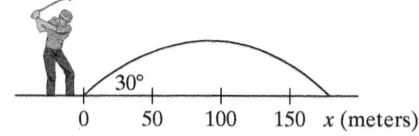

$$x = 23\sqrt{3}t$$

a. What is the horizontal position of the ball after 2 sec? Round the answer to the nearest meter.

b. What is the horizontal position of the ball after 4 sec? Round the answer to the nearest meter.

76. A long-jumper leaves the ground at an angle of 30° at a speed of 9 m/sec. The horizontal position of the long jumper, x (measured in meters), depends on the number of seconds, t, after he leaves the ground according to the equation:

$$x = 4.5\sqrt{3}t$$

a. What is the horizontal position of the long-jumper after 0.5 sec? Round the answer to the nearest hundredth of a meter.

b. What is the horizontal position of the long-jumper after 0.75 sec? Round the answer to the nearest hundredth of a meter.

Section 15.4 | Multiplication of Radicals

1. Multiplication Property of Radicals

In this section, we will learn how to multiply radicals that have the same index. Recall from Section 15.2 the multiplication property of radicals.

> **PROPERTY** Multiplication Property of Radicals
>
> Let a and b represent real numbers such that $\sqrt[n]{a}$ and $\sqrt[n]{b}$ are both real. Then,
> $$\sqrt[n]{a} \cdot \sqrt[n]{b} = \sqrt[n]{ab}$$

To multiply two radical expressions, use the multiplication property of radicals along with the commutative and associative properties of multiplication.

Skill Practice

Multiply the expressions and simplify the result. Assume the variables represent positive real numbers.

1. $\sqrt{2} \cdot \sqrt{5}$
2. $(-5z\sqrt{6})(4z\sqrt{2})$
3. $(9y\sqrt{x})\left(\frac{1}{3}y\sqrt{xy}\right)$

Example 1 Multiplying Radical Expressions

Multiply the expressions and simplify the result. Assume the variables represent positive real numbers.

a. $\sqrt{3} \cdot \sqrt{2}$ b. $(5\sqrt{3})(2\sqrt{15})$ c. $(6a\sqrt{ab})\left(\frac{1}{3}a\sqrt{a}\right)$

Solution:

a. $\sqrt{3} \cdot \sqrt{2} = \sqrt{6}$ Multiplication property of radicals

b. $(5\sqrt{3})(2\sqrt{15}) = (5 \cdot 2)(\sqrt{3} \cdot \sqrt{15})$ Commutative and associative properties of multiplication

$= 10\sqrt{45}$ Multiplication property of radicals

$= 10\sqrt{3^2 \cdot 5}$ Simplify the radical.

$= 10 \cdot 3\sqrt{5}$

$= 30\sqrt{5}$

c. $(6a\sqrt{ab})\left(\frac{1}{3}a\sqrt{a}\right) = \left(6a \cdot \frac{1}{3}a\right)(\sqrt{ab} \cdot \sqrt{a})$ Commutative and associative properties of multiplication

$= 2a^2\sqrt{a^2b}$ Multiplication property of radicals

$= 2a^2 \cdot a\sqrt{b}$ Simplify the radical.

$= 2a^3\sqrt{b}$

When multiplying radical expressions with more than one term, we use the distributive property.

Answers

1. $\sqrt{10}$ 2. $-40z^2\sqrt{3}$
3. $3xy^2\sqrt{y}$

Example 2 | **Multiplying Radical Expressions with Multiple Terms**

Multiply the expressions. Assume the variables represent positive real numbers.

a. $\sqrt{5}(4 + 3\sqrt{5})$ **b.** $(\sqrt{x} - 10)(\sqrt{y} + 4)$ **c.** $(2\sqrt{3} - \sqrt{5})(\sqrt{3} + 6\sqrt{5})$

Solution:

a. $\sqrt{5}(4 + 3\sqrt{5})$

$= \sqrt{5}(4) + \sqrt{5}(3\sqrt{5})$ Apply the distributive property.

$= 4\sqrt{5} + 3\sqrt{5^2}$ Multiplication property of radicals

$= 4\sqrt{5} + 3 \cdot 5$ Simplify the radical.

$= 4\sqrt{5} + 15$

b. $(\sqrt{x} - 10)(\sqrt{y} + 4)$

$= \sqrt{x}(\sqrt{y}) + \sqrt{x}(4) - 10(\sqrt{y}) - 10(4)$ Apply the distributive property.

$= \sqrt{xy} + 4\sqrt{x} - 10\sqrt{y} - 40$ Simplify.

c. $(2\sqrt{3} - \sqrt{5})(\sqrt{3} + 6\sqrt{5})$

$= 2\sqrt{3}(\sqrt{3}) + 2\sqrt{3}(6\sqrt{5}) - \sqrt{5}(\sqrt{3}) - \sqrt{5}(6\sqrt{5})$ Apply the distributive property.

$= 2\sqrt{3^2} + 12\sqrt{15} - \sqrt{15} - 6\sqrt{5^2}$ Multiplication property of radicals

$= 2 \cdot 3 + 11\sqrt{15} - 6 \cdot 5$ Simplify radicals. Combine *like* radicals.

$= 6 + 11\sqrt{15} - 30$

$= -24 + 11\sqrt{15}$ Combine *like* terms.

2. Expressions of the Form $(\sqrt[n]{a})^n$

The multiplication property of radicals can be used to simplify an expression of the form $(\sqrt{a})^2$, where $a \geq 0$.

$$(\sqrt{a})^2 = \sqrt{a} \cdot \sqrt{a} = \sqrt{a^2} = a$$

This logic can be applied to nth-roots. If $\sqrt[n]{a}$ is a real number, then $(\sqrt[n]{a})^n = a$.

Example 3 | **Simplifying Radical Expressions**

Simplify the expressions. Assume $x \geq 0$.

a. $(\sqrt{7})^2$ **b.** $(\sqrt[4]{x})^4$ **c.** $(3\sqrt{2})^2$

Solution:

a. $(\sqrt{7})^2 = 7$ **b.** $(\sqrt[4]{x})^4 = x$ **c.** $(3\sqrt{2})^2 = 3^2 \cdot (\sqrt{2})^2 = 9 \cdot 2 = 18$

3. Special Case Products

From Example 2, you may have noticed a similarity between multiplying radical expressions and multiplying polynomials.

Recall from Section 12.6 that the square of a binomial results in a perfect square trinomial.

$$(a + b)^2 = a^2 + 2ab + b^2$$
$$(a - b)^2 = a^2 - 2ab + b^2$$

The same patterns occur when squaring a radical expression with two terms.

Skill Practice

Square the radical expression. Assume $p \geq 0$.

10. $(\sqrt{p} + 3)^2$

Example 4 **Squaring a Two-Term Radical Expression**

Square the radical expression. Assume the variables represent positive real numbers.

$$(\sqrt{x} + \sqrt{y})^2$$

Solution:

$(\sqrt{x} + \sqrt{y})^2$ — This expression is in the form $(a + b)^2$, where $a = \sqrt{x}$ and $b = \sqrt{y}$.

$$\overset{a^2 + 2ab + b^2}{= (\sqrt{x})^2 + 2(\sqrt{x})(\sqrt{y}) + (\sqrt{y})^2}$$ — Apply the formula $(a + b)^2 = a^2 + 2ab + b^2$.

$$= x + 2\sqrt{xy} + y$$ — Simplify.

TIP: The product $(\sqrt{x} + \sqrt{y})^2$ can also be found using the distributive property.

$$(\sqrt{x} + \sqrt{y})^2 = (\sqrt{x} + \sqrt{y})(\sqrt{x} + \sqrt{y}) = \sqrt{x} \cdot \sqrt{x} + \sqrt{x} \cdot \sqrt{y} + \sqrt{y} \cdot \sqrt{x} + \sqrt{y} \cdot \sqrt{y}$$
$$= \sqrt{x^2} + \sqrt{xy} + \sqrt{xy} + \sqrt{y^2}$$
$$= x + 2\sqrt{xy} + y$$

Skill Practice

Square the radical expression.

11. $(\sqrt{5} - 3\sqrt{2})^2$

Example 5 **Square a Two-Term Radical Expression**

Square the radical expression. $(\sqrt{2} - 4\sqrt{3})^2$

Solution:

$(\sqrt{2} - 4\sqrt{3})^2$ — This expression is in the form $(a - b)^2$, where $a = \sqrt{2}$ and $b = 4\sqrt{3}$.

$$\overset{a^2 - 2ab + b^2}{(\sqrt{2})^2 - 2(\sqrt{2})(4\sqrt{3}) + (4\sqrt{3})^2}$$ — Apply the formula $(a - b)^2 = a^2 - 2ab + b^2$.

$$= 2 - 8\sqrt{6} + 16 \cdot 3$$ — Simplify.

$$= 2 - 8\sqrt{6} + 48$$

$$= 50 - 8\sqrt{6}$$

Answers

10. $p + 6\sqrt{p} + 9$
11. $23 - 6\sqrt{10}$

4. Multiplying Conjugate Radical Expressions

Recall from Section 12.6 that the product of two conjugate binomials results in a difference of squares.

$$(a + b)(a - b) = a^2 - b^2$$

The same pattern occurs when multiplying two conjugate radical expressions.

| Example 6 | Multiplying Conjugate Radical Expressions |

Multiply the radical expressions. $(\sqrt{5} + 4)(\sqrt{5} - 4)$

Solution:

$(\sqrt{5} + 4)(\sqrt{5} - 4)$ This expression is in the form $(a + b)(a - b)$, where $a = \sqrt{5}$ and $b = 4$.

$\overset{a^2 - b^2}{= (\sqrt{5})^2 - (4)^2}$ Apply the formula $(a + b)(a - b) = a^2 - b^2$.

$= 5 - 16$ Simplify.

$= -11$

TIP: The product $(\sqrt{5} + 4)(\sqrt{5} - 4)$ can also be found using the distributive property.

$(\sqrt{5} + 4)(\sqrt{5} - 4) = \sqrt{5} \cdot (\sqrt{5}) + \sqrt{5} \cdot (-4) + 4 \cdot (\sqrt{5}) + 4 \cdot (-4)$
$= 5 - 4\sqrt{5} + 4\sqrt{5} - 16$
$= 5 - 16$
$= -11$

| Example 7 | Multiply Conjugate Radical Expressions |

Multiply the radical expressions. Assume the variables represent positive real numbers.

$$(2\sqrt{c} - 3\sqrt{d})(2\sqrt{c} + 3\sqrt{d})$$

Solution:

$(2\sqrt{c} - 3\sqrt{d})(2\sqrt{c} + 3\sqrt{d})$ This expression is in the form $(a - b)(a + b)$, where $a = 2\sqrt{c}$ and $b = 3\sqrt{d}$.

$\overset{a^2 - b^2}{= (2\sqrt{c})^2 - (3\sqrt{d})^2}$ Apply the formula $(a + b)(a - b) = a^2 - b^2$.

$= 4c - 9d$

Answers
12. -3 **13.** $25a - b$

Section 15.4 Practice Exercises

Study Skills Exercise

1. When writing a radical expression, be sure to note the difference between an exponent on a coefficient and an index to a radical. Write an algebraic expression for each of the following:

   x cubed times the square root of y

   x times the cube root of y

Review Exercises

For Exercises 2–5, perform the indicated operations and simplify. Assume the variables represent positive real numbers.

2. $\sqrt{25} + \sqrt{16} - \sqrt{36}$ 3. $\sqrt{100} - \sqrt{4} + \sqrt{9}$ 4. $6x\sqrt{18} + 2\sqrt{2x^2}$ 5. $10\sqrt{zw^4} - w^2\sqrt{49z}$

6. What three conditions are needed for a radical expression to be in simplified form?

Objective 1: Multiplication Property of Radicals

For Exercises 7–26, multiply the expressions. **(See Example 1.)**

7. $\sqrt{5} \cdot \sqrt{3}$

8. $\sqrt{7} \cdot \sqrt{6}$

9. $\sqrt{47} \cdot \sqrt{47}$

10. $\sqrt{59} \cdot \sqrt{59}$

11. $\sqrt{b} \cdot \sqrt{b}$

12. $\sqrt{t} \cdot \sqrt{t}$

13. $(2\sqrt{15})(3\sqrt{p})$

14. $(4\sqrt{2})(5\sqrt{q})$

15. $\sqrt{10} \cdot \sqrt{5}$

16. $\sqrt{2} \cdot \sqrt{10}$

17. $(-\sqrt{7})(-2\sqrt{14})$

18. $(-6\sqrt{2})(-\sqrt{22})$

19. $(3x\sqrt{2})(\sqrt{14})$

20. $(4y\sqrt{3})(\sqrt{6})$

21. $\left(\frac{1}{6}x\sqrt{xy}\right)(24x\sqrt{x})$

22. $\left(\frac{1}{4}u\sqrt{uv}\right)(8u\sqrt{v})$

23. $(6w\sqrt{5})(w\sqrt{8})$

24. $(t\sqrt{2})(5\sqrt{6t})$

25. $(-2\sqrt{3})(4\sqrt{5})$

26. $(-\sqrt{7})(2\sqrt{3})$

For Exercises 27–28, find the exact perimeter and exact area of the rectangles.

27.

$\sqrt{5}$ ft

$\sqrt{20}$ ft

28.

$\sqrt{8}$ in.

$\sqrt{2}$ in.

For Exercises 29–30, find the exact area of the triangles.

29.

$\sqrt{12}$ cm

$\sqrt{3}$ cm

30.

$\sqrt{28}$ m

$\sqrt{7}$ m

For Exercises 31–44, multiply the expressions. Assume the variables represent positive real numbers. **(See Example 2.)**

31. $\sqrt{3w} \cdot \sqrt{3w}$ **32.** $\sqrt{6p} \cdot \sqrt{6p}$ **33.** $(8\sqrt{5y})(-2\sqrt{2})$ **34.** $(4\sqrt{5x})(7\sqrt{3})$

35. $\sqrt{2}(\sqrt{6} - \sqrt{3})$ **36.** $\sqrt{5}(\sqrt{10} + \sqrt{7})$ **37.** $4\sqrt{x}(\sqrt{x} + 5)$ **38.** $2\sqrt{y}(3 - \sqrt{y})$

39. $(\sqrt{3} + 2\sqrt{10})(4\sqrt{3} - \sqrt{10})$ **40.** $(8\sqrt{7} - \sqrt{5})(\sqrt{7} + 3\sqrt{5})$

41. $(\sqrt{a} - 3b)(9\sqrt{a} - b)$ **42.** $(11\sqrt{m} + 4n)(\sqrt{m} + n)$

43. $(p + 2\sqrt{p})(8p + 3\sqrt{p} - 4)$ **44.** $(5s - \sqrt{s})(s + 5\sqrt{s} + 6)$

Objective 2: Expressions of the Form $(\sqrt[n]{a})^n$

For Exercises 45–52, simplify the expressions. Assume the variables represent positive real numbers. **(See Example 3.)**

45. $(\sqrt{10})^2$ **46.** $(\sqrt{23})^2$ **47.** $(\sqrt[3]{4})^3$ **48.** $(\sqrt[3]{29})^3$

49. $(\sqrt[4]{t})^4$ **50.** $(\sqrt[4]{xy})^4$ **51.** $(4\sqrt{c})^2$ **52.** $(10\sqrt{2pq})^2$

Objective 3: Special Case Products

For Exercises 53–60, multiply the radical expressions. Assume the variables represent positive real numbers. **(See Examples 4–5.)**

53. $(\sqrt{13} + 4)^2$ **54.** $(6 - \sqrt{11})^2$ **55.** $(\sqrt{a} - 2)^2$ **56.** $(\sqrt{p} + 3)^2$

57. $(2\sqrt{a} - 3)^2$ **58.** $(3\sqrt{w} + 4)^2$ **59.** $(\sqrt{10} - \sqrt{11})^2$ **60.** $(\sqrt{3} - \sqrt{2})^2$

Objective 4: Multiplying Conjugate Radical Expressions

For Exercises 61–72, multiply the radical expressions. Assume the variables represent positive real numbers. **(See Examples 6–7.)**

61. $(\sqrt{5} + 2)(\sqrt{5} - 2)$ **62.** $(\sqrt{3} - 4)(\sqrt{3} + 4)$ **63.** $(\sqrt{x} + \sqrt{y})(\sqrt{x} - \sqrt{y})$

64. $(\sqrt{a} + \sqrt{b})(\sqrt{a} - \sqrt{b})$ **65.** $(\sqrt{10} - \sqrt{11})(\sqrt{10} + \sqrt{11})$ **66.** $(\sqrt{3} - \sqrt{2})(\sqrt{3} + \sqrt{2})$

67. $(\sqrt{6} + \sqrt{2})(\sqrt{6} - \sqrt{2})$ **68.** $(\sqrt{15} - \sqrt{5})(\sqrt{15} + \sqrt{5})$ **69.** $(8\sqrt{x} - 2\sqrt{y})(8\sqrt{x} + 2\sqrt{y})$

70. $(4\sqrt{s} + 11\sqrt{t})(4\sqrt{s} - 11\sqrt{t})$ **71.** $(5\sqrt{3} - \sqrt{2})(5\sqrt{3} + \sqrt{2})$ **72.** $(2\sqrt{7} - 4\sqrt{3})(2\sqrt{7} + 4\sqrt{3})$

Mixed Exercises

For Exercises 73–84, multiply the expressions in parts (a) and (b) and compare the process used. Assume the variables represent positive real numbers.

73. a. $3(x + 2)$ **74. a.** $-5(6 + y)$ **75. a.** $(2a + 3)^2$
    b. $\sqrt{3}(\sqrt{x} + \sqrt{2})$ **b.** $-\sqrt{5}(\sqrt{6} + \sqrt{y})$ **b.** $(2\sqrt{a} + 3)^2$

76. a. $(6 - z)^2$ **77. a.** $(b - 5)(b + 5)$ **78. a.** $(3w - 1)(3w + 1)$
    b. $(\sqrt{6} - z)^2$ **b.** $(\sqrt{b} - 5)(\sqrt{b} + 5)$ **b.** $(3\sqrt{w} - 1)(3\sqrt{w} + 1)$

79. a. $(x - 2y)^2$ **80. a.** $(5c + 2d)^2$ **81. a.** $(p - q)(p + q)$
    b. $(\sqrt{x} - 2\sqrt{y})^2$ **b.** $(5\sqrt{c} + 2\sqrt{d})^2$ **b.** $(\sqrt{p} - \sqrt{q})(\sqrt{p} + \sqrt{q})$

82. a. $(t - 3)(t + 3)$ **83. a.** $(y - 3)^2$ **84. a.** $(p + 4)^2$
    b. $(\sqrt{t} - \sqrt{3})(\sqrt{t} + \sqrt{3})$ **b.** $(\sqrt{x - 2} - 3)^2$ **b.** $(\sqrt{x + 1} + 4)^2$

Division of Radicals and Rationalization

1. Simplified Form of a Radical

Recall the conditions for a radical to be simplified.

> **DEFINITION** Simplified Form of a Radical
>
> Consider any radical expression where the radicand is written as a product of prime factors. The expression is in simplified form if all of the following conditions are met:
>
> 1. The radicand has no factor raised to a power greater than or equal to the index.
> 2. There are no radicals in the denominator of a fraction.
> 3. The radicand does not contain a fraction.

The basis of the second and third conditions, which restrict radicals from the denominator of an expression, are largely historical. In some cases, removing a radical from the denominator of a fraction will create an expression that is computationally simpler.

The process to remove a radical from the denominator is called **rationalizing the denominator**. In this section, we will show three approaches that can be used to achieve the second and third conditions of a simplified radical.

1. Rationalizing by applying the division property of radicals.
2. Rationalizing when the denominator contains a singe radical term.
3. Rationalizing when the denominator contains two terms involving square roots.

2. Division Property of Radicals

The multiplication property of radicals enables a product within a radical to be separated and written as a product of radicals. We now state a similar property for radicals involving quotients.

> **PROPERTY** Division Property of Radicals
>
> Let a and b represent real numbers such that $\sqrt[n]{a}$ and $\sqrt[n]{b}$ are both real. Then,
>
> $$\sqrt[n]{\frac{a}{b}} = \frac{\sqrt[n]{a}}{\sqrt[n]{b}} \qquad b \neq 0$$

The division property of radicals indicates that a quotient within a radicand can be written as a quotient of radicals provided the roots are real numbers. For example:

$$\sqrt{\frac{4}{9}} = \frac{\sqrt{4}}{\sqrt{9}}$$

The reverse process is also true. A quotient of radicals can be written as a single radical provided that the roots are real numbers and they have the same indices.

$$\text{same index} \left[\frac{\sqrt[3]{125}}{\sqrt[3]{8}} = \sqrt[3]{\frac{125}{8}} \right.$$

In Examples 1 and 2, we will apply the division property of radicals to simplify radical expressions.

Example 1 — Using the Division Property to Simplify Radicals

Use the division property of radicals to simplify the expressions. Assume the variables represent positive real numbers.

a. $\sqrt{\dfrac{a^{10}}{b^4}}$ **b.** $\sqrt{\dfrac{20x^3}{9}}$

Skill Practice

Simplify the expressions.

1. $\sqrt{\dfrac{c^4}{49}}$

2. $\sqrt{\dfrac{12b^5}{25}}$

Solution:

a. $\sqrt{\dfrac{a^{10}}{b^4}}$ The radicand contains an irreducible fraction.

$= \dfrac{\sqrt{a^{10}}}{\sqrt{b^4}}$ Apply the division property to rewrite as a quotient of radicals.

$= \dfrac{a^5}{b^2}$ Simplify the radicals.

b. $\sqrt{\dfrac{20x^3}{9}}$ The radicand contains an irreducible fraction.

$= \dfrac{\sqrt{20x^3}}{\sqrt{9}}$ Apply the division property to rewrite as a quotient of radicals.

$= \dfrac{\sqrt{2^2 \cdot 5 \cdot x^2 \cdot x}}{\sqrt{9}}$ Factor the radicand in the numerator to simplify the radical.

$= \dfrac{2x\sqrt{5x}}{3}$ Simplify the radicals in the numerator and denominator. The expression is simplified since it now satisfies all conditions.

Answers

1. $\dfrac{c^2}{7}$ 2. $\dfrac{2b^2\sqrt{3b}}{5}$

Example 2 Using the Division Property to Simplify Radicals

Use the division property of radicals to simplify the expressions. Assume the variables represent positive real numbers.

a. $\dfrac{\sqrt[3]{9}}{\sqrt[3]{72}}$ b. $\dfrac{\sqrt{7y^3}}{\sqrt{y}}$

Solution:

a. $\dfrac{\sqrt[3]{9}}{\sqrt[3]{72}}$ There is a radical in the denominator of the fraction.

$= \sqrt[3]{\dfrac{9}{72}}$ Apply the division property to write the quotient under a single radical.

$= \sqrt[3]{\dfrac{1}{8}}$ Reduce to lowest terms.

$= \dfrac{1}{2}$ Simplify the radical.

b. $\dfrac{\sqrt{7y^3}}{\sqrt{y}}$ There is a radical in the denominator of the fraction.

$= \sqrt{\dfrac{7y^3}{y}}$ Apply the division property to write the quotient under a single radical.

$= \sqrt{7y^2}$ Simplify the fraction.

$= y\sqrt{7}$ Simplify the radical.

Examples 1 and 2 show that radical expressions can sometimes be simplified by using the division property of radicals. However, there are cases where other methods are needed. For example:

$\dfrac{2}{\sqrt{2}}$ and $\dfrac{2}{\sqrt{5}+\sqrt{3}}$ are two such cases.

3. Rationalizing the Denominator: One Term

To begin the first case, recall that the nth-root of a perfect nth power is easily simplified. For example:

$$\sqrt{x^2} = x \quad x \geq 0$$

Example 3 Rationalizing the Denominator: One Term

Simplify the expression. $\dfrac{2}{\sqrt{2}}$

Solution:

A square root of a perfect square is needed in the denominator to remove the radical.

$\dfrac{2}{\sqrt{2}} = \dfrac{2}{\sqrt{2}} \cdot \dfrac{\sqrt{2}}{\sqrt{2}}$ Multiply the numerator and denominator by $\sqrt{2}$ because $\sqrt{2} \cdot \sqrt{2} = \sqrt{2^2}$.

$= \dfrac{2\sqrt{2}}{\sqrt{2^2}}$ Multiply the radicals.

$$= \frac{2\sqrt{2}}{2} \qquad \text{Simplify.}$$

$$= \frac{2\sqrt{2}}{2} \qquad \text{Reduce the fraction to lowest terms.}$$

$$= \sqrt{2}$$

Example 4 **Rationalizing the Denominator: One Term**

Simplify the expression. Assume x represents a positive real number. $\sqrt{\dfrac{x}{5}}$

Solution:

$$\sqrt{\frac{x}{5}} \qquad \text{The radicand contains an irreducible fraction.}$$

$$= \frac{\sqrt{x}}{\sqrt{5}} \qquad \text{Apply the division property of radicals.}$$

$$= \frac{\sqrt{x}}{\sqrt{5}} \cdot \frac{\sqrt{5}}{\sqrt{5}} \qquad \text{Multiply the numerator and denominator by } \sqrt{5} \text{ because } \sqrt{5} \cdot \sqrt{5} = \sqrt{5^2}.$$

$$= \frac{\sqrt{5x}}{\sqrt{5^2}} \qquad \text{Multiply the radicals.}$$

$$= \frac{\sqrt{5x}}{5} \qquad \text{Simplify the radicals.}$$

Skill Practice

Simplify the expression by rationalizing the denominator.

6. $\sqrt{\dfrac{7}{10}}$

Avoiding Mistakes

In the expression $\dfrac{\sqrt{5x}}{5}$, do not try to "cancel" the factor of $\sqrt{5}$ from the numerator with the factor of 5 in the denominator. $\sqrt{5}$ and 5 are not equal.

Example 5 **Rationalizing the Denominator: One Term**

Simplify the expression. Assume w represents a positive real number.

$$\frac{14\sqrt{w}}{\sqrt{7}}$$

Solution:

$$\frac{14\sqrt{w}}{\sqrt{7}} \qquad \text{Fraction contains a radical in the denominator.}$$

$$= \frac{14\sqrt{w}}{\sqrt{7}} \cdot \frac{\sqrt{7}}{\sqrt{7}} \qquad \text{Multiply the numerator and denominator by } \sqrt{7} \text{ because } \sqrt{7} \cdot \sqrt{7} = \sqrt{7^2}.$$

$$= \frac{14\sqrt{7w}}{\sqrt{7^2}} \qquad \text{Multiply the radicals.}$$

$$= \frac{14\sqrt{7w}}{7} \qquad \text{Simplify.}$$

$$= \frac{\overset{2}{14}\sqrt{7w}}{\underset{1}{7}} \qquad \text{Reduce to lowest terms.}$$

$$= 2\sqrt{7w}$$

Skill Practice

Simplify the expression by rationalizing the denominator.

7. $\dfrac{6y}{\sqrt{3}}$

TIP: In the expression

$$\frac{14\sqrt{7w}}{7}$$

the factor of 14 and the factor of 7 may be reduced because both factors are outside the radical.

$$\frac{14\sqrt{7w}}{7} = \frac{14}{7} \cdot \sqrt{7w}$$

$$= 2\sqrt{7w}$$

Answers

6. $\dfrac{\sqrt{70}}{10}$ 7. $2y\sqrt{3}$

Example 6 **Rationalizing the Denominator: One Term**

Simplify the expression. Assume w represents a positive real number.

$$\sqrt{\frac{w}{12}}$$

Solution:

$\sqrt{\dfrac{w}{12}}$ The radical contains an irreducible fraction.

$= \dfrac{\sqrt{w}}{\sqrt{12}}$ Apply the division property of radicals.

$= \dfrac{\sqrt{w}}{\sqrt{2^2 \cdot 3}}$ Factor 12 to simplify the radical.

$= \dfrac{\sqrt{w}}{2\sqrt{3}}$ The $\sqrt{3}$ in the denominator needs to be rationalized.

$= \dfrac{\sqrt{w}}{2\sqrt{3}} \cdot \dfrac{\sqrt{3}}{\sqrt{3}}$ Multiply the numerator and denominator by $\sqrt{3}$ because $\sqrt{3} \cdot \sqrt{3} = \sqrt{3^2}$.

$= \dfrac{\sqrt{3w}}{2\sqrt{3^2}}$ Multiply the radicals.

$= \dfrac{\sqrt{3w}}{2 \cdot 3}$ Simplify.

$= \dfrac{\sqrt{3w}}{6}$ This cannot be simplified further because 3 is inside the radical and 6 is not.

4. Rationalizing the Denominator: Two Terms

Recall from the multiplication of polynomials that the product of two conjugates results in a difference of squares.

$$(a + b)(a - b) = a^2 - b^2$$

If either a or b has a square root factor, the expression will simplify without a radical; that is, the expression is rationalized. For example,

$$(\sqrt{5} - \sqrt{3})(\sqrt{5} + \sqrt{3}) = (\sqrt{5})^2 - (\sqrt{3})^2$$
$$= 5 - 3$$
$$= 2$$

Multiplying a binomial by its conjugate is the basis for rationalizing a denominator with two terms involving square roots.

Example 7   **Rationalizing the Denominator: Two Terms**

Simplify the expression by rationalizing the denominator.

$$\frac{2}{\sqrt{5} + \sqrt{3}}$$

Skill Practice

Simplify the expression by rationalizing the denominator.

9. $\dfrac{6}{\sqrt{3} - 1}$

Solution:

$\dfrac{2}{\sqrt{5} + \sqrt{3}}$ To rationalize a denominator with two terms, multiply the numerator and denominator by the conjugate of the denominator.

$= \dfrac{2}{(\sqrt{5} + \sqrt{3})} \cdot \dfrac{(\sqrt{5} - \sqrt{3})}{(\sqrt{5} - \sqrt{3})}$

Conjugates

The denominator is in the form $(a + b)(a - b)$, where $a = \sqrt{5}$ and $b = \sqrt{3}$.

$= \dfrac{2(\sqrt{5} - \sqrt{3})}{(\sqrt{5})^2 - (\sqrt{3})^2}$ In the denominator, apply the formula $(a + b)(a - b) = a^2 - b^2$.

$= \dfrac{2(\sqrt{5} - \sqrt{3})}{5 - 3}$ Simplify.

$= \dfrac{2(\sqrt{5} - \sqrt{3})}{2}$

$= \dfrac{2(\sqrt{5} - \sqrt{3})}{2}$ Reduce to lowest terms.

$= \sqrt{5} - \sqrt{3}$

Example 8   **Rationalizing the Denominator: Two Terms**

Simplify the expression by rationalizing the denominator.

$$\frac{\sqrt{x} + \sqrt{2}}{\sqrt{x} - \sqrt{2}}$$

Skill Practice

Simplify the expression by rationalizing the denominators.

10. $\dfrac{\sqrt{y} - \sqrt{5}}{\sqrt{y} + \sqrt{5}}$

Solution:

$\dfrac{\sqrt{x} + \sqrt{2}}{\sqrt{x} - \sqrt{2}} = \dfrac{(\sqrt{x} + \sqrt{2})}{(\sqrt{x} - \sqrt{2})} \cdot \dfrac{(\sqrt{x} + \sqrt{2})}{(\sqrt{x} + \sqrt{2})}$ Multiply the numerator and denominator by the conjugate of the denominator.

Conjugates

$= \dfrac{(\sqrt{x} + \sqrt{2})^2}{(\sqrt{x} - \sqrt{2})(\sqrt{x} + \sqrt{2})}$

$= \dfrac{(\sqrt{x})^2 + 2(\sqrt{x})(\sqrt{2}) + (\sqrt{2})^2}{(\sqrt{x})^2 - (\sqrt{2})^2}$ Simplify using special case products.

$= \dfrac{x + 2\sqrt{2x} + 2}{x - 2}$ Simplify the radicals.

Answers

9. $3\sqrt{3} + 3$

10. $\dfrac{y - 2\sqrt{5y} + 5}{y - 5}$

5. Simplifying Quotients That Contain Radicals

Sometimes a radical expression within a quotient must be reduced to lowest terms. This is demonstrated in Example 9.

Example 9   **Simplifying a Radical Quotient to Lowest Terms**

Simplify the expression $\dfrac{4 - \sqrt{20}}{10}$.

Solution:

$$\frac{4 - \sqrt{20}}{10}$$ First simplify $\sqrt{20}$ by writing the radicand as a product of prime factors.

$$= \frac{4 - \sqrt{2^2 \cdot 5}}{10}$$

$$= \frac{4 - 2\sqrt{5}}{10}$$ Simplify the radical.

$$= \frac{2(2 - \sqrt{5})}{2 \cdot 5}$$ Factor out the GCF.

$$= \frac{2(2 - \sqrt{5})}{2 \cdot 5}$$ Reduce to lowest terms.

$$= \frac{2 - \sqrt{5}}{5}$$

Avoiding Mistakes

Remember that it is not correct to reduce *terms* within a rational expression. In the expression

$$\frac{4 - 2\sqrt{5}}{10}$$

do not try to reduce the 4 and the 10. Only common *factors* can be canceled.

Answer

11. $\dfrac{3 - \sqrt{6}}{6}$

Section 15.5 Practice Exercises

Study Skills Exercise

1. Define the key term **rationalizing the denominator**.

Review Exercises

For Exercises 2–10, perform the indicated operations. Assume the variables represent positive real numbers.

2. $x\sqrt{45} + 4\sqrt{20x^2}$

3. $(2\sqrt{y} + 3)(3\sqrt{y} + 7)$

4. $(4\sqrt{w} - 2)(2\sqrt{w} - 4)$

5. $4\sqrt{3} + \sqrt{5} \cdot \sqrt{15}$

6. $\sqrt{7} \cdot \sqrt{21} + 2\sqrt{27}$

7. $(5 - \sqrt{a})^2$

8. $(\sqrt{z} + 3)^2$

9. $(\sqrt{2} + \sqrt{7})(\sqrt{2} - \sqrt{7})$

10. $(\sqrt{3} + 5)(\sqrt{3} - 5)$

Objective 2: Division Property of Radicals

For Exercises 11–30, use the division property of radicals, if necessary, to simplify the expressions. Assume the variables represent positive real numbers. **(See Examples 1–2.)**

11. $\sqrt{\dfrac{3}{16}}$ **12.** $\sqrt{\dfrac{7}{25}}$ **13.** $\sqrt{\dfrac{a^4}{b^4}}$ **14.** $\sqrt{\dfrac{y^6}{z^2}}$

15. $\sqrt{\dfrac{c^3}{4}}$ **16.** $\sqrt{\dfrac{d^5}{9}}$ **17.** $\sqrt[3]{\dfrac{x^2}{27}}$ **18.** $\sqrt[3]{\dfrac{c^2}{8}}$

19. $\sqrt[3]{\dfrac{y^5}{27y^3}}$ **20.** $\sqrt[3]{\dfrac{7ac}{64c^4}}$ **21.** $\sqrt{\dfrac{200}{81}}$ **22.** $\sqrt{\dfrac{80}{49}}$

23. $\dfrac{\sqrt{8}}{\sqrt{50}}$ **24.** $\dfrac{\sqrt{21}}{\sqrt{12}}$ **25.** $\dfrac{\sqrt{p}}{\sqrt{4p^3}}$ **26.** $\dfrac{\sqrt{9t}}{\sqrt{t^5}}$

27. $\dfrac{\sqrt[3]{z^5}}{\sqrt[3]{z^2}}$ **28.** $\dfrac{\sqrt[3]{a^7}}{\sqrt[3]{a}}$ **29.** $\dfrac{\sqrt[3]{24x^5}}{\sqrt[3]{3x^4}}$ **30.** $\dfrac{\sqrt[3]{2y^8}}{\sqrt[3]{54y^7}}$

Objective 3: Rationalizing the Denominator: One Term

For Exercises 31–50, rationalize the denominators. Assume the variable expressions represent positive real numbers.
(See Examples 3–6.)

31. $\dfrac{1}{\sqrt{6}}$ **32.** $\dfrac{5}{\sqrt{2}}$ **33.** $\dfrac{15}{\sqrt{5}}$ **34.** $\dfrac{14}{\sqrt{7}}$

35. $\dfrac{6}{\sqrt{x+1}}$ **36.** $\dfrac{8}{\sqrt{y-3}}$ **37.** $\sqrt{\dfrac{6}{x}}$ **38.** $\sqrt{\dfrac{8}{y}}$

39. $\sqrt{\dfrac{3}{7}}$ **40.** $\sqrt{\dfrac{5}{11}}$ **41.** $\dfrac{10}{\sqrt{6y}}$ **42.** $\dfrac{15}{\sqrt{3w}}$

43. $\dfrac{9}{2\sqrt{6}}$ **44.** $\dfrac{15}{4\sqrt{10}}$ **45.** $\sqrt{\dfrac{p}{27}}$ **46.** $\sqrt{\dfrac{x}{32}}$

47. $\dfrac{5}{\sqrt{20}}$ **48.** $\dfrac{8}{\sqrt{24}}$ **49.** $\sqrt{\dfrac{x^2}{y^3}}$ **50.** $\sqrt{\dfrac{a}{b^5}}$

Objective 4: Rationalizing the Denominator: Two Terms

For Exercises 51–52, multiply the conjugates.

51. $(\sqrt{2}+3)(\sqrt{2}-3)$ **52.** $(\sqrt{3}+\sqrt{7})(\sqrt{3}-\sqrt{7})$

53. What is the conjugate of $\sqrt{5}-\sqrt{3}$? Multiply $\sqrt{5}-\sqrt{3}$ by its conjugate.

54. What is the conjugate of $\sqrt{7}+\sqrt{2}$? Multiply $\sqrt{7}+\sqrt{2}$ by its conjugate.

55. What is the conjugate of $\sqrt{x}+10$? Multiply $\sqrt{x}+10$ by its conjugate.

56. What is the conjugate of $12-\sqrt{y}$? Multiply $12-\sqrt{y}$ by its conjugate.

For Exercises 57–68, rationalize the denominators. Assume the variable expressions represent positive real numbers.
(See Examples 7–8.)

57. $\dfrac{4}{\sqrt{2}+3}$ **58.** $\dfrac{6}{4-\sqrt{3}}$ **59.** $\dfrac{1}{\sqrt{5}-\sqrt{2}}$ **60.** $\dfrac{2}{\sqrt{3}+\sqrt{7}}$

61. $\dfrac{\sqrt{8}}{\sqrt{3}+1}$

62. $\dfrac{\sqrt{18}}{1-\sqrt{2}}$

63. $\dfrac{1}{\sqrt{x}-\sqrt{3}}$

64. $\dfrac{1}{\sqrt{y}+\sqrt{5}}$

65. $\dfrac{2-\sqrt{3}}{2+\sqrt{3}}$

66. $\dfrac{\sqrt{3}-\sqrt{2}}{\sqrt{3}+\sqrt{2}}$

67. $\dfrac{\sqrt{5}+4}{2-\sqrt{5}}$

68. $\dfrac{3+\sqrt{2}}{\sqrt{2}-5}$

Objective 5: Simplifying Quotients That Contain Radicals

For Exercises 69–76, simplify the expression. **(See Example 9.)**

69. $\dfrac{10-\sqrt{50}}{5}$

70. $\dfrac{4+\sqrt{12}}{2}$

71. $\dfrac{21+\sqrt{98}}{14}$

72. $\dfrac{3-\sqrt{18}}{6}$

73. $\dfrac{2-\sqrt{28}}{2}$

74. $\dfrac{5+\sqrt{75}}{5}$

75. $\dfrac{14+\sqrt{72}}{6}$

76. $\dfrac{15-\sqrt{125}}{10}$

Recall that a radical is simplified if

1. The radicand has no factor raised to a power greater than or equal to the index.

2. There are no radicals in the denominator of a fraction.

3. The radicand does not contain a fraction.

For Exercises 77–80, state which condition(s) fails. Then simplify the radical.

77. a. $\sqrt{8x^9}$

b. $\dfrac{5}{\sqrt{5x}}$

c. $\sqrt{\dfrac{1}{3}}$

78. a. $\sqrt{\dfrac{7}{2}}$

b. $\sqrt{18y^6}$

c. $\dfrac{2}{\sqrt{4x}}$

79. a. $\dfrac{3}{\sqrt{x}+1}$

b. $\sqrt{\dfrac{9w^2}{t}}$

c. $\sqrt{24a^5b^9}$

80. a. $\sqrt{\dfrac{12}{z^3}}$

b. $\dfrac{4}{\sqrt{a}-\sqrt{b}}$

c. $\sqrt[3]{27m^3n^7}$

Mixed Exercises

For Exercises 81–96, simplify the radical expressions, if possible. Assume the variables represent positive real numbers.

81. $\sqrt{45}$

82. $-\sqrt{108y^4}$

83. $-\sqrt{\dfrac{18w^2}{25}}$

84. $\sqrt{\dfrac{8a^2}{7}}$

85. $\sqrt{-36}$

86. $\sqrt{54b^5}$

87. $\sqrt{\dfrac{s^2}{t}}$

88. $\dfrac{x+\sqrt{y}}{x-\sqrt{y}}$

89. $\dfrac{\sqrt{2m^5}}{\sqrt{8m}}$

90. $\dfrac{\sqrt{10w}}{\sqrt{5w^3}}$

91. $\sqrt{\dfrac{81}{t^3}}$

92. $-\sqrt{a^3bc^6}$

93. $\dfrac{3}{\sqrt{11}+\sqrt{5}}$

94. $\dfrac{4}{\sqrt{10}+\sqrt{2}}$

95. $\dfrac{\sqrt{a}+\sqrt{b}}{\sqrt{a}-\sqrt{b}}$

96. $\dfrac{\sqrt{x}+1}{\sqrt{x}-1}$

Expanding Your Skills

97. Find the slope of the line through the points: $(5\sqrt{2}, 3)$ and $(\sqrt{2}, 6)$.

98. Find the slope of the line through the points: $(4\sqrt{5}, -1)$ and $(6\sqrt{5}, -5)$.

99. Find the slope of the line through the points: $(\sqrt{3}, -1)$ and $(4\sqrt{3}, 0)$.

100. Find the slope of the line through the points: $(-2\sqrt{7}, -5)$ and $(\sqrt{7}, 2)$.

Problem Recognition Exercises

Operations on Radicals

Perform the indicated operations and simplify if possible. Assume that all variables represent positive real numbers.

1. $(\sqrt{3})(\sqrt{6})$

2. $(\sqrt{2})(\sqrt{14})$

3. $\sqrt{3} + \sqrt{6}$

4. $\sqrt{2} + \sqrt{14}$

5. $\dfrac{\sqrt{6}}{\sqrt{3}}$

6. $\dfrac{\sqrt{14}}{\sqrt{2}}$

7. $(3 + \sqrt{z})(3 - \sqrt{z})$

8. $(4 - \sqrt{y})(4 + \sqrt{y})$

9. $(2\sqrt{5} + 1)(\sqrt{5} - 2)$

10. $(4\sqrt{3} - 5)(\sqrt{3} + 4)$

11. $2\sqrt{x^2 y} - 3x\sqrt{y}$

12. $8\sqrt{a^3 b^2} + 3a\sqrt{ab^2}$

13. $-3\sqrt{2}\,(4\sqrt{2} + 2\sqrt{3} + 1)$

14. $-8\sqrt{5}\,(2\sqrt{5} - \sqrt{3} - 2)$

15. $\dfrac{2}{\sqrt{x} - 7}$

16. $\dfrac{5}{\sqrt{y} + 4}$

17. $\dfrac{9}{\sqrt{3}}$

18. $\dfrac{15}{\sqrt{5}}$

19. $\sqrt{\dfrac{7}{x}}$

20. $\sqrt{\dfrac{11}{y}}$

21. $\sqrt{y^4 z^{11}}$

22. $\sqrt{8q^6}$

23. $\sqrt[3]{27p^8}$

24. $\sqrt[3]{125u^{11} v^{12}}$

25. $\dfrac{\sqrt{10x^3}}{\sqrt{x}}$

26. $\dfrac{\sqrt{15y^3}}{\sqrt{5y}}$

27. $6\sqrt{75} - 5\sqrt{12}$

28. $\sqrt{90} - \sqrt{40}$

29. $(\sqrt{2} + 7)^2$

30. $(\sqrt{3} + \sqrt{5})^2$

31. $\dfrac{x - 5}{\sqrt{x} + \sqrt{5}}$

32. $\dfrac{y - 7}{\sqrt{y} + \sqrt{7}}$

33. $(4\sqrt{x} + \sqrt{y})(\sqrt{x} - 3\sqrt{y})$

34. $\sqrt[4]{\dfrac{1}{81}}$

35. $\sqrt[3]{\dfrac{125}{27}}$

36. $(\sqrt{5} - \sqrt{11})^2$

37. $(\sqrt{x} - 6)^2$

38. $2\sqrt{6} - 5\sqrt{6}$

39. $5\sqrt{a} + 7\sqrt{a} - \sqrt{a}$

40. $(2\sqrt{3} - 10)(2\sqrt{3} + 10)$

41. $(\sqrt{u} - 3\sqrt{v})(\sqrt{u} + 3\sqrt{v})$

42. $x\sqrt{18} + \sqrt{2x^2}$

43. $4\sqrt{75} - 20\sqrt{3}$

44. $\sqrt{5}(\sqrt{5} + \sqrt{7})$

45. $\sqrt{a}(\sqrt{a} + 2)$

46. $(3\sqrt{2} - 4)(5\sqrt{2} + 1)$

Section 15.6 Radical Equations

1. Solving Radical Equations

DEFINITION Radical Equation

An equation with one or more radicals containing a variable is called a **radical equation.**

For example, $\sqrt{x} = 5$ is a radical equation. Recall that $(\sqrt[n]{a})^n = a$ provided $\sqrt[n]{a}$ is a real number. The basis to solve a radical equation is to eliminate the radical by raising both sides of the equation to a power equal to the index of the radical.

To solve the equation $\sqrt{x} = 5$, square both sides of the equation.

$$\sqrt{x} = 5$$

$$(\sqrt{x})^2 = (5)^2$$

$$x = 25$$

By raising each side of a radical equation to a power equal to the index of the radical, a new equation is produced. However, it is important to note that the new equation may have **extraneous solutions**; that is, some or all of the solutions to the new equation may *not* be solutions to the original radical equation. For this reason, it is necessary to check *all* potential solutions in the original equation. For example, consider the equation $x = 4$. By squaring both sides we produce a quadratic equation.

Square both sides. $x = 4$

$(x)^2 = (4)^2$ Squaring both sides produces a quadratic equation.

$x^2 = 16$

$x^2 - 16 = 0$

$(x - 4)(x + 4) = 0$ Solving this equation, we find two solutions. However, $x = -4$ does not check. The value

$x = 4$ or $x = -4$ -4 is an extraneous solution because it is not a solution to the original equation, $x = 4$.

PROCEDURE Solving a Radical Equation

Step 1 Isolate the radical. If an equation has more than one radical, choose one of the radicals to isolate.

Step 2 Raise each side of the equation to a power equal to the index of the radical.

Step 3 Solve the resulting equation.

Step 4 Check the potential solutions in the original equation.*

*Extraneous solutions can only arise when both sides of the equation are raised to an *even power*. Therefore, an equation with odd-index roots will not have an extraneous solution. However, it is still recommended that you check *all* potential solutions regardless of the type of root.

Example 1   **Solving a Radical Equation**

Solve the equation. $\sqrt{2x+1} + 5 = 8$

Solution:

$$\sqrt{2x+1} + 5 = 8$$

$\sqrt{2x+1} = 8 - 5$	Isolate the radical.
$\sqrt{2x+1} = 3$	
$(\sqrt{2x+1})^2 = (3)^2$	Raise both sides to a power equal to the index of the radical.
$2x + 1 = 9$	Simplify both sides.
$2x = 8$	Solve the resulting equation. (The equation is linear.)
$x = 4$	

<u>Check:</u>   Check 4 as a potential solution.

$$\sqrt{2x+1} + 5 = 8$$
$$\sqrt{2(4)+1} + 5 \stackrel{?}{=} 8$$
$$\sqrt{8+1} + 5 \stackrel{?}{=} 8$$
$$\sqrt{9} + 5 \stackrel{?}{=} 8$$
$$3 + 5 \stackrel{?}{=} 8 \ ✔ \quad \text{The answer checks.}$$

The solution is 4.

Skill Practice

Solve the equation.
1. $\sqrt{p-4} - 2 = 4$

Example 2   **Solving a Radical Equation**

Solve the equation. $8 + \sqrt{x+2} = 7$

Solution:

$$8 + \sqrt{x+2} = 7$$

$\sqrt{x+2} = 7 - 8$	Isolate the radical.
$\sqrt{x+2} = -1$	
$(\sqrt{x+2})^2 = (-1)^2$	Raise both sides to a power equal to the index of the radical.
$x + 2 = 1$	Simplify.
$x = -1$	Solve the resulting equation.

<u>Check:</u>   Check -1 as a potential solution.

$$8 + \sqrt{x+2} = 7$$
$$8 + \sqrt{(-1)+2} \stackrel{?}{=} 7$$
$$8 + \sqrt{1} \stackrel{?}{=} 7$$
$$8 + 1 \neq 7 \quad \text{The value } -1 \text{ does not check. It is an extraneous solution.}$$

There is no solution to the equation.

Skill Practice

Solve the equation.
2. $\sqrt{2y+5} + 7 = 4$

TIP: After isolating the radical in Example 2, the equation shows a square root equated to a negative number.

$$\sqrt{x+2} = -1$$

By definition, a principal square root of any real number must be nonnegative. Therefore, there can be no solution to this equation.

Answers
1. 40
2. No solution; (The value 2 does not check.)

Example 3 Solving a Radical Equation

Solve the equation. $p + 4 = \sqrt{p + 6}$

Solution:

$p + 4 = \sqrt{p + 6}$	The radical is already isolated.
$(p + 4)^2 = (\sqrt{p + 6})^2$	Raise both sides to a power equal to the index.
$p^2 + 8p + 16 = p + 6$	
$p^2 + 7p + 10 = 0$	Solve the resulting equation. (The equation is quadratic).
$(p + 5)(p + 2) = 0$	Set the equation equal to zero and factor.

$p + 5 = 0$	or	$p + 2 = 0$	Set each factor equal to zero.
$p = -5$	or	$p = -2$	Solve for p.

Check: $p = -5$ Check: $p = -2$

$p + 4 = \sqrt{p + 6}$ $p + 4 = \sqrt{p + 6}$

$(-5) + 4 \stackrel{?}{=} \sqrt{(-5) + 6}$ $(-2) + 4 \stackrel{?}{=} \sqrt{(-2) + 6}$

$-1 \stackrel{?}{=} \sqrt{1}$ $2 \stackrel{?}{=} \sqrt{4}$

$-1 \neq 1$ Does not check. $2 \stackrel{?}{=} 2$ ✔ The solution checks.

The only solution is -2. (The value -5 does not check).

Example 4 Solving a Radical Equation

Solve the equation. $2\sqrt[3]{2x - 3} - \sqrt[3]{x + 6} = 0$

Solution:

$2\sqrt[3]{2x - 3} - \sqrt[3]{x + 6} = 0$

$2\sqrt[3]{2x - 3} = \sqrt[3]{x + 6}$	Isolate one of the radicals.
$\left(2\sqrt[3]{2x - 3}\right)^3 = \left(\sqrt[3]{x + 6}\right)^3$	Raise both sides to a power equal to the index.
$(2)^3\left(\sqrt[3]{2x - 3}\right)^3 = \left(\sqrt[3]{x + 6}\right)^3$	On the left-hand side, be sure to cube both factors, $(2)^3$ and $\left(\sqrt[3]{2x - 3}\right)^3$.
$8(2x - 3) = x + 6$	Solve the resulting equation.
$16x - 24 = x + 6$	
$15x = 30$	
$x = 2$	

Check:

$2\sqrt[3]{2x - 3} - \sqrt[3]{x + 6} = 0$ Check the potential solution, 2.

$2\sqrt[3]{2(2) - 3} - \sqrt[3]{2 + 6} \stackrel{?}{=} 0$

$2\sqrt[3]{4 - 3} - \sqrt[3]{8} \stackrel{?}{=} 0$

$2\sqrt[3]{1} - 2 \stackrel{?}{=} 0$

$2 - 2 \stackrel{?}{=} 0$ ✔   The solution checks.

The solution is 2.

2. Translations Involving Radical Equations

Example 5 Translating English Form into Algebraic Form

The principal square root of the sum of a number and three is equal to seven. Find the number.

Solution:

Let x represent the number.   Label the variable.

$$\sqrt{x + 3} = 7$$ Translate the verbal model into an algebraic equation.

$$(\sqrt{x + 3})^2 = (7)^2$$ The radical is already isolated. Square both sides.

$$x + 3 = 49$$ The resulting equation is linear.

$$x = 46$$ Solve for x.

<u>Check:</u> Check 46 as a potential solution.

$$\sqrt{x + 3} = 7$$

$$\sqrt{46 + 3} \stackrel{?}{=} 7$$

$$\sqrt{49} \stackrel{?}{=} 7$$

$$7 \stackrel{?}{=} 7 \checkmark$$ The solution checks.

The number is 46.

Skill Practice

5. The principal square root of the sum of a number and 5 is 2. Find the number.

3. Applications of Radical Equations

Example 6 Using a Radical Equation in an Application

For a small company, the weekly sales, y, of its product are related to the money spent on advertising, x, according to the equation:

$$y = 100\sqrt{x}$$

a. Find the amount in sales if the company spends \$100 on advertising.

b. Find the amount in sales if the company spends \$625 on advertising.

c. Find the amount the company spent on advertising if its sales for 1 week totaled \$2000.

Solution:

a. $y = 100\sqrt{x}$

$= 100\sqrt{100}$ Substitute $x = 100$.

$= 100(10)$

$= 1000$

The amount in sales is \$1000.

Skill Practice

6. If the small company mentioned in Example 6 changes its advertising media, the equation relating money spent on advertising, x, to weekly sales, y, is $y = 100\sqrt{2x}$.
  a. Use the given equation to find the amount in sales if the company spends \$200 on advertising.
  b. Find the amount spent on advertising if the sales for 1 week totaled \$3000.

Answers
5. The number is −1.
6. **a.** \$2000   **b.** \$450

b. $y = 100\sqrt{x}$

$\quad\quad = 100\sqrt{625}$ Substitute $x = 625$.

$\quad\quad = 100(25)$

$\quad\quad = 2500$

The amount in sales is $2500.

c. $y = 100\sqrt{x}$

$\quad 2000 = 100\sqrt{x}$ Substitute $y = 2000$.

$\quad \dfrac{2000}{100} = \dfrac{\cancel{100}\sqrt{x}}{\cancel{100}}$ Isolate the radical. Divide both sides by 100.

$\quad\quad 20 = \sqrt{x}$ Simplify.

$\quad (20)^2 = (\sqrt{x})^2$ Raise both sides to a power equal to the index.

$\quad\quad 400 = x$ Simplify both sides.

$\quad \underline{\text{Check:}}$ Check 400 as a potential solution.

$\quad\quad y = 100\sqrt{x}$

$\quad 2000 \overset{?}{=} 100\sqrt{400}$

$\quad 2000 \overset{?}{=} 100(20)$

$\quad 2000 \overset{?}{=} 2000\ \checkmark$ The solution checks.

The amount spent on advertising was $400.

Section 15.6 Practice Exercises

Boost *your* GRADE at
ALEKS.com!

 ALEKS
version 3.0

- Practice Problems
- Self-Tests
- NetTutor

- e-Professors
- Videos

Study Skills Exercise

1. Define the key terms:

    a. Radical equation   **b. Extraneous solution**

Review Exercises

For Exercises 2–5, rationalize the denominators.

2. $\dfrac{1}{\sqrt{3} - \sqrt{7}}$ **3.** $\dfrac{1}{\sqrt{2} + \sqrt{10}}$ **4.** $\dfrac{6}{\sqrt{6}}$ **5.** $\dfrac{2\sqrt{2}}{\sqrt{3}}$

6. Simplify the expression. $\dfrac{10 - \sqrt{75}}{5}$

For Exercises 7–10, square the binomials.

7. $(x + 4)^2$ **8.** $(3 - y)^2$ **9.** $(\sqrt{x} + 4)^2$ **10.** $(\sqrt{3} - \sqrt{y})^2$

For Exercises 11–14, simplify the expressions. Assume the variable expressions represent positive real numbers.

11. $(\sqrt{2x-3})^2$ **12.** $(\sqrt{m+6})^2$ **13.** $(t+1)^2$ **14.** $(y-4)^2$

Objective 1: Solving Radical Equations

For Exercises 15–47, solve the equations. Be sure to check all of the potential answers. **(See Examples 1–4.)**

15. $\sqrt{t}=6$ **16.** $\sqrt{p}=5$ **17.** $\sqrt{x+1}=4$

18. $\sqrt{x-3}=7$ **19.** $\sqrt{y-4}=-5$ **20.** $\sqrt{p+6}=-1$

21. $\sqrt{5-t}=0$ **22.** $\sqrt{13+m}=0$ **23.** $\sqrt{2n+10}=3$

24. $\sqrt{1-q}=15$ **25.** $\sqrt{6w}-8=-2$ **26.** $\sqrt{2z}-11=-3$

27. $\sqrt{5a-4}-2=4$ **28.** $\sqrt{3b+4}-3=2$ **29.** $\sqrt{2x-3}+7=3$

30. $\sqrt{8y+1}+5=1$ **31.** $5\sqrt{c}=\sqrt{10c+15}$ **32.** $4\sqrt{x}=\sqrt{10x+6}$

33. $\sqrt{x^2-x}=\sqrt{12}$ **34.** $\sqrt{x^2+5x}=\sqrt{150}$ **35.** $\sqrt{9y^2-8y+1}=3y+1$

36. $\sqrt{4x^2+2x+20}=2x$ **37.** $\sqrt{x^2+4x+16}=x$ **38.** $\sqrt{x^2+3x-2}=4$

39. $\sqrt{2k^2-3k-4}=k$ **40.** $\sqrt{6t+7}=t+2$ **41.** $\sqrt{y+1}=y+1$

42. $\sqrt{3p+3}+5=p$ **43.** $\sqrt{2m+1}+7=m$ **44.** $\sqrt[3]{3y+7}=\sqrt[3]{2y-1}$

45. $\sqrt[3]{p-5}-\sqrt[3]{2p+1}=0$ **46.** $\sqrt[3]{2x-8}-\sqrt[3]{-x+1}=0$ **47.** $\sqrt[3]{a-3}=\sqrt[3]{5a+1}$

Objective 2: Translations Involving Radical Equations

For Exercises 48–53, translate the English sentence to a radical equation and solve the equation. **(See Example 5.)**

48. The square root of the sum of a number and 8 equals 12. Find the number.

49. The square root of the sum of a number and 10 equals 1. Find the number.

50. The square root of a number is 2 less than the number. Find the number.

51. The square root of twice a number is 4 less than the number. Find the number.

52. The cube root of the sum of a number and 4 is −5. Find the number.

53. The cube root of the sum of a number and 1 is 2. Find the number.

Objective 3: Applications of Radical Equations

54. Ignoring air resistance, the time, t (in seconds), required for an object to fall x feet is given by the equation:

$$t=\frac{\sqrt{x}}{4}$$

a. Find the time required for an object to fall 64 ft.

b. Find the distance an object will fall in 4 sec.

55. Ignoring air resistance, the velocity, v (in feet per second: ft/sec), of an object in free fall depends on the distance it has fallen, x (in feet), according to the equation:

$$v=8\sqrt{x}$$

a. Find the velocity of an object that has fallen 100 ft.

b. Find the distance that an object has fallen if its velocity is 136 ft/sec. **(See Example 6.)**

56. The speed of a car, s (in miles per hour), before the brakes were applied can be approximated by the length of its skid marks, x (in feet), according to the equation:

$$s = 4\sqrt{x}$$

a. Find the speed of a car before the brakes were applied if its skid marks are 324 ft long.

b. How long would you expect the skid marks to be if the car had been traveling the speed limit of 60 mph?

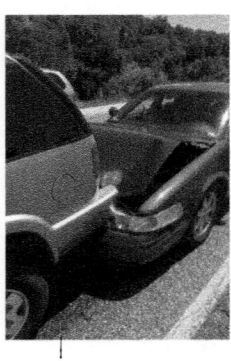

57. The height of a sunflower plant, y (in inches), can be determined by the time, t (in weeks), after the seed has germinated according to the equation:

$$y = 8\sqrt{t} \quad 0 \le t \le 40$$

a. Find the height of the plant after 4 weeks.

b. In how many weeks will the plant be 40 in. tall?

Expanding Your Skills

For Exercises 58–61, solve the equations. First isolate one of the radical terms. Then square both sides. The resulting equation will still have a radical. Repeat the process by isolating the radical and squaring both sides again.

58. $\sqrt{t + 8} = \sqrt{t} + 2$

59. $\sqrt{5x - 9} = \sqrt{5x} - 3$

60. $\sqrt{z + 1} + \sqrt{2z + 3} = 1$

61. $\sqrt{2m + 6} = 1 + \sqrt{7 - 2m}$

Group Activity

Approximating Square Roots

Materials: A calculator

Estimated Time: 15 minutes

Group Size: 2

Suppose that n represents a positive real number that is *not* a perfect square. To approximate $\sqrt{n}$, we will make repeated use of the formula:

$$\sqrt{n} \approx \frac{1}{2}\left(x + \frac{n}{x}\right) \quad \text{where } x \text{ is an approximation of the square root of } n.$$

We will outline the steps to use this formula and demonstrate by approximating $\sqrt{8}$.

Step 1: Begin by letting x be the nonzero whole number that is closest to the square root of n.

Step 1: To approximate $\sqrt{8}$ we begin with $x = 3$, because 3 is equal to $\sqrt{9}$ which is close to $\sqrt{8}$.

Step 2: Substitute the starting value of x and the value of n into the formula.

Step 2: $\sqrt{n} \approx \frac{1}{2}\left(x + \frac{n}{x}\right)$

$$\sqrt{8} \approx \frac{1}{2}\left(3 + \frac{8}{3}\right)$$

$$\approx 2.83333333333$$

Step 3: Replace x by the answer obtained in step 2. Then apply the formula again, using the new value of x.

Step 3: New value of $x = 2.8\overline{3}$

$$\sqrt{8} \approx \frac{1}{2}\left(2.8\overline{3} + \frac{8}{2.8\overline{3}}\right)$$

$$\approx 2.828431373$$

Step 4: Repeatedly apply step 3, each time using the new value of x from the previous step. You can repeat this process until two consecutive answers differ by less than the desired level of accuracy you want.

TIP: You can check to determine if your answer is reasonable by squaring the result.

$$(2.828431373)^2 \approx 8.000024029$$

1. Use the process outlined to approximate $\sqrt{28}$ accurate to 0.0001.

2. Use the process outlined to approximate $\sqrt{104}$ accurate to 0.00001.

Chapter 15   Summary

Section 15.1   Introduction to Roots and Radicals

Key Concepts	Examples

Key Concepts

b is a **square root** of a if $b^2 = a$.

The expression $\sqrt{a}$ represents the **principal square root** of a.

b is an nth-root of a if $b^n = a$.

1. If n is a positive *even* integer and $a > 0$, then $\sqrt[n]{a}$ is the principal (positive) nth-root of a.
2. If $n > 1$ is a positive *odd* integer, then $\sqrt[n]{a}$ is the nth-root of a.
3. If $n > 1$ is any positive integer, then $\sqrt[n]{0} = 0$.

$\sqrt[n]{a^n} = |a|$ if n is even.

$\sqrt[n]{a^n} = a$ if n is odd.

$\sqrt[n]{a}$ is not a real number if a is *negative* and n is even.

Pythagorean Theorem

$a^2 + b^2 = c^2$

Examples

Example 1

The square roots of 16 are 4 and -4 because $(4)^2 = 16$ and $(-4)^2 = 16$.

$\sqrt{16} = 4$ Because $4^2 = 16$

$\sqrt[4]{16} = 2$ Because $2^4 = 16$

$\sqrt[3]{125} = 5$ Because $5^3 = 125$

Example 2

$\sqrt{y^2} = |y|$ $\sqrt[3]{y^3} = y$ $\sqrt[4]{y^4} = |y|$

Example 3

$\sqrt[4]{-16}$ is not a real number.

Example 4

Find the length of the unknown side.

$$a^2 + b^2 = c^2$$
$$(8)^2 + b^2 = (17)^2$$
$$64 + b^2 = 289$$
$$b^2 = 289 - 64$$
$$b^2 = 225$$
$$b = \sqrt{225}$$
$$b = 15$$

Because b denotes a length, b must be the positive square root of 225.

b $c = 17$ cm

$a = 8$ cm

The third side is 15 cm.

Section 15.2 Simplifying Radicals

Key Concepts

Multiplication Property of Radicals

If $\sqrt[n]{a}$ and $\sqrt[n]{b}$ are both real, then

$$\sqrt[n]{ab} = \sqrt[n]{a} \cdot \sqrt[n]{b}$$

Simplifying Radicals

Consider a radical expression whose radicand is written as a product of prime factors. Then the radical is in simplified form if each of the following criteria are met:

1. The radicand has no factor raised to a power greater than or equal to the index.
2. There are no radicals in the denominator of a fraction.
3. The radicand does not contain a fraction.

Examples

Example 1

$$\sqrt{3} \cdot \sqrt{5} = \sqrt{3 \cdot 5} = \sqrt{15}$$

Example 2

$$\sqrt{\frac{b^7}{b^3}} = \sqrt{b^4} = b^2$$

Example 3

$$\sqrt[3]{16x^5y^7} = \sqrt[3]{2^4x^5y^7}$$
$$= \sqrt[3]{2^3x^3y^6 \cdot 2x^2y}$$
$$= \sqrt[3]{2^3x^3y^6} \cdot \sqrt[3]{2x^2y}$$
$$= 2xy^2\sqrt[3]{2x^2y}$$

Section 15.3 Addition and Subtraction of Radicals

Key Concepts

Two radical terms are *like* radicals if they have the same index and the same radicand.

Use the distributive property to add or subtract *like* radicals.

Examples

Example 1

Like radicals. $\sqrt[3]{5z}, \quad 6\sqrt[3]{5z}$

Example 2

$$3\sqrt{7} - 10\sqrt{7} + \sqrt{7}$$
$$= (3 - 10 + 1)\sqrt{7}$$
$$= -6\sqrt{7}$$

Section 15.4 Multiplication of Radicals

Key Concepts

Multiplication Property of Radicals

$\sqrt[n]{a} \cdot \sqrt[n]{b} = \sqrt[n]{ab}$ provided $\sqrt[n]{a}$ and $\sqrt[n]{b}$ are both real.

Examples

Example 1

$(6\sqrt{5})(4\sqrt{3}) = 6 \cdot 4\sqrt{5 \cdot 3}$
$$= 24\sqrt{15}$$

Example 2

$3\sqrt{2}(\sqrt{2} + 5\sqrt{7} - \sqrt{6}) = 3\sqrt{4} + 15\sqrt{14} - 3\sqrt{12}$
$$= 3\sqrt{2^2} + 15\sqrt{14} - 3\sqrt{2^2 \cdot 3}$$
$$= 3 \cdot 2 + 15\sqrt{14} - 3 \cdot 2\sqrt{3}$$
$$= 6 + 15\sqrt{14} - 6\sqrt{3}$$

Special Case Products

$(a + b)(a - b) = a^2 - b^2$

$(a + b)^2 = a^2 + 2ab + b^2$

$(a - b)^2 = a^2 - 2ab + b^2$

Example 3

$(4\sqrt{x} + \sqrt{2})(4\sqrt{x} - \sqrt{2}) = (4\sqrt{x})^2 - (\sqrt{2})^2$
$$= 16x - 2$$

Example 4

$(\sqrt{x} - \sqrt{5y})^2 = (\sqrt{x})^2 - 2(\sqrt{x})(\sqrt{5y}) + (\sqrt{5y})^2$
$$= x - 2\sqrt{5xy} + 5y$$

Section 15.5 Division of Radicals and Rationalization

Key Concepts

Division Property of Radicals

If $\sqrt[n]{a}$ and $\sqrt[n]{b}$ are both real, then

$\sqrt[n]{\dfrac{a}{b}} = \dfrac{\sqrt[n]{a}}{\sqrt[n]{b}}$ $b \neq 0$

Rationalizing the Denominator with One Term

Multiply the numerator and denominator by an appropriate expression to create an nth-root of an nth-power in the denominator.

Rationalizing a Two-Term Denominator Involving Square Roots

Multiply the numerator and denominator by the conjugate of the denominator.

Examples

Example 1

$\dfrac{\sqrt{x^{11}}}{\sqrt{x^3}} = \sqrt{\dfrac{x^{11}}{x^3}} = \sqrt{x^8} = x^4$

Example 2

$\dfrac{10}{\sqrt{5}} = \dfrac{10}{\sqrt{5}} \cdot \dfrac{\sqrt{5}}{\sqrt{5}} = \dfrac{10\sqrt{5}}{\sqrt{5^2}} = \dfrac{10\sqrt{5}}{5} = 2\sqrt{5}$

Example 3

$\dfrac{\sqrt{2}}{\sqrt{x} - \sqrt{3}} = \dfrac{\sqrt{2}}{(\sqrt{x} - \sqrt{3})} \cdot \dfrac{(\sqrt{x} + \sqrt{3})}{(\sqrt{x} + \sqrt{3})}$
$$= \dfrac{\sqrt{2x} + \sqrt{6}}{x - 3}$$

Section 15.6   Radical Equations

Key Concepts

An equation with one or more radicals containing a variable is a **radical equation**.

Steps for Solving a Radical Equation

1. Isolate the radical. If an equation has more than one radical, choose one of the radicals to isolate.
2. Raise each side of the equation to a power equal to the index of the radical.
3. Solve the resulting equation.
4. Check the potential solutions in the original equation.

Note: Raising both sides of an equation to an even power may result in extraneous solutions.

Examples

Example 1

Solve. $\sqrt{2x - 4} + 3 = 7$

Step 1: $\qquad \sqrt{2x - 4} = 4$

Step 2: $\quad (\sqrt{2x - 4})^2 = (4)^2$

Step 3: $\qquad\qquad 2x - 4 = 16$

$\qquad\qquad\qquad\qquad 2x = 20$

$\qquad\qquad\qquad\qquad\; x = 10$

Step 4:

Check:

$$\sqrt{2x - 4} + 3 = 7$$

$$\sqrt{2(10) - 4} + 3 \stackrel{?}{=} 7$$

$$\sqrt{20 - 4} + 3 \stackrel{?}{=} 7$$

$$\sqrt{16} + 3 \stackrel{?}{=} 7$$

$$4 + 3 \stackrel{?}{=} 7 \; ✔ \qquad \text{The solution checks.}$$

The solution is 10.

Chapter 15   Review Exercises

Section 15.1

For Exercises 1–4, state the principal square root and the negative square root.

1. 196   **2.** 1.44

3. 0.64   **4.** 225

5. Explain why $\sqrt{-64}$ is *not* a real number.

6. Explain why $\sqrt[3]{-64}$ *is* a real number.

For Exercises 7–18, simplify the expressions, if possible.

7. $-\sqrt{144}$ **8.** $-\sqrt{25}$ **9.** $\sqrt{-144}$

10. $\sqrt{-25}$ **11.** $\sqrt{y^2}$ **12.** $\sqrt[3]{y^3}$

13. $\sqrt[4]{y^4}$ **14.** $-\sqrt[3]{125}$ **15.** $-\sqrt[4]{625}$

16. $\sqrt[3]{p^{12}}$ **17.** $\sqrt[4]{\dfrac{81}{t^8}}$ **18.** $\sqrt[3]{\dfrac{-27}{w^3}}$

19. The radius, r, of a circle can be found from the area of the circle according to the formula:

$$r = \sqrt{\dfrac{A}{\pi}}$$

    a. What is the radius of a circular garden whose area is 160 m²? Round to the nearest tenth of a meter.

    b. What is the radius of a circular fountain whose area is 1600 ft²? Round to the nearest tenth of a foot.

20. Suppose a ball is thrown with an initial velocity of 76 ft/sec at an angle of 30° (see figure). Then the horizontal position of the ball, x (measured in feet), depends on the number of seconds, t, after the ball is thrown according to the equation:

$$x = 38\sqrt{3}t$$

a. What is the horizontal position of the ball after 1 sec? Round your answer to the nearest tenth of a foot.

b. What is the horizontal position of the ball after 2 sec? Round your answer to the nearest tenth of a foot.

For Exercises 21–22, translate the English phrases into algebraic expressions.

21. The square of b plus the principal square root of 5.

22. The difference of the cube root of y and the fourth root of x.

For Exercises 23–24, translate the algebraic expressions into English phrases. (Answers may vary.)

23. $\dfrac{2}{\sqrt{p}}$

24. $8\sqrt{q}$

25. A hedge extends 5 ft from the wall of a house. A 13-ft ladder is placed at the edge of the hedge. How far up the house is the tip of the ladder?

13 ft   ?

5 ft

26. Nashville, TN, is north of Birmingham, Alabama, a distance of 182 miles. Augusta, Georgia, is east of Birmingham, a distance of 277 miles. How far is it from Augusta to Nashville? Round the answer to the nearest mile.

Nashville

182 miles

Birmingham   277 miles   Augusta

Section 15.2

For Exercises 27–32, use the multiplication property of radicals to simplify. Assume the variables represent positive real numbers.

27. $\sqrt{x^{17}}$ **28.** $\sqrt[3]{40}$ **29.** $\sqrt{28}$

30. $5\sqrt{18x^3}$ **31.** $\sqrt[3]{27y^{10}}$ **32.** $2\sqrt{27y^{10}}$

For Exercises 33–42, use order of operations to simplify. Assume the variables represent positive real numbers.

33. $\sqrt{\dfrac{c^5}{c^3}}$ **34.** $\sqrt{\dfrac{t^9}{t^3}}$

35. $\sqrt{\dfrac{200y^5}{2y}}$ **36.** $\sqrt{\dfrac{18x^3}{2x}}$

37. $\sqrt[3]{\dfrac{48x^4}{6x}}$ **38.** $\sqrt[3]{\dfrac{128a^{17}}{2a^2}}$

39. $\dfrac{5\sqrt{12}}{2}$ **40.** $\dfrac{2\sqrt{45}}{6}$

41. $\dfrac{12 - \sqrt{49}}{5}$ **42.** $\dfrac{20 + \sqrt{100}}{5}$

Section 15.3

For Exercises 43–48, add or subtract as indicated. Assume the variables represent positive real numbers.

43. $8\sqrt{6} - \sqrt{6}$

44. $1.6\sqrt{y} - 1.4\sqrt{y} + 0.6\sqrt{y}$

45. $x\sqrt{20} - 2\sqrt{45x^2}$

46. $y\sqrt{64y} + 3\sqrt{y^3}$

47. $3\sqrt{75} - 4\sqrt{28} + \sqrt{7}$

48. $2\sqrt{50} - 4\sqrt{20} - 6\sqrt{2}$

For Exercises 49–50, translate the English phrases into algebraic expressions and simplify.

49. The sum of the principal square root of the fourth power of x and the square of $5x$.

50. The difference of the principal square root of 128 and the square root of 2.

51. Find the exact perimeter of the triangle.

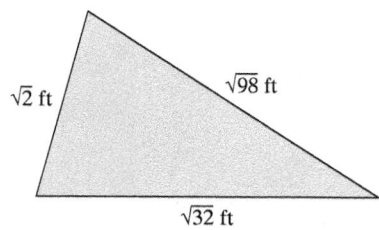

$\sqrt{2}$ ft

$\sqrt{98}$ ft

$\sqrt{32}$ ft

52. Find the exact perimeter of a square whose sides are $3\sqrt{48}$ m.

Section 15.4

For Exercises 53–62, multiply the expressions. Assume the variables represent positive real numbers.

53. $\sqrt{5} \cdot \sqrt{125}$

54. $\sqrt{10p} \cdot \sqrt{6}$

55. $(5\sqrt{6})(7\sqrt{2x})$

56. $(3\sqrt{y})(-2z\sqrt{11y})$

57. $8\sqrt{m}(\sqrt{m} + 3)$

58. $\sqrt{2}(\sqrt{7} + 8)$

59. $(5\sqrt{2} + \sqrt{13})(-\sqrt{2} - 3\sqrt{13})$

60. $(\sqrt{p} + 2\sqrt{q})(4\sqrt{p} - \sqrt{q})$

61. $(8\sqrt{w} - \sqrt{z})(8\sqrt{w} + \sqrt{z})$

62. $(2x - \sqrt{y})^2$

63. Find the exact volume of the box.

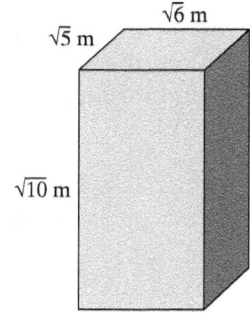

$\sqrt{6}$ m

$\sqrt{5}$ m

$\sqrt{10}$ m

Section 15.5

For Exercises 64–67, use the division property of radicals to write the radicals in simplified form. Assume all variables are positive real numbers.

64. $\dfrac{\sqrt[3]{x^7}}{\sqrt[3]{x^4}}$

65. $\dfrac{\sqrt{a^{11}}}{\sqrt{a}}$

66. $\dfrac{\sqrt{250c}}{\sqrt{10}}$

67. $\dfrac{\sqrt{96y^3}}{\sqrt{6y^2}}$

68. To rationalize the denominator in the expression

$$\frac{6}{\sqrt{a} + 5}$$

which quantity would you multiply by in the numerator and denominator?

a. $\sqrt{a} + 5$ **b.** $\sqrt{a} - 5$ **c.** $\sqrt{a}$ **d.** -5

69. To rationalize the denominator in the expression

$$\frac{w}{\sqrt{w} - 4}$$

which quantity would you multiply by in the numerator and denominator?

a. $\sqrt{w} - 4$

b. $\sqrt{w} + 4$

c. $\sqrt{w}$

d. 4

For Exercises 70–75, rationalize the denominators. Assume the variables represent positive real numbers.

70. $\dfrac{11}{\sqrt{7}}$

71. $\sqrt{\dfrac{18}{y}}$

72. $\dfrac{\sqrt{24}}{\sqrt{6x^7}}$

73. $\dfrac{10}{\sqrt{7} - \sqrt{2}}$

74. $\dfrac{6}{\sqrt{w} + 2}$

75. $\dfrac{\sqrt{7} + 3}{\sqrt{7} - 3}$

76. The velocity of an object, v (in meters per second: m/sec) depends on the kinetic energy, E (in joules: J), and mass, m (in kilograms: kg), of the object according to the formula:

$$v = \sqrt{\frac{2E}{m}}$$

a. What is the exact velocity of a 3-kg object whose kinetic energy is 100 J?

b. What is the exact velocity of a 5-kg object whose kinetic energy is 162 J?

Section 15.6

For Exercises 77–85, solve the equations. Be sure to check the potential solutions.

77. $\sqrt{p + 6} = 12$

78. $\sqrt{k + 1} = -7$

79. $\sqrt{3x - 17} - 10 = 0$

80. $\sqrt{14n + 10} = 4\sqrt{n}$

81. $\sqrt{2z + 2} = \sqrt{3z - 5}$

82. $\sqrt{5y - 5} - \sqrt{4y + 1} = 0$

83. $\sqrt{2m + 5} = m + 1$

84. $\sqrt{3n - 8} - n + 2 = 0$

85. $\sqrt[3]{2y + 13} = -5$

86. The length of the sides of a cube is related to the volume of the cube according to the formula: $x = \sqrt[3]{V}$.

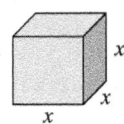

a. What is the volume of the cube if the side length is 21 in.?

b. What is the volume of the cube if the side length is 15 cm?

Chapter 15   Test

1. State the conditions for a radical expression to be in simplified form.

For Exercises 2–7, simplify the radicals, if possible. Assume the variables represent positive real numbers.

2. $\sqrt{242x^2}$ **3.** $\sqrt[3]{48y^4}$ **4.** $\sqrt{-64}$

5. $\sqrt{\dfrac{5a^6}{81}}$ **6.** $\dfrac{9}{\sqrt{6}}$ **7.** $\dfrac{2}{\sqrt{5}+6}$

8. Translate the English phrases into algebraic expressions and simplify.

a. The sum of the principal square root of twenty-five and the cube of five.

b. The difference of the square of four and the principal square root of 16.

9. A baseball player hits the ball at an angle of 30° with an initial velocity of 112 ft/sec. The horizontal position of the ball, x (measured in feet), depends on the number of seconds, t, after the ball is struck according to the equation

$$x = 56\sqrt{3}t$$

a. What is the horizontal position of the ball after 1 sec? Round the answer to the nearest foot.

b. What is the horizontal position of the ball after 3.5 sec? Round the answer to the nearest foot.

For Exercises 10–19, perform the indicated operations. Assume the variables represent positive real numbers.

10. $6\sqrt{z} - 3\sqrt{z} + 5\sqrt{z}$

11. $\sqrt{3}(4\sqrt{2} - 5\sqrt{3})$

12. $\sqrt{50t^2} - t\sqrt{288}$

13. $\sqrt{360} + \sqrt{250} - \sqrt{40}$

14. $(3\sqrt{5} - 1)^2$

15. $(6\sqrt{2} - \sqrt{5})(\sqrt{2} + 4\sqrt{5})$ **16.** $\dfrac{\sqrt{2m^3n}}{\sqrt{72m^5}}$

17. $(4 - 3\sqrt{x})(4 + 3\sqrt{x})$ **18.** $\sqrt{\dfrac{2}{11}}$

19. $\dfrac{6}{\sqrt{7} - \sqrt{3}}$

20. A triathlon consists of a swim, followed by a bike ride, followed by a run. The swim begins on a beach at point A. The swimmers must swim 50 yd to a buoy at point B, then 200 yd to a buoy at point C, and then return to point A on the beach. How far is the distance from point C to point A? (Round to the nearest yard.)

For Exercises 21–23, solve the equations.

21. $\sqrt{2x + 7} + 6 = 2$

22. $\sqrt{1 - 7x} = 1 - x$

23. $\sqrt[3]{x + 6} = \sqrt[3]{2x - 8}$

24. The height, y (in inches), of a tomato plant can be approximated by the time, t (in weeks), after the seed has germinated according to the equation

$$y = 6\sqrt{t}$$

a. Use the equation to find the height of the plant after 4 weeks.

b. Use the equation to find the height of the plant after 9 weeks.

c. Use the equation to find the time required for the plant to reach a height of 30 in. Verify your answer from the graph.

Chapters 1–15   Cumulative Review Exercises

1. Simplify. $\dfrac{|-3 - 12 \div 6 + 2|}{\sqrt{5^2 - 4^2}}$

2. Solve.
$2 - 5(2y + 4) - (-3y - 1) = -(y + 5)$

3. Simplify. Write the final answer with positive exponents only.

$$\left(\frac{1}{3}\right)^0 - \left(\frac{1}{4}\right)^{-2}$$

4. Perform the indicated operations:
$2(x - 3) - (3x + 4)(3x - 4)$

5. Divide:

$$\frac{14x^3y - 7x^2y^2 + 28xy^2}{7x^2y^2}$$

6. Factor completely. $50c^2 + 40c + 8$

7. Solve. $10x^2 = x + 2$

8. Perform the indicated operations:

$$\frac{5a^2 + 2ab - 3b^2}{10a + 10b} \div \frac{25a^2 - 9b^2}{50a + 30b}$$

9. Solve for z. $\dfrac{1}{5} + \dfrac{z}{z - 5} = \dfrac{5}{z - 5}$

10. Simplify:

$$\frac{\dfrac{5}{4} + \dfrac{2}{x}}{\dfrac{4}{x} - \dfrac{4}{x^2}}$$

11. Graph. $3y = 6$

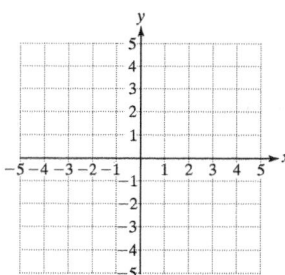

12. The equation $y = 210x + 250$ represents the cost, y (in dollars), of renting office space for x months.

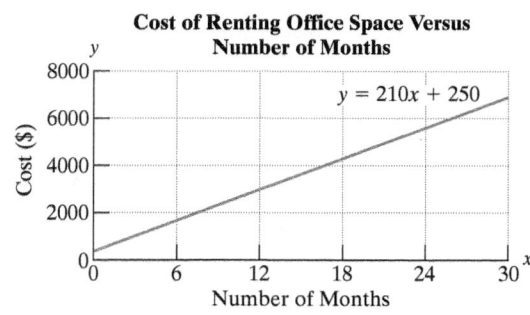

a. Find y when x is 3. Interpret the result in the context of the problem.

b. Find x when y is $2770. Interpret the result in the context of the problem.

c. What is the slope of the line? Interpret the meaning of the slope in the context of the problem.

d. What is the y-intercept? Interpret the meaning of the y-intercept in the context of the problem.

13. Write an equation of the line passing through the points $(2, -1)$ and $(-3, 4)$. Write the answer in slope-intercept form.

14. Solve the system of equations using the addition method. If the system has no solution or infinitely many solutions, so state:

$$3x - 5y = 23$$
$$2x + 4y = -14$$

15. Graph the solution to the inequality:
$$-2x - y > 3$$

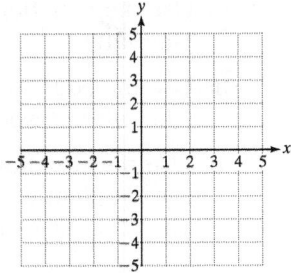

16. How many liters (L) of 20% acid solution must be mixed with a 50% acid solution to obtain 12 L of a 30% acid solution?

17. Simplify. $\sqrt{99}$

18. Perform the indicated operation.
$$5x\sqrt{3} + \sqrt{12x^2}$$

19. Rationalize the denominator. $\dfrac{\sqrt{x}}{\sqrt{x} - \sqrt{y}}$

20. Solve. $\sqrt{2y - 1} - 4 = -1$

More Quadratic Equations and Functions

16

Chapter 16

In earlier chapters, we solved quadratic equations by factoring and applying the zero product rule. In Chapter 16, we present additional techniques to solve quadratic equations. These new techniques can be used to solve quadratic equations even if a quadratic expression does not factor.

Are You Prepared?

This puzzle will help you recall the characteristics of a quadratic equation. Circle the number-letter of each true statement. Then write the letter in the matching numbered blank to complete the sentence.

| 1 − P | $m(m + 5) = 8$ is a linear equation. |

| 3 − O | $x^2 + 5x + 3 = x(x + 2)$ is a linear equation. |

| 3 − R | $x(x^2 - 4x - 1) = 2x^2 + 1$ is a quadratic equation. |

| 2 − W | $3(x - 8) = 10x$ is a linear equation. |

| 2 − S | $12x(x - 1) + 1 = 6$ is a linear equation. |

| 1 − T | $2x^3 + 3x = 2x(x^2 + 4)$ is a linear equation. |

| 3 − A | $4x(x - 1) = 7x + 10$ is a linear equation. |

| 2 − E | $x^2(x^2 + 8) = x(x^2 - 2x + 1)$ is a quadratic equation. |

A quadratic equation has at most ___ ___ ___ solutions.
                                              1   2   3

Section 16.1 The Square Root Property

1. Review of the Zero Product Rule

In Section 13.6, we learned that an equation that can be written in the form $ax^2 + bx + c = 0$, where $a \neq 0$, is a quadratic equation. One method to solve a quadratic equation is to factor the equation and apply the zero product rule. Recall that the zero product rule states that if $a \cdot b = 0$, then $a = 0$ or $b = 0$. This is reviewed in Examples 1–3.

Skill Practice

Solve the quadratic equation by using the zero product rule.

1. $2x^2 + 3x - 20 = 0$

Example 1 Solving a Quadratic Equation Using the Zero Product Rule

Solve the equation by factoring and applying the zero product rule.

$$2x^2 - 7x - 30 = 0$$

Solution:

$2x^2 - 7x - 30 = 0$	The equation is in the form $ax^2 + bx + c = 0$.
$(2x + 5)(x - 6) = 0$	Factor.
$2x + 5 = 0 \quad$ or $\quad x - 6 = 0$	Set each factor equal to zero.
$2x = -5 \quad$ or $\quad x = 6$	Solve the resulting equations.
$x = -\dfrac{5}{2}$	

The solutions are $-\dfrac{5}{2}$ and 6.

Skill Practice

Solve the quadratic equation by using the zero product rule.

2. $y(y - 1) = 2y + 10$

Example 2 Solving a Quadratic Equation Using the Zero Product Rule

Solve the equation by factoring and applying the zero product rule.

$$2x(x + 4) = x^2 - 15$$

Solution:

$2x(x + 4) = x^2 - 15$	
$2x^2 + 8x = x^2 - 15$	Clear parentheses and combine like terms.
$x^2 + 8x + 15 = 0$	Set one side of the equation equal to zero. The equation is now in the form $ax^2 + bx + c = 0$.
$(x + 5)(x + 3) = 0$	Factor.

Answers

1. $-4, \dfrac{5}{2}$

2. $5, -2$

$$x + 5 = 0 \quad \text{or} \quad x + 3 = 0 \qquad \text{Set each factor equal to zero.}$$
$$x = -5 \quad \text{or} \qquad x = -3 \qquad \text{Solve each equation.}$$

The solutions are -5 and -3.

TIP: The solutions to an equation can be checked in the original equation.

Check: $x = -5$

$$2x(x + 4) = x^2 - 15$$
$$2(-5)(-5 + 4) \stackrel{?}{=} (-5)^2 - 15$$
$$-10(-1) \stackrel{?}{=} 25 - 15$$
$$10 \stackrel{?}{=} 10 \checkmark$$

Check: $x = -3$

$$2x(x + 4) = x^2 - 15$$
$$2(-3)(-3 + 4) \stackrel{?}{=} (-3)^2 - 15$$
$$-6(1) \stackrel{?}{=} 9 - 15$$
$$-6 \stackrel{?}{=} -6 \checkmark$$

Example 3 **Solving a Quadratic Equation Using the Zero Product Rule**

Solve the equation by factoring and applying the zero product rule.

$$x^2 = 25$$

Solution:

$$x^2 = 25$$
$$x^2 - 25 = 0 \qquad \qquad \text{Set one side of the equation equal to zero.}$$
$$(x - 5)(x + 5) = 0 \qquad \text{Factor.}$$
$$x - 5 = 0 \quad \text{or} \quad x + 5 = 0 \qquad \text{Set each factor equal to zero.}$$
$$x = 5 \quad \text{or} \qquad x = -5$$

The solutions are 5 and -5.

Skill Practice

Solve the quadratic equation by using the zero product rule.

3. $t^2 = 49$

2. Solving Quadratic Equations Using the Square Root Property

In Examples 1–3, the quadratic equations were all factorable. In this chapter, we learn techniques to solve *all* quadratic equations, factorable and nonfactorable. The first technique uses the **square root property**.

PROPERTY **Square Root Property**

For any real number, k, if $x^2 = k$, then $x = \sqrt{k}$ or $x = -\sqrt{k}$.

Note: The solution can also be written as $x = \pm\sqrt{k}$, read as "x equals plus or minus the square root of k."

Answer

3. $7, -7$

Example 4 **Solving a Quadratic Equation Using the Square Root Property**

Use the square root property to solve the equation.

$$x^2 = 25$$

Solution:

$$x^2 = 25 \qquad \text{The equation is in the form } x^2 = k.$$

$$x = \pm\sqrt{25} \qquad \text{Apply the square root property.}$$

$$x = \pm 5$$

The solutions are 5 and -5. Note that this result is the same as in Example 3.

Example 5 **Solving a Quadratic Equation Using the Square Root Property**

Use the square root property to solve the equation.

$$2x^2 - 10 = 0$$

Solution:

$$2x^2 - 10 = 0 \qquad \text{To apply the square root property, the equation must be in the form } x^2 = k, \text{ that is, we must isolate } x^2.$$

$$2x^2 = 10 \qquad \text{Add 10 to both sides.}$$

$$x^2 = 5 \qquad \text{Divide both sides by 2. The equation is in the form } x^2 = k.$$

$$x = \pm\sqrt{5} \qquad \text{Apply the square root property.}$$

$$\underline{\text{Check: } x = \sqrt{5}} \qquad\qquad \underline{\text{Check: } x = -\sqrt{5}}$$

$$2x^2 - 10 = 0 \qquad\qquad 2x^2 - 10 = 0$$

$$2(\sqrt{5})^2 - 10 \stackrel{?}{=} 0 \qquad 2(-\sqrt{5})^2 - 10 \stackrel{?}{=} 0$$

$$2(5) - 10 \stackrel{?}{=} 0 \qquad\qquad 2(5) - 10 \stackrel{?}{=} 0$$

$$10 - 10 \stackrel{?}{=} 0 \checkmark \qquad\qquad 10 - 10 \stackrel{?}{=} 0 \checkmark$$

The solutions are $\sqrt{5}$ and $-\sqrt{5}$.

Example 6 **Solving a Quadratic Equation Using the Square Root Property**

Use the square root property to solve the equation.

$$(t - 4)^2 = 12$$

Solution:

$$(t - 4)^2 = 12 \qquad \text{The equation is in the form } x^2 = k, \text{ where } x = (t - 4).$$

$$t - 4 = \pm\sqrt{12} \qquad \text{Apply the square root property.}$$

$$t - 4 = \pm\sqrt{2^2 \cdot 3} \qquad \text{Simplify the radical.}$$
$$t - 4 = \pm 2\sqrt{3}$$
$$t = 4 \pm 2\sqrt{3} \qquad \text{Solve for } t.$$

Check: $t = 4 + 2\sqrt{3}$ 　　　　　 Check: $t = 4 - 2\sqrt{3}$

$$(t - 4)^2 = 12 \qquad\qquad (t - 4)^2 = 12$$
$$(4 + 2\sqrt{3} - 4)^2 \overset{?}{=} 12 \qquad (4 - 2\sqrt{3} - 4)^2 \overset{?}{=} 12$$
$$(2\sqrt{3})^2 \overset{?}{=} 12 \qquad\qquad (-2\sqrt{3})^2 \overset{?}{=} 12$$
$$4 \cdot 3 \overset{?}{=} 12 \qquad\qquad 4 \cdot 3 \overset{?}{=} 12$$
$$12 \overset{?}{=} 12 \checkmark \qquad\qquad 12 \overset{?}{=} 12 \checkmark$$

The solutions are: $4 + 2\sqrt{3}$ and $4 - 2\sqrt{3}$.

Example 7   **Solving a Quadratic Equation Using the Square Root Property**

Use the square root property to solve the equation.

$$y^2 = -4$$

Solution:

$$y^2 = -4 \qquad \text{The equation is in the form } y^2 = k.$$
$$y = \pm\sqrt{-4}$$

The expression $\sqrt{-4}$ is not a real number. Thus, the equation, $y^2 = -4$, has no real-valued solutions.

Skill Practice

Use the square root property to solve the equation.

7. $z^2 = -9$

Answer

7. The equation has no real-valued solutions.

Section 16.1   Practice Exercises

Boost *your* GRADE at ALEKS.com!

ALEKS version 3.0

- Practice Problems
- Self-Tests
- NetTutor
- e-Professors
- Videos

Study Skills Exercise

1. Define the key term **square root property**.

Objective 1: Review of the Zero Product Rule

2. Identify the equations as linear or quadratic.

　a. $2x - 5 = 3(x + 2) - 1$

　b. $2x(x - 5) = 3(x + 2) - 1$

　c. $ax^2 + bx + c = 0$
　　(a, b, and c are real numbers, and $a \ne 0$)

3. Identify the equations as linear or quadratic.

　a. $ax + b = 0$
　　(a and b are real numbers, and $a \ne 0$)

　b. $\dfrac{1}{2}p - \dfrac{3}{4}p^2 = 0$

　c. $\dfrac{1}{2}(p - 3) = 5$

For Exercises 4–19, solve using the zero product rule. **(See Examples 1–3.)**

4. $(3z - 2)(4z + 5) = 0$ **5.** $(t + 5)(2t - 1) = 0$ **6.** $r^2 + 7r + 12 = 0$ **7.** $y^2 - 2y - 35 = 0$

8. $10x^2 = 13x - 4$ **9.** $6p^2 = -13p - 2$ **10.** $2m(m - 1) = 3m - 3$ **11.** $2x^2 + 10x = -7(x + 3)$

12. $x^2 = 4$ **13.** $c^2 = 144$ **14.** $(x - 1)^2 = 16$ **15.** $(x - 3)^2 = 25$

16. $3p^2 + 4p = 15$ **17.** $4a^2 + 7a = 2$ **18.** $(x + 2)(x + 3) = 2$ **19.** $(x + 2)(x + 6) = 5$

Objective 2: Solving Quadratic Equations Using the Square Root Property

20. The symbol "$\pm$" is read as …

For Exercises 21–44, solve the equations using the square root property. **(See Examples 4–7.)**

21. $x^2 = 49$ **22.** $x^2 = 16$ **23.** $k^2 - 100 = 0$ **24.** $m^2 - 64 = 0$

25. $p^2 = -24$ **26.** $q^2 = -50$ **27.** $3w^2 - 9 = 0$ **28.** $4v^2 - 24 = 0$

29. $(a - 5)^2 = 16$ **30.** $(b + 3)^2 = 1$ **31.** $(y - 5)^2 = 36$ **32.** $(y + 4)^2 = 4$

33. $(x - 11)^2 = 5$ **34.** $(z - 2)^2 = 7$ **35.** $(a + 1)^2 = 18$ **36.** $(b - 1)^2 = 12$

37. $\left(t - \frac{1}{4}\right)^2 = \frac{7}{16}$ **38.** $\left(t - \frac{1}{3}\right)^2 = \frac{1}{9}$ **39.** $\left(x - \frac{1}{2}\right)^2 + 5 = 20$ **40.** $\left(x + \frac{5}{2}\right)^2 - 3 = 18$

41. $(p - 3)^2 = -16$ **42.** $(t + 4)^2 = -9$ **43.** $12t^2 = 75$ **44.** $8p^2 = 18$

45. Check the solution $-3 + \sqrt{5}$ in the equation $(x + 3)^2 = 5$.

46. Check the solution $-5 - \sqrt{7}$ in the equation $(p + 5)^2 = 7$.

For Exercises 47–48, answer true or false. If a statement is false, explain why.

47. The only solution to the equation $x^2 = 64$ is 8.

48. There are two real solutions to every quadratic equation of the form $x^2 = k$, where $k \geq 0$ is a real number.

49. Ignoring air resistance, the distance, d (in feet), that an object drops in t seconds is given by the equation

$$d = 16t^2$$

a. Find the distance traveled in 2 sec.

b. Find the time required for the object to fall 200 ft. Round to the nearest tenth of a second.

c. Find the time required for an object to fall from the top of the Empire State Building in New York City if the building is 1250 ft high. Round to the nearest tenth of a second.

50. Ignoring air resistance, the distance, d (in meters), that an object drops in t seconds is given by the equation

$$d = 4.9t^2$$

a. Find the distance traveled in 5 sec.

b. Find the time required for the object to fall 50 m. Round to the nearest tenth of a second.

c. Find the time required for an object to fall from the top of the Canada Trust Tower in Toronto, Canada, if the building is 261 m high. Round to the nearest tenth of a second.

51. A right triangle has legs of equal length. If the hypotenuse is 10 m long, find the length (in meters) of each leg. Round the answer to the nearest tenth of a meter.

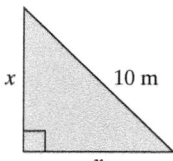

52. The diagonal of a square computer monitor screen is 24 in. long. Find the length of the sides to the nearest tenth of an inch.

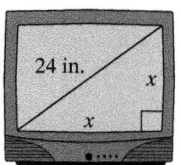

53. The area of a circular wading pool is approximately 200 ft². Find the radius to the nearest tenth of a foot.

54. According to the International Swimming Federation, the volume of an eight-lane Olympic size pool should be 2500 m³. The length of the pool is twice the width, and the depth is 2 m. Use a calculator to find the length and width of the pool.

Completing the Square

Section 16.2

1. Completing the Square

Objectives

1. Completing the Square
2. Solving Quadratic Equations by Completing the Square

In Section 16.1, Example 6, we used the square root property to solve an equation in which the square of a binomial was equal to a constant.

$$\underbrace{(t - 4)^2}_{\substack{\text{Square of a} \\ \text{binomial}}} = \underset{\text{Constant}}{12}$$

Furthermore, any equation $ax^2 + bx + c = 0$ $(a \neq 0)$ can be rewritten as the square of a binomial equal to a constant by using a process called **completing the square**.

We begin our discussion of completing the square with some vocabulary. For a trinomial $ax^2 + bx + c$ $(a \neq 0)$, the term ax^2 is called the **quadratic term**. The term bx is called the **linear term**, and the term c is called the **constant term**.

Next, notice that the square of a binomial is the factored form of a perfect square trinomial.

Perfect Square Trinomial   **Factored Form**

$$x^2 + 10x + 25 \longrightarrow (x + 5)^2$$

$$t^2 - 6t + 9 \longrightarrow (t - 3)^2$$

$$p^2 - 14p + 49 \longrightarrow (p - 7)^2$$

Furthermore, for a perfect square trinomial with a leading coefficient of 1, the constant term is the square of half the coefficient of the linear term. For example:

$$x^2 + 10x + 25 \longleftarrow \qquad t^2 - 6t + 9 \longleftarrow \qquad p^2 - 14p + 49 \longleftarrow$$

$$\left[\frac{1}{2}(10)\right]^2 = [5]^2 = 25 \quad\quad \left[\frac{1}{2}(-6)\right]^2 = [-3]^2 = 9 \quad\quad \left[\frac{1}{2}(-14)\right]^2 = [-7]^2 = 49$$

In general, an expression of the form $x^2 + bx$ will result in a perfect square trinomial if the square of half the linear term coefficient, $(\frac{1}{2}b)^2$, is added to the expression.

── **Skill Practice** ──

Complete the square for each expression and then factor the polynomial.

1. $q^2 + 8q$

2. $t^2 - 10t$

3. $v^2 + 3v$

4. $y^2 + \frac{1}{4}y$

Example 1   **Completing the Square**

Complete the square for each expression. Then factor the expression as the square of a binomial.

a. $x^2 + 12x$ **b.** $x^2 - 22x$ **c.** $x^2 + 5x$ **d.** $x^2 - \frac{3}{5}x$

Solution:

The expressions are in the form $x^2 + bx$. Add the square of half the linear term coefficient, $(\frac{1}{2}b)^2$.

a. $x^2 + 12x$

$\quad x^2 + 12x + 36$ Add $\frac{1}{2}$ of 12, squared. $[\frac{1}{2}(12)]^2 = (6)^2 = 36$.

$\quad (x + 6)^2$ Factored form

b. $x^2 - 22x$

$\quad x^2 - 22x + 121$ Add $\frac{1}{2}$ of -22, squared. $[\frac{1}{2}(-22)]^2 = (-11)^2 = 121$.

$\quad (x - 11)^2$ Factored form

c. $x^2 + 5x$

$\quad x^2 + 5x + \dfrac{25}{4}$ Add $\frac{1}{2}$ of 5, squared. $[\frac{1}{2}(5)]^2 = (\frac{5}{2})^2 = \frac{25}{4}$.

$\quad \left(x + \dfrac{5}{2}\right)^2$ Factored form

d. $x^2 - \dfrac{3}{5}x$

$\quad x^2 - \dfrac{3}{5}x + \dfrac{9}{100}$ Add $\frac{1}{2}$ of $-\frac{3}{5}$, squared.

$$\left[\frac{1}{2}\left(-\frac{3}{5}\right)\right]^2 = \left(-\frac{3}{10}\right)^2 = \frac{9}{100}$$

$\quad \left(x - \dfrac{3}{10}\right)^2$ Factored form

Answers

1. $q^2 + 8q + 16; (q + 4)^2$

2. $t^2 - 10t + 25; (t - 5)^2$

3. $v^2 + 3v + \dfrac{9}{4}; \left(v + \dfrac{3}{2}\right)^2$

4. $y^2 + \dfrac{1}{4}y + \dfrac{1}{64}; \left(y + \dfrac{1}{8}\right)^2$

2. Solving Quadratic Equations by Completing the Square

A quadratic equation can be solved by completing the square and applying the square root property. The following steps outline the procedure.

PROCEDURE Solving a Quadratic Equation in the Form $ax^2 + bx + c = 0$ ($a \neq 0$) by Completing the Square and Applying the Square Root Property

Step 1 Divide both sides by a to make the leading coefficient 1.

Step 2 Isolate the variable terms on one side of the equation.

Step 3 Complete the square by adding the square of one-half the linear term coefficient to both sides of the equation. Then factor the resulting perfect square trinomial.

Step 4 Apply the square root property and solve for x.

Example 2 **Solving a Quadratic Equation by Completing the Square and Applying the Square Root Property**

Solve the quadratic equation by completing the square and applying the square root property.

$$x^2 + 6x - 8 = 0$$

Solution:

$x^2 + 6x - 8 = 0$	The equation is in the form $ax^2 + bx + c = 0$.
	Step 1: The leading coefficient is already 1.
$x^2 + 6x = 8$	**Step 2:** Isolate the variable terms on one side.
$x^2 + 6x + 9 = 8 + 9$	**Step 3:** To complete the square, add $[\frac{1}{2}(6)]^2 = (3)^2 = 9$ to both sides.
$(x + 3)^2 = 17$	Factor the perfect square trinomial.
$x + 3 = \pm\sqrt{17}$	**Step 4:** Apply the square root property.
$x = -3 \pm \sqrt{17}$	Solve for x.

The solutions are $-3 - \sqrt{17}$ and $-3 + \sqrt{17}$.

Skill Practice

Solve the equation by completing the square and applying the square root property.

5. $t^2 + 6t + 2 = 0$

Answer

5. $-3 \pm \sqrt{7}$

Example 3 Solving a Quadratic Equation by Completing the Square and Applying the Square Root Property

Solve the quadratic equation by completing the square and applying the square root property.

$$2x^2 - 16x - 24 = 0$$

Solution:

$2x^2 - 16x - 24 = 0$ The equation is in the form $ax^2 + bx + c = 0$.

$\dfrac{2x^2}{2} - \dfrac{16x}{2} - \dfrac{24}{2} = \dfrac{0}{2}$ **Step 1:** Divide both sides by the leading coefficient, 2.

$x^2 - 8x - 12 = 0$

$x^2 - 8x = 12$ **Step 2:** Isolate the variable terms on one side.

$x^2 - 8x + 16 = 12 + 16$ **Step 3:** To complete the square, add $[\frac{1}{2}(-8)]^2 = 16$ to both sides of the equation.

$(x - 4)^2 = 28$ Factor the perfect square trinomial.

$x - 4 = \pm\sqrt{28}$ **Step 4:** Apply the square root property.

$x - 4 = \pm 2\sqrt{7}$ Simplify the radical.

$x = 4 \pm 2\sqrt{7}$ Solve for x.

The solutions are $4 + 2\sqrt{7}$ and $4 - 2\sqrt{7}$.

Example 4 Solving a Quadratic Equation by Completing the Square and Applying the Square Root Property

Solve the quadratic equation by completing the square and applying the square root property.

$$x(2x - 5) - 3 = 0$$

Solution:

$x(2x - 5) - 3 = 0$ Clear parentheses.

$2x^2 - 5x - 3 = 0$ The equation is in the form $ax^2 + bx + c = 0$.

$\dfrac{2x^2}{2} - \dfrac{5x}{2} - \dfrac{3}{2} = \dfrac{0}{2}$ **Step 1:** Divide both sides by the leading coefficient, 2.

$x^2 - \dfrac{5}{2}x - \dfrac{3}{2} = 0$

$x^2 - \dfrac{5}{2}x = \dfrac{3}{2}$ **Step 2:** Isolate the variable terms on one side.

Answers

6. $1 \pm 3\sqrt{2}$

7. $\dfrac{3}{5}, -2$

$$x^2 - \frac{5}{2}x + \frac{25}{16} = \frac{3}{2} + \frac{25}{16}$$

Step 3: Add $[\frac{1}{2}(-\frac{5}{2})]^2 = (-\frac{5}{4})^2 = \frac{25}{16}$ to both sides.

$$\left(x - \frac{5}{4}\right)^2 = \frac{24}{16} + \frac{25}{16}$$

Factor the perfect square trinomial. Rewrite the right-hand side with a common denominator and simplify.

$$\left(x - \frac{5}{4}\right)^2 = \frac{49}{16}$$

$$x - \frac{5}{4} = \pm\sqrt{\frac{49}{16}}$$

Step 4: Apply the square root property.

$$x - \frac{5}{4} = \pm\frac{7}{4}$$

Simplify the radical.

$$x = \frac{5}{4} \pm \frac{7}{4}$$

Solve for x.

We have

$$x = \begin{cases} \frac{5}{4} + \frac{7}{4} = \frac{12}{4} = 3 \\\\ \frac{5}{4} - \frac{7}{4} = -\frac{2}{4} = -\frac{1}{2} \end{cases}$$

The solutions are 3 and $-\frac{1}{2}$.

TIP: Since the solutions to the equation $x(2x - 5) - 3 = 0$ are rational numbers, the equation could have been solved by factoring and using the zero product rule:

$$x(2x - 5) - 3 = 0$$
$$2x^2 - 5x - 3 = 0$$
$$(2x + 1)(x - 3) = 0$$
$$2x + 1 = 0 \quad \text{or} \quad x - 3 = 0$$
$$x = -\frac{1}{2} \quad \text{or} \quad x = 3$$

Section 16.2   Practice Exercises

Boost *your* GRADE at ALEKS.com!

- Practice Problems
- Self-Tests
- NetTutor
- e-Professors
- Videos

Study Skills Exercise

1. Define the key terms:

    a. Completing the square   **b. Quadratic term**

    c. Linear term   **d. Constant term**

Review Exercises

For Exercises 2–4, solve the quadratic equation using the square root property.

    2. $x^2 = 21$ **3.** $(x - 5)^2 = 21$ **4.** $(x - 5)^2 = -21$

Objective 1: Completing the Square

For Exercises 5–16, find the constant that should be added to the expression to make it a perfect square trinomial. Then factor the trinomial. **(See Example 1.)**

5. $y^2 + 4y$

6. $w^2 - 6w$

7. $p^2 - 12p$

8. $q^2 + 16q$

9. $x^2 - 9x$

⊙ 10. $a^2 - 5a$

11. $d^2 + \frac{5}{3}d$

12. $t^2 + \frac{1}{4}t$

13. $m^2 - \frac{1}{5}m$

14. $n^2 - \frac{5}{7}n$

15. $u^2 + u$

16. $v^2 - v$

Objective 2: Solving Quadratic Equations by Completing the Square

For Exercises 17–36, solve the equations by completing the square and applying the square root property. **(See Examples 2–4.)**

17. $x^2 + 4x = 12$

18. $x^2 - 2x = 8$

19. $y^2 + 6y = -5$

20. $t^2 + 10t = 11$

21. $x^2 = 2x + 1$

22. $x^2 = 6x - 2$

23. $3x^2 - 6x - 15 = 0$

⊙ 24. $5x^2 + 10x - 30 = 0$

25. $4p^2 + 16p = -4$

26. $2t^2 - 12t = 12$

27. $w^2 + w - 3 = 0$

28. $z^2 - 3z - 5 = 0$

29. $x(x + 2) = 40$

30. $y(y - 4) = 10$

31. $a^2 - 4a - 1 = 0$

32. $c^2 - 2c - 9 = 0$

33. $2r^2 + 12r + 16 = 0$

34. $3p^2 + 12p + 9 = 0$

35. $h(h - 11) = -24$

36. $k(k - 8) = -7$

Mixed Exercises

For Exercises 37–64, solve the quadratic equation by using the zero product rule or the square root property. (*Hint:* For some exercises, you may have to factor or complete the square first.)

37. $y^2 = 121$

38. $x^2 = 81$

39. $(p + 2)^2 = 2$

40. $(q - 6)^2 = 3$

41. $(k + 13)(k - 5) = 0$

42. $(r - 10)(r + 12) = 0$

43. $(x - 13)^2 = 0$

44. $(p + 14)^2 = 0$

45. $z^2 - 8z - 20 = 0$

46. $b^2 - 14b + 48 = 0$

47. $(x - 3)^2 = 16$

48. $(x + 2)^2 = 49$

49. $a^2 - 8a + 1 = 0$

50. $x^2 + 12x - 4 = 0$

51. $2y^2 + 4y = 10$

52. $3z^2 - 48z = 6$

53. $x^2 - 9x - 22 = 0$

54. $y^2 + 11y + 18 = 0$

55. $5h(h - 7) = 0$

56. $-2w(w + 9) = 0$

57. $8t^2 + 2t - 3 = 0$

58. $18a^2 - 21a + 5 = 0$

59. $t^2 = 14$

60. $s^2 = 17$

61. $c^2 + 9 = 0$

62. $k^2 + 25 = 0$

63. $4x^2 - 8x = -4$

64. $3x^2 + 12x = -12$

Expanding Your Skills

For Exercises 65–66, solve by completing the square.

65. To comply with FAA regulations, a piece of luggage must be checked to the luggage compartment of the plane if its combined linear measurement of length, width, and height is over 45 in. Katie's suitcase has a total volume of 4200 in.³ Its length is 30 in., and its width is 4 in. greater than the height. Find the dimensions of the suitcase. Will this suitcase need to be checked?

66. Luggage that is checked to the baggage compartment of an airplane must not exceed the dimensional requirements set by the carrier. Most carriers do not allow bags that exceed 30 in. in any dimension. They also require that the combined length, width, and height of the bag not exceed 62 in. Suppose a suitcase has a total volume of 5040 in.^{3} If the length is 28 in., and the width is 8 in. greater than the height, find the dimensions of the bag. Can this bag be checked to the luggage compartment of the plane?

Quadratic Formula

1. Derivation of the Quadratic Formula

Objectives

If we solve a general quadratic equation $ax^2 + bx + c = 0, a > 0$, by completing the square and using the square root property, the result is a formula that gives the solutions for x in terms of a, b, and c.

1. Derivation of the Quadratic Formula
2. Solving Quadratic Equations Using the Quadratic Formula
3. Review of the Methods for Solving a Quadratic Equation
4. Applications of Quadratic Equations

$$ax^2 + bx + c = 0$$

Begin with a quadratic equation in standard form.

$$\frac{ax^2}{a} + \frac{b}{a}x + \frac{c}{a} = \frac{0}{a}$$

Divide by the leading coefficient.

$$x^2 + \frac{b}{a}x = -\frac{c}{a}$$

Isolate the terms containing x.

$$x^2 + \frac{b}{a}x + \left(\frac{1}{2} \cdot \frac{b}{a}\right)^2 = \left(\frac{1}{2} \cdot \frac{b}{a}\right)^2 - \frac{c}{a}$$

Add the square of $\frac{1}{2}$ the linear term coefficient to both sides of the equation.

$$\left(x + \frac{b}{2a}\right)^2 = \frac{b^2}{4a^2} - \frac{c}{a}$$

Factor the left side as a perfect square.

$$\left(x + \frac{b}{2a}\right)^2 = \frac{b^2}{4a^2} - \frac{c}{a} \cdot \frac{(4a)}{(4a)}$$

On the right side, write the fractions with the common denominator, $4a^2$.

$$\left(x + \frac{b}{2a}\right)^2 = \frac{b^2 - 4ac}{4a^2}$$

Combine the fractions.

$$x + \frac{b}{2a} = \pm\sqrt{\frac{b^2 - 4ac}{4a^2}}$$

Apply the square root property.

$$x + \frac{b}{2a} = \frac{\pm\sqrt{b^2 - 4ac}}{2a}$$

Simplify the denominator.

$$x = -\frac{b}{2a} \pm \frac{\sqrt{b^2 - 4ac}}{2a}$$

Subtract $\frac{b}{2a}$ from both sides.

$$= \frac{-b \pm \sqrt{b^2 - 4ac}}{2a}$$

Combine fractions.

Concept Connections

Write each quadratic equation in the form $ax^2 + bx + c = 0$. Then identify a, b, and c.

1. $4x^2 - 9x + 1 = 0$
2. $3x^2 = 2x + 8$
3. $x(x + 6) = x + 15$

FORMULA Quadratic Formula

For any quadratic equation of the form $ax^2 + bx + c = 0, (a \neq 0)$ the solutions are

$$x = \frac{-b \pm \sqrt{b^2 - 4ac}}{2a}$$

Answers

1. $4x^2 - 9x + 1 = 0$;
$a = 4; b = -9; c = 1$
2. $3x^2 - 2x - 8 = 0$;
$a = 3; b = -2; c = -8$
3. $x^2 + 5x - 15 = 0$;
$a = 1; b = 5; c = -15$

2. Solving Quadratic Equations Using the Quadratic Formula

Example 1 Solving Quadratic Equations Using the Quadratic Formula

Solve the quadratic equation using the quadratic formula: $3x^2 - 7x = -2$

Solution:

$$3x^2 - 7x = -2$$

$$3x^2 - 7x + 2 = 0 \qquad \text{Write the equation in the form } ax^2 + bx + c = 0.$$

$$a = 3, b = -7, c = 2 \qquad \text{Identify } a, b, \text{ and } c.$$

$$x = \frac{-b \pm \sqrt{b^2 - 4ac}}{2a}$$

$$x = \frac{-(-7) \pm \sqrt{(-7)^2 - 4(3)(2)}}{2(3)} \qquad \text{Apply the quadratic formula.}$$

$$x = \frac{7 \pm \sqrt{49 - 24}}{6} \qquad \text{Simplify.}$$

$$= \frac{7 \pm \sqrt{25}}{6}$$

$$= \frac{7 \pm 5}{6}$$

There are two rational solutions.

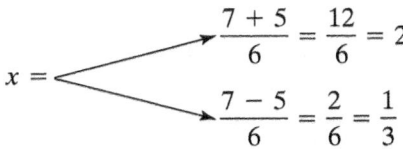

$$x = \begin{cases} \dfrac{7 + 5}{6} = \dfrac{12}{6} = 2 \\[2ex] \dfrac{7 - 5}{6} = \dfrac{2}{6} = \dfrac{1}{3} \end{cases}$$

The solutions are 2 and $\frac{1}{3}$.

TIP: Because the solutions to the equation $3x^2 - 7x = -2$ are rational numbers, the equation could have been solved by factoring and using the zero product rule.

$$3x^2 - 7x = -2$$
$$3x^2 - 7x + 2 = 0$$
$$(3x - 1)(x - 2) = 0$$
$$3x - 1 = 0 \quad \text{or} \quad x - 2 = 0$$
$$x = \frac{1}{3} \quad \text{or} \quad x = 2$$

The solutions are $\frac{1}{3}$ and 2.

Example 2 Solving a Quadratic Equation Using the Quadratic Formula

Solve the quadratic equation using the quadratic formula. Then approximate the solutions to three decimal places.

$$2x(x - 1) - 6 = 0$$

Solution:

$2x(x - 1) - 6 = 0$

$2x^2 - 2x - 6 = 0$ Write the equation in the form $ax^2 + bx + c = 0$.

$a = 2, b = -2, c = -6$ Identify a, b, and c.

$x = \dfrac{-b \pm \sqrt{b^2 - 4ac}}{2a}$

$x = \dfrac{-(-2) \pm \sqrt{(-2)^2 - 4(2)(-6)}}{2(2)}$ Apply the quadratic formula.

$= \dfrac{2 \pm \sqrt{4 + 48}}{4}$ Simplify.

$= \dfrac{2 \pm \sqrt{52}}{4}$

$= \dfrac{2 \pm \sqrt{2^2 \cdot 13}}{4}$ Simplify the radical.

$= \dfrac{2 \pm 2\sqrt{13}}{4}$

$= \dfrac{\overset{1}{2}(1 \pm \sqrt{13})}{\underset{2}{4}}$ Simplify the fraction.

$= \dfrac{1 \pm \sqrt{13}}{2}$ $x = \dfrac{1 + \sqrt{13}}{2} \approx 2.303$

                   $x = \dfrac{1 - \sqrt{13}}{2} \approx -1.303$

The exact solutions are $\dfrac{1 + \sqrt{13}}{2}$ and $\dfrac{1 - \sqrt{13}}{2}$. The approximate solutions are 2.303 and −1.303.

Example 3 **Solving a Quadratic Equation Using the Quadratic Formula**

Solve the quadratic equation using the quadratic formula.

$$\frac{1}{4}w^2 - \frac{1}{2}w - \frac{5}{4} = 0$$

Solution:

$$\frac{1}{4}w^2 - \frac{1}{2}w - \frac{5}{4} = 0 \qquad \text{To simplify the equation, multiply both sides by 4.}$$

$$4\left(\frac{1}{4}w^2 - \frac{1}{2}w - \frac{5}{4}\right) = 4(0) \qquad \text{Clear fractions.}$$

$$w^2 - 2w - 5 = 0 \qquad \text{The equation is in the form } ax^2 + bx + c = 0.$$

$$a = 1, b = -2, c = -5 \qquad \text{Identify } a, b, \text{ and } c.$$

$$w = \frac{-b \pm \sqrt{b^2 - 4ac}}{2a}$$

$$w = \frac{-(-2) \pm \sqrt{(-2)^2 - 4(1)(-5)}}{2(1)} \qquad \text{Apply the quadratic formula.}$$

$$= \frac{2 \pm \sqrt{4 + 20}}{2} \qquad \text{Simplify.}$$

$$= \frac{2 \pm \sqrt{24}}{2}$$

$$= \frac{2 \pm 2\sqrt{6}}{2} \qquad \text{The solutions are irrational numbers.}$$

$$= \frac{2(1 \pm \sqrt{6})}{2} \qquad \text{Factor and simplify.}$$

$$= 1 \pm \sqrt{6}$$

The solutions are $1 + \sqrt{6}$ and $1 - \sqrt{6}$.

3. Review of the Methods for Solving a Quadratic Equation

Three methods have been presented for solving quadratic equations.

PROCEDURE **Methods for Solving a Quadratic Equation**
- Factor and use the zero product rule (Section 13.6).
- Use the square root property. Complete the square if necessary (Sections 16.1 and 16.2).
- Use the quadratic formula (Section 16.3).

Using the zero product rule only works if you can factor the equation. The square root property and the quadratic formula can be used to solve any quadratic equation. Before solving a quadratic equation, take a minute to analyze it. Each problem must be evaluated individually before choosing the most efficient method to find its solutions.

Example 4 **Solving Quadratic Equations Using Any Method**

Solve the quadratic equations using any method.

a. $(x + 1)^2 = 5$ **b.** $t^2 - t - 30 = 0$ **c.** $2x^2 + 5x + 1 = 0$

Solution:

a. $(x + 1)^2 = 5$ — Because the equation is the square of a binomial equal to a constant, the square root property can be applied easily.

$x + 1 = \pm\sqrt{5}$ — Apply the square root property.

$x = -1 \pm \sqrt{5}$ — Isolate x.

The solutions are $-1 + \sqrt{5}$ and $-1 - \sqrt{5}$.

b. $t^2 - t - 30 = 0$ — This equation factors.

$(t - 6)(t + 5) = 0$ — Factor and apply the zero product rule.

$t = 6$ or $t = -5$

The solutions are 6 and -5.

c. $2x^2 + 5x + 1 = 0$ — The equation does not factor. Because it is already in the form $ax^2 + bx + c = 0$, use the quadratic formula.

$a = 2, b = 5, c = 1$ — Identify a, b, and c.

$x = \dfrac{-(5) \pm \sqrt{(5)^2 - 4(2)(1)}}{2(2)}$ — Apply the quadratic formula.

$x = \dfrac{-5 \pm \sqrt{25 - 8}}{4}$ — Simplify.

$x = \dfrac{-5 \pm \sqrt{17}}{4}$

The solutions are $\dfrac{-5 + \sqrt{17}}{4}$ and $\dfrac{-5 - \sqrt{17}}{4}$.

Skill Practice

Solve the equations using any method.

7. $p^2 + 7p + 12 = 0$
8. $5y^2 + 7y + 1 = 0$
9. $(w - 8)^2 = 3$

Answers

7. $-3, -4$
8. $\dfrac{-7 \pm \sqrt{29}}{10}$
9. $8 \pm \sqrt{3}$

4. Applications of Quadratic Equations

Example 5   **Solving a Quadratic Equation in an Application**

The length of a box is 2 in. longer than the width. The height of the box is 4 in., and the volume of the box is 200 in.^{3} Find the exact dimensions of the box. Then use a calculator to approximate the dimensions to the nearest tenth of an inch.

Solution:

Label the box as follows (Figure 16-1):

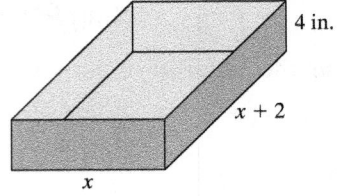
4 in.
$x + 2$
x

Figure 16-1

> Width = x
>
> Length = $x + 2$
>
> Height = 4

The volume of a box is given by the formula: $V = lwh$

$$V = l \cdot w \cdot h$$

$$200 = (x + 2)(x)(4)$$ Substitute $V = 200$, $l = x + 2$, $w = x$, and $h = 4$.

$$200 = (x + 2)4x$$

$$200 = 4x^2 + 8x$$

$$0 = 4x^2 + 8x - 200$$

$$4x^2 + 8x - 200 = 0$$ The equation is in the form $ax^2 + bx + c = 0$.

$$\frac{4x^2}{4} + \frac{8x}{4} - \frac{200}{4} = \frac{0}{4}$$ The coefficients are all divisible by 4. Dividing by 4 will create smaller values of a, b, and c to be used in the quadratic formula.

$$x^2 + 2x - 50 = 0$$ $a = 1$, $b = 2$, $c = -50$

$$x = \frac{-2 \pm \sqrt{(2)^2 - 4(1)(-50)}}{2(1)}$$ Apply the quadratic formula.

$$= \frac{-2 \pm \sqrt{4 + 200}}{2}$$ Simplify.

$$= \frac{-2 \pm \sqrt{204}}{2}$$

$$= \frac{-2 \pm 2\sqrt{51}}{2}$$ Simplify the radical. $\sqrt{204} = \sqrt{2^2 \cdot 51} = 2\sqrt{51}$

$$= \frac{\overset{1}{2}(-1 \pm \sqrt{51})}{\underset{1}{2}}$$ Factor and simplify.

$$= -1 \pm \sqrt{51}$$

Because the width of the box must be positive, use $x = -1 + \sqrt{51}$.

> The width is $(-1 + \sqrt{51})$ in. ≈ 6.1 in.
>
> The length is $x + 2$: $(-1 + \sqrt{51} + 2)$ in. or $(1 + \sqrt{51})$ in. ≈ 8.1 in.
>
> The height is 4 in.

Calculator Connections

Topic: Entering Values in the Quadratic Formula on a Calculator

Use the quadratic formula to verify that the solutions to the equation $x(x + 7) + 4 = 0$ are

$$x = \frac{-7 + \sqrt{33}}{2} \quad \text{and} \quad x = \frac{-7 - \sqrt{33}}{2}$$

A calculator can be used to obtain decimal approximations for the irrational solutions of a quadratic equation.

Scientific Calculator

Enter: 7 [+/-]   [+]   33 [√]   [=]   [÷] 2 [=]   **Result:** $\boxed{-0.6277186767}$

Enter: 7 [+/-]   [−]   33 [√]   [=]   [÷] 2 [=]   **Result:** $\boxed{-6.372281323}$

Graphing Calculator

```
(-7+√(33))/2
         -.6277186767
(-7-√(33))/2
         -6.372281323
```

Calculator Exercises

Use a calculator to obtain a decimal approximation of each expression.

1. $\dfrac{-5 + \sqrt{17}}{4}$ and $\dfrac{-5 - \sqrt{17}}{4}$ **2.** $\dfrac{-40 + \sqrt{1920}}{-32}$ and $\dfrac{-40 - \sqrt{1920}}{-32}$

Section 16.3   Practice Exercises

Boost *your* GRADE at ALEKS.com!   ALEKS version 3.0
• Practice Problems   • e-Professors
• Self-Tests   • Videos
• NetTutor

Review Exercises

For Exercises 1–4, apply the square root property to solve the equation.

1. $z^2 = 169$ **2.** $p^2 = 1$ **3.** $(x - 4)^2 = 28$ **4.** $(y + 3)^2 = 7$

For Exercises 5–6, solve the equations by completing the square.

5. $3a^2 - 12a - 12 = 0$ **6.** $x^2 - 5x + 1 = 0$

Objective 1: Derivation of the Quadratic Formula

7. State the quadratic formula from memory.

8. Can all quadratic equations be solved by using the quadratic formula?

For Exercises 9–14, write the equations in the form $ax^2 + bx + c = 0$. Then identify the values of a, b, and c.

9. $2x^2 - x = 5$ **10.** $5(x^2 + 2) = -3x$ **11.** $-3x(x - 4) = -2x$

12. $x(x - 2) = 3(x + 1)$ **13.** $x^2 - 9 = 0$ **14.** $x^2 + 25 = 0$

Objective 2: Solving Quadratic Equations Using the Quadratic Formula

For Exercises 15–32, solve the equations using the quadratic formula. **(See Examples 1–3.)**

15. $t^2 + 16t + 64 = 0$

16. $y^2 - 10y + 25 = 0$

17. $6k^2 - k - 2 = 0$

18. $3n^2 + 5n - 2 = 0$

19. $5t^2 - t = 3$

20. $2a^2 + 5a = 1$

21. $x(x - 2) = 1$

22. $2y(y - 3) = -1$

23. $2p^2 = -10p - 11$

24. $z^2 = 4z + 1$

25. $-4y^2 - y + 1 = 0$

26. $-5z^2 - 3z + 4 = 0$

27. $2x(x + 1) = 3 - x$

28. $3m(m - 2) = -m + 1$

29. $0.2y^2 = -1.5y - 1$

30. $0.2t^2 = t + 0.5$

31. $\frac{2}{3}x^2 + \frac{4}{9}x = \frac{1}{3}$

32. $\frac{1}{2}x^2 + \frac{1}{6}x = 1$

Objective 3: Review of the Methods for Solving a Quadratic Equation

For Exercises 33–56, choose any method to solve the quadratic equations. **(See Example 4.)**

33. $16x^2 - 9 = 0$

34. $\frac{1}{4}x^2 + 5x + 13 = 0$

35. $(x - 5)^2 = -21$

36. $2x^2 + x + 5 = 0$

37. $\frac{1}{9}x^2 + \frac{8}{3}x + 11 = 0$

38. $7x^2 = 12x$

39. $2x^2 - 6x - 3 = 0$

40. $4(x + 1)^2 = -15$

41. $9x^2 = 11x$

42. $25x^2 - 4 = 0$

43. $(2y - 3)^2 = 5$

44. $(6z + 1)^2 = 7$

45. $0.4x^2 = 0.2x + 1$

46. $0.6x^2 = 0.1x + 0.8$

47. $9z^2 - z = 0$

48. $16p^2 - p = 0$

49. $r^2 - 52 = 0$

50. $y^2 - 32 = 0$

51. $-2.5t(t - 4) = 1.5$

52. $1.6p(p - 2) = 0.8$

53. $(m - 3)(m + 2) = 9$

54. $(h - 6)(h - 1) = 12$

55. $x^2 + x + 3 = 0$

56. $3x^2 - 20x + 12 = 0$

Objective 4: Applications of Quadratic Equations

57. In a rectangle, the length is 1 m less than twice the width, and the area is 100 m². Approximate the dimensions to the nearest tenth of a meter. **(See Example 5.)**

58. In a triangle, the height is 2 cm more than the base. The area is 72 cm². Approximate the base and height to the nearest tenth of a centimeter.

59. The volume of a rectangular storage area is 240 ft³. The length is 2 ft more than the width. The height is 6 ft. Approximate the dimensions to the nearest tenth of a foot.

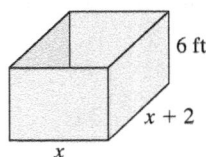
6 ft
$x + 2$
x

60. In a right triangle, one leg is 2 ft shorter than the other leg. The hypotenuse is 12 ft. Approximate the lengths of the legs to the nearest tenth of a foot.

61. In a rectangle, the length is 4 ft longer than the width. The area is 72 ft². Approximate the dimensions to the nearest tenth of a foot.

62. In a triangle, the base is 4 cm less than twice the height. The area is 60 cm². Approximate the base and height to the nearest tenth of a centimeter.

63. In a right triangle, one leg is 3 m longer than the other leg. The hypotenuse is 13 m. Approximate the lengths of the legs to the nearest tenth of a meter.

Problem Recognition Exercises

Solving Quadratic Equations

For Exercises 1–2, solve the equations using each of the three methods.

    a. Factoring and applying the zero product rule

    b. Completing the square and applying the square root property

    c. Applying the quadratic formula

1. $6x^2 + 7x - 3 = 0$ **2.** $y^2 + 14y + 49 = 0$

For Exercises 3–22, solve using any method.

3. $x(x - 8) = 6$ **4.** $2 - 6y = -y^2$

5. $(t - 3)^2 - 8 = 0$ **6.** $(p + 11)^2 - 12 = 0$

7. $6m^2 = 5m$ **8.** $12n^2 = 6n$

9. $\frac{1}{36}w^2 - 1 = 0$ **10.** $\frac{25}{49}y^2 - 1 = 0$

11. $8x^2 - 22x + 5 = 0$ **12.** $9w^2 - 15w + 4 = 0$

13. $p^2 + 20 = 0$ **14.** $m^2 + 15 = 0$

15. $y(y + 8) = -1$ **16.** $t(t + 6) = -3$

17. $\frac{1}{2}a^2 - 4a + 8 = 0$ **18.** $\frac{1}{3}b^2 + 2b + 3 = 0$

19. $2x^2 - 14x = -20$ **20.** $3n^2 - 6n = 9$

21. $(w + 1)^2 = 100$ **22.** $(u - 5)^2 = 64$

Section 16.4   Graphing Quadratic Equations

1. Quadratic Equations in Two Variables

In Chapter 10, we learned how to graph the solutions to linear equations in two variables. Now suppose we want to graph the *nonlinear* equation, $y = x^2$. To begin, we create a table of points representing several solutions to the equation (Table 16-1). These points form the curve shown in Figure 16-2.

Table 16-1

x	y
-3	9
-2	4
-1	1
0	0
1	1
2	4
3	9

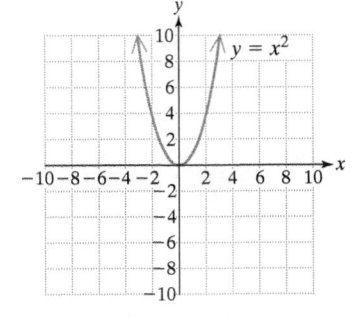

Figure 16-2

The equation $y = x^2$ is a quadratic equation in two variables, and its graph is in the shape of a **parabola**.

DEFINITION   Quadratic Equation in Two Variables

Let a, b, and c represent real numbers such that $a \neq 0$. Then an equation in the form $y = ax^2 + bx + c$ is called a **quadratic equation in two variables**.

The graph of a quadratic equation is a parabola that opens upward or downward. The leading coefficient, a, determines the direction of the parabola. For the quadratic equation $y = ax^2 + bx + c$:

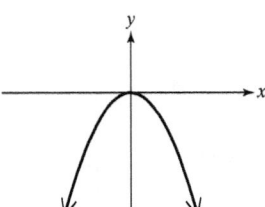

If $a > 0$, the parabola opens *upward*.
For example: $y = x^2$.

If $a < 0$, the parabola opens *downward*.
For example: $y = -x^2$.

If a parabola opens upward, the **vertex** is the lowest point on the graph. If a parabola opens downward, the **vertex** is the highest point on the graph. For a parabola, the **axis of symmetry** is the vertical line that passes through the vertex. Notice that the graph of the parabola is its own mirror image to the left and right of the axis of symmetry.

Here are four quadratic equations and their graphs.

$y = 0.5x^2 + 2x + 3$
$a > 0$
Vertex $(-2, 1)$
Axis of symmetry: $x = -2$

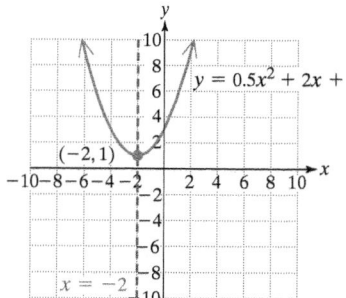

$y = x^2 - 6x + 9$
$a > 0$
Vertex $(3, 0)$
Axis of symmetry: $x = 3$

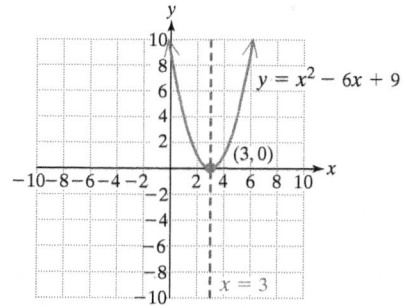

$y = -x^2 + 4x$
$a < 0$
Vertex $(2, 4)$
Axis of symmetry: $x = 2$

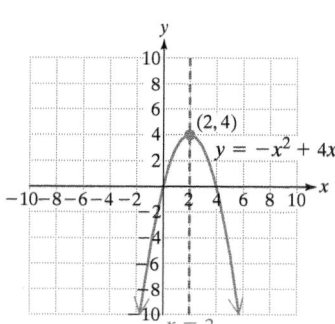

$y = -2x^2 - 4$
$a < 0$
Vertex $(0, -4)$
Axis of symmetry: $x = 0$

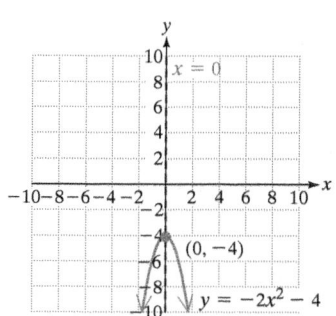

Concept Connections

2. Refer to the graph shown:

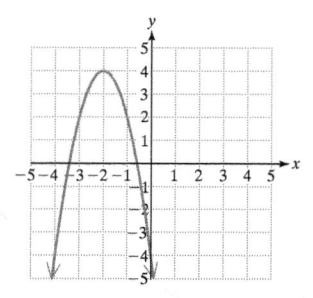

a. Determine the vertex of the parabola.
b. Determine the axis of symmetry of the parabola.

2. Vertex of a Parabola

Quadratic equations arise in many applications of mathematics and applied sciences. For example, an object thrown through the air follows a parabolic path. The mirror inside a reflecting telescope is parabolic in shape. In applications, it is often advantageous to analyze the graph of a parabola. In particular, we want to find the location of the x- and y-intercepts and the vertex.

To find the vertex of a parabola defined by $y = ax^2 + bx + c \ (a \neq 0)$, we use the following steps:

PROCEDURE Finding the Vertex of a Parabola

Step 1 The x-coordinate of the vertex of the parabola defined by $y = ax^2 + bx + c \ (a \neq 0)$ is given by

$$x = \frac{-b}{2a}$$

Step 2 To find the corresponding y-coordinate of the vertex, substitute the value of the x-coordinate found in step 1 and solve for y.

Answers
2. a. $(-2, 4)$ **b.** $x = -2$

Skill Practice

3. Given $y = -x^2 - 4x$, perform parts (a)–(e), as in Example 1.

Example 1   **Analyzing a Quadratic Equation**

Given $y = -x^2 + 4x - 3$,

a. Determine whether the parabola opens upward or downward.

b. Find the vertex of the parabola.

c. Find the x-intercept(s).

d. Find the y-intercept.

e. Sketch the parabola.

Solution:

a. The equation $y = -x^2 + 4x - 3$ is written in the form $y = ax^2 + bx + c$, where $a = -1$, $b = 4$, and $c = -3$. Because the value of a is negative, the parabola opens *downward*.

b. The x-coordinate of the vertex is given by $x = \dfrac{-b}{2a}$.

$$x = \frac{-b}{2a} = \frac{-(4)}{2(-1)} \qquad \text{Substitute } b = 4 \text{ and } a = -1.$$

$$= \frac{-4}{-2} \qquad \text{Simplify.}$$

$$= 2$$

The y-coordinate of the vertex is found by substituting $x = 2$ into the equation and solving for y.

$$y = -x^2 + 4x - 3$$

$$= -(2)^2 + 4(2) - 3 \qquad \text{Substitute } x = 2.$$

$$= -4 + 8 - 3$$

$$= 1$$

The vertex is $(2, 1)$.   Because the parabola opens downward, the vertex is the maximum point on the graph of the parabola.

c. To find the x-intercept(s), substitute $y = 0$ and solve for x.

$$y = -x^2 + 4x - 3$$

$$0 = -x^2 + 4x - 3 \qquad \text{Substitute } y = 0. \text{ The resulting equation is quadratic.}$$

$$0 = -1(x^2 - 4x + 3) \qquad \text{Factor out } -1.$$

$$0 = -1(x - 3)(x - 1) \qquad \text{Factor the trinomial.}$$

$$x - 3 = 0 \quad \text{or} \quad x - 1 = 0 \qquad \text{Apply the zero product rule.}$$

$$x = 3 \quad \text{or} \quad x = 1$$

The x-intercepts are $(3, 0)$ and $(1, 0)$.

Answers

3. a. downward
b. $(-2, 4)$
c. $(0, 0)$ and $(-4, 0)$
d. $(0, 0)$
e.

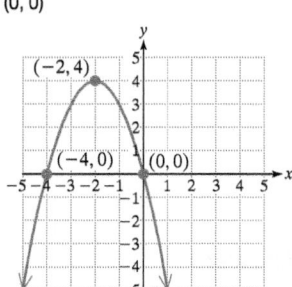

d. To find the y-intercept, substitute $x = 0$ and solve for y.

$y = -x^2 + 4x - 3$

$\quad = -(0)^2 + 4(0) - 3 \qquad\qquad$ Substitute $x = 0$.

$\quad = -3$

The y-intercept is $(0, -3)$.

e. Using the results of parts (a)–(d), we have a parabola that opens downward with vertex $(2, 1)$, x-intercepts at $(3, 0)$ and $(1, 0)$, and y-intercept at $(0, -3)$ (Figure 16-3).

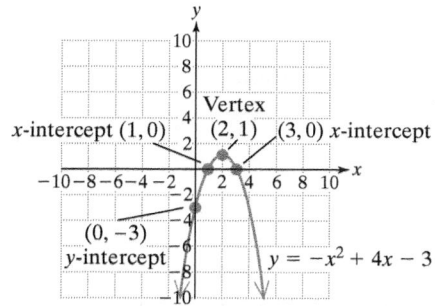

Figure 16-3

3. Graphing a Parabola

Example 1 illustrates a process to sketch a quadratic equation by finding the location of the defining characteristics of the parabola. These include the vertex and the x- and y-intercepts. Furthermore, notice that the parabola defining the graph of a quadratic equation is symmetric with respect to the axis of symmetry.

To analyze the graph of a parabola, we recommend the following guidelines.

PROCEDURE Graphing a Parabola

Given a quadratic equation in the form $y = ax^2 + bx + c \, (a \neq 0)$, consider the following guidelines to graph the parabola.

Step 1 Determine whether the parabola opens upward or downward.
- If $a > 0$, the parabola opens upward.
- If $a < 0$, the parabola opens downward.

Step 2 Find the vertex.

- The x-coordinate is given by $x = \dfrac{-b}{2a}$

- To find the y-coordinate, substitute the x-coordinate of the vertex into the equation and solve for y.

Step 3 Find the x-intercept(s) by substituting $y = 0$ and solving the equation for x.
- *Note:* If the solutions to the equation in step 3 are not real numbers, then the graph has no x-intercepts.

Step 4 Find the y-intercept by substituting $x = 0$ and solving the equation for y.

Step 5 Plot the vertex and x- and y-intercepts. If necessary, find and plot additional points near the vertex. Then use the symmetry of the parabola to sketch the curve through the points. (*Note:* The axis of symmetry is the vertical line that passes through the vertex.)

Skill Practice

4. Graph $y = x^2 - 2x + 1$.

Example 2   **Graphing a Parabola**

Graph $y = x^2 - 6x + 9$.

Solution:

1. The equation $y = x^2 - 6x + 9$ is written in the form $y = ax^2 + bx + c$, where $a = 1$, $b = -6$, and $c = 9$. Because the value of a is positive, the parabola opens upward.

2. The x-coordinate of the vertex is given by

$$x = \frac{-b}{2a} = \frac{-(-6)}{2(1)} = 3$$

Substituting $x = 3$ into the equation, we have

$$y = (3)^2 - 6(3) + 9$$
$$= 9 - 18 + 9$$
$$= 0$$

The vertex is $(3, 0)$.

3. To find the x-intercept(s), substitute $y = 0$ and solve for x.

$$y = x^2 - 6x + 9 \longrightarrow 0 = x^2 - 6x + 9$$
$$0 = (x - 3)^2 \qquad \text{Factor.}$$
$$x = 3 \qquad \text{Apply the zero product rule.}$$

The x-intercept is $(3, 0)$.

4. To find the y-intercept, substitute $x = 0$ and solve for y.

$$y = x^2 - 6x + 9 \longrightarrow y = (0)^2 - 6(0) + 9$$
$$= 9$$

The y-intercept is $(0, 9)$.

5. Sketch the parabola through the x- and y-intercepts and vertex (Figure 16-4).

TIP: Using the symmetry of the parabola, we know that the points to the right of the vertex must mirror the points to the left of the vertex.

Figure 16-4

Answer

4.

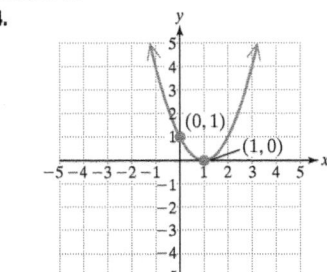

Example 3   **Graphing a Parabola**

Graph $y = -x^2 - 4$.

Solution:

1. The equation $y = -x^2 - 4$ is written in the form $y = ax^2 + bx + c$, where $a = -1$, $b = 0$, and $c = -4$. Because the value of a is negative, the parabola opens downward.

2. The x-coordinate of the vertex is given by

$$x = \frac{-b}{2a} = \frac{-(0)}{2(-1)} = 0$$

Substituting $x = 0$ into the equation, we have

$$y = -(0)^2 - 4$$
$$= -4$$

The vertex is $(0, -4)$.

3. Because the vertex is below the x-axis and the parabola opens downward, the graph cannot have an x-intercept.

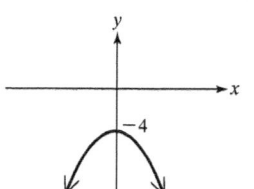

> **TIP:** Substituting $y = 0$ into the equation $y = -x^2 - 4$ results in an equation with no real solutions. Therefore, the graph $y = -x^2 - 4$ has no x-intercepts.
>
> $$y = -x^2 - 4$$
> $$0 = -x^2 - 4$$
> $$x^2 = -4$$
> $$x = \pm\sqrt{-4} \quad \text{Not a real number}$$

4. The vertex is $(0, -4)$. This is also the y-intercept.

5. Sketch the parabola through the y-intercept and vertex (Figure 16-5).

    To gauge how "wide" to graph the parabola, find additional points to the right or left of the vertex and use the symmetry of the parabola to sketch the curve.

x	y
1	-5
2	-8
3	-13

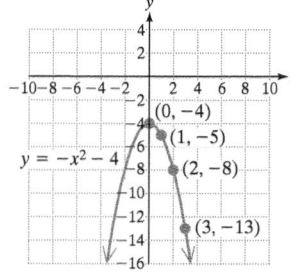

Figure 16-5

Skill Practice

5. Graph $y = x^2 + 1$.

Answer

5.

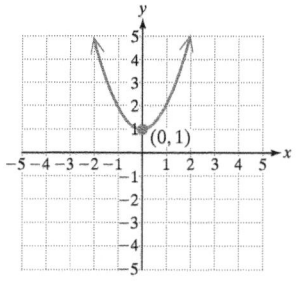

4. Applications of Quadratic Equations

Example 4   Using a Quadratic Equation in an Application

A golfer hits a ball at an angle of 30°. The height of the ball y (in feet) can be represented by

$$y = -16x^2 + 60x$$ where x is the time in seconds after the ball was hit (Figure 16-6).

Find the maximum height of the ball. In how many seconds will the ball reach its maximum height?

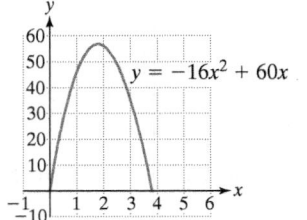

Figure 16-6

Solution:

The equation is written in the form $y = ax^2 + bx + c$, where $a = -16$, $b = 60$, and $c = 0$. Because a is negative, the parabola opens downward. Therefore, the maximum height of the ball occurs at the vertex of the parabola.

The x-coordinate of the vertex is given by

$$x = \frac{-b}{2a} = \frac{-(60)}{2(-16)} = \frac{-60}{-32} = \frac{15}{8}$$

Substituting $x = \dfrac{15}{8}$ into the equation, we have

$$y = -16\left(\frac{15}{8}\right)^2 + 60\left(\frac{15}{8}\right)$$

$$= -16\left(\frac{225}{64}\right) + \frac{900}{8}$$

$$= -\frac{225}{4} + \frac{450}{4}$$

$$= \frac{225}{4}$$

The vertex is $\left(\dfrac{15}{8}, \dfrac{225}{4}\right)$ or equivalently $(1.875, 56.25)$.

The ball reaches its maximum height of 56.25 ft after 1.875 sec.

Calculator Connections

Topic: Evaluating the Maximum or Minimum Value of a Parabola

Some graphing calculators have *Minimum* and *Maximum* features that enable the user to approximate the minimum or maximum value of a parabola. Otherwise, *Zoom* and *Trace* can be used.

For example, the maximum value of the parabola from Example 4, $y = -16x^2 + 60x$, can be found using the *Maximum* feature.

The minimum value of the parabola from Example 2, $y = x^2 - 6x + 9$, can be found using the *Minimum* feature.

Calculator Exercises

For Exercises 1–6, find the vertex of each parabola without using a calculator. Then verify the answer using a graphing calculator.

1. $y = x^2 + 4x + 7$ **2.** $y = x^2 - 20x + 105$ **3.** $y = -x^2 - 3x - 4.85$

4. $y = -x^2 + 3.5x - 0.5625$ **5.** $y = 2x^2 - 10x + \dfrac{25}{2}$ **6.** $y = 3x^2 + 16x + \dfrac{64}{3}$

7. Use a graphing calculator to graph the equations on the same screen. Describe the relationship between the graph of $y = x^2$ and the graphs in parts (b) and (c).

     a. $y = x^2$ **b.** $y = x^2 + 4$ **c.** $y = x^2 - 3$

8. Use a graphing calculator to graph the equations on the same screen. Describe the relationship between the graph of $y = x^2$ and the graphs in parts (b) and (c).

     a. $y = x^2$ **b.** $y = (x - 3)^2$ **c.** $y = (x + 2)^2$

9. Use a graphing calculator to graph the equations on the same screen. Describe the relationship between the graph of $y = x^2$ and the graphs in parts (b) and (c).

     a. $y = x^2$ **b.** $y = 2x^2$ **c.** $y = \frac{1}{2}x^2$

10. Use a graphing calculator to graph the equations on the same screen. Describe the relationship between the graph of $y = x^2$ and the graphs in parts (b) and (c).

     a. $y = x^2$ **b.** $y = -2x^2$ **c.** $y = -\frac{1}{2}x^2$

Section 16.4 Practice Exercises

Study Skills Exercise

1. Define the key terms.

   a. **Quadratic equation in two variables**   b. **Parabola**
   c. **Vertex of a parabola**   d. **Axis of symmetry**

Review Exercises

For Exercises 2–8, solve the quadratic equations using any one of the following methods: factoring, the square root property, or the quadratic formula.

2. $3(y^2 + 1) = 10y$ **3.** $3 + a(a + 2) = 18$ **4.** $4t^2 - 7 = 0$ **5.** $2z^2 + 4z - 10 = 0$

6. $(b + 1)^2 = 6$ **7.** $(x - 2)^2 = 8$ **8.** $3p^2 - 12p - 12 = 0$

Objective 1: Quadratic Equations in Two Variables

For Exercises 9–20, identify the equations as linear, quadratic, or neither.

9. $y = -8x + 3$ **10.** $y = 5x - 12$ **11.** $y = 4x^2 - 8x + 22$ **12.** $y = x^2 + 10x - 3$

13. $y = -5x^3 - 8x + 14$ **14.** $y = -3x^4 + 7x - 11$ **15.** $y = 15x$ **16.** $y = -9x$

17. $y = -21x^2$ **18.** $y = 3x^2$ **19.** $y = -x^3 + 1$ **20.** $y = 7x^4 - 4$

Objective 2: Vertex of a Parabola

21. How do you determine whether the graph of the parabola $y = ax^2 + bx + c$ $(a \neq 0)$ opens upward or downward?

For Exercises 22–25, identify a and determine if the parabola opens upward or downward. **(See Example 1.)**

22. $y = x^2 - 15$ **23.** $y = 2x^2 + 23$ **24.** $y = -3x^2 + x - 18$ ⬤ **25.** $y = -10x^2 - 6x - 20$

26. How do you find the vertex of a parabola?

For Exercises 27–34, find the vertex of the parabola. **(See Example 1.)**

⬤ **27.** $y = 2x^2 + 4x - 6$ **28.** $y = x^2 - 4x - 4$ **29.** $y = -x^2 + 2x - 5$ **30.** $y = 2x^2 - 4x - 6$

31. $y = x^2 - 2x + 3$ **32.** $y = -x^2 + 4x - 2$ **33.** $y = 3x^2 - 4$ **34.** $y = 4x^2 - 1$

Objective 3: Graphing a Parabola

For Exercises 35–38, find the x- and y-intercepts. Then match each equation with its graph. **(See Example 1.)**

35. $y = x^2 - 7$ **36.** $y = x^2 - 9$ **37.** $y = (x + 3)^2 - 4$ **38.** $y = (x - 2)^2 - 1$

a.   **b.**   **c.**   **d.**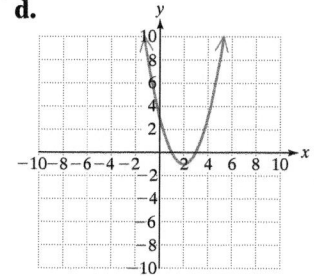

For Exercises 39–50, **(See Examples 1–3.)**

   a. Determine whether the graph of the parabola opens upward or downward.

   b. Find the vertex.

   c. Find the x-intercept(s), if possible.

   d. Find the y-intercept.

   e. Sketch the parabola.

39. $y = x^2 - 9$

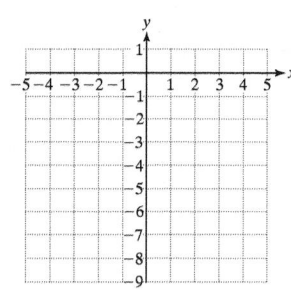

40. $y = x^2 - 4$

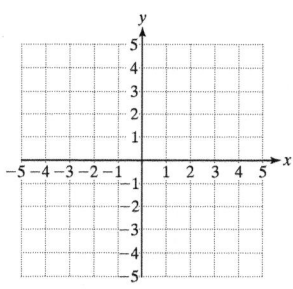

41. $y = x^2 - 2x - 8$

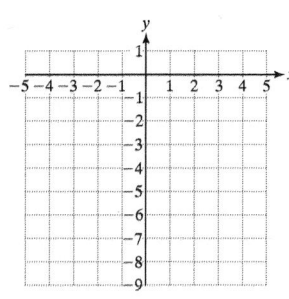

42. $y = x^2 + 2x - 24$

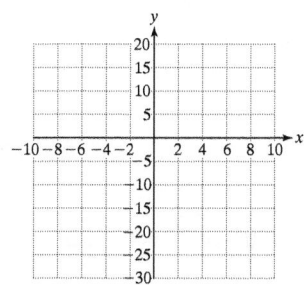

43. $y = -x^2 + 6x - 9$

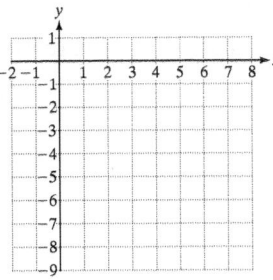

44. $y = -x^2 + 10x - 25$

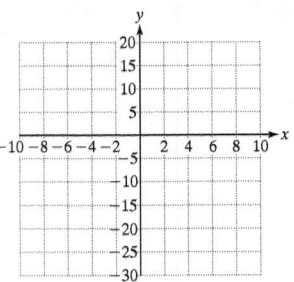

45. $y = -x^2 + 8x - 15$

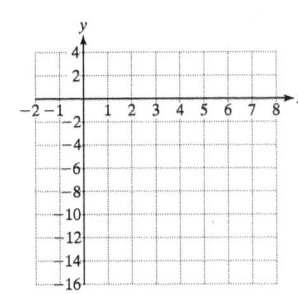

46. $y = -x^2 - 4x + 5$

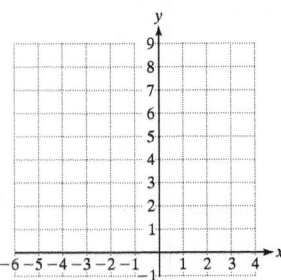

47. $y = x^2 + 6x + 10$

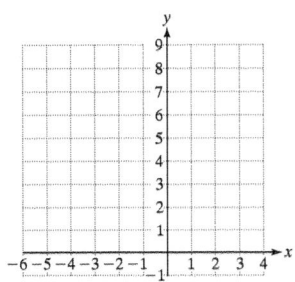

48. $y = x^2 + 4x + 5$

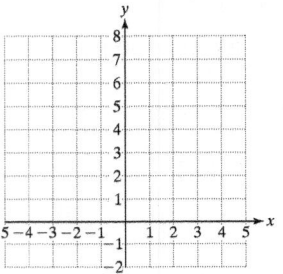

49. $y = -2x^2 - 2$

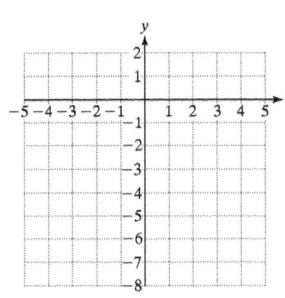

50. $y = -x^2 - 5$

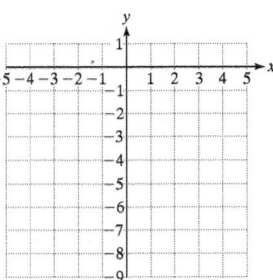

51. True or False: The parabola $y = -5x^2$ has a maximum value but no minimum value.

52. True or False: The graph of $y = -4x^2 + 9x - 6$ opens upward.

53. True or False: The graph of $y = 1.5x^2 - 6x - 3$ opens downward.

54. True or False: The parabola $y = 2x^2 - 5x + 4$ has a maximum value but no minimum value.

Objective 4: Applications of Quadratic Equations

55. A child kicks a ball into the air, and the height of the ball, y (in feet), can be approximated by

$y = -16t^2 + 40t + 3$ where t is the number of seconds after the ball was kicked.

a. Find the maximum height of the ball. **(See Example 4.)**

b. How long will it take the ball to reach its maximum height?

56. A concession stand at the Arthur Ashe Tennis Center sells a hamburger/drink combination dinner for $5. The profit, y (in dollars), can be approximated by

$y = -0.001x^2 + 3.6x - 400$ where x is the number of dinners prepared.

a. Find the number of dinners that should be prepared to maximize profit.

b. What is the maximum profit?

57. For a fund raising activity, a charitable organization produces calendars to sell in the community. The profit, y (in dollars), can be approximated by

$y = -\dfrac{1}{40}x^2 + 10x - 500$ where x is the number of calendars produced.

a. Find the number of calendars that should be produced to maximize the profit.

b. What is the maximum profit?

58. The pressure, x, in an automobile tire can affect its wear. Both over-inflated and under-inflated tires can lead to poor performance and poor mileage. For one particular tire, the number of miles that a tire lasts, y (in thousands), is given by

$y = -0.875x^2 + 57.25x - 900$ where x is the tire pressure in pounds per square inch (psi).

a. Find the tire pressure that will yield the maximum number of miles that a tire will last. Round to the nearest whole unit.

b. Find the maximum number of miles that a tire will last if the proper tire pressure is maintained. Round to the nearest thousand miles.

Section 16.5 | Introduction to Functions

1. Definition of a Relation

The number of points scored by LeBron James during the first six games of a recent basketball season is shown in Table 16-2.

Table 16-2

Game, x	Number of Points, y		Ordered Pair
1	26	$\longrightarrow$	$(1, 26)$
2	35	$\longrightarrow$	$(2, 35)$
3	16	$\longrightarrow$	$(3, 16)$
4	34	$\longrightarrow$	$(4, 34)$
5	19	$\longrightarrow$	$(5, 19)$
6	38	$\longrightarrow$	$(6, 38)$

Each ordered pair from Table 16-2 shows a correspondence, or relationship, between the game number and the number of points scored by LeBron James. The set of ordered pairs: $\{(1, 26), (2, 35), (3, 16), (4, 34), (5, 19), (6, 38)\}$ defines a relation between the game number and the number of points scored.

DEFINITION Relation in x and y

Any set of ordered pairs, (x, y), is called a **relation** in x and y. Furthermore:

- The set of first components in the ordered pairs is called the **domain** of the relation.
- The set of second components in the ordered pairs is called the **range** of the relation.

Skill Practice

1. Find the domain and range of the relation. $\{(0, 1), (4, 5), (-6, 8), (4, 13), (-8, 8)\}$

Example 1 Finding the Domain and Range of a Relation

Find the domain and range of the relation linking the game number to the number of points scored by James in the first six games of the season:

$$\{(1, 26), (2, 35), (3, 16), (4, 34), (5, 19), (6, 38)\}$$

Solution:

Domain: $\{1, 2, 3, 4, 5, 6\}$ (Set of first coordinates)

Range: $\{26, 35, 16, 34, 19, 38\}$ (Set of second coordinates)

The domain consists of the game numbers for the first six games of the season. The range represents the corresponding number of points.

Answer

1. Domain: $\{0, 4, -6, -8\}$;
   Range: $\{1, 5, 8, 13\}$

Example 2 Finding the Domain and Range of a Relation

The three women represented in Figure 16-7 each have children. Molly has one child, Peggy has two children, and Joanne has three children.

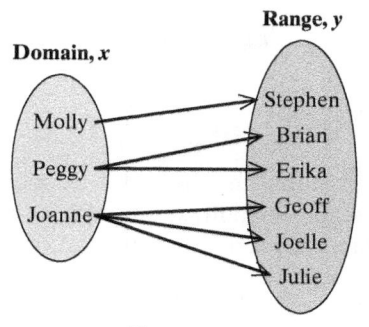

a. If the set of mothers is given as the domain and the set of children is the range, write a set of ordered pairs defining the relation given in Figure 16-7.

b. Write the domain and range of the relation.

Figure 16-7

Solution:

a. {(Molly, Stephen), (Peggy, Brian), (Peggy, Erika), (Joanne, Geoff), (Joanne, Joelle), (Joanne, Julie)}

b. Domain: {Molly, Peggy, Joanne}
Range: {Stephen, Brian, Erika, Geoff, Joelle, Julie}

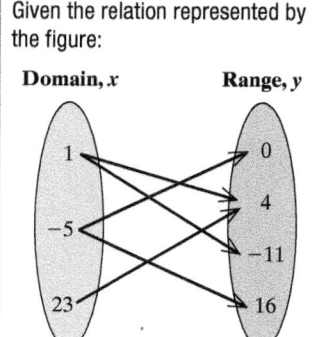
2. Definition of a Function

In mathematics, a special type of relation, called a function, is used extensively.

DEFINITION Function

Given a relation in x and y, we say "y is a **function** of x" if for each element x in the domain, there is exactly one value of y in the range.

Note: This means that no two ordered pairs may have the same first coordinate and different second coordinates.

To understand the difference between a relation that is a function and one that is not a function, consider Example 3.

Example 3 Determining Whether a Relation Is a Function

Determine whether the following relations are functions:

a. $\{(2, -3), (4, 1), (3, -1), (2, 4)\}$ **b.** $\{(-3, 1), (0, 2), (4, -3), (1, 5), (-2, 1)\}$

Solution:

a. This relation is defined by the set of ordered pairs.

same x-values

$$\{(2, -3), (4, 1), (3, -1), (2, 4)\}$$

different y-values

When $x = 2$, there are two possibilities for y: $y = -3$ and $y = 4$.

This relation is *not* a function because for $x = 2$, there is more than one corresponding element in the range.

b. This relation is defined by the set of ordered pairs: $\{(-3, 1), (0, 2), (4, -3), (1, 5), (-2, 1)\}$. Notice that no two ordered pairs have the same value of x but different values of y. Therefore, this relation *is* a function.

In Example 2, the relation linking the set of mothers with their respective children is *not* a function. The domain elements, "Peggy" and "Joanne," each have more than one child. Because these *x*-values in the domain have more than one corresponding *y*-value in the range, the relation is not a function.

3. Vertical Line Test

A relation that is not a function has at least one domain element, *x*, paired with more than one range element, *y*. For example, the ordered pairs (2, 1) and (2, 4) do not make a function. On a graph, these two points are aligned vertically in the *xy*-plane, and a vertical line drawn through one point also intersects the other point (Figure 16-8). Thus, if a vertical line drawn through a graph of a relation intersects the graph in more than one point, the relation cannot be a function. This idea is stated formally as the **vertical line test**.

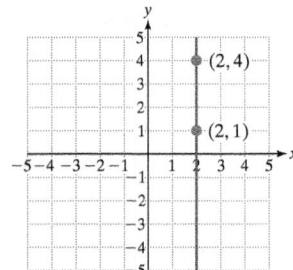

Figure 16-8

PROCEDURE Using the Vertical Line Test

Consider a relation defined by a set of points (*x*, *y*) on a rectangular coordinate system. Then the graph defines *y* as a function of *x* if no vertical line intersects the graph in more than one point.

The vertical line test also implies that if any vertical line drawn through the graph of a relation intersects the relation in more than one point, then the relation does *not* define *y* as a function of *x*.

The vertical line test can be demonstrated by graphing the ordered pairs from the relations in Example 3 (Figure 16-9 and Figure 16-10).

$$\{(2, -3), (4, 1), (3, -1), (2, 4)\} \qquad \{(-3, 1), (0, 2), (4, -3), (1, 5), (-2, 1)\}$$

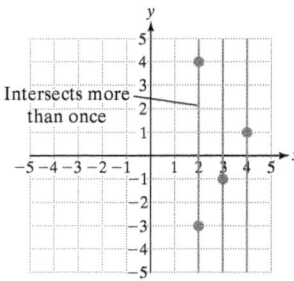

Figure 16-9

Not a Function

A vertical line intersects in
more than one point.

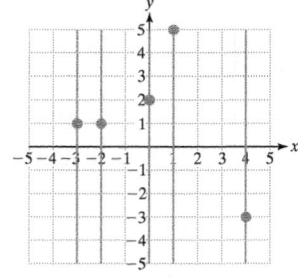

Figure 16-10

Function

No vertical line intersects
more than once.

The relations in Examples 1, 2, and 3 consist of a finite number of ordered pairs. A relation may, however, consist of an *infinite* number of points defined by an equation or by a graph. For example, the equation $y = x + 1$ defines infinitely many ordered pairs whose *y*-coordinate is one more than its *x*-coordinate. These ordered pairs cannot all be listed but can be depicted in a graph.

The vertical line test is especially helpful in determining whether a relation is a function based on its graph.

Example 4 **Using the Vertical Line Test**

Use the vertical line test to determine whether the following relations are functions.

a.

b.

Solution:

a.

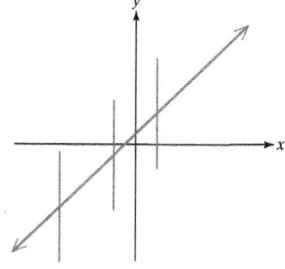

Function
No vertical line intersects
more than once.

b.

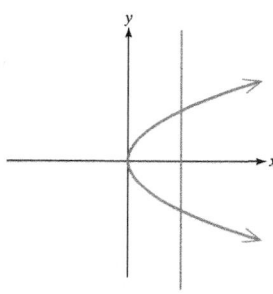

Not a Function
A vertical line intersects
in more than one point.

4. Function Notation

A function is defined as a relation with the added restriction that each value of the domain corresponds to only one value in the range. In mathematics, functions are often given by rules or equations to define the relationship between two or more variables. For example, the equation, $y = x + 1$ defines the set of ordered pairs such that the y-value is one more than the x-value.

When a function is defined by an equation, we often use **function notation**. For example, the equation $y = x + 1$ may be written in function notation as

$$f(x) = x + 1$$

where f is the name of the function, x is an input value from the domain of the function, and $f(x)$ is the function value (or y-value) corresponding to x.

The notation $f(x)$ is read as "f of x" or "the value of the function, f, at x."

A function may be evaluated at different values of x by substituting values of x from the domain into the function. For example, for the function defined by $f(x) = x + 1$ we can evaluate f at $x = 3$ by using substitution.

$$f(x) = x + 1$$

$$f(3) = (3) + 1$$

$$f(3) = 4 \qquad \text{This is read as "}f\text{ of 3 equals 4."}$$

Thus, when $x = 3$, the corresponding function value is 4. This can also be interpreted as an ordered pair: $(3, 4)$

The names of functions are often given by either lowercase letters or uppercase letters such as f, g, h, p, k, M, and so on.

Avoiding Mistakes

The notation $f(x)$ is read as "f of x"
and does *not* imply multiplication.

Answers

6. Function   **7.** Not a function

Skill Practice

Given the function defined by $f(x) = x^2 - 5x$, find the function values.

8. $f(1)$ **9.** $f(0)$
10. $f(-3)$ **11.** $f(2)$
12. $f(-1)$

Example 5 **Evaluating a Function**

Given the function defined by $h(x) = x^2 - 2$, find the function values.

a. $h(0)$ **b.** $h(1)$ **c.** $h(2)$ **d.** $h(-1)$ **e.** $h(-2)$

Solution:

a. $h(x) = x^2 - 2$

$h(0) = (0)^2 - 2$ Substitute $x = 0$ into the function.

$= 0 - 2$

$= -2$ $h(0) = -2$ means that when $x = 0, y = -2$, yielding the ordered pair $(0, -2)$.

b. $h(x) = x^2 - 2$

$h(1) = (1)^2 - 2$ Substitute $x = 1$ into the function.

$= 1 - 2$

$= -1$ $h(1) = -1$ means that when $x = 1, y = -1$, yielding the ordered pair $(1, -1)$.

c. $h(x) = x^2 - 2$

$h(2) = (2)^2 - 2$ Substitute $x = 2$ into the function.

$= 4 - 2$

$= 2$ $h(2) = 2$ means that when $x = 2, y = 2$, yielding the ordered pair $(2, 2)$.

d. $h(x) = x^2 - 2$

$h(-1) = (-1)^2 - 2$ Substitute $x = -1$ into the function.

$= 1 - 2$

$= -1$ $h(-1) = -1$ means that when $x = -1, y = -1$, yielding the ordered pair $(-1, -1)$.

e. $h(x) = x^2 - 2$

$h(-2) = (-2)^2 - 2$ Substitute $x = -2$ into the function.

$= 4 - 2$

$= 2$ $h(-2) = 2$ means that when $x = -2, y = 2$, yielding the ordered pair $(-2, 2)$.

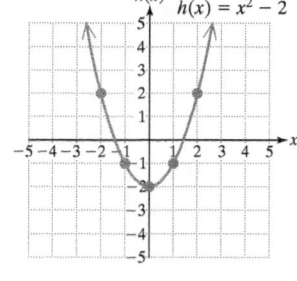

Figure 16-11

The rule $h(x) = x^2 - 2$ is equivalent to the equation $y = x^2 - 2$. The function values $h(0), h(1), h(2), h(-1)$, and $h(-2)$ correspond to the y-values in the ordered pairs $(0, -2), (1, -1), (2, 2), (-1, -1)$, and $(-2, 2)$, respectively. These points can be used to sketch a graph of the function (Figure 16-11).

Answers

8. -4 **9.** 0 **10.** 24
11. -6 **12.** 6

5. Domain and Range of a Function

A function is a relation, and it is often necessary to determine its domain and range. Consider a function defined by the equation $y = f(x)$. The domain of f is the set of all x-values within the ordered pairs that make up the function. The range is the set of y-values.

Example 6 **Finding the Domain and Range of a Function**

Find the domain and range of the functions based on the graph of the function. Express the answers in interval notation.

a.

b.

Solution:

a.

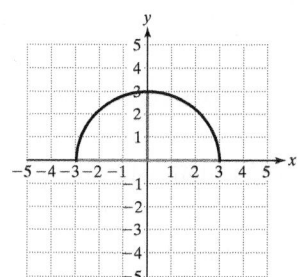

The horizontal "span" of the graph is determined by the x-values of the points. This is the domain. In this graph, the x-values in the domain are bounded between -3 and 3 (shown in blue).

Domain: $[-3, 3]$

The vertical "span" of the graph is determined by the y-values of the points. This is the range.

The y-values in the range are bounded between 0 and 3 (shown in red).

Range: $[0, 3]$

b.

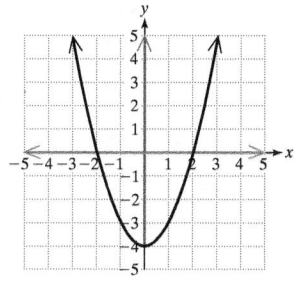

The function extends infinitely far to the left and right. The domain is shown in blue.

Domain: $(-\infty, \infty)$

The y-values extend infinitely far in the positive direction, but are bounded below at $y = -4$ (shown in red).

Range: $[-4, \infty)$

13.

14.

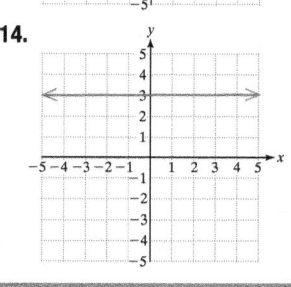

Answers

13. Domain: $[0, 5]$
Range: $[2, 4]$
14. Domain: $(-\infty, \infty)$
Range: $\{3\}$

6. Applications of Functions

Example 7   Using a Function in an Application

The score a student receives on an exam is a function of the number of hours the student spends studying. The function defined by

$$P(x) = \frac{100x^2}{40 + x^2} \quad (x \geq 0)$$

indicates that a student will achieve a score of $P\%$ after studying for x hours.

a. Evaluate $P(0)$, $P(10)$, and $P(20)$.

b. Interpret the function values from part (a) in the context of this problem.

Solution:

a. $P(x) = \dfrac{100x^2}{40 + x^2}$

$$P(0) = \frac{100(0)^2}{40 + (0)^2} \qquad P(10) = \frac{100(10)^2}{40 + (10)^2} \qquad P(20) = \frac{100(20)^2}{40 + (20)^2}$$

$$P(0) = \frac{0}{40} \qquad\qquad P(10) = \frac{10{,}000}{140} \qquad\qquad P(20) = \frac{40{,}000}{440}$$

$$P(0) = 0 \qquad\qquad P(10) = \frac{500}{7} \approx 71.4 \qquad P(20) = \frac{1000}{11} \approx 90.9$$

b. $P(0) = 0$ means that for 0 hr spent studying, the student will receive 0% on the exam.

$P(10) \approx 71.4$ means that for 10 hr spent studying, the student will receive approximately 71.4% on the exam.

$P(20) \approx 90.9$ means that for 20 hr spent studying, the student will receive approximately 90.9% on the exam.

The graph of $P(x) = \dfrac{100x^2}{40 + x^2}$ is shown in Figure 16-12.

Student Score (Percent) as a Function of Study Time

Figure 16-12

Calculator Connections

Topic: Graphing Functions

A graphing calculator can be used to graph a function. We replace $f(x)$ by y and enter the defining expression into the calculator. For example,

$$f(x) = \frac{1}{4}x^3 - x^2 - x + 4 \quad \text{becomes} \quad y = \frac{1}{4}x^3 - x^2 - x + 4.$$

Calculator Exercises

Use a graphing calculator to graph the following functions.

1. $f(x) = x^2 - 5x + 2$ **2.** $g(x) = -x^2 + 4x + 5$

3. $m(x) = \frac{1}{3}x^3 + x^2 - 3x - 1$ **4.** $n(x) = x^3 - 9x$

Section 16.5   Practice Exercises

Study Skills Exercises

1. Define the key terms:

     a. Domain   **b. Function**   **c. Function notation**

     d. Range   **e. Relation**   **f. Vertical line test**

Review Exercises

For Exercises 2–4, refer to the equation $y = x^2 - 2x - 3$.

2. Find the vertex of the parabola.

3. Does the parabola open upward or downward?

4. Find the x- and y-intercepts.

Objective 1: Definition of a Relation

For Exercises 5–14, determine the domain and range of the relation. **(See Examples 1–2.)**

5. $\{(4, 2), (3, 7), (4, 1), (0, 6)\}$ **6.** $\{(-3, -1), (-2, 6), (1, 3), (1, -2)\}$

7. $\{(\frac{1}{2}, 3), (0, 3), (1, 3)\}$ **8.** $\{(9, 6), (4, 6), (-\frac{1}{3}, 6)\}$

9. $\{(0, 0), (5, 0), (-8, 2), (8, 5)\}$ **10.** $\{(\frac{1}{2}, -\frac{1}{2}), (-4, 0), (0, -\frac{1}{2}), (\frac{1}{2}, 0)\}$

11.

12.

13.

14.

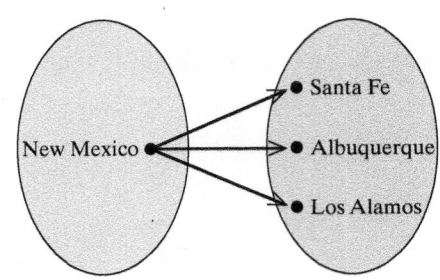

Objective 2: Definition of a Function

15. How can you tell if a set of ordered pairs represents a function?

16. Refer back to Exercises 6, 8, 10, 12, and 14. Identify which relations are functions.

17. Refer back to Exercises 5, 7, 9, 11, and 13. Identify which relations are functions. **(See Example 3.)**

Objective 3: Vertical Line Test

18. How can you tell from the graph of a relation if the relation is a function?

For Exercises 19–27, determine if the relation defines y as a function of x. **(See Example 4.)**

19.

20.

21.

22.

23.

24.

25.

26.

27.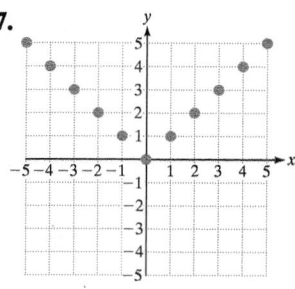

Objective 4: Function Notation

28. Explain how you would evaluate $f(x) = 3x^2$ at $x = -1$.

For Exercises 29–36, evaluate the given functions. **(See Example 5.)**

29. Let $f(x) = 2x - 5$.

Find: $f(0)$
  $f(2)$
  $f(-3)$

30. Let $g(x) = x^2 + 1$.

Find: $g(0)$
  $g(-1)$
  $g(3)$

31. Let $h(x) = \dfrac{1}{x + 4}$.

Find: $h(1)$ $\frac{1}{5}$
  $h(0)$ $\frac{1}{4}$
  $h(-2)$ $\frac{1}{2}$

32. Let $p(x) = \sqrt{x + 4}$.

Find: $p(0)$
  $p(-4)$
  $p(5)$

33. Let $m(x) = |5x - 7|$.

Find: $m(0)$
  $m(1)$
  $m(2)$

34. Let $w(x) = |2x - 3|$.

Find: $w(0)$
  $w(1)$
  $w(2)$

35. Let $n(x) = \sqrt{x - 2}$.

Find: $n(2)$
  $n(3)$
  $n(6)$

36. Let $t(x) = \dfrac{1}{x - 3}$.

Find: $t(1)$ $\frac{1}{2}$
  $t(-1)$ $\frac{1}{4}$
  $t(2)$

Objective 5: Domain and Range of a Function

For Exercises 37–40, match the domain and range given with a possible graph. **(See Example 6.)**

37. Domain: $(-\infty, \infty)$

Range: $[1, \infty)$

38. Domain: $[-4, 4]$

Range: $[-2, 0]$

39. Domain: $[-2, \infty)$

Range: $(-\infty, 0]$

40. Domain: $(-\infty, \infty)$

Range: $(-\infty, \infty)$

a.

b.

c.

d.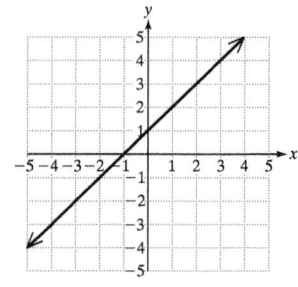

For Exercises 41–44, translate the expressions into English phrases.

41. $f(6) = 2$ **42.** $f(-2) = -14$ **43.** $g\left(\dfrac{1}{2}\right) = \dfrac{1}{4}$ **44.** $h(k) = k^2$

45. Consider a function defined by $y = f(x)$. The function value $f(2) = 7$ corresponds to what ordered pair?

46. Consider a function defined by $y = f(x)$. The function value $f(-3) = -4$ corresponds to what ordered pair?

47. Consider a function defined by $y = f(x)$. The function value $f(0) = 8$ corresponds to what ordered pair?

48. Consider a function defined by $y = f(x)$. The function value $f(4) = 0$ corresponds to what ordered pair?

Objective 6: Applications of Functions

49. In the absence of air resistance, the speed, s (in feet per second: ft/sec), of an object in free fall is a function of the number of seconds, t, after it was dropped: **(See Example 7.)**

$$s(t) = 32t$$

a. Find $s(1)$ and interpret the meaning of this function value in terms of speed and time.

b. Find $s(2)$ and interpret the meaning in terms of speed and time.

c. Find $s(10)$ and interpret the meaning in terms of speed and time.

d. A ball dropped from the top of the Sears Tower in Chicago falls for approximately 9.2 sec. How fast was the ball going the instant before it hit the ground?

50. The number of people diagnosed with skin cancer, $N(x)$, can be approximated by $N(x) = 45{,}625(1 + 0.029x)$. For this function, x represents the number of years since 2003. (*Source:* Centers for Disease Control)

a. Evaluate $N(0)$ and interpret its meaning in the context of this problem.

b. Evaluate $N(7)$ and interpret its meaning in the context of this problem. Round to the nearest whole number.

51. A punter kicks a football straight up with an initial velocity of 64 ft/sec. The height of the ball, h (in feet), is a function of the number of seconds, t, after the ball is kicked:

$$h(t) = -16t^2 + 64t + 3$$

a. Find $h(0)$ and interpret the meaning of the function value in terms of time and height.

b. Find $h(1)$ and interpret the meaning in terms of time and height.

c. Find $h(2)$ and interpret the meaning in terms of time and height.

d. Find $h(4)$ and interpret the meaning in terms of time and height.

52. For people 16 years old and older, the maximum recommended heart rate, M (in beats per minute: beats/min), is a function of a person's age, x (in years).

$$M(x) = 220 - x \text{ for } x \geq 16$$

a. Find $M(16)$ and interpret the meaning in terms of maximum recommended heart rate and age.

b. Find $M(30)$ and interpret the meaning in terms of maximum recommended heart rate and age.

c. Find $M(60)$ and interpret the meaning in terms of maximum recommended heart rate and age.

d. Find your own maximum recommended heart rate.

Group Activity

Maximizing Volume

Materials: A calculator and a sheet of $8\frac{1}{2}$ by 11 in. paper.

Estimated Time: 25–30 minutes

Group Size: 3

Antonio is going to build a custom gutter system for his house. He plans to use rectangular strips of aluminum that are $8\frac{1}{2}$ in. wide and 72 in. long. Each piece of aluminum will be turned up at a distance of x in. from the sides to form a gutter. See Figure 16-13.

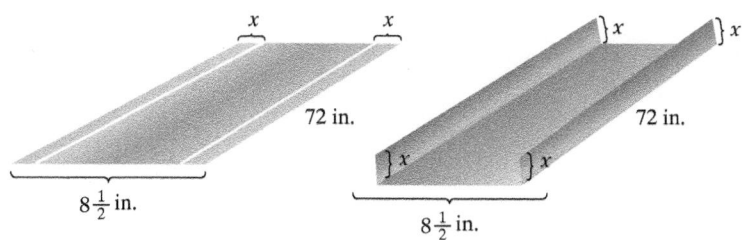

Figure 16-13

Antonio wants to maximize the volume of water that the gutters can hold. To do this, he must determine the distance, x, that should be turned up to form the height of the gutter.

1. To familiarize yourself with this problem, we will simulate the gutter problem using an $8\frac{1}{2}$ by 11 in. piece of paper. For each value of x in the table, turn up the sides of the paper x in. from the edge. Then measure the base, the height, and the length of the paper "gutter," and calculate the volume.

Height, x	Base	Length	Volume
0.5 in.		11 in.	
1.0 in.		11 in.	
1.5 in.		11 in.	
2.0 in.		11 in.	
2.5 in.		11 in.	
3.0 in.		11 in.	
3.5 in.		11 in.	

2. Now follow these steps to find the optimal distance, x, that you should fold the paper to make the greatest volume within the paper gutter.

   a. If the height of the paper gutter is x in., write an expression for the base of the paper gutter.

   b. Write a function for the volume of the paper gutter.

   c. Find the vertex of the parabola defined by the function in part (b).

   d. Interpret the meaning of the vertex from part (c).

3. Use the concept from the paper gutter to write a function for the volume of Antonio's aluminum gutter that is 72 in. long.

4. Now find the optimal distance, x, that he should fold the aluminum sheet to make the greatest volume within the 72-in.-long aluminum gutter. What is the maximum volume?

Chapter 16   Summary

Section 16.1   The Square Root Property

Key Concepts

Square Root Property

If $x^2 = k$, then $x = \pm\sqrt{k}$.

The square root property can be used to solve a quadratic equation written as a square of a binomial equal to a constant.

Example

Example 1

$$(x - 5)^2 = 13$$

$$x - 5 = \pm\sqrt{13} \qquad \text{Square root property}$$

$$x = 5 \pm \sqrt{13} \qquad \text{Solve for } x.$$

Section 16.2   Completing the Square

Key Concepts

Solving a Quadratic Equation of the Form
$ax^2 + bx + c = 0$ ($a \neq 0$) **by Completing the Square and Applying the Square Root Property**

1. Divide both sides by a to make the leading coefficient 1.
2. Isolate the variable terms on one side of the equation.
3. Complete the square by adding the square of $\frac{1}{2}$ the linear term coefficient to both sides of the equation. Then factor the resulting perfect square trinomial.
4. Apply the square root property and solve for x.

Example

Example 1

$$2x^2 - 8x - 6 = 0$$

Step 1: $\dfrac{2x^2}{2} - \dfrac{8x}{2} - \dfrac{6}{2} = \dfrac{0}{2}$

$$x^2 - 4x - 3 = 0$$

Step 2: $x^2 - 4x = 3$

Step 3: $x^2 - 4x + 4 = 3 + 4$ Note that

$$(x - 2)^2 = 7 \qquad [\tfrac{1}{2}(-4)]^2 = (-2)^2 = 4$$

Step 4: $\qquad x - 2 = \pm\sqrt{7}$

$$x = 2 \pm \sqrt{7}$$

Section 16.3   Quadratic Formula

Key Concepts

The solutions to a quadratic equation of the form $ax^2 + bx + c = 0$ $(a \neq 0)$ are given by the **quadratic formula**:

$$x = \frac{-b \pm \sqrt{b^2 - 4ac}}{2a}$$

Three Methods for Solving a Quadratic Equation

1. Factoring
2. Completing the square and applying the square root property
3. Using the quadratic formula

Example

Example 1

$$3x^2 = 2x + 4$$

$$3x^2 - 2x - 4 = 0 \qquad a = 3, b = -2, c = -4$$

$$x = \frac{-(-2) \pm \sqrt{(-2)^2 - 4(3)(-4)}}{2(3)}$$

$$= \frac{2 \pm \sqrt{4 + 48}}{6}$$

$$= \frac{2 \pm \sqrt{52}}{6}$$

$$= \frac{2 \pm 2\sqrt{13}}{6} \qquad \text{Simplify the radical.}$$

$$= \frac{2(1 \pm \sqrt{13})}{6} \qquad \text{Factor.}$$

$$= \frac{1 \pm \sqrt{13}}{3} \qquad \text{Simplify.}$$

Section 16.4   Graphing Quadratic Equations

Key Concepts

Let a, b, and c represent real numbers such that $a \neq 0$. Then an equation in the form $y = ax^2 + bx + c$ is called a **quadratic equation in two variables**.

The graph of a quadratic equation in two variables is called a **parabola**.

The leading coefficient, a, of a quadratic equation, $y = ax^2 + bx + c$, determines if the parabola will open upward or downward. If $a > 0$, then the parabola opens upward. If $a < 0$, then the parabola opens downward.

Finding the Vertex of a Parabola

1. The x-coordinate of the vertex of the parabola with equation $y = ax^2 + bx + c$ $(a \neq 0)$ is given by

$$x = \frac{-b}{2a}$$

2. To find the corresponding y-coordinate of the vertex, substitute the value of the x-coordinate found in step 1 and solve for y.

If a parabola opens upward, the vertex is the lowest point on the graph. If a parabola opens downward, the vertex is the highest point on the graph.

Examples

Example 1

$y = x^2 - 4x - 3$ is a quadratic equation. Its graph is in the shape of a parabola.

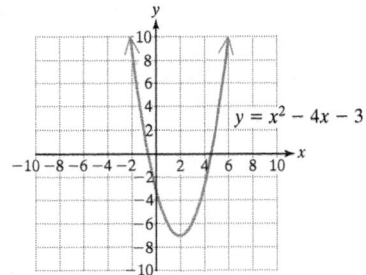

Example 2

Find the vertex of the parabola defined by $y = 3x^2 + 6x - 1$.

$$x = \frac{-b}{2a} = \frac{-6}{2 \cdot 3} = -1$$

$$y = 3(-1)^2 + 6(-1) - 1 = -4$$

The vertex is $(-1, -4)$.

For the equation $y = 3x^2 + 6x - 1$, $a = 3 > 0$. Therefore, the parabola opens upward. The vertex $(-1, -4)$ represents the lowest point of the graph.

Section 16.5 Introduction to Functions

Key Concepts

Any set of ordered pairs, (x, y), is called a **relation** in x and y.

The **domain** of a relation is the set of first components in the ordered pairs in the relation. The **range** of a relation is the set of second components in the ordered pairs.

Given a relation in x and y, we say "y is a **function** of x" if for each element x in the domain, there is exactly one value y in the range.

Vertical Line Test for Functions

Consider any relation defined by a set of points (x, y) on a rectangular coordinate system. Then the graph defines y as a function of x if no vertical line intersects the graph in more than one point.

Function Notation

$f(x)$ is the value of the function, f, at x.

Examples

Example 1

Find the domain and range of the relation.

$\{(0, 0), (1, 1), (2, 4), (3, 9), (-1, 1), (-2, 4), (-3, 9)\}$

Domain: $\{0, 1, 2, 3, -1, -2, -3\}$

Range: $\{0, 1, 4, 9\}$

Example 2

Function: $\{(1, 3), (2, 5), (6, 3)\}$

Not a function: $\{(1, 3), (2, 5), (1, -2)\}$

different y-values for the same x-value

Example 3

 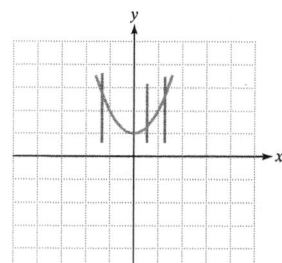

Not a Function
Vertical line intersects more than once.

Function
No vertical line intersects more than once.

Example 4

Given $f(x) = -3x^2 + 5x$, find $f(-2)$.

$f(-2) = -3(-2)^2 + 5(-2)$

$= -12 - 10$

$= -22$

Chapter 16   Review Exercises

Section 16.1

For Exercises 1–4, identify the equations as linear or quadratic.

1. $5x - 10 = 3x - 6$ **2.** $(x + 6)^2 = 6$

3. $x(x - 4) = 5x - 2$ **4.** $3(x + 6) = 18(x - 1)$

For Exercises 5–12, solve the equations using the square root property.

5. $x^2 = 25$ **6.** $x^2 - 19 = 0$

7. $x^2 + 49 = 0$ **8.** $x^2 = -48$

9. $(x + 1)^2 = 14$ **10.** $(x - 2)^2 = 60$

11. $\left(x - \dfrac{1}{8}\right)^2 = \dfrac{3}{64}$ **12.** $(2x - 3)^2 = 20$

Section 16.2

For Exercises 13–16, find the constant that should be added to each expression to make it a perfect square trinomial.

13. $x^2 + 12x$ **14.** $x^2 - 18x$

15. $x^2 - 5x$ **16.** $x^2 + 7x$

For Exercises 17–20, solve the quadratic equations by completing the square and applying the square root property.

17. $x^2 + 8x + 3 = 0$ **18.** $x^2 - 2x - 4 = 0$

19. $2x^2 - 6x - 6 = 0$ **20.** $3x^2 - 7x - 3 = 0$

21. A right triangle has legs of equal length. If the hypotenuse is 15 ft long, find the length of each leg. Round the answer to the nearest tenth of a foot.

22. A can in the shape of a right circular cylinder holds approximately 362 cm³ of liquid. If the height of the can is 12.1 cm, find the radius of the can. Round to the nearest tenth of a centimeter. (*Hint:* The volume of a right circular cylinder is given by: $V = \pi r^2 h$)

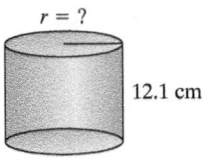

$r = ?$

12.1 cm

Section 16.3

23. Write the quadratic formula from memory.

For Exercises 24–33, solve the quadratic equations using the quadratic formula.

24. $5x^2 + x - 7 = 0$ **25.** $x^2 + 4x + 4 = 0$

26. $3x^2 - 2x + 2 = 0$ **27.** $2x^2 - x - 3 = 0$

28. $\dfrac{1}{8}x^2 + x = \dfrac{5}{2}$ **29.** $\dfrac{1}{6}x^2 + x + \dfrac{1}{3} = 0$

30. $1.2x^2 + 6x = 7.2$

31. $0.01x^2 - 0.02x - 0.04 = 0$

32. $(x + 6)(x + 2) = 10$

33. $(x - 1)(x - 7) = -18$

34. One number is two more than another number. Their product is 11.25. Find the numbers.

35. The base of a parallelogram is 1 cm longer than the height, and the area is 24 cm². Find the exact values of the base and height of the parallelogram. Then use a calculator to approximate the values to the nearest tenth of a centimeter.

36. An astronaut on the moon tosses a rock upward with an initial velocity of 25 ft/sec. The height of the rock, $h(t)$ (in feet), is determined by the number of seconds, t, after the rock is released according to the equation:

$$h(t) = -2.7t^2 + 25t + 5$$

Find the time required for the rock to hit the ground. [*Hint:* At ground level, $h(t) = 0$.] Round to the nearest tenth of a second.

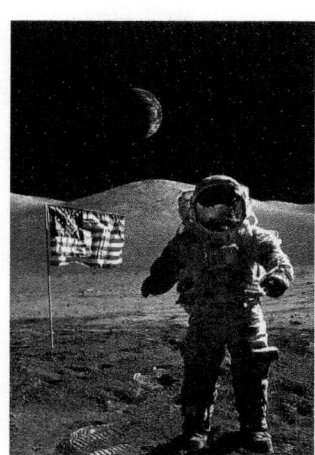

Section 16.4

For Exercises 37–40, identify a and determine if the parabola opens upward or downward.

37. $y = x^2 - 3x + 1$ **38.** $y = -x^2 + 8x + 2$

39. $y = -2x^2 + x - 12$ **40.** $y = 5x^2 - 2x - 6$

For Exercises 41–44, find the vertex for each parabola.

41. $y = 3x^2 + 6x + 4$ **42.** $y = -x^2 + 8x + 3$

43. $y = -2x^2 + 12x - 5$ **44.** $y = 2x^2 + 2x - 1$

For Exercises 45–48,

   a. Determine whether the graph of the parabola opens upward or downward.

   b. Find the vertex.

   c. Find the x-intercept(s) if possible.

   d. Find the y-intercept.

   e. Sketch the parabola.

45. $y = 3x^2 + 12x + 9$

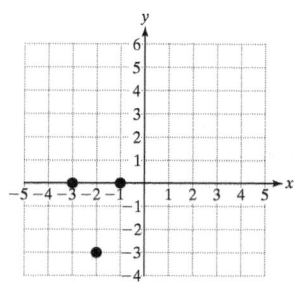

46. $y = -3x^2 + 12x - 10$

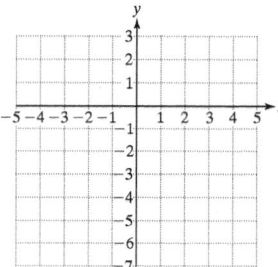

47. $y = -8x^2 - 16x - 12$

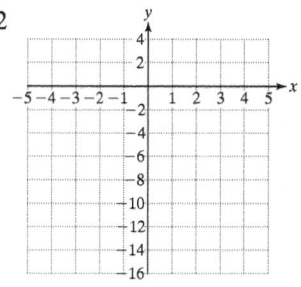

48. $y = 2x^2 + 4x - 1$

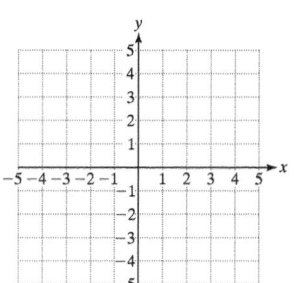

49. An object is launched into the air from ground level with an initial velocity of 256 ft/sec. The height of the object, y (in feet), can be approximated by

$$y = -16t^2 + 256t$$ where t is the number of seconds after launch.

a. Find the maximum height of the object.

b. Find the time required for the object to reach its maximum height.

Section 16.5

For Exercises 50–55, state the domain and range of each relation. Then determine whether the relation is a function.

50. $\{(6, 3), (10, 3), (-1, 3), (0, 3)\}$

51. $\{(2, 0), (2, 1), (2, -5), (2, 2)\}$

52.

53.

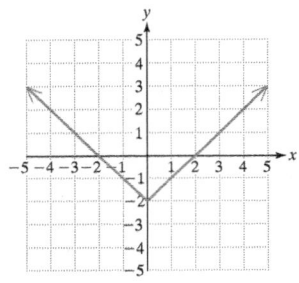

54. $\{(4, 23), (3, -2), (-6, 5), (4, 6)\}$

55. $\{(3, 0), (-4, \frac{1}{2}), (0, 3), (2, -12)\}$

56. Given the function defined by $f(x) = x^3$ find:

a. $f(0)$ **b.** $f(2)$ **c.** $f(-3)$

d. $f(-1)$ **e.** $f(4)$

57. Given the function defined by $g(x) = \dfrac{x}{5 - x}$. Find:

a. $g(0)$ **b.** $g(4)$ **c.** $g(-1)$

d. $g(3)$ **e.** $g(-5)$

58. The landing distance that a certain plane will travel on a runway is determined by the initial landing speed at the instant the plane touches down. The following function relates landing distance, $D(x)$, to initial landing speed, x, where $x \geq 15$.

$$D(x) = \frac{1}{10}x^2 - 3x + 22$$ where D is in feet and x is in feet per second.

a. Find $D(90)$ and interpret the meaning of the function value in terms of landing speed and length of the runway.

b. Find $D(110)$ and interpret the meaning in terms of landing speed and length of the runway.

Chapter 16 Test

1. Solve the equation by applying the square root property.

$$(3x + 1)^2 = -14$$

2. Solve the equation by completing the square and applying the square root property.

$$x^2 - 8x - 5 = 0$$

3. Solve the equation by using the quadratic formula.

$$3x^2 - 5x = -1$$

For Exercises 4–10, solve the equations using any method.

4. $5x^2 + x - 2 = 0$ 5. $(c - 12)^2 = 12$

6. $y^2 + 14y - 1 = 0$ 7. $3t^2 = 30$

8. $4x(3x + 2) = 15$ 9. $6p^2 - 11p = 0$

10. $\frac{1}{4}x^2 - \frac{3}{2}x = \frac{11}{4}$

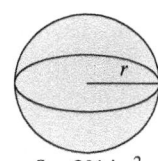

11. The surface area, S, of a sphere is given by the formula $S = 4\pi r^2$, where r is the radius of the sphere. Find the radius of a sphere whose surface area is 201 in.^{2} Round to the nearest tenth of an inch.

$S = 201$ in.^{2}

12. The height of a triangle is 2 m longer than twice the base, and the area is 24 m^2. Find the exact values of the base and height. Then use a calculator to approximate the base and height to the nearest tenth of a meter.

13. Explain how to determine if a parabola opens upward or downward.

For Exercises 14–16, find the vertex of the parabola.

14. $y = x^2 - 10x + 25$ 15. $y = 3x^2 - 6x + 8$

16. $y = -x^2 - 16$

17. Suppose a parabola opens upward and the vertex is located at $(-4, 3)$. How many x-intercepts does the parabola have?

18. Given the parabola, $y = x^2 + 6x + 8$

   a. Determine whether the parabola opens upward or downward.

   b. Find the vertex of the parabola.

   c. Find the x-intercepts.

   d. Find the y-intercept.

   e. Graph the parabola.

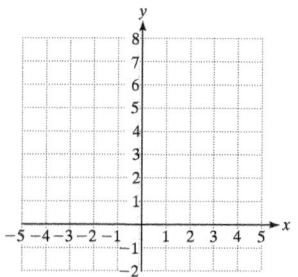

19. Graph the parabola and label the vertex, x-intercepts, and y-intercept.

$$y = -x^2 + 25$$

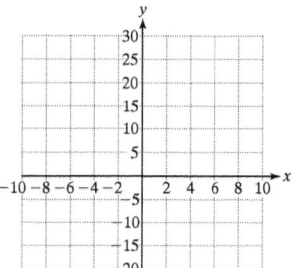

20. The Phelps Arena in Atlanta holds 20,000 seats. If the Atlanta Hawks charge x dollars per ticket for a game, then the total revenue, y (in dollars), can be approximated by

$$y = -400x^2 + 20{,}000x \qquad \text{where } x \text{ is the price per ticket.}$$

   a. Find the ticket price that will produce the maximum revenue.

   b. What is the maximum revenue?

21. Given the relation $\{(0, -1), (2, 3), (-15, -8),$ $(4, 4), (9, -1)\}$:

   a. State the domain.

   b. State the range.

   c. Determine whether the relation is a function.

22. Given the function defined by $f(x) = x^2 - x$, find

   a. $f(3)$ **b.** $f(-3)$

Chapters 1–16   Cumulative Review Exercises

1. Simplify. $-3^2 - 4^2$

2. Solve. $3x - 5 = 2(x - 2)$

3. Solve for h. $A = \frac{1}{2}bh$

4. Solve. $\frac{1}{2}y - \frac{5}{6} = \frac{1}{4}y + 2$

5. Graph the solution to the inequality: $-3x + 4 < x + 8$. Then write the solution in set-builder notation and in interval notation.

---

6. The following data give the ages of 12 students at a college graduation. Find the mean, median, and mode. Round to one decimal place if necessary.

   22 24 24 28 29 29
   52 32 29 40 29 21

7. The triangles are similar. Find the missing value of x.

8. Find the volume.

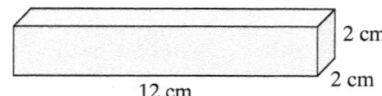

9. The tax on a \$44 pair of slacks was \$2.20. What is the tax rate?

10. Simplify completely. Write the final answer with positive exponents only.

$$\left(\frac{2a^2b^{-3}}{c}\right)^{-1} \cdot \left(\frac{4a^{-1}}{b^2}\right)^2$$

11. Approximately 5.2×10^7 disposable diapers are thrown into the trash each day in the United States and Canada. How many diapers are thrown away each year?

12. Perform the indicated operation.
$(2x - 3)^2 - 4(x - 1)$

13. Divide using long division.
$(2y^4 - 4y^3 + y - 5) \div (y - 2)$

14. Factor. $2x^2 - 9x - 35$

15. Factor completely. $2xy + 8xa - 3by - 12ab$

16. The base of a triangle is 1 m more than the height. If the area is 36 m², find the base and height.

17. Multiply. $\dfrac{x^2 + 10x + 9}{x^2 - 81} \cdot \dfrac{18 - 2x}{x^2 + 2x + 1}$

18. Reduce to lowest terms.
$$\frac{5x + 10}{x^2 - 4}$$

19. Perform the indicated operations.
$$\frac{x^2}{x - 5} - \frac{10x - 25}{x - 5}$$

20. Simplify completely.
$$\frac{\dfrac{1}{x + 1} - \dfrac{1}{x - 1}}{\dfrac{x}{x^2 - 1}}$$

21. Solve.
$$1 - \frac{1}{y} = \frac{12}{y^2}$$

22. At Lake George, a fishing enthusiast must release any fish that is less than 8 inches in length. If a fish is caught and measured at 20 cm, must the fish be released back to the lake? (*Hint:* 1 in. = 2.54 cm)

23. Write an equation of the line passing through the point $(-2, 3)$ and having a slope of $\frac{1}{2}$. Write the final answer in slope-intercept form.

For Exercises 24–25,

    a. Find the x-intercept (if it exists).

    b. Find the y-intercept (if it exists).

    c. Find the slope (if it exists).

    d. Graph the line.

24. $2x - 4y = 12$

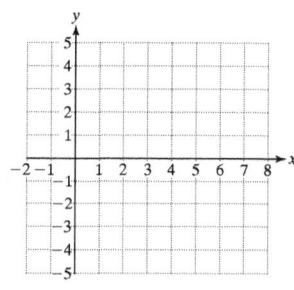

25. $4x + 12 = 0$

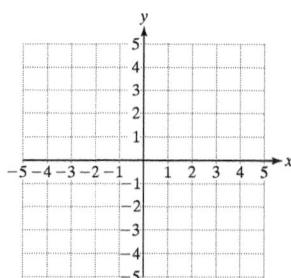

26. Solve the system by using the addition method. If the system has no solution or infinitely many solutions, so state.

$$\frac{1}{2}x - \frac{1}{4}y = \frac{1}{6}$$
$$12x - 3y = 8$$

27. Solve the system by using the substitution method. If the system has no solution or infinitely many solutions, so state.

$$2x - y = 8$$
$$4x - 4y = 3x - 3$$

28. In a right triangle, one acute angle is 2° more than three times the other acute angle. Find the measure of each angle.

29. Sketch the inequality, $x - y \le 4$.

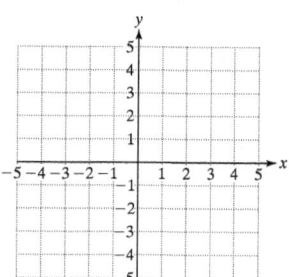

30. Which of the following are irrational numbers? $\{0, -\frac{2}{3}, \pi, \sqrt{7}, 1.2, \sqrt{25}\}$

For Exercises 31–32, simplify the radicals.

31. $\sqrt{\dfrac{1}{7}}$

32. $\dfrac{\sqrt{16x^4}}{\sqrt{2x}}$

33. Perform the indicated operation. $(4\sqrt{3} + \sqrt{x})^2$

34. Add the radicals. $-3\sqrt{2x} + \sqrt{50x}$

35. Rationalize the denominator.

$$\frac{4}{2 - \sqrt{a}}$$

36. Solve. $\sqrt{x + 11} = x + 5$

37. Which graph defines y as a function of x?

    a.   **b.**

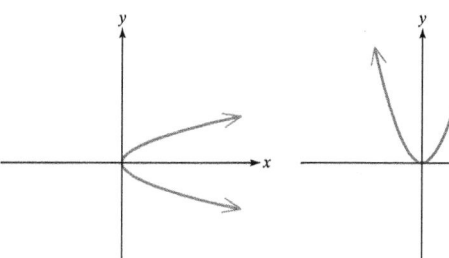

38. Given the functions defined by $f(x) = -\frac{1}{2}x + 4$ and $g(x) = x^2$, find

    a. $f(6)$ **b.** $g(-2)$ **c.** $f(0) + g(3)$

39. Find the domain and range of the function.
$\{(2, 4), (-1, 3), (9, 2), (-6, 8)\}$

40. Find the slope of the line passing through the points $(3, -1)$ and $(-4, -6)$.

41. Find the slope of the line defined by $-4x - 5y = 10$.

42. What value of k would make the expression a perfect square trinomial?

$$x^2 + 10x + k$$

43. Solve the quadratic equation by completing the square and applying the square root property. $2x^2 + 12x + 6 = 0$.

44. Solve the quadratic equation by using the quadratic formula. $2x^2 + 12x + 6 = 0$.

45. Graph the parabola defined by the equation. Label the vertex, x-intercepts, and y-intercept.

$$y = x^2 + 4x + 4$$

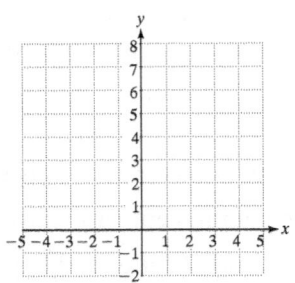

Additional Topic Appendix

Sum and Difference of Cubes

1. Factoring a Sum or Difference of Cubes

A binomial $a^2 - b^2$ is a difference of squares and can be factored as $(a - b)(a + b)$. Furthermore, if a and b share no common factors, then a sum of squares $a^2 + b^2$ is not factorable over the real numbers. In this section, we will learn that both a difference of cubes, $a^3 - b^3$, and a sum of cubes, $a^3 + b^3$, are factorable.

Objectives

1. Factoring a Sum or Difference of Cubes
2. Factoring Binomials: A Summary

FORMULA Factored Form of a Sum or Difference of Cubes

Sum of Cubes: $\qquad\qquad a^3 + b^3 = (a + b)(a^2 - ab + b^2)$

Difference of Cubes: $\qquad a^3 - b^3 = (a - b)(a^2 + ab + b^2)$

Multiplication can be used to confirm the formulas for factoring a sum or difference of cubes:

$$(a + b)(a^2 - ab + b^2) = a^3 - \cancel{a^2b} + \cancel{ab^2} + \cancel{a^2b} - \cancel{ab^2} + b^3 = a^3 + b^3 \;\checkmark$$

$$(a - b)(a^2 + ab + b^2) = a^3 + \cancel{a^2b} + \cancel{ab^2} - \cancel{a^2b} - \cancel{ab^2} - b^3 = a^3 - b^3 \;\checkmark$$

To help you remember the formulas for factoring a sum or difference of cubes, keep the following guidelines in mind:

- The factored form is the product of a binomial and a trinomial.
- The first and third terms in the trinomial are the squares of the terms within the binomial factor.
- Without regard to signs, the middle term in the trinomial is the product of terms in the binomial factor.

Square the first term of the binomial.　　　Product of terms in the binomial

$$x^3 + 8 = (x)^3 + (2)^3 = (x + 2)[(x)^2 - (x)(2) + (2)^2]$$

Square the last term of the binomial.

- The sign within the binomial factor is the same as the sign of the original binomial.
- The first and third terms in the trinomial are always positive.
- The sign of the middle term in the trinomial is opposite the sign within the binomial.

Same sign　　　　　　Positive

$$x^3 + 8 = (x)^3 + (2)^3 = (x + 2)[(x)^2 - (x)(2) + (2)^2]$$

Opposite signs

To help you recognize a sum or difference of cubes, we recommend that you familiarize yourself with the first several perfect cubes:

Perfect Cubes	Perfect Cubes
$1 = (1)^3$	$216 = (6)^3$
$8 = (2)^3$	$343 = (7)^3$
$27 = (3)^3$	$512 = (8)^3$
$64 = (4)^3$	$729 = (9)^3$
$125 = (5)^3$	$1000 = (10)^3$

It is also helpful to recognize that a variable expression is a perfect cube if its exponent is a multiple of 3. For example:

Perfect Cubes

$$x^3 = (x)^3$$
$$x^6 = (x^2)^3$$
$$x^9 = (x^3)^3$$
$$x^{12} = (x^4)^3$$

Skill Practice

Factor.
  1. $p^3 + 125$

Example 1   Factoring a Sum of Cubes

Factor: $w^3 + 64$

Solution:

$w^3 + 64$	w^3 and 64 are perfect cubes.
$= (w)^3 + (4)^3$	Write as $a^3 + b^3$, where $a = w, b = 4$.
$a^3 + b^3 = (a + b)(a^2 - ab + b^2)$	Apply the formula for a sum of cubes.
$(w)^3 + (4)^3 = (w + 4)[(w)^2 - (w)(4) + (4)^2]$	
$= (w + 4)(w^2 - 4w + 16)$	Simplify.

Skill Practice

Factor.
  2. $8y^3 - 27z^3$

Example 2   Factoring a Difference of Cubes

Factor: $27p^3 - 1000q^3$

Solution:

$27p^3 - 1000q^3$	$27p^3$ and $1000q^3$ are perfect cubes.
$(3p)^3 - (10q)^3$	Write as $a^3 - b^3$, where $a = 3p, b = 10q$.
$a^3 - b^3 = (a - b)(a^2 + ab + b^2)$	Apply the formula for a difference of cubes.
$(3p)^3 - (10q)^3 = (3p - 10q)[(3p)^2 + (3p)(10q) + (10q)^2]$	
$= (3p - 10q)(9p^2 + 30pq + 100q^2)$	Simplify.

Answers

1. $(p + 5)(p^2 - 5p + 25)$
2. $(2y - 3z)(4y^2 + 6yz + 9z^2)$

2. Factoring Binomials: A Summary

After removing the GCF, the next step in any factoring problem is to recognize what type of pattern it follows. Exponents that are divisible by 2 are perfect squares and those divisible by 3 are perfect cubes. The formulas for factoring binomials are summarized in the following box:

FORMULA Factored Forms of Binomials

Difference of Squares: $a^2 - b^2 = (a + b)(a - b)$
Difference of Cubes: $a^3 - b^3 = (a - b)(a^2 + ab + b^2)$
Sum of Cubes: $a^3 + b^3 = (a + b)(a^2 - ab + b^2)$

Example 3 Factoring Binomials

Factor completely.

a. $27y^3 + 1$ **b.** $m^2 - \dfrac{1}{4}$ **c.** $z^6 - 8w^3$

Solution:

a. $27y^3 + 1$ Sum of cubes: $27y^3 = (3y)^3$ and $1 = (1)^3$.

$= (3y)^3 + (1)^3$ Write as $a^3 + b^3$, where $a = 3y$ and $b = 1$.

$= (3y + 1)((3y)^2 - (3y)(1) + (1)^2)$ Apply the formula $a^3 + b^3 = (a + b)(a^2 - ab + b^2)$.

$= (3y + 1)(9y^2 - 3y + 1)$ Simplify.

b. $m^2 - \dfrac{1}{4}$ Difference of squares

$= (m)^2 - \left(\dfrac{1}{2}\right)^2$ Write as $a^2 - b^2$, where $a = m$ and $b = \frac{1}{2}$.

$= \left(m + \dfrac{1}{2}\right)\left(m - \dfrac{1}{2}\right)$ Apply the formula $a^2 - b^2 = (a + b)(a - b)$.

c. $z^6 - 8w^3$ Difference of cubes: $z^6 = (z^2)^3$ and $8w^3 = (2w)^3$

$= (z^2)^3 - (2w)^3$ Write as $a^3 - b^3$, where $a = z^2$ and $b = 2w$.

$= (z^2 - 2w)[(z^2)^2 + (z^2)(2w) + (2w)^2]$ Apply the formula $a^3 - b^3 = (a - b)(a^2 + ab + b^2)$.

$= (z^2 - 2w)(z^4 + 2z^2w + 4w^2)$ Simplify.

Each of the factorizations in Example 3 can be checked by multiplying.

Skill Practice

Factor completely.
3. $1000x^3 + 1$
4. $25p^2 - \dfrac{1}{9}$
5. $27a^6 - b^3$

Some factoring problems require more than one method of factoring. In general, when factoring a polynomial, be sure to factor completely.

Answers
3. $(10x + 1)(100x^2 - 10x + 1)$
4. $\left(5p - \dfrac{1}{3}\right)\left(5p + \dfrac{1}{3}\right)$
5. $(3a^2 - b)(9a^4 + 3a^2b + b^2)$

Example 4   **Factoring Polynomials**

Factor completely. $3y^4 - 48$

Solution:

$3y^4 - 48$

$= 3(y^4 - 16)$ Factor out the GCF. The binomial is a difference of squares.

$= 3[(y^2)^2 - (4)^2]$ Write as $a^2 - b^2$, where $a = y^2$ and $b = 4$.

$= 3(y^2 + 4)(y^2 - 4)$ Apply the formula $a^2 - b^2 = (a + b)(a - b)$.

    $y^2 + 4$ is a sum of squares and cannot be factored.

$= 3(y^2 + 4)(y + 2)(y - 2)$ $y^2 - 4$ is a difference of squares and can be factored further.

Example 5   **Factoring Polynomials**

Factor completely. $4x^3 + 4x^2 - 25x - 25$

Solution:

$4x^3 + 4x^2 - 25x - 25$ The GCF is 1.

$= 4x^3 + 4x^2 - 25x - 25$ The polynomial has four terms. Factor by grouping.

$= 4x^2(x + 1) - 25(x + 1)$

$= (x + 1)(4x^2 - 25)$ $4x^2 - 25$ is a difference of squares.

$= (x + 1)(2x + 5)(2x - 5)$

Example 6   **Factoring Binomials**

Factor the binomial $x^6 - y^6$ as

a. A difference of cubes   **b.** A difference of squares

Solution:

a. $x^6 - y^6$

Difference of cubes

$= (x^2)^3 - (y^2)^3$ Write as $a^3 - b^3$, where $a = x^2$ and $b = y^2$.

$= (x^2 - y^2)[(x^2)^2 + (x^2)(y^2) + (y^2)^2]$ Apply the formula $a^3 - b^3 = (a - b)(a^2 + ab + b^2)$.

$= (x^2 - y^2)(x^4 + x^2y^2 + y^4)$ Factor $x^2 - y^2$ as a difference of squares.

$= (x + y)(x - y)(x^4 + x^2y^2 + y^4)$

b. $x^6 - y^6$

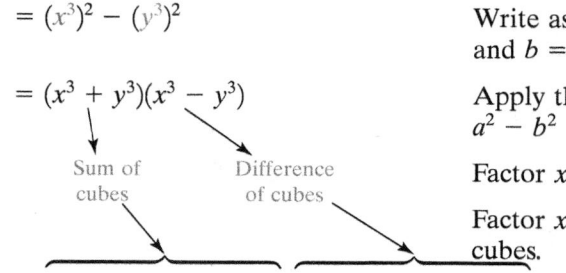

$= (x^3)^2 - (y^3)^2$ Write as $a^2 - b^2$, where $a = x^3$ and $b = y^3$.

$= (x^3 + y^3)(x^3 - y^3)$ Apply the formula $a^2 - b^2 = (a + b)(a - b)$.

Factor $x^3 + y^3$ as a sum of cubes.

Factor $x^3 - y^3$ as a difference of cubes.

$= (x + y)(x^2 - xy + y^2)(x - y)(x^2 + xy + y^2)$

    Notice that the expressions x^6 and y^6 are both perfect squares and perfect cubes because both exponents are multiples of 2 and of 3. Consequently, $x^6 - y^6$ can be factored initially as either the difference of squares or as the difference of cubes. In such a case, it is recommended that you factor the expression as a difference of squares first because it factors more completely into polynomials of lower degree.

$$x^6 - y^6 = (x + y)(x^2 - xy + y^2)(x - y)(x^2 + xy + y^2)$$

Section A.1   Practice Exercises

Study Skills Exercise

1. Define the key terms.

    a. Sum of cubes   **b. Difference of cubes**

Objective 1: Factoring a Sum or Difference of Cubes

2. Identify the expressions that are perfect cubes:
$\{36, t^3, -1, 27, a^3b^6, -9, 125, -8x^2, y^6, 25\}$

3. Identify the expressions that are perfect cubes:
$\{x^3, 8, 9, y^6, a^4, b^2, 3p^3, 27q^3, w^{12}, r^3s^6\}$

4. Identify the expressions that are perfect cubes:
$\{z^9, -81, 30, 8, 6x^3, y^{15}, 27a^3, b^2, p^3q^2, -1\}$

5. From memory, write the formula to factor a sum of cubes:
$$a^3 + b^3 = \rule{3cm}{0.4pt}$$

6. From memory, write the formula to factor a difference of cubes:
$$a^3 - b^3 = \rule{3cm}{0.4pt}$$

For Exercises 7–22, factor the sums or differences of cubes. **(See Examples 1–2.)**

7. $y^3 - 8$ **8.** $x^3 + 27$ **9.** $1 - p^3$ **10.** $q^3 + 1$

11. $w^3 + 64$ **12.** $8 - t^3$ **13.** $x^3 - 1000$ **14.** $8y^3 - 27$

15. $64t^3 + 1$ **16.** $125r^3 + 1$ **17.** $1000a^3 + 27$ **18.** $216b^3 - 125$

19. $n^3 - \dfrac{1}{8}$ **20.** $\dfrac{8}{27} + m^3$ **21.** $125m^3 + 8$ **22.** $27p^3 - 64$

Objective 2: Factoring Binomials: A Summary

For Exercises 23–58, factor completely. **(See Examples 3–6.)**

23. $x^4 - 4$ **24.** $b^4 - 25$ **25.** $a^2 + 9$ **26.** $w^2 + 36$

27. $t^3 + 64$ **28.** $u^3 + 27$ **29.** $g^3 - 4$ **30.** $h^3 - 25$

31. $4b^3 + 108$ **32.** $3c^3 - 24$ **33.** $5p^2 - 125$ **34.** $2q^4 - 8$

35. $\dfrac{1}{64} - 8h^3$ **36.** $\dfrac{1}{125} + k^6$ **37.** $x^4 - 16$ **38.** $p^4 - 81$

39. $q^6 - 64$ **40.** $a^6 - 1$ **41.** $\dfrac{4x^2}{9} - w^2$ **42.** $\dfrac{16y^2}{25} - x^2$

43. $x^9 + 64y^3$ **44.** $125w^3 - z^9$ **45.** $2x^3 + 3x^2 - 2x - 3$ **46.** $3x^3 + x^2 - 12x - 4$

47. $16x^4 - y^4$ **48.** $1 - t^4$ **49.** $81y^4 - 16$ **50.** $u^5 - 256u$

51. $a^3 + b^6$ **52.** $u^6 - v^3$ **53.** $x^4 - y^4$ **54.** $a^4 - b^4$

55. $k^3 + 4k^2 - 9k - 36$ **56.** $w^3 - 2w^2 - 4w + 8$ **57.** $2t^3 - 10t^2 - 2t + 10$ **58.** $9a^3 + 27a^2 - 4a - 12$

Expanding Your Skills

For Exercises 59–62, factor completely.

59. $\dfrac{64}{125}p^3 - \dfrac{1}{8}q^3$ **60.** $\dfrac{1}{1000}r^3 + \dfrac{8}{27}s^3$ **61.** $a^{12} + b^{12}$ **62.** $a^9 - b^9$

Use Exercises 63–64 to investigate the relationship between division and factoring.

63. a. Use long division to divide $x^3 - 8$ by $(x - 2)$.

   b. Factor $x^3 - 8$.

64. a. Use long division to divide $y^3 + 27$ by $(y + 3)$.

   b. Factor $y^3 + 27$.

65. What trinomial multiplied by $(x - 4)$ gives a difference of cubes?

66. What trinomial multiplied by $(p + 5)$ gives a sum of cubes?

67. Write a binomial that when multiplied by $(4x^2 - 2x + 1)$ produces a sum of cubes.

68. Write a binomial that when multiplied by $(9y^2 + 15y + 25)$ produces a difference of cubes.

Introduction to Probability

1. Basic Definitions

The probability of an event measures the likelihood of the event to occur. It is of particular interest because of its application to everyday life.

- The probability of picking the winning six-number combination for the New York lotto grand prize is $\frac{1}{45,057,474}$.

- Genetic DNA analysis can be used to determine the risk that a child will be born with cystic fibrosis. If both parents test positive, the probability is 25% that a child will be born with cystic fibrosis.

To begin our discussion, we must first understand some basic definitions.

An activity with observable outcomes such as flipping a coin or rolling a die is called an **experiment**. The collection (or set) of all possible outcomes of an experiment is called the **sample space** of the experiment.

Objectives

1. Basic Definitions
2. Probability of an Event
3. Estimating Probabilities from Observed Data
4. Complementary Events

Example 1 Determining the Sample Space of an Experiment

a. Suppose a single die is rolled. Determine the sample space of the experiment.

b. Suppose a coin is flipped. Determine the sample space of the experiment.

Solution:

a. A die is a single six-sided cube on which each side has between 1 and 6 dots painted on it. When the die is rolled, any of the six sides may come up.

The sample space is $\{1, 2, 3, 4, 5, 6\}$.   Notice that the symbols { } (called *set braces*) are used to enclose the elements.

b. The coin may land as a head H or as a tail T.
The sample space is $\{H, T\}$.

Skill Practice

1. Suppose one ball is selected from those shown and the color is recorded. Write the sample space for this experiment.

2. For an individual birth, the gender of the baby is recorded. Determine the sample space for this experiment.

---

2. Probability of an Event

Any part of a sample space is called an **event**. For example, if we roll a die, the event of rolling number 5 or a greater number consists of the outcomes 5 and 6. In mathematics, we measure the likelihood of an event to occur by its probability.

DEFINITION Probability of an Event

$$\text{Probability of an event} = \frac{\text{number of elements in event}}{\text{number of elements in sample space}}$$

Avoiding Mistakes

From the definition, a probability value can never be negative or greater than 1.

Answers
1. {red, green, blue, yellow}
2. {male, female}

Skill Practice

3. Find the probability of selecting a yellow ball from those shown.

4. Find the probability of a random birth resulting in a girl.

Example 2   Finding the Probability of an Event

a. Find the probability of rolling a 5 or greater on a die.

b. Find the probability of flipping a coin and having it land as heads.

Solution:

a. The event can occur in 2 ways: The die lands as a 5 or 6. The sample space has 6 elements: 1, 2, 3, 4, 5, and 6.

The probability of rolling a 5 or greater: $\dfrac{2}{6}$ ← number of ways to roll a 5 or greater
← number of elements in the sample space

$= \dfrac{1}{3}$ Simplify to lowest terms.

b. The event can occur in 1 way (the coin lands head side up). The sample space has 2 outcomes: heads or tails.

The probability of flipping a head on a coin: $\dfrac{1}{2}$ ← number of ways to get heads

← number of elements in the sample space

The value of a probability can be written as a fraction, as a decimal, or as a percent. For example, the probability of a coin landing as heads is $\frac{1}{2}$ or 0.5 or 50%. In words, this means that if we flip a coin many times, theoretically we expect one-half (50%) of the outcomes to land as heads.

Skill Practice

A group of registered voters has 9 Republicans, 8 Democrats, and 3 Independents. Suppose one person from the group is selected at random.

5. What is the probability that the person is a Democrat?
6. What is the probability that the person is an Independent?
7. What is the probability that the person is registered with the Libertarian Party?

Example 3   Finding Probabilities

A class has 4 freshmen, 12 sophomores, and 6 juniors. If one individual is selected at random from the class, find the probability of selecting

a. A sophomore

b. A junior

c. A senior

4 freshmen

12 sophomores

6 juniors

Solution:

In this case, there are 22 members of the class (4 freshmen + 12 sophomores + 6 juniors). This means that the sample space has 22 elements.

a. There are 12 sophomores in the class. The probability of selecting a sophomore is

$\dfrac{12}{22}$ There are 12 sophomores out of 22 people in the sample space.

$= \dfrac{6}{11}$ Simplify to lowest terms.

Answers

3. $\dfrac{1}{4}$ or 0.25   4. $\dfrac{1}{2}$ or 0.5

5. $\dfrac{2}{5}$ or 0.4   6. $\dfrac{3}{20}$ or 0.15   7. 0

b. There are 6 juniors out of 22 people in the sample space. The probability of selecting a junior is

$$\frac{6}{22} \quad \text{or} \quad \frac{3}{11}$$

c. There are no seniors in the class. The probability of selecting a senior is

$$\frac{0}{22} \quad \text{or} \quad 0$$

A probability of 0 indicates that the event is impossible. It is impossible to select a senior from a class that has no seniors.

3. Estimating Probabilities from Observed Data

We were able to compute the probabilities in Examples 2 and 3 because the sample space was known. Sometimes we need to collect information to help us estimate probabilities.

Example 4 **Estimating Probabilities form Observed Data**

A dental hygienist records the number of times a day her patients say that they brush their teeth. Table A.2-1 displays the results.

Table A.2-1

Number of Times of Brushing Teeth per Day	Frequency
1	6
2	10
3	4
More than 3	1

If one of her patients is selected at random,

a. What is the probability of selecting a patient who brushes only one time a day?

b. What is the probability of selecting a patient who brushes more than once a day?

Solution:

a. The table shows that there are 6 patients who brush once a day. To get the total number of patients we add all of the frequencies (6 + 10 + 4 + 1 = 21). The probability of selecting a patient who brushes only once a day is

$$\frac{6}{21} \quad \text{or} \quad \frac{2}{7}$$

b. To find the number of patients who brush more than once a day, we add the frequencies for the patients who brush 2 times, 3 times, and more than 3 times (10 + 4 + 1 = 15). The probability of selecting a patient who brushes more that once a day is

$$\frac{15}{21} \quad \text{or} \quad \frac{5}{7}$$

Skill Practice

Refer to Table 9-8 in Example 4.

8. What is the probability of selecting a patient who brushes twice a day?

9. What is the probability of selecting a patient who brushes more than twice a day?

Answers

8. $\frac{10}{21}$ **9.** $\frac{5}{21}$

4. Complementary Events

The events in Example 4(a) and 4(b) are called complementary events. The **complement of an event** is the set of all elements in the sample space that are not in the event. In this case, the number of patients who brush once a day and the number of patients who brush more than once a day make up the entire sample space, yet do not overlap. For this reason, the probability of an event plus the probability of its complement is 1. For Example 4, we have $\frac{2}{7} + \frac{5}{7} = \frac{7}{7} = 1$.

Skill Practice

10. For one particular medicine, the probability that a patient will experience side effects is $\frac{1}{20}$. What is the probability that a patient will *not* experience side effects?

11. The probability that a flight arrives on time is 0.18. What is the probability that a flight will *not* arrive on time?

Example 5   **Finding the Probability of Complementary Events**

Find the indicated probability.

a. The probability of getting a winter cold is $\frac{3}{10}$. What is the probability of *not* getting a winter cold?

b. If the probability that a washing machine will break before the end of the warranty period is 0.0042, what is the probability that a washing machine will *not* break before the end of the warranty period?

Solution:

a. The probability of an event plus the probability of its complement must add up to 1. Therefore, we have an addition problem with a missing addend. This may also be expressed as subtraction.

$$\frac{3}{10} + \,? = 1 \qquad \text{or equivalently} \qquad 1 - \frac{3}{10} = \,?$$

$$\frac{10}{10} - \frac{3}{10} = \frac{7}{10} \qquad \text{Find a common denominator and subtract.}$$

There is a $\frac{7}{10}$ chance (70% chance) of *not* getting a winter cold.

b. The probability that a washing machine will break before the end of the warranty period is 0.0042. Then the probability that a machine will *not* break before the end of the warranty period is given by

$$1 - 0.0042 = 0.9958 \text{ or equivalently } 99.58\%$$

Answers

10. $\frac{19}{20}$ 11. 0.82

Study Skills Exercise

1. Define the key terms.

   a. **Experiment**   b. **Sample space**   c. **Event**

   d. **Probability of an event**   e. **Complement of an event**

Objectives 1: Basic Definitions

2. If a die is rolled, in how many ways can a number less than 6 come up?

3. A card is chosen from a deck consisting of 10 cards numbered 1–10. Determine the sample space of this experiment. **(See Example 1.)**

4. A marble is chosen from a jar containing a yellow marble, a red marble, a blue marble, a green marble, and a white marble. Determine the sample space of this experiment.

5. Two dice are thrown, and the sum of the top sides is observed. Determine the sample space of this experiment.

6. A coin is tossed twice. Determine the sample space of this experiment.

Objective 2: Probability of an Event

7. Which of the values can represent the probability of an event?

    a. 1.62   **b.** $-\dfrac{7}{5}$ **c.** 0   **d.** 1

    e. 200%   **f.** 4.5   **g.** 4.5%   **h.** 0.87

8. Which of the values can represent the probability of an event?

    a. 1.5   **b.** 0   **c.** $\dfrac{2}{3}$ **d.** 1

    e. 150%   **f.** 3.7   **g.** 3.7%   **h.** 0.92

9. If a single die is rolled, what is the probability that it will come up as a number less than 3? **(See Example 2.)**

10. If a single die is rolled, what is the probability that it will come up as a number greater than 5?

11. If a single die is rolled, what is the probability that it will come up with an even number?

12. If a single die is rolled, what is the probability that it will come up as an odd number?

For Exercises 13–16, refer to the figure. A sock drawer contains 2 white socks, 5 gray socks, and 1 blue sock. **(See Example 3.)**

13. What is the probability of choosing a gray sock from the drawer?

14. What is the probability of choosing a white sock from the drawer?

15. What is the probability of choosing a blue sock from the drawer?

16. What is the probability of choosing a purple sock from the drawer?

17. If a die is tossed, what is the probability that a number from 1 to 6 will come up?

18. If a die is tossed, what is the probability of getting a 7?

19. What is the probability of an impossible event?

20. What is the sum of the probabilities of an event and its complement?

21. In a deck of cards there are 12 face cards and 40 cards with numbers. What is the probability of selecting a face card from the deck?

22. In a deck of cards, 13 are diamonds, 13 are spades, 13 are clubs, and 13 are hearts. Find the probability of selecting a diamond from the deck.

23. A jar contains 7 yellow marbles, 5 red marbles, and 4 green marbles. What is the probability of selecting a red marble or a yellow marble?

24. A jar contains 10 black marbles, 12 white marbles, and 4 blue marbles. What is the probability of selecting a blue marble or a black marble?

Objective 3: Estimating Probabilities from Observed Data

25. The table displays the length of stay for vacationers at a small motel. **(See Example 4.)**

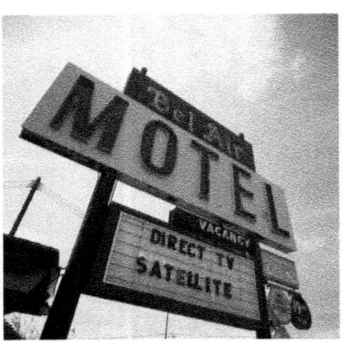

Length of Stay in Days	Frequency
2	14
3	13
4	18
5	28
6	11
7	30
8	6

a. What is the probability that a vacationer will stay for 4 days?

b. What is the probability that a vacationer will stay for less than 4 days?

c. Based on the information from the table, what percent of vacationers stay for more than 6 days?

26. A number of students at a large university were asked if they owned a car. The table shows the results.

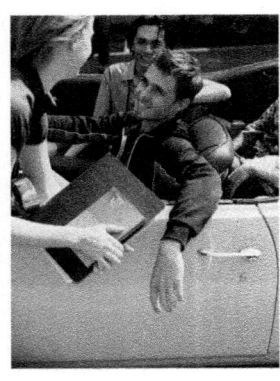

	Number of Car Owners	Number Who Do Not Own a Car
Dorm resident	32	88
Lives off campus	59	26

a. What is the probability that a student selected at random lives in a dorm?

b. What is the probability that a student selected at random does not own a car?

27. A survey was made of 60 participants, asking if they drive an American-made car, a Japanese car, or a car manufactured in another foreign country. The table displays the results.

	Frequency
American	21
Japanese	30
Other	9

a. What is the probability that a randomly selected car is manufactured in America?

b. What percent of cars is manufactured in some country other than Japan?

28. The number of customer complaints for service representatives is given in the table. If one representative is picked at random, find the probability that the representative received

a. Exactly 3 complaints

b. Between 1 and 5 complaints, inclusive

c. At least 4 complaints

d. More than 5 complaints or fewer than 2 complaints

Number of Complaints	Number of Representatives
0	4
1	2
2	14
3	10
4	16
5	18
6	10
7	6

29. Mr. Gutierrez noted the times in which his students entered his classroom and constructed the following chart.

a. What is the probability that a student will be early to class?

b. What is the probability that a student will be late to class?

c. What percent of students arrive on time or early? Round to the nearest whole percent.

Time	Number of Students
About 10 min early	1
About 5 min early	6
On time	11
About 5 min late	7
About 10 min late	3
About 15 min late	1

30. Each person at an office party purchased a raffle ticket. The graph shows the results of the raffle.

a. How many people bought raffle tickets?

b. What is the probability of winning the TV set?

c. What percent of people won some type of prize?

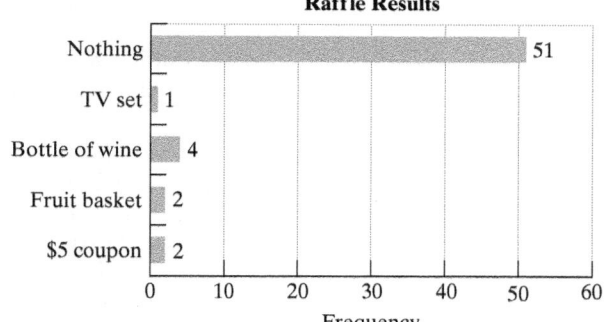

Raffle Results

Objective 4: Complementary Events

31. If the probability of the horse Sugar 'N Spice to win is $\frac{2}{11}$, what is the probability that he will lose? **(See Example 5.)**

32. If the probability of being hit by lighting is $\frac{1}{1,000,000}$, what is the probability of not getting hit by lighting?

33. If the probability of having twins is 1.2%, what is the probability of not having twins?

34. The probability of a woman's surviving breast cancer is 88%. What is the probability that a woman would not survive breast cancer?

Section A.3   Variation

1. Definition of Direct and Inverse Variation

In this section, we introduce the concept of variation. Direct and inverse variation models can show how one quantity varies in proportion to another.

> **DEFINITION   Direct and Inverse Variation**
>
> Let k be a nonzero constant real number. Then the following statements are equivalent:
>
> **1.** y varies **directly** as x.
> y is directly proportional to x. $\Big\}$ $y = kx$
>
> **2.** y varies **inversely** as x.
> y is inversely proportional to x. $\Big\}$ $y = \dfrac{k}{x}$
>
> *Note:* The value of k is called the constant of variation.

For a car traveling 30 mph, the equation $d = 30t$ indicates that the distance traveled is *directly proportional* to the time of travel. For positive values of k, when two variables are directly related, as one variable increases, the other variable will also increase. Likewise, if one variable decreases, the other will decrease. In the equation $d = 30t$, the longer the time of the trip, the greater the distance traveled. The shorter the time of the trip, the shorter the distance traveled.

For positive values of k, when two positive variables are *inversely related*, as one variable increases, the other will decrease, and vice versa. Consider a car traveling between Toronto and Montreal, a distance of 500 km. The time required to make the trip is inversely proportional to the speed of travel: $t = 500/r$. As the rate of speed, r, increases, the quotient $500/r$ will decrease. Thus the time will decrease. Similarly, as the rate of speed decreases, the trip will take longer.

2. Translations Involving Variation

The first step in using a variation model is to translate an English phrase into an equivalent mathematical equation.

Example 1   Translating to a Variation Model

Translate each expression into an equivalent mathematical model.

a. The circumference of a circle varies directly as the radius.

b. At a constant temperature, the volume of a gas varies inversely as the pressure.

c. The length of time of a meeting is directly proportional to the *square* of the number of people present.

Solution:

a. Let C represent circumference and r represent radius. The variables are directly related, so use the model $C = kr$.

b. Let V represent volume and P represent pressure. Because the variables are inversely related, use the model $V = k/P$.

c. Let t represent time, and let N be the number of people present at a meeting. Because t is directly related to N^2, use the model $t = kN^2$.

Sometimes a variable varies directly as the product of two or more other variables. In this case, we have joint variation.

DEFINITION Joint Variation

Let k be a nonzero constant real number. Then the following statements are equivalent:

y varies **jointly** as w and z.

y is jointly proportional to w and z. $\Big\}$ $y = kwz$

Example 2 Translating to a Variation Model

Translate each expression into an equivalent mathematical model.

a. y varies jointly as u and the square root of v.

b. The gravitational force of attraction between two planets varies jointly as the product of their masses and inversely as the square of the distance between them.

Solution:

a. $y = ku\sqrt{v}$

b. Let m_1 and m_2 represent the masses of the two planets. Let F represent the gravitational force of attraction and d represent the distance between the planets.

The variation model is $F = \dfrac{km_1m_2}{d^2}$

3. Applications of Variation

Consider the variation models $y = kx$ and $y = k/x$. In either case, if values for x and y are known, we can solve for k. Once k is known, we can use the variation equation to find y if x is known, or to find x if y is known. This concept is the basis for solving many problems involving variation.

PROCEDURE Finding a Variation Model

Step 1 Write a general variation model that relates the variables given in the problem. Let k represent the constant of variation.

Step 2 Solve for k by substituting known values of the variables into the model from step 1.

Step 3 Substitute the value of k into the original variation model from step 1.

Skill Practice

Translate each expression into an equivalent mathematical model.

1. The distance, d, driven in a particular time varies directly with the speed of the car, s.
2. The weight of an individual kitten, w, varies inversely with the number of kittens in the litter, n.
3. The value of v varies inversely as the square root of b.

Skill Practice

Translate each expression into an equivalent mathematical model.

4. The value of q varies jointly as u and v.
5. The value of x varies directly as the square of y and inversely as z.

Answers

1. $d = ks$ 2. $w = \dfrac{k}{n}$
3. $v = \dfrac{k}{\sqrt{b}}$ 4. $q = kuv$
5. $x = \dfrac{ky^2}{z}$

The variable t varies directly as the square of v. When v is 8, t is 32.

6. Write a variation model for this relationship.

7. Solve for the constant of variation.

8. Find t when $v = 10$.

Example 3 Solving an Application Involving Direct Variation

The variable z varies directly as w. When w is 16, z is 56.

  a. Write a variation model for this situation. Use k as the constant of variation.

  b. Solve for the constant of variation.

  c. Find the value of z when w is 84.

Solution:

  a. $z = kw$

  b. $z = kw$

$$56 = k(16)$$ Substitute known values for z and w. Then solve for the unknown value of k.

$$\frac{56}{16} = \frac{k(16)}{16}$$ To isolate k, divide both sides by 16.

$$\frac{7}{2} = k$$ Simplify $\frac{56}{16}$ to $\frac{7}{2}$.

  c. With the value of k known, the variation model can now be written as
$$z = \frac{7}{2}w.$$

$$z = \frac{7}{2}(84)$$ To find z when $w = 84$, substitute $w = 84$ into the equation.

$$z = 294$$

9. The amount of water needed by a mountain hiker varies directly as the time spent hiking. The hiker needs 2.4 L for a 4-hr hike. How much water will be needed for a 5-hr hike?

Example 4 Solving an Application Involving Direct Variation

The speed of a racing canoe in still water varies directly as the square root of the length of the canoe.

  a. If a 16-ft canoe can travel 6.2 mph in still water, find a variation model that relates the speed of a canoe to its length.

  b. Find the speed of a 25-ft canoe.

Solution:

  a. Let s represent the speed of the canoe and L represent the length. The general variation model is $s = k\sqrt{L}$. To solve for k, substitute the known values for s and L.

$$s = k\sqrt{L}$$

$$6.2 = k\sqrt{16}$$ Substitute $s = 6.2$ mph and $L = 16$ ft.

$$6.2 = k \cdot 4$$

$$\frac{6.2}{4} = \frac{\cancel{4}k}{\cancel{4}}$$ Solve for k.

$$k = 1.55$$

$$s = 1.55\sqrt{L}$$ Substitute $k = 1.55$ into the model $s = k\sqrt{L}$.

Answers

6. $t = kv^2$ **7.** $\dfrac{1}{2}$

8. 50   **9.** 3 L

b. $s = 1.55\sqrt{L}$

$= 1.55\sqrt{25}$ Find the speed when $L = 25$ ft.

$= 7.75$ mph   The speed is 7.75 mph.

Example 5 **Solving an Application Involving Inverse Variation**

The loudness of sound measured in decibels varies inversely as the square of the distance between the listener and the source of the sound. If the loudness of sound is 17.92 decibels at a distance of 10 ft from a stereo speaker, what is the decibel level 20 ft from the speaker?

Solution:

Let L represent the loudness of sound in decibels and d represent the distance in feet. The inverse relationship between decibel level and the square of the distance is modeled by

$$L = \frac{k}{d^2}$$

$17.92 = \dfrac{k}{(10)^2}$ Substitute $L = 17.92$ decibels and $d = 10$ ft.

$17.92 = \dfrac{k}{100}$

$(17.92)100 = \dfrac{k}{100} \cdot 100$ Solve for k (clear fractions).

$k = 1792$

$L = \dfrac{1792}{d^2}$ Substitute $k = 1792$ into the original model $L = \dfrac{k}{d^2}$.

With the value of k known, we can find L for any value of d.

$L = \dfrac{1792}{(20)^2}$ Find the loudness when $d = 20$ ft.

$= 4.48$ decibels   The loudness is 4.48 decibels.

Notice that the loudness of sound is 17.92 decibels at a distance 10 ft from the speaker. When the distance from the speaker is increased to 20 ft, the decibel level decreases to 4.48 decibels. This is consistent with an inverse relationship. For $k > 0$, as one variable is increased, the other is decreased. It also seems reasonable that the further one moves away from the source of a sound, the softer the sound becomes.

Skill Practice

10. The yield on a bond varies inversely as the price. The yield on a particular bond is 5% when the price is $100. Find the yield when the price is $125.

Answer
10. 4%

--- Skill Practice ---

11. The amount of simple interest earned in an account varies jointly as the interest rate and time of the investment. An account earns $72 in 4 yr at 2% interest. How much interest would be earned in 3 yr at a rate of 5%?

Example 6   **Solving an Application Involving Joint Variation**

The kinetic energy of an object varies jointly as the weight of the object at sea level and as the square of its velocity. During a hurricane, a 0.5-lb stone traveling at 60 mph has 81 J (joules) of kinetic energy. Suppose the wind speed doubles to 120 mph. Find the kinetic energy.

Solution:

Let E represent the kinetic energy, let w represent the weight, and let v represent the velocity of the stone. The variation model is

$$E = kwv^2$$

$$81 = k(0.5)(60)^2 \qquad \text{Substitute } E = 81 \text{ J}, w = 0.5 \text{ lb}, \text{ and } v = 60 \text{ mph.}$$

$$81 = k(0.5)(3600) \qquad \text{Simplify exponents.}$$

$$81 = k(1800)$$

$$\frac{81}{1800} = \frac{k(1800)}{1800} \qquad \text{Divide by 1800.}$$

$$0.045 = k \qquad \text{Solve for } k.$$

With the value of k known, the model $E = kwv^2$ can now be written as $E = 0.045wv^2$. We now find the kinetic energy of a 0.5-lb stone traveling at 120 mph.

$$E = 0.045(0.5)(120)^2$$

$$= 324$$

The kinetic energy of a 0.5-lb stone traveling at 120 mph is 324 J.

In Example 6, when the velocity increased by 2 times, the kinetic energy increased by 4 times (note that 324 J = 4 · 81 J). This factor of 4 occurs because the kinetic energy is proportional to the *square* of the velocity. When the velocity increased by 2 times, the kinetic energy increased by 2^2 times.

Answer

11. $135

Section A.3   Practice Exercises

Study Skills Exercise

1. Define the key terms:

    a. Direct variation   **b. Inverse variation**   **c. Joint variation**

Objective 1: Definition of Direct and Inverse Variation

2. In the equation $r = kt$, does r vary directly or inversely with t?

3. In the equation $w = \dfrac{k}{v}$, does w vary directly or inversely with v?

4. In the equation $P = \dfrac{k \cdot c}{v}$, does P vary directly or inversely as v?

Objective 2: Translations Involving Variation

For Exercises 5–16, write a variation model. Use k as the constant of variation. **(See Examples 1–2.)**

5. T varies directly as q.

6. W varies directly as z.

7. b varies inversely as c.

8. m varies inversely as t.

9. Q is directly proportional to x and inversely proportional to y.

10. d is directly proportional to p and inversely proportional to n.

11. c varies jointly as s and t.

12. w varies jointly as p and f.

13. L varies jointly as w and the square root of v.

14. q varies jointly as v and the square root of w.

15. x varies directly as the square of y and inversely as z.

16. a varies directly as n and inversely as the square of d.

For Exercises 17–22, find the constant of variation, k. **(See Example 3.)**

17. y varies directly as x and when x is 4, y is 18.

18. m varies directly as x and when x is 8, m is 22.

19. p varies inversely as q and when q is 16, p is 32.

20. T varies inversely as x and when x is 40, T is 200.

21. y varies jointly as w and v. When w is 50 and v is 0.1, y is 8.75.

22. N varies jointly as t and p. When t is 1 and p is 7.5, N is 330.

Objective 3: Applications of Variation

Solve Exercises 23–34 using the steps found on page A-15. **(See Example 3.)**

23. x varies directly as p. If $x = 50$ when $p = 10$, find x when p is 14.

24. y is directly proportional to z. If $y = 12$ when $z = 36$, find y when z is 21.

25. b is inversely proportional to c. If b is 4 when c is 3, find b when $c = 2$.

26. q varies inversely as w. If q is 8 when w is 50, find q when w is 125.

27. Z varies directly as the square of w. If $Z = 14$ when $w = 4$, find Z when $w = 8$.

28. m varies directly as the square of x. If $m = 200$ when $x = 20$, find m when x is 32.

29. Q varies inversely as the square of p. If $Q = 4$ when $p = 3$, find Q when $p = 2$.

30. z is inversely proportional to the square of t. If $z = 15$ when $t = 4$, find z when $t = 10$.

31. L varies jointly as a and the square root of b. If $L = 72$ when $a = 8$ and $b = 9$, find L when $a = \frac{1}{2}$ and $b = 36$.

32. Y varies jointly as the cube of x and the square root of w. $Y = 128$ when $x = 2$ and $w = 16$. Find Y when $x = \frac{1}{2}$ and $w = 64$.

33. B varies directly as m and inversely as n. $B = 20$ when $m = 10$ and $n = 3$. Find B when $m = 15$ and $n = 12$.

34. R varies directly as s and inversely as t. $R = 14$ when $s = 2$ and $t = 9$. Find R when $s = 4$ and $t = 3$.

For Exercises 35–50, use a variation model to solve for the unknown value. **(See Examples 4–6.)**

35. The amount of medicine that a physician prescribes for a patient varies directly as the weight of the patient. A physician prescribes 3 g of a medicine for a 150-lb person.

    a. How many grams should be prescribed for a 180-lb person?

    b. How many grams should be prescribed for a 225-lb person?

    c. How many grams should be prescribed for a 120-lb person?

36. The number of turkeys needed for a banquet is directly proportional to the number of guests that must be fed. Master Chef Rico knows that he needs to cook 3 turkeys to feed 42 guests.

    a. How many turkeys should he cook to feed 70 guests?

    b. How many turkeys should he cook to feed 140 guests?

    c. How many turkeys should be cooked to feed 700 guests at an inaugural ball?

    d. How many turkeys should be cooked for a wedding with 100 guests?

37. The unit cost of producing CDs is inversely proportional to the number of CDs produced. If 5000 CDs are produced, the cost per CD is $0.48.

    a. What would be the unit cost if 6000 CDs were produced?

    b. What would be the unit cost if 8000 CDs were produced?

    c. What would be the unit cost if 2400 CDs were produced?

38. An author self-publishes a book and finds that the number of books she can sell per month varies inversely as the price of the book. The author can sell 1500 books per month when the price is set at $8 per book.

    a. How many books would she expect to sell if the price were $12?

    b. How many books would she expect to sell if the price were $15?

    c. How many books would she expect to sell if the price were $6?

39. The amount of pollution entering the atmosphere over a given time varies directly as the number of people living in an area. If 80,000 people cause 56,800 tons of pollutants, how many tons enter the atmosphere in a city with a population of 500,000?

40. The area of a picture projected on a wall varies directly as the square of the distance from the projector to the wall. If a 10-ft distance produces a 16-ft^2 picture, what is the area of a picture produced when the projection unit is moved to a distance 20 ft from the wall?

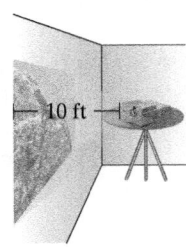

41. The stopping distance of a car varies directly as the square of the speed of the car. If a car traveling at 40 mph has a stopping distance of 109 ft, find the stopping distance of a car that is traveling at 25 mph. (Round your answer to one decimal place.)

42. The intensity of a light source varies inversely as the square of the distance from the source. If the intensity is 400 lumens/m^2 at a distance of 5 m, what is the intensity when the distance is 8 m?

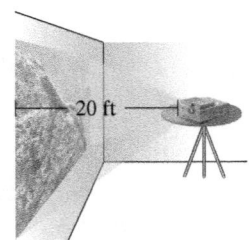

43. The power in an electric circuit varies jointly as the current and the square of the resistance. If the power is 144 W (watts) when the current is 4 A and the resistance is 6 Ω, find the power when the current is 3 A and the resistance is 10 Ω.

44. The current in a wire varies directly as the voltage and inversely as the resistance. If the current is 9 A (amperes) when the voltage is 90 V (volts) and the resistance is 10 Ω (ohms), find the current when the voltage is 185 V and the resistance is 10 Ω.

45. The resistance of a wire varies directly as its length and inversely as the square of its diameter. A 40-ft wire 0.1 in. in diameter has a resistance of 4 Ω. What is the resistance of a 50-ft wire with a diameter of 0.2 in.?

46. Some body-builders claim that, within safe limits, the number of repetitions that a person can complete on a given weight-lifting exercise is inversely proportional to the amount of weight lifted. Roxanne can bench press 45 lb for 15 repetitions.

a. How many repetitions can Roxanne bench with 60 lb of weight?

b. How many repetitions can Roxanne bench with 75 lb of weight?

c. How many repetitions can Roxanne bench with 100 lb of weight?

47. The weight of a medicine ball varies directly as the cube of its radius. A ball with a radius of 3 in. weighs 4.32 lb. How much would a medicine ball weigh if its radius is 5 in.?

48. The surface area of a cube varies directly as the square of the length of an edge. The surface area is 24 ft² when the length of an edge is 2 ft. Find the surface area of a cube with an edge that is 5 ft.

49. The amount of simple interest earned in an account varies jointly as the amount of principal invested and the amount of time the money is invested. If $2500 in principal earns $500 in interest after 4 yr, then how much interest will be earned on $7000 invested for 10 yr?

50. The amount of simple interest earned in an account varies jointly as the amount of principal invested and the amount of time the money is invested. If $6000 in principal earns $840 in interest after 2 yr, then how much interest will be earned on $4500 invested for 8 yr?

Student Answer Appendix

Chapter 1
Chapter Opener Puzzle

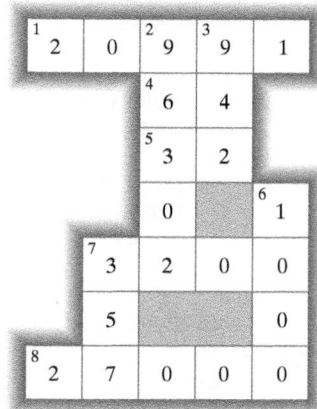

Section 1.2 Practice Exercises, pp. 9–12

3. 7: ones; 5: tens; 4: hundreds; 3: thousands;
1: ten-thousands; 2: hundred-thousands; 8: millions
5. Tens   **7.** Ones   **9.** Hundreds   **11.** Thousands
13. Hundred-thousands   **15.** Billions
17. Ten-thousands   **19.** Millions   **21.** Ten-millions
23. Billions   **25.** 5 tens + 8 ones
27. 5 hundreds + 3 tens + 9 ones
29. 5 thousands + 2 hundreds + 3 ones
31. 1 ten-thousand + 2 hundreds + 4 tens + 1 one
33. 524   **35.** 150   **37.** 1906   **39.** 85,007
41. Ones, thousands, millions, billions
43. Two hundred forty-one   **45.** Six hundred three
47. Thirty-one thousand, five hundred thirty
49. One hundred thousand, two hundred thirty-four
51. Nine thousand, five hundred thirty-five
53. Twenty thousand, three hundred twenty
55. Five hundred ninety thousand, seven hundred twelve
57. 6005   **59.** 672,000   **61.** 1,484,250
63.

65. 10   **67.** 4
69. 8 is greater than 2, or 2 is less than 8
71. 3 is less than 7, or 7 is greater than 3
73. <   **75.** >   **77.** <   **79.** >   **81.** <   **83.** <
85. False   **87.** 99   **89.** There is no greatest whole
number.   **91.** 7   **93.** 964

Section 1.3 Practice Exercises, pp. 22–26

3. 3 hundreds + 5 tens + 1 one
5. 4012

7.

+	0	1	2	3	4	5	6	7	8	9
0	0	1	2	3	4	5	6	7	8	9
1	1	2	3	4	5	6	7	8	9	10
2	2	3	4	5	6	7	8	9	10	11
3	3	4	5	6	7	8	9	10	11	12
4	4	5	6	7	8	9	10	11	12	13
5	5	6	7	8	9	10	11	12	13	14
6	6	7	8	9	10	11	12	13	14	15
7	7	8	9	10	11	12	13	14	15	16
8	8	9	10	11	12	13	14	15	16	17
9	9	10	11	12	13	14	15	16	17	18

9. Addends: 1, 13, 4; sum: 18   **11.** 75   **13.** 59
15. 997   **17.** 119   **19.** 121   **21.** 111
23. 889   **25.** 701   **27.** 203   **29.** 15,203
31. 40,985   **33.** 44 + 101   **35.** $y + x$
37. 23 + (9 + 10)   **39.** $(r + s) + t$
41. The commutative property changes the order of the
addends, and the associative property changes the grouping.
43. Minuend: 12; subtrahend: 8; difference: 4
45. 18 + 9 = 27   **47.** 27 + 75 = 102   **49.** 5
51. 3   **53.** 1126   **55.** 1103   **57.** 17   **59.** 521
61. 4764   **63.** 1403   **65.** 2217   **67.** 713
69. 30,941   **71.** 5,662,119   **73.** The expression $7 - 4$
means 7 minus 4, yielding a difference of 3. The expression
$4 - 7$ means 4 minus 7 which results in a difference of -3.
(This is a mathematical skill we have not yet learned.)
75. 13 + 7; 20   **77.** 7 + 45; 52   **79.** 18 + 5; 23
81. 1523 + 90; 1613   **83.** 5 + 39 + 81; 125
85. 422 − 100; 322   **87.** 1090 − 72; 1018
89. 50 − 13; 37   **91.** 103 − 35; 68
93. 74,283,000 viewers   **95.** 423 desks
97. Denali is 6074 ft higher than White Mountain Peak.
99. 7748   **101.** 195,489   **103.** 821,024 nonteachers
105. 4256 ft   **107.** Jeannette will pay $29,560 for 1 year.
109. 104 cm   **111.** 42 yd   **113.** 288 ft   **115.** 13 m

Section 1.3 Calculator Connections, p. 27

117. 192,780   **118.** 21,491,394   **119.** 5,257,179
120. 4,447,302   **121.** 897,058,513   **122.** 2,906,455
123. 49,408 mi^2 **124.** 17,139 mi^2 **125.** 96,572 mi^2
126. 224,368 mi^2

Section 1.4 Practice Exercises, pp. 32–34

3. 26   **5.** 5007   **7.** Ten-thousands
9. If the digit in the tens place is 0, 1, 2, 3, or 4, then change
the tens and ones digits to 0. If the digit in the tens place is 5,
6, 7, 8, or 9, increase the digit in the hundreds place by 1 and
change the tens and ones digits to 0.
11. 340   **13.** 730   **15.** 9400   **17.** 8500
19. 35,000   **21.** 3000   **23.** 10,000   **25.** 109,000

27. 490,000   **29.** $148,000,000   **31.** 239,000 mi
33. 160   **35.** 220   **37.** 1000   **39.** 2100
41. $151,000,000   **43.** $11,000,000 more
45. $10,000,000   **47. a.** 2003; $3,500,000   **b.** 2005;
$2,000,000   **49.** Massachusetts; 79,000 students
51. 71,000 students   **53.** 10,000 mm   **55.** 440 in.

Section 1.5 Practice Exercises, pp. 43–46

3. 1,010,000   **5.** 5400   **7.** 6×5; 30   **9.** 3×9; 27
11. Factors: 13, 42; product: 546
13. Factors: 3, 5, 2; product: 30
15. For example: 5×12; $5 \cdot 12$; 5(12)
17. d   **19.** e   **21.** c   **23.** $8 \cdot 14$ **25.** $(6 \cdot 2) \cdot 10$
27. $(5 \cdot 7) + (5 \cdot 4)$ **29.** 144   **31.** 52   **33.** 655
35. 1376   **37.** 11,280   **39.** 23,184   **41.** 378,126
43. 448   **45.** 1632   **47.** 864   **49.** 2431   **51.** 6631
53. 19,177   **55.** 186,702   **57.** 21,241,448
59. 4,047,804   **61.** 24,000   **63.** 2,100,000
65. 72,000,000   **67.** 36,000,000   **69.** 60,000,000
71. 2,400,000,000   **73.** $1000   **75.** $1,370,000
77. 4000 min   **79.** $1665   **81.** 144 fl oz
83. 287,500 sheets   **85.** 372 mi   **87.** 276 ft^2
89. 5329 cm^2 **91.** 105,300 mi^2 **93. a.** 2400 in.^{2}
b. 42 windows   **c.** 100,800 in.^{2} **95.** 128 ft^2

Section 1.6 Practice Exercises, pp. 54–56

3. 4944   **5.** 1253   **7.** 664,210   **9.** 902
11. 9; the dividend is 72; the divisor is 8; the quotient is 9
13. 8; the dividend is 64; the divisor is 8; the quotient is 8
15. 5; the dividend is 45; the divisor is 9; the quotient is 5
17. You cannot divide a number by zero (the quotient is
undefined). If you divide zero by a number (other than zero),
the quotient is always zero.
19. 15   **21.** 0   **23.** Undefined   **25.** 1
27. Undefined   **29.** 0   **31.** $2 \cdot 3 = 6$, $2 \cdot 6 \neq 3$
33. Multiply the quotient and the divisor to get the dividend.
35. 13   **37.** 41   **39.** 486   **41.** 409
43. 203   **45.** 822   **47.** Correct   **49.** Incorrect; 253 R2
51. Correct   **53.** Incorrect; 25 R3   **55.** 7 R5
57. 10 R2   **59.** 27 R1   **61.** 197 R2   **63.** 42 R4
65. 1557 R1   **67.** 751 R6   **69.** 835 R2   **71.** 479 R9
73. 43 R19   **75.** 308   **77.** 1259 R26   **79.** 22
81. 35 R1   **83.** 229 R96   **85.** 302   **87.** $497 \div 71$; 7
89. $877 \div 14$; 62 R9   **91.** $42 \div 6$; 7
93. 14 classrooms   **95.** 5 cases; 8 cans left over
97. There will be 120 classes of Beginning Algebra.
99. It will use 9 gal.
101. $1200 \div 20 = 60$; approximately 60 words per minute
103. Yes, they can all attend if they sit in the second balcony.

Section 1.6 Calculator Connections, p. 57

105. 7,665,000,000 bbl   **106.** 13,000 min
107. $211 billion   **108.** Each crate weighs 255 lb.

Chapter 1 Problem Recognition Exercises, p. 57

1. a. 120   **b.** 72   **c.** 2304   **d.** 4
2. a. 575   **b.** 525   **c.** 13,750   **d.** 22
3. a. 946   **b.** 612   **4. a.** 278   **b.** 612
5. a. 1201   **b.** 5500   **6. a.** 34,855   **b.** 22,718
7. a. 20,000   **b.** 400   **8. a.** 34,524   **b.** 548

9. a. 230   **b.** 5060   **10. a.** 15   **b.** 1875
11. a. 328   **b.** 4   **12. a.** 8   **b.** 547
13. a. 4180   **b.** 41,800   **c.** 418,000   **d.** 4,180,000
14. a. 35,000   **b.** 3500   **c.** 350   **d.** 35

Section 1.7 Practice Exercises, pp. 63–65

3. True   **5.** False   **7.** True   **9.** 9^4
11. 3^6 **13.** $4^4 \cdot 2^3$ **15.** $8 \cdot 8 \cdot 8 \cdot 8$
17. $4 \cdot 4 \cdot 4 \cdot 4 \cdot 4 \cdot 4 \cdot 4 \cdot 4$ **19.** 8   **21.** 9
23. 27   **25.** 125   **27.** 32   **29.** 81
31. The number 1 raised to any power is 1.   **33.** 1000
35. 100,000   **37.** 2   **39.** 6   **41.** 10   **43.** 0
45. No, addition and subtraction should be performed in
the order in which they appear from left to right.
47. 26   **49.** 1   **51.** 49   **53.** 3   **55.** 2
57. 53   **59.** 8   **61.** 45   **63.** 24   **65.** 4
67. 40   **69.** 5   **71.** 26   **73.** 4   **75.** 50
77. 2   **79.** 0   **81.** 5   **83.** 6   **85.** 3
87. 201   **89.** 6   **91.** 15   **93.** 32   **95.** 24
97. 75   **99.** 400   **101.** 3

Section 1.7 Calculator Connections, p. 65

102. 24,336   **103.** 174,724   **104.** 248,832
105. 1,500,625   **106.** 79,507   **107.** 357,911
108. 8028   **109.** 293,834   **110.** 66,049
111. 1728   **112.** 35   **113.** 43

Section 1.8 Practice Exercises, pp. 69–73

3. $71 + 14$; 85   **5.** $2 \cdot 14$; 28   **7.** $102 - 32$; 70
9. $10 \cdot 13$; 130   **11.** $24 \div 6$; 4   **13.** $5 + 13 + 25$; 43
15. Lucio's monthly payment was $85.
17. The interstate will take 4 hr, and the back roads will
take 5 hr. The interstate will take less time.
19. Area   **21.** It will cost $1650.   **23.** The cost is $720.
25. There will be $2676 left in Jose's account.
27. The amount of money required is $924.
29. a. Shevona's paycheck is worth $320.   **b.** She will have
$192 left.   **31.** There will be 2 in. of matte between the
pictures.   **33. a.** The difference between the number of
male and female doctors is 424,400.   **b.** The total number of
doctors is 836,200.   **35. a.** The distance is 320 mi.   **b.** 15
in. represents 600 mi.   **37.** 354 containers will be filled
completely with 9 eggs left over.   **39. a.** Byron needs six
$10 bills.   **b.** He will receive $6 in change.   **41.** The total
amount paid was $2748.   **43.** 109   **45.** 18   **47.** 78¢ per
pound   **49.** 121 mm per month

Chapter 1 Review Exercises, pp. 78–82

1. Ten-thousands   **3.** 92,046
5. 3 millions + 4 hundred-thousands + 8 hundreds + 2 tens
7. Two hundred forty-five   **9.** 3602
11.
13. True   **15.** Addends: 105, 119; sum: 224   **17.** 71
19. 17,410   **21. a.** Commutative property
b. Associative property   **c.** Commutative property
23. Minuend: 102; subtrahend: 78; difference: 24   **25.** 20
27. 1090   **29.** 34,188   **31.** $44 + 92$; 136
33. $111 - 15$; 96   **35.** $23 + 6$; 29   **37.** $90 - 52$; 38
39. 45,797 thousand seniors   **41.** 45,096 thousand

43. $21,772,784   **45.** 5,000,000   **47.** 800,000
49. 17,000,000 people   **51.** Factors: 33, 40; product: 1320
53. c   **55.** d   **57.** b   **59.** 52,224   **61** $429
63. 7; divisor: 6, dividend: 42, quotient: 7   **65.** 3
67. Undefined   **69.** Multiply the quotient and the divisor to get the dividend.   **71.** 58   **73.** 52 R3
75. $9\overline{)108}$; 12   **77. a.** 4 T-shirts **b.** 5 hats   **79.** $2^4 \cdot 5^3$
81. 256   **83.** 1,000,000   **85.** 12   **87.** 75   **89.** 15
91. 55   **93.** 42   **95.** 4   **97. a.** 21 mi **b.** 840 mi
99. a. She should purchase 48 plants.   **b.** The plants will cost $144.   **c.** The fence will cost $80.   **d.** Aletha's total cost will be $224.   **101.** $89

Chapter 1 Test, pp. 82–83

1. a. Hundreds **b.** Thousands **c.** Millions
d. Ten-thousands   **2. a.** 4,065,000 **b.** Twenty-one million, three hundred twenty-five thousand **c.** Twelve million, two hundred eighty-seven thousand **d.** 729,000
e. Eleven million, four hundred ten thousand
3. a. 14 > 6 **b.** 72 < 81   **4.** 129   **5.** 328
6. 113   **7.** 227   **8.** 2842   **9.** 447
10. 21 R9   **11.** 546   **12.** 8103   **13.** 20
14. 1,500,000,000   **15.** 336   **16.** 0   **17.** Undefined
18. a. The associative property of multiplication; the expression shows a change in grouping.
b. The commutative property of multiplication; the expression shows a change in the order of the factors.
19. a. 4900 **b.** 12,000 **c.** 8,000,000
20. There were approximately 1,430,000 people.   **21.** 4
22. 24   **23.** 48   **24.** 33   **25.** 57   **26.** 9
27. Jennifer has a higher average of 29. Brittany has an average of 28.   **28. a.** 23,418 thousand subscribers
b. The largest increase was between the years 2004 and 2005.
29. The North Side Fire Department is the busiest with five calls per week.   **30.** 156 mm   **31.** Perimeter: 350 ft; area: 6016 ft^2 **32.** 4,560,000 m^2

Chapter 2
Chapter Opener Puzzle

1	A5	2	B3	6	4
C6	3	D4	2	5	1
E4	2	3	5	F1	6
5	G1	6	4	3	H2
3	4	1	I6	2	J5
2	K6	L5	1	M4	3

Section 2.1 Practice Exercises, pp. 89–92

3. −86 m   **5.** $3800   **7.** −$500   **9.** −14 lb
11. 1,400,000
13.

15. −2   **17.** >   **19.** >   **21.** <   **23.** <
25. 2   **27.** 2   **29.** 427   **31.** 100,000   **33. a.** −8
b. |−12| **35. a.** 7 **b.** |7| **37.** |−5| **39.** Neither, they are equal.   **41.** −5   **43.** 12   **45.** 0   **47.** 1
49. 15   **51.** −15   **53.** −15   **55.** 15   **57.** 36
59. −107   **61. a.** 6 **b.** 6 **c.** −6 **d.** 6 **e.** −6
63. −8 **b.** 8 **c.** −8 **d.** 8 **e.** 8   **65.** −6   **67.** −(−2)
69. |7| **71.** |−3| **73.** −|14| **75.** =   **77.** >
79. >   **81.** <   **83.** <   **85.** 25°F   **87.** −22°F
89. −2°F   **91.** 44°F   **93.** September   **95.** −60, −|−46|, |−12|, −(−24), 5^2 **97.** Positive   **99.** Negative

Section 2.2 Practice Exercises, pp. 97–99

3. >   **5.** =   **7.** <   **9.** 2   **11.** −2   **13.** −8
15. 6   **17.** −7   **19.** −4   **21.** To add two numbers with the same sign, add their absolute values and apply the common sign.   **23.** 15   **25.** −16   **27.** −124
29. 89   **31.** −3   **33.** 5   **35.** −24   **37.** 45   **39.** 0
41. 0   **43.** 9   **45.** −26   **47.** −41   **49.** −150
51. −17   **53.** −41   **55.** 2   **57.** −30   **59.** 10
61. −8   **63.** 0   **65.** −12   **67.** −23 + 49; 26
69. 3 + (−10) + 5; −2   **71.** (−8 + 6) + (−5); −7
73. 7 in.; Marquette had above average snowfall.
75. −8   **77.** 8°F   **79.** $333   **81.** $600   **83.** 0
85. For example: −12 + 2   **87.** For example: −1 + (−1)

Section 2.2 Calculator Connections, p. 99

89. −120   **90.** −566   **91.** −28,414   **92.** −24,325
93. 711   **94.** 339

Section 2.3 Practice Exercises, pp. 102–105

3. −47   **5.** −26   **7.** −8   **9.** 2 + (−9); −7
11. 4 + 3; 7   **13.** −3 + (−15); −18   **15.** −11 + 13; 2
17. 52   **19.** −33   **21.** −12   **23.** 8   **25.** 0
27. 161   **29.** −34   **31.** −22   **33.** −26   **35.** −1
37. 32   **39.** −15   **41.** 0   **43.** −1   **45.** 52
47. minus, difference, decreased, less than, subtract from
49. 14 − 23; −9   **51.** 105 − 110; −5
53. 320 − (−20); 340   **55.** 5 − 12; −7
57. −34 − 21; −55   **59.** −35 − 24; −59
61. 6423°F   **63.** His balance is −$375.
65. The balance is $18,084   **67.** 164   **69.** −112
71. The range is 3° − (−8°) = 11°.   **73.** For example: 4 − 10
75. −11, −15, −19   **77.** Positive   **79.** Positive
81. Negative   **83.** Negative

Section 2.3 Calculator Connections, p. 105

85. −413   **86.** −433   **87.** −14,623   **88.** 19,906
89. 916,450   **90.** 129,777   **91.** 64,827 ft   **92.** 4478 m

Section 2.4 Practice Exercises, pp. 110–113

3. 19   **5.** −44   **7.** 17   **9.** −15   **11.** 40
13. −21   **15.** 48   **17.** −45   **19.** −72   **21.** 0
23. 95   **25.** −3(−1); 3   **27.** −5 · 3; −15

29. $3(-5)$; -15 **31.** 400   **33.** -88 **35.** 0   **37.** 1
39. 32   **41.** -100 **43.** 100   **45.** -1000
47. -1000 **49.** -625 **51.** 625   **53.** 1   **55.** -1
57. -20 **59.** 7   **61.** -3 **63.** 21   **65.** Undefined
67. 0   **69.** 4   **71.** -34 **73.** $-100 \div 20$; -5
75. $-64 \div (-32)$; 2   **77.** $-52 \div 13$; -4 **79.** -6 ft/min
81. $-13°$F   **83.** $-$$235   **85.** -18 ft   **87.** -108
89. -3 **91.** 108   **93.** 15   **95.** 0   **97.** Undefined
99. 40   **101.** 49   **103. a.** 7 **b.** -7 **105.** $+1$
107. -2 **109.** Negative   **111.** Negative   **113.** Positive

Section 2.4 Calculator Connections, p. 113
115. $-359,723$ **116.** 594,125   **117.** 54   **118.** -629

Chapter 2 Problem Recognition Exercises, p. 114
1. a. 48 **b.** -22 **c.** -26 **d.** 12   **2. a.** -36 **b.** 15
c. 9 **d.** -4 **3.** $-5 + (-3)$; -8 **4.** $9(-5)$; -45
5. $-3 - (-7)$; 4   **6.** $\dfrac{28}{-4}$; -7 **7.** $-23(-2)$; 46
8. $-4 - 18$; -22 **9.** $\dfrac{42}{-2}$; -21 **10.** $-18 + (-13)$; -31
11. $10 - (-12)$; 22   **12.** $\dfrac{-21}{-7}$; 3   **13.** $-6(-9)$; 54
14. $-7 + 4 + 8 + (-16) + (-5)$; -16 **15. a.** 20 **b.** -75
c. 10 **d.** -3 **16. a.** 72 **b.** -34 **c.** 18 **d.** -38
17. a. -80 **b.** 80 **c.** -80 **d.** 80   **18. a.** -16 **b.** -90
19. a. -5 **b.** 25   **20. a.** 24 **b.** 24 **c.** -24 **d.** -24
21. a. 50 **b.** 50 **c.** 50 **d.** -50 **22.** 0   **23.** Undefined
24. 90   **25.** -593 **26.** -30 **27.** 40   **28.** 0
29. 0   **30.** 81   **31.** -32 **32.** -81 **33.** -32
34. Undefined   **35.** 0   **36.** $-10,149$ **37.** $-85,048$

Section 2.5 Practice Exercises, pp. 119–121
3. 25   **5.** 400   **7.** 144   **9.** -17 **11.** 120
13. 1   **15.** 16   **17.** -44 **19.** -150
21. 56   **23.** 110   **25.** -3 **27.** -4 **29.** 16
31. 13   **33.** 11   **35.** 2   **37.** -5 **39.** 8
41. -16 **43.** 6   **45.** -1 **47.** 1   **49.** 14
51. -5 **53.** 38   **55.** $15x$ **57.** $t + 4$
59. $v - 6$ **61.** $2g$ **63.** $-12n$ **65.** $-9 - x$
67. $\dfrac{t}{-2}$ **69.** $y + (-14)$ **71.** $2(c + d)$ **73.** $x - (-8)$
75. -37 **77.** 17   **79.** 7   **81.** -48 **83.** 9
85. -4 **87.** 9   **89.** -9 **91.** -52
93. -5 **95.** $-2°$ **97.** -3

Chapter 2 Review Exercises, pp. 125–127
1. -4250 ft
3., 5.

7. Opposite: 4; absolute value: 4   **9.** 3   **11.** 74
13. 9   **15.** -20 **17.** $<$ **19.** $>$ **21.** 4
23. -5 **25.** See page 93.   **27.** 13   **29.** -70 **31.** 3
33. $23 + (-35)$; -12 **35.** $-5 + (-13) + 20$; 2
37. $-12 + 3$; -9 **39.** -2 in.; Caribou had below average
snowfall.   **41.** See page 100.   **43.** -25 **45.** -419
47. 40   **49.** 100   **51.** For example: 14 subtracted from -2.

53. The temperature rose 5°F.   **55.** The average is
1 above par.   **57.** -18 **59.** 15   **61.** -4 **63.** 96
65. Undefined   **67.** -125 **69.** 36   **71.** 1
73. Negative   **75.** $-45 \div (-15)$; 3   **77.** $-3°$F
79. 38   **81.** -11 **83.** -7 **85.** -2 **87.** 17
89. $a + 8$ **91.** $-5x$ **93.** $(a + b) + 2$ **95.** $y - (-8)$
97. -23 **99.** -18 **101.** -2 **103.** -10

Chapter 2 Test, pp. 128–129
1. $-$$220   **2.** 26   **3.** $<$ **4.** $>$ **5.** $<$ **6.** $=$
7. $<$ **8.** $<$ **9.** 10   **10.** 10   **11.** -5
12. -28 **13.** 9   **14.** -41 **15.** 6   **16.** -23
17. -72 **18.** 88   **19.** 2   **20.** -18
21. Undefined   **22.** 0   **23.** $-3(-7)$; 21
24. $-13 + 8$; -5 **25.** $18 -(-4)$; 22   **26.** $6 \div (-2)$; -3
27. $-8 + 5$; -3 **28.** $-3 + 15 + (-6) + (-1)$; 5
29. -7 in.; Atlanta had below average rainfall.
30. $-7°$F   **31. a.** 64 **b.** -64 **c.** -64 **d.** -64
32. 3   **33.** -60 **34.** 0   **35.** -19 **36.** -55
37. 3   **38.** $18m$ **39.** -15 **40.** 12

Chapters 1–2 Cumulative Review Exercises, p. 129
1. Ten-thousands place   **2.** One hundred thirty is less
than two hundred forty-four.   **3.** 1200 ft   **4.** 114
5. 42   **6.** -196 **7.** 766   **8.** -248 **9.** 193
10. 105 R2   **11.** 93,252   **12.** 0   **13.** Undefined
14. 140 m^2 **15. a.** -4 **b.** 4 **c.** -16 **d.** 16   **16.** 18
17. 21   **18.** 5   **19. a.** Torie can take the herb for
40 days if she takes 3 a day.   **b.** Torie can take the herb for
60 days if she takes 2 a day.   **20.** $-4°$F

Chapter 3
Chapter Opener Puzzle
1. Yes   **2.** No   **3.** Yes   **4.** No   **5.** Yes
6. Yes   **7.** No   **8.** Yes

Section 3.1 Practice Exercises, pp. 138–140
3. -16 **5.** 6   **7.** -144 **9.** $2a$: variable term; $5b^2$:
variable term; 6: constant term   **11.** 8: constant term; $9a$:
variable term   **13.** 6, -4 **15.** -1, -12
17. *Like* terms   **19.** Unlike terms; different variables
21. Unlike terms; different powers of y **23.** Unlike
terms; different variables   **25.** $w + 5$ **27.** $2r$ **29.** $-st$
31. $7 - p$ **33.** $(3 + 8) + t$; $11 + t$ **35.** $(-2 \cdot 6)b$; $-12b$
37. $(3 \cdot 6)x$; $18x$ **39.** $[-9 + (-12)] + h$; $-21 + h$
41. $4x + 32$ **43.** $4a + 16b - 4c$ **45.** $-2p - 8$
47. $-3x - 9 + 5y$ **49.** $-12 + 4n^2$ **51.** $15q + 6s + 9t$
53. $12x$ **55.** $12 + 6x$ **57.** $-4 - p$ **59.** $-32 + 8p$
61. $14r$ **63.** $7h$ **65.** $-2a^2b$ **67.** $6x - 15y + 9$
69. $-3k - 4$ **71.** $4uv + 6u$ **73.** $5t - 28$
75. $-6x - 16$ **77.** $6y - 14$ **79.** $7q$ **81.** $-2n - 4$
83. $4x + 23$ **85.** $2z - 11$ **87.** $-w - 4y + 9$
89. $8a - 9b$ **91.** $-5m + 6n - 10$ **93.** $12z^2 + 7$
95. a. 6 **b.** 6   **97. a.** 5 **b.** 5   **99. a.** -45 **b.** -45
101. a. 36 **b.** 36

Section 3.2 Practice Exercises, pp. 145–146

3. $-13a + 16b$ **5.** $8h - 2k + 13$ **7.** $-3z + 4$
9. Yes   **11.** No   **13.** Yes   **15.** No
17. Equation   **19.** Expression   **21.** Equation
23. 0   **25.** 7   **27.** 3   **29.** 37   **31.** 16   **33.** -15
35. 16   **37.** -78 **39.** 34   **41.** 52   **43.** 0
45. 100   **47.** -28 **49.** 3   **51.** -46 **53.** 61
55. -55 **57.** 42   **59.** -1 **61.** -6 **63.** 12
65. -5 **67.** -1 **69.** 11   **71.** -1 **73.** 10
75. 3   **77.** 28

Section 3.3 Practice Exercises, pp. 151–152

3. $6x + 4y$ **5.** $2m - 10n$ **7.** 45   **9.** -36
11. 3   **13.** -7 **15.** 2   **17.** 13   **19.** -5
21. -21 **23.** 30   **25.** -28 **27.** 4   **29.** 0
31. 0   **33.** 6   **35.** If the operation between the
variable and a number is subtraction, use the addition property
to isolate the variable.   **37.** If the operation between the
variable and a number is multiplication, use the division
property to isolate the variable.   **39.** -16 **41.** -3
43. -8 **45.** -48 **47.** 2   **49.** 30   **51.** -15
53. -57 **55.** 0   **57.** 20   **59.** -31 **61.** 5
63. 13   **65.** 3   **67.** -2 **69.** 1   **71.** -5
73. -1

Section 3.4 Practice Exercises, pp. 156–157

3. -12 **5.** 1   **7.** -19 **9.** 0   **11.** 6   **13.** 6
15. 5   **17.** 2   **19.** 9   **21.** -12 **23.** -60
25. -21 **27.** -3 **29.** 2   **31.** 1   **33.** 4
35. -3 **37.** -4 **39.** -13 **41.** 3   **43.** -12
45. -2 **47.** 0   **49.** 15   **51.** 6   **53.** 1   **55.** 5

Chapter 3 Problem Recognition Exercises, pp. 157–158

1. Equation   **2.** Expression   **3.** Expression
4. Equation   **5.** Equation   **6.** Expression   **7.** 4
8. 6   **9.** $-15t$ **10.** $-30x$ **11.** $5w - 15$
12. $6x - 12$ **13.** 7   **14.** 8   **15.** 15   **16.** 30
17. $t + 25$ **18.** $x + 42$ **19.** -1 **20.** 9   **21.** 2
22. 3   **23.** $11u + 74$ **24.** $61w + 129$ **25.** $-3x + 26$
26. $-7x + 21$ **27.** 14   **28.** -7 **29.** 8   **30.** -34

Section 3.5 Practice Exercises, pp. 164–167

3. -3 **5.** -45 **7.** 6   **9. a.** $x + 6 = 19$ **b.** The
number is 13.   **11. a.** $x - 14 = 20$ **b.** The number is 34.
13. a. $\frac{x}{3} = -8$ **b.** The number is -24.
15. a. $-6x = -60$ **b.** The number is 10.
17. a. $-2 - x = -14$ **b.** The number is 12.
19. a. $13 + x = -100$ **b.** The number is -113.
21. a. $60 = -5x$ **b.** The number is -12.
23. a. $3x + 9 = 15$ **b.** The number is 2.
25. a. $5x - 12 = -27$ **b.** The number is -3.
27. a. $\frac{x}{4} - 5 = -12$ **b.** The number is -28.
29. a. $8 - 3x = 5$ **b.** The number is 1.
31. a. $3(x + 4) = -24$ **b.** The number is -12.

33. a. $-4(3 - x) = -20$ **b.** The number is -2.
35. a. $-12x = x + 26$ **b.** The number is -2.
37. a. $10(x + 5) = 80$ **b.** The number is 3.
39. a. $3x = 2x - 10$ **b.** The number is -10.
41. $5x$ **43.** $6n$ **45.** $A - 30$ **47.** $p + 1481$
49. $5r$ **51.** $2c$ **53.** The pieces should be 2 ft and 6 ft.
55. The distance between Minneapolis and Madison is
240 mi.   **57.** The Beatles had 19 and Elvis had 10.
59. The Giants scored 17 points and the Patriots scored
14 points.   **61.** Charlene's rent is $650 a month and the
security deposit is $300.   **63.** Stefan worked 6 hr of overtime.

Chapter 3 Review Exercises, pp. 172–174

1. $3a^2$ is a variable term with coefficient 3; $-5a$ is a
variable term with coefficient -5; 12 is a constant term with
coefficient 12.   **3.** Unlike terms   **5.** *Like* terms
7. $-5 + t$ **9.** $(-4 \cdot 2)p$; $-8p$ **11.** $6b + 15$
13. $-4c + 6d$ **15.** $2x$ **17.** $6x + 4y + 10$
19. $-2x + 26$ **21.** $-u - 17v$ **23.** -3 is a solution.
25. -35 **27.** 14   **29.** 13   **31.** 2   **33.** -7
35. 26   **37.** 6   **39.** -1 **41.** 8   **43.** 32
45. -28 **47.** -4 **49.** -1 **51.** -3
53. $x - 4 = 13$; The number is 17.   **55.** $-4x + 3 = -17$;
The number is 5.   **57.** $2(x + 10) = 16$; The number is -2.
59. $9n$ **61.** $x + 2$ **63.** Monique drove 120 mi, and
Michael drove 360 mi.   **65.** Tom Hanks starred in 35 films
and Tom Cruise starred in 30 films

Chapter 3 Test, pp. 174–175

1. d   **2.** a   **3.** c   **4.** e   **5.** b   **6.** $-7x$
7. $5a + b$ **8.** $4a + 24$ **9.** $-13b + 8$
10. $12y + 39$ **11.** $-5w - 3$ **12.** An expression is a
collection of terms. An equation has an equal sign that
indicates that two expressions are equal.   **13.** Expression
14. Equation   **15.** Equation   **16.** Expression
17. 21   **18.** 18   **19.** -3 **20.** 7   **21.** -7
22. -10 **23.** -21 **24.** 32   **25.** -2 **26.** 18
27. -72 **28.** -2 **29.** 7   **30.** -3 **31.** -84
32. -14 **33.** 4   **34.** 3   **35.** 0   **36.** 2   **37.** The
number is -5.   **38.** The number is -3.   **39.** $15m$
40. $a + 5$ **41.** Phil makes $252 and Monica makes $504.
42. The computer costs $570 and the monitor costs $329.

Chapters 1–3 Cumulative Review Exercises, pp. 175–176

1. a. hundreds   **b.** ten-thousands   **c.** hundred-thousands
2. 46,000   **3.** 1,290,000   **4.** 25,400
5. Dividend is 39,190; divisor is 46; quotient 851; remainder is 44.
6. Sarah makes $20 per room.   **7.** 10   **8.** 365 ft
9. 20   **10.** -5 **11.** -25 **12.** -9
13. Undefined   **14.** -12 **15.** $-5x + 29$
16. $-2y - 18$ **17.** -4 **18.** -8 **19.** 4
20. Kanye received 10 nominations and Alicia Keys
received 8 nominations.

Chapter 4
Chapter Opener Puzzle

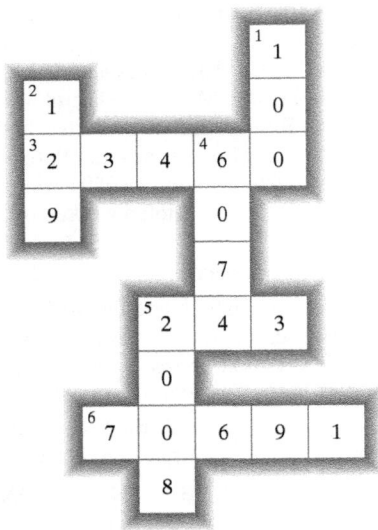

Section 4.1 Practice Exercises, pp. 184–188

3. Numerator: 8; denominator: 9
5. Numerator: $7p$; denominator: $9q$
7. $\dfrac{5}{9}$ **9.** $\dfrac{3}{8}$ **11.** $\dfrac{4}{7}$ **13.** $\dfrac{1}{8}$ **15.** $\dfrac{41}{103}$
17. $\dfrac{10}{21}$ **19.** -13 **21.** 1   **23.** 0   **25.** Undefined
27. $\dfrac{9}{10}$ **29.** b, c   **31.** a, b, c   **33.** Proper
35. Improper   **37.** Improper   **39.** $\dfrac{5}{2}$ **41.** $\dfrac{12}{4}$
43. $\dfrac{7}{4}; 1\dfrac{3}{4}$ **45.** $\dfrac{13}{8}$ in.; $1\dfrac{5}{8}$ in.   **47.** $\dfrac{7}{4}$ **49.** $-\dfrac{38}{9}$
51. $-\dfrac{24}{7}$ **53.** $\dfrac{27}{4}$ **55.** $\dfrac{137}{12}$ **57.** $-\dfrac{171}{8}$
59. 30   **61.** 19   **63.** 7   **65.** $4\dfrac{5}{8}$ **67.** $-7\dfrac{4}{5}$
69. $-2\dfrac{7}{10}$ **71.** $5\dfrac{7}{9}$ **73.** $12\dfrac{1}{11}$ **75.** $-3\dfrac{5}{6}$
77. $44\dfrac{1}{7}$ **79.** $1056\dfrac{1}{5}$ **81.** $810\dfrac{3}{11}$ **83.** $12\dfrac{7}{15}$

85. ![number line with point at 3/4 between 0 and 1]

87. ![number line with point at 1/3 between 0 and 1]

89. ![number line with point at −2/3 between −1 and 0]

91. ![number line with point at 1 1/6 between 1 and 2]

93. ![number line with point at −1 1/3 between −2 and −1]

95. $\dfrac{3}{4}$ **97.** $\dfrac{1}{10}$ **99.** $-\dfrac{7}{3}$ **101.** $\dfrac{7}{3}$
103. False   **105.** True

Section 4.2 Practice Exercises, pp. 196–200

3. $\dfrac{5}{2}, \dfrac{1}{2}$ **5.** $4\dfrac{3}{5}$ **7.** For example: $2 \cdot 4$ and $1 \cdot 8$
9. For example: $4 \cdot 6$ and $2 \cdot 2 \cdot 2 \cdot 3$
11. A whole number is divisible by 2 if it is an even number.
13. A whole number is divisible by 3 if the sum of its digits is divisible by 3.
15. a. No   **b.** Yes   **c.** Yes   **d.** No
17. a. No   **b.** No   **c.** No   **d.** No
19. a. Yes   **b.** Yes   **c.** No   **d.** No
21. a. Yes   **b.** No   **c.** Yes   **d.** Yes
23. Yes   **25.** Prime   **27.** Composite   **29.** Neither
31. Prime   **33.** $2, 3, 5, 7, 11, 13, 17, 19, 23, 29, 31, 37, 41, 43, 47$
35. False   **37.** No, 9 is not a prime number.   **39.** Yes
41. $2 \cdot 5 \cdot 7$ **43.** $2 \cdot 2 \cdot 5 \cdot 13$ or $2^2 \cdot 5 \cdot 13$
45. $3 \cdot 7 \cdot 7$ or $3 \cdot 7^2$
47. $2 \cdot 2 \cdot 2 \cdot 7 \cdot 11$ or $2^3 \cdot 7 \cdot 11$

49.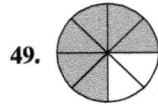

51. False   **53.** $\ne$ **55.** $=$ **57.** $=$ **59.** $\ne$
61. $\dfrac{1}{2}$ **63.** $\dfrac{1}{3}$ **65.** $-\dfrac{9}{5}$ **67.** $-\dfrac{5}{4}$ **69.** 1
71. $\dfrac{3}{4}$ **73.** -3 **75.** $\dfrac{7}{10}$ **77.** $\dfrac{77}{39}$ **79.** $\dfrac{2}{5}$ **81.** $\dfrac{3}{4}$
83. $-\dfrac{5}{3}$ **85.** $\dfrac{21}{11}$ **87.** $\dfrac{17}{100}$ **89.** $\dfrac{8b}{5}$ **91.** $2xy$
93. $\dfrac{x}{3}$ **95.** $-\dfrac{1}{2c^2}$ **97.** Heads: $\dfrac{5}{12}$; tails: $\dfrac{7}{12}$
99. a. $\dfrac{3}{13}$ **b.** $\dfrac{10}{13}$ **c.** $\dfrac{3}{25}$ **101. a.** Jonathan: $\dfrac{5}{7}$; Jared: $\dfrac{6}{7}$
b. Jared sold the greater fractional part.   **103. a.** Raymond: $\dfrac{10}{11}$; Travis: $\dfrac{9}{11}$ **b.** Raymond read the greater fractional part.
105. a. $300,000,000$ **b.** $36,000,000$ **c.** $\dfrac{3}{25}$ **107.** For example: $\dfrac{6}{8}, \dfrac{9}{12}, \dfrac{12}{16}$ **109.** For example: $-\dfrac{6}{9}, -\dfrac{4}{6}, -\dfrac{2}{3}$

Section 4.2 Calculator Connections, p. 200

111. $\dfrac{8}{9}$ **112.** $\dfrac{13}{14}$ **113.** $\dfrac{41}{51}$ **114.** $\dfrac{21}{10}$
115. $\dfrac{29}{30}$ **116.** $\dfrac{13}{7}$ **117.** $\dfrac{3}{2}$ **118.** $\dfrac{31}{19}$

Section 4.3 Practice Exercises, pp. 210–213

3. Numerator: 2100; denominator: 7000; $\dfrac{3}{10}$ **5.** $\dfrac{23}{8}$

7.   **9.** $\dfrac{3}{16}$ **11.** $\dfrac{24}{35}$ **13.** $\dfrac{8}{11}$

15. $-\dfrac{24}{5}$ **17.** $\dfrac{2}{15}$ **19.** $\dfrac{5}{8}$ **21.** $\dfrac{35}{4}$ **23.** $-\dfrac{8}{3}$

25. $\dfrac{4}{5}$ **27.** $\dfrac{30}{7}$ **29.** $\dfrac{3}{2}$ **31.** $-\dfrac{a}{10}$ **33.** $\dfrac{1}{20y}$

35. $4m^2$ **37.**   **39.**

41. 44 cm^2 **43.** 32 m^2 **45.** 4 yd^2 **47.** $\dfrac{8}{7}$

49. $-\dfrac{9}{10}$ **51.** $-\dfrac{1}{4}$ **53.** No reciprocal exists.   **55.** $\dfrac{1}{3}$

57. multiplying   **59.** $\dfrac{8}{25}$ **61.** $\dfrac{35}{26}$ **63.** $\dfrac{35}{9}$

65. -5 **67.** 1   **69.** $-\dfrac{21}{2}$ **71.** $\dfrac{3}{5}$ **73.** $-\dfrac{90}{13}$

75. $\dfrac{6y}{7}$ **77.** $-4c^2d$ **79.** $\dfrac{7}{2}$ **81.** $\dfrac{5}{36}$ **83.** -8

85. $\dfrac{2}{5}$ **87.** 2   **89.** $\dfrac{3}{2}$ **91.** $-\dfrac{xy}{2}$ **93.** $\dfrac{2}{d}$

95. Li wrapped 54 packages.   **97.** 24 cups of juice
99. The stack will be 12 in. high.   **101. a.** 27
commercials in 1 hr   **b.** 648 commercials in 1 day
103. a. Ricardo's mother will pay $16,000.   **b.** Ricardo
will have to pay $8000.   **c.** He will have to finance $216,000.
105. Frankie mowed 960 yd^2. He has 480 yd^2 left to mow.
107. $\dfrac{1}{10}$ of the sample has O negative blood.

109. She can prepare 14 samples.   **111. a.** 455 gal was
required to transport the 130 gal.   **b.** A total of 585 gal was
used.   **113.** 18   **115.** $\dfrac{2}{25}$ **117.** 12 ft, because $30 \div \dfrac{5}{2} = 12$.

119. $\dfrac{1}{32}$ **121.** They are the same.

Section 4.4 Practice Exercises, pp. 219–222

3. $\dfrac{3y}{2x^2}$ **5.** $-\dfrac{10}{7}$ **7.** $-\dfrac{23}{4}$ **9. a.** 48, 72, 240
b. 4, 8, 12   **11. a.** 72, 360, 108   **b.** 6, 12, 9
13. 50   **15.** 48   **17.** 72   **19.** 60   **21.** 210
23. 120   **25.** 60   **27.** 240   **29.** 180   **31.** 180
33. The shortest length of floor space is 60 in. (5 ft).
35. It will take 120 hr (5 days) for the satellites to be lined
up again.

37. $\dfrac{14}{21}$ **39.** $\dfrac{10}{16}$ **41.** $-\dfrac{12}{16}$ **43.** $\dfrac{-12}{15}$ **45.** $\dfrac{49}{42}$

47. $\dfrac{121}{99}$ **49.** $\dfrac{20}{4}$ **51.** $\dfrac{11,000}{4000}$ **53.** $-\dfrac{55}{15}$ **55.** $\dfrac{-15}{24}$

57. $\dfrac{16y}{28}$ **59.** $\dfrac{3y}{8y}$ **61.** $\dfrac{15p}{25p}$ **63.** $\dfrac{2x}{x^2}$ **65.** $\dfrac{8b^2}{ab^3}$

67. $>$ **69.** $<$ **71.** $=$ **73.** $>$ **75.** $\dfrac{7}{8}$

77. $\dfrac{2}{3}, \dfrac{3}{4}, \dfrac{7}{8}$ **79.** $-\dfrac{3}{8}, -\dfrac{5}{16}, -\dfrac{1}{4}$ **81.** $-\dfrac{4}{3}, \dfrac{13}{12}, \dfrac{17}{15}$

83. The longest cut is above the left eye. The shortest cut is
on the right hand.   **85.** The least amount is $\frac{3}{4}$ lb of cheddar,
and the greatest amount is $\frac{7}{8}$ lb of Swiss.   **87.** a and b
89. 336   **91.** 540

Section 4.5 Practice Exercises, pp. 229–231

3. $-\dfrac{12}{14}$ **5.** $\dfrac{25}{5}$ **7.** $\dfrac{4t^2}{t^3}$

9.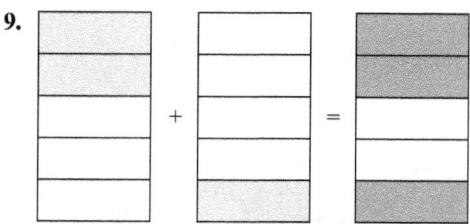

11.

13. $\dfrac{3}{2}$ **15.** $\dfrac{2}{3}$ **17.** $\dfrac{5}{2}$ **19.** $\dfrac{4}{5}$ **21.** $-\dfrac{5}{2}$

23. $-\dfrac{7}{4}$ **25.** $\dfrac{3y+5}{2w}$ **27.** $-\dfrac{2x}{5y}$ **29.** $\dfrac{19}{16}$ **31.** $\dfrac{1}{6}$

33. $\dfrac{83}{42}$ **35.** $\dfrac{3}{8}$ **37.** $\dfrac{1}{3}$ **39.** $-\dfrac{55}{36}$ **41.** $-\dfrac{7}{8}$

43. $\dfrac{8}{3}$ **45.** $-\dfrac{2}{7}$ **47.** $-\dfrac{1}{100}$ **49.** $\dfrac{391}{1000}$ **51.** $\dfrac{9}{8}$

53. $-\dfrac{1}{8}$ **55.** $\dfrac{9}{16}$ **57.** $\dfrac{3x+8}{4x}$ **59.** $\dfrac{10y+7x}{xy}$

61. $\dfrac{10x-2}{x^2}$ **63.** $\dfrac{5-2x}{3x}$ **65.** Inez added $\frac{9}{8}$ cups or $1\frac{1}{8}$ cups.

67. The storm delivered $\frac{5}{32}$ in. of rain.   **69. a.** $\dfrac{13}{36}$ **b.** $\dfrac{23}{36}$

71. $\dfrac{13}{5}$ m or $2\dfrac{3}{5}$ m   **73.** Perimeter: 3 ft   **75.** b

Section 4.6 Practice Exercises, pp. 241–245

1. $\dfrac{24}{5}$ **3.** $\dfrac{13}{6}$ **5.** $\dfrac{12}{11}$ **7.** $\dfrac{1}{2}$ **9.** $\dfrac{17}{5}$

11. $-12\dfrac{5}{6}$ **13.** $7\dfrac{2}{5}$ **15.** $15\dfrac{2}{5}$ **17.** -38 **19.** $27\dfrac{2}{3}$

21. $72\dfrac{1}{2}$ **23.** 2   **25.** $-4\dfrac{5}{12}$ **27.** $2\dfrac{6}{17}$ **29.** $\dfrac{3}{5}$

31. $-2\dfrac{3}{4}$ **33.** $7\dfrac{4}{11}$ **35.** $15\dfrac{3}{7}$ **37.** $15\dfrac{9}{16}$ **39.** $10\dfrac{13}{15}$

41. 5   **43.** 2   **45.** $3\dfrac{1}{5}$ **47.** $8\dfrac{2}{3}$ **49.** $14\dfrac{1}{2}$

51. $23\dfrac{1}{8}$ **53.** $19\dfrac{17}{48}$ **55.** $9\dfrac{5}{12}$ **57.** $12\dfrac{19}{24}$ **59.** $9\dfrac{7}{8}$

61. $171\dfrac{1}{2}$ **63.** $11\dfrac{3}{5}$ **65.** $12\dfrac{1}{6}$ **67.** $11\dfrac{1}{2}$ **69.** $1\dfrac{3}{4}$

71. $7\dfrac{13}{14}$ **73.** $3\dfrac{1}{6}$ **75.** $2\dfrac{7}{9}$ **77.** $\dfrac{11}{16}$ **79.** $\dfrac{32}{35}$

81. $-7\dfrac{11}{14}$ **83.** $2\dfrac{7}{8}$ **85.** $5\dfrac{3}{4}$ **87.** $-2\dfrac{5}{6}$ **89.** $-\dfrac{36}{5}$

91. $\dfrac{7}{24}$ **93.** $\dfrac{50}{13}$ **95.** $\dfrac{61}{30}$ **97.** $7\dfrac{3}{4}$ in.

99. The index finger is longer.   **101.** Tabitha earned $38.

103. $642\frac{1}{2}$ lb   **105.** The total is $16\dfrac{11}{12}$ hr.

107. a. 7 weeks old **b.** $8\frac{1}{2}$ weeks old   **109. a.** Lucy earned $72 more than Ricky. **b.** Together they earned $922.

111. $3\frac{5}{12}$ ft   **113.** The printing area width is 6 in.

115. a. $3\frac{3}{8}$ L **b.** $\frac{5}{8}$ L   **117.** $2\frac{2}{3}$ **119.** $2\frac{1}{6}$

Section 4.6 Calculator Connections, p. 246

121. $318\frac{1}{4}$ **122.** $3\frac{1}{15}$ **123.** $17\frac{18}{19}$ **124.** $466\frac{1}{5}$

125. $1\frac{43}{168}$ **126.** $\frac{11}{30}$ **127.** $\frac{37}{132}$ **128.** $\frac{137}{391}$

129. $46\frac{25}{54}$ **130.** $25\frac{71}{84}$ **131.** $5\frac{17}{77}$ **132.** $3\frac{9}{68}$

Chapter 4 Problem Recognition Exercises, p. 247

1. a. -1 **b.** $-\frac{14}{25}$ **c.** $-\frac{7}{2}$ or $-3\frac{1}{2}$ **d.** $-\frac{9}{5}$ or $-1\frac{4}{5}$

2. a. $\frac{10}{9}$ or $1\frac{1}{9}$ **b.** $\frac{8}{5}$ or $1\frac{3}{5}$ **c.** $\frac{13}{6}$ or $2\frac{1}{6}$ **d.** $\frac{1}{2}$

3. a. $\frac{5}{4}$ or $1\frac{1}{4}$ **b.** $\frac{17}{4}$ or $4\frac{1}{4}$ **c.** $-\frac{11}{6}$ or $-1\frac{5}{6}$

d. $-\frac{33}{8}$ or $-4\frac{1}{8}$ **4. a.** $\frac{221}{18}$ or $12\frac{5}{18}$ **b.** $\frac{26}{17}$ or $1\frac{9}{17}$

c. $\frac{3}{2}$ or $1\frac{1}{2}$ **d.** $\frac{43}{6}$ or $7\frac{1}{6}$ **5. a.** $-\frac{35}{8}$ or $-4\frac{3}{8}$

b. $-\frac{3}{2}$ or $-1\frac{1}{2}$ **c.** $-\frac{32}{3}$ or $-10\frac{2}{3}$ **d.** $-\frac{29}{8}$ or $-3\frac{5}{8}$

6. a. $\frac{11}{6}$ or $1\frac{5}{6}$ **b.** $\frac{5}{3}$ or $1\frac{2}{3}$ **c.** $\frac{17}{3}$ or $5\frac{2}{3}$ **d.** $\frac{22}{3}$ or $7\frac{1}{3}$

7. a. $-\frac{53}{15}$ or $-3\frac{8}{15}$ **b.** $-\frac{73}{15}$ or $-4\frac{13}{15}$ **c.** $\frac{14}{5}$ or $2\frac{4}{5}$

d. $\frac{63}{10}$ or $6\frac{3}{10}$ **8. a.** $\frac{25}{18}$ or $1\frac{7}{18}$ **b.** $\frac{50}{9}$ or $5\frac{5}{9}$ **c.** $\frac{7}{9}$

d. $\frac{43}{9}$ or $4\frac{7}{9}$ **9. a.** -1 **b.** $-\frac{56}{45}$ or $-1\frac{11}{45}$

c. $-\frac{81}{25}$ or $-3\frac{6}{25}$ **d.** $-\frac{106}{45}$ or $-2\frac{16}{45}$

10. a. 1 **b.** 1 **c.** 1 **d.** 1

Section 4.7 Practice Exercises, pp. 252–254

3. $-\frac{47}{30}$ **5.** $-\frac{12}{35}$ **7.** $-9\frac{5}{24}$ **9.** $\frac{1}{81}$ **11.** $\frac{1}{81}$

13. $-\frac{27}{8}$ **15.** $-\frac{27}{8}$ **17.** $\frac{1}{1000}$ **19.** $\frac{1}{1,000,000}$

21. $-\frac{1}{1000}$ **23.** -27 **25.** $4\frac{1}{4}$ **27.** 42

29. -2 **31.** $\frac{2}{9}$ **33.** 3   **35.** $2\frac{3}{8}$ **37.** $\frac{5}{3}$

39. $\frac{1}{36}$ **41.** $\frac{23}{24}$ **43.** $1\frac{3}{7}$ **45.** $\frac{25}{3}$ **47.** $5\frac{1}{4}$

49. -7 **51.** $7\frac{7}{9}$ **53.** $\frac{5}{6}$ **55.** $-\frac{7}{4}$ **57.** $\frac{x}{28}$

59. $-\frac{3}{5}$ **61.** $\frac{7}{4}$ **63.** $\frac{28}{11}$ **65.** -11 **67.** $\frac{2}{9}$

69. $2y$ **71.** $\frac{5}{8}a$ **73.** $\frac{17}{30}x$ **75.** $\frac{4}{3}y - \frac{7}{4}z$

77. a. $\frac{1}{36}$ **b.** $\frac{1}{6}$ **79.** $\frac{1}{5}$ **81.** $\frac{8}{9}$

Section 4.8 Practice Exercises, pp. 259–261

3. $\frac{25}{36}$ **5.** $-\frac{65}{36}$ **7.** $-10\frac{1}{24}$ **9.** $\frac{7}{6}$ **11.** $-\frac{13}{10}$

13. $\frac{13}{12}$ **15.** $\frac{13}{8}$ **17.** 2   **19.** $\frac{7}{6}$ **21.** $-\frac{2}{5}$

23. -24 **25.** 21   **27.** -21 **29.** 30   **31.** 0

33. $\frac{2}{5}$ **35.** $\frac{1}{18}$ **37.** $\frac{35}{8}$ **39.** -5 **41.** $\frac{1}{4}$

43. 1   **45.** $-\frac{7}{2}$ **47.** $\frac{2}{3}$ **49.** $\frac{10}{9}$ **51.** 7

53. 5   **55.** -48 **57.** $\frac{1}{3}$ **59.** $-\frac{21}{10}$ **61.** $-\frac{1}{12}$

63. $\frac{7}{10}$ **65.** -12 **67.** $\frac{1}{3}$ **69.** $\frac{8}{5}$ **71.** $-\frac{44}{15}$

73. 6   **75.** $\frac{9}{5}$

Chapter 4 Problem Recognition Exercises, pp. 261–262

1. Equation; $\frac{1}{10}$ **2.** Equation; $\frac{6}{7}$ **3.** Expression; $\frac{3}{2}$

4. Expression; $\frac{1}{8}$ **5.** Expression; $\frac{7}{5}$ **6.** Expression; $\frac{9}{5}$

7. Equation; $-\frac{2}{5}$ **8.** Equation; $-\frac{4}{5}$ **9.** Equation; 4

10. Equation; $\frac{5}{3}$ **11.** Expression; $\frac{4}{9}$

12. Expression; 0   **13.** Equation; 6   **14.** Equation; $-\frac{5}{2}$

15. Expression; $6x - 24$ **16.** Expression; $2x + 30$

17. Equation; $\frac{8}{3}$ **18.** Equation; 7   **19.** Expression; $\frac{3}{2}$

20. Expression; $\frac{25}{7}$ **21.** Equation; $\frac{2}{7}$ **22.** Equation; $\frac{3}{4}$

23. Expression; $\frac{18}{7}c$ **24.** Expression; $\frac{21}{4}d$

Chapter 4 Review Exercises, pp. 272–275

1. $\frac{1}{2}$ **3. a.** $\frac{5}{3}$ **b.** Improper   **5. a.** $\frac{3}{8}$ **b.** $\frac{2}{3}$ **c.** $\frac{4}{9}$

7. $\frac{7}{6}$ or $1\frac{1}{6}$ **9.** $\frac{57}{5}$ **11.** $1\frac{2}{21}$

13., 15.

17. $60\frac{11}{13}$ **19.** 55, 140, 260, 1200

21. 12, 27, 51, 63, 130   **23.** $2 \cdot 2 \cdot 3 \cdot 3 \cdot 5 \cdot 5$ or $2^2 \cdot 3^2 \cdot 5^2$

25. =   **27.** $\frac{1}{5}$ **29.** $-\frac{7}{3}$ **31.** $\frac{7}{1000}$ **33.** $\frac{4t^2}{5}$

35. a. $\frac{3}{5}$ **b.** $\frac{2}{5}$ **37.** $-\frac{3}{2}$ **39.** 15   **41.** $\frac{3y^2}{2}$

43. 51 ft²   **45.** 1   **47.** $-\frac{1}{7}$ **49.** $\frac{7}{5}$ **51.** −14

53. $\frac{3y^2}{2}$ **55.** Yes. $9 \div \frac{3}{8} = 24$ so he will have 24 pieces,

which is more than enough for his class.
57. There are 300 Asian American students.   **59. a.** $2^2 \cdot 5^2$
b. $5 \cdot 13$ **c.** $2 \cdot 5 \cdot 7$ **61.** 96   **63.** $\frac{15}{48}$ **65.** $\frac{35y}{60y}$

67. <   **69.** =   **71.** $\frac{3}{2}$ **73.** $\frac{29}{100}$ **75.** $-\frac{47}{11}$

77. $\frac{17}{40}$ **79.** $\frac{17}{5w}$ **81. a.** $\frac{35}{4}$ m or $8\frac{3}{4}$ m   **b.** $\frac{315}{128}$ m²

or $2\frac{59}{128}$ m²   **83.** $23\frac{7}{15}$ **85.** $\frac{10}{11}$ **87.** $-2\frac{3}{11}$

89. $50; 50\frac{9}{40}$ **91.** $11\frac{11}{63}$ **93.** $2\frac{5}{8}$ **95.** $3\frac{2}{5}$

97. $63\frac{15}{16}$ **99.** $-2\frac{5}{6}$ **101.** Corry drove a total of $8\frac{1}{6}$ hr.

103. It will take $3\frac{1}{8}$ gal.   **105.** $\frac{9}{64}$

107. $-\frac{1}{100,000}$ **109.** $-\frac{29}{10}$ **111.** $\frac{1}{6}$ **113.** $\frac{14}{5}$

115. $-\frac{3}{7}$ **117.** $-\frac{4}{3}$ **119.** $\frac{5}{16}$ **121.** $-\frac{17}{12}x$

123. $\frac{2}{3}a + \frac{1}{6}c$ **125.** $\frac{19}{15}$ **127.** $\frac{10}{9}$ **129.** $\frac{3}{5}$

131. −1   **133.** −15

Chapter 4 Test, pp. 276–277

1. a. $\frac{5}{8}$ **b.** Proper   **2. a.** $\frac{7}{3}$ **b.** Improper

3. a. $3\frac{2}{3}$. **b.** $\frac{34}{9}$

4.

5.

6. $\frac{2}{11}$ **7.** $-\frac{2}{11}$ **8.** $\frac{2}{11}$ **9. a.** Composite
b. Neither **c.** Prime **d.** Neither **e.** Prime **f.** Composite
10. $3 \cdot 3 \cdot 5$ or $3^2 \cdot 5$ **11.** Add the digits of the number.

If the sum is divisible by 3, then the original number is
divisible by 3.   **b.** Yes   **12. a.** No **b.** Yes **c.** Yes **d.** No

13. =   **14.** ≠   **15.** $\frac{10}{7}$ or $1\frac{3}{7}$ **16.** $\frac{2}{7b}$

17. a. Christine: $\frac{3}{5}$; Brad: $\frac{4}{5}$

b. Brad has the greater fractional part completed.
18. $\frac{19}{69}$ **19.** $\frac{25}{2}$ or $12\frac{1}{2}$ **20.** $\frac{4}{9}$ **21.** $-\frac{1}{2}$ **22.** $\frac{2y}{3}$

23. $-5bc$ **24.** $\frac{44}{3}$ cm² or $14\frac{2}{3}$ cm²   **25.** $20 \div \frac{1}{4}$

26. 48 quarter-pounders

27. They can build on a maximum of $\frac{2}{5}$ acre.

28. a. 24, 48, 72, 96   **b.** 1, 2, 3, 4, 6, 8, 12, 24
c. $2 \cdot 2 \cdot 2 \cdot 3$ or $2^3 \cdot 3$

29. 240   **30.** $\frac{35}{63}$ **31.** $\frac{22w}{42w}$ **32.** $-\frac{5}{3}, -\frac{4}{7}, -\frac{11}{21}$

33. When subtracting like fractions, keep the same
denominator and subtract the numerators. When multiplying
fractions, multiply the denominators as well as the numerators.

34. $\frac{9}{16}$ **35.** $\frac{1}{3}$ **36.** $-\frac{1}{3}$ **37.** $\frac{12y - 6}{y^2}$ **38.** $-1\frac{21}{25}$

39. $9\frac{3}{5}$ **40.** $17\frac{3}{8}$ **41.** $2\frac{1}{11}$ **42.** $-7\frac{4}{9}$ **43.** $3\frac{9}{10}$

44. 1 lb is needed.   **45.** Area: $25\frac{2}{25}$ m²; perimeter: $20\frac{1}{5}$ m

46. $\frac{36}{49}$ **47.** $-\frac{1}{1000}$ **48.** $-\frac{4}{15}$ **49.** $\frac{9}{7}$ **50.** $-\frac{1}{17}$

51. $\frac{3}{2}$ **52.** $\frac{8}{15}m$ **53.** $\frac{11}{9}$ **54.** $-\frac{6}{5}$ **55.** $-\frac{2}{11}$

56. 16   **57.** $-\frac{7}{2}$ **58.** $\frac{20}{3}$

Chapters 1–4 Cumulative Review Exercises, p. 278

1. Ten-thousands place   **2.** One hundred thirty is less
than two hundred forty-four
3. $2 \cdot 2 \cdot 2 \cdot 3 \cdot 3 \cdot 5$ or $2^3 \cdot 3^2 \cdot 5$ **4.** 42   **5.** $-\frac{3}{8}$

6. −92   **7.** 0   **8.** $\frac{1}{8}$ **9.** $\frac{2}{5}$ **10.** $\frac{26}{17}$ or $1\frac{9}{17}$

11. $\frac{10}{3}$ or $3\frac{1}{3}$ **12.** $\frac{1}{5}$

13.

14. a. −4 **b.** 4 **c.** −16 **d.** 16   **15.** 18
16. $-11x - 3y - 5$ **17.** $-7x + 18$ **18.** 24

19. $\frac{1}{4}$ **20.** 14

Chapter 5

Chapter Opener Puzzle

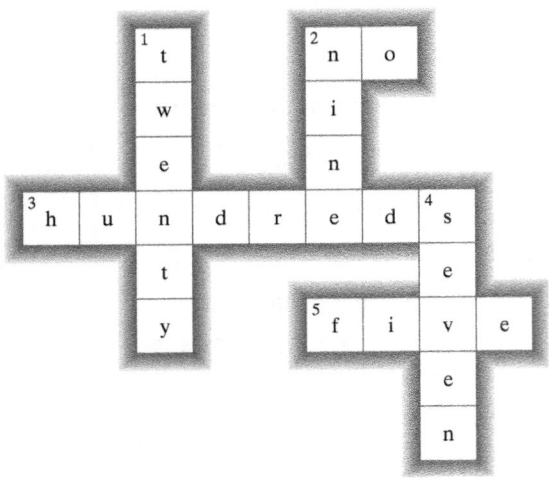

Section 5.1 Practice Exercises, pp. 287–289

3. 100   **5.** 10,000   **7.** $\dfrac{1}{100}$ **9.** $\dfrac{1}{10,000}$
11. Tenths   **13.** Hundredths   **15.** Tens
17. Ten-thousandths   **19.** Thousandths   **21.** Ones
23. Nine-tenths   **25.** Twenty-three hundredths
27. Negative thirty-three thousandths
29. Four hundred seven ten-thousandths
31. Three and twenty-four hundredths
33. Negative five and nine-tenths
35. Fifty-two and three-tenths
37. Six and two hundred nineteen thousandths
39. −8472.014   **41.** 700.07   **43.** −2,469,000.506
45. $3\dfrac{7}{10}$ **47.** $2\dfrac{4}{5}$ **49.** $\dfrac{1}{4}$ **51.** $-\dfrac{11}{20}$ **53.** $20\dfrac{203}{250}$
55. $-15\dfrac{1}{2000}$ **57.** $\dfrac{42}{5}$ **59.** $\dfrac{157}{50}$ **61.** $-\dfrac{47}{2}$
63. $\dfrac{1191}{100}$ **65.** <   **67.** >   **69.** <
71. >   **73.** a, b   **75.** 0.3444, 0.3493, 0.3558, 0.3585, 0.3664   **77.** These numbers are equivalent, but they represent different levels of accuracy.   **79.** 7.1   **81.** 49.9
83. 33.42   **85.** −9.096   **87.** 21.0   **89.** 7.000
91. 0.0079   **93.** 0.0036 mph

	Number	Hundreds	Tens	Tenths	Hun-dredths	Thou-sandths
95.	971.0948	1000	970	971.1	971.09	971.095
97.	21.9754	0	20	22.0	21.98	21.975

99. 0.972

Section 5.2 Practice Exercises, pp. 295–298

1. a, c   **3.** 23.5   **5.** 8.603   **7.** 2.8300   **9.** 63.2
11. 8.951   **13.** 15.991   **15.** 79.8005   **17.** 31.0148
19. 62.6032   **21.** 100.414   **23.** 128.44   **25.** 82.063
27. 14.24   **29.** 3.68   **31.** 12.32   **33.** 5.677
35. 1.877   **37.** 21.6646   **39.** 14.765   **41.** 159.558
43. 0.9012   **45.** −422.94   **47.** −1.359   **49.** 50.979
51. −3.27   **53.** −4.432   **55.** 1.4   **57.** −111.2
59. 0.5346
61.

Check No.	Description	Debit	Credit	Balance
				$ 245.62
2409	Electric bill	$ 52.48		193.14
2410	Groceries	72.44		120.70
2411	Department store	108.34		12.36
	Paycheck		$1084.90	1097.26
2412	Restaurant	23.87		1073.39
	Transfer from savings		200	1273.39

63. 1.35 million cells per microliter
65. a. The water is rising 1.7 in./hr.   **b.** At 1:00 P.M. the level will be 11 in.   **c.** At 3:00 P.M. the level will be 14.4 in.
67. The pile containing the two nickels and two pennies is higher.   **69.** $x = 8.9$ in.; $y = 15.4$ in.; the perimeter is 98.8 in.
71. $x = 2.075$ ft; $y = 2.59$ ft; the perimeter is 22.17 ft.
73. 27.2 mi   **75.** $3.87t$ **77.** $-13.2p$ **79.** $0.4y$
81. $0.845x + 0.52y$ **83.** $c - 5d$

Section 5.2 Calculator Connections, p. 299

85. IBM increased by $5.90 per share.   **86.** FedEx decreased by $3.66 per share.   **87.** Between February and March, FedEx increased the most, by $2.27 per share.
88. Between April and May, IBM increased the most, by $7.96 per share.   **89.** Between March and April, FedEx decreased the most, by $8.09 per share.   **90.** Between February and March, IBM decreased the most, by $6.73 per share.

Section 5.3 Practice Exercises, pp. 306–311

3. 50.0   **5.** −0.003   **7.** 7.958   **9.** 0.4   **11.** 3.6
13. 0.18   **15.** 17.904   **17.** 37.35   **19.** 4.176
21. −4.736   **23.** 2.891   **25.** 114.88   **27.** 2.248
29. −0.00144   **31. a.** 51   **b.** 510   **c.** 5100   **d.** 51,000
33. a. 0.51   **b.** 0.051   **c.** 0.0051   **d.** 0.00051   **35.** 3490
37. 96,590   **39.** −0.933   **41.** 0.05403
43. 2,600,000   **45.** 400,000   **47.** $20,549,000,000
49. a. 201.6 lb of gasoline   **b.** 640 lb of CO_2
51. The bill was $312.17.   **53.** $2.81 can be saved.
55. 0.00115 km^2 **57.** The area is 333 yd^2.   **59.** 0.16
61. 1.69   **63.** 0.001   **65.** −0.04   **67.** The length of a radius is one-half the length of a diameter.   **69.** 12.2 in.

71. 83 m   **73.** 62.8 cm   **75.** 15.7 km   **77.** 18.84 cm
79. 14.13 in.   **81.** 314 mm^2 **83.** 121 ft^2
85. 16.642 mi   **87.** 2826 ft^2
89. a. 62.8 in.   **b.** 23 times   **91.** 69,080 in. or 5757 ft

Section 5.3 Calculator Connections, p. 311

93. Area ≈ 517.1341 cm^2; circumference ≈ 80.6133 cm
94. Area ≈ 81.7128 ft^2; circumference ≈ 32.0442 ft
95. Area ≈ 70.8822 in.^{2}; circumference ≈ 29.8451 in.
96. Area ≈ 8371.1644 mm^2; circumference ≈ 324.3380 mm

Section 5.4 Practice Exercises, pp. 319–322

3. −10.203   **5.** −101.161   **7.** −0.00528   **9.** 314 ft^2
11. 0.9   **13.** 0.18   **15.** 0.53   **17.** 21.1   **19.** 1.96
21. 0.035   **23.** 16.84   **25.** 0.12   **27.** −0.16
29. 5.$\overline{3}$ **31.** 3.1$\overline{6}$ **33.** 2.$\overline{15}$ **35.** 503
37. 9.92   **39.** −56   **41.** 2.975   **43.** 208.$\overline{3}$
45. 48.5   **47.** 1100   **49.** 42,060   **51.** The decimal
point will move to the left two places.   **53.** 0.03923
55. −9.802   **57.** 0.00027   **59.** 0.00102
61. a. 2.4   **b.** 2.44   **c.** 2.444
63. a. 1.8   **b.** 1.79   **c.** 1.789
65. a. 3.6   **b.** 3.63   **c.** 3.626
67. 0.26   **69.** −14.8   **71.** 20.667   **73.** 35.67
75. 111.3   **77.** Unreasonable; $960
79. Unreasonable; $140,000   **81.** The monthly payment
is $42.50.   **83. a.** 13 bulbs would be needed (rounded up to
the nearest whole unit).   **b.** $9.75   **c.** The energy efficient
fluorescent bulb would be more cost effective.
85. Babe Ruth's batting average was 0.342.
87. 2.2 mph   **89.** −47.265   **91.** b, d

Section 5.4 Calculator Connections, pp. 322-323

93. 1149686.166   **94.** 3411.4045   **95.** 1914.0625
96. 69,568.83693   **97.** 95.6627907   **98.** 293.5070423
99. Answers will vary.   **100.** Answers will vary.
101. a. 0.27   **b.** Yes the claim is accurate. The decimal, 0.27
is close to 0.25, which is equal to $\frac{1}{4}$.   **102.** 272 people per
square mile   **103. a.** 1,600,000 mi per day
b. 66,666.$\overline{6}$ mph   **104.** When we say that 1 year is 365
days, we are ignoring the 0.256 day each year. In 4 years, that
amount is 4 × 0.256 = 1.024, which is another whole day. This
is why we add one more day to the calendar every 4 years.

Chapter 5 Problem Recognition Exercises, pp. 323–324

1. a. 223.04   **b.** 12,304   **c.** 23.04   **d.** 1.2304   **e.** 123.05
f. 1.2304   **g.** 12,304   **h.** 123.03
2. a. 6078.3   **b.** 5,078,300   **c.** 4078.3   **d.** 5.0783
e. 5078.301   **f.** 5.0783   **g.** 5,078,300   **h.** 5078.299
3. a. −7.191   **b.** 7.191   **4. a.** −730.4634   **b.** 730.4634
5. a. 52.64   **b.** 52.64   **6. a.** 59.384   **b.** 59.384
7. a. 86.4   **b.** −5.4   **8. a.** 185   **b.** −46.25
9. a. −80   **b.** −448   **10. a.** −54   **b.** −496.8
11. 1   **12.** 1   **13.** 4000   **14.** 6,400,000

15. 200,000   **16.** 2700   **17.** 1,350,000,000
18. 1,700,000   **19.** 4.4001   **20.** 76.7001
21. 5.73   **22.** 0.055   **23.** −12.67   **24.** −0.139

Section 5.5 Practice Exercises, pp. 333–336

3. 0.0225   **5.** 6.4   **7.** −0.756   **9.** $\frac{4}{10}$; 0.4
11. $\frac{98}{100}$; 0.98   **13.** 0.28   **15.** −0.632   **17.** −3.2
19. −5.25   **21.** 0.75   **23.** 7.45   **25.** 3.$\overline{8}$
27. 0.52$\overline{7}$ **29.** −0.1$\overline{26}$ **31.** 1.1$\overline{36}$ **33.** 0.9
35. 0.143   **37.** 0.08   **39.** −0.71
41. a. 0.$\overline{1}$ **b.** 0.$\overline{2}$ **c.** 0.$\overline{4}$ **d.** 0.$\overline{5}$
If we memorize that $\frac{1}{9} = 0.\overline{1}$, then $\frac{2}{9} = 2 \cdot \frac{1}{9} = 2 \cdot 0.\overline{1} = 0.\overline{2}$,
and so on.

43.

	Decimal Form	Fraction Form
a.	0.45	$\frac{9}{20}$
b.	1.625	$1\frac{5}{8}$ or $\frac{13}{8}$
c.	−0.$\overline{7}$	$-\frac{7}{9}$
d.	−0.$\overline{45}$	$-\frac{5}{11}$

45.

	Decimal Form	Fraction Form
a.	0.$\overline{3}$	$\frac{1}{3}$
b.	−2.125	$-2\frac{1}{8}$ or $-\frac{17}{8}$
c.	−0.8$\overline{63}$	$-\frac{19}{22}$
d.	1.68	$\frac{42}{25}$

47. Rational   **49.** Rational   **51.** Rational
53. Irrational   **55.** Irrational   **57.** Rational
59. =   **61.** <   **63.** >   **65.** >
67. 1.75, 1.$\overline{7}$, 1.8

69. $-\frac{1}{5}$, −0.$\overline{1}$, $-\frac{1}{10}$

71. 6.25   **73.** 10   **75.** 8.77   **77.** 25.75   **79.** −2
81. −8.58   **83.** 67.35   **85.** 25.05   **87.** 23.4
89. 1.28   **91.** −10.83   **93.** 2.84   **95.** 43.46 cm^2
97. 84.78   **99.** −78.4   **101. a.** 471 mi   **b.** 62.8 mph
103. Jorge will be charged $98.75.   **105.** She has 24.3 g
left for dinner.   **107.** Hannah should get $4.77 in change.
109. 3.475   **111.** 0.52

Section 5.5 Calculator Connections, p. 337

113. a. 237 shares **b.** $13.90 will be left.
114. a. Approximately 921,800 homes could be powered.
b. Approximately 342,678 additional homes could be powered.   **115. a.** The BMI is approximately 30.1. The person is at high risk. **b.** The BMI is approximately 19.8. The person has a lower risk.   **116. a.** Marty will have to finance $120,000. **b.** There are 360 months in 30 yr. **c.** He will pay $287,409.60 **d.** He will pay $167,409.60 in interest.
117. Each person will get approximately $13,410.10.

Section 5.6 Practice Exercises, pp. 342–344

1. area: 0.0314 m²; circumference: 0.628 m   **3.** 2.25
5. −2.23   **7.** 0.51x **9.** −22.1z + 6.2   **11.** 0.86
13. −4.78   **15.** −49.9   **17.** 0.095   **19.** 42.78
21. −0.12   **23.** −2.9   **25.** 19   **27.** 5   **29.** 9
31. −24   **33.** 6.72   **35.** 50   **37.** −4
39. −600   **41.** 10   **43.** The number is 4.5.
45. The number is 2.7.   **47.** The number is −9.4.
49. The number is 7.6.   **51.** The sides are 4.6 yd, 7.7 yd, and 9.2 yd.   **53.** Rafa made $65.25, Toni made $43.20, and Henri made $59.35 in tips.   **55.** The painter rented the pressure cleaner for 3.5 hr.   **57.** The previous balance is $104.75, and the new charges amount to $277.15.
59. Madeline rode for 54.25 min, and Kim rode for 62.5 min.

Chapter 5 Review Exercises, pp. 352–355

1. The 3 is in the tens place, 2 is in the ones place, 1 is in the tenths place, and 6 is in the hundredths place.
3. Five and seven-tenths   **5.** Negative fifty-one and eight thousandths   **7.** 33,015.047   **9.** $-4\frac{4}{5}$ **11.** $\frac{13}{10}$
13. <   **15.** 4.3875, 4.3953, 4.4839, 4.5000, 4.5142
17. 34.890   **19.** a, b   **21.** 49.743   **23.** 5.45
25. −244.04   **27.** 7.809   **29.** 0.5y **31. a.** Between days 1 and 2, the increase was $0.194. **b.** Between days 3 and 4, the decrease was $0.209.   **33.** 4.113   **35.** −346.5
37. 100.34   **39.** 1.0422   **41.** 33,800,000   **43.** The call will cost $1.61.   **45. a.** 7280 people **b.** 18,000 people
47. 13.6 ft   **49.** Area: 2826 yd²; circumference: 188.4 yd
51. 42.8   **53.** 8.7$\overline{6}$ **55.** −0.03   **57.** 9.0234
59. 260   **61.** −11.62   **63. a.** $0.50 per roll
b. $0.57 per roll   **c.** The 12-pack is better.
65. 3.52   **67.** −0.4375   **69.** 1.52$\overline{7}$ **71.** 0.29
73. −3.667   **75.** $\frac{2}{9}$

77.

Stock	Closing Price ($) (Decimal)	Closing Price ($) (Fraction)
Sun	5.20	$5\frac{1}{5}$
Sony	55.53	$55\frac{53}{100}$
Verizon	41.16	$41\frac{4}{25}$

79. >   **81.** −5.52   **83.** 1.6   **85.** −2   **87.** Marvin must drive 34 mi more.   **89.** −1.53   **91.** −11.32

93. 2.5   **95.** 110   **97.** Multiply by 100; solution: −1.48
99. The number is 6.5.   **101.** The number is 1600.
103. The sides are 5.6 yd, 8 yd, and 11.2 yd.
105. Mykeshia can rent space for 6 months.

Chapter 5 Test, pp. 355–357

1. a. Tens place **b.** Hundredths place
2. Negative five hundred nine and twenty-four thousandths
3. $1\frac{13}{50}; \frac{63}{50}$ **4.** 0.4419, 0.4484, 0.4489, 0.4495
5. b is correct.   **6.** −45.172   **7.** −46.89
8. −126.45   **9.** −5.08   **10.** 1.22   **11.** 12.2243
12. 120.$\overline{6}$ **13.** 439.81   **14.** 4.592   **15.** 57,923
16. 8012   **17.** 0.002931   **18.** 5.66x **19.** 14.6y − 3.3
20. 24.4 ft   **21.** Circumference: 50 cm; area: 201 cm²
22. a. 61.4°F **b.** 1.4°F   **23. a.** 1,040,000,000 tons
b. 360,000,000 tons **c.** 680,000,000 tons   **24. a.** 67.5 in.²
b. 75.5 in.² **c.** 157.3 in.²
25. He made $3094.75.   **26.** She will pay approximately $37.50 per month.   **27.** He will use 10 gal of gas.
28. $-3.\overline{5}, -3\frac{1}{2}, -3.2$

29. 9.57   **30.** 47.25   **31.** −1.21   **32. a.** Rational
b. Irrational **c.** Irrational **d.** Rational
33. −0.008   **34.** 177.5   **35.** 18.66   **36.** 3.4
37. −2   **38.** 5.5   **39.** The number is −6.2.
40. The number is 0.24.

Chapters 1–5 Cumulative Review Exercises, p. 357

1. 14   **2.** 2,415,000   **3.** The difference between sales for Wal-Mart and Sears is $181,956 million.
4. $\frac{6}{55}$ **5.** $\frac{4}{7}$ **6.** $\frac{49}{100}$ **7.** $\frac{2}{3}$
8. There is $9000 left.   **9.** $\frac{2}{5}$ **10.** $\frac{38}{11}$ **11.** $-\frac{3}{2}$
12. Area: $\frac{15}{64}$ ft²; perimeter: 2 ft   **13.** −72.33
14. 668.79   **15.** −75.275   **16.** 16
17. 3.66x − 8.65   **18.** Circumference: 6.28 m; area: 3.14 m²   **19.** −0.86   **20.** −6

Chapter 6

Chapter Opener Puzzle

H	O	U	S	E		O	F		P	I
1	2	3	4	5		2	6		7	8

Section 6.1 Practice Exercises, pp. 364–367

3. 5 : 6 and $\frac{5}{6}$ **5.** 11 to 4 and $\frac{11}{4}$ **7.** 1 : 2 and 1 to 2
9. a. $\frac{5}{3}$ **b.** $\frac{3}{5}$ **c.** $\frac{3}{8}$ **11. a.** $\frac{2}{15}$ **b.** $\frac{2}{13}$

13. a. $\frac{7}{18}$ **b.** $\frac{7}{25}$ **15.** $\frac{2}{3}$ **17.** $\frac{1}{5}$ **19.** $\frac{4}{1}$ **21.** $\frac{11}{5}$

23. $\frac{6}{5}$ **25.** $\frac{1}{2}$ **27.** $\frac{3}{2}$ **29.** $\frac{6}{7}$ **31.** $\frac{8}{9}$ **33.** $\frac{7}{1}$

35. $\frac{1}{8}$ **37.** $\frac{5}{4}$ **39. a.** 315 ft **b.** $\frac{63}{1}$ **41. a.** $\frac{2}{9}$ **b.** $\frac{2}{9}$

43. $\frac{1}{11}$ **45.** $\frac{10}{1}$ **47.** $\frac{15}{32}$ **49.** $\frac{20}{61}$ **51.** $\frac{2}{3}$

53. $\frac{1}{4}$ **55.** 13 units **57. a.** 1.5 **b.** $1.\overline{6}$ **c.** 1.6

d. 1.625; yes **59.** Answers will vary.

Section 6.2 Practice Exercises, pp. 371–374

3. 4 to 1 and $\frac{4}{1}$ **5.** $\frac{9}{17}$ **7.** $\frac{\$32}{5\,\text{ft}^2}$ **9.** $\frac{117\,\text{mi}}{2\,\text{hr}}$

11. $\frac{\$29}{4\,\text{hr}}$ **13.** $\frac{1\,\text{page}}{2\,\text{sec}}$ **15.** $\frac{65\,\text{calories}}{4\,\text{crackers}}$ **17.** $-\frac{9°\text{F}}{4\,\text{hr}}$

19. a, c, d **21.** 113 mi/day **23.** −400 m/hr
25. $55 per payment **27.** $0.69/lb **29.** $256,000 per person **31.** 14.29 m/sec **33.** $0.150 per oz
35. $0.995 per liter **37.** $52.50 per tire **39.** $5.417 per bodysuit **41. a.** $0.075/oz **b.** $0.075/oz **c.** Both sizes cost the same amount per ounce. **43.** The larger can is $0.055 per ounce. The smaller can is $0.073 per ounce. The larger can is the better buy. **45.** Coca-Cola: 3.25 g/fl oz; Mello Yello: 3.92 g/fl oz; Ginger Ale: 3 g/fl oz; Mello Yello has the greatest amount per fluid oz. **47.** Coca-Cola: 12 cal/fl oz; Mello Yello: 14.2 cal/fl oz; Ginger Ale: 11.25 cal/fl oz; Ginger Ale has the least number of calories per fluid oz.
49. 295,000 vehicles/year **51. a.** 2.2 million per year **b.** 2.04 million per year **c.** Mexico **53.** Cheetah: 29 m/sec; antelope: 24 m/sec. The cheetah is faster.

Section 6.2 Calculator Connections, pp. 374–375

54. a. 9.9 wins/yr **b.** 8.6 wins/yr **c.** Shula
55. a. 2.1 wins/loss **b.** 1.5 wins/loss **c.** Shula
56. a. $0.29 per ounce **b.** $0.21 per ounce **c.** $0.19 per ounce; The best buy is Irish Spring. **57.** The unit prices are $0.175 per ounce, $0.237 per ounce, and $0.324 per ounce. The best buy is the 32-oz jar. **58. a.** $0.333 per ounce **b.** $0.262 per ounce **c.** $0.377 per ounce The best buy is the 4-pack of 6-oz cans for $6.29. **59. a.** $0.017 per ounce **b.** $0.052 per ounce The case of 24 twelve-oz cans for $4.99 is the better buy.

Section 6.3 Practice Exercises, pp. 381–384

3. $\frac{1\,\text{teacher}}{15\,\text{students}}$ **5.** $\frac{3}{1}$ **7.** 28.1 mpg **9.** $\frac{4}{16}=\frac{5}{20}$

11. $\frac{-25}{15}=\frac{-10}{6}$ **13.** $\frac{2}{3}=\frac{4}{6}$ **15.** $\frac{-30}{-25}=\frac{12}{10}$

17. $\frac{\$6.25}{1\,\text{hr}}=\frac{\$187.50}{30\,\text{hr}}$ **19.** $\frac{1\,\text{in.}}{7\,\text{mi}}=\frac{5\,\text{in.}}{35\,\text{mi}}$ **21.** No

23. Yes **25.** Yes **27.** Yes **29.** Yes
31. Yes **33.** No **35.** Yes **37.** No

39. 4 **41.** 3 **43.** −75 **45.** $\frac{3}{4}$

47. $-\frac{65}{4}$ or $-16\frac{1}{4}$ or −16.25 **49.** $\frac{15}{2}$ or $7\frac{1}{2}$ or 7.5

51. 3 **53.** 2.5 **55.** 4 **57.** $-\frac{1}{80}$ **59.** 36

61. 7.5 **63.** 30 **65.** Pam can drive 610 mi on 10 gal of gas. **67.** 78 kg of crushed rock will be required.
69. The actual distance is about 80 mi. **71.** There are 3800 male students. **73.** Heads would come up about 315 times. **75.** There would be approximately 3 earned runs for a 9-inning game. **77.** Pierre can buy 576 Euros.
79. 9 g **81.** There are approximately 357 bass in the lake. **83.** There are approximately 4000 bison in the park.
85. $\frac{8}{7}$ **87.** −3 **89.** 12 **91.** −6

Section 6.3 Calculator Connections, p. 385
93. There were approximately 166,005 crimes committed.
94. The Washington Monument is approximately 555 ft tall.
95. Approximately 15,400 women would be expected to have breast cancer. **96.** Approximately 295,000 men would be expected to have prostate disease.

Chapter 6 Problem Recognition Exercises, p. 385

1. a. Proportion; $\frac{15}{2}$ **b.** Product of fractions; $\frac{15}{32}$

2. a. Product of fractions; $\frac{3}{25}$ **b.** Proportion; 4

3. a. Product of fractions; $\frac{3}{49}$ **b.** Proportion; 4

4. a. Proportion; 2 **b.** Product of fractions; $\frac{6}{25}$

5. a. Proportion; 9 **b.** Product of fractions; 32

6. a. Product of fractions; 8 **b.** Proportion; $\frac{98}{5}$

7a. 14 **b.** $\frac{5}{2}$ **c.** $\frac{3}{5}$ **d.** $\frac{18}{245}$ **8a.** $\frac{3}{25}$ **b.** $\frac{3}{5}$

c. $\frac{16}{3}$ **d.** $-\frac{88}{15}$ **9a.** 4 **b.** $\frac{98}{5}$ **c.** $\frac{48}{35}$

d. $\frac{49}{25}$ **10a.** 18 **b.** $\frac{29}{3}$ **c.** $\frac{11}{18}$ **d.** 22

Section 6.4 Practice Exercises, pp. 394–397
3. 84% **5.** 10% **7.** 2% **9.** 70% **11.** Replace the symbol % by $\times\frac{1}{100}$ (or ÷ 100). Then reduce the fraction to lowest terms. **13.** $\frac{3}{100}$ **15.** $\frac{21}{25}$ **17.** $\frac{17}{500}$

19. $\frac{23}{20}$ or $1\frac{3}{20}$ **21.** $\frac{1}{200}$ **23.** $\frac{1}{400}$ **25.** $\frac{31}{600}$

27. $\frac{249}{200}$ **29.** Replace the % symbol by × 0.01 (or ÷ 100).
31. 0.58 **33.** 0.085 **35.** 1.42 **37.** 0.0055
39. 0.264 **41.** 0.5505 **43.** 27% **45.** 19%
47. 175% **49.** 12.4% **51.** 0.6% **53.** 101.4%
55. 71% **57.** 87.5% or $87\frac{1}{2}$% **59.** $83.\overline{3}$% or $83\frac{1}{3}$%
61. 175% **63.** $122.\overline{2}$% or $122\frac{2}{9}$% **65.** $166.\overline{6}$% or $166\frac{2}{3}$%
67. 42.9% **69.** 7.7% **71.** 45.5% **73.** 86.7%
75. c **77.** e **79.** f **81.** e **83.** f **85.** a

87.

	Fraction	Decimal	Percent
a.	$\frac{1}{4}$	0.25	25%
b.	$\frac{23}{25}$	0.92	92%
c.	$\frac{3}{20}$	0.15	15%
d.	$\frac{8}{5}$ or $1\frac{3}{5}$	1.6	160%
e.	$\frac{1}{100}$	0.01	1%
f.	$\frac{1}{125}$	0.008	0.8%

89.

	Fraction	Decimal	Percent
a.	$\frac{7}{50}$	0.14	14%
b.	$\frac{87}{100}$	0.87	87%
c.	1	1	100%
d.	$\frac{1}{3}$	$0.\overline{3}$	$33.\overline{3}\%$ or $33\frac{1}{3}\%$
e.	$\frac{1}{500}$	0.002	0.2%
f.	$\frac{19}{20}$	0.95	95%

91. 25%   **93.** 10%   **95.** 0.058; $\frac{29}{500}$ **97.** 0.084; $\frac{21}{250}$
99. The fraction $\frac{1}{2} = 0.5$ and $\frac{1}{2}\% = 0.5\% = 0.005$.
101. 25% = 0.25 and 0.25% = 0.0025   **103.** a, c
105. a, c   **107.** 1.4 > 100%   **109.** 0.052 < 50%

Section 6.5 Practice Exercises, pp. 402–406

3. 130%   **5.** 37.5% or $37\frac{1}{2}\%$ **7.** 1%   **9.** $\frac{1}{50}$

11. 0.82   **13.** 1   **15.** Amount: 12; base: 20; $p = 60$

17. Amount: 99; base: 200; $p = 49.5$ **19.** Amount: 50; base: 40; $p = 125$ **21.** $\frac{10}{100} = \frac{12}{120}$ **23.** $\frac{80}{100} = \frac{72}{90}$

25. $\frac{104}{100} = \frac{21{,}684}{20{,}850}$ **27.** 108 employees   **29.** 0.2

31. 560   **33.** Pedro pays $20,160 in taxes.   **35.** Jesse Ventura received approximately 762,200 votes.   **37.** 36
39. 230 lb   **41.** 1350   **43.** Albert makes $1600 per month.
45. Aimee has a total of 35 e-mails.   **47.** 35%
49. 120%   **51.** 87.5%   **53.** She answered 72.5% correctly.   **55.** 20%   **57.** 26.7%   **59.** 7.5   **61.** 40%
63. 92   **65.** 77   **67.** 8800   **69.** 160%   **71.** 70 mm of rain fell in August.   **73.** Approximately 2110 freshmen were admitted.   **75.** The hospital is filled to 84% occupancy.   **77. a.** 22 women would be expected to relapse.   **b.** 465 would not be expected to relapse.
79. 73 were Chevys.   **81.** There were 180 total vehicles.
83. $331.20   **85.** $11.60   **87.** $6.30

Section 6.6 Practice Exercises, pp. 411–414

3. 146%   **5.** 0.0002; $\frac{1}{5000}$ **7.** 4   **9.** 700
11. $x = (0.35)(700); x = 245$ **13.** $(0.0055)(900) = x; x = 4.95$
15. $x = (1.33)(600); x = 798$ **17.** 50% equals one-half of the number. So multiply the number by $\frac{1}{2}$.   **19.** $2 \cdot 14 = 28$
21. $\frac{1}{2} \cdot 40 = 20$ **23.** There is 3.84 oz of sodium hypochlorite.   **25.** Marino completed approximately 5015 passes.   **27.** $18 = 0.4x; x = 45$ **29.** $0.92x = 41.4$; $x = 45$ **31.** $3.09 = 1.03x; x = 3$ **33.** There were 1175 subjects tested.   **35.** At that time, the population was about 280 million.   **37.** $x \cdot 480 = 120; x = 25\%$
39. $666 = x \cdot 740; x = 90\%$ **41.** $x \cdot 300 = 400$; $x = 133.3\%$ **43.** 5% of American Peace Corps volunteers were over 50 years old.   **45. a.** There are 80 total employees. **b.** 12.5% missed 3 days of work.   **c.** 75% missed 1 to 5 days of work.   **47.** 27.9   **49.** 20%   **51.** 150   **53.** 555
55. 600   **57.** 0.2%   **59.** There were 35 million total hospital stays that year.   **61.** Approximately 12.6% of Florida's panthers live in Everglades National Park.
63. 416 parents would be expected to have started saving for their children's education.   **65.** The total cost is $2400.
67. a. $40,200 **b.** $41,614   **69.** 12,240 accidents involved drivers 35–44 years old.   **71.** There were 40,000 traffic fatalities.   **73. a.** 200 beats per minute **b.** Between 120 and 170 beats per minute

Chapter 6 Problem Recognition Exercises, p. 415

1. 41%   **2.** 75%   **3.** $33\frac{1}{3}\%$ **4.** 100%
5. Greater than   **6.** Less than   **7.** Greater than
8. Greater than   **9.** 3000   **10.** 24%   **11.** 4.8
12. 15%   **13.** 70   **14.** 36   **15.** 6.3   **16.** 250
17. 300%   **18.** 0.7   **19.** 75,000   **20.** 37.5%
21. 25   **22.** 135   **23.** 100   **24.** 6000   **25.** 0.8%
26. 125%   **27.** 260   **28.** 20   **29.** 2.6   **30.** 6.05
31. 75%   **32.** 25%   **33.** $133\frac{1}{3}\%$ **34.** 400%
35. 8.2   **36.** 4.1   **37.** 16.4   **38.** 41   **39.** 164
40. 12.3

Section 6.7 Practice Exercises, pp. 423–427

3. 12   **5.** 40   **7.** 26,000   **9.** 24%   **11.** 8.8

13.	Cost of Item	Sales Tax Rate	Amount of Tax	Total Cost
a.	$20	5%	$1.00	$21.00
b.	$12.50	4%	$0.50	$13.00
c.	$110	2.5%	$2.75	$112.75
d.	$55	6%	$3.30	$58.30

15. The total bill is $71.66. **17.** The tax rate is 7%.
19. The price is $44.50.

21.	Total Sales	Commission Rate	Amount of Commission
a.	$20,000	5%	$1000
b.	$125,000	8%	$10,000
c.	$5400	10%	$540

23. Zach made $3360 in commission. **25.** Rodney's commission rate is 15%. **27.** Her sales were $1,400,000.

29.	Original Price	Discount Rate	Amount of Discount	Sale Price
a.	$56	20%	$11.20	$44.80
b.	$900	$33\frac{1}{3}$%	$300	$600
c.	$85	10%	$8.50	$76.50
d.	$76	50%	$38	$38

31.	Original Price	Markup Rate	Amount of Markup	Retail Price
a.	$92	5%	$4.60	$96.60
b.	$110	8%	$8.80	$118.80
c.	$325	30%	$97.50	$422.50
d.	$45	20%	$9	$54

33. The discounted lunch bill is $4.76. **35.** The discount rate is 25%. **37. a.** The markup is $27.00. **b.** The retail price is $177.00. **c.** The total price is $189.39. **39.** The markup rate is 25%. **41.** The discount is $80.70, and the sale price is $188.30. **43.** The markup rate is 54%.
45. The discount is $11.00, and the sale price is $98.99.
47. c **49.** 100% **51.** 10% **53.** 7% **55.** 29.5%
57. 5% **59.** 68% **61.** 15% **63. a.** $49 per ticket
b. 43.4%

Section 6.7 Calculator Connections, p. 427

	Stock	Price Jan. 2000 ($ per share)	Price Jan. 2008 ($ per share)	Change ($)	Percent Increase
64.	eBay Inc.	$16.84	$26.15	$9.31	55.3%
65.	Starbucks Corp.	$6.06	$16.92	$10.86	179.2%
66.	Apple Inc.	$28.66	$178.85	$150.19	524.0%
67.	IBM Corp.	$118.37	$127.52	$9.15	7.7%

Section 6.8 Practice Exercises, pp. 433–435

3. 0.0225 **5.** 25.3% **7.** $900, $6900 **9.** $1212, $6262
11. $2160, $14,160 **13.** $1890.00, $12,390.00 **15. a.** $350
b. $2850 **17. a.** $48 **b.** $448 **19.** $12,360

21. $5625 **23.** There are 6 total compounding periods.
25. There are 24 total compounding periods.
27. a. $560 **b.**

Year	Interest Earned	Total Amount in Account
1	$20.00	$520.00
2	20.80	540.80
3	21.63	**562.43**

29. a. $26,400 **b.**

Period	Interest Earned	Total Amount in Account
1st	$600	$24,600
2nd	615	25,215
3rd	630.38	25,845.38
4th	646.13	**26,491.51**

31. A = total amount in the account; P = principal; r = annual interest rate; n = number of compounding periods per year; t = time in years

Section 6.8 Calculator Connections, p. 435

33. $6230.91 **34.** $14,725.49 **35.** $6622.88
36. $4373.77 **37.** $10,934.43 **38.** $9941.60
39. $16,019.47 **40.** $10,555.99

Chapter 6 Review Exercises, pp. 444–449

1. 5 to 4 and $\frac{5}{4}$ **3.** 8 : 7 and 8 to 7

5. a. $\frac{4}{5}$ **b.** $\frac{5}{4}$ **c.** $\frac{5}{9}$ **7.** $\frac{4}{1}$ **9.** $\frac{2}{5}$ **11.** $\frac{9}{2}$ **13.** $\frac{4}{3}$

15. a. This year's enrollment is 1520 students. **b.** $\frac{4}{19}$

17. $\frac{1}{5}$ **19.** $\frac{4 \text{ hot dogs}}{9 \text{ min}}$ **21.** $-\frac{\$1700}{3 \text{ months}}$

23. All unit rates have a denominator of 1, and reduced rates may not. **25.** $-4°$ per hour **27.** 11 min/lawn
29. $3.333 per towel **31. a.** $0.078/oz **b.** $0.075/oz
c. The 48-oz jar is the best buy. **33.** The difference is about 8¢ per roll or $0.08 per roll. **35. a.** There was an increase of 120,000 hybrid vehicles. **b.** There will be 10,000 additional hybrid vehicles per month. **37.** $\frac{16}{14} = \frac{12}{10\frac{1}{2}}$

39. $\frac{-5}{3} = \frac{-10}{6}$ **41.** $\frac{\$11}{1 \text{ hr}} = \frac{\$88}{8 \text{ hr}}$ **43.** No
45. Yes **47.** Yes **49.** No **51.** 4 **53.** 3
55. -13.6 **57.** The human equivalent is 84 years.
59. Alabama had approximately 4,600,000 people.

61. 75%   **63.** 125%   **65.** b, c   **67.** $\frac{3}{10}$; 0.3

69. $\frac{27}{20}$; 1.35   **71.** $\frac{1}{500}$; 0.002   **73.** $\frac{2}{3}$; $0.\overline{6}$ **75.** 62.5%

77. 175%   **79.** 0.6%   **81.** 400%   **83.** 42.9%

85. $\frac{6}{8} = \frac{75}{100}$ **87.** $\frac{840}{420} = \frac{200}{100}$ **89.** 6   **91.** 12.5%

93. 39   **95.** Approximately 11 people would be no-shows.
97. Victoria spends 40% on rent.
99. $0.18 \cdot 900 = x$; $x = 162$ **101.** $18.90 = x \cdot 63$; $x = 30\%$
103. $30 = 0.25 \cdot x$; $x = 120$ **105.** The original price
was $68.00.   **107.** Elaine can consume 720 fat calories.
109. The sales tax is $76.74.   **111.** The cost before tax was
$8.80. The cost per photo is $0.22.   **113.** The commission
rate was approximately 10.6%.   **115.** Sela will earn $75
that day.   **117.** The discount is $8.69. The sale price
is $20.26.   **119.** The markup rate is 30%.   **121.** 55.9%
123. $1224, $11,424   **125.** Jean-Luc will have to pay $2687.50.
127.

Year	Interest	Total
1	$240.00	$6240.00
2	249.60	6489.60
3	259.58	6749.18

129. $995.91   **131.** $16,976.32

Chapter 6 Test, pp. 449–451

1. 25 to 521, 25 : 521, $\frac{25}{521}$ **2. a.** $\frac{44}{27}$ **b.** $\frac{27}{71}$

3. $\frac{5}{8}$ **4. a.** $\frac{21}{125}$ **b.** $\frac{9}{125}$

c. The poverty ratio was greater in New Mexico.
5. a. $\frac{\frac{1}{2}}{1\frac{1}{2}} = \frac{1}{3}$ **b.** $\frac{30}{90} = \frac{1}{3}$ **6.** $\frac{85 \text{ mi}}{2 \text{ hr}}$ **7.** $\frac{10 \text{ lb}}{3 \text{ weeks}}$
8. 21.45 g/cm³   **9.** 2.29 oz/lb
10. $0.22 per ounce   **11.** $1.10 per ring
12. $\frac{-42}{15} = \frac{-28}{10}$ **13.** $\frac{20 \text{ pages}}{12 \text{ min}} = \frac{30 \text{ pages}}{18 \text{ min}}$
14. $\frac{\$15}{1 \text{ hr}} = \frac{\$75}{5 \text{ hr}}$ **15.** -35 **16.** 12.5
17. 5   **18.** -6 **19.** Cherise spends 30 hr each week
on homework outside of class.   **20.** There are
approximately 27 fish in her pond.   **21.** 22%

22. $0.054; \frac{27}{500}$ **23.** $0.0015; \frac{3}{2000}$ **24.** $1.70; \frac{17}{10}$

25. a. $\frac{1}{100}$ **b.** $\frac{1}{4}$ **c.** $\frac{1}{3}$ **d.** $\frac{1}{2}$ **e.** $\frac{2}{3}$ **f.** $\frac{3}{4}$ **g.** 1   **h.** $\frac{3}{2}$

26. 60%   **27.** 0.4%   **28.** 175%   **29.** 71.4%
30. 32%   **31.** 5.2%   **32.** 130%   **33.** 0.6%
34. 19.2   **35.** 350   **36.** 90%   **37. a.** 730 mg
b. 98.6%   **38.** 390 m³   **39.** 420 m³   **40.** Her salary
before the raise was $52,000. Her new salary is $56,160.

41. a. The amount of sales tax is $2.10.   **b.** The sales tax
rate is 7%.   **42.** The discount rate of this product is 60%.
43. a. The dining room set is $1250 from the manufacturer.
b. The retail price is $1625.   **c.** The cost after sales tax is
$1722.50.   **44. a.** $1200   **b.** $6200   **45.** $31,268.76

Chapters 1–6 Cumulative Review Exercises, p. 452

1. Millions place   **2.** 3,488,200   **3.** 87   **4.** 11
5. $\frac{4}{3}$ or $1\frac{1}{3}$ **6.** $\frac{3}{2}$ or $1\frac{1}{2}$ **7.** 9 km

8. $229\frac{1}{2}$ in.² or 229.5 in.²

9. a. 18, 36, 54, 72   **b.** 1, 2, 3, 6, 9, 18   **c.** $2 \cdot 3^2$

10. a. $\frac{5}{2}$ **b.** $\frac{5}{6}$ **11.** 0.375   **12.** 87.5%

13. $-7x + 39$ **14.** -4 **15.** 15   **16.** 20   **17.** $6\frac{1}{2}$
18. The DC-10 flew 514 mph.   **19.** Kevin will have $15,080.
20. There is $91,473.02 paid in interest.

Chapter 7

Chapter Opener Puzzle

1. f   **2.** e   **3.** b   **4.** g   **5.** c   **6.** d
7. a   **8.** h

Section 7.1 Practice Exercises, pp. 460–463

3. 3 yd   **5.** 42 in.   **7.** $2\frac{1}{4}$ mi   **9.** $4\frac{2}{3}$ yd

11. 563,200 yd   **13.** $4\frac{3}{4}$ yd   **15.** 72 in.

17. 50,688 in.   **19.** $\frac{1}{2}$ mi   **21. a.** 76 in.   **b.** $6\frac{1}{3}$ ft

23. a. 8 ft   **b.** $2\frac{2}{3}$ yd   **25.** 6 ft   **27.** 3 ft 4 in.

29. 4′4″   **31.** 730 days   **33.** $1\frac{1}{2}$ hr   **35.** 3 min

37. 3 days   **39.** 1 hr   **41.** 1512 hr   **43.** 80.5 min
45. 175.25 min   **47.** 2 lb   **49.** 4000 lb   **51.** 6500 lb
53. 10 lb 8 oz   **55.** 8 lb 2 oz   **57.** 6 lb 8 oz   **59.** 2 c

61. 24 qt   **63.** 16 c   **65.** $\frac{1}{2}$ gal   **67.** 16 fl oz

69. 6 tsp   **71.** Yes, 3 c is 24 oz, so the 48-oz jar will suffice.
73. The plumber used 7′2″ of pipe.   **75.** 7 ft is left over.

77. $5\frac{1}{2}$ ft   **79.** The unit price for the 24-fl-oz jar is about

$0.112 per ounce, and the unit price for the 1-qt jar is about
$0.103 per ounce; therefore the 1-qt jar is the better buy.
81. The total length is 46′.   **83.** The total weight is 312 lb
8 oz.   **85.** 18 pieces of border are needed.   **87.** Gil ran
for 5 hr 35 min.   **89.** The total time is 1 hr 34 min.
91. 6 yd²   **93.** 3 ft²   **95.** 720 in.²   **97.** 27 ft²

Section 7.2 Practice Exercises, pp. 471–475

3. 4 pt   **5.** 1440 min   **7.** 56 oz   **9.** b, f, g
11. 3.2 cm or 32 mm   **13.** a   **15.** d   **17.** d
19. 2.43 km   **21.** 50,000 mm   **23.** 4000 m
25. 43.1 mm   **27.** 0.3328 km   **29.** 300 m
31. 0.539 kg   **33.** 2500 g   **35.** 33.4 mg   **37.** 4.09 g
39. <   **41.** =   **43.** Cubic centimeter   **45.** 3.2 L
47. 700 cL   **49.** 0.42 dL   **51.** 64 mL   **53.** 40 cc
55. b, f   **57.** a, f

	Object	mm	cm	m	km
59.	Length of the Mississippi River	3,766,000,000	376,600,000	3,766,000	3766
61.	Diameter of a quarter	24.3	2.43	0.0243	0.0000243

	Object	mg	cg	g	kg
63.	Bag of rice	907,000	90,700	907	0.907
65.	Hockey puck	170,000	17,000	170	0.17

	Object	mL	cL	L	kL
67.	Bottle of vanilla extract	59	5.9	0.059	0.000059
69.	Capacity of a gasoline tank	75,700	7570	75.7	0.0757

71. 4,669,000 m   **73.** 305,000 mg   **75.** 250 mL
77. Cliff drives 17.4 km per week.
79. 8 cans hold 0.96 kL.   **81.** The bottle contains 49.5 cL.
83. 3.6 g   **85.** No, she needs 1.04 m of molding.
87. The difference is 4500 m.   **89.** 65 km^2
91. 0.56 m^2 **93.** 5.78 metric tons   **95.** 8500 kg

Section 7.3 Practice Exercises, pp. 481–484

3. d, f   **5.** b, e   **7.** c, f   **9.** b, g   **11.** b
13. a   **15.** 5.1 cm   **17.** 8.8 yd   **19.** 122 m
21. 1.1 m   **23.** 15.2 cm   **25.** 2.7 kg   **27.** 0.4 oz
29. 1.2 lb   **31.** 1980 kg   **33.** 5.7 L   **35.** 4 fl oz
37. 32 fl oz   **39.** The box of sugar costs $0.100 per ounce, and the packets cost $0.118 per ounce. The 2-lb box is the better buy.   **41.** 18 mi is about 28.98 km. Therefore the 30-km race is longer than 18 mi.   **43.** 97 lb is approximately 43.65 kg.
45. The price is approximately $7.22 per gallon.
47. A hockey puck is 1 in. thick.   **49.** Tony weighs about 222 lb.   **51.** 45 cc is 1.5 fl oz.   **53.** 40.8 ft
55. 77°F   **57.** 20°C   **59.** 86°F
61. 7232°F   **63.** It is a hot day. The temperature is 95°F.

65. $F = \frac{9}{5}C + 32 = \frac{9}{5} \cdot 100 + 32 = 9(20) + 32$
$= 180 + 32 = 212$ **67.** 184 g   **69.** The Navigator weighs approximately 2.565 metric tons.   **71.** The average weight of the blue whale is approximately 240,000 lb.

Chapter 7 Problem Recognition Exercises, p. 484

1. 9 qt   **2.** 2.2 m   **3.** 12 oz   **4.** 300 mL
5. 4 yd   **6.** 6030 g   **7.** 4.5 m   **8.** $\frac{3}{4}$ ft
9. 2640 ft   **10.** 3 tons   **11.** 4 qt   **12.** $\frac{1}{2}$ T
13. 0.021 km   **14.** 6.8 cg   **15.** 36 cc   **16.** 4 lb
17. 4.322 kg   **18.** 5000 mm   **19.** 2.5 c   **20.** 8.5 min
21. 0.5 gal   **22.** 3.25 c   **23.** 5460 g   **24.** 902 cL
25. 16,016 yd   **26.** 3 lb   **27.** 3240 lb   **28.** 4600 m
29. 2.5 days   **30.** 8 mL   **31.** 512.4 min   **32.** 336 hr

Section 7.4 Practice Exercises, pp. 486–488

3. 4280 m   **5.** 8 cg   **7.** 9000 mL   **9.** 6.$\overline{2}$ lb
11. 10 mcg   **13.** 7.5 mg   **15.** 0.05 cg   **17.** 500 mcg
19. 200 mcg   **21.** 1 mg   **23. a.** 400 mg   **b.** 8000 mg or 8 g   **25.** 3 mL   **27.** 5.25 g of the drug would be given in 1 wk.   **29.** 2 mL   **31.** 500 people   **33.** 9.6 mg
35. 3.6 g

Section 7.5 Practice Exercises, pp. 493–496

3. A line extends forever in both directions. A ray begins at an endpoint and extends forever in one direction.
5. Ray   **7.** Point   **9.** Line
11. For example:

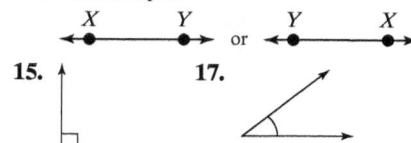

13. For example:

15.   **17.**

19. 20°   **21.** 90°   **23.** 148°   **25.** Right
27. Obtuse   **29.** Acute   **31.** Straight
33. 10°   **35.** 63°   **37.** 60.5°   **39.** 1°
41. 100°   **43.** 53°   **45.** 142.6°   **47.** 1°
49. No, because the sum of two angles that are both greater than 90° will be more than 180°.   **51.** Yes. For two angles to add to 90°, the angles themselves must both be less than 90°.   **53.** A 90° angle
55.   **57.**

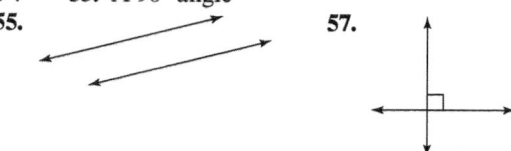

59. $m(\angle a) = 41°$; $m(\angle b) = 139°$; $m(\angle c) = 139°$
61. $m(\angle a) = 26°$; $m(\angle b) = 112°$; $m(\angle c) = 26°$; $m(\angle d) = 42°$
63. The two lines are perpendicular.   **65.** Vertical angles
67. a, c or b, h or e, g or f, d **69.** a, e or f, b
71. $m(\angle a) = 55°$; $m(\angle b) = 125°$; $m(\angle c) = 55°$; $m(\angle d) = 55°$; $m(\angle e) = 125°$; $m(\angle f) = 55°$; $m(\angle g) = 125°$
73. True   **75.** True   **77.** False   **79.** True
81. True   **83.** 70°   **85.** 90°   **87. a.** 48°   **b.** 48°
c. 132°   **89.** 180°   **91.** 120°

Section 7.6 Practice Exercises, pp. 503–506

3. Yes   **5.** No   **7.** No   **9.** $m(\angle a) = 54°$
11. $m(\angle b) = 78°$ **13.** $m(\angle a) = 60°, m(\angle b) = 80°$
15. $m(\angle a) = 40°, m(\angle b) = 72°$ **17.** c, f   **19.** b, d
21. b, c, e   **23.** $c = 5$ m   **25.** $b = 12$ yd
27. Leg = 10 ft   **29.** Hypotenuse = 40 in.
31. The brace is 20 in. long.   **33.** The height is 9 km.
35. The car is 25 mi from the starting point.
37. $x = 4$ cm; $y = 5$ cm   **39.** $x = 3.75$ cm; $y = 4.5$ cm
41. The height of the pole is 7 m.   **43.** The light post is
24 ft high.   **45.** 24 m   **47.** 30 km

Section 7.6 Calculator Connections, pp. 506–507

	Square Root	Estimate	Calculator Approximation (Round to 3 Decimal Places)
	$\sqrt{50}$	is between 7 and 8	7.071
49.	$\sqrt{10}$	is between 3 and 4	3.162
50.	$\sqrt{90}$	is between 9 and 10	9.487
51.	$\sqrt{116}$	is between 10 and 11	10.770
52.	$\sqrt{65}$	is between 8 and 9	8.062
53.	$\sqrt{5}$	is between 2 and 3	2.236
54.	$\sqrt{48}$	is between 6 and 7	6.928

55. 20.682   **56.** 56.434   **57.** 1116.244   **58.** 7100.423
59. 0.7   **60.** 0.5   **61.** 0.748   **62.** 0.906
63. $b = 21$ ft   **64.** $a = 16$ cm
65. Hypotenuse = 11.180 mi
66. Hypotenuse = 8.246 m   **67.** Leg = 18.439 in.
68. Leg = 9.950 ft   **69.** The diagonal length is 1.41 ft.
70. The length of the diagonal is 134.16 ft.
71. The length of the diagonal is 35.36 ft.

Section 7.7 Practice Exercises, pp. 514–518

3. An isosceles triangle has two sides of equal length.
5. An acute triangle has all acute angles.   **7.** An obtuse
triangle has an obtuse angle.   **9.** A quadrilateral is a
polygon with four sides.   **11.** A trapezoid has one pair of
opposite sides that are parallel.   **13.** A rectangle has four
right angles.   **15.** 80 cm   **17.** 260 mm   **19.** 10.7 m
21. 25.12 ft   **23.** 2.4 km or 2400 m
25. 10 ft 6 in.   **27.** 5 ft or 60 in.   **29.** $x = 550$ mm;
$y = 3$ dm; perimeter = 26 dm or 2600 mm
31. 280 ft of rain gutters is needed.   **33.** 576 yd^2
35. 23 in.^{2} **37.** 18.4 ft^2 **39.** 54 m^2
41. 656 in.^{2} **43.** 217.54 ft^2 **45.** 154 m^2
47. $346\frac{1}{2}$ cm^2 **49.** 113 mm^2 **51.** 5 ft^2 **53.** The
area of the sign is 16.5 yd^2.   **55.** $956.25
57. a. The area is 483 ft^2.   **b.** They will need 2 paint kits.
59. 13.5 cm^2 **61.** 18.28 in.^{2} **63.** Perimeter = 72 ft

Chapter 7 Problem Recognition Exercises, p. 519

1. Area = 25 ft^2; perimeter = 20 ft
2. Area = 144 m^2; perimeter = 48 m   **3.** Area = 12 m^2
or 120,000 cm^2; perimeter = 14 m or 1400 cm

4. Area = 1 ft^2 or 144 in.^{2}; perimeter = 5 ft or 60 in.
5. Area = $\frac{1}{3}$ yd^2 or 3 ft^2; perimeter = 3 yd or 9 ft
6. Area = 0.473 km^2 or 473,000 m^2; perimeter = 3.24 km
or 3240 m
7. Area = 6 yd^2; perimeter = 12 yd
8. Area = 30 cm^2; perimeter = 30 cm
9. Area = 44 m^2; perimeter = 32 m
10. Area = 88 in.^{2}; perimeter = 40 in.
11. Area ≈ 28.26 yd^2; circumference ≈ 18.84 yd
12. Area ≈ 1256 cm^2; circumference ≈ 125.6 cm
13. Area ≈ 2464 cm^2; circumference ≈ 176 cm
14. Area ≈ 616 ft^2; circumference ≈ 88 ft
15. a. perimeter   **b.** 64 yd
16. a. circumference   **b.** $\frac{11}{2}$ ft or $5\frac{1}{2}$ ft
17. a. area   **b.** 125 ft^2 **18. a.** area   **b.** 314 m^2

Section 7.8 Practice Exercises, pp. 524–528

3. Complement: 66°; supplement: 156°
5. $m(\angle a) = 70°, m(\angle b) = 110°, m(\angle c) = 70°,$
$m(\angle d) = 70°, m(\angle e) = 110°, m(\angle f) = 70°, m(\angle g) = 110°$
7. 2.744 cm^3 **9.** 48 ft^3 **11.** 12.56 mm^3
13. 3052.08 yd^3 **15.** 235.5 cm^3 **17.** 452.16 ft^3
19. 289 in.^{3} **21.** 314 ft^3 **23.** 10 ft^3 **25. a.** 2575 ft^3
b. 19,260 gal   **27.** 342 in.^{2} **29.** 13.5 cm^2
31. 113.0 in.^{2} **33.** 211.1 in.^{2} **35.** 492 ft^2
37. 96 cm^2 **39.** 1356.48 in.^{2} **41.** 1256 mm^2
43. $\frac{11}{36}$ ft^3 or 0.306 ft^3 or 528 in.^{3} **45.** 109.3 in.^{3}
47. 502.4 mm^3 **49.** 621.72 ft^3 **51.** 84.78 in.^{3}
53. 50,240 cm^3 **55.** 400 ft^3

Chapter 7 Review Exercises, pp. 537–541

1. 4 ft   **3.** 3520 yd   **5.** 2640 ft   **7.** 9 ft 3 in.
9. 2'10"   **11.** $7\frac{1}{2}$ ft   **13.** 3 days   **15.** 80 oz
17. $1\frac{1}{2}$ c   **19.** $1\frac{3}{4}$ tons   **21.** $\frac{3}{4}$ lb   **23.** 144.5 min
25. b   **27.** 520 mm   **29.** 3.4 m   **31.** 0.04 m
33. 610 cg   **35.** 3.212 g   **37.** 8.3 L   **39.** 22.5 cL
41. Perimeter: 6.5 m; area: 2.5 m^2 **43.** The difference is
64.8 kg.   **45.** 15.75 cm   **47.** 5 oz   **49.** 1.04 m
51. 74.53 mi   **53.** 45 cc   **55.** The difference in height
is 38.2 cm.   **57.** The marathon is approximately 26.2 mi.
59. 82.2°C to 85°C   **61.** 46.4°F   **63.** 1500 mcg
65. 0.5 cg   **67. a.** 3.2 mg   **b.** 44.8 mg
69. There is 1.2 cc or 1.2 mL of fluid left.   **71.** d
73. c   **75.** The measure of an acute angle is between 0°
and 90°.   **77.** The measure of a right angle is 90°.
79. a. 70°   **b.** 160°   **81.** 118°   **83.** 62°
85. $m(\angle x) = 40°$ **87.** An equilateral triangle has three
sides of equal length and three angles of equal measure.
89. 5   **91.** $b = 7$ cm   **93.** 13 m of string is extended.
95. 90 cm   **97.** 15.5 ft   **99.** 20 in.^{2} **101.** 7056 ft^2
103. 314 cm^2 **105.** Volume: 25,000 cm^3; SA: 5250 cm^2
107. Volume: 14,130 in.^{3}; SA: 2826 in.^{2} **109.** 37.68 m^3
111. 113 in.^{3} **113.** 335 cm^3

Chapter 7 Test, pp. 541–544

1. c, d, g, j   **2.** f, h, i   **3.** a, b, e   **4.** $8\frac{1}{3}$ yd

5. 5.5 tons   **6.** 10 mi   **7.** 10 oz of liquid
8. 20 min   **9.** 9′   **10.** 4′2″   **11.** He lost 7 oz.
12. 19 ft 7 in.   **13.** 75.25 min   **14.** 2.4 cm or 24 mm
15. c   **16.** 1.158 km   **17.** 15 mL
18. a. Cubic centimeters **b.** 235 cc **c.** 1000 cc
19. 41,100 cg   **20.** 7 servings   **21.** 2.1 qt   **22.** 109 yd
23. 2.8 mi   **24.** 2929 m   **25.** 50.8 cm tall and 96.52-cm
wingspan **26.** 11 lb   **27.** 190.6°C   **28.** 35.6°F
29. 28 mg   **30.** 1750 mcg per week   **31.** d   **32.** c
33. 74°   **34.** 33°   **35.** 103°   **36.** $a = 5.6$; $b = 12$
37. Perimeter: 28 cm; area 36 cm²   **38.** 70,650 ft²
39. 48 ft²   **40.** $m(\angle x) = 125°$, $m(\angle y) = 55°$
41. They are each 45°.   **42.** $m(\angle S) = 49°$
43. $m(\angle A) = 80°$ **44.** 12 ft   **45.** 100 m
46. 3 rolls are needed.   **47.** The area is 72 in.²
48. The volume is about 151 ft³.   **49.** The volume is 1260 in.³
50. 65.94 in.³   **51.** 113.04 cm³   **52.** 113.04 cm²   **53.** 824 in.²

Chapters 1–7 Cumulative Review Exercises, pp. 544–545

1. $9\frac{1}{2}$ **2.** $18\frac{8}{9}$ **3.** $2\frac{6}{17}$ **4.** $3\frac{5}{6}$ **5.** −6

6. −36   **7.** $-3a + 19b$ **8.** −7   **9.** −18
10. 90 cars   **11.** 80%   **12.** 2290 trees
13. 6%   **14.** $1020 in interest   **15.** 182.9 cm
16. 6 ft   **17.** 96 in.   **18.** 5 ft   **19.** 57°
20. Volume: 840 cm³; SA: 604 cm²

Chapter 8

Chapter Opener Puzzle

Ranch	Horses	Cattle	Bison	Liamas	Total
Stevens	125	200	0	0	325
Raven	0	150	0	0	150
Summit	12	125	32	0	169
Yellowstone	32	0	73	0	105
Ellis	6	225	0	20	251
Total	175	700	105	20	1000

1. 1000 animals   2. Stevens Ranch   3. 17.5%   4. 40%   5. 105 animals

Section 8.1 Practice Exercises, pp. 553–558

3. Asia   **5.** 2514 ft   **7.** 3.6 yr   **9.** 2.8 yr   **11.** Men
13.

	Dog	Cat	Neither
Boy	4	1	3
Girl	3	4	5

15. a. Students had the best access to a computer in 2007. Only four students were sharing a computer.
b.

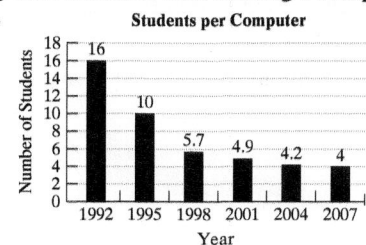

17.

Number of Cellular Phone Subscriptions

2006	238
2005	208
2004	182
2003	159
2002	141

Cellular Phone Subscriptions (millions)

19. a. One icon represents 100 servings sold. **b.** About 450 servings **c.** Sunday   **21. a.** Barnes & Noble/B. Dalton has approximately $4.5 billion in book sales.
b. There is approximately $11.5 billion in book sales.
23. 48.4%   **25.** The trend for women over 65 in the labor force shows a slight increase.   **27.** For example: 18%
29. In January 2007, the most hybrids were sold. There were 14,900 sold.   **31.** 4400   **33.** Between 2005 and 2006
35.

Average Height for Girls, Ages 2–9

37. There are 14 servings per container, which means that there is 8 g × 14 = 112 g of fat in one container.
39. The daily value of fat is approximately 61.5 g.

Section 8.2 Practice Exercises pp. 561–564

3. There are 72 data.   **5.** 9–12
7.

Class Intervals (Age in Years)	Tally	Frequency (Number of Professors)
56–58	||	2
59–61	|	1
62–64	|	1
65–67	IIII II	7
68–70	IIII	5
71–73	IIII	4

a. The class of 65–67 has the most values.
b. There are 20 values represented in the table.
c. Of the professors, 25% retire when they are 68 to 70 yr old.
9.

Class Intervals (Amount in Gal)	Tally	Frequency (Number of Customers)
8.0–9.9	IIII	4
10.0–11.9	|	1
12.0–13.9	IIII	5
14.0–15.9	IIII	4
16.0–17.9		0
18.0–19.9	||	2

a. The 12.0–13.9 class has the highest frequency.
b. There are 16 data values represented in the table.
c. Of the customers, 12.5% purchased 18 to 19.9 gal of gas.
11. The class widths are not the same.   **13.** There are too few classes.   **15.** The class intervals overlap. For example,

it is unclear whether the data value 12 should be placed in the first class or the second class.

17.

Class Interval (Height, in.)	Frequency (Number of Students)
62–63	2
64–65	3
66–67	4
68–69	4
70–71	4
72–73	3

19.

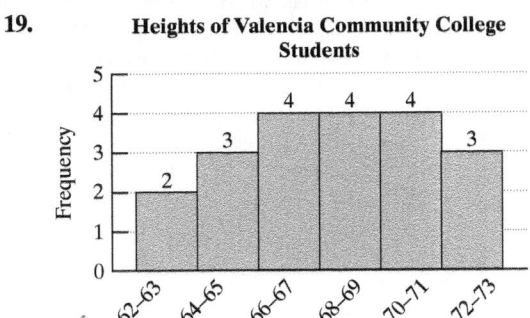

Heights of Valencia Community College Students

21.

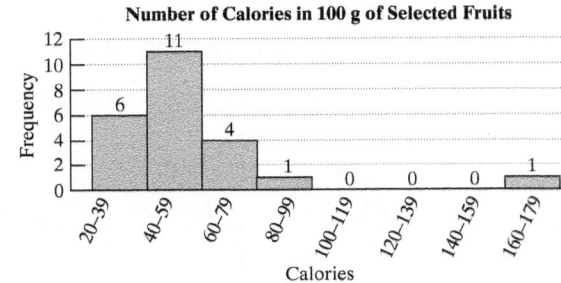

Number of Calories in 100 g of Selected Fruits

Section 8.3 Practice Exercises, pp. 569–571

3. 64,000   **5.** 640   **7.** 25%   **9.** 2.5 times
11. There are 20 million viewers represented.
13. 1.8 times as many viewers.   **15.** Of the viewers, 18% watch *General Hospital.*   **17.** There are 960 Latina CDs.
19. There are 640 CDs that are classical or jazz.
21. There were 9 Super Bowls played in Louisiana.
23. There were 2 Super Bowls played in Georgia.
25.   **27.**   **29.**

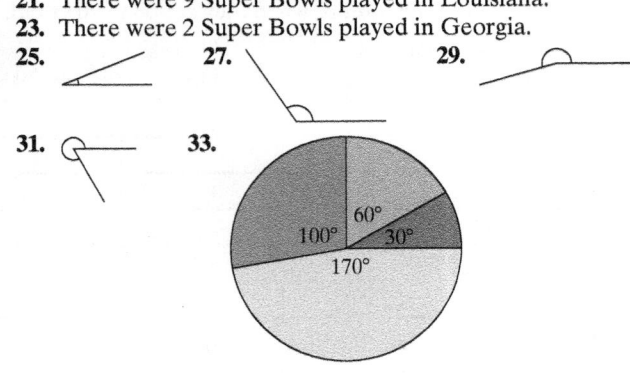

31.   **33.**

35. a.

	Expenses	Percent	Number of Degrees
Tuition	$9000	75%	270°
Books	600	5%	18°
Housing	2400	20%	72°

b.

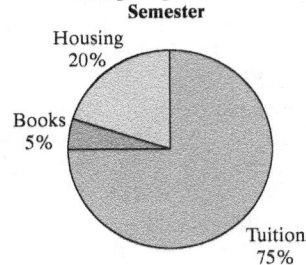

College Expenses for a Semester

Housing 20%
Books 5%
Tuition 75%

37.

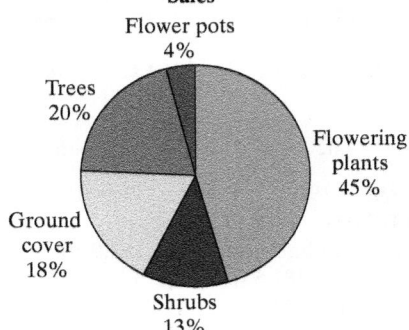

Sunshine Nursery Distribution of Sales

Flower pots 4%
Trees 20%
Flowering plants 45%
Ground cover 18%
Shrubs 13%

Section 8.4 Practice Exercises, pp. 577–581

3. 6   **5.** 4   **7.** 15.2   **9.** 8.76 in.   **11.** 5.8 hr
13. a. 397 Cal   **b.** 386 Cal   **c.** There is only an 11-Cal difference in the means.   **15. a.** 86.5%   **b.** 81%
c. The low score of 59% decreased Zach's average by 5.5%.
17. 17   **19.** 110.5   **21.** 52.5   **23.** 3.93 deaths per 1000
25. 58 years old   **27.** 51.7 million passengers   **29.** 4
31. No mode   **33.** 21, 24   **35.** $600   **37.** 5.2%
39. These data are bimodal: $2.49 and $2.51.
41. Mean: 85.5%; median: 94.5%; The median gave Jonathan a better overall score.   **43.** Mean: $250; median: $256; mode: There is no mode.   **45.** Mean: $942,500; median: $848,500; mode: $850,000

47.

Age (yr)	Number of Students	Product
16	2	32
17	9	153
18	6	108
19	3	57
Total:	20	350

The mean age is 17.5 years.

49. The weighted mean is about 26 students.   **51.** 3.59
53. 2.73

Chapter 8 Review Exercises, pp. 586–588

1. Godiva   **3.** Blue Bell has 2 times more sodium than Edy's Grand.   **5.** 374 acres   **7.** The difference is 4 acres.   **9.** 1 icon represents 50 tornadoes.
11. June   **13.** 2005   **15.** Increasing
17.

19.

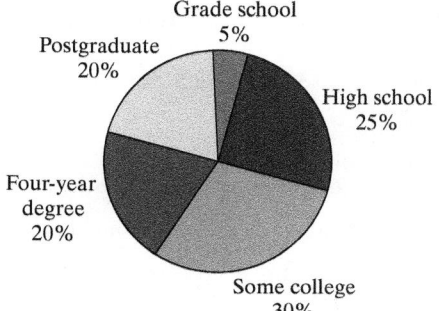

21. $\frac{2}{3}$ of the subs contain beef.

23. a.

Education Level	Number of People	Percent	Number of Degrees
Grade school	10	5%	18°
High school	50	25%	90°
Some college	60	30%	108°
Four-year degree	40	20%	72°
Post graduate	40	20%	72°

b.   Percent by Education Level

Grade school 5%
Postgraduate 20%
High school 25%
Four-year degree 20%
Some college 30%

25. The mean daily calcium intake is approximately 1060 mg.
27. 4

Chapter 8 Test, pp. 589–590

1.

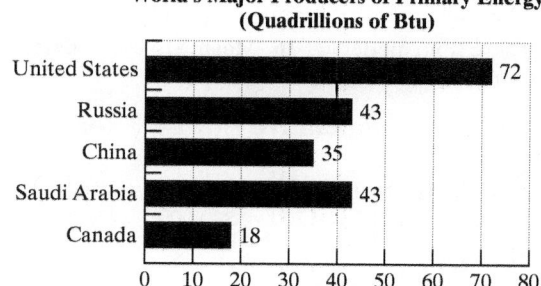

2. a. The year 1820 had the greatest percent of workers employed in farm occupations. This was 72%.

b.

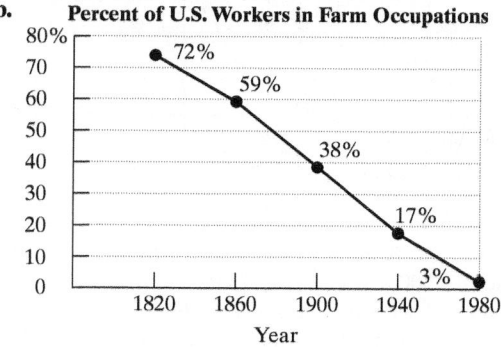

c. Approximately 10% of U.S. workers were employed in farm occupations in the year 1960.
3. $1000   **4.** $4500   **5.** February   **6.** Seattle
7. 1.73 in.   **8.** The mean for Salt Lake City is 1.4 in., and the mean for Seattle is 2.05 in.
9.

Number of Minutes Used Monthly	Tally	Frequency
51–100	ⅢⅢ I	6
101–150	II	2
151–200	III	3
201–250	II	2
251–300	IIII	4
301–350	III	3

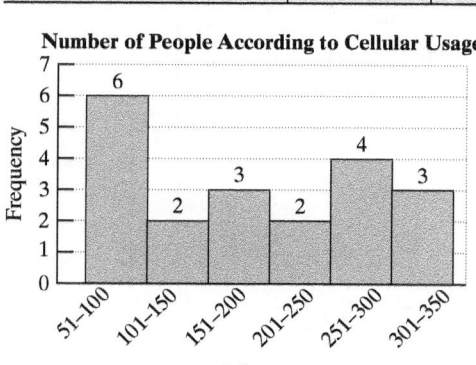

10. 66 people would have carpet.   **11.** 40 people would have tile.   **12.** 270 people would have something other than linoleum.   **13.** 19,173 ft   **14.** 19,340 ft
15. There is no mode.   **16.** Mean: $14.60; median: $15; mode $16

Chapters 1–8 Cumulative Review Exercises, p. 591

1. a. Millions   **b.** Ten-thousands   **c.** Hundreds
2. 12,645   **3.** $700 \times 1200 = 840,000$
4. $\dfrac{3}{8}$ **5.** $\dfrac{3}{2}$

6.

Stock	Yesterday's Closing Price ($)	Increase/ Decrease	Today's Closing Price ($)
RylGold	13.28	0.27	13.55
NetSolve	9.51	−0.17	9.34
Metals USA	14.35	0.10	14.45
PAM Transpt	18.09	0.09	18.18
Steel Tch	21.63	−0.37	21.26

7. 6841.2   **8.** 68,412   **9. a.** 0.7 million km² or equivalently, 700,000 km²   **b.** 18.9%
10. Quick Cut Lawn Company's rate is 0.55 hr per customer. Speedy Lawn Company's rate is 0.5 hr per customer. Speedy Lawn Company is faster.
11. 125 min or 2 hr 5 min   **12.** $x = 5$ m, $y = 22.4$ m
13. $1404   **14.** 29 in.   **15.** 9 yd 1 ft
16. 4 lb 3 oz   **17.** Obtuse   **18.** Right
19. Mean: 105; median: 123   **20.** 3

Chapter 9

Chapter Opener Puzzle

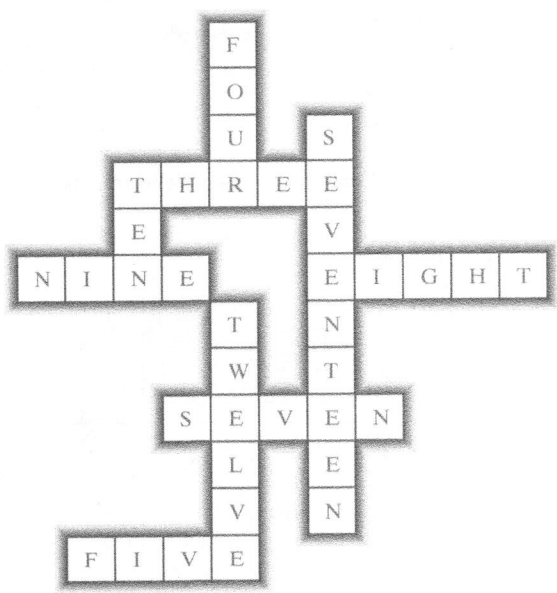

$8 \cdot \left(\dfrac{3}{8}\right) =$ ___three___ $6 \cdot \left(\dfrac{2}{3}\right) =$ ___four___

$100(0.17) =$ ___seventeen___ $100(0.09) =$ ___nine___

___five___ $\cdot \left(\dfrac{2}{5}\right) = 2$ ___seven___ $\cdot \left(\dfrac{6}{7}\right) = 6$

___eight___ $\cdot \left(\dfrac{3}{4}\right) = 6$ ___twelve___ $\cdot \left(\dfrac{5}{6}\right) = 10$

___ten___ $\cdot (0.4) = 4$

Section 9.1 Practice Exercises, pp. 599–601

3.

$$-\pi \quad -\tfrac{5}{2}\,-2 \qquad 0 \quad 1 \qquad\qquad 5.1$$

(number line from −6 to 6)

5. a; rational   **7. b**; rational   **9. a**; rational
11. c; irrational   **13. a**; rational   **15. a**; rational
17. b; rational   **19. c**; irrational
21. For example: $\pi, -\sqrt{2}, \sqrt{3}$ **23.** For example: $-4, -1, 0$
25. For example: $-\dfrac{3}{4}, \dfrac{1}{2}, 0.206$ **27.** $-\dfrac{3}{2}, -4, 0.\overline{6}, 0, 1$
29. 1   **31.** $-4, 0, 1$ **33. a.** >   **b.** >   **c.** <   **d.** >
35. 2   **37.** 1.5   **39.** -1.5 **41.** $\dfrac{3}{2}$ **43.** -10
45. $-\dfrac{1}{2}$ **47.** False, $|n|$ is never negative.   **49.** True
51. False   **53.** True   **55.** False   **57.** False
59. False   **61.** True   **63.** True   **65.** False
67. True   **69.** True   **71.** True   **73.** For all $a < 0$

Section 9.2 Practice Exercises, pp. 609–611

3. -6 **5.** -23 **7.** $\dfrac{3}{2}$ **9.** 10   **11.** $-\dfrac{1}{9}$
13. -12 **15.** $\dfrac{22}{3}$ **17.** -36 **19.** 16   **21.** 2
23. $-\dfrac{7}{4}$ **25.** 2   **27.** 6   **29.** $\dfrac{5}{2}$ **31.** 5   **33.** -4
35. -26 **37.** 10   **39.** -8 **41.** 0   **43.** -3
45. -2 **47.** $-\dfrac{1}{3}$ **49.** -6 **51.** 0   **53.** -2
55. $-\dfrac{25}{4}$ **57.** $\dfrac{10}{3}$ **59.** Contradiction; no solution
61. Conditional equation; -15
63. Identity; all real numbers
65. One solution   **67.** Infinitely many solutions
69. 7   **71.** $\dfrac{1}{2}$ **73.** 0   **75.** All real numbers
77. -46 **79.** 2   **81.** $\dfrac{13}{2}$ **83.** -5
85. No solution   **87.** 2.205   **89.** 10   **91.** -1
93. $a = 15$ **95.** $a = 4$
97. For example: $5x + 2 = 2 + 5x$

Section 9.3 Practice Exercises, pp. 616–618

3. -2 **5.** -5 **7.** No solution   **9.** $18, 36$

11. $100; 1000; 10,000$ **13.** $30, 60$ **15.** 4 **17.** $-\dfrac{19}{2}$

19. $-\dfrac{15}{4}$ **21.** 8 **23.** 3 **25.** 15

27. No solution   **29.** All real numbers   **31.** 5

33. 2 **35.** -15 **37.** 6 **39.** 3

41. All real numbers   **43.** 67 **45.** 90 **47.** 4

49. -3.8 **51.** No solution   **53.** -0.25 **55.** -6

57. $\dfrac{8}{3}$ or $2\dfrac{2}{3}$ **59.** -9 **61.** $\dfrac{1}{10}$ **63.** -2

65. -1 **67.** 2

Chapter 9 Problem Recognition Exercises, p. 618

1. Expression; $-4b + 18$ **2.** Expression; $20p - 30$

3. Equation; -8 **4.** Equation; -14 **5.** Equation; $\dfrac{1}{3}$

6. Equation; $-\dfrac{4}{3}$ **7.** Expression; $6z - 23$

8. Expression; $-x - 9$ **9.** Equation; $\dfrac{7}{9}$

10. Equation; $-\dfrac{13}{10}$ **11.** Equation; 20

12. Equation; -3 **13.** Equation; $\dfrac{1}{2}$ **14.** Equation; -6

15. Expression; $\dfrac{5}{8}x + \dfrac{7}{4}$ **16.** Expression; $-26t + 18$

17. Equation; no solution   **18.** Equation; no solution

19. Equation; $\dfrac{23}{12}$ **20.** Equation; $\dfrac{5}{8}$

21. Equation; all real numbers
22. Equation; all real numbers

23. Equation; $\dfrac{1}{2}$ **24.** Equation; 0 **25.** Expression; 0

26. Expression; -1 **27.** Expression; $2a + 13$
28. Expression; $8q + 3$ **29.** Equation; 10

30. Equation; $-\dfrac{1}{20}$

Section 9.4 Practice Exercises, pp. 625–628

3. $x + 5$ **5.** $3x$ **7.** $3x + 20$ **9.** The number is -4.
11. The number is -3.   **13.** The number is 5.
15. The number is -5.   **17.** The number is 9.
19. a. $x + 1, x + 2$ **b.** $x - 1, x - 2$ **21.** The integers are -34 and -33.   **23.** The integers are 13 and 15.
25. The sides are 14 in., 15 in., 16 in., 17 in., and 18 in.
27. The integers are 42, 44, and 46.   **29.** The integers are 13, 15, and 17.   **31.** The lengths of the pieces are 33 cm and 53 cm.   **33.** Karen's age is 35, and Clarann's age is 23.
35. There were 201 Republicans and 232 Democrats.
37. 4.698 million watch *The Dr. Phil Show*.   **39.** The Congo River is 4370 km long, and the Nile River is 6825 km.
41. The area of Africa is 30,065,000 km^2. The area of Asia is 44,579,000 km^2.   **43.** They walked 12.3 mi on the first day and 8.2 mi on the second.   **45.** The pieces are 6 in., 18 in., and

24 in.   **47.** The integers are 42, 43, and 44   **49.** Jennifer Lopez made $37 million, and U2 made $69 million.   **51.** The number is 11.   **53.** The page numbers are 470 and 471.
55. The number is 10.   **57.** The deepest point in the Arctic Ocean is 5122 m.   **59.** The number is $\dfrac{7}{16}$.   **61.** The number is 2.5.

Section 9.5 Practice Exercises, pp. 633–635

3. The numbers are 21 and 22.   **5.** 12.5%   **7.** 85%
9. 0.75   **11.** 1050.8   **13.** 885   **15.** 2200
17. Molly will have to pay $106.99.   **19.** Approximately 231,000 cases   **21.** 2%   **23.** Javon's taxable income was $84,000.   **25.** Pam will earn $420.
27. Bob borrowed $1200.   **29.** The rate is 6%.
31. Penny needs to invest $3302.   **33. a.** $20.40
b. $149.60   **35.** The original price was $470.59.
37. The discount rate is 12%.   **39.** The original cost was $60.   **41.** The tax rate is 5%.   **43.** The ticket price was $67.   **45.** The original price was $210,000.
47. Alina made $4600 that month.   **49.** Diane sold $645 over $200 worth of merchandise.

Section 9.6 Practice Exercises, pp. 640–643

3. -5 **5.** 0 **7.** -2 **9.** $a = P - b - c$

11. $y = x + z$ **13.** $q = p - 250$ **15.** $b = \dfrac{A}{h}$

17. $t = \dfrac{PV}{nr}$ **19.** $x = 5 + y$ **21.** $y = -3x - 19$

23. $y = \dfrac{-2x + 6}{3}$ or $y = -\dfrac{2}{3}x + 2$

25. $x = \dfrac{y + 9}{-2}$ or $x = -\dfrac{1}{2}y - \dfrac{9}{2}$

27. $y = \dfrac{-4x + 12}{-3}$ or $y = \dfrac{4}{3}x - 4$

29. $y = \dfrac{-ax + c}{b}$ or $y = -\dfrac{a}{b}x + \dfrac{c}{b}$

31. $t = \dfrac{A - P}{Pr}$ or $t = \dfrac{A}{Pr} - \dfrac{1}{r}$

33. $c = \dfrac{a - 2b}{2}$ or $c = \dfrac{a}{2} - b$ **35.** $y = 2Q - x$

37. $a = MS$ **39.** $R = \dfrac{P}{I^2}$

41. The length is 7 ft, and the width is 5 ft.
43. The length is 120 yd, and the width is 30 yd.
45. The length is 195 m, and the width is 100 m.
47. The sides are 22 m, 22 m, and 27 m.
49. "Adjacent supplementary angles form a straight angle." The words *Supplementary* and *Straight* both begin with the same letter.   **51.** The angles are 55° and 35°.
53. The angles are 45° and 135°.
55. $x = 20$; the vertical angles measure 37°.
57. The measures of the angles are 30°, 60°, and 90°.
59. The measures of the angles are 42°, 54°, and 84°.
61. $x = 17$; the measures of the angles are 34° and 56°.

63. a. $A = lw$ **b.** $w = \dfrac{A}{l}$ **c.** The width is 29.5 ft.

65. a. $P = 2l + 2w$ **b.** $l = \dfrac{P - 2w}{2}$ **c.** The length is 103 m.

67. a. $C = 2\pi r$ **b.** $r = \dfrac{C}{2\pi}$ **c.** The radius is approximately 140 ft.   **69. a.** 415.48 m²   **b.** 10,386.89 m³

Section 9.7 Practice Exercises, pp. 653–658

3. -3

Set-Builder Notation	Graph	Interval Notation
5. $\{x \mid x \geq 6\}$	6	$[6, \infty)$
7. $\{x \mid x \leq 2.1\}$	2.1	$(-\infty, 2.1]$
9. $\{x \mid -2 < x \leq 7\}$	-2 7	$(-2, 7]$

Set-Builder Notation	Graph	Interval Notation
11. $\left\{x \mid x > \dfrac{3}{4}\right\}$	$\frac{3}{4}$	$\left(\dfrac{3}{4}, \infty\right)$
13. $\{x \mid -1 < x < 8\}$	-1 8	$(-1, 8)$
15. $\{x \mid x \leq -14\}$	-14	$(-\infty, -14]$

Set-Builder Notation	Graph	Interval Notation
17. $\{x \mid x \geq 18\}$	18	$[18, \infty)$
19. $\{x \mid x < -0.6\}$	-0.6	$(-\infty, -0.6)$
21. $\{x \mid -3.5 \leq x < 7.1\}$	-3.5 7.1	$[-3.5, 7.1)$

23. a. $x = 3$ **b.** $x > 3$
3

25. a. $p = 13$ **b.** $p \leq 13$
13

27. a. $c = -3$ **b.** $c < -3$
-3

29. a. $z = -\dfrac{3}{2}$ **b.** $z \geq -\dfrac{3}{2}$
$-\frac{3}{2}$

31.
-1 4

33. $-3 < x < 5$
-3 5

35. $2 \leq x \leq 6$
2 6

37. $(-\infty, 1]$
1

39. $(10, \infty)$
10

41. $(3, \infty)$
3

43. $(-\infty, 8]$
8

45. $(2, \infty)$
2

47. $(-\infty, -2)$
-2

49. $[14, \infty)$
14

51. $[-24, \infty)$
-24

53. $[-3, 3)$
-3 3

55. $\left(0, \dfrac{5}{2}\right)$
0 $\frac{5}{2}$

57. $(10, 12)$
10 12

59. $[-1, 4)$
-1 4

61. $[90, \infty)$
90

63. $(-9, \infty)$
-9

65. $\left[-\dfrac{15}{2}, \infty\right)$
$-\frac{15}{2}$

67. $(-\infty, -3)$
-3

69. $\left[-\dfrac{1}{3}, \infty\right)$
$-\frac{1}{3}$

71. $(-3, \infty)$
-3

73. $(-\infty, 7)$
7

75. $(-\infty, -5]$
-5

77. $\left(-\infty, \dfrac{15}{4}\right]$
$\frac{15}{4}$

79. $(-\infty, -9)$
-9

81. $(-3, \infty)$
-3

83. $(-\infty, 0]$
0

85. No   **87.** Yes

89. a. A $[93, 100]$; B+ $[89, 93)$; B $[84, 89)$; C+ $[80, 84)$; C $[75, 80)$; F $[0, 75)$ **b.** B   **c.** C   **91.** $L \geq 10$

93. $w > 75$ **95.** $t \leq 72$ **97.** $L \geq 8$ **99.** $2 < h < 5$

101. More than 10.2 in. of rain is needed.

103. a. \$1539   **b.** 200 birdhouses cost \$1440. It is cheaper to purchase 200 birdhouses because the discount is greater.

105. a. $2.00x > 75 + 0.17x$ **b.** $x \geq 41$; profit occurs when 41 or more lemonades are sold.

107. $[13, \infty)$
13

109. $[-4, \infty)$
-4

111. $(14.5, \infty)$
14.5

Chapter 9 Review Exercises, pp. 664–667

1. a. $7, 1$ **b.** $7, -4, 0, 1$ **c.** $7, 0, 1$ **d.** $7, \frac{1}{3}, -4, 0, -0.\overline{2}, 1$ **e.** $-\sqrt{3}, \pi$ **f.** $7, \frac{1}{3}, -4, 0, -\sqrt{3}, -0.\overline{2}, \pi, 1$ **3.** 6   **5.** 0

7. False   **9.** True   **11.** True   **13.** True   **15.** -8

17. $\dfrac{21}{4}$ **19.** $-\dfrac{21}{5}$ **21.** $-\dfrac{10}{7}$ **23.** 1   **25.** $\dfrac{9}{4}$

27. -3 **29.** $\dfrac{3}{4}$ **31.** 0   **33.** $\dfrac{3}{8}$

35. A contradiction has no solution and an identity is true for all real numbers.   **37.** 6   **39.** 13   **41.** -10

43. $\dfrac{5}{3}$ **45.** 2.5   **47.** -4.2 **49.** -312

51. No solution   **53.** All real numbers
55. The number is 30.   **57.** The number is -7.
59. The integers are 66, 68, and 70.

61. The sides are 25 in., 26 in., and 27 in.
63. The minimum salary was $30,000 in 1980.
65. 23.8   **67.** 12.5%   **69.** 160   **71.** The novel originally cost $29.50.   **73. a.** $840   **b.** $3840

75. $K = C + 273$ **77.** $s = \dfrac{P}{4}$ **79.** $x = \dfrac{y-b}{m}$

81. $y = \dfrac{-2x - 2}{5}$ **83. a.** $h = \dfrac{3V}{\pi r^2}$ **b.** The height is 5.1 in.

85. The angles are 22°, 78°, and 80°.   **87.** The length is 5 ft, and the width is 4 ft.   **89.** The measure of angle y is 53°.

91. $\left(-\infty, \dfrac{1}{2}\right]$

93. a. $637   **b.** 300 plants cost $1410, and 295 plants cost $1416. 300 plants cost less.

95. $\left(-\dfrac{1}{3}, \infty\right)$ **97.** $\left(-\infty, -\dfrac{14}{5}\right]$

99. $(-\infty, 34.5)$ **101.** $\left(-\infty, \dfrac{5}{2}\right]$

103. $[-6, 5]$

105. a. $1.50x > 33 + 0.4x$ **b.** $x > 30$; a profit is realized if more than 30 hot dogs are sold.

Chapter 9 Test, pp. 667–668

1. a. b, d   **2. a.** $5x + 7$ **b.** 9   **3.** −16   **4.** 12

5. $-\dfrac{16}{9}$ **6.** $\dfrac{7}{3}$ **7.** 15   **8.** $\dfrac{13}{4}$ **9.** $\dfrac{20}{21}$

10. No solution   **11.** −3   **12.** −47

13. All real numbers   **14.** $y = -3x - 4$ **15.** $r = \dfrac{C}{2\pi}$

16. 90   **17.** The numbers are 18 and 13.
18. The sides are 61 in., 62 in., 63 in., 64 in., and 65 in.
19. The cost was $82.00.   **20.** Each basketball ticket was $36.32, and each hockey ticket was $40.64.
21. Clarita originally borrowed $5000.   **22.** The field is 110 m long and 75 m wide.   **23.** $y = 30$; The measures of the angles are 30°, 39°, and 111°.
24. The measures of the angles are 32° and 58°.
25. a. $(-\infty, 0)$ **b.** $[-2, 5)$

26. $(-2, \infty)$ **27.** $(-\infty, -4]$

28. $\left(-\dfrac{3}{2}, \infty\right)$ **29.** $[-5, 1]$

30. More than 26.5 in. is required.

Chapters 1–9 Cumulative Review Exercises, pp. 668–669

1. Three hundred-thousand, three hundred and three hundredths

2. $\dfrac{1}{2}$ **3.** −7   **4.** 16

5. $\sqrt{5^2 - 9}$; 4   **6.** $-14 + 12$; −2

7. $9x + 13$ **8.** −7.2

9. All real numbers   **10.** −8   **11.** $-\dfrac{4}{7}$

12. The numbers are 77 and 79.   **13.** The cost before tax was $350.00.   **14.** 6,900,000 people   **15. a.** 40   **b.** 15%   **c.** 27%   **16.** Mean: 29.9 yr; median: 29 yr; mode: 29 yr
17. Diameter: 12 ft; circumference: 37.68 ft; 113.04 ft²
18. The height is $\dfrac{41}{6}$ cm or $6\dfrac{5}{6}$ cm.
19. $(-2, \infty)$ **20.** $[-1, 9]$

Chapter 10

Chapter Opener Puzzle

In a rectangular coordinate system, we use an
$\underset{6}{O}\ \underset{1}{R}\ \underset{5}{D}\ \underset{2}{E}\ \underset{1}{R}\ \underset{2}{E}\ \underset{5}{D}$ $\underset{3}{P}\ \underset{7}{A}\ \underset{4}{I}\ \underset{1}{R}$
to represent the location of a $\underset{3}{P}\ \underset{6}{O}\ \underset{4}{I}\ \underset{8}{N}\ \underset{9}{T}$.

Section 10.1 Practice Exercises, pp. 676–681

3. a. Month 10   **b.** 30   **c.** Between months 3 and 5 and between months 10 and 12   **d.** Months 8 and 9
e. Month 3   **f.** 80
5. a. On day 1 the price per share was $89.25.
b. $1.75   **c.** −$2.75
7.

9.

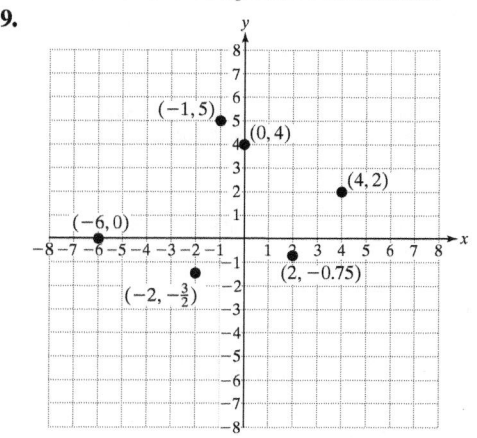

11. IV   **13.** II   **15.** III   **17.** I

19. $(0, -5)$ lies on the y-axis.

21. $(\frac{7}{8}, 0)$ is located on the x-axis.

23. $A(-4, 2), B(\frac{1}{2}, 4), C(3, -4), D(-3, -4), E(0, -3), F(5, 0)$

25. a. $A(400, 200), B(200, -150), C(-300, -200),$
$D(-300, 250), E(0, 450)$ **b** 450 m

27. a. $(250, 225), (175, 193), (315, 330), (220, 209), (450, 570), (400, 480), (190, 185)$; the ordered pair $(250, 225)$ means that 250 people produce \$225 in popcorn sales.

b.

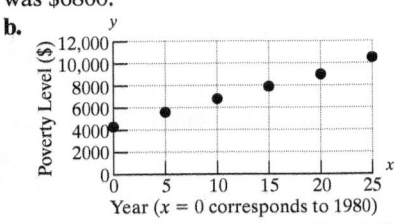

29. a. $(10, 6800)$ means that in 1990, the poverty level was \$6800.

b.

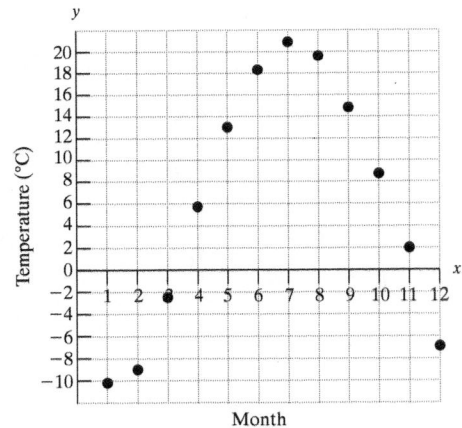

31. a. $(1, -10.2), (2, -9.0), (3, -2.5), (4, 5.7), (5, 13.0),$
$(6, 18.3), (7, 20.9), (8, 19.6), (9, 14.8), (10, 8.7), (11, 2.0),$
$(12, -6.9).$

b.

33. a.

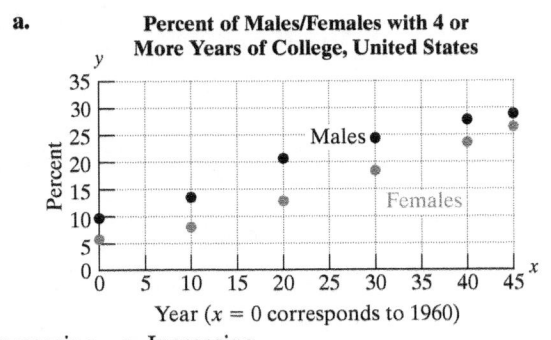

b. Increasing   **c.** Increasing

Section 10.2 Calculator Connections, pp. 689–690

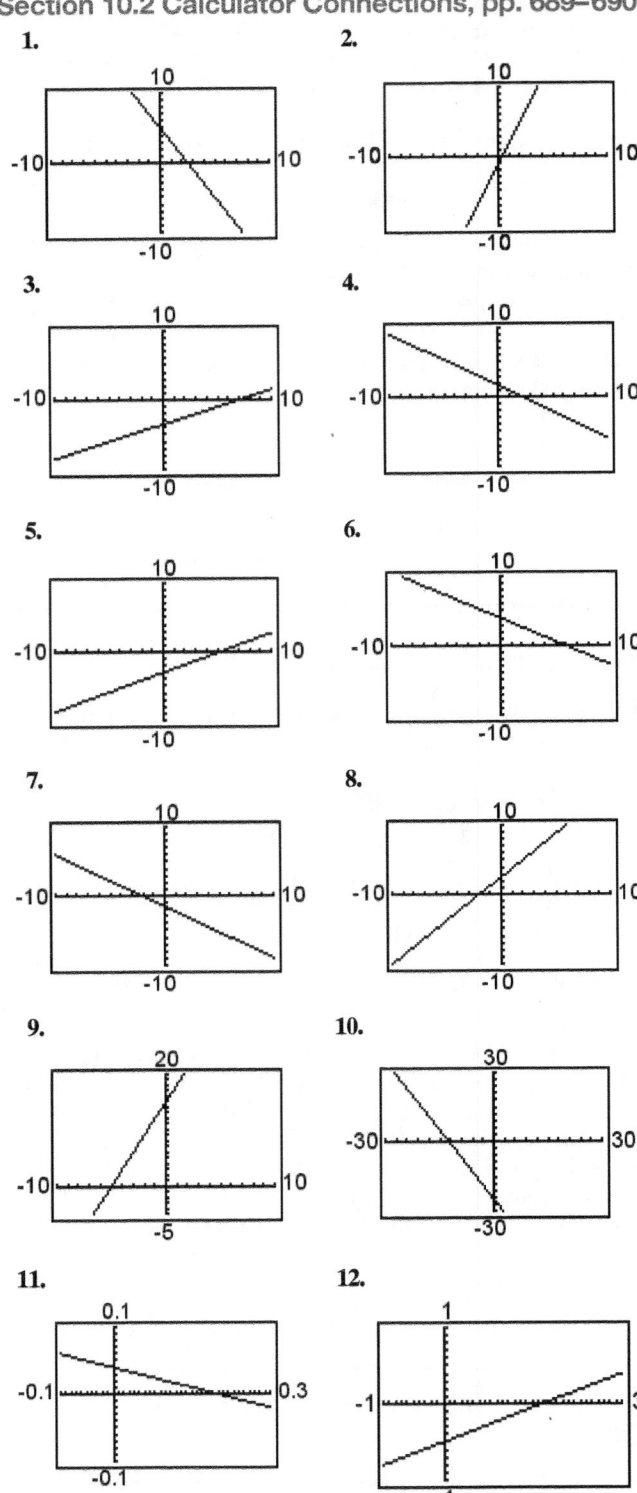

Section 10.2 Practice Exercises, pp. 690–696

3. $(2, 4)$; quadrant I   **5.** $(0, -1)$; y-axis

7. $(3, -4)$; quadrant IV   **9.** Yes   **11.** Yes   **13.** No

15. No   **17.** Yes

19.

x	*y*
1	−3
−2	0
−3	1
−4	2

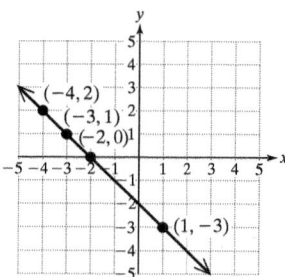

21.

x	*y*
−2	3
−1	0
−4	9

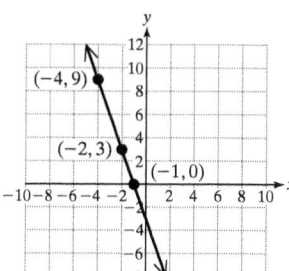

23.

x	*y*
0	4
2	0
3	−2

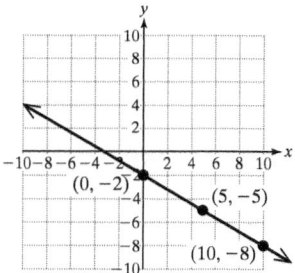

25.

x	*y*
0	−2
5	−5
10	−8

27.

x	*y*
0	−2
−3	−2
5	−2

29.

x	*y*
3/2	−1
3/2	2
3/2	−3

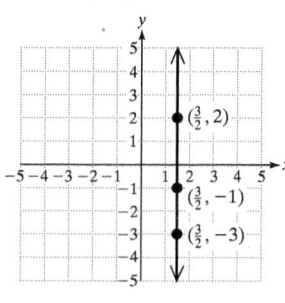

31.

x	*y*
0	4.6
1	3.4
2	2.2

33.

35.

37.

39.

41.

43.

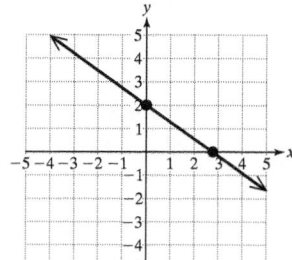

45. *y*-axis   **47.** *x*-intercept: (−1, 0); *y*-intercept: (0, −3)

49. *x*-intercept: (−4, 0); *y*-intercept: (0, 1)

51. *x*-intercept: $\left(-\frac{9}{4}, 0\right)$;

y-intercept: (0, 3)

53. *x*-intercept: $\left(\frac{8}{3}, 0\right)$;

y-intercept: (0, 2)

55. x-intercept: $(-4, 0)$;
y-intercept: $(0, 8)$

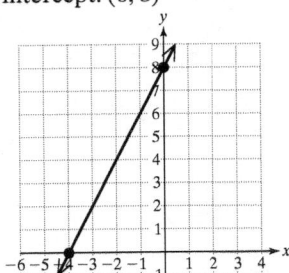

57. x-intercept: $(0, 0)$;
y-intercept: $(0, 0)$

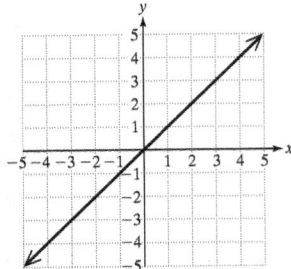

Section 10.3 Practice Exercises, pp. 703–709

3. x-intercept: $(6, 0)$;
y-intercept: $(0, -2)$

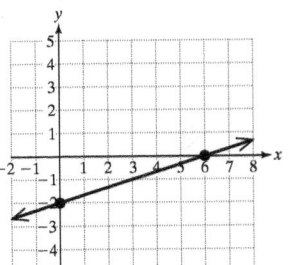

5. x-intercept: $(0, 0)$;
y-intercept: $(0, 0)$

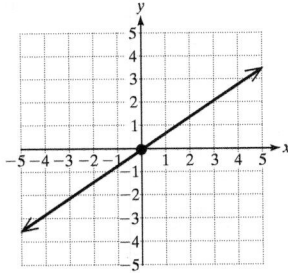

59. x-intercept: $(10, 0)$;
y-intercept: $(0, 5)$

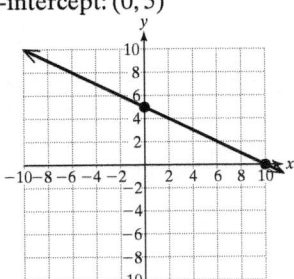

61. x-intercept: $(0, 0)$;
y-intercept: $(0, 0)$

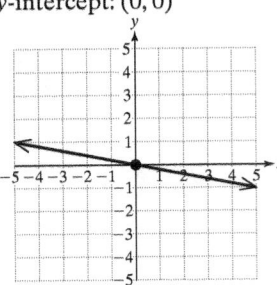

7. x-intercept: $(2, 0)$;
y-intercept: $(0, 8)$

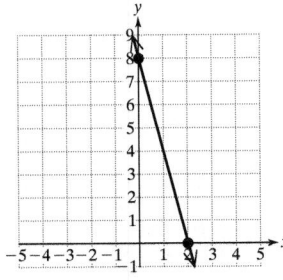

63. True
67. a. Horizontal
c. no x-intercept;
y-intercept: $(0, -1)$

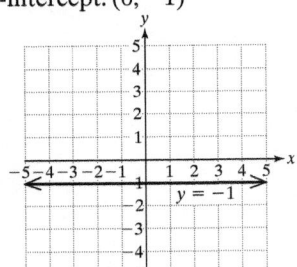

65. True
69. a. Vertical
c. x-intercept: $(4, 0)$;
no y-intercept

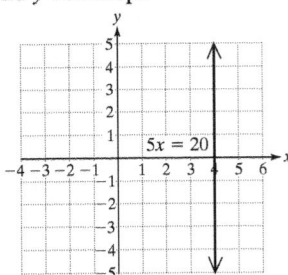

9. $m = \dfrac{1}{3}$ **11.** $m = \dfrac{6}{11}$ **13.** Undefined
15. Positive   **17.** Negative   **19.** Zero
21. Undefined   **23.** Positive   **25.** Negative
27. $m = \dfrac{1}{2}$ **29.** $m = -3$ **31.** $m = 0$
33. The slope is undefined.   **35.** $\dfrac{1}{3}$ **37.** -3
39. $\dfrac{3}{5}$ **41.** Zero   **43.** Undefined   **45.** $\dfrac{28}{5}$ **47.** $-\dfrac{7}{8}$
49. -0.45 or $-\dfrac{9}{20}$ **51.** -0.15 or $-\dfrac{3}{20}$
53. a. -2 **b.** $\dfrac{1}{2}$ **55. a.** 0 **b.** undefined
57. a. $\dfrac{4}{5}$ **b.** $-\dfrac{5}{4}$ **59. a.** 1 **b.** -1
61. Perpendicular   **63.** Parallel   **65.** Neither
67. l_1: $m = 2$, l_2: $m = 2$; parallel
69. l_1: $m = 5$, l_2: $m = -\dfrac{1}{5}$; perpendicular
71. l_1: $m = \dfrac{1}{4}$, l_2: $m = 4$; neither
73. a. $m = 47$ **b.** The number of male prisoners increased at a rate of 47 thousand per year during this time period.
75. a. $m \approx 0.009$ **b.** The slope $m = 0.009$ means that postage increased by about $0.009 per year (or equivalently 0.9¢ per year) during this time.
77. $m = \dfrac{3}{4}$ **79.** $m = 0$

71. a. Horizontal
c. no x-intercept;
y-intercept $(0, -5)$

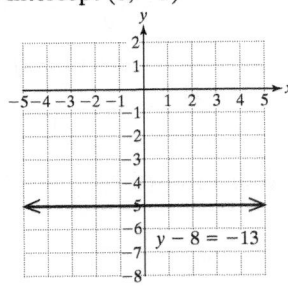

73. a. Vertical
c. All points on the y-axis are y-intercepts; x-intercept: $(0, 0)$

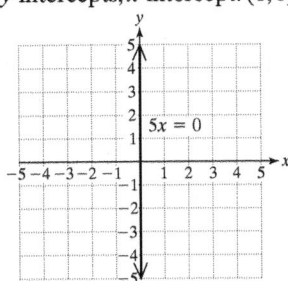

75. A horizontal line may not have an x-intercept. A vertical line may not have a y-intercept.   **77.** a b, d
79. a. $y = 10{,}068$ **b.** $x = 3$ **c.** $(1, 10068)$ One year after purchase the value of the car is $10,068. $(3, 7006)$ Three years after purchase the value of the car is $7006.

81. For example:
(4, 0) and (−2, −4)

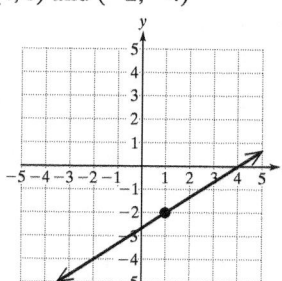

83. For example:
(3, −1) and (1, 5)

85.

87.

89.

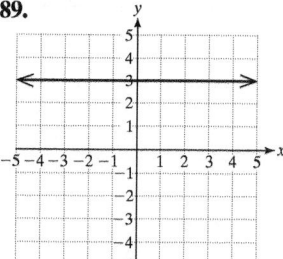

91. $\dfrac{3m - 3n}{2b}$ or $\dfrac{-3m + 3n}{-2b}$ **93.** $\left(\dfrac{c}{a}, 0\right)$

95. For example: (7, 1)

Section 10.4 Calculator Connections, p. 713

1. Perpendicular

2. Parallel

3. Neither

4. The lines may appear parallel; however, they are not parallel because the slopes are different.

5. The lines may appear to coincide on a graph; however, they are not the same line because the y-intercepts are different.

6. The line may appear to be horizontal, but it is not. The slope is 0.001 rather than 0.

Section 10.4 Practice Exercises, pp. 714–717

3. x-intercept: (10, 0); y-intercept: (0, −2)

5. x-intercept: none; y-intercept: (0, −3)

7. x-intercept: (0, 0); y-intercept: (0, 0)

9. x-intercept: (4, 0); ; y-intercept: none

11. $m = -2$; y-intercept: (0, 3)   **13.** $m = 1$; y-intercept: (0, −2)   **15.** $m = -1$; y-intercept: (0, 0)

17. $m = \dfrac{3}{4}$; y-intercept: (0, −1)   **19.** $m = \dfrac{2}{5}$; y-intercept: $\left(0, -\dfrac{4}{5}\right)$ **21.** $m = 3$; y-intercept: (0, −5)

23. $m = -1$; y-intercept: (0, 6)   **25.** Undefined slope; no y-intercept   **27.** $m = 0$; y-intercept: $\left(0, -\dfrac{1}{4}\right)$

29. $m = \dfrac{2}{3}$; y-intercept: (0, 0)

31.

33.

35. b   **37.** e   **39.** c

41. $y = \dfrac{1}{2}x - 3$

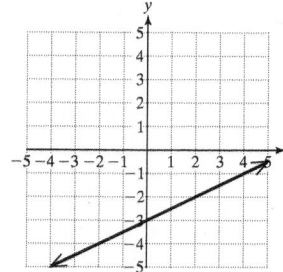

43. $y = -2x + 9$

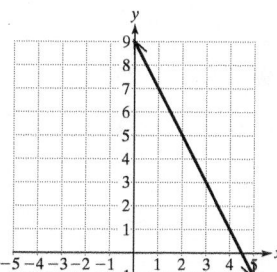

45. $y = -\frac{1}{2}x + \frac{3}{2}$

47. $y = -x$

49. $y = \frac{4}{5}x$

51. $y = -\frac{2}{3}$

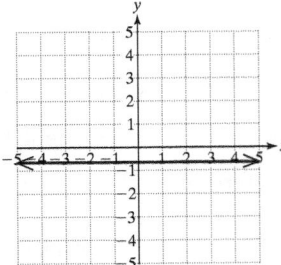

53. Perpendicular   **55.** Neither   **57.** Parallel
59. Perpendicular   **61.** Parallel   **63.** Perpendicular
65. Neither   **67.** Parallel   **69.** $y = -\frac{1}{3}x + 2$
71. $y = 10x - 19$ **73.** $y = -11$ **75.** $y = 5x$
77. $y = 6x - 2$ **79. a.** $m = 49.95$. The cost increases
$49.95 per day.   **b.** $(0, 31.95)$. The base fee for renting a car
is $31.95.   **c.** $381.60   **81.** $y = -\frac{A}{B}x + \frac{C}{B}$; the slope is $-\frac{A}{B}$.
83. $m = -\frac{6}{7}$ **85.** $m = \frac{11}{8}$

Chapter 10 Problem Recognition Exercises, p. 718

1. a, c, d   **2.** b, f, h   **3.** a   **4.** f   **5.** b, f   **6.** c
7. c, d   **8.** f   **9.** e   **10.** g   **11.** b   **12.** h
13. g   **14.** e   **15.** c   **16.** b, h   **17.** e   **18.** e
19. b, f, h   **20.** c, d

Section 10.5 Practice Exercises, pp. 723–726

3.

5.

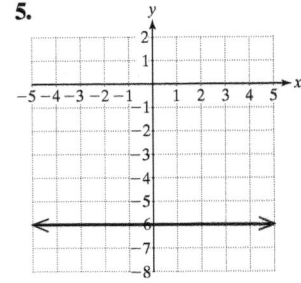

7. 9   **9.** 0   **11.** $y = 3x + 7$ or $3x - y = -7$
13. $y = -4x - 14$ or $4x + y = -14$ **15.** $y = -\frac{1}{2}x - \frac{1}{2}$

or $x + 2y = -1$ **17.** $y = \frac{1}{4}x + 8$ or $x - 4y = -32$
19. $y = 4.5x - 25.6$ or $45x - 10y = 256$ **21.** $y = -2$
23. $y = 2x - 2$ or $2x - y = 2$ **25.** $y = -x - 4$ or
$x + y = -4$ **27.** $y = -0.2x - 2.86$ or
$20x + 100y = -286$ **29.** $y = -2x + 1$
31. $y = 2x + 4$ **33.** $y = \frac{1}{2}x - 1$ **35.** $y = 4x + 13$ or
$4x - y = -13$ **37.** $y = -\frac{3}{2}x + 6$ or $3x + 2y = 12$
39. $y = -2x - 8$ or $2x + y = -8$ **41.** $y = -\frac{1}{5}x - 6$
or $x + 5y = -30$ **43.** $y = 3x - 8$ or $3x - y = 8$
45. iv   **47.** vi   **49.** iii   **51.** $y = 1$ **53.** $x = 2$
55. $y = 2$ **57.** $x = -6$ **59.** $x = -4$

Section 10.6 Calculator Connections, p. 729

1. 13.3

2. −42.3

3. 345

4. 95

Section 10.6 Practice Exercises, pp. 730–733

3. x-intercept: $(6, 0)$; y-intercept: $(0, 5)$ **5.** x-intercept:
$(-2, 0)$; y-intercept: $(0, -4)$ **7.** x-intercept: none;
y-intercept: $(0, -9)$ **9. a.** $3.00   **b.** $7.20
c. The y-intercept is $(0, 1.6)$. This indicates that the minimum
wage was $1.60 per hour in the year 1970.   **d.** The slope is
0.14. This indicates that the minimum wage has risen
approximately $0.14 per year during this period.
11. a. $30.7°$ **b.** $13.4°$ **c.** $m = -2.333$. The average
temperature in January decreases at a rate of $2.333°$ per $1°$
of latitude.   **d.** $(53.2, 0)$. At $53.2°$ latitude, the average
temperature in January is $0°$.
13. a. $95   **b.** $190   **c.** $(0, 0)$. For 0 kilowatt-hours used,
the cost is $0.   **d.** $m = 0.095$. The cost increases by $0.095
for each kilowatt-hour used.   **15. a.** $y = -0.08x + 7.6$
b. 5 days   **17. a.** $y = 2.5x + 31$ **b.** 43.5 in.
19. a. $y = 0.25x + 20$ **b.** $84.50   **21. a.** $y = 90x + 105$
b. $1185.00   **23. a.** $y = 0.8x + 100$ **b.** $260.00

Chapter 10 Review Exercises, pp. 740–743

1.

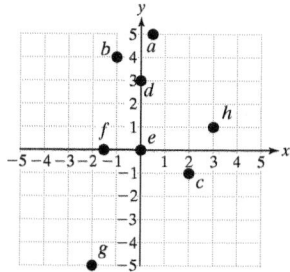

3. III   **5.** IV   **7.** IV   **9.** x-axis
11. a. On day 1, the price was $26.25.   **b.** Day 2   **c.** $2.25
13. No   **15.** Yes

17.

x	y
2	1
3	4
1	−2

19.

x	y
0	−1
3	1
−6	−5

21.

23.

25. Vertical   **27.** Horizontal

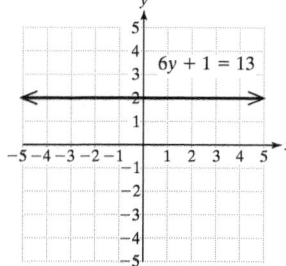

29. x-intercept: $(-3, 0)$; y-intercept: $\left(0, \dfrac{3}{2}\right)$

31. x-intercept: $(0, 0)$; y-intercept: $(0, 0)$

33. x-intercept: none; y-intercept: $(0, -4)$

35. x-intercept: $\left(-\dfrac{5}{2}, 0\right)$; y-intercept: none

37. $m = \dfrac{12}{5}$ **39.** $-\dfrac{2}{3}$ **41.** Undefined

43. a. -5 **b.** $\dfrac{1}{5}$ **45.** $m_1 = \dfrac{2}{3}; m_2 = \dfrac{2}{3}$; parallel

47. $m_1 = -\dfrac{5}{12}; m_2 = \dfrac{12}{5}$; perpendicular   **49.** $y = \dfrac{5}{2}x - 5$;

$m = \dfrac{5}{2}$; y-intercept: $(0, -5)$ **51.** $y = \dfrac{1}{3}x$;

$m = \dfrac{1}{3}$; y-intercept: $(0, 0)$ **53.** $y = -\dfrac{5}{2}$; $m = 0$;

y-intercept: $\left(0, -\dfrac{5}{2}\right)$ **55.** Neither   **57.** Parallel

59. Perpendicular   **61.** $y = 5x$ or $5x - y = 0$
63. For example: $5x + 2y = -4$ **65.** $y - y_1 = m(x - x_1)$

67. For example: $y = -5$ **69.** $y = \dfrac{2}{3}x + \dfrac{5}{3}$ or

$2x - 3y = -5$ **71.** $y = -5$

73. $y = 4x + 31$ or $4x - y = -31$
75. a. $m = 137$ **b.** The number of prescriptions
increased by 137 million per year during this time period.
c. $y = 137x + 2140$ **d.** 4195 million
77. a. $y = 8x + 700$ **b.** $1340

Chapter 10 Test, pp. 744–746

1. a. II   **b.** IV   **c.** III   **2.** 0   **3.** 0
4. a. $(5, 46)$ At age 5 the boy's height was 46 in. $(7, 50)$
$(9, 55)$ $(11, 60)$
b.

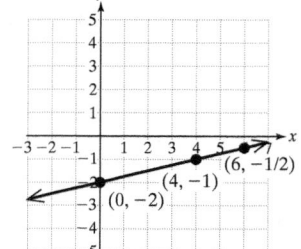

c. 57.5 in.   **d.** No, his height will maximize in his teen years.
5. a. No   **b.** Yes   **c.** Yes   **d.** Yes
6.

x	y
0	−2
4	−1
6	$-\dfrac{1}{2}$

7. a. 202 beats per minute   **b.** $(20, 200), (30, 190), (40, 180)$
$(50, 170), (60, 160)$

8. Horizontal

9. Vertical

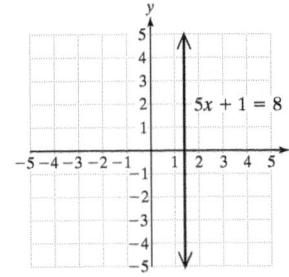

10. x-intercept: $\left(-\frac{3}{2}, 0\right)$; y-intercept: $(0, 2)$

11. x-intercept: $(0, 0)$; y-intercept: $(0, 0)$

12. x-intercept: $(4, 0)$; y-intercept: none

13. x-intercept: none; y-intercept: $(0, 3)$ **14.** $\frac{2}{5}$

15. a. $\frac{1}{3}$ **b.** $\frac{4}{3}$ **16. a.** $-\frac{1}{4}$ **b.** 4

17. a. Undefined   **b.** 0

18.

19.

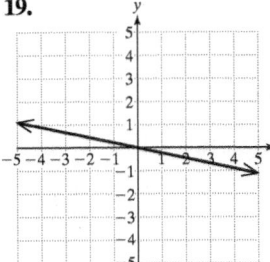

20. Perpendicular   **21.** $y = \frac{1}{4}x + \frac{1}{2}$ or $x - 4y = -2$

22. $y = -\frac{7}{2}x + 15$ or $7x + 2y = 30$ **23.** $y = -6$

24. $y = -\frac{1}{3}x + 1$ or $x + 3y = 3$ **25.** $y = 3x + 8$ or

$3x - y = -8$ **26. a.** $\frac{3}{4}$ **b.** $\frac{1}{2}$ **27. a.** $y = 1.5x + 10$

b. \$25   **28. a.** $m = 20$; The slope indicates that there is
an increase of 20 thousand medical doctors per year.
b. $y = 20x + 414$ **c.** 1014 thousand or, equivalently,
1,014,000

Chapters 1–10 Cumulative Review Exercises, p. 746

1. a. Rational   **b.** Rational   **c.** Irrational   **d.** Rational

2. a. $\frac{2}{3}; \frac{2}{3}$ **b.** $-5.3; 5.3$ **3.** 69

4. $\frac{3}{4} \div -\frac{7}{8}; -\frac{6}{7}$ **5.** $(-2.1)(-6); 12.6$

6. 12 yd   **7.** Area: 36 cm²; perimeter: 28 cm

8. \$0.324 per oz   **9.** 4   **10.** 5

11. $-\frac{9}{2}$ **12.** -2 **13.** 9241 mi²   **14.** $a = \frac{c - b}{3}$

15.

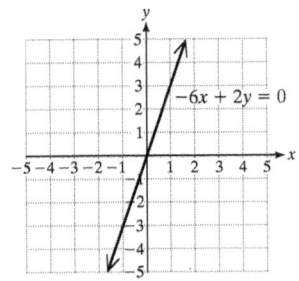

16. x-intercept: $(-2, 0)$; y-intercept: $(0, 1)$

17. $y = -\frac{3}{2}x - 6$;   slope: $-\frac{3}{2}$; y-intercept: $(0, -6)$

18. $2x + 3 = 5$ can be written as $x = 1$, which represents a
vertical line. A vertical line of the form $x = k$ $(k \neq 0)$ has an
x-intercept of $(k, 0)$ and no y-intercept.

19. $y = -3x + 1$ or $3x + y = 1$ **20.** $y = \frac{2}{3}x + 6$ or
$2x - 3y = -18$

Chapter 11

Chapter Opener Puzzle

One drink costs \$3.00, and one small popcorn costs \$4.50.

Section 11.1 Calculator Connections, pp. 752–753

1. $(2, 1)$

2. $(6, -1)$

3. $(3, 1)$

4. $(-2, 0)$

5. No solution

6. Infinitely many solutions

Section 11.1 Practice Exercises, pp. 753–758

3. Yes   **5.** No   **7.** Yes   **9.** No   **11.** b   **13.** d

15. a.

b.

c.

17. c   **19.** a   **21.** a   **23.** b   **25.** c

27.

29.

31.

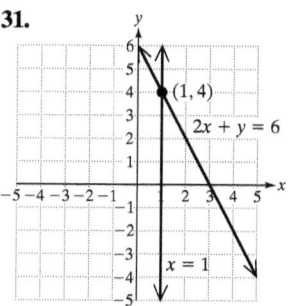

33. No solution; inconsistent system

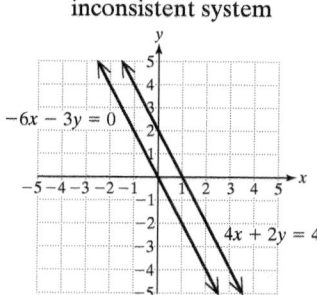

35. Infinitely many solutions; $\{(x, y)\,|\,-2x + y = 3\}$; dependent equations

37.

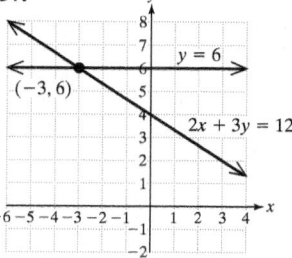

39. Infinitely many solutions; $\{(x, y)\,|\,y = \frac{5}{3}x - 3\}$; dependent equations

41.

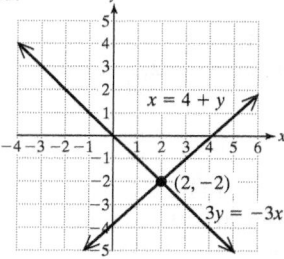

43. No solution; inconsistent system

45.

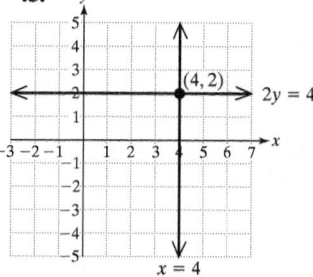

47. No solution; inconsistent system

49.

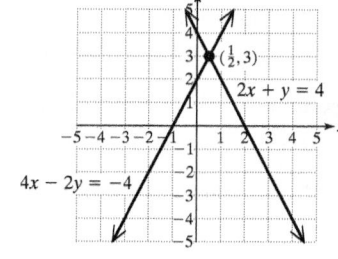

51. Infinitely many solutions; $\{(x, y)|y = 0.5x + 2\}$; dependent equations

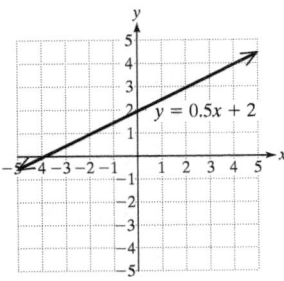

53. 4 lessons will cost $120 for each instructor.   **55.** The point of intersection is below the x-axis so it cannot have a positive y-coordinate.   **57.** For example: $4x + y = 9$; $-2x - y = -5$ **59.** For example: $2x + 2y = 1$

Section 11.2 Practice Exercises, pp. 766–767

1. $y = 2x - 4$; $y = 2x - 4$; coinciding lines
3. $y = -\frac{2}{3}x + 2$; $y = x - 5$; intersecting lines
5. $y = 4x - 4$; $y = 4x - 13$; parallel lines
7. $(3, -6)$ **9.** $(0, 4)$ **11. a.** y in the second equation is easiest to isolate because its coefficient is 1.   **b.** $(1, 5)$
13. $(5, 2)$ **15.** $(10, 5)$ **17.** $\left(\frac{1}{2}, 3\right)$ **19.** $(5, 3)$
21. $(1, 0)$ **23.** $(1, 4)$ **25.** No solution; inconsistent system   **27.** Infinitely many solutions; $\{(x, y)|2x - 6y = -2\}$; dependent equations   **29.** $(5, -7)$
31. $\left(-5, \frac{3}{2}\right)$ **33.** $(2, -5)$ **35.** $(-4, 6)$ **37.** $(0, 2)$
39. Infinitely many solutions; $\{(x, y)|y = 0.25x + 1\}$; dependent equations   **41.** $(1, 1)$ **43.** No solution; inconsistent system   **45.** $(-1, 5)$ **47.** $(-6, -4)$
49. The numbers are 48 and 58.   **51.** The numbers are 13 and 39.   **53.** The angles are 165° and 15°.   **55.** The angles are 70° and 20°.   **57.** The angles are 42° and 48°.
59. For example: $(0, 3)$, $(1, 5)$, $(-1, 1)$

Section 11.3 Practice Exercises, pp. 774–776

3. No   **5.** Yes   **7. a.** True   **b.** False, multiply the second equation by 5.   **9. a.** x would be easier.
b. $(0, -3)$ **11.** $(4, -1)$ **13.** $(4, 3)$ **15.** $(2, 3)$
17. $(1, -4)$ **19.** $(1, -1)$ **21.** $(-4, -6)$
23. $\left(\frac{7}{9}, \frac{5}{9}\right)$ **25.** $\left(\frac{7}{16}, -\frac{7}{8}\right)$
27. There are infinitely many solutions. The lines coincide.
29. The system will have no solution. The lines are parallel.
31. The system will have one solution. The lines intersect at a point whose y-coordinate is 0.   **33.** No solution; inconsistent system   **35.** Infinitely many solutions; $\{(x, y)|4x - 3y = 6\}$; dependent equations   **37.** $(2, -2)$
39. $(0, 3)$ **41.** $(5, 2)$ **43.** No solution; inconsistent system   **45.** $(-5, 0)$ **47.** $(2.5, -0.5)$
49. $\left(\frac{1}{2}, 0\right)$ **51.** $(-3, 2)$ **53.** $\left(\frac{7}{4}, 3\right)$ **55.** $(0, 1)$
57. No solution; inconsistent system   **59.** $(0, -5)$

61. $(4, -2)$ **63.** Infinitely many solutions; $\{(a, b)|a = 5 + 2b\}$; dependent equations
65. The numbers are 17 and 19.   **67.** The numbers are -1 and 3.   **69.** $(1, 3)$ **71.** One line within the system of equations would have to "bend" for the system to have exactly two points of intersection. This is not possible.
73. $A = -5, B = 2$

Chapter 11 Problem Recognition Exercises, p. 777

1. Infinitely many solutions. The equations represent the same line.   **2.** No solution. The equations represent parallel lines.   **3.** One solution. The equations represent intersecting lines.   **4.** One solution. The equations represent intersecting lines.   **5.** No solution. The equations represent parallel lines.   **6.** Infinitely many solutions. The equations represent the same line.   **7.** $(5, 0)$
8. $(1, -7)$ **9.** $(4, -5)$ **10.** $(2, 3)$ **11.** $(2, 0)$
12. $(8, 10)$ **13.** $\left(2, -\frac{5}{7}\right)$ **14.** $\left(-\frac{14}{3}, -4\right)$
15. No solution; inconsistent system   **16.** No solution; inconsistent system   **17.** $(-1, 0)$ **18.** $(5, 0)$
19. Infinitely many solutions; $\{(x, y)|y = 2x - 14\}$; dependent equations   **20.** Infinitely many solutions; $\{(x, y)|x = 5y - 9\}$; dependent equations
21. $(2200, 1000)$ **22.** $(3300, 1200)$ **23.** $(5, -7)$
24. $(2, -1)$ **25.** $\left(\frac{2}{3}, \frac{1}{2}\right)$ **26.** $\left(\frac{1}{4}, -\frac{3}{2}\right)$

Section 11.4 Practice Exercises, pp. 783–787

1. $(-1, 4)$ **3.** $\left(\frac{5}{2}, 1\right)$ **5.** The numbers are 4 and 16.
7. The angles are 80° and 10°.   **9.** DVDs are $10.50 each, and CDs are $15.50 each.   **11.** Technology stock costs $16 per share, and the mutual fund costs $11 per share.
13. Patricia bought forty 44¢ stamps and ten 29¢ stamps.
15. Shanelle invested $3500 in the 10% account and $6500 in the 7% account.   **17.** $9000 was borrowed at 6%, and $3000 was borrowed at 9%.   **19.** Invest $12,000 in the bond fund and $18,000 in the stock fund.   **21.** 15 gal of the 50% mixture should be mixed with 10 gal of the 40% mixture.   **23.** 12 gal of the 45% disinfectant solution should be mixed with 8 gal of the 30% disinfectant solution.
25. She should mix 20 mL of the 13% solution with 30 mL of the 18% solution.   **27.** The speed of the boat in still water is 6 mph, and the speed of the current is 2 mph.   **29.** The speed of the plane in still air is 300 mph, and the wind is 20 mph.   **31.** The speed of the plane in still air is 525 mph, and the speed of the wind is 75 mph.   **33.** There are 17 dimes and 22 nickels.   **35. a.** 835 free throws and 1597 field goals   **b.** 4029 points   **c.** Approximately 50 points per game   **37.** The speed of the plane in still air is 160 mph, and the wind is 40 mph.   **39.** 12 lb of candy should be mixed with 8 lb of nuts.   **41.** $15,000 was invested in the 5.5% account, and $45,000 was invested in the 6.5% account.
43. Dallas scored 30 points, and Buffalo scored 13 points.
45. There were 300 women and 200 men in the survey.

Section 11.5 Practice Exercises, pp. 793–797

3.

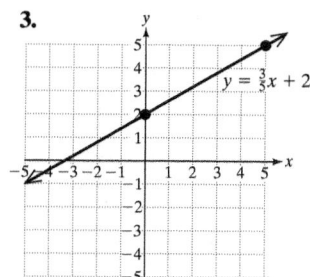

5. When the inequality symbol is $\leq$ or $\geq$
7. All of the points in the shaded region are solutions to the inequality. **9.** a

11. For example:
$(0, 5)\ (2, 7)\ (-1, 8)$

13. For example:
$(1, -1)\ (3, 0)\ (-2, -9)$

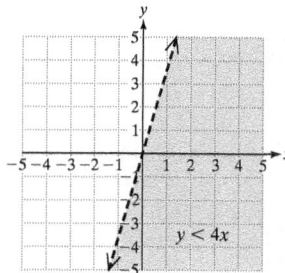

15. For example:
$(0, 0)\ (0, 2)\ (-1, -3)$

17.

19.

21.

23.

25.

27.

29.

31.

33.

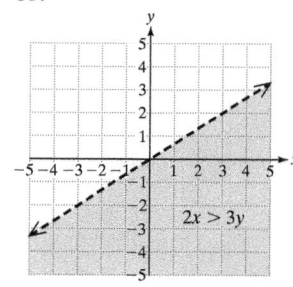

35. a. The set of ordered pairs above the line $x + y = 4$, for example, $(6, 3)(-2, 8)(0, 5)$ **b.** The set of ordered pairs on the line $x + y = 4$, for example, $(0, 4)(4, 0)(2, 2)$ **c.** The set of ordered pairs below the line $x + y = 4$, for example, $(0, 0)(-2, 1)(3, 0)$

37.

39.

41.

43.

45.

47.

49.

51.

53.

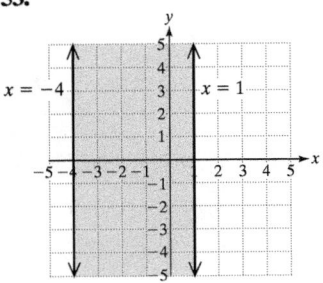

Chapter 11 Review Exercises, pp. 804–807

1. Yes   **3.** No   **5.** Intersecting lines (The lines have different slopes.)   **7.** Parallel lines (The lines have the same slope but different y-intercepts.)   **9.** Coinciding lines (The lines have the same slope and same y-intercept.)
11. $(0, -2)$

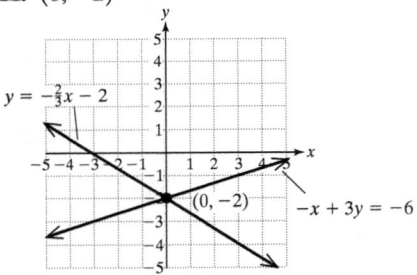

13. Infinitely many solutions; $\{(x, y) | 2x + y = 5\}$; dependent equations

15. $(1, -1)$

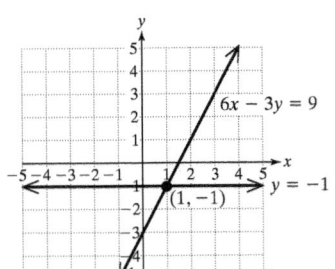

17. No solution; inconsistent system

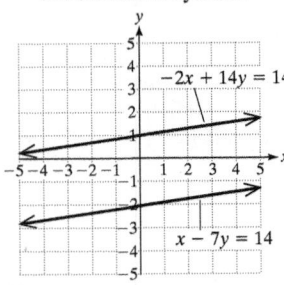

19. 200 mi   **21.** $(-4, 1)$ **23.** Infinitely many solutions; $\{(x, y) | y = -2x + 2\}$ **25. a.** y in the second equation is easiest to isolate because its coefficient is 1.
b. $\left(\dfrac{9}{2}, 3\right)$ **27.** $(0, 4)$ **29.** No solution
31. The angles are 42° and 48°.
33. See page 769.   **35. b.** $(2, 2)$ **37.** $(-6, 2)$
39. $\left(\dfrac{1}{4}, -\dfrac{2}{5}\right)$ **41.** No solution
43. $(1, 0)$ **45. b.** $(-2, -1)$ **47.** He should invest $75,000 at 12% and $525,000 at 4%.   **49.** The speed of the boat is 18 mph, and that of the current is 2 mph.
51. A hot dog costs $4.50, and a drink costs $3.50.
53. The score was 72 on the first round and 82 on the second round.
55. For example: $(5, 5)(4, 0)(0, 7)$

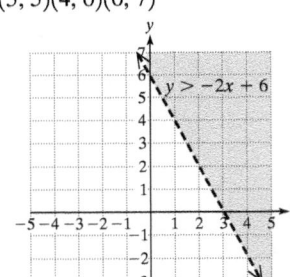

57. For example: $(0, 0)(0, -5)(-1, 1)$

59.

61.

63.

65.

67.

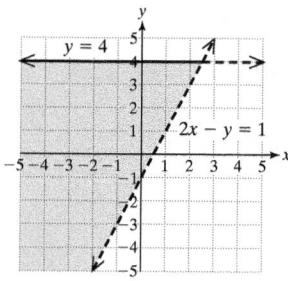

Chapter 11 Test, pp. 808–809

1. $y = -\dfrac{5}{2}x - 3$; $y = -\dfrac{5}{2}x + 3$; Parallel lines

2.

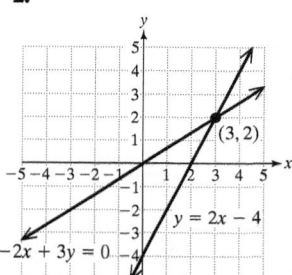

3. Infinitely many solutions; $\{(x, y) \mid 2x + 4y = 6\}$

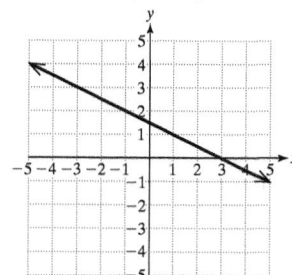

4. $(-2, 0)$ **5.** Swoopes scored 614 points, and Jackson scored 597.   **6.** $\left(2, -\dfrac{1}{3}\right)$ **7.** 12 mL of the 50% acid solution should be mixed with 24 mL of the 20% solution.
8. a. No solution   **b.** Infinitely many solutions   **c.** One solution   **9.** $(-5, 4)$ **10.** No solution   **11.** $(3, -5)$ **12.** $(-1, 2)$ **13.** Infinitely many solutions; $\{(x, y) \mid 10x + 2y = -8\}$ **14.** $(1, -2)$ **15.** CDs cost $8

each and DVDs cost $11 each.   **16. a.** $18 was required. **b.** They used 24 quarters and 12 $1 bills.   **17.** $1200 was borrowed at 10%, and $3800 was borrowed at 8%.
18. He scored 155 receiving touchdowns and 10 touchdowns rushing.   **19.** The plane travels 500 mph in still air, and the wind speed is 45 mph.   **20.** The cake has 340 calories, and the ice cream has 120 calories.
21. 60 mL of 10% solution and 40 mL of 25% solution.

22.

23.

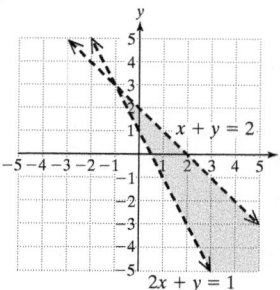

Chapters 1–11 Cumulative Review Exercises, pp. 809–810

1. $\dfrac{11}{6}$ **2.** The perimeter is $16\dfrac{1}{4}$ in., and the area is $14\dfrac{25}{32}$ in.^{2} **3.** 2.625   **4.** 925   **5.** 28.8

6. Mean: 84; median: 83.5; mode: 93

7. $-\dfrac{21}{2}$ **8.** No solution   **9.** $y = \dfrac{3}{2}x - 3$

10. $\left[\dfrac{3}{11}, \infty\right)$ ⊢━━━━━━➤ $\frac{3}{11}$

11. The angles are 37°, 33°, and 110°.
12. 36% of the goal has been achieved.

13. The angles are 36.5° and 53.5°.   **14. a.** $-\dfrac{2}{3}$ **b.** $\dfrac{3}{2}$

15. $y = -3x + 3$ **16.** $(0, 2)$

17. a.   **b.**

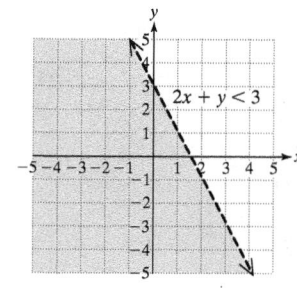

c. Part (a) represents the solutions to an equation. Part (b) represents the solutions to a strict inequality.   **18.** 20 gal of the 15% solution should be mixed with 40 gal of the 60% solution.   **19.** x is 27°; y is 63°   **20. a.** 1.4   **b.** Between 1920 and 1990, the winning speed in the Indianapolis 500 increased on average by 1.4 mph per year.

Chapter 12

Chapter Opener Puzzle

The numerical factor within a term is called the

$\underset{1}{C}\ \underset{2}{O}\ \underset{3}{E}\ \underset{4}{F}\ \underset{5}{F}\ \underset{6}{I}\ \underset{7}{C}\ \underset{8}{I}\ \underset{9}{E}\ \underset{10}{N}\ \underset{11}{T}.$

Section 12.1 Practice Exercises, pp. 817–819

3. Base: x; exponent: 4   **5.** Base: 3; exponent: 5
7. Base: -1; exponent: 4   **9.** Base: q; exponent: 1
11. v **13.** 1   **15.** $(-6b)^2$ **17.** $-6b^2$ **19.** $(y+2)^4$

21. $\dfrac{-2}{t^3}$ **23.** No; $-5^2 = -25$ and $(-5)^2 = 25$

25. Yes; $-2^5 = -32$ and $(-2)^5 = -32$ **27.** Yes; $\left(\dfrac{1}{2}\right)^3 = \dfrac{1}{8}$

and $\dfrac{1}{2^3} = \dfrac{1}{8}$ **29.** Yes; $\left(\dfrac{3}{10}\right)^2 = \dfrac{9}{100}$ and $(0.3)^2 = 0.09$

31. 16   **33.** -1 **35.** $\dfrac{1}{9}$ **37.** $-\dfrac{4}{25}$ **39.** 48

41. 4   **43.** 9   **45.** 50   **47.** -100 **49.** 400
51. 1   **53.** 1   **55.** 1000   **57.** -800
59. a. $(x \cdot x \cdot x \cdot x)(x \cdot x \cdot x) = x^7$
b. $(5 \cdot 5 \cdot 5 \cdot 5)(5 \cdot 5 \cdot 5) = 5^7$ **61.** z^8 **63.** a^9

65. 4^{14} **67.** $\left(\dfrac{2}{3}\right)^4$ **69.** c^{14} **71.** x^{18}

73. a. $\dfrac{p \cdot p \cdot p \cdot p \cdot p \cdot p \cdot p \cdot p}{p \cdot p \cdot p} = p^5$

b. $\dfrac{8 \cdot 8 \cdot 8 \cdot 8 \cdot 8 \cdot 8 \cdot 8 \cdot 8}{8 \cdot 8 \cdot 8} = 8^5$

75. x^2 **77.** a^9 **79.** 7^7 **81.** 5^7 **83.** y **85.** h^4
87. 7^7 **89.** 10^9 **91.** $6x^7$ **93.** $40a^5b^5$ **95.** $13r^8s^5$
97. s^9t^{16} **99.** $-30v^8$ **101.** $16m^{20}n^{10}$ **103.** $2cd^4$

105. z^4 **107.** $\dfrac{25hjk^4}{12}$ **109.** $-8p^7q^9r^6$ **111.** $-3stu$

113. x^{2n+1} **115.** p^{2m+3} **117.** z **119.** r^3

Section 12.2 Practice Exercises, pp. 823–824

1. 4^9 **3.** a^{20} **5.** d^9 **7.** 7^6 **9.** When multiplying
expressions with the same base, add the exponents. When
dividing expressions with the same base, subtract the
exponents.   **11.** 5^{12} **13.** 12^6 **15.** y^{14} **17.** w^{25}
19. a^{36} **21.** y^{14} **23.** They are both equal to 2^6.
25. $2^{(2^4)} = 2^{16}$ $(2^2)^4 = 2^8$; the expression $2^{(2^4)}$ is greater than
$(2^2)^4$.   **27.** $25w^2$ **29.** $s^4r^4t^4$

31. $\dfrac{16}{r^4}$ **33.** $\dfrac{x^5}{y^5}$ **35.** $81a^4$ **37.** $-27a^3b^3c^3$

39. $-\dfrac{64}{x^3}$ **41.** $\dfrac{a^2}{b^2}$ **43.** $6^3u^6v^{12}$ or $216\,u^6v^{12}$

45. $5x^8y^4$ **47.** $-h^{28}$ **49.** m^{12} **51.** $\dfrac{4^5}{r^5s^{20}}$ or $\dfrac{1024}{r^5s^{20}}$

53. $\dfrac{3^5p^5}{q^{15}}$ or $\dfrac{243p^5}{q^{15}}$ **55.** y^{14} **57.** x^{31} **59.** $200a^{14}b^9$

61. $16p^8q^{16}$ **63.** $-m^{35}n^{15}$ **65.** $25a^{18}b^6$ **67.** $\dfrac{4c^2d^6}{9}$

69. $\dfrac{c^{27}d^{31}}{2}$ **71.** $-\dfrac{27a^9b^3}{c^6}$ **73.** $16b^{26}$ **75.** x^{2m}

77. $125a^{6n}$ **79.** $\dfrac{m^{2b}}{n^{3b}}$ **81.** $\dfrac{3^na^{3n}}{5^nb^{4n}}$

Section 12.3 Practice Exercises, pp. 831–833

3. c^9 **5.** y **7.** 3^6 or 729   **9.** $7^4w^{28}z^8$ or $2401w^{28}z^8$
11. a. 1   **b.** 1   **13.** 1   **15.** 1   **17.** -1 **19.** 1

21. 1   **23.** -7 **25. a.** $\dfrac{1}{t^5}$ **b.** $\dfrac{1}{t^5}$ **27.** $\dfrac{343}{8}$ **29.** 25

31. $\dfrac{1}{a^3}$ **33.** $\dfrac{1}{12}$ **35.** $\dfrac{1}{16b^2}$ **37.** $\dfrac{6}{x^2}$ **39.** $\dfrac{1}{64}$

41. $-\dfrac{3}{y^4}$ **43.** $-\dfrac{1}{t^3}$ **45.** a^5 **47.** $\dfrac{x^4}{x^{-6}} = x^{4-(-6)} = x^{10}$

49. $2a^{-3} = 2 \cdot \dfrac{1}{a^3} = \dfrac{2}{a^3}$ **51.** $\dfrac{1}{x^4}$ **53.** 1   **55.** y^4

57. $\dfrac{n^{27}}{m^{18}}$ **59.** $\dfrac{81k^{24}}{j^{20}}$ **61.** $\dfrac{1}{p^6}$ **63.** $\dfrac{1}{r^3}$ **65.** a^8

67. $\dfrac{1}{y^8}$ **69.** $\dfrac{1}{7^7}$ **71.** 1   **73.** $\dfrac{1}{a^4b^6}$ **75.** $\dfrac{1}{w^{21}}$

77. $\dfrac{1}{27}$ **79.** 1   **81.** $\dfrac{1}{64x^6}$ **83.** $-\dfrac{16y^4}{z^2}$ **85.** $-\dfrac{a^{12}}{6}$

87. $80c^{21}d^{24}$ **89.** $\dfrac{p^{27}}{8}$ **91.** $\dfrac{4d^{16}}{c^2}$ **93.** $\dfrac{9y^2}{2x}$

95. $\dfrac{9}{20}$ **97.** $\dfrac{9}{10}$ **99.** $\dfrac{5}{4}$ **101.** $\dfrac{10}{3}$

Section 12.4 Calculator Connections, p. 836

1.–2.

```
(5.2E6)*(4.6E-3)
            23920
(2.19E-8)*(7.84E
-4)
      1.71696E-11
```

3.–4.

```
(4.76E-5)/(2.38E
9)
           2E-14
(8.5E4)/(4.0E-1)
          212500
```

5.

```
((9.6E7)*(4.0E-3
))/(2.0E-2)
        19200000
```

6.

```
((5.0E-12)*(6.4E
-5))/((1.6E-8)*(
4.0E2))
            5E-11
```

Section 12.4 Practice Exercises, pp. 837–839

3. b^{13} **5.** 10^{13} **7.** $\dfrac{1}{y^5}$ **9.** $\dfrac{x^{20}}{y^{12}}$ **11.** w^4 **13.** 10^4

15. Move the decimal point between the 2 and 3 and
multiply by 10^{-10}; 2.3×10^{-10}.   **17.** 5×10^4
19. 2.08×10^5 **21.** 6.01×10^6 **23.** 8×10^{-6}
25. 1.25×10^{-4} **27.** 6.708×10^{-3} **29.** 1.7×10^{-24} g
31. $\$2.7 \times 10^{10}$ **33.** 6.8×10^7 gal; 1×10^2 miles
35. Move the decimal point nine places to the left;
0.000 000 0031.   **37.** 0.00005   **39.** 2800   **41.** 0.000603
43. 2,400,000   **45.** 0.019   **47.** 7032
49. 0.000 000 000 001 g   **51.** 1600 calories and 2800 calories
53. 5×10^4 **55.** 3.6×10^{11} **57.** 2.2×10^4
59. 2.25×10^{-13} **61.** 3.2×10^{14} **63.** 2.432×10^{-10}
65. 3×10^{13} **67.** 6×10^5 **69.** 1.38×10^1
71. 5×10^{-14} **73.** 3.75 in.   **75.** $\$2.97 \times 10^{10}$
77. a. 6.5×10^7 **b.** 2.3725×10^{10} days
c. 5.694×10^{11} hr   **d.** 2.04984×10^{15} sec

Chapter 12 Problem Recognition Exercises, p. 839

1. t^8 **2.** 2^8 or 256 **3.** y^5 **4.** p^6 **5.** $r^4 s^8$

6. $a^3 b^9 c^6$ **7.** w^6 **8.** $\dfrac{1}{m^{16}}$ **9.** $\dfrac{x^4 z^3}{y^7}$ **10.** $\dfrac{a^3 c^8}{b^6}$

11. 1.25×10^3 **12.** 1.24×10^5 **13.** 8×10^8

14. 6×10^{-9} **15.** p^{15} **16.** p^{15} **17.** $\dfrac{1}{v^2}$

18. $c^{50} d^{40}$ **19.** 3 **20.** -4 **21.** $\dfrac{b^9}{2^{15}}$ **22.** $\dfrac{81}{y^6}$

23. $\dfrac{16 y^4}{81 x^4}$ **24.** $\dfrac{25 d^6}{36 c^2}$ **25.** $3 a^7 b^5$ **26.** $64 x^7 y^{11}$

27. $\dfrac{y^4}{x^8}$ **28.** $\dfrac{1}{a^{10} b^{10}}$ **29.** $\dfrac{1}{t^2}$ **30.** $\dfrac{1}{p^7}$ **31.** $\dfrac{8 w^6 x^9}{27}$

32. $\dfrac{25 b^8}{16 c^6}$ **33.** $\dfrac{q^3 s}{r^2 t^5}$ **34.** $\dfrac{m^2 p^3 q}{n^3}$ **35.** $\dfrac{1}{y^{13}}$ **36.** w^{10}

37. $-\dfrac{1}{8 a^{18} b^6}$ **38.** $\dfrac{4 x^{18}}{9 y^{10}}$ **39.** $\dfrac{k^8}{5 h^6}$ **40.** $\dfrac{6 n^{10}}{m^{12}}$

Section 12.5 Practice Exercises, pp. 845–848

3. $\dfrac{45}{x^2}$ **5.** $\dfrac{2}{t^4}$ **7.** $\dfrac{1}{3^{12}}$

9. 4.0×10^{-2} is in scientific notation in which 10 is raised to the -2 power. 4^{-2} is not in scientific notation and 4 is being raised to the -2 power. **11.** $-7x^4 + 7x^2 + 9x + 6$
13. Binomial; $10; 2$ **15.** Monomial; $6; 2$
17. Binomial; $-1; 4$ **19.** Trinomial; $12; 4$
21. Monomial; $23; 0$ **23.** Monomial; $-32; 3$
25. The exponents on the x-factors are different.
27. $35 x^2 y$ **29.** $10 y$ **31.** $8 b^5 d^2 - 9 d$

33. $4 y^2 + y - 9$ **35.** $4a - 8c$ **37.** $a - \dfrac{1}{2} b - 2$

39. $\dfrac{4}{3} z^2 - \dfrac{5}{3}$ **41.** $7.9 t^3 - 3.4 t^2 + 6t - 4.2$ **43.** $-4h + 5$
45. $2 m^2 - 3m + 15$ **47.** $-3 v^3 - 5 v^2 - 10 v - 22$
49. $-8 a^3 b^2$ **51.** $-53 x^3$ **53.** $-5a - 3$ **55.** $16 k + 9$
57. $2s - 14$ **59.** $3 t^2 - 4t - 3$ **61.** $-2r - 3s + 3t$

63. $\dfrac{3}{4} x + \dfrac{1}{3} y - \dfrac{3}{10}$ **65.** $-\dfrac{2}{3} h^2 + \dfrac{3}{5} h - \dfrac{5}{2}$
67. $2.4 x^4 - 3.1 x^2 - 4.4 x - 6.7$
69. $4 b^3 + 12 b^2 - 5b - 12$ **71.** $-3 x^3 - 2 x^2 + 11 x - 31$
73. $4 y^3 + 2 y^2 + 2$ **75.** $3 a^2 - 3a + 5$
77. $9 a b^2 - 3 a b + 16 a^2 b$ **79.** $4 z^5 + z^4 + 9 z^3 - 3z - 2$
81. $2 x^4 + 11 x^3 - 3 x^2 + 8x - 4$ **83.** $-2 w^2 - 7w + 18$
85. $-p^2 q - 4 p q^2 + 3 p q$ **87.** 0 **89.** $-5 a b + 6 a b^2$
91. $11 y^2 - 10 y - 4$ **93.** For example, $x^3 + 6$
95. For example, $8 x^5$ **97.** For example, $-6 x^2 + 2x + 5$

Section 12.6 Practice Exercises, pp. 854–857

3. $-2 y^2$ **5.** $-8 y^4$ **7.** $8 u v w^2$ **9.** $7 u^2 v^2 w^4$
11. $-12 y$ **13.** $21 p$ **15.** $12 a^{14} b^8$ **17.** $-2 c^{10} d^{12}$
19. $16 p^2 q^2 - 24 p^2 q + 40 p q^2$ **21.** $-4 k^3 + 52 k^2 + 24 k$
23. $-45 p^3 q - 15 p^4 q^3 + 30 p q^2$ **25.** $y^2 - y - 90$
27. $m^2 - 14 m + 24$ **29.** $12 p^2 - 5p - 2$
31. $12 w^2 - 32 w + 16$ **33.** $p^2 - 14 p w + 33 w^2$
35. $12 x^2 + 28 x - 5$ **37.** $8 a^2 - 22 a + 9$
39. $9 t^2 - 18 t - 7$ **41.** $3 m^2 + 28 m n + 32 n^2$

43. $5 s^3 + 8 s^2 - 7s - 6$ **45.** $27 w^3 - 8$
47. $p^4 + 5 p^3 - 2 p^2 - 21 p + 5$
49. $6 a^3 - 23 a^2 + 38 a - 45$
51. $8 x^3 - 36 x^2 y + 54 x y^2 - 27 y^3$ **53.** $9 a^2 - 16 b^2$
55. $81 k^2 - 36$ **57.** $\dfrac{1}{4} - t^2$ **59.** $u^6 - 25 v^2$

61. $4 - 9 a^2$ **63.** $\dfrac{4}{9} - p^2$ **65.** $a^2 + 10 a + 25$
67. $x^2 - 2 x y + y^2$ **69.** $4 c^2 + 20 c + 25$
71. $9 t^4 - 24 s t^2 + 16 s^2$ **73.** $t^2 - 14 t + 49$
75. $16 q^2 + 24 q + 9$ **77. a.** 36 **b.** 20
c. $(a + b)^2 \neq a^2 + b^2$ in general. **79. a.** $9 x^2 + 6 x y + y^2$
b. $9 x^2 y^2$ **81.** $36 - y^2$ **83.** $49 q^2 - 42 q + 9$
85. $r^3 - 15 r^2 + 63 r - 49$ **87.** $3 t^3 - 12 t$
89. $81 w^2 - 16 z^2$ **91.** $25 s^2 - 30 s t + 9 t^2$

93. $10 a^2 - 13 a b + 4 b^2$ **95.** $s^2 + \dfrac{147}{5} s - 18$

97. $4 k^3 - 4 k^2 - 5k - 25$ **99.** $u^3 + u^2 - 10 u + 8$

101. $w^3 + w^2 + 4w + 12$ **103.** $\dfrac{4}{25} p^2 - \dfrac{4}{5} p q + q^2$

105. $4 v^4 + 48 v^3$ **107.** $4 h^2 - 7.29$ **109.** $5 k^6 - 19 k^3 + 18$
111. $6.25 y^2 + 5.5 y + 1.21$ **113.** $h^3 + 9 h^2 + 27 h + 27$
115. $8 a^3 - 48 a^2 + 96 a - 64$ **117.** $6 w^4 + w^3 - 15 w^2 - 11 w - 5$
119. $30 x^3 + 55 x^2 - 10 x$ **121.** $2 y^3 - y^2 - 15 y + 18$
123. $x + 6$ **125.** $k = 6$ or -6

Section 12.7 Practice Exercises, pp. 862–864

1. $6 z^5 - 10 z^4 - 4 z^3 - z^2 - 6$ **3.** $10 x^2 - 29 x y - 3 y^2$

5. $11 x - 2 y$ **7.** $y^2 - \dfrac{3}{4} y + \dfrac{1}{2}$ **9.** $a^3 + 27$

11. Use long division when the divisor is a polynomial with two or more terms. **13.** $5 t^2 + 6t$ **15.** $3 a^2 + 2a - 7$

17. $x^2 + 4x - 1$ **19.** $3 p^2 - p$ **21.** $1 + \dfrac{2}{m}$

23. $-2 y^2 + y - 3$ **25.** $x^2 - 6x - \dfrac{1}{4} + \dfrac{2}{x}$

27. $a - 1 + \dfrac{b}{a}$ **29.** $3t - 1 + \dfrac{3}{2t} - \dfrac{1}{2 t^2} + \dfrac{2}{t^3}$

31. a. $z + 2 + \dfrac{1}{z + 5}$ **33.** $t + 3 + \dfrac{2}{t + 1}$

35. $7b + 4$ **37.** $k - 6$ **39.** $2 p^2 + 3p - 4$

41. $k - 2 + \dfrac{-4}{k + 1}$ **43.** $2 x^2 - x + 6 + \dfrac{2}{2x - 3}$

45. $y^2 + 2y + 1 + \dfrac{2}{3y - 1}$ **47.** $a - 3 + \dfrac{18}{a + 3}$

49. $4 x^2 + 8x + 13$ **51.** $w^2 + 5w - 2 + \dfrac{1}{w^2 - 3}$

53. $n^2 + n - 6$ **55.** $x - 1 + \dfrac{-8}{5 x^2 + 5x + 1}$

57. Multiply $(x - 2)(x^2 + 4) = x^3 - 2 x^2 + 4x - 8$, which does not equal $x^3 - 8$. **59.** Monomial division; $3 a^2 + 4a$
61. Long division; $p + 2$ **63.** Long division;
$t^3 - 2 t^2 + 5t - 10 + \dfrac{4}{t + 2}$ **65.** Long division;
$w^2 + 3 + \dfrac{1}{w^2 - 2}$ **67.** Long division; $n^2 + 4n + 16$

69. Monomial division; $-3r + 4 - \dfrac{3}{r^2}$ **71.** $x + 1$

73. $x^3 + x^2 + x + 1$ **75.** $x + 1 + \dfrac{1}{x - 1}$

77. $x^3 + x^2 + x + 1 + \dfrac{1}{x - 1}$

Chapter 12 Problem Recognition Exercises, p. 865

1. $2x^3 - 8x^2 + 14x - 12$ **2.** $-3y^4 - 20y^2 - 32$
3. $x^2 - 1$ **4.** $4y^2 + 12$ **5.** $36y^2 - 84y + 49$
6. $9z^2 + 12z + 4$ **7.** $36y^2 - 49$ **8.** $9z^2 - 4$
9. $16x^2 + 8xy + y^2$ **10.** $4a^2 + 4ab + b^2$ **11.** $16x^2y^2$
12. $4a^2b^2$ **13.** $-x^2 - 3x + 4$ **14.** $5m^2 - 4m + 1$
15. $-7m^2 - 16m$ **16.** $-4n^5 + n^4 + 6n^2 - 7n + 2$
17. $8x^2 + 16x + 34 + \dfrac{74}{x - 2}$
18. $-4x^2 - 10x - 30 + \dfrac{-95}{x - 3}$
19. $6x^3 + 5x^2y - 6xy^2 + y^3$ **20.** $6a^3 - a^2b + 5ab^2 + 2b^3$
21. $x^3 + y^6$ **22.** $m^6 + 1$ **23.** $4b$ **24.** $-12z$
25. $a^4 - 4b^2$ **26.** $y^6 - 36z^2$ **27.** $64u^2 + 48uv + 9v^2$
28. $4p^2 - 4pt + t^2$ **29.** $4p + 4 + \dfrac{-2}{2p - 1}$
30. $2v - 7 + \dfrac{29}{2v + 3}$ **31.** $4x^2y^2$ **32.** $-9pq$
33. $10a^2 - 57a + 54$ **34.** $28a^2 - 17a - 3$
35. $\dfrac{9}{49}x^2 - \dfrac{1}{4}$ **36.** $\dfrac{4}{25}y^2 - \dfrac{16}{9}$
37. $-\dfrac{11}{9}x^3 + \dfrac{5}{9}x^2 - \dfrac{1}{2}x - 4$ **38.** $-\dfrac{13}{10}y^2 - \dfrac{9}{10}y + \dfrac{4}{15}$
39. $1.3x^2 - 0.3x - 0.5$ **40.** $5w^3 - 4.1w^2 + 2.8w - 1.2$

Chapter 12 Review Exercises, pp. 870–873

1. Base: 5; exponent: 3   **3.** Base: -2; exponent: 0
5. a. 36   **b.** 36   **c.** -36 **7.** 5^{13} **9.** x^9 **11.** 10^3
13. b^8 **15.** k **17.** 2^8 **19.** $-12x^3y^5$
21. Exponents are added only when multiplying factors with the same base. In such a case, the base does not change.
23. 7^{12} **25.** p^{18} **27.** $\dfrac{a^2}{b^2}$ **29.** $\dfrac{5^2}{c^4 d^{10}}$ **31.** $2^4 a^4 b^8$
33. $-\dfrac{3^3 x^9}{5^3 y^6 z^3}$ **35.** a^{11} **37.** $4h^{14}$ **39.** $\dfrac{x^6 y^2}{4}$ **41.** 1
43. -1 **45.** 2   **47.** $\dfrac{1}{z^5}$ **49.** $\dfrac{1}{36a^2}$ **51.** $\dfrac{17}{16}$
53. $\dfrac{1}{t^8}$ **55.** $\dfrac{2y^7}{x^6}$ **57.** $\dfrac{n^{16}}{16m^8}$ **59.** $\dfrac{k^{21}}{5}$ **61.** $\dfrac{1}{2}$
63. a. 9.74×10^7 **b.** 4.2×10^{-3} in.   **65.** 9.43×10^5
67. 2.5×10^8 **69.** $\approx 9.5367 \times 10^{13}$. This number is too big to fit on most calculator displays.
71. a. $\approx 5.84 \times 10^8$ mi   **b.** $\approx 6.67 \times 10^4$ mph
73. a. Trinomial   **b.** 4   **c.** 7   **75.** $7x - 3$
77. $14a^2 - 2a - 6$ **79.** $10w^4 + 2w^3 - 7w + 4$
81. $-2x^2 - 9x - 6$ **83.** For example, $-5x^2 + 2x - 4$
85. $6w + 6$ **87.** $18a^8 b^4$ **89.** $-2x^3 - 10x^2 + 6x$
91. $20t^2 + 3t - 2$ **93.** $2a^2 + 4a - 30$
95. $b^2 - 8b + 16$ **97.** $-2w^3 - 5w^2 - 5w + 4$

99. $12a^3 + 11a^2 - 13a - 10$ **101.** $\dfrac{1}{9}r^8 - s^4$
103. $2h^5 + h^4 - h^3 + h^2 - h + 3$ **105.** $4y^2 - 2y$
107. $-3x^2 + 2x - 1$ **109.** $x + 2$
111. $p - 3 + \dfrac{5}{2p + 7}$ **113.** $b^2 + 5b + 25$
115. $y^2 - 4y + 2 + \dfrac{9y - 4}{y^2 + 3}$ **117.** $w^2 + w - 1$

Chapter 12 Test, pp. 873–874

1. $\dfrac{(3 \cdot 3 \cdot 3 \cdot 3) \cdot (3 \cdot 3 \cdot 3)}{3 \cdot 3 \cdot 3 \cdot 3 \cdot 3 \cdot 3} = 3$ **2.** 9^6 **3.** q^8
4. $27a^6 b^3$ **5.** $\dfrac{16x^4}{y^{12}}$ **6.** 1   **7.** $\dfrac{1}{c^3}$ **8.** 14
9. $49s^{18}t$ **10.** $\dfrac{4}{b^{12}}$ **11.** $\dfrac{16a^{12}}{9b^6}$
12. a. 4.3×10^{10} **b.** $0.000\,0056$ **13. a.** $2.4192 \times 10^8\,\text{m}^3$
b. $8.83008 \times 10^{10}\,\text{m}^3$ **14.** $5x^3 - 7x^2 + 4x + 11$ **a.** 3
b. 5   **15.** $24w^2 - 3w - 4$ **16.** $15x^3 - 7x^2 - 2x + 1$
17. $-10x^5 - 2x^4 + 30x^3$ **18.** $8a^2 - 10a + 3$
19. $4y^3 - 25y^2 + 37y - 15$ **20.** $4 - 9b^2$
21. $25z^2 - 60z + 36$ **22.** $15x^2 - x - 6$
23. $y^3 - 11y^2 + 32y - 12$ **24.** Perimeter: $12x - 2$;
area: $5x^2 - 13x - 6$ **25.** $-3x^6 + \dfrac{x^4}{4} - 2x$ **26.** $2y - 7$
27. $w^2 - 4w + 5 + \dfrac{-10}{2w + 3}$ **28.** $3x^2 + x - 12 + \dfrac{15}{x^2 + 4}$

Chapters 1–12 Cumulative Review Exercises, pp. 874–875

1. Undefined   **2.** $2 \cdot 3 \cdot 5 \cdot 11$ **3.** $5^2 - \sqrt{4}$; 23
4. $\dfrac{28}{3}$ **5.** All real numbers   **6.** 37.68 m
7. $113.04\,\text{m}^2$ **8.** Quadrant III   **9.** y-axis
10.

(graph of $y = -2x + 8$)

11. The measures are $31°, 54°, 95°$.   **12.** $-\dfrac{1}{3}$
13. a. 12 in.   **b.** 19.5 in.   **c.** 5.5 hr   **14.** $(-3, 4)$
15. $[-5, \infty)$
16. $-2y^2 - 13yz - 15z^2$ **17.** $16t^2 - 24t + 9$
18. $-4a^3 b^2 + 2ab - 1$ **19.** $4m^2 + 8m + 11 + \dfrac{24}{m - 2}$
20. $\dfrac{c^2}{16d^4}$

Chapter 13
Chapter Opener Puzzle

5	2	6	^{A}1	3	^{B}4
3	^{C}1	4	2	^{D}6	^{E}5
^{F}4	6	1	5	^{G}2	^{H}3
2	3	5	4	1	6
1	4	3	6	5	2
6	5	2	3	4	1

Section 13.1 Practice Exercises, pp. 885–887

3. 7 **5.** 6 **7.** y **9.** $4w^2z$ **11.** $2xy^4z^2$
13. $(x - y)$ **15. a.** $3x - 6y$ **b.** $3(x - 2y)$
17. $4(p + 3)$ **19.** $5(c^2 - 2c + 3)$ **21.** $x^3(x^2 + 1)$
23. $t(t^3 - 4 + 8t)$ **25.** $2ab(1 + 2a^2)$ **27.** $19x^2y(2 - y^3)$
29. $6xy^5(x^2 - 3y^4z)$ **31.** The expression is prime because
it is not factorable. **33.** $7pq^2(6p^2 + 2 - p^3q^2)$
35. $t^2(t^3 + 2rt - 3t^2 + 4r^2)$ **37. a.** $-2x(x^2 + 2x - 4)$
b. $2x(-x^2 - 2x + 4)$ **39.** $-1(8t^2 + 9t + 2)$
41. $-15p^2(p + 2)$ **43.** $-q(q^3 - 2q + 9)$
45. $-1(7x + 6y + 2z)$ **47.** $(a + 6)(13 - 4b)$
49. $(w^2 - 2)(8v + 1)$ **51.** $7x(x + 3)^2$
53. $(2a - b)(4a + 3c)$ **55.** $(q + p)(3 + r)$
57. $(2x + 1)(3x + 2)$ **59.** $(t + 3)(2t - 5)$
61. $(3y - 1)(2y - 3)$ **63.** $(b + 1)(b^3 - 4)$
65. $(j^2 + 5)(3k + 1)$ **67.** $(2x^6 + 1)(7w^6 - 1)$
69. $(y + x)(a + b)$ **71.** $(vw + 1)(w - 3)$
73. $5x(x^2 + y^2)(3x + 2y)$ **75.** $4b(a - b)(x - 1)$
77. $6t(t - 3)(s - t^2)$ **79.** $P = 2(l + w)$
81. $S = 2\pi r(r + h)$ **83.** $\frac{1}{7}(x^2 + 3x - 5)$

85. $\frac{1}{4}(5w^2 + 3w + 9)$ **87.** For example, $6x^2 + 9x$

89. For example, $16p^4q^2 + 8p^3q - 4p^2q$

Section 13.2 Practice Exercises, pp. 891–893

3. $4xy^5(x^2y^2 - 3x^3 + 2y^3)$ **5.** $(a + 2b)(x - 5)$
7. $(x + 8)(x + 2)$ **9.** $(z - 9)(z - 2)$
11. $(z - 6)(z + 3)$ **13.** $(p - 8)(p + 5)$
15. $(t + 10)(t - 4)$ **17.** Prime **19.** $(n + 4)^2$
21. a **23.** c **25.** They are both correct because
multiplication of polynomials is a commutative operation.
27. The expressions are equal, and both are correct.
29. Descending order **31.** $(x - 15)(x + 2)$
33. $(w - 13)(w - 5)$ **35.** $(t + 18)(t + 4)$
37. $3(x - 12)(x + 2)$ **39.** $8p(p - 1)(p - 4)$
41. $y^2z^2(y - 6)(y - 6)$ or $y^2z^2(y - 6)^2$
43. $-(x - 4)(x - 6)$ **45.** $-(m + 2)(m - 3)$
47. $-2(c + 2)(c + 1)$ **49.** $xy^3(x - 4)(x - 15)$
51. $12(p - 7)(p - 1)$ **53.** $-2(m - 10)(m - 1)$
55. $(c + 5d)(c + d)$ **57.** $(a - 2b)(a - 7b)$ **59.** Prime

61. $(q - 7)(q + 9)$ **63.** $(x + 10)^2$ **65.** $(t + 20)(t - 2)$
67. The student forgot to factor out the GCF before factoring
the trinomial further. The polynomial is not factored
completely, because $(2x - 4)$ has a common factor of 2.
69. $x^2 + 9x - 52$ **71.** $(x^2 + 1)(x^2 + 9)$
73. $(w^2 + 5)(w^2 - 3)$ **75.** $7, 5, -7, -5$
77. For example: $c = -16$

Section 13.3 Practice Exercises, pp. 900–902

3. $3ab(7ab + 4b - 5a)$ **5.** $(n - 1)(m - 2)$
7. $6(a - 7)(a + 2)$ **9.** a **11.** b
13. $(2y + 1)(y - 2)$ **15.** $(3n + 1)(n + 4)$
17. $(5x + 1)(x - 3)$ **19.** $(4c + 1)(3c - 2)$
21. $(10w - 3)(w + 4)$ **23.** $(3q + 2)(2q - 3)$
25. Prime **27.** $(5m + 2)(5m - 4)$
29. $(6y - 5x)(y + 4x)$ **31.** $2(m + 4)(m - 10)$
33. $y^3(2y + 1)(y + 6)$ **35.** $-(a + 17)(a - 2)$
37. $10(4m + p)(2m - 3p)$ **39.** $(x^2 + 1)(x^2 + 9)$
41. $(w^2 + 5)(w^2 - 3)$ **43.** $(2x^2 + 3)(x^2 - 5)$
45. $-2(z - 9)(z - 1)$ **47.** $(q - 7)(q - 6)$
49. $(2t + 3)(3t - 1)$ **51.** $(2m - 5)^2$ **53.** Prime
55. $(2x - 5y)(3x - 2y)$ **57.** $(4m + 5n)(3m - n)$
59. $5(3r + 2)(2r - 1)$ **61.** Prime **63.** $(2t - 5)(5t + 1)$
65. $(7w - 4)(2w + 3)$ **67.** $(x + 9)(x - 2)$
69. $(a - 12)(a + 2)$ **71.** $(r + 8)(r - 3)$
73. $(x + 5y)(x + 4y)$ **75.** Prime
77. $(a + 20b)(a + b)$ **79.** $(t - 7)(t - 3)$
81. $d(5d^2 + 3d - 10)$ **83.** $4b(b - 5)(b + 4)$
85. $y^2(x - 3)(x - 10)$ **87.** $-2u(2u + 5)(3u - 2)$
89. $(2x^2 + 3)(4x^2 + 1)$ **91.** $(5z^2 - 3)(2z^2 + 3)$
93. a. $(x - 12)(x + 2)$ **b.** $(x - 6)(x - 4)$
95. a. $(x - 6)(x + 1)$ **b.** $(x - 2)(x - 3)$

Section 13.4 Practice Exercises, pp. 906–907

3. $(y + 5)(8 + 9y)$ **5.** $12, 1$ **7.** $-8, -1$ **9.** $5, -4$
11. $9, -2$ **13.** $(x + 4)(3x + 1)$ **15.** $(w - 2)(4w - 1)$
17. $(m + 3)(2m - 1)$ **19.** $(4k + 3)(2k - 3)$
21. $(2k - 5)^2$ **23.** Prime **25.** $(3z - 5)(3z - 2)$
27. $2(7y + 4)(y + 3)$ **29.** $(6y - 5z)(2y + 3z)$
31. $-(3w - 5)(5w + 1)$ **33.** $-4(x - y)(3x - 2y)$
35. $6y(y + 1)(3y + 7)$ **37.** $(a^2 + 2)(a^2 + 3)$
39. $(3x^2 - 5)(2x^2 + 3)$ **41.** $(8p^2 - 3)(p^2 + 5)$
43. $(5p - 1)(4p - 3)$ **45.** $(3u - 2v)(2u - 5v)$
47. $(4a + 5b)(3a - b)$ **49.** $(h + 7k)(3h - 2k)$
51. Prime **53.** $(8w + 1)(2w + 1)$ **55.** $(q - 1)^2$
57. $-2(a - 1)(a - 9)$ **59.** $(m + 3)(m - 2)$
61. $2(10y + 1)(y - 4)$ **63.** $w^3(w - 4)(w - 7)$
65. $r(4r - 5)(r + 2)$ **67.** $4q(q - 5)(q + 4)$
69. $b^2(a + 10)(a + 3)$ **71.** $-1(m - 2)(m + 17)$
73. $-2(h - 9)(h - 5)$ **75.** $(m^2 + 3)(m^2 + 7)$
77. No. $(5x - 10)$ contains a common factor of 5.

Section 13.5 Practice Exercises, pp. 913–914

3. $(3x - 1)(2x - 5)$ **5.** $5xy^5(3x - 2y)$
7. $(x + b)(a - 6)$ **9.** $(y + 10)(y - 4)$
11. $x^2 - 25$ **13.** $4p^2 - 9q^2$ **15.** $(x - 6)(x + 6)$
17. $3(w + 10)(w - 10)$ **19.** $(2a - 11b)(2a + 11b)$
21. $(7m - 4n)(7m + 4n)$ **23.** Prime
25. $(y + 2z)(y - 2z)$ **27.** $(a - b^2)(a + b^2)$
29. $(5pq - 1)(5pq + 1)$ **31.** $(c^3 - 5)(c^3 + 5)$

33. $2(5 - 4t)(5 + 4t)$ **35.** $(z + 2)(z - 2)(z^2 + 4)$

37. $\left(a + \dfrac{1}{3}\right)\left(a - \dfrac{1}{3}\right)\left(a^2 + \dfrac{1}{9}\right)$ **39.** $(x + 3)(x - 3)(x + 5)$

41. $(c + 5)(c - 5)(c - 1)$ **43.** $(2 + y)(x + 3)(x - 3)$

45. $(x + 2)(x - 2)(y + 3)(y - 3)$ **47.** $9x^2 + 30x + 25$

49. a. $x^2 + 4x + 4$ is a perfect square trinomial.

b. $x^2 + 4x + 4 = (x + 2)^2$; $x^2 + 5x + 4 = (x + 1)(x + 4)$

51. $(x + 9)^2$ **53.** $(5z - 2)^2$ **55.** $(7a + 3b)^2$

57. $(y - 1)^2$ **59.** $5(4z + 3w)^2$ **61.** $(3y + 25)(3y + 1)$

63. $2(a - 5)^2$ **65.** Prime **67.** $(2x + y)^2$

69. $y(y - 6)$ **71.** $(2p - 5)(2p + 7)$

73. $(-t + 2)(t + 6)$ or $-(t - 2)(t + 6)$

75. $(-2b + 15)(2b + 5)$ or $-(2b - 15)(2b + 5)$

77. a. $a^2 - b^2$ **b.** $(a - b)(a + b)$

Chapter 13 Problem Recognition Exercises, pp. 914–916

1. A prime factor cannot be factored further. **2.** Factor out the GCF. **3.** Look for a difference of squares: $a^2 - b^2$.

4. Grouping **5. a.** Difference of squares

b. $2(a - 9)(a + 9)$ **6. a.** Nonperfect square trinomial

b. $(y + 3)(y + 1)$ **7. a.** None of these **b.** $6w(w - 1)$

8. a. Difference of squares **b.** $(2z + 3)(2z - 3)(4z^2 + 9)$

9. a. Nonperfect square trinomial **b.** $(3t + 1)(t + 4)$

10. a. Four terms-grouping **b.** $(3c + d)(a - b)$

11. a. Nonperfect square trinomial **b.** $(7p - 1)(p - 4)$

12. a. Nonperfect square trinomial **b.** $3(q - 4)(q + 1)$

13. a. Perfect square trinomial **b.** $-2(x - 2)^2$

14. a. None of these **b.** $6a(3a + 2)$

15. a. Difference of squares **b.** $4(t - 5)(t + 5)$

16. a. Nonperfect square trinomial **b.** $(4t + 1)(t - 8)$

17. a. Nonperfect square trinomial **b.** $10(c^2 + c + 1)$

18. a. Four terms-grouping **b.** $(w - 5)(2x + 3y)$

19. a. Difference of squares **b.** $(2q - 3)(2q + 3)$

20. a. Perfect square trinomial **b.** $(8 + k)^2$

21. a. Four terms-grouping **b.** $(t + 6)(s^2 + 5)$

22. a. Four terms-grouping **b.** $(x + 1)(2x - y)$

23. a. Nonperfect square trinomial **b.** Prime

24. a. Nonperfect square trinomial **b.** Prime

25. a. Perfect square trinomial **b.** $(a + 1)^2$

26. a. Perfect square trinomial **b.** $(b + 5)^2$

27. a. Nonperfect square trinomial **b.** $-1(t + 8)(t - 4)$

28. a. Nonperfect square trinomial **b.** $-p(p + 4)(p + 1)$

29. a. Difference of squares **b.** $(xy - 7)(xy + 7)$

30. a. Nonperfect square trinomial **b.** $3(2x + 3)(x - 5)$

31. a. Nonperfect square trinomial **b.** $2(5y - 1)(2y - 1)$

32. a. None of these **b.** $abc^2(5ac - 7)$

33. a. Difference of squares **b.** $2(2a - 5)(2a + 5)$

34. a. Nonperfect square trinomial **b.** $(t + 9)(t - 7)$

35. a. Nonperfect square trinomial **b.** $(b + 10)(b - 8)$

36. a. Four terms-grouping **b.** $(b + y)(a - b)$

37. a. None of these **b.** $3x^2y^4(2x + y)$

38. a. Nonperfect square trinomial **b.** $(7u - 2v)(2u - v)$

39. a. Nonperfect square trinomial **b.** Prime

40. a. Nonperfect square trinomial **b.** $2(2q^2 - 4q - 3)$

41. a. Nonperfect square trinomial **b.** $3(3w^2 + w - 5)$

42. a. Sum of squares **b.** Prime

43. a. Perfect square trinomial **b.** $5(b - 3)^2$

44. a. Nonperfect square trinomial **b.** $(3r + 1)(2r + 3)$

45. a. Nonperfect square trinomial **b.** $(2s - 3)(2s + 5)$

46. a. Difference of squares **b.** $(2a - 1)(2a + 1)(4a^2 + 1)$

47. a. Four terms-grouping **b.** $(p + c)(p - 3)(p + 3)$

48. a. Perfect square trinomial **b.** $(9u - 5v)^2$

49. a. Sum of squares **b.** $4(x^2 + 4)$

50. a. Nonperfect square trinomial **b.** $(x - 6)(x + 1)$

51. a. Nonperfect square trinomial **b.** Prime

52. a. a. Four terms-grouping **b.** $2(x - 3y)(a + 2b)$

53. a. Nonperfect square trinomial

b. $m(4m + 1)(2m - 3)$ **54. a.** Nonperfect square trinomial **b.** $x^2y(3x + 5)(7x + 2)$

55. a. Difference of squares **b.** $2(m^2 - 8)(m^2 + 8)$

56. a. Four terms-grouping **b.** $(4v - 3)(2u + 3)$

57. a. Four terms-grouping **b.** $(t - 5)(4t + s)$

58. a. Perfect square trinomial **b.** $3(2x - 1)^2$

59. a. Perfect square trinomial **b.** $(p + q)^2$

60. a. Nonperfect square trinomial **b.** $n(2n - 1)(3n + 4)$

61. a. Nonperfect square trinomial **b.** $k(2k - 1)(2k + 3)$

62. a. Difference of squares **b.** $(8 - y)(8 + y)$

63. a. Difference of squares **b.** $b(6 - b)(6 + b)$

64. a. Nonperfect square trinomial **b.** Prime

65. a. Nonperfect square trinomial **b.** $(y + 4)(y + 2)$

66. a. Nonperfect square trinomial **b.** $(c^2 - 10)(c^2 - 2)$

Section 13.6 Practice Exercises, pp. 920–922

3. $4(b - 5)(b - 6)$ **5.** $(3x - 2)(x + 4)$ **7.** $4(x^2 + 4y^2)$

9. Neither **11.** Quadratic **13.** Linear **15.** $-3, 1$

17. $\dfrac{7}{2}, -\dfrac{7}{2}$ **19.** -5 **21.** $0, \dfrac{1}{5}$ **23.** The polynomial must be factored completely. **25.** $5, -3$ **27.** $-12, 2$

29. $4, -\dfrac{1}{2}$ **31.** $\dfrac{2}{3}, -\dfrac{2}{3}$ **33.** $6, 8$ **35.** $0, -\dfrac{3}{2}, 4$

37. $-\dfrac{1}{3}, 3, -6$ **39.** $0, 4, -\dfrac{3}{2}$ **41.** $0, -\dfrac{9}{2}, 11$

43. $0, 4, -4$ **45.** $-6, 0$ **47.** $\dfrac{3}{4}, -\dfrac{3}{4}$ **49.** $0, -5, -2$

51. $-\dfrac{14}{3}$ **53.** $5, 3$ **55.** $0, -2$ **57.** -3 **59.** $-3, 1$

61. $\dfrac{3}{2}$ **63.** $0, \dfrac{1}{3}$ **65.** $0, 2$ **67.** $3, -2, 2$ **69.** $-5, 4$

71. $-5, -1$

Chapter 13 Problem Recognition Exercises, p. 922

1. a. $(x + 7)(x - 1)$ **b.** $-7, 1$ **2. a.** $(c + 6)(c + 2)$

b. $-6, -2$ **3. a.** $(2y + 1)(y + 3)$ **b.** $-\dfrac{1}{2}, -3$

4. a. $(3x - 5)(x - 1)$ **b.** $\dfrac{5}{3}, 1$ **5. a.** $\dfrac{4}{5}, -1$

b. $(5q - 4)(q + 1)$ **6. a.** $-\dfrac{1}{3}, \dfrac{3}{2}$ **b.** $(3a + 1)(2a - 3)$

7. a. $(2b + 9)(2b - 9)$ **b.** $-\dfrac{9}{2}, \dfrac{9}{2}$

8. a. $(6t + 7)(6t - 7)$ **b.** $-\dfrac{7}{6}, \dfrac{7}{6}$

9. a. $-\dfrac{3}{2}, -\dfrac{1}{2}$ **b.** $2(2x + 3)(2x + 1)$

10. a. $-\dfrac{4}{3}, -2$ **b.** $4(3y + 4)(y + 2)$

11. a. $x(x - 10)(x + 2)$ **b.** $0, 10, -2$
12. a. $k(k + 7)(k - 2)$ **b.** $0, -7, 2$
13. a. $-1, 3, -3$ **b.** $(b + 1)(b - 3)(b + 3)$
14. a. $8, -2, 2$ **b.** $(x - 8)(x + 2)(x - 2)$
15. $(s - 3)(2s + r)$ **16.** $(2t + 1)(3t + 5u)$
17. $-\dfrac{1}{2}, 0, \dfrac{1}{2}$ **18.** $-5, 0, 5$ **19.** $0, 1$ **20.** $-3, 0$
21. $\dfrac{1}{3}$ **22.** $-\dfrac{7}{12}$ **23.** $-\dfrac{7}{5}, 1$ **24.** $-6, -\dfrac{1}{4}$
25. $-\dfrac{2}{3}, -5$ **26.** $-1, -\dfrac{1}{2}$ **27.** 3
28. 0 **29.** $1, 6$ **30.** $-2, -12$

Section 13.7 Practice Exercises, pp. 927–929

1. $-\dfrac{1}{6}, -4$ **3.** $\dfrac{5}{7}, -\dfrac{5}{7}$ **5.** $6, -1$ **7.** 9
9. The numbers are 7 and -7. **11.** The numbers are 10 and -4. **13.** The numbers are -9 and -7, or 7 and 9.
15. The numbers are 5 and 6, or -1 and 0. **17.** The room is 15 yd by 20 yd. **19. a.** The slab is 7 m by 4 m.
b. 22 m **21.** The base is 7 ft, and the height is 4 ft.
23. 3 sec **25.** 0 sec and 1.5 sec
27.

29. $c = 25$ cm **31.** $a = 15$ in.
33. The brace is 20 in. long. **35.** The kite is 19 yd high.
37. The bottom of the ladder is 8 ft from the house. The distance from the top of the ladder to the ground is 15 ft.
39. The hypotenuse is 10 m.

Chapter 13 Review Exercises, pp. 935–936

1. $3a^2b$ **3.** $2c(3c - 5)$ **5.** $2x(3x + x^3 - 4)$
7. $t(-t + 5)$ or $-t(t - 5)$ **9.** $(b + 2)(3b - 7)$
11. $(w + 2)(7w + b)$ **13.** $3(4y - 3)(5y - 1)$
15. $(x - 3)(x - 7)$ **17.** $(z - 12)(z + 6)$
19. $3w(p + 10)(p + 2)$ **21.** $-(t - 8)(t - 2)$
23. $(a + b)(a + 11b)$ **25.** Different **27.** Both positive **29.** $(2y + 3)(y - 4)$ **31.** $(2z + 5)(5z + 2)$
33. Prime **35.** $10(w - 9)(w + 3)$ **37.** $(3c - 5d)^2$
39. $(v^2 + 1)(v^2 - 3)$ **41.** The trinomials in Exercises 37 and 38. **43.** $-3, -5$ **45.** $(y + 3)(4y + 1)$
47. $x(x + 5)(4x - 3)$ **49.** $(p - 3q)(p - 5q)$
51. $10(4s - 5)(s + 2)$ **53.** $2z^4(z + 7)(z - 3)$
55. $(3p + 2)(2p + 5)$ **57.** $(3w - z)^2$
59. $(a - b)(a + b)$ **61.** $(a - 7)(a + 7)$
63. $(10 - 9t)(10 + 9t)$ **65.** Prime **67.** $(y + 6)^2$
69. $(3a - 2)^2$ **71.** $-3(v + 2)^2$ **73.** $2(c^2 - 3)(c^2 + 3)$
75. $(p + 3)(p - 4)(p + 4)$ **77.** $(x - 3)(2x + 1) = 0$ can be solved directly by the zero product rule because it is a product of factors set equal to zero.

79. $9, \dfrac{1}{2}$ **81.** $0, 7, \dfrac{9}{4}$ **83.** $-\dfrac{1}{4}, 6$ **85.** $5, -5$
87. $4, 2$ **89.** $-\dfrac{2}{3}$ **91.** $\dfrac{11}{2}, -12$ **93.** $0, 2, -2$
95. The ball is at ground level at 0 and 1 sec.
97. The legs are 6 ft and 8 ft; the hypotenuse is 10 ft.
99. The numbers are 29 and 30, or -2 and -1.

Chapter 13 Test, p. 937

1. $3x(5x^3 - 1 + 2x^2)$ **2.** $(a - 5)(7 - a)$
3. $(6w - 1)(w - 7)$ **4.** $(13 - p)(13 + p)$
5. $(q - 8)^2$ **6.** $(a + 4)(a + 8)$ **7.** $(x + 7)(x - 6)$
8. $(2y - 1)(y - 8)$ **9.** $(2z + 1)(3z + 8)$
10. $(3t - 10)(3t + 10)$ **11.** $(v + 9)(v - 9)$
12. $3(a + 6b)(a + 3b)$ **13.** $(c - 1)(c + 1)(c^2 + 1)$
14. $(y - 7)(x + 3)$ **15.** Prime **16.** $-10(u - 2)(u - 1)$
17. $3(2t - 5)(2t + 5)$ **18.** $5(y - 5)^2$ **19.** $7q(3q + 2)$
20. $(2x + 1)(x - 2)(x + 2)$ **21.** $(mn - 9)(mn + 9)$
22. $16(a - 2b)(a + 2b)$ **23.** $3y(x - 4)(x + 2)$
24. $\dfrac{3}{2}, -5$ **25.** $0, 7$ **26.** $8, -2$ **27.** $\dfrac{1}{5}, -1$
28. $3, -3, -10$ **29.** The tennis court is 12 yd by 26 yd.
30. The two integers are 5 and 7, or -5 and -7.
31. The base is 12 in., and the height is 7 in.
32. The shorter leg is 5 ft.

Chapters 1–13 Cumulative Review Exercises, p. 938

1. $\dfrac{7}{5}$ **2.** -3 **3.** $y = \dfrac{3}{2}x - 4$
4. 1200 students were surveyed.
5. $[-4, \infty)$ $\xrightarrow{}$ **6. a.** Yes **b.** 1
c. $(0, 4)$ **d.** $(-4, 0)$ **e.**

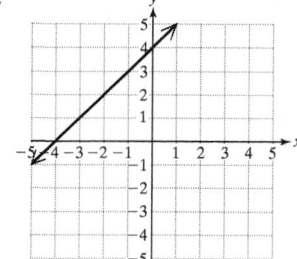

7. a. Vertical line **b.** Undefined **c.** $(5, 0)$ **d.** Does not exist **8.** $y = 3x + 14$ **9.** $(5, 2)$
10. $-\dfrac{7}{2}y^2 - 5y - 14$ **11.** $8p^3 - 22p^2 + 13p + 3$
12. $4w^2 - 28w + 49$ **13.** $r^3 + 5r^2 + 15r + 40 + \dfrac{121}{r - 3}$
14. c^4 **15.** 1.6×10^3 **16.** $(w - 2)(w + 2)(w^2 + 4)$
17. $(a + 5b)(2x - 3y)$ **18.** $(2x - 5)(2x + 1)$
19. $5(y^2 + 4)$ **20.** $0, \dfrac{1}{2}, -5$

Chapter 14

Chapter Opener Puzzle

$$\underset{4}{\underline{p}}\ \underset{1}{\underline{r}}\ \underset{2}{\underline{o}}\ \underline{c}\ \underset{1}{\underline{r}}\ \underset{5}{\underline{a}}\ \underline{s}\ \underset{3}{\underline{t}}\ \underline{i}\ \underline{n}\ \underset{5}{\underline{a}}\ \underset{3}{\underline{t}}\ \underline{i}\ \underset{2}{\underline{o}}\ \underline{n}$$

Section 14.1 Practice Exercises, pp. 947–949

3. a. A number $\dfrac{p}{q}$, where p and q are integers and $q \neq 0$

b. An expression $\dfrac{p}{q}$, where p and q are polynomials and

$q \neq 0$ **5.** $-\dfrac{1}{8}$ **7.** $-\dfrac{1}{2}$ **9.** Undefined

11. a. $3\frac{1}{5}$ hr or 3.2 hr   **b.** $1\frac{3}{4}$ hr or 1.75 hr

13. $k = -2$ **15.** $x = \dfrac{5}{2}, x = -8$ **17.** $b = -2, b = -3$

19. There are no restricted values.   **21.** There are no restricted values.   **23.** $t = 0$

25. For example: $\dfrac{1}{x - 2}$ **27.** For example: $\dfrac{1}{(x + 3)(x - 7)}$

29. a. $\dfrac{2}{5}$ **b.** $\dfrac{2}{5}$ **31. a.** Undefined   **b.** Undefined

33. a. $y = -2$ **b.** $\dfrac{1}{2}$ **35. a.** $t = -1$ **b.** $t - 1$

37. a. $w = 0, w = \frac{5}{3}$ **b.** $\dfrac{1}{3w - 5}$ **39. a.** $x = -\frac{2}{3}$

b. $\dfrac{3x - 2}{2}$ **41. a.** $a = -3, a = 2$ **b.** $\dfrac{a + 5}{a + 3}$ **43.** $\dfrac{b}{3}$

45. $\dfrac{3t^2}{2}$ **47.** $-\dfrac{3xy}{z^2}$ **49.** $\dfrac{1}{2}$ **51.** $\dfrac{p - 3}{p + 4}$

53. $\dfrac{1}{4(m - 11)}$ **55.** $\dfrac{2x + 1}{4x^2}$ **57.** $\dfrac{1}{4a - 5}$

59. $\dfrac{4}{w + 2}$ **61.** $\dfrac{x - 2}{3(y + 2)}$ **63.** $\dfrac{2}{x - 5}$

65. $a + 7$ **67.** Cannot simplify   **69.** $\dfrac{y + 3}{2y - 5}$

71. $\dfrac{3x - 2}{x + 4}$ **73.** $\dfrac{5}{(q + 1)(q - 1)}$ **75.** $\dfrac{c - d}{2c + d}$

77. $\dfrac{1}{t(t - 5)}$ **79.** $\dfrac{7p - 2q}{2}$ **81.** $5x + 4$ **83.** $\dfrac{x + y}{x - 4y}$

85. They are opposites.   **87.** -1 **89.** -1 **91.** $-\dfrac{1}{2}$

93. Cannot simplify   **95.** $\dfrac{5x - 6}{5x + 6}$ **97.** $-\dfrac{x + 3}{4 + x}$

Section 14.2 Practice Exercises, pp. 954–955

1. $\dfrac{3}{10}$ **3.** 2   **5.** $\dfrac{5}{2}$ **7.** $\dfrac{15}{4}$ **9.** $\dfrac{3}{2x}$ **11.** $3xy^4$

13. $\dfrac{x - 6}{8}$ **15.** $\dfrac{2}{y}$ **17.** $-\dfrac{5}{8}$ **19.** $-\dfrac{b + a}{a - b}$

21. $\dfrac{y + 1}{5}$ **23.** $\dfrac{2(x + 6)}{2x + 1}$ **25.** 6   **27.** $\dfrac{m^6}{n^2}$ **29.** $\dfrac{10}{9}$

31. $\dfrac{6}{7}$ **33.** $-m(m + n)$ **35.** $\dfrac{3p + 4q}{4(p + 2q)}$ **37.** $\dfrac{p}{p - 1}$

39. $\dfrac{w}{2w - 1}$ **41.** $\dfrac{5}{6}$ **43.** $\dfrac{q + 1}{q - 6}$ **45.** $\dfrac{1}{4}$

47. $\dfrac{y + 9}{y - 6}$ **49.** $\dfrac{t + 4}{t + 2}$ **51.** $\dfrac{3t + 8}{t + 2}$ **53.** $\dfrac{x + 4}{x + 1}$

55. $-\dfrac{w - 3}{2}$ **57.** $\dfrac{k + 6}{k + 3}$ **59.** $\dfrac{2}{a}$ **61.** $2y(y + 1)$

63. $x + y$ **65.** 2   **67.** $\dfrac{1}{a - 2}$

Section 14.3 Practice Exercises, pp. 959–961

3. $x = 1, x = -1$; $\dfrac{3}{5(x - 1)}$

5. $\dfrac{a + 5}{a + 7}$ **7.** $\dfrac{2}{3y}$ **9.** a, b, c, d

11. x^5 is the greatest power of x that appears in any denominator.   **13.** 45   **15.** 48   **17.** 63   **19.** $9x^2y^3$

21. w^2y **23.** $(p + 3)(p - 1)(p + 2)$ **25.** $9t(t + 1)^2$

27. $(y - 2)(y + 2)(y + 3)$ **29.** $3 - x$ or $x - 3$

31. Because $(b - 1)$ and $(1 - b)$ are opposites; they differ by a factor of -1.

33. $\dfrac{6}{5x^2}; \dfrac{5x}{5x^2}$ **35.** $\dfrac{24x}{30x^3}; \dfrac{5y}{30x^3}$ **37.** $\dfrac{10}{12a^2b}; \dfrac{a^3}{12a^2b}$

39. $\dfrac{6m - 6}{(m + 4)(m - 1)}; \dfrac{3m + 12}{(m + 4)(m - 1)}$

41. $\dfrac{6x + 18}{(2x - 5)(x + 3)}; \dfrac{2x - 5}{(2x - 5)(x + 3)}$

43. $\dfrac{6w + 6}{(w + 3)(w - 8)(w + 1)}; \dfrac{w^2 + 3w}{(w + 3)(w - 8)(w + 1)}$

45. $\dfrac{6p^2 + 12p}{(p - 2)(p + 2)^2}; \dfrac{3p - 6}{(p - 2)(p + 2)^2}$

47. $\dfrac{1}{a - 4}; \dfrac{-a}{a - 4}$ or $\dfrac{-1}{4 - a}; \dfrac{a}{4 - a}$

49. $\dfrac{8}{2(x - 7)}; \dfrac{-y}{2(x - 7)}$ or $\dfrac{-8}{2(7 - x)}; \dfrac{y}{2(7 - x)}$

51. $\dfrac{1}{a + b}; \dfrac{-6}{a + b}$ or $\dfrac{-1}{-a - b}; \dfrac{6}{-a - b}$

53. $\dfrac{-9}{24(3y + 1)}; \dfrac{20}{24(3y + 1)}$ **55.** $\dfrac{3z + 12}{5z(z + 4)}; \dfrac{5z}{5z(z + 4)}$

57. $\dfrac{z^2 + 3z}{(z + 2)(z + 7)(z + 3)}; \dfrac{-3z^2 - 6z}{(z + 2)(z + 7)(z + 3)}; \dfrac{5z + 35}{(z + 2)(z + 7)(z + 3)}$

Section 14.4 Practice Exercises, pp. 968–970

1. a. $-\dfrac{1}{2}, -2, 0$, undefined, undefined

b. $(x - 5)(x - 2); x = 5, x = 2$

c. $\dfrac{x + 1}{x - 2}$ **3.** $\dfrac{2(2b - 3)}{(b - 3)(b - 1)}$ **5.** $\dfrac{5}{4}$ **7.** $\dfrac{3}{8}$

9. 2   **11.** 5   **13.** $\dfrac{-2(t - 2)}{t - 8}$ **15.** $3x + 7$

17. $m + 5$ **19.** 2   **21.** $x - 5$ **23.** $\dfrac{1}{r + 1}$

25. $\dfrac{1}{y+7}$ **27.** $\dfrac{15x}{y}$ **29.** $\dfrac{5a+6}{4a}$ **31.** $\dfrac{2(6+x^2y)}{15xy^3}$

33. $\dfrac{2s-3t^2}{s^4t^3}$ **35.** $-\dfrac{2}{3}$ **37.** $\dfrac{19}{3(a+1)}$

39. $\dfrac{-3(k+4)}{(k-3)(k+3)}$ **41.** $\dfrac{a-4}{2a}$ **43.** $\dfrac{(x+6)(x-2)}{(x-4)(x+1)}$

45. $\dfrac{2(4a-b)}{(a+b)(a-b)}$ **47.** $\dfrac{5p-1}{3}$ or $\dfrac{-5p+1}{-3}$

49. $\dfrac{6n-1}{n-8}$ or $\dfrac{-6n+1}{8-n}$ **51.** $\dfrac{2(4x+5)}{x(x+2)}$

53. $\dfrac{3p+1}{(p-3)(p-1)}$ **55.** $\dfrac{3y}{2(2y+1)}$ **57.** $\dfrac{2(w-3)}{(w+3)(w-1)}$

59. $\dfrac{4a-13}{(a-3)(a-4)}$ **61.** $\dfrac{4x(x+1)}{(x+3)(x-2)(x+2)}$

63. $\dfrac{-y(y+8)}{(2y+1)(y-1)(y-4)}$ **65.** $\dfrac{1}{2p+1}$

67. $\dfrac{-2mn+1}{(m+n)(m-n)}$ **69.** 0 **71.** $\dfrac{2(3x+7)}{(x+3)(x+2)}$

73. $\dfrac{1}{n}$ **75.** $\dfrac{5}{n+2}$ **77.** $n+\left(7\cdot\dfrac{1}{n}\right)$; $\dfrac{n^2+7}{n}$

79. $\dfrac{1}{n}-\dfrac{2}{n}$; $-\dfrac{1}{n}$ **81.** $\dfrac{p^2-2p+7}{(p+2)(p+3)(p-1)}$

83. $\dfrac{-m-21}{2(m+5)(m-2)}$ or $\dfrac{m+21}{2(m+5)(2-m)}$ **85.** $\dfrac{3k+5}{4k+7}$

87. $\dfrac{1}{a}$

Chapter 14 Problem Recognition Exercises, p. 971

1. $\dfrac{-2x+9}{3x+1}$ **2.** $\dfrac{1}{w-4}$ **3.** $\dfrac{y-5}{2y-3}$

4. $\dfrac{7}{(x+3)(2x-1)}$ **5.** $-\dfrac{1}{x}$ **6.** $\dfrac{1}{3}$ **7.** $\dfrac{c+3}{c}$

8. $\dfrac{x+3}{5}$ **9.** $\dfrac{a}{12b^4c}$ **10.** $\dfrac{2a-b}{a-b}$ **11.** $\dfrac{p-q}{5}$

12. 4 **13.** $\dfrac{10}{2x+1}$ **14.** $\dfrac{w+2z}{w+z}$ **15.** $\dfrac{3}{2x+5}$

16. $\dfrac{y+7}{x+a}$ **17.** $\dfrac{1}{2(a+3)}$ **18.** $\dfrac{2(3y+10)}{(y-6)(y+6)(y+2)}$

19. $(t+8)^2$ **20.** $6b+5$

Section 14.5 Practice Exercises, pp. 977–978

3. $a=\dfrac{3}{2},\ a=-5;\ \dfrac{1}{2a-3}$

5. $\dfrac{3(2k-5)}{5(k-2)}$ **7.** $\dfrac{7}{4y}$ **9.** $\dfrac{1}{2y}$ **11.** $\dfrac{24b}{a^3}$ **13.** $\dfrac{2r^5t^4}{s^6}$

15. $\dfrac{35}{2}$ **17.** $k+h$ **19.** $\dfrac{n+1}{2(n-3)}$ **21.** $\dfrac{2x+1}{4x+1}$

23. $m-7$ **25.** $\dfrac{2y(y-5)}{7y^2+10}$ **27.** $-\dfrac{a+8}{a-2}$ or $\dfrac{a+8}{2-a}$

29. $\dfrac{t-2}{t-4}$ **31.** $\dfrac{t+3}{t-5}$ **33.** $\dfrac{1}{2}$ **35.** $\dfrac{\frac{1}{2}+\frac{2}{3}}{5}$; $\dfrac{7}{30}$

37. $\dfrac{3}{\frac{2}{3}+\frac{3}{4}}$; $\dfrac{36}{17}$ **39. a.** $\dfrac{6}{5}\ \Omega$ **b.** $6\ \Omega$ **41.** $\dfrac{y+4x}{2y}$

43. $\dfrac{1}{n^2+m^2}$ **45.** $\dfrac{2z-5}{3(z+3)}$ **47.** $-\dfrac{x+1}{x-1}$ or $\dfrac{x+1}{1-x}$

49. $\dfrac{3}{2}$

Section 14.6 Practice Exercises, pp. 986–988

3. $\dfrac{2}{4x-1}$ **5.** $5(h+1)$ **7.** $\dfrac{(x+4)(x-3)}{x^2}$

9. 3 **11.** $\dfrac{5}{11}$ **13.** $\dfrac{1}{3}$

15. a. $z=0$ **b.** $5z$ **c.** 5

17. $-\dfrac{200}{19}$ **19.** 8 **21.** $\dfrac{47}{6}$ **23.** $3,-1$ **25.** 4

27. 5; (The value 0 does not check.)   **29.** -5

31. No solution; (The value 4 does not check.)   **33.** 4

35. $4,-3$ **37.** -4; (The value 1 does not check.)

39. No solution; (The value -4 does not check.)

41. 4; (The value -6 does not check.)   **43.** -25

45. -1 **47.** The number is 8.   **49.** The number is -26.

51. $m=\dfrac{FK}{a}$ **53.** $E=\dfrac{IR}{K}$

55. $R=\dfrac{E-Ir}{I}$ or $R=\dfrac{E}{I}-r$

57. $B=\dfrac{2A-hb}{h}$ or $B=\dfrac{2A}{h}-b$ **59.** $h=\dfrac{V}{r^2\pi}$

61. $t=\dfrac{b}{x-a}$ or $t=\dfrac{-b}{a-x}$ **63.** $x=\dfrac{y}{1-yz}$ or $x=\dfrac{-y}{yz-1}$ **65.** $h=\dfrac{2A}{a+b}$ **67.** $R=\dfrac{R_1R_2}{R_2+R_1}$

Chapter 14 Problem Recognition Exercises, p. 989

1. $\dfrac{y-2}{2y}$ **2.** 6 **3.** 2 **4.** $\dfrac{3a-17}{a-5}$ **5.** $\dfrac{4p+27}{18p^2}$

6. $\dfrac{b(b-5)}{(b-1)(b+1)}$ **7.** 5 **8.** $\dfrac{2w+5}{(w+1)^2}$ **9.** 7

10. 5 **11.** $\dfrac{3x+14}{4(x+1)}$ **12.** $\dfrac{11}{3}$

Section 14.7 Practice Exercises, pp. 997–1001

3. Expression; $\dfrac{m^2+m+2}{(m-1)(m+3)}$ **5.** Expression; $\dfrac{3}{10}$

7. Equation; 2   **9.** 95   **11.** 1   **13.** $\dfrac{40}{3}$ **15.** 40

17. 3   **19.** -1 **21.** 1   **23. a.** $V_f=\dfrac{V_iT_f}{T_i}$

b. $T_f=\dfrac{T_iV_f}{V_i}$ **25.** Toni can drive 297 mi on 9 gal of gas.

27. They would produce 1536 lb.   **29.** 5 oz contains 12 g of carbohydrate.   **31.** This represents 262.5 mi.

33. The flagpole is 12 ft high.   **35.** The platform is 2.4 m high.   **37.** $x=17.5$ in.   **39.** $x=21$ ft; $y=21$ ft; $z=53.2$ ft

41. The speed of the boat is 20 mph.

43. The plane flies 210 mph in still air. **45.** He runs 8 mph and bikes 16 mph. **47.** Floyd walks 4 mph, and Rachel walks 2 mph. **49.** Sergio rode 12 mph, and walked 3 mph. **51.** $\frac{1}{2}$ of the room **53.** $5\frac{5}{11}$ $(5.\overline{45})$ min **55.** $22\frac{2}{9}$ $(22.\overline{2})$ min **57.** 48 hr **59.** $3\frac{1}{3}$ $(3.\overline{3})$ days **61.** There are 40 smokers and 140 nonsmokers. **63.** There are 240 men and 200 women.

Chapter 14 Review Exercises pp. 1008–1010

1. a. $-\frac{2}{9}, -\frac{1}{10}, 0, -\frac{5}{6}$, undefined
b. $t = -9$ **3.** a, c, d
5. $h = -\frac{1}{3}, h = -7; \frac{1}{3h+1}$
7. $w = 4, w = -4; \frac{2w+3}{w-4}$
9. $k = 0, k = 5; -\frac{3}{2k}$
11. $m = -1; \frac{m-5}{3}$
13. $p = -7; \frac{1}{p+7}$ **15.** $\frac{u^2}{2}$
17. $\frac{3}{2(x-5)}$ **19.** $\frac{q-2}{4}$ **21.** $4s(s-4)$
23. $\frac{1}{n-2}$ **25.** $\frac{1}{m+3}$ **27.** $-\frac{2y-1}{y+1}$
29. LCD $= 12xy; \frac{21y}{12xy}; \frac{22x}{12xy}$
31. LCD $= ab^3c^2; \frac{5c^2}{ab^3c^2}; \frac{3b^3}{ab^3c^2}$
33. LCD $= q(q+8); \frac{6q+48}{q(q+8)}; \frac{q}{q(q+8)}$
35. LCD $= (m+4)(m-4)(m+3)$
37. $3-x$ or $x-3$ **39.** 2 **41.** $x-7$
43. $\frac{t^2+2t+3}{(2-t)(2+t)}$ **45.** $\frac{3(r-4)}{2r(r+6)}$ **47.** $\frac{q}{(q+5)(q+4)}$
49. $\frac{1}{3}$ **51.** $\frac{3(z+5)}{z(z-5)}$ **53.** $\frac{8}{y}$ **55.** $-(b+a)$
57. $-\frac{k+10}{k+4}$ **59.** -2 **61.** 2 **63.** 3 **65.** $-11, 1$
67. $h = \frac{3V}{\pi r^2}$ **69.** $\frac{6}{5}$ **71.** 10 g **73.** Together the pumps would fill the pool in 16.8 min.
75. $x = 1.6$ yd, $y = 1.8$ yd

Chapter 14 Test pp. 1010–1011

1. a. $x = 2$ **b.** $-\frac{x+1}{6}$
2. a. $a = 0, a = 6, a = -2$
b. $\frac{7}{a+2}$ **3.** b, c, d **4.** $\frac{y+7}{3(y+3)(y+1)}$
5. $-\frac{b+3}{5}$ **6.** $\frac{1}{w+1}$ **7.** $\frac{t+4}{t+2}$
8. $\frac{x(x+5)}{(x+4)(x-2)}$ **9.** $\frac{1}{m+4}$ **10.** $\frac{8}{5}$ **11.** 2
12. 1 **13.** No solution; (The value 4 does not check.)
14. $r = \frac{2A}{C}$ **15.** The number is $-\frac{2}{5}$. **16.** -8
17. $1\frac{1}{4}$ (1.25) cups of carrots **18.** The speed of the current is 5 mph. **19.** It would take the second printer 3 hr to do the job working alone.

20. $x = 10.8$ cm, $y = 30$ cm
21. a. $15(x+3)$ **b.** $3x^2y^2$ **22.** 8.25 mL

Chapters 1–14 Cumulative Review Exercises pp. 1011–1012

1. 32 **2.** 7 **3.** $\frac{10}{9}$

4.

Set-Builder Notation	Graph	Interval Notation
$\{x \mid x \geq -1\}$	$\xrightarrow{}$ at -1	$[-1, \infty)$
$\{x \mid x < 5\}$	$\xleftarrow{}$ at 5	$(-\infty, 5)$

5. The width is 17 m, and the length is 35 m.
6. The base is 10 in., and the height is 8 in. **7.** $\frac{x^2yz^{17}}{2}$
8. a. $6x+4$ **b.** $2x^2+x-3$ **9.** $(5x-3)^2$
10. $(2c+1)(5d-3)$ **11.** $x = 5, x = -\frac{1}{2}$
12. $\frac{x-3}{x+5}$ **13.** $\frac{1}{5(x+4)}$ **14.** -3 **15.** 1 **16.** $-\frac{7}{2}$
17. a. x-intercept: $(-4, 0)$; y-intercept: $(0, 2)$
b. x-intercept: $(0, 0)$; y-intercept: $(0, 0)$
18. a. $m = -\frac{7}{5}$ **b.** $m = -\frac{2}{3}$ **c.** $m = 4$ **d.** $m = -\frac{1}{4}$
19. $y = 5x - 3$ **20.** One large popcorn costs \$3.50, and one drink costs \$1.50.

Chapter 15

Chapter Opener Puzzle

P	Y	T	H	A	G	O	R	E	A	N	T	H	E	O	R	E	M
	5		2		4		1						6		3		

Section 15.1 Calculator Connections, p. 1021

1. 2.236 **3.** 7.071 **5.** 5.745 **7.** 8.944
9. 1.913 **11.** 4.021

Section 15.1 Practice Exercises, pp. 1021–1025

3. $12, -12$ **5.** There are no real-valued square roots of -49. **7.** 0 **9.** $\frac{1}{5}, -\frac{1}{5}$ **11. a.** 13 **b.** -13 **13.** 0
15. 9, 16, 25, 36, 64, 121, 169 **17.** 2 **19.** 7 **21.** 0.4
23. 0.3 **25.** $\frac{5}{4}$ **27.** $\frac{1}{12}$ **29.** 5 **31.** 9
33. There is no real value of b for which $b^2 = -16$.
35. -2 **37.** Not a real number **39.** Not a real number
41. Not a real number **43.** -20 **45.** Not a real number
47. 0, 1, 27, 125 **49.** Yes, -3 **51.** 3 **53.** 4
55. -2 **57.** Not a real number **59.** Not a real number
61. -2 **63.** -1 **65.** 0 **67.** 4 **69.** 4 **71.** 5
73. -5 **75.** 2 **77.** 2 **79.** $|a|$ **81.** y **83.** $|w|$
85. x **87.** $x^2, y^4, (ab)^6, w^8x^8, m^{10}$. The expression is a perfect square if the exponent is even. **89.** $p^4, t^8, (cd)^{12}$. The expression is a perfect fourth power if the exponent is a multiple of 4. **91.** y^6 **93.** a^4b^{15} **95.** q^8 **97.** $2w^2$
99. $5x$ **101.** $-5x$ **103.** $5p^2$ **105.** $5p^2$

107. $\sqrt{q} + p^2$ **109.** $\dfrac{6}{\sqrt[4]{x}}$ **111.** 9 cm **113.** 5 ft

115. 6.9 cm **117.** 17.0 in. **119.** 31.3 in.
121. 268 km **123.** $x \ge 0$

Section 15.2 Calculator Connections, p. 1030

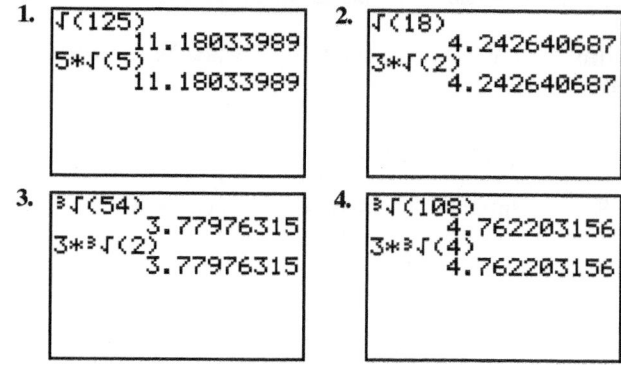

Section 15.2 Practice Exercises, pp. 1031–1033

3. $8, 27, y^3, y^9, y^{12}, y^{27}$ **5.** -5 **7.** -3 **9.** a^2
11. $2xy^2$ **13.** 446 km **15.** $3\sqrt{2}$ **17.** $2\sqrt{7}$
19. $12\sqrt{5}$ **21.** $-10\sqrt{2}$ **23.** $a^2\sqrt{a}$ **25.** w^{11}
27. $m^2n^2\sqrt{n}$ **29.** $x^7y^5\sqrt{x}$ **31.** $3t^5$ **33.** $2x\sqrt{2x}$
35. $4z\sqrt{z}$ **37.** $-3w^3\sqrt{5}$ **39.** $z^{12}\sqrt{z}$ **41.** $-z^5\sqrt{15z}$
43. $10ab^3\sqrt{26b}$ **45.** $\sqrt{26pq}$ **47.** m^6n^8
49. $4ab^2c^2\sqrt{3ab}$ **51.** a^4 **53.** y^5 **55.** $\dfrac{1}{2}$

57. 2 **59.** $2x$ **61.** $5p^3$ **63.** $3\sqrt{5}$ **65.** $\sqrt{6}$
67. 4 **69.** 7 **71.** $11\sqrt{2}$ ft **73.** $2\sqrt{66}$ cm
75. $a^2\sqrt[3]{a^2}$ **77.** $14z\sqrt[3]{2}$ **79.** $2ab^2\sqrt[3]{2a^2}$ **81.** z

83. -2 **85.** $2\sqrt[3]{5}$ **87.** $\dfrac{1}{3}$ **89.** $4a\sqrt{a}$

91. $2x$ **93.** $2p\sqrt{2q}$ **95.** $4\sqrt{2}$ **97.** $2u^2v^3\sqrt{13v}$
99. $6\sqrt{6}$ **101.** 6 **103.** $2a\sqrt[3]{2}$ **105.** x

107. $-\sqrt{5}$ **109.** $-\dfrac{1}{2}$ **111.** $5\sqrt{2}$ **113.** $x + 5$

Section 15.3 Practice Exercises, pp. 1037–1039

3. $2y$ **5.** $6x\sqrt{x}$ **7.** $\dfrac{5c^3}{4}$ **9.** Not a real number

11. For example, $2\sqrt{3}, 6\sqrt[3]{3}$ **13.** c **15.** $8\sqrt{2}$
17. $4\sqrt{7}$ **19.** $2\sqrt{10}$ **21.** $11\sqrt{y}$ **23.** 0
25. $5y\sqrt{15}$ **27.** $x\sqrt{y} - y\sqrt{x}$ **29.** $3\sqrt[3]{6} + 8\sqrt[3]{6}; 11\sqrt[3]{6}$
31. $4\sqrt{5} - 6\sqrt{5}; -2\sqrt{5}$ **33.** $8\sqrt{3}$ **35.** 0 **37.** $2\sqrt{2}$
39. $16p^2\sqrt{5}$ **41.** $10\sqrt{2k}$ **43.** $a^2\sqrt{b}$ **45.** $3\sqrt{5}$
47. $\dfrac{29}{18}z\sqrt{6}$ **49.** $-1.7\sqrt{10}$ **51.** $2x\sqrt{x}$ **53.** $3\sqrt{7}$
55. $4\sqrt{w} + 2\sqrt{6w} + 2\sqrt{10w}$ **57.** $6x^3\sqrt{y}$
59. $2\sqrt{3} - 4\sqrt{6}$ **61.** $-4x\sqrt{2} + \sqrt{2x}$ **63.** $9\sqrt{2}$ m
65. $16\sqrt{3}$ in. **67.** Radicands are not the same.
69. One term has a radical. One does not.

71. The indices are different. **73.** $\dfrac{\sqrt{3}}{3}$ **75. a.** 80 m
b. 159 m

Section 15.4 Practice Exercises, pp. 1044–1045

3. 11 **5.** $3w^2\sqrt{z}$ **7.** $\sqrt{15}$ **9.** 47 **11.** b
13. $6\sqrt{15p}$ **15.** $5\sqrt{2}$ **17.** $14\sqrt{2}$ **19.** $6x\sqrt{7}$

21. $4x^3\sqrt{y}$ **23.** $12w^2\sqrt{10}$ **25.** $-8\sqrt{15}$
27. Perimeter: $6\sqrt{5}$ ft; area: 10 ft^2 **29.** 3 cm^2 **31.** $3w$
33. $-16\sqrt{10y}$ **35.** $2\sqrt{3} - \sqrt{6}$ **37.** $4x + 20\sqrt{x}$
39. $-8 + 7\sqrt{30}$ **41.** $9a - 28b\sqrt{a} + 3b^2$
43. $8p^2 + 19p\sqrt{p} + 2p - 8\sqrt{p}$ **45.** 10 **47.** 4
49. t **51.** $16c$ **53.** $29 + 8\sqrt{13}$ **55.** $a - 4\sqrt{a} + 4$
57. $4a - 12\sqrt{a} + 9$ **59.** $21 - 2\sqrt{110}$ **61.** 1
63. $x - y$ **65.** -1 **67.** 4 **69.** $64x - 4y$ **71.** 73
73. a. $3x + 6$ **b.** $\sqrt{3x} + \sqrt{6}$ **75. a.** $4a^2 + 12a + 9$
b. $4a + 12\sqrt{a} + 9$ **77. a.** $b^2 - 25$ **b.** $b - 25$
79. a. $x^2 - 4xy + 4y^2$ **b.** $x - 4\sqrt{xy} + 4y$
81. a. $p^2 - q^2$ **b.** $p - q$ **83. a.** $y^2 - 6y + 9$
b. $x - 6\sqrt{x - 2} + 7$

Section 15.5 Practice Exercises, pp. 1052–1055

3. $6y + 23\sqrt{y} + 21$ **5.** $9\sqrt{3}$ **7.** $25 - 10\sqrt{a} + a$
9. -5 **11.** $\dfrac{\sqrt{3}}{4}$ **13.** $\dfrac{a^2}{b^2}$ **15.** $\dfrac{c\sqrt{c}}{2}$ **17.** $\dfrac{\sqrt[3]{x^2}}{3}$
19. $\dfrac{\sqrt[3]{y^2}}{3}$ **21.** $\dfrac{10\sqrt{2}}{9}$ **23.** $\dfrac{2}{5}$ **25.** $\dfrac{1}{2p}$ **27.** z
29. $2\sqrt[3]{x}$ **31.** $\dfrac{\sqrt{6}}{6}$ **33.** $3\sqrt{5}$ **35.** $\dfrac{6\sqrt{x+1}}{x+1}$
37. $\dfrac{\sqrt{6x}}{x}$ **39.** $\dfrac{\sqrt{21}}{7}$ **41.** $\dfrac{5\sqrt{6y}}{3y}$ **43.** $\dfrac{3\sqrt{6}}{4}$
45. $\dfrac{\sqrt{3p}}{9}$ **47.** $\dfrac{\sqrt{5}}{2}$ **49.** $\dfrac{x\sqrt{y}}{y^2}$ **51.** -7
53. $\sqrt{5} + \sqrt{3}; 2$ **55.** $\sqrt{x} - 10; x - 100$
57. $\dfrac{4\sqrt{2} - 12}{-7}$ or $\dfrac{12 - 4\sqrt{2}}{7}$ **59.** $\dfrac{\sqrt{5} + \sqrt{2}}{3}$
61. $\sqrt{6} - \sqrt{2}$ **63.** $\dfrac{\sqrt{x} + \sqrt{3}}{x - 3}$ **65.** $7 - 4\sqrt{3}$
67. $-13 - 6\sqrt{5}$ **69.** $2 - \sqrt{2}$ **71.** $\dfrac{3 + \sqrt{2}}{2}$
73. $1 - \sqrt{7}$ **75.** $\dfrac{7 + 3\sqrt{2}}{3}$ **77. a.** Condition 1 fails;
$2x^4\sqrt{2x}$ **b.** Condition 2 fails; $\dfrac{\sqrt{5x}}{x}$ **c.** Condition 3 fails;
$\dfrac{\sqrt{3}}{3}$ **79. a.** Condition 2 fails; $\dfrac{3\sqrt{x} - 3}{x - 1}$ **b.** Conditions
1 and 3 fail; $\dfrac{3w\sqrt{t}}{t}$ **c.** Condition 1 fails; $2a^2b^4\sqrt{6ab}$
81. $3\sqrt{5}$ **83.** $-\dfrac{3w\sqrt{2}}{5}$ **85.** Not a real number
87. $\dfrac{s\sqrt{t}}{t}$ **89.** $\dfrac{m^2}{2}$ **91.** $\dfrac{9\sqrt{t}}{t^2}$ **93.** $\dfrac{\sqrt{11} - \sqrt{5}}{2}$
95. $\dfrac{a + 2\sqrt{ab} + b}{a - b}$ **97.** $-\dfrac{3\sqrt{2}}{8}$ **99.** $\dfrac{\sqrt{3}}{9}$

Chapter 15 Problem Recognition Exercises, p. 1055

1. $3\sqrt{2}$ **2.** $2\sqrt{7}$ **3.** Cannot be simplified further
4. Cannot be simplified further **5.** $\sqrt{2}$ **6.** $\sqrt{7}$
7. $9 - z$ **8.** $16 - y$ **9.** $8 - 3\sqrt{5}$
10. $-8 + 11\sqrt{3}$ **11.** $-x\sqrt{y}$ **12.** $11ab\sqrt{a}$
13. $-24 - 6\sqrt{6} - 3\sqrt{2}$ **14.** $-80 + 8\sqrt{15} + 16\sqrt{5}$
15. $\dfrac{2\sqrt{x} + 14}{x - 49}$ **16.** $\dfrac{5\sqrt{y} - 20}{y - 16}$ **17.** $3\sqrt{3}$

18. $3\sqrt{5}$ **19.** $\dfrac{\sqrt{7x}}{x}$ **20.** $\dfrac{\sqrt{11y}}{y}$ **21.** $y^2z^5\sqrt{z}$

22. $2q^3\sqrt{2}$ **23.** $3p^2\sqrt[3]{p^2}$ **24.** $5u^3v^4\sqrt[3]{u^2}$ **25.** $x\sqrt{10}$
26. $y\sqrt{3}$ **27.** $20\sqrt{3}$ **28.** $\sqrt{10}$ **29.** $51 + 14\sqrt{2}$
30. $8 + 2\sqrt{15}$ **31.** $\sqrt{x} - \sqrt{5}$ **32.** $\sqrt{y} - \sqrt{7}$

33. $4x - 11\sqrt{xy} - 3y$ **34.** $\dfrac{1}{3}$ **35.** $\dfrac{5}{3}$

36. $16 - 2\sqrt{55}$ **37.** $x - 12\sqrt{x} + 36$ **38.** $-3\sqrt{6}$
39. $11\sqrt{a}$ **40.** -88 **41.** $u - 9v$ **42.** $4x\sqrt{2}$
43. 0 **44.** $5 + \sqrt{35}$ **45.** $a + 2\sqrt{a}$
46. $26 - 17\sqrt{2}$

Section 15.6 Practice Exercises, pp. 1060–1062

3. $\dfrac{\sqrt{2} - \sqrt{10}}{-8}$ or $\dfrac{\sqrt{10} - \sqrt{2}}{8}$ **5.** $\dfrac{2\sqrt{6}}{3}$

7. $x^2 + 8x + 16$ **9.** $x + 8\sqrt{x} + 16$ **11.** $2x - 3$
13. $t^2 + 2t + 1$ **15.** 36 **17.** 15 **19.** No solution;

(The value 29 does not check.) **21.** 5 **23.** $-\dfrac{1}{2}$

25. 6 **27.** 8 **29.** No solution; (The value $\frac{19}{2}$ does
not check.) **31.** 1 **33.** $4, -3$ **35.** 0
37. No solution; (The value -4 does not check.)
39. 4; (The value -1 does not check.) **41.** $0, -1$
43. 12; (The value 4 does not check.) **45.** -6 **47.** -1
49. $\sqrt{x + 10} = 1$; -9 **51.** $\sqrt{2x} = x - 4$; 8
53. $\sqrt[3]{x + 1} = 2$; 7 **55. a.** 80 ft/sec **b.** 289 ft
57. a. 16 in. **b.** 25 weeks **59.** $\dfrac{9}{5}$

61. $\dfrac{3}{2}$; (The value -1 does not check.)

Chapter 15 Review Exercises, pp. 1067–1070

1. Principal square root: 14; negative square root: -14
3. Principal square root: 0.8; negative square root: -0.8
5. There is no real number b such that $b^2 = -64$. **7.** -12
9. Not a real number **11.** $|y|$ **13.** $|y|$ **15.** -5

17. $\dfrac{3}{t^2}$ **19. a.** 7.1 m **b.** 22.6 ft **21.** $b^2 + \sqrt{5}$

23. The quotient of 2 and the principal square root of p
25. 12 ft **27.** $x^8\sqrt{x}$ **29.** $2\sqrt{7}$ **31.** $3y^3\sqrt[3]{y}$
33. c **35.** $10y^2$ **37.** $2x$ **39.** $5\sqrt{3}$ **41.** 1
43. $7\sqrt{6}$ **45.** $-4x\sqrt{5}$ **47.** $15\sqrt{3} - 7\sqrt{7}$
49. $\sqrt{x^4 + (5x)^2}$; $26x^2$ **51.** $12\sqrt{2}$ ft **53.** 25
55. $70\sqrt{3x}$ **57.** $8m + 24\sqrt{m}$ **59.** $-49 - 16\sqrt{26}$
61. $64w - z$ **63.** $10\sqrt{3}$ m^3 **65.** a^5 **67.** $4\sqrt{y}$

69. b **71.** $\dfrac{3\sqrt{2y}}{y}$ **73.** $2\sqrt{7} + 2\sqrt{2}$

75. $-8 - 3\sqrt{7}$ **77.** 138 **79.** 39 **81.** 7
83. 2; (The value -2 does not check.) **85.** -69

Chapter 15 Test, pp. 1070–1071

1. 1. The radicand has no factor raised to a power greater
than or equal to the index. 2. There are no radicals in the
denominator of a fraction. 3. The radicand does not contain a
fraction. **2.** $11x\sqrt{2}$ **3.** $2y\sqrt[3]{6y}$ **4.** Not a real number

5. $\dfrac{a^3\sqrt{5}}{9}$ **6.** $\dfrac{3\sqrt{6}}{2}$ **7.** $\dfrac{2\sqrt{5} - 12}{-31}$ or $\dfrac{12 - 2\sqrt{5}}{31}$

8. a. $\sqrt{25} + 5^3$; 130 **b.** $4^2 - \sqrt{16}$; 12 **9. a.** 97 ft

b. 339 ft **10.** $8\sqrt{z}$ **11.** $4\sqrt{6} - 15$ **12.** $-7t\sqrt{2}$
13. $9\sqrt{10}$ **14.** $46 - 6\sqrt{5}$ **15.** $-8 + 23\sqrt{10}$

16. $\dfrac{\sqrt{n}}{6m}$ **17.** $16 - 9x$ **18.** $\dfrac{\sqrt{22}}{11}$ **19.** $\dfrac{3\sqrt{7} + 3\sqrt{3}}{2}$

20. 206 yd **21.** No solution; (The value $\frac{9}{2}$ does not check.)
22. $0, -5$ **23.** 14 **24. a.** 12 in. **b.** 18 in. **c.** 25 weeks

Chapters 1–15 Cumulative Review Exercises, pp. 1071–1072

1. 1 **2.** -2 **3.** -15 **4.** $-9x^2 + 2x + 10$

5. $\dfrac{2x}{y} - 1 + \dfrac{4}{x}$ **6.** $2(5c + 2)^2$ **7.** $-\dfrac{2}{5}, \dfrac{1}{2}$ **8.** 1

9. No solution; (The value 5 does not check.)

10. $\dfrac{x(5x + 8)}{16(x - 1)}$ **11.**

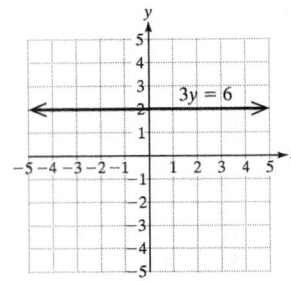

12. a. $y = 880$; the cost of renting the office space for
3 months is \$880. **b.** $x = 12$; the cost of renting office space
for 12 months is \$2770. **c.** $m = 210$; the cost increases at a
rate of \$210 per month. **d.** $(0, 250)$; the down payment of
renting the office space is \$250. **13.** $y = -x + 1$
14. $(1, -4)$ **15.**

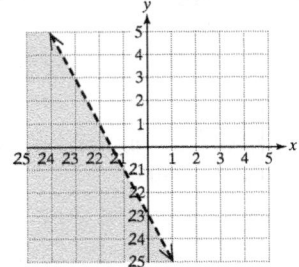

16. 8 L of 20% solution should be mixed with 4 L of 50%
solution. **17.** $3\sqrt{11}$ **18.** $7x\sqrt{3}$

19. $\dfrac{x + \sqrt{xy}}{x - y}$ **20.** 5

Chapter 16

Chapter Opener Puzzle

$3 - $ O; $2 - $ W; $1 - $ T

A quadratic equation has at most $\dfrac{\text{T}}{1}\dfrac{\text{W}}{2}\dfrac{\text{O}}{3}$ solutions.

Section 16.1 Practice Exercises, pp. 1077–1079

3. a. Linear **b.** Quadratic **c.** Linear **5.** $-5, \dfrac{1}{2}$

7. $7, -5$ **9.** $-2, -\dfrac{1}{6}$ **11.** $-7, -\dfrac{3}{2}$ **13.** $12, -12$

15. $8, -2$ **17.** $\dfrac{1}{4}, -2$ **19.** $-1, -7$ **21.** ± 7

23. ± 10 **25.** There are no real-valued solutions.

27. $\pm\sqrt{3}$ **29.** 9, 1 **31.** 11, -1 **33.** 11 $\pm\sqrt{5}$

35. $-1 \pm 3\sqrt{2}$ **37.** $\frac{1}{4} \pm \frac{\sqrt{7}}{4}$ **39.** $\frac{1}{2} \pm \sqrt{15}$

41. There are no real-valued solutions. **43.** $\pm\frac{5}{2}$

45. The solution checks. **47.** False. -8 is also a solution.
49. a. 64 ft **b.** 3.5 sec **c.** 8.8 sec **51.** 7.1 m
53. 8.0 ft

Section 16.2 Practice Exercises, pp. 1083–1085

3. $5 \pm \sqrt{21}$ **5.** $4; y^2 + 4y + 4 = (y + 2)^2$

7. $36; p^2 - 12p + 36 = (p - 6)^2$

9. $\frac{81}{4}; x^2 - 9x + \frac{81}{4} = \left(x - \frac{9}{2}\right)^2$

11. $\frac{25}{36}; d^2 + \frac{5}{3}d + \frac{25}{36} = \left(d + \frac{5}{6}\right)^2$

13. $\frac{1}{100}; m^2 - \frac{1}{5}m + \frac{1}{100} = \left(m - \frac{1}{10}\right)^2$

15. $\frac{1}{4}; u^2 + u + \frac{1}{4} = \left(u + \frac{1}{2}\right)^2$ **17.** 2, -6

19. $-1, -5$ **21.** $1 \pm \sqrt{2}$ **23.** $1 \pm \sqrt{6}$

25. $-2 \pm \sqrt{3}$ **27.** $-\frac{1}{2} \pm \frac{\sqrt{13}}{2}$

29. $-1 \pm \sqrt{41}$ **31.** $2 \pm \sqrt{5}$ **33.** $-2, -4$
35. 3, 8 **37.** ± 11 **39.** $-2 \pm \sqrt{2}$ **41.** $-13, 5$
43. 13 **45.** 10, -2 **47.** 7, -1 **49.** $4 \pm \sqrt{15}$

51. $-1 \pm \sqrt{6}$ **53.** 11, -2 **55.** 0, 7 **57.** $\frac{1}{2}, -\frac{3}{4}$

59. $\pm\sqrt{14}$ **61.** There are no real-valued solutions.
63. 1 **65.** The suitcase is 10 in. by 14 in. by 30 in. The
bag must be checked because 10 in. + 14 in. + 30 in. = 54 in.,
which is greater than 45 in.

Section 16.3 Calculator Connections, p. 1091

1.

```
(-5+J(17))/4
       -.2192235936
(-5-J(17))/4
       -2.280776406
```

2.

```
(-40+J(1920))/-3
2
       -.1193063938
(-40-J(1920))/-3
2
       2.619306394
```

Section 16.3 Practice Exercises, pp. 1091–1093

1. ± 13 **3.** $4 \pm 2\sqrt{7}$ **5.** $2 \pm 2\sqrt{2}$

7. For $ax^2 + bx + c = 0, x = \dfrac{-b \pm \sqrt{b^2 - 4ac}}{2a}$

9. $2x^2 - x - 5 = 0; a = 2, b = -1, c = -5$
11. $-3x^2 + 14x + 0 = 0; a = -3, b = 14, c = 0$
13. $x^2 + 0x - 9 = 0; a = 1, b = 0, c = -9$

15. -8 **17.** $\frac{2}{3}, -\frac{1}{2}$ **19.** $\dfrac{1 \pm \sqrt{61}}{10}$ **21.** $1 \pm \sqrt{2}$

23. $\dfrac{-5 \pm \sqrt{3}}{2}$ **25.** $\dfrac{1 \pm \sqrt{17}}{-8}$ or $\dfrac{-1 \pm \sqrt{17}}{8}$

27. $\dfrac{-3 \pm \sqrt{33}}{4}$ **29.** $\dfrac{-15 \pm \sqrt{145}}{4}$

31. $\dfrac{-2 \pm \sqrt{22}}{6}$ **33.** $\dfrac{3}{4}, -\dfrac{3}{4}$

35. There are no real-valued solutions. **37.** $-12 \pm 3\sqrt{5}$

39. $\dfrac{3 \pm \sqrt{15}}{2}$ **41.** $0, \dfrac{11}{9}$ **43.** $\dfrac{3 \pm \sqrt{5}}{2}$

45. $\dfrac{1 \pm \sqrt{41}}{4}$ **47.** $0, \dfrac{1}{9}$ **49.** $\pm 2\sqrt{13}$

51. $\dfrac{-10 \pm \sqrt{85}}{-5}$ or $\dfrac{10 \pm \sqrt{85}}{5}$ **53.** $\dfrac{1 \pm \sqrt{61}}{2}$

55. There are no real-valued solutions. **57.** The width is
$\dfrac{1 + 3\sqrt{89}}{4} \approx 7.3$ m. The length is $\dfrac{-1 + 3\sqrt{89}}{2} \approx 13.6$ m
59. The length is $1 + \sqrt{41} \approx 7.4$ ft. The width is
$-1 + \sqrt{41} \approx 5.4$ ft. The height is 6 ft. **61.** The width is
$-2 + 2\sqrt{19} \approx 6.7$ ft. The length is $2 + 2\sqrt{19} \approx 10.7$ ft.

63. The legs are $\dfrac{3 + \sqrt{329}}{2} \approx 10.6$ m and

$\dfrac{-3 + \sqrt{329}}{2} \approx 7.6$ m.

Chapter 16 Problem Recognition Exercises, p. 1093

1. $\dfrac{1}{3}, -\dfrac{3}{2}$ **2.** -7 **3.** $4 \pm \sqrt{22}$ **4.** $3 \pm \sqrt{7}$

5. $3 \pm 2\sqrt{2}$ **6.** $-11 \pm 2\sqrt{3}$ **7.** $0, \dfrac{5}{6}$ **8.** $0, \dfrac{1}{2}$

9. ± 6 **10.** $\pm\dfrac{7}{5}$ **11.** $\dfrac{5}{2}, \dfrac{1}{4}$ **12.** $\dfrac{4}{3}, \dfrac{1}{3}$

13. There are no real-valued solutions. **14.** There are no
real-valued solutions. **15.** $-4 \pm \sqrt{15}$ **16.** $-3 \pm \sqrt{6}$
17. 4 **18.** -3 **19.** 5, 2 **20.** 3, -1 **21.** 9, -11
22. 13, -3

Section 16.4 Calculator Connections, p. 1101

1. $(-2, 3)$

2. 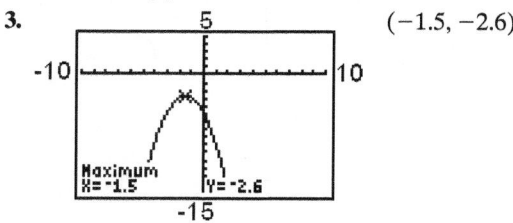 $(10, 5)$

3. $(-1.5, -2.6)$

4.

(1.75, 2.5)

5.

$\left(\dfrac{5}{2}, 0\right)$

6.

$\left(-\dfrac{8}{3}, 0\right)$

7. The graph in part (b) is shifted up 4 units. The graph in part (c) is shifted down 3 units.

8. In part (b), the graph is shifted to the right 3 units. In part (c), the graph is shifted to the left 2 units.

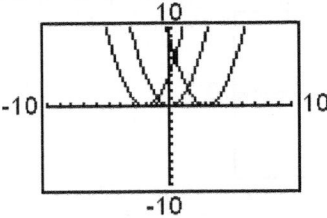

9. In part (b), the graph is stretched vertically by a factor of 2. In part (c), the graph is shrunk vertically by a factor of $\frac{1}{2}$.

10. In part (b), the graph has been stretched vertically and reflected across the x-axis. In part (c), the graph has been shrunk vertically and reflected across the x-axis.

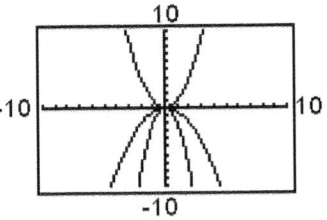

Section 16.4 Practice Exercises, pp. 1102–1105

3. $-5, 3$ **5.** $-1 \pm \sqrt{6}$ **7.** $2 \pm 2\sqrt{2}$
9. Linear   **11.** Quadratic   **13.** Neither
15. Linear   **17.** Quadratic   **19.** Neither
21. If $a > 0$ the graph opens upward; if $a < 0$ the graph opens downward.   **23.** $a = 2$; upward   **25.** $a = -10$; downward   **27.** $(-1, -8)$ **29.** $(1, -4)$ **31.** $(1, 2)$
33. $(0, -4)$ **35.** c; x-intercepts: $(\sqrt{7}, 0)(-\sqrt{7}, 0)$; y-intercept: $(0, -7)$ **37.** a; x-intercepts: $(-1, 0)(-5, 0)$; y-intercept: $(0, 5)$
39. a. Upward   **b.** $(0, -9)$ **c.** $(3, 0)(-3, 0)$ **d.** $(0, -9)$
e.

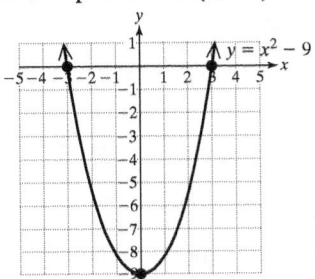

41. a. Upward   **b.** $(1, -9)$ **c.** $(4, 0)(-2, 0)$ **d.** $(0, -8)$
e.

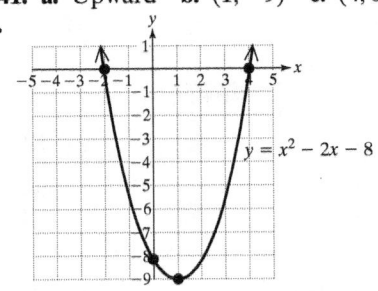

43. a. Downward   **b.** $(3, 0)$ **c.** $(3, 0)$ **d.** $(0, -9)$
e.

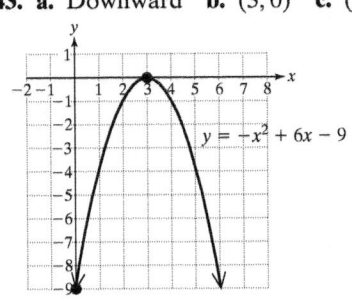

45. a. Downward **b.** $(4, 1)$ **c.** $(3, 0)(5, 0)$ **d.** $(0, -15)$
e.

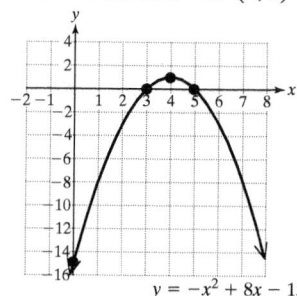

$y = -x^2 + 8x - 15$

47. a. Upward **b.** $(-3, 1)$ **c.** none **d.** $(0, 10)$
e.

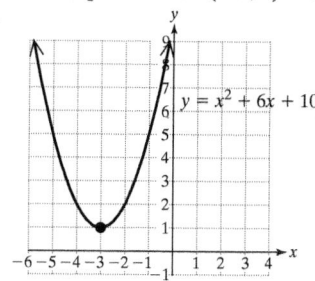

$y = x^2 + 6x + 10$

49. a. Downward **b.** $(0, -2)$ **c.** none **d.** $(0, -2)$
e.

$y = -2x^2 + 2$

51. True **53.** False **55. a.** 28 ft **b.** 1.25 sec
57. a. 200 calendars **b.** $500

Section 16.5 Calculator Connections, p. 1113

1.

2.

3.

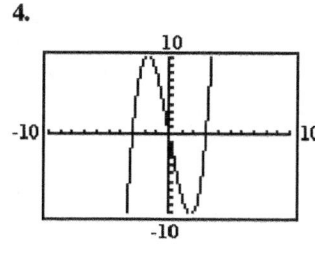

4.

(4. graph)

Section 16.5 Practice Exercises, pp. 1113–1117

3. Upward **5.** Domain: $\{4, 3, 0\}$; range: $\{2, 7, 1, 6\}$
7. Domain: $\{\frac{1}{2}, 0, 1\}$; range: $\{3\}$ **9.** Domain: $\{0, 5, -8, 8\}$;
range: $\{0, 2, 5\}$ **11.** Domain: $\{$Atlanta, Macon, Pittsburgh$\}$;
range: $\{$GA, PA$\}$ **13.** Domain: $\{$New York, California$\}$;
range: $\{$Albany, Los Angeles, Buffalo$\}$ **15.** The relation is
a function if each element in the domain has exactly one
corresponding element in the range.
17. The relations in Exercises 7, 9, and 11 are functions.
19. Yes **21.** No **23.** No **25.** Yes **27.** Yes
29. $-5, -1, -11$ **31.** $\frac{1}{5}, \frac{1}{4}, \frac{1}{2}$ **33.** $7, 2, 3$ **35.** $0, 1, 2$
37. b **39.** c **41.** The function value at $x = 6$ is 2.
43. The function value at $x = \frac{1}{2}$ is $\frac{1}{4}$. **45.** $(2, 7)$
47. $(0, 8)$ **49. a.** $s(1) = 32$. The speed of an object
1 sec after being dropped is 32 ft/sec. **b.** $s(2) = 64$. The
speed of an object 2 sec after being dropped is 64 ft/sec.
c. $s(10) = 320$. The speed of an object 10 sec after being
dropped is 320 ft/sec. **d.** 294.4 ft/sec
51. a. $h(0) = 3$. The initial height of the ball is 3 ft.
b. $h(1) = 51$. The height of the ball 1 sec after being kicked
is 51 ft. **c.** $h(2) = 67$. The height of the ball 2 sec after being
kicked is 67 ft. **d.** $h(4) = 3$. The height of the ball 4 sec after
being kicked is 3 ft.

Chapter 16 Review Exercises, pp. 1122–1124

1. Linear **3.** Quadratic **5.** ± 5 **7.** The equation
has no real-valued solutions. **9.** $-1 \pm \sqrt{14}$
11. $\frac{1}{8} \pm \frac{\sqrt{3}}{8}$ **13.** 36 **15.** $\frac{25}{4}$ **17.** $-4 \pm \sqrt{13}$
19. $\frac{3}{2} \pm \frac{\sqrt{21}}{2}$ **21.** 10.6 ft **23.** For $ax^2 + bx + c = 0$,
$x = \dfrac{-b \pm \sqrt{b^2 - 4ac}}{2a}$ **25.** -2 **27.** $\frac{3}{2}, -1$
29. $-3 \pm \sqrt{7}$ **31.** $1 \pm \sqrt{5}$
33. The equation has no real-valued solutions.
35. The height is $\dfrac{-1 + \sqrt{97}}{2} \approx 4.4$ cm. The base is
$\dfrac{1 + \sqrt{97}}{2} \approx 5.4$ cm. **37.** $a = 1$; upward **39.** $a = -2$;
downward **41.** Vertex: $(-1, 1)$ **43.** Vertex: $(3, 13)$
45. a. Upward **b.** $(-2, -3)$ **c.** $(-3, 0)(-1, 0)$ **d.** $(0, 9)$
e.

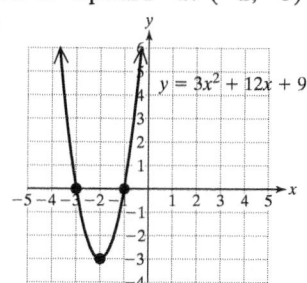

$y = 3x^2 + 12x + 9$

47. a. Downward   **b.** $(-1, -4)$ **c.** No x-intercepts
d. $(0, -12)$
e.

$y = -8x^2 - 16x - 12$

49. a. 1024 ft   **b.** 8 sec
51. Domain: $\{2\}$; range: $\{0, 1, -5, 2\}$; not a function
53. Domain: $(-\infty, \infty)$; range: $[-2, \infty)$; function
55. Domain: $\{3, -4, 0, 2\}$; range: $\{0, \frac{1}{2}, 3, -12\}$; function
57. a. 0   **b.** 4   **c.** $-\frac{1}{6}$ **d.** $\frac{3}{2}$ **e.** $-\frac{1}{2}$

Chapter 16 Test, pp. 1125–1126

1. The equation has no real-valued solutions.
2. $4 \pm \sqrt{21}$ **3.** $\dfrac{5 \pm \sqrt{13}}{6}$ **4.** $\dfrac{-1 \pm \sqrt{41}}{10}$
5. $12 \pm 2\sqrt{3}$ **6.** $-7 \pm 5\sqrt{2}$ **7.** $\pm\sqrt{10}$
8. $\dfrac{5}{6}, -\dfrac{3}{2}$ **9.** $0, \dfrac{11}{6}$ **10.** $3 \pm 2\sqrt{5}$ **11.** 4.0 in.

12. The base is $\dfrac{-1 + \sqrt{97}}{2} \approx 4.4$ m. The height is
$1 + \sqrt{97} \approx 10.8$ m.   **13.** For $y = ax^2 + bx + c$, if $a > 0$
the parabola opens upward, if $a < 0$ the parabola opens
downward.   **14.** $(5, 0)$ **15.** $(1, 5)$ **16.** $(0, -16)$
17. The parabola has no x-intercepts.
18. a. Opens upward   **b.** Vertex: $(-3, -1)$
c. x-intercepts: $(-2, 0)$ and $(-4, 0)$ **d.** y-intercept: $(0, 8)$
e.

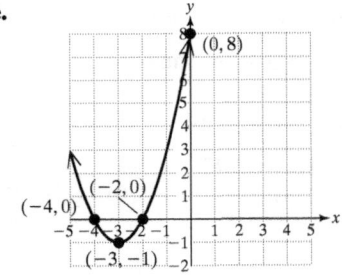
$(0, 8)$
$(-2, 0)$
$(-4, 0)$
$(-3, -1)$

19. Vertex: $(0, 25)$; x-intercepts: $(-5, 0)(5, 0)$; y-intercept:
$(0, 25)$

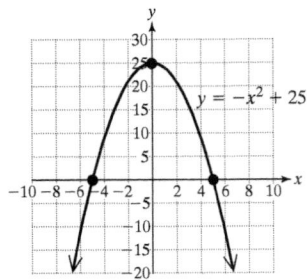
$y = -x^2 + 25$

20. a. $25 per ticket   **b.** $250,000
21. a. $\{0, 2, -15, 4, 9\}$ **b.** $\{-1, 3, -8, 4\}$ **c.** Function
22. a. 6   **b.** 12

Chapters 1–16 Cumulative Review Exercises, pp. 1126–1128

1. -25 **2.** 1   **3.** $h = \dfrac{2A}{b}$ **4.** $\dfrac{34}{3}$
5. $\{x \mid x > -1\}$; $(-1, \infty)$

-1

6. Mean: 29.9 yr; median: 29 yr; mode: 29 yr
7. 3.2 ft   **8.** 48 cm^3 **9.** The tax rate is 5%.
10. $\dfrac{8c}{a^4 b}$ **11.** 1.898×10^{10} diapers   **12.** $4x^2 - 16x + 13$
13. $2y^3 + 1 - \dfrac{3}{y - 2}$ **14.** $(2x + 5)(x - 7)$
15. $(y + 4a)(2x - 3b)$ **16.** The base is 9 m, and the
height is 8 m.   **17.** $-\dfrac{2}{x + 1}$ **18.** $\dfrac{5}{x - 2}$ **19.** $x - 5$
20. $-\dfrac{2}{x}$ **21.** $4, -3$ **22.** 20 cm $\approx$ 7.9 in. The fish
must be released.   **23.** $y = \dfrac{1}{2}x + 4$
24. a. $(6, 0)$ **b.** $(0, -3)$ **c.** $\frac{1}{2}$
d.

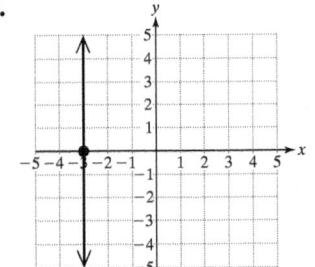

25. a. $(-3, 0)$ **b.** No y-intercept   **c.** Slope is undefined.
d.

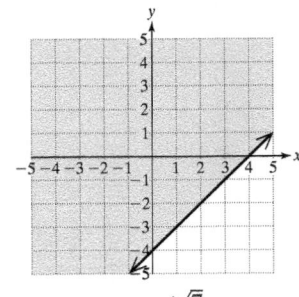

26. $\left(1, \dfrac{4}{3}\right)$ **27.** $(5, 2)$ **28.** The angles are 22° and 68°.
29.

$y = $

30. $\pi, \sqrt{7}$ **31.** $\dfrac{\sqrt{7}}{7}$ **32.** $2x\sqrt{2x}$
33. $48 + 8\sqrt{3x} + x$ **34.** $2\sqrt{2x}$ **35.** $\dfrac{8 + 4\sqrt{a}}{4 - a}$
36. -2; (The value -7 does not check.)   **37.** b

38. a. 1   **b.** 4   **c.** 13
39. Domain: $\{2, -1, 9, -6\}$; range: $\{4, 3, 2, 8\}$
40. $m = \dfrac{5}{7}$ **41.** $m = -\dfrac{4}{5}$ **42.** 25
43. $-3 \pm \sqrt{6}$ **44.** $-3 \pm \sqrt{6}$
45.

$y = x^2 + 4x + 4$
$(0, 4)$
$(-2, 0)$

Section A.1 Practice Exercises, pp. A-5–A-6

3. $x^3, 8, y^6, 27q^3, w^{12}, r^3s^6$ **5.** $(a + b)(a^2 - ab + b^2)$
7. $(y - 2)(y^2 + 2y + 4)$ **9.** $(1 - p)(1 + p + p^2)$
11. $(w + 4)(w^2 - 4w + 16)$
13. $(x - 10)(x^2 + 10x + 100)$ **15.** $(4t + 1)(16t^2 - 4t + 1)$
17. $(10a + 3)(100a^2 - 30a + 9)$
19. $\left(n - \dfrac{1}{2}\right)\left(n^2 + \dfrac{1}{2}n + \dfrac{1}{4}\right)$
21. $(5m + 2)(25m^2 - 10m + 4)$ **23.** $(x^2 - 2)(x^2 + 2)$
25. Prime   **27.** $(t + 4)(t^2 - 4t + 16)$
29. Prime   **31.** $4(b + 3)(b^2 - 3b + 9)$
33. $5(p - 5)(p + 5)$ **35.** $(\frac{1}{4} - 2h)(\frac{1}{16} + \frac{1}{2}h + 4h^2)$
37. $(x - 2)(x + 2)(x^2 + 4)$ **39.** $(q - 2)(q^2 + 2q + 4)$
$(q + 2)(q^2 - 2q + 4)$ **41.** $\left(\dfrac{2x}{3} - w\right)\left(\dfrac{2x}{3} + w\right)$
43. $(x^3 + 4y)(x^6 - 4x^3y + 16y^2)$
45. $(2x + 3)(x - 1)(x + 1)$
47. $(2x - y)(2x + y)(4x^2 + y^2)$
49. $(3y - 2)(3y + 2)(9y^2 + 4)$
51. $(a + b^2)(a^2 - ab^2 + b^4)$ **53.** $(x^2 + y^2)(x - y)(x + y)$

55. $(k + 4)(k - 3)(k + 3)$ **57.** $2(t - 5)(t - 1)(t + 1)$
59. $\left(\dfrac{4}{5}p - \dfrac{1}{2}q\right)\left(\dfrac{16}{25}p^2 + \dfrac{2}{5}pq + \dfrac{1}{4}q^2\right)$
61. $(a^4 + b^4)(a^8 - a^4b^4 + b^8)$ **63. a.** The quotient is
$x^2 + 2x + 4$.   **b.** $(x - 2)(x^2 + 2x + 4)$
65. $x^2 + 4x + 16$ **67.** $2x + 1$

Section A.2 Practice Exercises, pp. A-10–A-13

3. $\{1, 2, 3, 4, 5, 6, 7, 8, 9, 10\}$ **5.** $\{2, 3, 4, 5, 6, 7, 8, 9, 10, 11, 12\}$
7. c, d, g, h   **9.** $\dfrac{2}{6} = \dfrac{1}{3}$ **11.** $\dfrac{3}{6} = \dfrac{1}{2}$ **13.** $\dfrac{5}{8}$
15. $\dfrac{1}{8}$ **17.** 1
19. An impossible event is one in which the probability is 0.
21. $\dfrac{12}{52} = \dfrac{3}{13}$ **23.** $\dfrac{12}{16} = \dfrac{3}{4}$
25. a. $\dfrac{18}{120} = \dfrac{3}{20}$ **b.** $\dfrac{27}{120} = \dfrac{9}{40}$ **c.** 30%
27. a. $\dfrac{21}{60} = \dfrac{7}{20}$ **b.** 50%   **29. a.** $\dfrac{7}{29}$ **b.** $\dfrac{11}{29}$ **c.** 62%
31. $1 - \dfrac{2}{11} = \dfrac{9}{11}$ **33.** $100\% - 1.2\% = 98.8\%$

Section A.3 Practice Exercises, pp. A-18–A-21

3. Inversely   **5.** $T = kq$ **7.** $b = \dfrac{k}{c}$ **9.** $Q = \dfrac{kx}{y}$
11. $c = kst$ **13.** $L = kw\sqrt{v}$ **15.** $x = \dfrac{ky^2}{z}$
17. $k = \dfrac{9}{2}$ **19.** $k = 512$ **21.** $k = 1.75$ **23.** $x = 70$
25. $b = 6$ **27.** $Z = 56$ **29.** $Q = 9$ **31.** $L = 9$
33. $B = \dfrac{15}{2}$ **35. a.** 3.6 g   **b.** 4.5 g   **c.** 2.4 g
37. a. $0.40   **b.** $0.30   **c.** $1.00   **39.** 355,000 tons
41. 42.6 ft   **43.** 300 W   **45.** 1.25 Ω   **47.** 20 lb
49. $3500

Photo Credits

Page 2: © Getty Images/Blend Images RF; p. 3: © Photodisc/Getty RF; p. 6: © RF/Corbis; p. 7: © SMSU-WP Photo: Vickie Driskell; p. 10: © BrandX Pictures/Punchstock RF; p. 11(left): © Royalty-Free/Corbis; p. 11(right): © BrandX Pictures/Punchstock RF; p. 15: © The McGraw-Hill Companies, Inc./Jill Braaten, photographer; p. 25(left): © Corbis RF; p. 25(right): © The McGraw-Hill Companies, Inc./Jill Braaten, photographer; p. 28: © Julie Miller; p. 33(top): © Corbis RF; p. 33(bottom): © Banana Stock/agefotostock RF; p. 40: © Corbis RF; p. 45(top): © Veer RF; p. 45(bottom left): © PhotoDisc/Getty RF; p. 45(bottom right): © The McGraw-Hill Companies, Inc./Jill Braaten, photographer; p. 50: © BrandX/Jupiter RF; p. 52: © PhotoLink/Getty RF; p. 53: © Corbis RF; p. 56: © Corbis RF; p. 66: © Corbis/Jupiterimages RF; p. 71(top): © Getty RF; p. 71(bottom): © Julie Miller; p. 72(top): © Vol. 43 PhotoDisc/Getty RF; p. 72(bottom): © Getty RF; p. 73: © Vol. 156/Corbis RF; p. 80(top): © IMS/Capstone Design RF; p. 80(bottom): © Lynette King; p. 81: © Comstock/PunchStock RF; p. 82: © Photodisc/Getty Images RF; p. 83: © Buzzshotz/Alamy RF; p. 86: © 2006 Glowimages RF; p. 89: © Doug Sherman/Geofile; p. 90(top): © Imagestate Media (John Foxx)/Imagestate RF; p. 90(bottom): © Fancy Photography/Veer RF; p. 98: National Park Service, photo by DL Coe; p. 99: © Ilene MacDonald/Alamy RF; p. 104(left): © Getty Images/Purestock RF; p. 104(right): © Ingram Publishing/SuperStock RF; p. 105: © J. Luke/PhotoLink/Getty Images RF; p. 112(top): © ImageState/Punchstock RF; p. 112(bottom): © StockTrek/SuperStock RF; p. 117: © BananaStock/Punchstock RF; p. 120(top): © Imagestate Media (John Foxx)/Imagestate RF; p. 120(bottom): © Somos Images/Corbis RF; p. 121: © BananaStock/Punchstock RF; p. 122: © Siede Preis/Getty Images RF; p. 126: © Stockdisc RF; p. 127: © Randy Faris/Corbis RF; p. 128: © Getty Images/Digital Vision RF; p. 129: © Fancy Photography/Veer RF; p. 161: © Purestock/PunchStock RF; p. 162: © Alamy RF; p. 166(top): © Comstock Images/SuperStock RF; p. 166(bottom): © Brand X Pictures RF; p. 167(top): © Corbis RF; p. 167(bottom): © Ingram Publishing/SuperStock RF; p. 174(left): © Stock 4B RF; p. 174(right): © Dynamic Graphics/JupiterImages RF;

p. 175(top): © Tetra Images/Alamy RF; p. 175(bottom): © Burke/Triolo/Brand X Pictures RF; p. 178: © The McGraw-Hill Companies, Inc./Mark Dierker, photographer; p. 182: © The McGraw-Hill Companies, Inc./Mark Dierker, photographer; p. 185(top): © Royalty-Free/Corbis; p. 185(bottom): © liquidlibrary/PictureQuest RF; p. 187: © The McGraw-Hill Companies, Inc./Jill Braaten, photographer; p. 196: © Image100 Ltd. RF; p. 199(top left): © BrandX/Punchstock RF; p. 199(top right): © Banana Stock/Punchstock RF; p. 199(bottom top): © Banana Stock/Jupiterimages RF; p. 199 (bottom bottom): © PhotoAlto/PunchStock RF; p. 212: © Corbis RF; p. 213(top): © Digital Vision/Getty Images RF; p. 213(middle): © C Squared Studies/Getty Images RF; p. 213(bottom): © BrandX/Punchstock RF; p. 221: © Vol. 85/PhotoDisc/Getty RF; p. 230: © Corbis RF; p. 244(top): © Corbis RF; p. 244(bottom): © Comstock/Alamy RF; p. 245(top): © BrandX Pictures/Jupiter RF; p. 245(bottom): Photo by Benjamin Schott; p. 274: © Tanya Constantine/Blend Images/Getty Images RF; p. 275(top): © Stockbyte/SuperStock RF; p. 275(bottom): © Brand X Pictures RF; p. 277(left): © Dynamic Graphics/PunchStock RF; p. 277(right): © Brand X Pictures/PunchStock RF; p. 288(left): © Mastefile RF; p. 288(right): U.S. Air Force Photo by Master Sgt. Michael A. Kaplan; p. 289: © EP4 PhotoDisc/Getty RF; p. 297(top): © NASA; p. 297(bottom): © Bob Jacobson/Corbis RF; p. 303(top): © Creatas/Punchstock RF; p. 303(bottom): © The McGraw-Hill Companies, Inc./Ken Karp, photographer; p. 308: © The McGraw-Hill Companies, Inc./Lars A. Niki, photographer; p. 309(left): © The McGraw-Hill Companies, Inc./Mark Dierker, photographer; p. 309(right): © The McGraw-Hill Companies, Inc./Mark Dierker, photographer; p. 310(left): © Art Vandalay/Getty Images RF; p. 310(right): © Stockbyte/PunchStock RF; p. 318: © Vol. 190/Getty RF; p. 321(top): © Getty RF; p. 321(bottom): © Brownstock Inc./Alamy RF; p. 332: © The McGraw-Hill Companies, Inc./Gary He, photographer; p. 336: © Vol. 49/Getty RF; p. 342: © BananaStock/Jupiterimages RF; p. 344(top): © Brand X Pictures/PunchStock RF; p. 344(bottom): © Corbis - All Rights Reserved RF; p. 356: © Getty Images/Digital Vision RF; p. 360: © moodboard/Corbis RF; p. 361: © Molly O'Neill; p. 362: © Lars A.

Niki; p. 363(top): © Brand X Pictures/PunchStock RF; p. 363(bottom): © Corbis RF; p. 364(left): © Corbis RF; p. 364(right): © Kent Knudson/PhotoLink/Getty Images RF; p. 365: © Photograph courtesy of USGS, Water Resources Division; p. 366(top): © Vol. 77/PhotoDisc/Getty RF; p. 366(bottom): © MIXA/PunchStock RF; p. 370a: © The McGraw-Hill Companies, Inc./Jill Braaten, photographer; p. 370b: © The McGraw-Hill Companies, Inc./Jill Braaten, photographer; p. 370c: © The McGraw-Hill Companies, Inc./Jill Braaten, photographer; p. 372(top): © Getty RF; p. 372(bottom): © bildagentur-online.com/th-foto/Alamy RF; p. 373: © Vol. 101 PhotoDisc/Getty RF; p. 374(top): © Digital Vision/Punchstock RF; p. 374(bottom): © EP073/Getty RF; p. 381: © Corbis RF; p. 383: © Corbis RF; p. 383(top): © The McGraw-Hill Companies, Inc./Mark Dierker, photographer; p. 383(middle): © Don Farrall/Getty Images RF; p. 384(bottom): © Corbis RF; p. 392(top): © Royalty-Free/CORBIS RF; p. 392(bottom): © C Squared Studios/Getty Images RF; p. 396: © PhotoDisc/Getty RF; p. 401(top): © Stockbyte/Punchstock RF; p. 401(bottom): © Stockbyte/Getty Images RF; p. 403: © PhotoDisc/Getty RF; p. 404: © BrandX RF; p. 405: © Medioimages/Punchstock RF; p. 406: © Blend Images/Getty Images RF; p. 410: © Digital Vison/Getty RF; p. 411: © The McGraw-Hill Companies, Inc./Jill Braaten, photographer; p. 412: © The McGraw-Hill Companies, Inc./Jill Braaten, photographer; p. 413: © Creatas/Punchstock RF; p. 414: © Getty RF; p. 418: © Image100/Corbis RF; p. 424(top): © OS23/Getty RF; p. 424(bottom): © Creatas/PictureQuest RF; p. 425(top): © RF/Corbis RF; p. 425(bottom): © Digital Vision/Getty Images RF; p. 427: © Julie Miller; p. 434: © Getty RF RF; p. 444: © David Tietz/Editorial Image, LLC; p. 446(left): © Imagestate Media (John Foxx)/Imagestate RF; p. 446(right): © Jarvell Jardey/Alamy RF; p. 448: © Big Cheese Photo/PunchStock RF; p. 457: © LCPL Casey N. Thurston, USMC/DoD Media RF; p. 458: © Vol. 1/PhotoDisc/Getty RF; p. 460: © The McGraw-Hill Companies, Inc./Jill Braaten, photographer; p. 462(left): The McGraw-Hill Companies, Inc./Mark Dierker, photographer; p. 462(right): The McGraw-Hill Companies, Inc./Mark Dierker, photographer; p. 463(top): © RF/Corbis RF; p. 463(bottom): © Corbis-All Rights Reserved RF; p. 465: © Image Club RF; p. 472(left): © Ingram Publishing/Alam RF;

Application Index

Biology/Health/Life Sciences

Aerobic range heart rate, 414
African elephant weight, 458
Age and systolic blood pressure of women, 679
Age differences, 121, 127, 166, 175, 626, 627
Age of dog equated to human age, 446
Age of kitten, 244
Age versus height of children, 744
Average height of boys and girls, 558, 732, 743
Bass population in lake, 384
Bison population in Wyoming, 384
Blood alcohol concentration, 487
Blood platelet counts, 374
Blood types, 185, 213
Blood volume pumped by human heart, 837
Body mass index, 337, 537, 658
Body measurement conversion, 542
Breast cancer rate in women, 442
Breast cancer relapse risk, 405
Butterfly wingspan, 577
Calcium intake daily, 588
Calories burned per hour, 53
Calories in food, 577, 586, 809
Calories reduced per day, 427
Carbohydrates in food, 998
Deer population in Michigan, 384
Drug dosage, 71, 485–487, 533, 538, 543, 634
Drug prescription increase, 743
Drug testing, 412
Electrolyte solution needed by patient, 245
Elk population, 381
Endangered species in U.S., 442, 449
Fat amounts in food, 384, 586, 1007, 1009
Fat calories allowed on diet, 448
Goldfish population of pond, 450
Grams of fat allowed on diet, 336
Grams of protein in supplement bar, 46
Growth rate of child, 443
Height differences between brothers, 120, 174
Hemoglobin grams in blood, 488
Herb capsule dosage, 129
Hospital stays by year, 732
Leading forms of cancer in men, 633
Lengths of birds, 244
Lengths of cuts needing stitches, 222

Liver transplants, 586
Manatee population in Florida, 384
Maximum recommended heart rate by age, 414, 744, 1117
Medical exam cost for cats, 45
Medication according to weight of human, 1011
Migration distance of whales, 1024
Mortality rates, 371
Occupancy of hospital beds, 405
Pain medication dosage, 220, 487
Panther population of Everglades National Park, 413
Panther population of Florida, 410
Patients served by hospice care center, 676
Percent increase in health insurance premiums, 426
Placebos received by women, 555
Population diagnosed with skin cancer, 1116
Population with heart disease, 412
Potassium daily allowance, 475
Pounds of food eaten by whales, 80
Pulse beats per minute, 383, 998
Ratio of cats to dogs at humane society, 1001
Ratio of height to arm/shoulder in humans, 367, 732
Ratio of insured to noninsured persons, 364
Red blood cell count in humans, 297
Running speed of selected animals, 374
Salt solution mixtures, 785
Sodium content of food, 451, 596
Sugar content of beverages, 373–374
Tallest living tree, 474
Temperatures of humans, 577
Tiger population of India, 727
Total number of hospital stays, 413
Volume unit conversions, 483
Water weight before diet, 414
Weight loss of cat, 427
Weight units conversion, 458, 483–484, 537, 541

Business and Economics

Absentee record for a business, 413
Airline revenue from tickets, 40
Albums sold, median number of, 578
Amount in sales after advertising, 1059–1060
Amount spent on advertising, 1059–1060

Annual salaries, 572–573
Average annual income, 321
Average cost to manufacture mountain bikes, 947
Beach parking revenue, 33
Cellular phone subscriptions, 555
Checking account, 24, 70, 99, 104, 112, 126, 127, 296
Commercials on radio/television, 212
Commission calculation, 418–419, 424–425, 433, 443, 448, 635
Containers filled with eggs, 72
Cost before discount, 632
Cost difference of tire brands, 308
Cost for each item versus bulk cost, 354
Cost of land, 244
Cost of merchandise before tax, 417–418, 663, 666
Cost of tennis ball cans plus tax, 303
Currency exchange rate, 384, 446
Delivery scheduling, 24
Depreciation, 696
Desks delivered to supply store, 24
Discount rate calculation, 420, 425–426, 443, 445, 448, 451, 632, 634, 657, 666
Dow Jones Industrial Average, 104
Down payments, 212–213
Earnings by working together, 245
Earnings differences between two persons, 161, 175, 336
Earnings of three house painters, 52
Electric bill charges, 732
Energy consumers in the world, 556
Fixed cost and rate of change, 729, 733, 743
Food mixtures by pound needed, 786
Fuel needed for equipment, 213
Fundraising, 199, 810
Gas prices, 405, 483
Health insurance costs, 579
Home prices, 580
Homes sold per month, 82
Hours of work scheduled for employees, 46
Hours worked per week, 244
Income tax paid, 403
iPod and CD storage minutes, 45
Lots sold by developer, 212
Lottery winnings, 839
Markdowns/markups, 297, 420–421, 425–427, 448–449, 451, 634
Mean prices, 578
Median income for U.S. males, 702–703

Subject Index

A

Absolute value
  explanation of, 87
  of fraction, 184
  method to find, 88
  notation for, 88, 598
  of real numbers, 598–599
AC-method to factor trinomials,
    902–906, 932
Acute angles, 490
Acute triangles, 498
Addends, 12
Addition
  on calculators, 27
  carrying in, 13, 17, 235
  of decimals, 290–294, 347
  explanation of, 12
  of fractions, 223–228, 268
  of integers, 92–96, 123
  of like terms, 136
  of mixed numbers, 234–236, 239
  of mixed units of measurement,
    456–457
  of polynomials, 841–842, 869
  of radicals, 1033–1036, 1065
  of rational expressions, 962–967, 1004
  repeated, 35
  symbol for, 12, 18
  of whole numbers, 12–15, 73
  words for, 19–20
Addition method
  explanation of, 768
  to solve systems of linear equations,
    768–773, 801
Addition properties
  associative, 15, 133, 134
  commutative, 14–15, 95, 133, 134
  distributive property of
    multiplication over addition,
    37, 38, 133, 135
  of equality, 141–144, 152–154, 170,
    254, 255, 338, 602–603
  of inequality, 648–649
  of zero, 14
Additive inverse property, 95
Adjacent angles, 492
Algebraic expressions
  in applications, 117
  decimals in, 294
  evaluation of, 62–63, 117–119, 125,
    249, 332
  explanation of, 62
  simplification of, 251–252

  translating English expressions to,
    340–341
Amount, of percent proportion, 398
Angles
  acute, 490
  adjacent, 492
  alternate exterior, 492
  alternate interior, 492
  complementary, 490–491, 638–639
  congruent, 490
  corresponding, 492
  explanation of, 489, 533
  measurement of, 489–490, 493
  obtuse, 490
  properties of, 492
  right, 489
  straight, 489
  supplementary, 490–491
  symbol for, 489
  of triangles, 487–498
  vertex of, 489
  vertical, 491
Applications. *See also* Applications
    Index
  addition in, 20–21, 96
  algebraic expressions in, 117
  area in, 41–42, 513–514
  consecutive integers in, 622–623
  converting units in, 478–479
  decimals in, 292–294, 303–304,
    318–319, 332
  discount and markup in, 632
  distance, rate, and time in, 781–783,
    993–995
  division in, 52, 53
  estimation in, 31, 40
  fractions in, 196, 208–209, 228, 332
  functions in, 1112
  geometry in, 341, 637–640, 663, 845,
    853, 923–924
  interest in, 631
  least common multiple in, 216
  linear equations in, 161–163, 340–342,
    623–625, 662, 727–729, 739, 802
  linear inequalities in, 652–653
  measurement in, 478–479, 485–486,
    532–533
  medical, 485–486, 532–533
  mixed numbers in, 240
  multiple operations in, 66–69
  multiplication in, 41
  percent equations in, 409–411, 442
  percent in, 416–423, 442–443,
    629–631, 663

  percent proportions in, 400–402, 441
  plotting points in, 675
  proportions in, 379–381, 439, 440,
    990–991, 1007
  Pythagorean theorem in, 500–501,
    925–926
  quadratic equations in, 923–926, 934,
    1090, 1100
  radical equations in, 1059–1060
  rates in, 371
  rational equations in, 990
  ratios in, 363
  similar triangles in, 502–503
  slope in, 697, 702–703
  steps to solve, 158, 172, 619
  substitution method in, 764–765
  subtraction in, 20–21
  systems of linear equations in,
    778–783
  work, 996–997
Approximation, 391. *See also*
    Estimation; Rounding
Area
  applications of, 41–42, 513–514
  of circles, 305–306, 510, 512–513
  explanation of, 510, 535
  formulas for, 203, 305, 510, 512
  method to find, 510–514
  of rectangles, 41–42, 76
  surface, 523–524, 536
  of triangles, 203–204
Associative properties
  of addition, 15, 95, 133
  of multiplication, 36, 133, 134
Average. *See* Mean
Axis of symmetry, 1094

B

Bar graphs
  construction of, 550–551
  explanation of, 550
  histograms as, 560–561
  pictograms as, 551
Base
  explanation of, 58
  multiplication and division of
    common, 814–816
  of percent proportion, 398
Binomial factors, 879, 882
Binomials. *See also* Polynomials
  explanation of, 840
  factoring, 909
  square of, 841

Perimeter and Circumference

Rectangle

$P = 2l + 2w$

Square

$P = 4s$

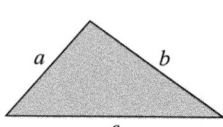

Triangle

$P = a + b + c$

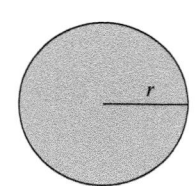

Circle

Circumference: $C = 2\pi r$

Area

Rectangle

$A = lw$

Square

$A = s^2$

Parallelogram

$A = bh$

Triangle

$A = \frac{1}{2}bh$

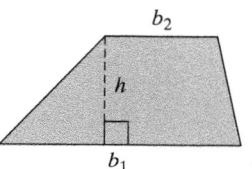

Trapezoid

$A = \frac{1}{2}(b_1 + b_2)h$

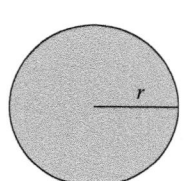

Circle

$A = \pi r^2$

Volume

Rectangular Solid

$V = lwh$

Cube

$V = s^3$

Right Circular Cylinder

$V = \pi r^2 h$

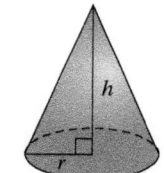

Right Circular Cone

$V = \frac{1}{3}\pi r^2 h$

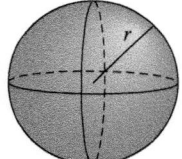

Sphere

$V = \frac{4}{3}\pi r^3$

Angles

- Two angles are **complementary** if the sum of their measures is 90°.

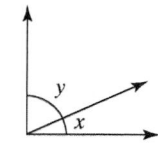

- Two angles are **supplementary** if the sum of their measures is 180°.

- $\angle a$ and $\angle c$ are vertical angles, and $\angle b$ and $\angle d$ are vertical angles. The measures of vertical angles are equal.

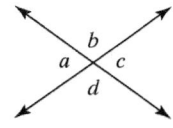

- The sum of the measures of the angles of a triangle is 180°.

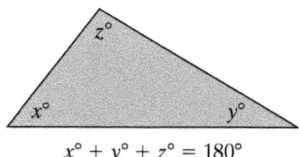

$x° + y° + z° = 180°$